A TEXTBOOK OF

NUCLEAR PHYSICS

PLATE I.

7 GeV proton synchrotron (Nimrod) at Rutherford High Energy Laboratory, N.I.R.N.S., Harwell, during construction.

A TEXTBOOK OF
NUCLEAR PHYSICS

BY

C. M. H. SMITH
Senior Lecturer in Physics
Oxford College of Technology

PERGAMON PRESS
OXFORD · LONDON · EDINBURGH · NEW YORK
TORONTO · PARIS · BRAUNSCHWEIG

Pergamon Press Ltd., Headington Hill Hall, Oxford
4 & 5 Fitzroy Square, London, W. 1

Pergamon Press (Scotland) Ltd., 2 & 3 Teviot Place, Edinburgh 1

Pergamon Press Inc., 44-01 21st Street, Long Island City, New York 11101

Pergamon of Canada, Ltd., 6 Adelaide Street East, Toronto, Ontario

Pergamon Press S.A.R.L., 24 rue des Écoles, Paris 5e

Vieweg & Sohn GmbH, Burgplatz 1, Braunschweig

First edition 1965
Student edition 1966

Library of Congress Catalog Card No. 63-18937

1343/66

CONTENTS

Chapter 10. Radioactive Decay

Chapter 11. The Detection of Nuclear Radiation

Chapter 12. Electronic Techniques

Chapter 13. Alpha and Gamma Radiation

CHAPTER 14. BETA DECAY

CHAPTER 15. THE NEUTRON

CHAPTER 19. NUCLEAR FORCES

CHAPTER 20. NUCLEAR REACTIONS AND NUCLEAR MODELS

CHAPTER 21. ELEMENTARY PARTICLES

PREFACE

THE main purpose of this book is to provide a general coverage of nuclear physics suitable for honours physics students. An attempt has been made to keep the subject matter as self-contained as possible and, for this reason, the first seven chapters deal with those parts of atomic physics, relativity, and quantum mechanics, which are a necessary prelude to the study of nuclear physics. It is, of course, impossible to give, for example, a comprehensive account of quantum mechanics in a single chapter, and it is hoped that the reader will already have some background to this most important aspect of modern physics, or be prepared to follow up the references given at the end of Chapter 6.

The second part of the book, Chapters 8 to 20 inclusive, is concerned with what may be described as "low energy nuclear processes and nuclear structure" the main field of study of nuclear physics in the post 1945 years. The penultimate chapter, on the other hand, deals with the rapidly developing subject of high energy nuclear physics and the light it throws on our knowledge of those peculiar objects we call "elementary particles". There is a growing inclination, an unfortunate one in the author's opinion, for the physics of finite nuclear matter to be divorced from the physics of elementary particles.† In an attempt to offset this tendency, a fairly long and detailed account of elementary particle physics is given in Chapter 21.

In the final chapter, an account is given of our present day knowledge of thermonuclear reactions in stars and also of one of the more successful theories of the origin of the elements. This chapter also illustrates the importance of not keeping the various branches of physics in rigidly separated compartments.

Throughout the book it has not always been possible to avoid the irritating phrase "it can be shown that"; but when this is inevitable, references to original sources have been given, and there is an adequate and up-to-date bibliography.

A few specific comments on some of the chapters may be helpful. Chapters 11 and 12 are devoted to the art of experimental techniques in nuclear physics: the range of detectors of nuclear radiation is continuously extending (the bubble chamber, the semiconduction counter, the spark chamber . . .); the chapter on "Electronic Techniques" does not attempt to give any detailed account of modern multi-channel pulse height analysers, nor does

† The importance of bearing in mind the properties of finite nuclei in studying elementary particles was the theme of Wilkinson's Rutherford Memorial Lecture (1962).

it include any discussion of the transistor equivalents of the thermionic vacuum tube circuits.

There is no attempt to cover any reactor physics; this is best regarded as a new brand of engineering physics, nor are current researches into laboratory controlled thermonuclear reactions mentioned.

Special emphasis should be made of parts of the subject matter of Chapter 16, "Nuclear Magnetism". Although the study of nuclear magnetic resonance in bulk matter is now mainly a sensitive tool for elucidating certain aspects of the solid and liquid state, the writer believes that it is worthwhile discussing such topics as spin–lattice and spin–spin relaxation effects. This chapter also includes a description of the elegant optical methods of determining nuclear magnetic moments. Finally, an account is given of one of the most refined experiments of recent years, the determination of the anomalous part of the gyromagnetic ratio of the muon at CERN.

The chapters need not be read in strict numerical order and it is possible to omit certain sections, such as that on "Angular Correlations in Nuclear Reactions" in Chapter 20, without any loss of understanding of the rest of the book.

Chapter 20, "Nuclear Reactions and Nuclear Models" attempts the well-nigh impossible task of covering an enormous field of "nuclear activity". For this reason, an extensive bibliography is given at the end of this chapter and the reader is urged to look at some of the review articles listed. The important section on the Nuclear Shell Model can be read separately, and it is probably wise to do this, for this model is referred to on several occasions in the earlier chapters.

There is no account included of cosmic ray physics and the remarkable high energy nuclear chain reactions known as extensive air showers. Here in the energy region from 10^{12} to 10^{20} electron volts we enter a domain which seems to be beyond the range of any foreseeable future advances in particle accelerators. These ultra-high energy reactions are omitted from the text,† as they belong to the province of the cosmic ray physicist. Another great problem of cosmic ray physics is also omitted from the book;—"where and how do the primary cosmic ray nuclei attain their enormous energies"?††

Two important contributions to nuclear physics in the past decade have been reluctantly omitted from the book because of the mathematical difficulties involved. The first is the theory of Brueckner‡ in which a determined attack has been made on the fundamental problem of the properties of nuclear matter, using a self-consistent field approach on the assumption that two-body interactions are dominant in the nucleus. The second is the

† The interested reader is referred to the book W. Galbraith, *Extensive Air Showers*, Butterworth's, London, 1958.

†† P. Morrison, *Rev. Mod. Phys.* **29**, 235, 1957.

‡ A useful introduction to Brueckner theory is given in the book D. J. Thouless, *The Quantum Mechanics of Many Body Systems*, Academic Press, 1961.

method of dispersion relations, which has become the cornerstone of theoretical elementary particle physics. A very brief reference to this method is given in Chapter 21.

The author is greatly indebted to Dr. J. E. Evans of A.E.R.E., Harwell, for his encouragement in writing this book. He has read most of the chapters and has provided much helpful constructive criticism. Dr. Evans is also responsible for writing the Section on "Angular Correlations in Nuclear Reactions" in Chapter 20.

It is also a pleasure to acknowledge the help of many of my colleagues at the College of Technology, Oxford, who have read several of the chapters.

The photographic plates numbers I, II, IV, were kindly provided by the Rutherford High Energy Laboratory, Harwell. I should like to thank Mr. T. F. Gubbins for his help in obtaining permission to include these photographs.

Oxford C. M. H. S.

ACKNOWLEDGEMENTS

The following figures have been reproduced by kind permission of the editors of the journals concerned:

Fig. 18, p. 60; G. P. Thomson, *The Wave Mechanics of Free Electrons*, University of Cornell Press, 1930.

Fig. 3, p. 166; and Fig. 7, p. 176, of *Ann. Rev. Nucl. Sci.* **8**, Ann. Reviews Inc.

Fig. 5, p. 262; Fig. 11, p. 277; Fig. 13, p. 287; Fig. 22, p. 304; Fig. 23, p. 307, of *Ann. Rev. Nucl. Sci.* **9**.

Fig. 9, p. 20, of *Ann. Rev. Nucl. Sci.* **10**.

Fig. 16, p. 726, *Nuclear Spectroscopy*, Part B, Editor F. Ajzenberg-Selove, Academic Press, New York.

Fig. 2, p. 381, *Canad. J. Phys.* **30**, 1952.

Fig. 15, p. 95, from L. I. Schiff, *Quantum Mechanics*, 2nd edition, McGraw-Hill, New York, 1955.

Fig. 1, p. 293; Fig. 2, p. 294, *Proc. Phys. Soc.* **A 62**, 1949.

Fig. 7, p. 255, *Proc. Phys. Soc.* **A 66**, 1953.

Diagram on p. 125 of *J. de Phys. et Rad.* **16**, 1955.

Diagram on p. 544 of *Phil. Mag.* **7**, 1904.

From the *Handbuch der Physik*, Springer-Verlag, Berlin: Vol. XLIV, Fig. 17, p. 147; Table 1, p. 162; Table 2, p. 166; Table 1, p. 231.
Vol. XXXIX, Table 5, p. 258.

Fig. 1, p. 639, from *Rev. Sci. Instr.* **27**, 1956.

Questions from the Graduateship of the Institute of Physics examination papers.

Many figures are redrawn from *The Physical Review*, *Physical Review Letters*, and *Reviews of Modern Physics*.

PREFACE TO THE STUDENT EDITION

THE subject matter of this book is nuclear physics at a level suitable for students in their final year of honours physics. To provide a background for the main part of the book, the earlier chapters cover those parts of atomic physics which form an essential prelude to the serious study of nuclear physics.

The opening chapter deals with the early days of atomic physics culminating in Rutherford's discovery of the atomic nucleus. The next four chapters cover the "old" quantum theory of Planck and Bohr, the special theory of relativity (many of the formulae derived here are needed in the later parts of the book) and X-ray and electron diffraction theory.

The chapter on Quantum Mechanics is a long one, but it attempts the difficult task of deriving or summarizing many of the important theoretical results required in later chapters. Nevertheless, it is hoped that the reader has already had an introductory course of quantum mechanics.

The last chapter in the first part of the book, Chapter 7, deals with the experimental methods of determining precise values of atomic masses. A notable feature of the subject matter is an account of the novel mass synchrometer of L. G. Smith.

The main part of the book, Chapters 8 to 20 inclusive, is concerned with low and medium-energy nuclear physics and its relation to our understanding of nuclear structure. It is not necessary to read these chapters in consecutive order. There are many cross-references between the sections of these chapters, a reflection of the closely integrated nature of the subject. It may be advisable to read the section in Chapter 20, on the nuclear shell model, before reading the rest of that long chapter. An important feature of the middle part of the book is the two chapters dealing with particle detection and the associated electronic techniques.

The penultimate chapter is concerned with the rapidly expanding subject of "elementary" particle physics. For this edition the author has added some recent material (1965), in the form of an appendix (Appendix D). This recent material includes a concise account of the prediction and discovery of the Ω^- particle and the apparent failure of time-reversal invariance in neutral K meson decay.

The last chapter is of special interest, illustrating the rich dividends resulting from the overlap and fusion of the disciplines of nuclear reaction theory and astrophysics. An account is given of our present state of knowledge of stellar energy sources and the cosmological origin of the chemical elements.

CHAPTER 1

INTRODUCTION

1.1. KINETIC THEORY OF MATTER

The atomic theory of matter discussed more than 2000 years ago by the Greek philosophers Democritus and Lucretius lay dormant until the beginning of the nineteenth century. John Dalton in 1808 pointed out that the quantitative laws of chemical composition, derived from the gravimetric measurements of the substances involved in chemical reactions, could be explained in terms of an atomic theory. The fact, for example, that gases combine chemically in simple proportions, was interpreted in terms of atoms of certain elements combining to form molecules. Atoms of the same element were postulated to be identical in all respects: size, shape, weight, chemical affinity. In spite of the great advance in chemistry brought about by the Dalton atomic theory there existed as late as 1900 a school of scientists who were reluctant to accept the reality of atoms. Their main objection was the lack of direct evidence of individual atoms and at the time it seemed unlikely that such evidence would ever be found.

The molecular theory of matter was developed in physics in relation to the properties of gases. The fact that the common gases obey the simple laws of Boyle, Charles and Dalton is a reflection of the gaseous state rather than of the individual properties of the constituent molecules. Maxwell and independently Boltzmann, in the second half of the nineteenth century, developed with great skill the statistical theory known as the "Kinetic Theory of Gases". In dealing with the enormous number of molecules in one cubic centimetre of gas, about 10^{19} at S.T.P., a mathematical theory dealing with the motion of each individual molecule is impossible. The only hope of deriving any useful theoretical results is to deal with a large collection of molecules by statistical methods.

Pressure of a Gas

The pressure exerted by a gas on the walls of its containing vessel is a macroscopic manifestation of the rate at which momentum is communicated to unit area of the walls by the rebounding molecules. The pressure p of an ideal gas is given by the expression

$$p = \frac{1}{3} mn\overline{c^2} \tag{1}$$

where m is the mass of a single molecule,
n is the number of molecules per unit volume,
$m\,n = \varrho$, where ϱ is the density of the gas.
$\overline{c^2}$ is the mean square speed of the molecules.

From equation (1), the root mean square speed, $c_{\text{R.M.S.}} = \sqrt{\overline{c^2}}$ is given by

$$c_{\text{R.M.S.}} = \sqrt{\frac{3p}{\varrho}} \tag{2}$$

Typical values at S.T.P. are 1,840 and 460 m per sec for hydrogen and oxygen respectively.

Equipartition of Energy

Combining equation (1) with the equation of state for 1 mole of ideal gas $PV = RT$, the average kinetic energy of a molecule can be expressed in terms of Boltzmann's constant k

$$\frac{1}{2} m\overline{c^2} = \frac{3}{2} kT \tag{3}$$

where $k = R/N$, N being Avogadro's number. Equation (3) is a special case of Boltzmann's Equipartition of Energy theorem which states that the average energy per degree of freedom of a molecule is equal to $\frac{1}{2}kT$. For a monatomic gas, each atom has three degrees of freedom corresponding to the three independent components of translational momentum of the centre of mass of the atom. Diatomic molecules in a gas have five degrees of freedom, the two extra degrees being associated with two independent internal rotations about axes perpendicular to the chemical bond joining the two atoms. Classical Physics cannot account for the absence of rotation of the molecule about the chemical bond or why, below 60°K, hydrogen gas molecules cease to rotate. This behaviour can only be explained in terms of the quantum theory. The equipartition theory is based on the assumption that as a result of many collisions between the particles of a system, a steady state is established with the total available energy equally divided between the individual degrees of freedom. A bold application of the theorem has been made by Fermi to explain the mechanism of acceleration of cosmic ray particles (mainly protons and other light atomic nuclei). There is strong astronomical evidence for the existence of moving clouds of gas in inter-stellar space. Statistically the protons and other cosmic ray nuclei gain energy in colliding with the magnetic fields of these clouds, until the total available energy is shared between the cosmic ray particles and the moving gas clouds† according to the equipartition principle.

† The "temperature" of the assembly of gas clouds is very high.

The Distribution of Molecular Speeds

The individual kinetic energies of the molecules of a gas are spread out over a wide range. This is not surprising in view of the fact that even if at some instant all the molecules had the same energy this state of affairs would not persist for long. At normal pressure and temperature a single molecule experiences about 10^9 intermolecular collisions per second. Some of the molecules will gain energy in collisions, some will lose energy, the average energy depending on the temperature. At each collision the energy of a molecule will in general change; nevertheless the number of molecules in

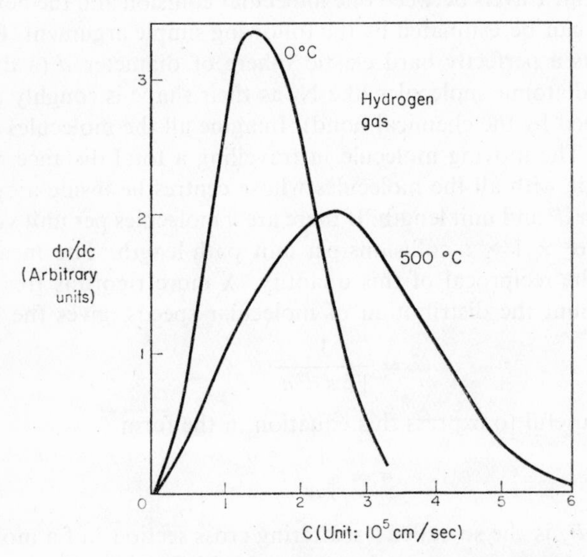

FIG. 1. Maxwell distribution of molecular velocities.

a definite small energy range will not alter, because, for every molecule scattered out of this narrow energy range one on average will be scattered into it. The steady state distribution of speeds amongst a large number of molecules in a gas at temperature T is given by the famous Maxwell law (1869).

The number of molecules dn out of a total number n, whose speed lies between c and $c + dc$ is given by

$$\frac{dn}{dc} = \frac{4n}{\sqrt{\pi}}\left(\frac{m}{2kT}\right)^{\frac{3}{2}} c^2 e^{-mc^2/2kT} \tag{4}$$

For small speeds, $mc^2/2kT \ll 1$, dn/dc is small as the term c^2 dominates the distribution; for high speeds the value of dn/dc is again small because the negative exponent of the exponential factor, which is the kinetic energy of a molecule of speed c divided by the thermal energy kT, is numerically large. The most probable speed at temperature T is found by finding the maximum of the curve dn/dc plotted against c. The peak of the curve corresponds to $\frac{1}{2}m\,c^2 = kT$. An important feature of the distribution curve (Fig. 1) is the existence of a small number of molecules with energies much greater than the most probable energy kT. This is of extreme importance in determining the rate of so-called thermonuclear reactions (Chapter 22).

Mean Free Path and Molecular Cross Section

The mean free path λ of a molecule in a gas is defined as the average distance a molecule travels between one molecular collision and the next. The magnitude of λ can be estimated by the following simple argument. Regard each molecule as a perfectly hard elastic sphere of diameter d (a dubious assumption for diatomic molecules like N_2 as their shape is roughly that of two spheres joined by the chemical bond). Imagine all the molecules except one are at rest. The moving molecule in travelling a total distance of unit length will collide with all the molecules whose centres lie inside a cylinder of cross section $\pi\,d^2$ and unit length. If there are n molecules per unit volume, there will be $\pi\,d^2 \times 1 \times n$ collisions per unit path length. The mean free path λ will be the reciprocal of this quantity. A more rigorous treatment, taking into account the distribution of molecular speeds, gives the result:

$$\lambda = \frac{1}{\sqrt{2}\,\pi\,d^2 n} \tag{5}$$

It is sometimes useful to express this equation in the form

$$\sigma = \frac{1}{\lambda n} \tag{6}$$

where $\sigma = \sqrt{2}\pi\,d^2$, is the so-called "scattering cross section" of a molecule. It has the dimensions of area and it can be regarded as an effective target area offered to a moving molecule in the gas. The larger the cross section the shorter the mean free path. The concept of cross section in atomic and nuclear physics is a useful one provided it is realised that it does not represent the geometrical cross sectional area of a molecule or nucleus.

It is not easy to measure mean free paths by direct experiment. M. Born and E. Bormann (1921) determined the mean free path of silver atoms, emerging from a slit in a small oven, passing through air. The principle of the method is to detect the number of silver atoms which succeed in crossing a plane at distance x from the slit for different values of x. The number $n(x)$ of silver atoms which travel across a plane normal to the beam at distance x without being scattered falls off exponentially with x:

$$n(x) = n(0)\,e^{-x/\lambda} \tag{7}$$

where $n(0)$ is the number of atoms crossing the plane at $x = 0$. It is important to note that more than 37% of the atoms have path lengths greater than the mean free path length λ.

A simpler, though more indirect method of determining λ, is that of Maxwell. He showed that the phenomena of heat conduction, viscosity, and diffusion in gases could be treated by elementary kinetic theory. The viscous forces in a gas arise as a result of the transport of momentum from one region of the gas to another. The coefficient of viscosity η is given by the expression

$$\eta = \frac{1}{3} m n \bar{c} \lambda \tag{8}$$

where $\bar{c}$ is the mean speed of the molecules of the gas

$$\left(\bar{c} = \sqrt{\frac{8}{3\pi}}\, c_{\text{R.M.S.}}\right)$$

Maxwell measured the viscosities of gases and made use of the theoretical result (eqn. 8) to calculate λ. He found values of λ of the order of 10^{-5} cm for gases at S.T.P. Inserting the value of λ in equation (5) one can then obtain a value for $n\,d^2$. A rough estimate of the value of $n\,d^3$ can be made as follows. If the gas could be solidified at room temperature, the concentration of atoms in the solid state n_s would be of the order of $n\,\varrho_s/\varrho$ where ϱ_s is the density in the solid state and ϱ the density in the gaseous state. Now the product $n_s\,d^3$, where d is the diameter of a molecule, is of the order of unit volume as the molecules are closely packed in the solid state. Combining the estimated values of $n\,d^2$ and $n\,d^3$ we find that n is of the order of 10^{19} molecules per cm^3, and d is of the order of 10^{-8} cm (1 Å). A better estimate of n and d is based on the experimental pressure–volume–temperature behaviour of a gas that can be represented by van der Waals' equation:

$$\left(P + \frac{a}{V^2}\right)(V - b) = RT$$

Experimental values of the constant b yield a volume of the order of four times the volume of space occupied by the molecules of the gas.

Molecular diameters deduced by different methods do not agree with one another. This means we should not blindly assume that the concept of molecular diameter is meaningful. In the first place, many gases have molecules which are not spherical. Secondly, the treatment of a molecular collision as a "billiard ball" elastic collision between rigid spheres is too superficial. When two molecules approach one another a complex electrical force of attraction is set up between the constituent electrons and nuclei of the two molecules. This force increases as the molecules approach one another and it changes over to a repulsive force when the electric charge distributions of the two molecules overlap. The effective time of the collision during which the forces are significant is of the order of 10^{-12} sec. It turns out that the closest distance of approach of two colliding molecules decreases with increasing relative velocity of approach. In other words, the effective molecular diameter decreases as the temperature increases! These ideas originated in the work of W. Sutherland (1893) to explain the observed increase of the viscosity of a gas with temperature faster than the $T^{\frac{1}{2}}$ law predicted by eqn. (8) ($\bar{c}$ is proportional to $T^{\frac{1}{2}}$).

Determination of Avogadro's Number N

Estimates of the number of molecules in 1 mole, the Avogadro number N, can be made by the approximate methods described above. One of the most interesting group of determinations of N is based on the physics of what are known as "Fluctuation Phenomena". One of the earliest determinations was carried out by Lord Rayleigh in 1871, who developed a theory to account for the blue of the sky. In considering one cubic centimetre of gas at S.T.P. we do not expect to find observable fluctuations in the density as this volume contains about 10^{19} molecules. However a sphere, whose diameter is of the order of the wavelength of visible light (5×10^{-5} cm), in the upper atmosphere will contain less than 10^6 molecules. The number of molecules in such a volume will experience fluctuations about a mean value. Rayleigh showed that these density fluctuations in the upper atmosphere are responsible for the scattering of sunlight. The effect is more pronounced for blue light than for red because the density fluctuations are more important over a distance corresponding to the shorter wavelength (blue).

Another fluctuation method is based on recording the irregular torsional oscillations of a lightweight coil suspended by a very fine fibre under the random impact of molecules of the air. This is an example of Brownian motion in a gas. The study of Brownian motion in liquids is easier and observations of the haphazard jerky movements of tiny colloidal particles, of diameter less than 10^{-4} cm, suspended in a liquid have led to determinations of N.

J. Perrin was the pioneer in studying the sedimentation equilibrium of a colloidal suspension in a liquid in a quantitative way. A. Westgren (1916) improved on Perrin's method and using smaller particles of colloidal gold obtained a value for N within 1% of the best modern value, a remarkable achievement. The principle of Perrin's method is the following. Consider a large number of tiny spherical particles of the same diameter (about 1 micron. i.e. 10^{-3} mm), suspended in a drop of water, shielded from heating effects, so that no convection currents are produced in the liquid. A bright parallel beam of light passes horizontally through the liquid cell (sealed to prevent loss of liquid by evaporation). The colloidal particles scatter the light and those rays scattered into the objective lens of a high power microscope reveal the positions of the particles if the microscope is focused on a particular horizontal plane in the liquid. Counts can be made at frequent intervals of the number of particles lying in this plane. If a sufficient number of counts is made the mean number n of particles in the plane at a height h

in the suspension can be found. The observations are then repeated with the microscope focused on planes at different heights h. The variation of n with height h is predicted as follows (Fig. 2).

The colloidal particles have a low particle density and can therefore be treated as an ideal gas at a uniform temperature T, corresponding to that of the water. The particles lying between the horizontal planes at height h and $h + dh$ are supported by the difference in pressure dp of the particle gas at these two levels.

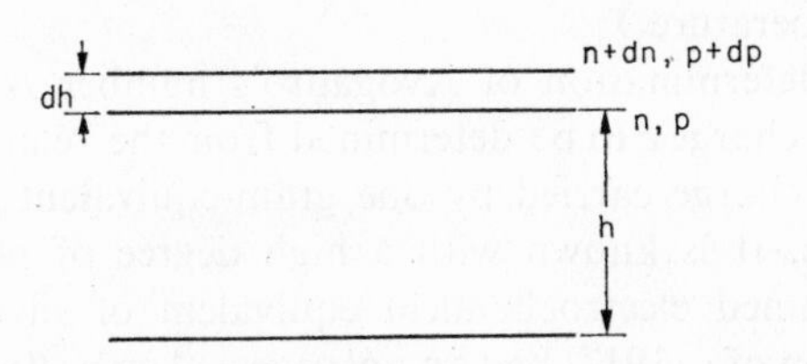

FIG. 2. Boltzmann distribution of particle density.

For a column of unit cross-section we have $-dp = mg \cdot n\,dh$, where mg is the apparent weight of a particle, and n is the number of particles per unit volume at height h. The particle gas pressure $p = nkT$

$$\therefore -dp = -kT\,dn$$

$$\therefore -kT\,dn = mg \cdot n\,dh$$

$$\therefore \int_{n_0}^{n} \frac{dn}{n} = -\int_{0}^{h} \frac{mg\,dh}{kT}$$

$$\therefore \ln\left(\frac{n}{n_0}\right) = -\frac{mgh}{kT} \qquad (9)$$

A plot of $\ln n$ against h enables k to be determined if the apparent weight of the particles can be found. Their radius can be found by observing their terminal velocity of fall in a cloud of particles with the aid of Stokes' law. This combined with a measurement of their density, by finding a liquid in which they neither rise nor sink, enables their weight to be found. From Boltzmann's constant k, we can deduce N from the definition of k as R/N. The steady state distribution of particles under the action of a field of force (gravity) and the effect of random thermal collisions of the surrounding molecules can be expressed by saying that the probability of a particle being found at the level where its potential energy in the field of force is E

($E = mgh$), is proportional to $\exp(-E/kT)$. This is an example of a general theorem due to Boltzmann. One recognizes two opposing influences the effect of random thermal motion, measured by kT, tending to produce all possible values of E with equal frequency, and the effect of the field of force tending to move all the particles to the position of stable equilibrium, i.e. the position of minimum potential energy ($h = 0$). This theorem is of importance when we consider the magnetic effects of atomic nuclei in orientating magnetic fields (Chapter 16). A magnetic dipole moment μ in a magnetic field H has a magnetic potential energy $-\mu H \cos\theta$ where θ is the angle between the axis of the dipole and the magnetic field. The probability of a dipole having an orientation θ will be proportional to $\exp\left(\frac{\mu H \cos\theta}{kT}\right)$, provided the system of dipoles is in thermodynamic equilibrium with the medium at a temperature T.

Any accurate determination of Avogadro's number N enables the fundamental electron charge e to be determined from the relation $F = Ne$. The Faraday F is the charge carried by one gram-equivalent of any species of ion in electrolysis. It is known with a high degree of precision from the accurately determined electrochemical equivalent of silver. Millikan's oil drop determination of e (1917) had an unsuspected error due to an inaccurate value of the viscosity of air being used in determining the radius of a falling droplet. Inserting a more accurate value of the viscosity of air in Millikan's calculation, the value of e agrees closely with the value obtained from the most accurate determination of N and F. The introduction of accurate optical grating methods of measuring X-ray wavelengths in the 1920's meant that the lattice spacing of good crystals such as calcite could be accurately determined. This enables an accurate value of Avogadro's number to be found (Chapter 4).

1.2. CATHODE RAYS AND X-RAYS

The gradual acceptance of the reality of atoms was brought about more by the series of experiments which showed that atoms had constituent parts, rather than by the predictions of chemistry and the kinetic theory of gases. From about 1870 to 1900 the study of electric discharges through rarefied gases excited great interest in the scientific world. This activity culminated in the discovery of the electron and its recognition as a sub-atomic particle. Sir William Crookes was one of the first to realise that the nature of the discharge in a gas at a pressure too low for the gas to be luminous represented a novel or "fourth state of matter". High energy negatively charged particles seemed to be emitted from the negative electrode, carrying with them considerable momentum, as small vanes mounted in the discharge tube were set in rotation. The cathode rays as they came to be called, travel in straight lines and excite fluorescence in the glass walls of the tube. For some time the nature of the rays had been hotly debated. Hertz had maintained that they were some form of aether vibration. Early attempts to deflect the rays with electrostatic fields failed as positive ions, produced by the cathode rays in an imperfect vacuum, accumulated on or near the deflecting plates thereby screening the negatively charged beam of particles from the deflecting field. J. J. Thomson was the first to succeed in improving the vacuum to the stage where the particles were deflected by an electrostatic field. One of the most puzzling properties of the rays was their ability to penetrate thin metallic foils mounted at the end of the discharge tube opposite the cathode. The rays passing through the foil caused the air outside the tube to fluoresce. How could electrically charged particles pass through the densely packed atoms in a metal foil? If the particles were charged atoms (ions) akin to those responsible for the conductivity of electrolytic solutions one would expect that they would be too big to pass through a foil several thousand atomic layers thick. These observations were difficult to reconcile with the particle theory of cathode rays.

J. J. Thomson's classic series of experiments in which he determined the charge to mass ratio e/m of the cathode ray corpuscles and their velocity v are too well known to merit description here. But a few points are worth mentioning. Thomson was too shrewd an investigator to assume that the velocity v of the particles could be calculated from the cathode–anode potential difference V and the e/m ratio by the equation

$$\tfrac{1}{2}mv^2 = Ve$$

This relation is valid provided the vacuum is high enough so that the electrons do not lose any energy in colliding with molecules of residual gas. Thomson determined the electron velocity v by balancing the electrostatic deflecting force against a coterminous magnetic deflecting force in the opposite direction. The velocity v was of the order of 15,000 km per sec a startling result if the mass of the electron was of the order of the mass of an atom. Early estimates of the electron charge e were very rough but they enabled Thomson to conjecture that electrons were sub-atomic particles with a mass of the order of one thousandth of that of the lighest atom (hydrogen). The value of e/m was found to be independent of the nature of the metal cathode and the same result was obtained for electrons ejected from clean metal surfaces by ultraviolet light. Once the reality of the electron as a sub-atomic particle was accepted, various atomic models were proposed in which the negatively charged electrons were assumed to be a part of every atom. Thomson favoured a model in which the electrons were embedded in a much larger sphere of positive electricity, rather like currants in a plum pudding. The atom as a unit is neutral so the charge of all the constituent electrons just balances the positive charge. Many speculations were made in this period (1900–1914) concerning the number Z

of electrons in an atom. This number is now identified with the position of the element in the Periodic Table, the atomic number. Thomson discussed three methods of determining Z: one based on the dispersive power of gases for visible light, the second based on the scattering of X-rays by the electrons in a gas, the third based on the absorption of the beta rays emitted spontaneously by certain radioactive substances (by this time they had been identified as swiftly moving electrons). The theory of the first method was found in the event of later developments to be fundamentally unsound. The second method, although it did not yield results of high accuracy, is of considerable interest and was used by Barkla who found that the number of electrons in an atom is about one half its atomic weight. Barkla's experiment is described later in this chapter. The third method gave results in general agreement with the X-ray scattering experiments.

X-rays

In November 1895 W. K. Röntgen announced the discovery of a new radiation which was emitted from the walls of a cathode ray tube. This X-radiation, as it came to be known in this country, is emitted by electrons when they strike the walls or a metal target mounted inside the discharge tube. Röntgen found that the radiation would pass through thin sheets of cardboard and metal and excite fluorescence in certain chemical salts. The discovery should have been made earlier as one worker ordered a laboratory steward to keep boxes of photographic plates away from the vicinity of a cathode ray tube as the plates become fogged! The ionizing effect of the rays, which is intimately connected with their action on a photographic emulsion, is one of their most useful properties. During the next fifteen years the nature of the X-rays was hotly debated. The ionizing property strongly suggested that they were particles. On the other hand, the rays could not be deflected by electric or magnetic fields. Attempts to refract the rays with prisms and to reflect them rather than diffusely scatter them from polished mirrors were unsuccessful. Haga and Wind in Germany in 1902 detected a broadening of the image of a fine wedged-shaped slit, and suggested that the degree of diffraction of the radiation passing through the fine slit was compatible with a wavelength of the order of 10^{-8} cm. These diffraction experiments were not considered as convincing proof of the electromagnetic wave nature of X-rays as they were difficult to reproduce and it was not certain whether the effects were due to the scattering of the radiation from the edge of the slit. J. J. Thomson and other people had realized that if X-rays were electromagnetic waves of wavelength of the order of 10^{-8} cm, the refractive index of media should be slightly less than unity and the refraction of the rays would be very difficult to observe. C. G. Barkla, a former research student of J. J. Thomson, carried out a number of experiments on the penetrating power of X-rays before and after they were diffusely scattered by light elements. The scattered radiation was of two kinds; one kind had the same absorption coefficient in aluminium foil as the primary radiation, the other kind was more homogeneous and more easily absorbed and was characteristic of the scattering element. The homogeneous X-rays proved to be fluorescent radiation excited by the primary radiation incident on the scatterer. Barkla showed by a double scattering experiment that the rays could be polarized, that is that the radiation scattered from the second scatterer is anisotropic. This was strong evidence for the transverse nature of the electromagnetic waves.

The conclusive demonstration that X-rays were electromagnetic waves of short wavelength came about in Munich in the following way. P. P. Ewald a young research student in 1912 consulted M. von Laue about a theoretical problem concerning the transmission of light through a crystal. He was interested in the interaction of the light with the atomic lattice. von Laue realized that if the wavelength was much shorter than that of visible light, in fact if it was of the order of 1 Å unit the crystal lattice might act as a three-dimensional diffraction grating. The waves scattered by the periodic lattice structure would in certain directions reinforce one another and produce detectable diffracted beams. von Laue suggested that such an experiment should be carried out using a fine beam of X-rays. W. Friedrich and P. Knipping carried out experiments and eventually succeeded in recording a diffraction pattern on a photographic plate placed behind a zinc sulphide crystal normal to the direction of the beam incident on the crystal. Later in the year, W. L. Bragg read a paper in Cambridge which treated the diffraction of X-rays by a crystal in a simple way. Each diffracted beam is produced as if it were due to the superposition of a large number of reflected beams from parallel planes inside the crystal which possess a high density of atoms. In general, these internally reflected beams are out of phase with one another and destructively interfere. However for certain angles of incidence on these internal lattice planes, the reflected waves are all in phase and an observable beam emerges from the crystal.

1.3. THE NUMBER OF ELECTRONS IN AN ATOM, Z

Soon after the discovery of the electron (1895) various atomic models were proposed. One method of determining the number of electrons per atom Z was suggested by J. J. Thomson's theory of the scattering of X-rays by free electrons. Barkla measured the scattered intensity of X-rays from light elements and gases and showed that for light atoms Z is about one half the atomic weight of the element A.

Consider a free or loosely bound electron set into forced oscillation by an electromagnetic wave $\boldsymbol{E} = \boldsymbol{E}_0 \sin\omega t$. The electron will have a forced acceleration $a = e\,(E_0/m) \sin\omega t$. According to Maxwell's electromagnetic theory an accelerated charged particle emits radiation at the rate

$$\frac{2}{3}\frac{e^2}{c^3}|\boldsymbol{a}|^2 \text{ ergs per sec} \tag{10}$$

where e is the charge in e.s.u.

c is the velocity of light *in vacuo* in c.g.s. units and $\boldsymbol{a}$ is the particle acceleration in c.g.s. units. The mean rate of emission of energy by the oscillating electron is given by P:

$$P = \frac{1}{3}\frac{e^2}{c^3}\left(\frac{eE_0}{m}\right)^2 \tag{11}$$

as the mean value of E^2 per oscillation is $E_0^2/2$.

The energy density of radiation in an electromagnetic field is given by

$$\frac{KE^2}{8\pi} + \frac{\mu H^2}{8\pi} = \frac{2KE^2}{8\pi} \tag{12}$$

where K is the dielectric constant of the medium and μ is the magnetic permeability of the medium; E is the electric field intensity; H is the magnetic field intensity.

$KE^2/8\pi = \mu H^2/8\pi$ for an electromagnetic wave in free space. The intensity I_0 of a parallel beam of X-rays is the energy crossing unit area normally per second. This is equal to the energy residing in a cylinder of length c and unit cross-sectional area.

$$I_0 = c \times \text{time average value of}\left(\frac{2KE^2}{8\pi}\right) = \frac{cE_0^2}{8\pi} \tag{13}$$

K, being taken to be unity (*in vacuo*).

The power P radiated by a single electron under the stimulus of an incident X-ray beam of intensity I_0 can be written in the form

$$P = \frac{1}{3}\frac{e^2}{c^3}\frac{e^2}{m^2}\frac{8\pi I_0}{c} = \left(\frac{8\pi}{3}\right)\left(\frac{e^2}{mc^2}\right)^2 I_0 \tag{14}$$

combining equations (11) and (13).

The quantity e^2/mc^2 is of the dimensions of length and is known as the classical electron radius ($2{\cdot}82 \times 10^{-13}$ cm). The concept of a sharply defined radius for an electron is inadmissible according to modern atomic theory.

An alternative and instructive method of deriving the ratio P/I_0 is the following. Consider a parallel beam of plane polarized X-rays travelling in the direction AB. The electric field E of the incident wave is normal to the plane of the diagram (Fig. 3 (a)). A free electron at B is set into vibration and we are interested in the amplitude of the scattered wave at P.

The oscillating electron at B radiates a wave of the same frequency ν as the incident wave and the effect can be considered as one of coherent scattering (Thomson scattering).

The amplitude of the scattered wave at P, $a_{r,\theta}$ will be independent of θ when the electric vector $\boldsymbol{E}$ of the incident wave is normal to the plane ABP. It is given by

$$a_{r,\theta} = \frac{a_0}{r} \cdot \left(\frac{e^2}{mc^2}\right) \tag{15}$$

where a_0 is the amplitude of the incident wave at B.

e^2/mc^2 is the classical electron radius (e is measured in e.s.u.). A naive argument suggests that at the "surface" of the electron $r = e^2/mc^2$, the scattered amplitude must equal the incident amplitude. This condition is satisfied by the equation.

For an incident wave train of amplitude a_0, plane polarized with the electric vector $\boldsymbol{E}$ lying in the plane ABP (Fig. 3(b)) the scattering is no

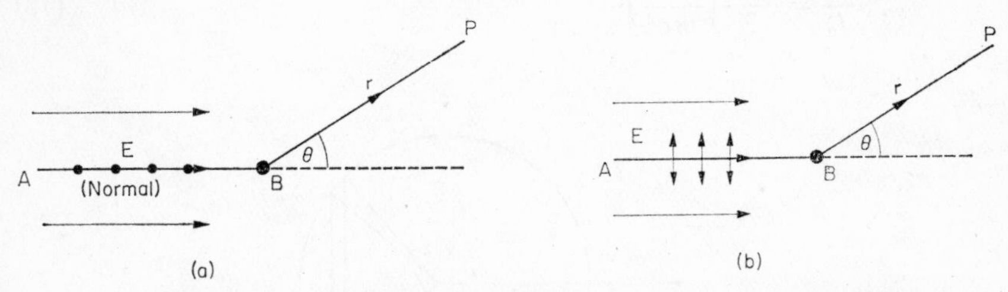

FIG. 3. Scattering of plane polarized X-ray wave train by a "free" electron (a) Electric vector $\boldsymbol{E}$ normal to the plane A B P, (b) Electric vector $\boldsymbol{E}$ in the plane A B P.

longer isotropic in the plane of the diagram. The effective component of the vibrating electron's displacement is the one transverse to the vector **BP**. The scattered amplitude at P, $a_{r,\theta}$ is now given by

$$a_{r,\theta} = \frac{a_0}{r} \left(\frac{e^2}{mc^2}\right) \cos\theta \tag{16}$$

The intensity $I_{r,\theta}$ of the scattered radiation at P for unpolarized incident radiation of intensity I_0 is given by

$$I_{r,\theta} = \frac{I_0}{r^2} \left(\frac{e^2}{mc^2}\right)^2 \left(\frac{1 + \cos^2\theta}{2}\right) \tag{17}$$

remembering that I is proportional to a^2 and averaging the two polarization components.

The total scattered energy per second is obtained by integrating $I_{r,\theta}$ over the surface of a sphere centre B and radius r (Fig. 4).

$$P = \int_S I_{r,\theta}\, dS$$

where dS is element of area cut off by two cones vertex B, semi-vertical angles θ and $\theta + d\theta$ on the surface of the sphere

$$dS = 2\pi r \sin\theta \cdot r d\theta$$

$$\therefore P = \int_0^{\pi} \frac{I_0}{r^2}\left(\frac{e^2}{mc^2}\right)^2 \left(\frac{1+\cos^2\theta}{2}\right) 2\pi r^2 \sin\theta\, d\theta$$

$$\therefore P = \pi I_0 \left(\frac{e^2}{mc^2}\right)^2 \int_0^{\pi} [\sin\theta + \cos^2\theta \sin\theta]\, d\theta$$

$$\therefore P = \pi I_0 \left(\frac{e^2}{mc^2}\right)^2 \left[-\cos\theta - \frac{\cos^3\theta}{3}\right]_0^{\pi} = \frac{8}{3}\pi I_0 \left(\frac{e^2}{mc^2}\right)^2$$

$$\therefore \frac{P}{I_0} = \frac{8\pi}{3}\left(\frac{e^2}{mc^2}\right)^2 \qquad (18)$$

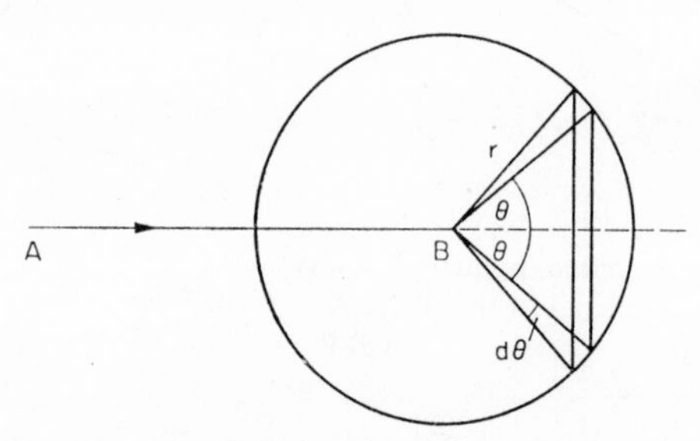

FIG. 4. Incident X-rays scattered by "free" electron at B into elementary cone lying between angles θ and $\theta + d\theta$.

This is the same as the result given by eqn. (14). The power of the scattered radiation is the product of I_0 and the Thomson scattering cross section of the electron σ_e

$$\sigma_e = \frac{8\pi}{3} \cdot \left(\frac{e^2}{mc^2}\right)^2 \text{cm}^2 = 6{\cdot}65 \times 10^{-25}\,\text{cm}^2$$

Consider the scattering by a large number of electrons acting independently in a gas, then the power scattered by one cubic centimetre of gas is

$$P = I_0 \sigma_e \times Z \times n \qquad (19)$$

where n is the number of atoms per cm^3, and Z is the number of electrons per atom.

Barkla (1904, 1911) measured the intensity of a beam of X-rays scattered by a known gas volume in the following way (Fig. 5). A beam of X-rays passed through two apertures Q and R in lead plates. Some of the rays scattered by the gas (air) in the volume ABCD ($\sim$200 cm³) were detected by the sensitive electroscope M. The rate of fall of the leaf of the electroscope was observed by means of a microscope. This was a measure of the rate of ionization and therefore of the rate at which scattered radiation entered the sensitive volume of the electroscope. The fraction of scattered radiation from the volume of gas ABCD which falls on the aperture V (5 cm $\times$ 5 cm) is $\omega/4\pi$, where ω is the solid angle subtended by the aperture at the point 0, the centre of the scattering region ABCD. Barkla verified that the scattered

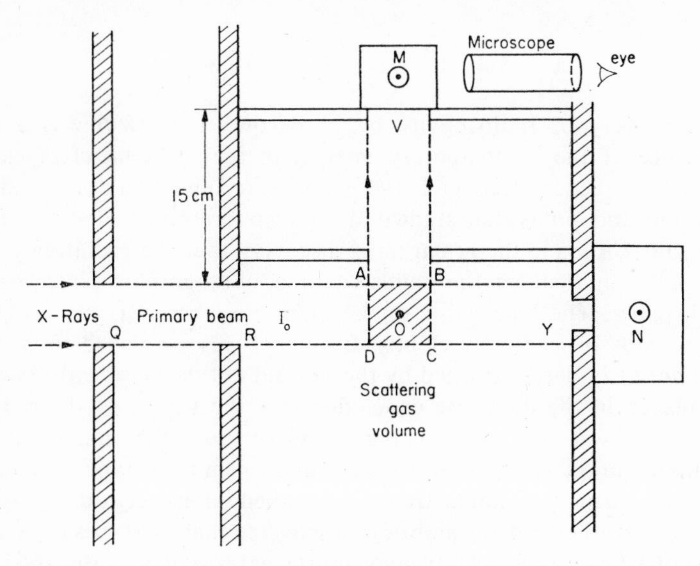

FIG. 5. Barkla's experiment on X-ray scattering by a gas to determine Z the number of electrons per atom.

radiation had the same absorption coefficient as the primary beam by placing thin foils over the apertures V and Y. The size of the aperture Y was much less than that of V so that the ionization rates in the sensitive volumes of the two electroscopes were of the same order. The ratio of the scattered power to the incident intensity depends on the ratio of the rates of discharge of M and N, the solid angle ω, and the ratio of the area of the two apertures. The scattered beam at V was as small as 10^{-5} times the primary beam intensity at 0.

The principle of the experiment assumed that the scattered radiation was of the same wavelength as the primary radiation and that it was scattered isotropically. At the time, the existence of scattered radiation of longer wavelength (the Compton effect) was unknown. It is essential that the electrons in the scattering volume ABCD scatter the primary X-rays so that phase differences between the scattered waves from the electrons are completely random. A single crystal or polycrystalline material or powder would produce coherent diffracted cones of X-rays in certain directions. In other words, the radiation is preferentially scattered in some directions and the fraction of radiation falling on the aperture V may be greater or smaller than $\omega/4\pi$ times the total scattered radiation. In spite of the difficulties and uncertainties of the method, Barkla succeeded in showing, that at least for elements of low atomic weight A, the number of electrons per atom is of the order of one half the mass number A.

1.4. RADIOACTIVITY

The discovery of radioactivity by H. Becquerel in 1896 was a direct consequence of the contemporary interest in the phenomena of cathode rays and fluorescence. Becquerel after exposing to sunlight a double sulphate of uranium and potassium studied the phosphorescent radiation emitted by this salt. He made the remarkable discovery that the radiation emitted by the salt would affect the emulsion of a photographic plate wrapped in black paper. The blackening of the plate, however, was just as intense if the sun was obscured by clouds. Becquerel was perplexed to find that the amount of radiation emitted by the salt did not decrease with time after it was placed in the dark. He concluded that the source of the radiation from the salt was not stored energy received from the sun. Other salts of uranium and the element itself were found to emit this type of radiation.

This phenomenon of radioactivity was studied intensively during the next few years. E. Rutherford at Cambridge discovered that two types of radiation were emitted: α-rays which strongly ionize gases and are absorbed by a thick sheet of paper, and β-rays which have a much smaller ionizing power but will penetrate absorbers ten to a hundred times the thickness of paper. The β-rays were deflected by a magnetic field in a direction corresponding to the hypothesis that the rays consist of negatively charged particles. Before long it was apparent that they were in fact swiftly moving electrons. Early attempts to deflect the α-rays with magnetic fields failed, but in 1903 Rutherford using strong fields (6000 gauss) showed that the rays consist of massive positively charged particles. Measurements of the charge-to-mass ratio and of the velocity of the α-particles agreed with the theory that they were high energy doubly charged helium ions He^{++}. This conclusion was verified in an elegant way by an experiment of Rutherford and Royds in 1909, in which the α-particles emitted by radon, a radioactive gas, passed through a very thin glass walled tube into a thick walled surrounding glass tube. After a few days it was shown spectroscopically that helium gas had slowly accumulated in the outer tube. The α-particles had been slowed down to rest in the wall of the outer tube and after acquiring two electrons, the neutral helium atoms slowly diffused out of the wall. Rutherford realized that the combination of a large mass for the α-particles, about 8000 times the electron mass, and a velocity of emission of the order of one tenth of the velocity of light, meant that the kinetic energy of an α-particle was of the order of 5 million electron volts! This discovery was so unexpected, it seemed to defy the law of conservation of energy, that the phenomena associated with radioactivity were regarded with deep suspicion. Rutherford was impressed with the high energy carried away by individual α-particles and he realized that many important discoveries might result from an active study of their properties. Later events justified this belief as the atomic nucleus and the first artificial nuclear transformation were discovered with the aid of α-rays.

Meanwhile, Pierre and Marie Curie in Paris had shown that thorium was a radioactive element and that the radioactivity of a uranium bearing ore known as pitchblende was higher than expected. They managed after much arduous toil in showing that the high activity of the pitchblende was due to the presence of two new radioactive elements. These elements were named polonium and radium. Great interest was aroused in the element radium as its activity gram for gram was more than a million times that of uranium!

Four years after the discovery of the radioactivity of uranium P. Villard (1900) discovered that radium emits, in addition to the alpha radiation, a very penetrating radiation, requiring 8 cm of aluminium to reduce the intensity by half. This γ-radiation as it was called, could not be deflected by magnetic fields. It was suspected that γ-radiation might be a form of short wavelength electromagnetic radiation, shorter in wavelength by a factor of ten compared with the newly discovered X-radiation. This was confirmed in 1914 when Rutherford and Andrade determined the wavelengths of the γ-rays emitted by the radioactive elements known as RaB and RaC by the crystal diffraction method.

The curious property of radioactivity that the rate of emission of the radiation decreases exponentially with time was not noticed at first. This is not surprising as the half-life of uranium, that is, the time for the activity to halve itself is $> 10^9$ years. A long and intricate series of investigations by many workers showed that there existed a number of radioactive elements deriving from uranium, thorium or actinium. The elements in these series had a wide range of half-life from 10^{10} y to about 10^{-6} sec. The uranium series starts with the decay of uranium and ends with a stable form of lead:

$$U \rightarrow A \rightarrow B \rightarrow C \rightarrow D \cdots Pb \text{ (stable)}$$

The symbols A, B, C, D, . . . , etc. denoting radioactive elements formed in the decay chain.

The stumbling block to an understanding of radioactivity is the apparent breakdown of the law of conservation of energy. The rate of emission of energy is uninfluenced by chemical composition, extremes of temperature and pressure, the exposure to ultraviolet light, etc. Nevertheless, in 1903 Rutherford and Soddy formulated the fundamental laws of radioactivity.

(1) Radioactive elements such as uranium and thorium are continuously being transformed into new kinds of matter, which are themselves radioactive.

(2) A certain fraction of the *atoms* of the radioactive element spontaneously transform themselves into new atoms of a different element. These changes involve the emission of energy and are of a different kind from those associated with chemical change.

(3) The number of atoms which disintegrate in unit time is directly proportional to the number of atoms of the radioactive element. This means that the number of atoms n of the radioelement decreases with time:

$$n = n_0 e^{-\lambda t}$$

where n_0 is the number of atoms at time $t = 0$ and λ is a constant characteristic of the element the so-called decay constant.

The rate of decay itself, dn/dt, follows an exponential decay law.

λ is uninfluenced by external conditions.

(4) It seemed likely that the change from one element to another was in fact due to the emission of either an α- or a β-particle. The possible emission of a γ-ray would not alter the chemical nature of the disintegrating atom.

A clear-cut statement of the last point is contained in the "Radioactive Displacement Laws" stated by A. S. Russell, K. Fajans and F. Soddy in 1913:

A disintegration of an atom by the emission of an alpha particle produces an atom two places lower down in the Periodic Table, of atomic weight approximately 4 units lower. A disintegration involving the emission of a beta particle produces an atom one place higher in the table, but does not change the atomic weight.

1.5. ISOTOPES

As long ago as 1815 Prout had suggested that the atoms of all elements are built up from hydrogen atoms. This hypothesis seemed unlikely when the atomic weights of elements were accurately determined and some of them were found to have non-integral values, the notable example being chlorine with an atomic weight of 35·46. In searching for the element that transforms into radium, Boltwood (1907) found that a radioactive element with half-life about 10^5 years is the parent element, but ionium, as it was named, could not be chemically separated from thorium. The end products of the radioactive uranium and thorium series were identified as lead but the two forms of lead were found to have atomic weights of 206 and 208 respectively. Soddy coined the word *isotope* for atomic species with different atomic weights but which are chemically inseparable (1905).

A few years later, J. J. Thomson showed that neon, a light stable element, possessed two isotopes of mass 20 and 22. A beam of positively charged neon ions was deflected by coterminous parallel electric and magnetic fields, the field directions being normal to the direction of travel of a fine beam of neon ions. The ions were recorded on a photographic plate placed at right angles to the undeflected beam direction. Ions with the same value of e/m but differing in velocity were recorded as a parabolic trace on the plate. Ions with different e/m form separate parabolas. The parabolic trace due to the neon 20 isotope was about ten times as intense as the neon 22 trace. This fits in with the chemical atomic weight of 22·2, if natural neon is a mixture of isotopes of mass 20 and 22 in the ratio of 9 to 1. The possibility of the mass 22 parabola being produced by NeH_2, where two hydrogen atoms combine with a Ne^{20} atom, although remote, could not be ruled out.

The experimental evidence for the existence of isotopes of many elements was firmly established by the pioneer work of Aston who invented the mass spectrograph (1919), which not only dispersed ions of different e/m but focused each group on a photographic plate for a wide range of velocity. Within the space of a few years Aston had determined the masses of the isotopes of many elements.

1.6. THE NUCLEAR MODEL OF THE ATOM

By 1911 it was known that:

(a) Electrons were much lighter than atoms and that the number of electrons per atom is about half the atomic weight.

(b) Alpha particles emitted by radioactive elements can pass through very thin foils.

(c) The energy of individual alpha particles is far in excess of the highest energies gained by the electrons or ions in cathode ray tubes.

(d) Alpha particles could be individually counted by observing the tiny flash of light emitted when they strike a zinc sulphide screen. (The first instance of the detection of *individual* atomic particles) (1903).

Rutherford and Geiger in 1908 carried out experiments to count α-particles with the gas counter newly invented by Geiger. Incidentally they needed to estimate the effect of scattering by atoms as the α-particles passed through matter. Geiger studied the small angle scattering and found nothing very unexpected or startling. A year later however, Geiger and Masden at Rutherford's suggestion, discovered the remarkable result that very occasionally an α-particle is so violently scattered in a thin foil that it emerges on the same side of the foil at which it entered. The α-particle was known to be a helium ion He^{++} and not a light particle like an electron and Rutherford believed that only a very strong repulsive electric field due to a concentrated positively charged *nucleus* at the centre of the atom could be responsible for the rare large angle deflections.

In view of the importance of Rutherford's theory it is worthwhile considering the possibility of large angle deflections arising as the result of multiple scattering events.

The effect of multiple atomic scattering experienced by an α-particle passing through a very thin foil can be treated by statistical methods.

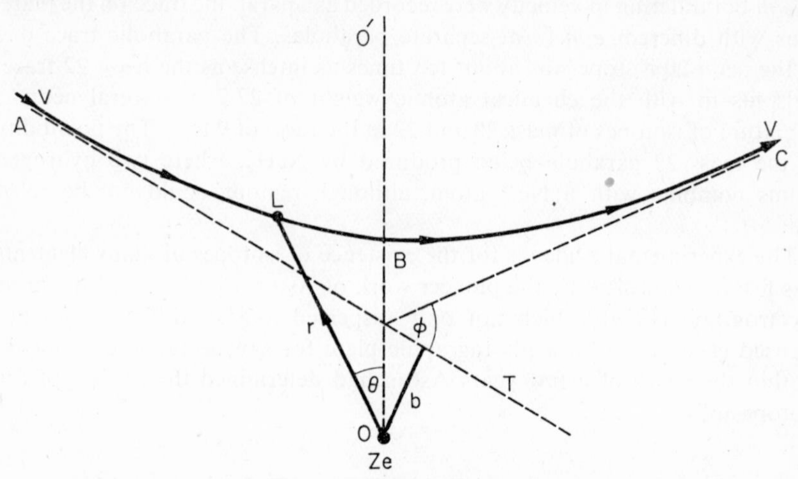

FIG. 6. Scattering of an α-particle by a heavy nucleus of charge *Ze*.

It can be shown that the probability of an α-particle being deflected through an angle $>\varphi_1$, in traversing a thin foil of thickness t is

$$\exp\left(-\frac{\varphi_1^2}{\overline{\varphi^2}}\right) \tag{20}$$

where $\overline{\varphi^2}$, the mean squared deflection is proportional to t.

It is found that for typical α-particles $\sqrt{\overline{\varphi^2}}$ is $\sim 1°$, for a gold foil 4×10^{-5} cm thick.

This means that the probability of an α-particle being deflected through an angle $\geqq 10°$ by multiple scattering is $\sim e^{-100}$. This is far too small, by many orders of magnitude, to account for the observed infrequent large angle deflections.

Let us now consider the Rutherford theory of large angle α-particle scattering. This is the result of a single scattering event when an incident α-particle closely approaches the concentrated atomic nucleus. For a foil of high atomic number, e.g. gold (79), the mass of the nucleus is $\gg$ mass of the α-particle and we can ignore the recoil motion of the nucleus resulting from the Coulomb interaction. An α-particle of velocity v (Fig. 6) travelling initially in the direction AT is deflected along a hyperbolic orbit ABC by the atomic nucleus of charge Ze at 0. If there were no Coloumb interaction between the α-particle, of charge ze, and the nucleus the closest distance between the two would be $= b$. (b is known as the "impact parameter".)

The line O O′ bisecting the initial and final directions of travel of the α-particle is a symmetry axis. Hence the only momentum component acquired by the particle during the Coulomb collision is parallel to the direction OO′.

The momentum p transferred to the α-particle during the collision is given by

$$p = 2mv\cos\left(\frac{\pi}{2} - \frac{\varphi}{2}\right) = 2mv\sin\frac{\varphi}{2} \tag{21}$$

Alternatively using Newton's second law of motion, $F = dp/dt$, where F is the force between the two bodies

$$p = \int_{-\infty}^{\infty} F(r)\cos\theta\, dt \tag{22}$$

where $F(r)$ is the Coulomb force when the α-particle is at distance r from the nucleus, the position vector **OL** making angle θ with the symmetry axis OO′

$$F(r) = \frac{Zze^2}{r^2}$$

Angular momentum of the α-particle about the nucleus must be conserved. Equating the value when the α-particle is a long way from O to the value at L:

$$mvb = mr^2\cdot\frac{d\theta}{dt} \tag{23}$$

where m is the mass of the α-particle. At L the moment of inertia of the α-particle about O is $m\,r^2$, and it is swinging about O with an instantaneous angular velocity $d\theta/dt$.

$$\therefore p = \int_{-(\pi/2-\varphi/2)}^{\pi/2-\varphi/2} \frac{Zze^2}{r^2}\cos\theta\,\frac{r^2}{vb}\,d\theta = \frac{2Zze^2}{vb}\cos\frac{\varphi}{2} \tag{24}$$

N.B. For any other law except the inverse square, the terms in r under the integral sign would not have cancelled and more information about the shape of the particle orbit would be required.

Equating eqns. (21) and (24) we find that

$$b = \frac{Zze^2}{mv^2}\cot\frac{\varphi}{2} \tag{25}$$

For a head-on collision ($b = 0$) $\varphi = \pi$, i.e. the α-particle is slowed down by the nucleus, brought to rest at a distance ($Zze^2/2mv^2$) from the nucleus, and then repelled away along its original trajectory.

Differentiating eqn. (25): $|db| = \dfrac{Zze^2}{2mv^2} \operatorname{cosec}^2 \dfrac{\varphi}{2}\, d\varphi$.

Consider an annular ring of area $2\pi b\, db$ (Fig. 7) described around the nucleus at O normal to the incident direction of travel of the α-particle beam. If, by chance, the particle has an impact parameter in the range b to $b + db$ it will be scattered between angles φ and $\varphi + d\varphi$. If this

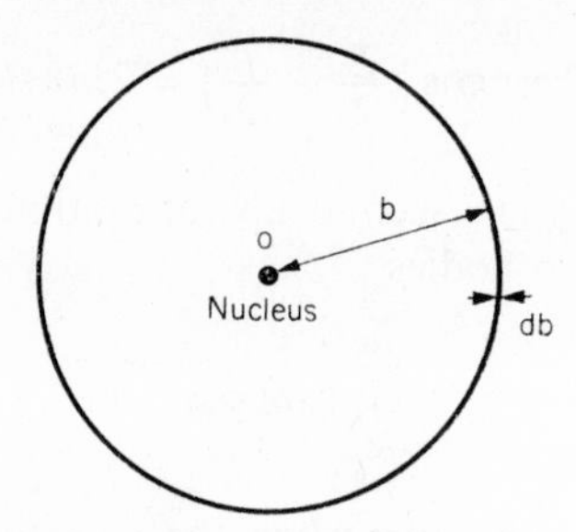

FIG. 7. Annular ring corresponding to impact parameters b and $b + db$ for an incident α-particle.

was the only nucleus in a foil of unit cross-sectional area, the probability of the incident α-particle passing within a range b to db would be the ratio of the area of the ring to the foil

$$\frac{2\pi b \cdot db}{1} = \pi \left(\frac{Zze^2}{mv^2}\right)^2 \cot \frac{\varphi}{2} \operatorname{cosec}^2 \frac{\varphi}{2}\, d\varphi \tag{26}$$

α-particles scattered between angles φ and $\varphi + d\varphi$ lie within two cones enclosing a solid angle $d\omega = 2\pi \sin\varphi\, d\varphi$.

The probability of the α-particle being deflected by a given nucleus through angle φ into a solid angle $d\omega$ is given by

$$d\sigma = \left(\frac{Zze^2}{2mv^2}\right)^2 \operatorname{cosec}^4 \frac{\varphi}{2}\, d\omega \tag{27}$$

$d\sigma/d\omega$ is known as the differential scattering cross section. The fraction F of incident α-particles scattered by a foil, containing nt atoms per cm^2, (t the thickness, n the number of atoms per cm^3), which strike a small screen of area dS distant r from the centre of the foil is

$$F = nt \left(\frac{Zze^2}{2mv^2}\right)^2 \operatorname{cosec}^4 \frac{\varphi}{2} \frac{dS}{r^2} \tag{28}$$

where φ is the angle between the incident α-particle direction and the line from the centre of the foil to the centre of the screen.

Geiger and Marsden's Experiment

A collimated beam of α-particles emerges from a fine channel in the block R (Fig. 8). The air is pumped out of the apparatus via the tube T. Alpha-particles scattered by the foil (typical thickness 3×10^{-5} cm) are detected by the scintillations produced in the small fluorescent screen dS

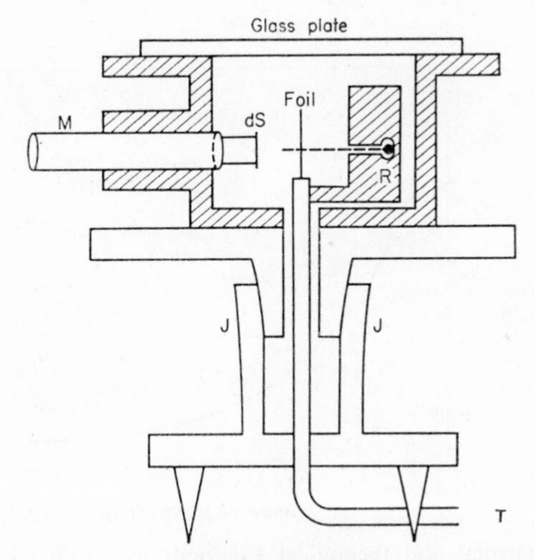

FIG. 8. Apparatus of Geiger and Marsden to study α-particle scattering. (Redrawn from RUTHERFORD, CHADWICK and ELLIS, *Radiations from Radioactive Substances*, Cambridge University Press.)

mounted in front of the objective of a low power microscope M. The microscope and screen could be rotated about a vertical axis in the plane of the foil by means of the ground conical joint J. The number of scintillations per unit time can be measured for different values of φ by rotating the microscope and screen. Visual observation is very tedious and if the scintillation rate is very small, some scintillations may be missed, if it is too fast the human eye cannot resolve them. Account must be taken of the decrease in the number of incident α-particles if the half life of the α-emitter is not enormously greater than the time of the experiment. F decreases very rapidly with increase of φ, $\text{cosec}^4(\varphi/2)$ decreases by a factor of more than 1000 between $\varphi = 10°$ and $\varphi = 60°$. For observations at small angles a much weaker source is necessary.

The dependence of F on the different variables can be tested one at a time:

(a) $F \propto Z^2$, where Z is the atomic number of the scattering foil.
(b) $F \propto 1/E^2$, where E is the kinetic energy of the α-particle.
(c) $F \propto \text{cosec}^4(\varphi/2)$.

The verification of the $\text{cosec}^4(\varphi/2)$ relation is a convincing demonstration of the correctness of Rutherford's theory (see Fig. 9).

These experiments not only demonstrated the correctness of the nuclear model of the atom but allowed estimates to be made of nuclear size. The fact that there are no observed deviations from the Coulomb scattering law for incident α-particle energies up to 8 MeV, means that even when the impact parameter b is zero, the incident particles are turned back ($\varphi = 180°$)

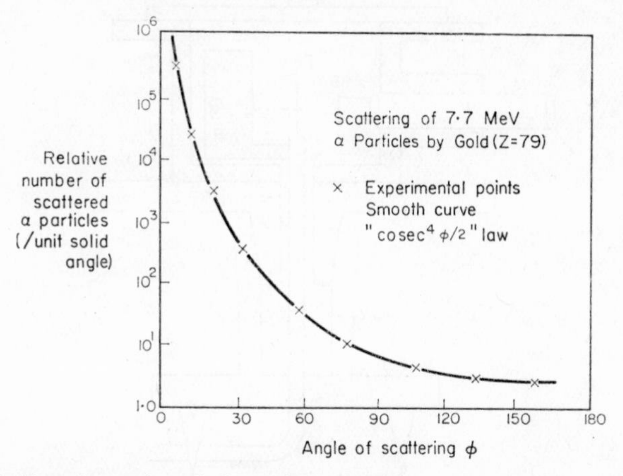

FIG. 9. Experimental and theoretical Coulomb scattering of α-particles.

before they reach the surface of the nucleus. This closest distance of approach sets an upper limit for the size of the nucleus.

In the case of gold ($Z = 79$), the upper limit to the nuclear radius R_{max} is given by

$Z z e^2/R_{max} = E$, (equating the loss of kinetic energy to the gain of potential energy)

for $E = 8$ MeV $= 8 \times 1{\cdot}6 \times 10^{-6}$ ergs,

$Z = 79$, $z = 2$, $e = 4{\cdot}8 \times 10^{-10}$ e.s.u.

we find $R_{max} = 2{\cdot}9 \times 10^{-12}$ cm.

This means that the nuclear radius is about 10^{-4} of the atomic radius.

Determination of Nuclear Charge

J. Chadwick (1920) used the nuclear (Coulomb) scattering of α-particles by very thin foils to determine in an absolute way the nuclear charge of several elements. In order to increase the number of α-particles scattered between angles φ_1, and φ_2 which impinge on a small scintillation screen, he mounted a very thin foil as an annular ring in a metal plate (Fig. 10).

Counting the number of α-particles scattered between angles φ_1, and φ_2 by a foil of known thickness t and atomic density n, and comparing this value with the incident number enables Z to be determined from eqn. (28) if the energy of the α-particles is known. Chadwick obtained the following values for Z:

Copper	Silver	Platinum
29·3	46·3	77·4

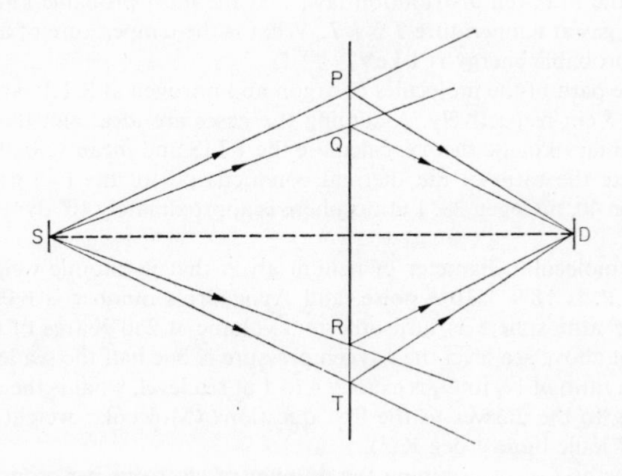

FIG. 10. Chadwick's determination of nuclear charge Z. α-particles emitted by source S are scattered by a thin annular foil P Q, R T, and detected by the scintillation screen at D.

corresponding to the atomic numbers in the Periodic Table of 29, 47 and 78 respectively. Considering the difficulties of attaining very high accuracy with the scintillation detector, this experiment confirms the suggestion first made by van den Broek in 1913 that the "Charge on the atomic nucleus is equal to the atomic number".

It is interesting to contrast Barkla's X-ray scattering determination of the number of electrons in an atom with Chadwick's determination of the number of positive units of charge in the nucleus. In the first method, the nucleus has a negligible effect in scattering the X-rays as the scattered intensity varies inversely as the square of the mass of the charged particle scattering the radiation, while in the second method the heavy α-particle is not sensibly deflected by the much lighter electrons in the foil. In a thick foil, however, the α-particles would transfer a lot of energy to the atomic electrons, thereby significantly reducing the energy E of the α-particle.

BIBLIOGRAPHY

Sir J. H. JEANS, *An Introduction to the Kinetic Theory of Gases*, Cambridge University Press, 1946.

E. H. KENNARD, *Kinetic Theory of Gases*, McGraw-Hill, New York 1938.

Lord RAYLEIGH, *The Life of Sir J. J. Thomson*, Cambridge University Press, 1942.

Sir E. RUTHERFORD, J. CHADWICK, C. D. ELLIS, *Radiations from Radioactive Substances*, Cambridge University Press, 1930.

Sir J. J. THOMSON and Sir G. P. THOMSON, *Conduction of Electricity through Gases*, 3rd Edition, Cambridge University Press, 1928.

Sir E. WHITTAKER, *A History of the Theories of Aether and Electricity*, Vol. 1, Nelson 1951.

EXAMPLES

1. Show, using the Maxwell distribution law, that the most probable kinetic energy of a molecule in a gas at temperature T is kT. What is the temperature of a gas of particles whose most probable energy is 1 keV?
2. The mean free path of the molecules of argon and nitrogen at S.T.P. are $6{\cdot}3 \times 10^{-6}$ cm and $5{\cdot}8 \times 10^{-6}$ cm respectively. Assuming the gases are ideal and that they obey the laws of elementary kinetic theory, calculate the RMS and mean velocities of the molecules. Estimate the ratio of the thermal conductivities of the two gases. (Molecular weights: argon 40, nitrogen 28. 1 atmosphere is approximately 10^6 dyne cm^{-2}). (Grad I. Physics.)
3. Estimate the molecular diameter of helium given that its atomic weight is 4, its viscosity at S.T.P. is $18{\cdot}9 \times 10^{-5}$ poise, and Avogadro's number is $6{\cdot}02 \times 10^{23}$.
4. Assuming the atmosphere is an isothermal volume at 280°K free of winds, calculate at what height above sea level the oxygen pressure is one half the sea level value. If the concentration ratio of N_2 to O_2 is exactly 4 to 1 at sea level, what is the ratio at the level corresponding to the answer to the first question? (Molecular weights: N is 28, O is 32. R is 8·317 joule mole^{-1} deg K^{-1}).
5. In Barkla's method of determining the number of electrons per atom (see Fig. 5), an X-ray tube emits 5 watts of X-rays. Assuming the centre of the scattering volume ABCD, O is 15 cm from the target of the X-ray bulb, calculate the intensity of the primary beam at O. If the volume ABCD is 30 cm³ and the gas is argon at N.T.P. calculate the total power scattered by the volume ABCD and the intensity of the scattered beam 15 cm from O. (Argon: atomic number is 18, atomic weight is 40; Avogadro's number is $6{\cdot}02 \times 10^{23}$).
6. The Thomson scattering cross section σ_T can be written as $\frac{8\pi}{3} b_e^2$ where b_e is the classical electron radius. In "Neutron Optics" the scattering cross section of *nuclei* for slow neutrons can be written as $4\pi\, b_n^2$, where b_n is a dimension of the order of nuclear radii. Why does one cross section contain the factor $\frac{8\pi}{3}$ and the other the factor 4π?
7. A collimated beam of monoenergetic alpha particles of kinetic energy 8 MeV, travelling in an evacuated vessel, pass through a very thin gold foil ($Z = 79$) and a few of them are scattered through 40° and strike a small fluorescent screen. What is the impact parameter of the particles striking the screen? If the incident beam of particles is slowed down to 4 MeV, by inserting a metal foil, before passing through the gold foil, what must be the angular position of the screen in order that the number of alpha particles striking the screen per minute is unchanged?
8. A stream of 4 MeV alpha particles is incident normally on an aluminium foil 2×10^{-5} cm thick. What fraction of the particles is scattered between 45° and 60° with the incident direction? (Density of Al is 2·70 g cm^{-3}, $N = 6{\cdot}02 \times 10^{23}$, atomic weight of Al is 27, electron charge is $4{\cdot}803 \times 10^{-10}$ e.s.u.)

CHAPTER 2

THE QUANTUM THEORY

2.1. PLANCK'S RADIATION LAW

In a lecture given at a meeting of the British Association in 1892 Schuster said:

"Efforts have been made to look on energy as something which can be labelled and identified through its various transformations. Thus we may feel a certain bit of energy radiating from a coal-fire, and if our knowledge was complete, we ought to be able to fix the time at which that identical bit of energy left the sun and arrived on the surface of the earth, setting up a chemical action in the leaves of the plants from which the coal has been derived. If we push this idea to a logical conclusion it seems to me that we must arrive at an atomic conception of energy, which some may consider an absurdity". Eight years later the quantum theory was born and the "absurd" idea of discrete amounts or quanta of electromagnetic radiation became the fundamental postulate of the new *quantum theory*.

Attempts to explain the wavelength distribution of energy radiated by a black-body, which depends only on its temperature, by W. Wien and by Rayleigh and Jeans had met with partial success. Wien's formula agreed with observations at short wavelengths, but completely failed in the long wavelength part of the spectrum. Rayleigh and Jeans' theory, on the other hand, agreed with experiment at very long wavelengths. Rayleigh and Jeans derived an expression for the number of independent modes of vibration of electromagnetic radiation in a cavity, whose walls are at temperature T. This number, in a cavity of unit volume in the wavelength band λ to $\lambda + d\lambda$ is

$$\frac{8\pi}{\lambda^4} d\lambda \dagger \tag{1}$$

Assuming that each vibration mode corresponds to two degrees of freedom, one associated with the kinetic the other associated with the potential

† For longitudinal vibrations, e.g. sound waves in a gas, the numerical factor is 4; this number is doubled for electromagnetic waves as there are two independent planes of polarization for transverse waves.

energy of the vibration, then the mean energy per mode of vibration should be given by Boltzmann's equipartition theorem

$$2 \times \frac{kT}{2} = kT, \text{ where } k \text{ is Boltzmann's constant.} \tag{2}$$

Combining eqns. (1) and (2) the radiant energy per unit wavelength interval, per unit volume is given by

$$E_\lambda = \frac{8\pi kT}{\lambda^4} \tag{3}$$

This is the Rayleigh–Jeans formula and it is illustrated in Fig. 1. It approaches the observed distribution curve at long wavelengths but it leads

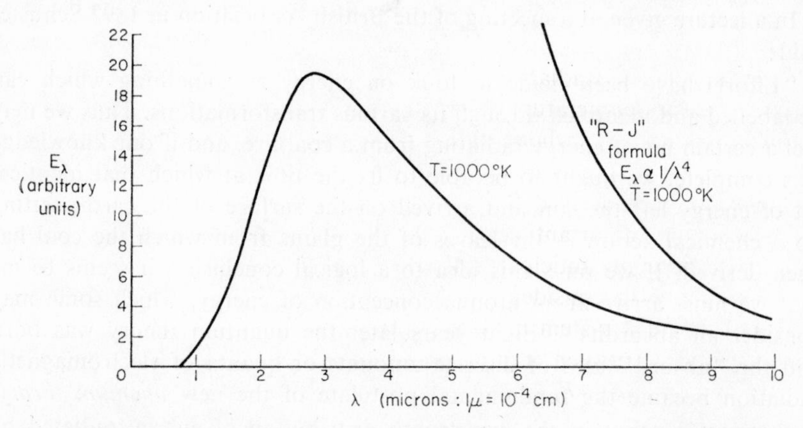

FIG. 1. Spectrum of black-body radiation (1000°K) and Rayleigh–Jeans theoretical curve.

to the absurd conclusion that at short wavelengths E_λ tends to infinity. Moreover the total amount of radiation is obtained by evaluating the integral $\int_0^\infty E_\lambda \cdot d\lambda$ and this diverges.

Max Planck succeeded in deriving a theoretical formula in close agreement with observation at all wavelengths, if the bold assumption is made that radiation is absorbed and emitted by atoms in definite discrete amounts or quanta. The energy ε of a quantum of radiation is related to the *frequency* ν of the emitted or absorbed wave train by the relation

$$\varepsilon = nh\nu \tag{4}$$

where n is a positive integer, and h is a universal constant of Nature (Planck's constant).

The constant h has dimensions "Energy × Time" a quantity in mechanics known as action. Action is of one of the few quantities which is invariant to a Lorentz transformation (Chapter 3), entropy is another, a strong indication that such a physical quantity may have a fundamental physical significance.

Using the quantum postulate, eqn. (4), the mean energy $\bar{\varepsilon}$ of the quantized radiation vibrations in a cavity can be derived

$$\bar{\varepsilon} = \frac{h\nu}{e^{h\nu/kT} - 1} \tag{5}$$

Multiplying by the number of modes of vibration per unit volume, per unit wavelength interval, the energy density E_λ of radiation per unit wavelength interval is

$$E_\lambda = \frac{8\pi}{\lambda^4} \frac{h\nu}{e^{h\nu/kT} - 1} \tag{6}$$

This is the Planck Radiation Formula (1900). The function E_λ is plotted in Fig. 1 for a temperature T of 1000°K. The peak of the curve occurs at a wavelength λ_m where $\lambda_m T =$ constant (Wien's displacement law). For $T = 1000$°K, λ_m is ~ 3 microns (in the infrared region). Planck's formula has been derived by many methods. Einstein's derivation (1916) introduced the important concept of emission and absorption transition probabilities thereby anticipating the methods of Quantum Mechanics (1925). It is instructive to consider this method.

The atoms of a system in thermodynamic equilibrium at temperature T are distributed between a number of quantum energy states of energy $E_1, E_2, E_3, \ldots, E_m, E_n, \ldots$ The number of atoms in a given state E_n is proportional to

$$e^{-E_n/kT} \tag{7}$$

An atom in state n, provided this is not the lowest energy state, has a definite probability A_{nm} of spontaneously making a transition to a lower energy state (E_m) in unit time. A quantum of radiation $\varepsilon = E_n - E_m$ being radiated.

The coefficient A_{nm} is called a "Transition Probability".

If the system is bathed in light, quantized radiation of energy $\varepsilon = E_n - E_m$ may, by a resonance process, *stimulate* atoms in state n to emit radiation and descend to state m. The probability of this happening to an atom in state n in unit time is

$$E\,B_{nm}, \tag{8}$$

where B_{nm} is the appropriate stimulated emission coefficient and E is the density of incident radiation of the required resonant energy.

On the other hand, atoms in the lower state m may absorb quanta of energy $\varepsilon = E_n - E_m$ and jump to the higher state n.

The probability of an atom in state m doing this in unit time is

$$E B_{mn} \tag{9}$$

Once the system, exposed to radiation, reaches an equilibrium state, the number of atoms going from state m to state n is equal to the number going from state n to state m.

$$\underset{m\to n}{e^{-E_m/kT}\,EB_{mn}} = \underset{n\to m}{e^{-E_n/kT}(EB_{nm}+A_{nm})} \tag{10}$$

The transition probabilities are "weighted" by the relative number of atoms in the given energy state.

As T tends to infinity:

$$B_{mn} = B_{nm} + \frac{A_{nm}}{E} \tag{11}$$

but we would expect the energy density of radiation E to approach infinity with T, hence

$$B_{mn} = B_{nm} \tag{12}$$

This is an important result and one we shall make use of in discussing the absorption of radiation by atomic nuclei which have a magnetic moment.

Equation (10) can now be written in the form

$$E = \frac{A_{nm}}{B_{nm}} \cdot \frac{1}{\exp[(E_n - E_m)/kT] - 1} \tag{13}$$

This is identical in form with Planck's formula (eqn. (6)) if we write

$$E_n - E_m = h\nu \tag{14}$$

and

$$\frac{A_{nm}}{B_{nm}} = \frac{8\pi h\nu}{\lambda^4} \tag{15}$$

2.2. THE PHOTOELECTRIC EFFECT

In 1888 Hallwachs discovered that a carefully insulated metal plate which had received a negative charge, lost this charge when exposed to ultraviolet radiation. This was the first clear cut observation of a *photoelectric* phenomenon. The effect is due to the emission of electrons from the surface of the metal when they absorb the incident radiation. If such a plate is mounted inside a vacuum tube and the emitted photoelectrons are attracted to a second electrode at a positive potential, the current flowing through this photoelectric cell, as it is called, is proportional to the rate of emission of electrons. Most metals do not respond to visible light, the only elements which do are the reactive alkali metals, Li, Na, K, Cs,...

The fundamental laws of photoelectric emission were investigated by Lenard in 1902 and they were established with greater accuracy by Millikan in 1916. Millikan realized the supreme importance of *clean* surfaces in studying the effect and his apparatus for cutting fresh surfaces *in vacuo* on cast cylinders of alkali metals is justly famous. The maximum kinetic energy of the released photoelectrons was measured by finding the retarding potential difference V which just prevented the electrons from reaching a gauze electrode.

Then $eV = \frac{1}{2}mv_m^2$

where e is the electron charge, m the electron mass and v_m the maximum speed of emission.

The following laws of photoelectricity are firmly established:

(1) For incident light of a given wavelength, the number of electrons ejected from the surface of a metal is directly proportional to the amount of radiant energy absorbed. (If the reflection coefficient of the surface for the incident wavelength is high, very little photoelectric emission will occur).

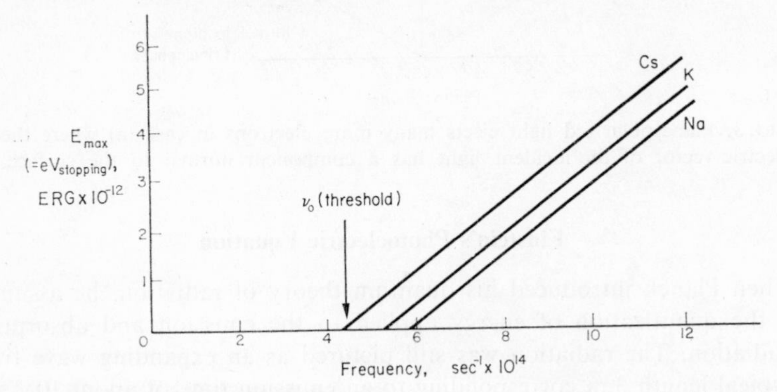

FIG. 2. Relation between max. kinetic energy and frequency of incident light for three alkali metals (N.B. all the graphs have the same slope h).

(2) For each surface, there exists a threshold frequency ν_0. Light of frequency less than ν_0 cannot eject any electrons from the surface. Corresponding to ν_0 is a threshold wavelength λ_0, given by $c = \nu_0 \lambda_0$, so that light of wavelength greater than λ_0 cannot release photoelectrons.

(3) If the incident light has a frequency ν above threshold, the emitted electrons have a continuous energy distribution up to a maximum value E_m. The maximum kinetic energy E_m is a linear function of the frequency ν (Fig. 2).

(4) Photoelectric emission may occur in a gas, if the incident frequency is high enough (ultraviolet light, X- or γ-radiation), the electron being ejected from a bound state in an atom or molecule in the gas.

(5) There is no observable time delay between the incidence of the light and the emission of a photoelectron. Lawrence and Beams in 1928, using a Kerr cell optical light shutter, established that the delay time is less than 3×10^{-9} sec.†

† E. O. LAWRENCE and J. W. BEAMS, *Phys. Rev.* **32**, 478, 1928.

(6) The probability of light ejecting electrons from a surface depends on the direction of vibration of the electric field if the light is polarized. Plane polarized light, incident at 60° on a potassium–sodium surface emitts 60 times as many electrons when the electric vector $\boldsymbol{E}$ lies in the plane of incidence compared with the case when $\boldsymbol{E}$ is normal to the plane of incidence (Fig. 3).

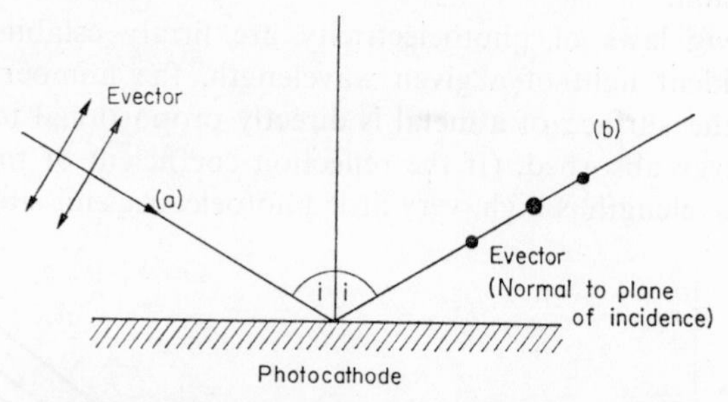

FIG. 3. Plane polarized light ejects many more electrons in case (a) where the electric vector of the incident light has a component normal to the surface.

Einstein's Photoelectric Equation

When Planck introduced his quantum theory of radiation, he assumed that the quantization of energy applied to the emission and absorption of radiation. The radiation was still pictured as an expanding wave train of typical length 3 m corresponding to an emission time of about 10^{-8} sec. In order to understand the photoelectric laws, in particular (2) and (3) above, Einstein made the startling assertion that the radiation in space travels as a stream of discrete localized particles of energy.† These particles of light energy (later named photons, by G. N. Lewis) travel with the same velocity c in empty space, but each one carries an energy ε and a momentum p,†† given by

$$\varepsilon = h\nu \tag{16}$$

$$p = \frac{\varepsilon}{c} = \frac{h\nu}{c} \tag{17}$$

Photons are emitted and absorbed by electrons. They are in fact responsible for the Coulomb interaction between elementary charged particles. A photon absorbed by an electron in the surface of a metal may transfer sufficient energy to the electron for it to escape through the surface. In the most

† It is shown by the new quantum mechanics, that it is not permissible to describe photons in space as sharply localized particles as this contradicts the Uncertainty Principle.

†† The possibility that photons carry angular momentum is not considered at this stage.

favourable case, the maximum kinetic energy of the ejected electron E_m is related to the photon energy by the Einstein equation

$$E_m = h\nu - W \tag{18}$$

where W is the minimum energy necessary to eject an electron from the surface. W is known as the work function.

If the electron is ejected from a bound energy state in a molecule of a gas, W is the binding energy of the electron in the molecule.

The work functions W, the threshold frequencies and wavelengths of some elements are given in Table 1.

TABLE 1

Surface	W (eV)†	ν_0 (in 10^{14} c/s)	λ_0 (Å)
Li	2·28	5·5	5400
Na	2·46	6·0	5000
K	2·24	5·4	5500
Cu	*ca.* 4·1	10	*ca.* 3000
Fe	4·72	11·5	2620

† 1 eV = $1{\cdot}602 \times 10^{-12}$ ergs.

If the frequency of the incident radiation is less than W/h, then no electrons will be emitted. The probability of an electron absorbing two photons and escaping is vanishingly small.

If the photon energy exceeds the work function, there is no guarantee that every photon will eject an electron; in fact the fraction of incident photons ejecting electrons is often less than 10^{-2}. A plot of E_m against ν, the incident frequency, is linear in agreement with experiment; different surfaces giving different intercepts on the frequency axis, but all having a common slope equal to Planck's constant h. Careful measurements of E_m, taking into account contact potential differences, from clean metal surfaces, enable h to be determined to an accuracy of the order of ½% (Fig. 2).

The absence of time delay, law (5) above, in photoelectric emission is readily explained, as an electron which escapes with, for example, a kinetic energy of 1 eV has a velocity of 6×10^7 cm sec^{-1} and the time it takes to pass through the surface, a few Ångström units thick, will be of the order of 10^{-15} sec.

Wave–Corpuscular Dual Nature of Light

The introduction in 1905 of the photon theory of radiation by Einstein was a break with the tradition of the wave theory of light, which in the previous hundred years had great success in describing the phenomena of interference, diffraction and polarization of light. The fact that the state of polarization of light influences its photoelectric emission properties is a reminder that the wave theory should not be abandoned too quickly. A number of interesting experiments and speculations have been made to demonstrate the photon nature of electromagnetic waves. J. J. Thomson had suggested that in order to understand the ionizing properties of X-rays, an effect closely related to photoelectricity, the energy of the radiation might be concentrated in narrow tubes. Even in a light beam of very low intensity, there would still be enough energy in one tube for an atom to absorb enough energy to release an electron. G. I. Taylor in 1909 followed up a suggestion of J. J. Thomson that if a light beam of very low intensity is diffracted by an obstacle, there ought to be an alteration in the visibility of the diffraction pattern. Taylor found no diminution in sharpness of the diffraction pattern formed by a needle when the light intensity was so low that an exposure of three months was required. Recent experiments confirm Taylor's results and it has been shown that in all problems of interference of light we cannot interpret the results in terms of interference between different photons.† Janossy and Náray in 1957 measured the intensity of the interference pattern formed in a Michelson interferometer with arms nearly 14 m long using such low light intensities that only one photon at a time was passing through the instrument! The interference pattern was found to be independent of the light intensity.

The corpuscular nature of radiation becomes more evident the higher the frequency, that is, the higher the photon energy. The fact that individual high energy photons can be counted with a Geiger counter is difficult to reconcile with the wave nature of radiation. If a weak γ-ray source is placed at the centre of a circular array of Geiger counters, first one counter and then another detects the passage of a γ-ray photon. If the radiation travelled from the source as a series of quantized expanding wave trains one would expect all or none of the Geiger counters to respond at a given instant. This is not observed. Over a sufficient length of time, the number of photons recorded by each counter is, of course, the same as the source is isotropic.

The paradox of the photon energy relation $\varepsilon = h\nu$, lies in the fact that we connect the particle property of quantized energy ε with the wave property of frequency ν. The dual properties of light are not unique. All material particles; electrons, neutrons, atoms have wave properties, which can be demonstrated under suitable conditions. Niels Bohr coined the word "complementarity" to describe this dual nature of radiation and matter. There is a breakdown in our traditional or classical way of thinking about physical problems. We begin to realize that there is a fundamental deficiency in our concepts employed in describing events on the atomic scale.

† The interference effect is a property of the individual photon.

The wave–particle paradox led to the development of wave mechanics—a new language for describing atomic phenomena.

2.3. ATOMIC SPECTRA

It was natural that the first attempts to understand the pattern of sharp frequencies radiated by elements, that is their line emission spectra, should be in terms of fundamental vibrations and their harmonics. Such attempts failed. Balmer in 1885 found that the visible line spectrum af atomic hydrogen could be represented by the simple series

$$k_n = R(1/2^2 - 1/n^2)$$

where n can equal 3, 4, 5, etc. R is a constant (Rydberg constant)

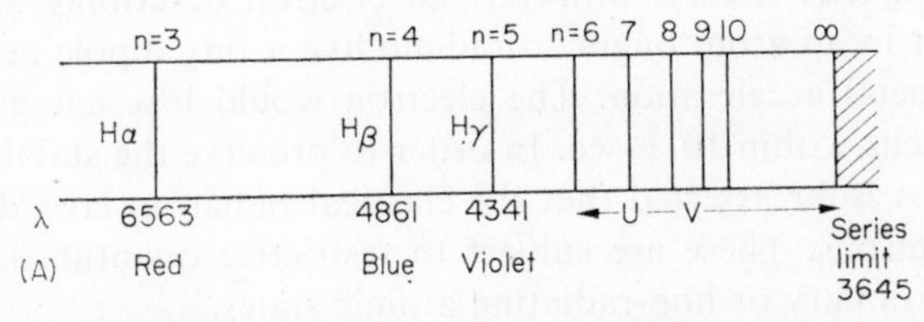

FIG. 4. Diagram of the Balmer Series. (Transitions from states of $n > 2$ to state $n = 2$.)

k_n is the wave-number (reciprocal of the wavelength) of a line in the Balmer series corresponding to an integral value of n ($n > 2$). The Balmer series is represented in Fig. 4.

Niels Bohr in 1913 developed his famous theory of atomic spectra and succeeded in explaining the Balmer and other series of spectral lines of atomic hydrogen. Moreover the empirical Rydberg constant R was deduced in terms of fundamental atomic constants. Before describing the Bohr theory we mention some important ideas put forward in the years between Balmer's discovery and Bohr's theory.

A. W. Conway at Dublin in 1907 was the first to enunciate the principle that a single atom radiates one spectral frequency at a time; it does not radiate a mixture of frequencies corresponding to a given series. There must be an enormous number of atoms radiating at one time. Conway stated that for an atom to radiate it must be in a disturbed or excited state. In this state, he suggested a single electron is stimulated to emit radiation of one single frequency for a time long enough for a fairly long wave train to be emitted.

Ritz's Combination Principle of Spectroscopy (1908) asserted that the frequencies of spectral lines can be expressed as differences between certain terms. The number of terms required is less than the observed number of lines. This principle was an important clue to the understanding of atomic spectra.

J. W. Nicholson in 1911 introduced the Rutherford atomic model and he realized that the production of atomic spectra must be closely connected with Planck's quantum of action. To Nicholson belongs the credit of realizing that the *angular momentum* of an atom can only change by discrete amounts.

N. Bohr's Theory of the Atomic Spectrum of Hydrogen

In 1913, Niels Bohr, at that time a research student of Rutherford's in Manchester, developed his theory of atomic spectra. Bohr had the insight to seize the right ideas of earlier workers and reject their mistakes. He assumed, like Conway, that atoms produce one spectral frequency at a time, and that the Rutherford model of the atom must be used. According to the classical electromagnetic theory, however, an electron describing an elliptic or circular orbit in an atom ought to radiate like a tiny dipole aerial, in view of its centripetal acceleration. The electron would lose energy and spiral into the nucleus within 10^{-10} sec. In order to preserve the stability of atoms and molecules Bohr asserted that the classical radiation laws do not apply to *bound* electrons. These are subject to restrictive quantum laws and are known as stationary or non-radiating atomic states.

Bohr considered the frequency change of an electron spiralling around the nucleus as it approaches from a great distance until it is caught in a stationary orbit. He succeeded in deriving a frequency law in agreement with the Balmer series and found that the angular momentum of an electron in a stationary orbit is quantized in units of $h/2\pi$ (written as $\hbar$). This was not the starting point of his theory as is often believed. It is, however, simpler to present Bohr's theory starting with the principle of angular momentum quantization, one of the most important discoveries in quantum physics. Bohr's original theory dealt with atomic hydrogen, but it can be applied to singly ionized helium, doubly ionized lithium, etc., i.e. a one electron atom or ion.

Consider an electron describing a circular orbit of radius r about a nucleus, charge Ze. (Fig. 5).

Equating the electrostatic force of attraction to the product of the electron mass m and its radial acceleration $\frac{v^2}{r}$ we have

$$\frac{Ze^2}{r^2} = m\frac{v^2}{r} \qquad \text{(in c.g.s. units)} \tag{19}$$

where e is the electron charge and v is the orbital speed.

Therefore, the electron kinetic energy

$$T = \frac{1}{2}mv^2 = \frac{1}{2}\frac{Ze^2}{r} \tag{20}$$

The electron potential energy in the Coulomb field of the nucleus is

$$V = \int_{\infty}^{r} \frac{Ze^2}{r^2} dr = -\frac{Ze^2}{r} \tag{21}$$

The zero level of potential energy is taken at $r = \infty$.

We note that the only stable orbits of an electron, according to classical physics correspond to

$$T = -\frac{1}{2}V \qquad \text{(Virial Theorem)} \tag{22}$$

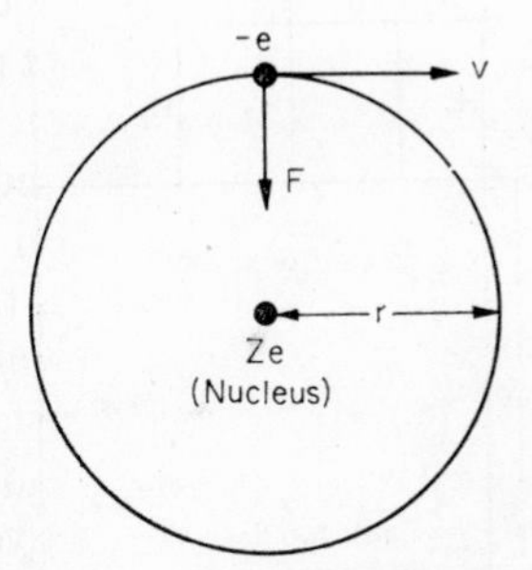

FIG. 5. Electron describing a circular orbit of radius r and speed v around the nuclear charge Ze.

The total energy

$$E = T + V = \frac{1}{2}V = -\frac{Ze^2}{2r} \tag{23}$$

This is far as one can go by classical theory. The quantum theory is introduced by postulating that only orbits corresponding to an angular momentum $n\hbar$ are allowed

$$mvr = n\hbar \qquad n = 1, 2, 3, \ldots \tag{24}$$

n is known as a quantum number.

Squaring eqn. (24) and dividing by eqn. (19) we get

$$r = \frac{n^2 \hbar^2}{Zme^2} \tag{25}$$

Combining eqns. (25) and (23)

$$E_n = -\frac{Z^2 m e^4}{2n^2 \hbar^2} \tag{26}$$

This result means that there exists a number of discrete energy levels or states corresponding to different values of the quantum number n. Normally the atom will exist in the state of lowest energy $n = 1$; the ground state. If the atom is disturbed sufficiently by thermal agitation, electron bombardment, etc. it may make an abrupt transition to a higher energy state.

This state has a finite lifetime (typically 10^{-8} sec) and in decaying to lower energy states the energy difference is radiated as a photon. In this way, Bohr accounts for the emission and absorption of radiation. (Fig. 6).

Thus the energy of a photon radiated when a hydrogen atom makes a transition from state n to a lower state m† is

$$\varepsilon = h\nu = E_n - E_m = \frac{Z^2 m e^4}{2\hbar^2}\left(\frac{1}{m^2} - \frac{1}{n^2}\right), \quad n > m \tag{27}$$

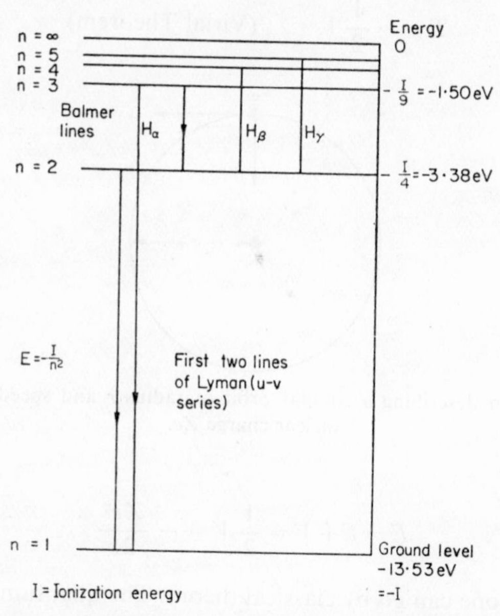

FIG. 6. Energy level diagram of atomic hydrogen. Transitions responsible for first three lines, and first two lines of Balmer and Lyman series respectively.

If $m = 2$, and n takes on the values 3, 4, 5, 6 ... we obtain the Balmer series of lines: $k = R\left(\frac{1}{2^2} - \frac{1}{n^2}\right)$ where the Rydberg constant for hydrogen is given by

$$R = \frac{m e^4}{4\pi c \hbar^3}, \quad \text{as} \quad Z = 1 \quad \text{and} \quad k = \frac{\nu}{c} \tag{28}$$

where c is the velocity of light.

The close agreement between the spectroscopic value of R and the value given by eqn. (28) is a striking confirmation of the theory.

$E_1 = -\frac{Z^2 m e^4}{2\hbar^2}$ measures the greatest energy through which a free

† There should be no confusion with the electron mass m.

electron can fall into a bound state. The energy to just free an electron from this ground state, the *ionization energy* of the hydrogen atom is given by $-E_1$, i.e., $\frac{m e^4}{2\hbar^2} \equiv 1$ rydberg $= 13{\cdot}5$ eV.

Bohr's theory gave a simple interpretation of Ritz's combination principle. The terms of Ritz's rule are now identified with the Bohr energy levels. Lyman (1914) discovered a series of lines in the ultraviolet spectrum of hydrogen corresponding to transitions from higher energy states to the ground state.† Later Paschen, Brackett and Pfund discovered series in the infrared.

$$k = \frac{1}{\lambda} = R\left(\frac{1}{1^2} - \frac{1}{n^2}\right), \quad n = 2, 3, 4, \ldots \quad \text{Lyman (ultraviolet) Series}$$

$$k = \frac{1}{\lambda} = R\left(\frac{1}{2^2} - \frac{1}{n^2}\right), \quad n = 3, 4, 5, \ldots \quad \text{Balmer (visible) Series}$$

$$k = \frac{1}{\lambda} = R\left(\frac{1}{3^2} - \frac{1}{n^2}\right), \quad n = 4, 5, 6, \ldots \quad \text{Paschen (infrared) Series}$$

$$k = \frac{1}{\lambda} = R\left(\frac{1}{4^2} - \frac{1}{n^2}\right), \quad n = 5, 6, 7, \ldots \quad \text{Brackett (infrared) Series}$$

$$k = \frac{1}{\lambda} = R\left(\frac{1}{5^2} - \frac{1}{n^2}\right), \quad n = 6, 7, 8, \ldots \quad \text{Pfund (infrared) Series}$$

The stationary energy states of the hydrogen atom, according to the simple Bohr theory are illustrated in Fig. 6. Emission and absorption of radiation in quanta occurs when transitions occur between two different energy levels.

The theory described above assumes that the electron circulates about a nucleus of infinite mass. Strictly speaking, the electron and the nucleus describe orbits about the centre of mass. The nucleus orbit is much smaller in radius than the electron orbit as the proton mass is 1836 times the electron mass. The effect of the finite mass of the nucleus is to increase slightly the energy values of the stationary states. In place of the electron mass m in eqn. (27) substitute the *reduced* electron mass m', given by

$$\frac{1}{m'} = \frac{1}{m} + \frac{1}{M} \tag{29}$$

where M is the mass of the nucleus.

The energy levels of atomic hydrogen (H^1), deuterium (H^2), and tritium (H^3) are therefore slightly different in view of the fact that the mass of the nuclei increase roughly in the ratio 1 : 2 : 3 respectively. The wavelengths

† The first line of the Lyman series, which like the other Lyman lines is absorbed in air, has recently been observed in the solar absorption spectrum from a high-altitude rocket.

of corresponding spectral lines of the three isotopes differ by a detectable amount and this difference was used by Urey in the discovery in 1932 of deuterium.

Notice also that the Rydberg constant depends on the mass of the nucleus. Moreover the Rydberg constant for singly ionized helium atom is not exactly four times ($R \propto Z^2$) the value for hydrogen as the reduced electron mass in He^+ is greater than the reduced electron mass in H^1.

How many spectral lines of the Balmer series are observed? The number depends on the conditions of excitation of the hydrogen gas. More lines are observed in stellar spectra than from a low pressure discharge tube. This can be explained when it is realized that quantized electron orbital radii r increase as n^2 (eqn. 25). For $n = 1$, $r \sim 0{\cdot}5$ Å, for $n = 32$, r is about 500 Å! Transitions between states of high n values are unlikely except at very low pressure (e.g. in the outer rarefied atmosphere of a star), in view of the large orbital radii.

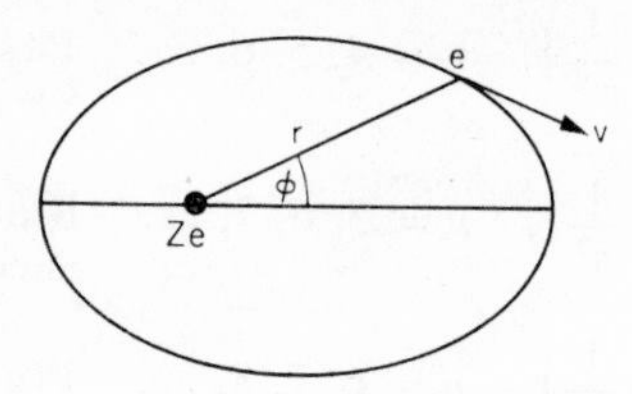

FIG. 7. Elliptic orbit of an electron (nucleus at one focus).

A high resolving power spectroscope shows that the lines of the Balmer series H_α, H_β, etc. are not single, but have a fine structure, i.e. each "line" consists of a group of lines close together. Bohr suggested that this might be the result of a relativistic increase of the electron mass, which would modify the energy levels, particularly in the case of elliptic orbits. The treatment of the quantized motion of the electron in an elliptic orbit was carried out independently by A. Sommerfeld and W. Wilson in 1916.

The orbiting electron now has two degrees of freedom, and it is convenient to describe its motion in terms of polar coordinates r and φ (Fig. 7). The nucleus is located at one of the foci and it is convenient to take this point as the origin of coordinates.

Two empirical quantization rules restrict the electron's motion

$$\oint p_r\, dr = n_r\, h \tag{30}$$

$$\oint p_\varphi\, d\varphi = n_\varphi\, h \tag{31}$$

where p_r and p_φ are the radial ($m_e \dot{r}$) and angular ($m_e r^2 \dot{\varphi}$) components of the electron's momentum,

n_r can assume the values 0, 1, 2, 3, . . . , etc. and is known as the *radial* quantum number,

n_φ can assume the values 1, 2, 3, . . ., etc. and is known as the *azimuthal* quantum number,

(N.B. $n_\varphi = 0$ is excluded, as this would correspond to a radial oscillation of the electron through the nucleus).

The definite integrals are evaluated for one complete orbit.

The second integral can be easily evaluated by using the principle of conservation of angular momentum.

As p_φ is independent of φ, we have,

$$\because \oint p_\varphi \, d\varphi = p_\varphi \oint d\varphi = p_\varphi \, . \, 2\pi = n_\varphi h$$

$$\therefore p_\varphi = n_\varphi \hbar \tag{32}$$

For a circular orbit, $p_r = 0$, and we return to one quantization condition, given by eqn. (32) which is identical with Bohr's original condition, provided we identify n_φ with n.

The energies of the stationary states are now given by the formula

$$E_{n_\varphi, n_r} = -\frac{Z^2 m e^4}{2\hbar^2} \frac{1}{(n_\varphi + n_r)^2} \tag{33}$$

and the semi-major axis a of the orbit is given by the formula

$$a = \frac{\hbar^2}{Z m e^2} (n_\varphi + n_r)^2 \tag{34}$$

The eccentricity ε of the orbit is given by the expression

$$1 - \varepsilon^2 = \left(\frac{n_\varphi}{n_\varphi + n_r} \right)^2 \tag{35}$$

The energy of the state depends on the sum of the quantum numbers n_φ and n_r.

We introduce the principal quantum n where

$$n = n_\varphi + n_r \tag{36}$$

as this defines the energy of a state.

Equation (35) means that only elliptic orbits in which the ratio of the lengths of the major and minor axes is a ratio of two integers occur. For a given value of n, there are n *degenerate* states, i.e. n different elliptic orbits with the same energy: e.g. for $n = 3$, there are three states $n = 3$, $n_\varphi = 3$ (circle); $n = 3$, $n_\varphi = 2$ (ellipse) and $n = 3$, $n_\varphi = 1$ (ellipse . . .) with the same value of E.

Sommerfeld showed that if the variation in mass with speed of the orbital electron is considered, this energy degeneracy for a given n is removed. The energy values can be represented by a series of rapidly converging terms:

$$E_{n, n_\varphi} = -\frac{Z^2 m e^4}{2\hbar^2 n^2} \left[1 + \frac{\alpha^2 Z^2}{n} \left(\frac{1}{n} - \frac{3}{4n} \right) + \cdots \text{smaller terms} \right] \tag{37}$$

where $\alpha = \dfrac{e^2}{\hbar c} = \dfrac{1}{137}$, a dimensionless ratio known as the fine structure constant. The fine structure term, the second inside the bracket of eqn. (37), is $< \left(\dfrac{1}{137}\right)^2$.

The statement that the energy of a state depends only on the value of n must now be modified. To a high degree of accuracy the energy is determined by n, but different n values yield slightly different values of E, according to eqn. (37). The fine splitting of the energy levels for a given n is a consequence of the fact that the fine structure constant α is much less than unity. The ratio $\dfrac{e^2}{\hbar c}$† is one of the most important constants of Nature and it determines the strength of electromagnetic interactions.

Although the explanation of the fine structure of the spectral lines of hydrogen represented a marked advance in the theory of spectra, the defects of the Bohr–Sommerfeld theory became more apparent when attention was paid to the question of predicting the relative intensities of the spectral lines. It was known that certain energy state transitions did not occur and a number of "Selection Rules" was formulated. Bohr introduced a "Correspondence Principle" which stated that the observed frequency, intensity, and state of polarization of the radiation emitted when an atom experiences a transition between two states of very high quantum number should agree with the predictions of classical theory (i.e. the frequency of the light should be equal to the orbital frequency of revolution of the electron). It is possible to arrive at the selection rules $\Delta n_\varphi = \pm 1$, with Δn unrestricted. Nevertheless, the quantization rules had no logical foundation and the theory did not predict the correct frequencies for atomic helium. The introduction of the new Quantum Mechanics in 1925–27, resolved many of these difficulties. It is now customary to replace the azimuthal quantum number n_φ with the orbital angular momentum quantum number l, where $1 = n_\varphi - 1$, as the number l is found to occur logically when the problem is solved, using quantum mechanics. For historical reasons connected with the classification of spectral series (sharp, principal, diffuse, fundamental . . ., etc.), electron orbital states with

$l = 0, 1, 2, 3, 4, 5$, etc. are described as s, p, d, f, g, h states.

† The ratio $\dfrac{e^2}{\hbar c}$ is equal to the ratio of two fundamental measures of the quantity "action". Consider the Coulomb potential energy of two protons, distance r apart, e^2/r. Multiply this by the time for a photon emitted by one of the protons to reach the other and we obtain

$$\frac{e^2}{r} \times \frac{r}{c} = \frac{e^2}{c} \cdots$$

a "quantity" of action. Divide this by $\hbar$ the quantum of action and we obtain a fundamental action ratio. (N.B. e in e.s.u.)

Space Quantization

The orbital angular momentum of an electron can be represented by a vector, whose direction is normal to the plane of the orbit, of magnitude $\sqrt{[l(l+1)]}\,\hbar$,† according to quantum mechanics. l can have values 0, 1, 2, ... up to $n-1$, for a given principal quantum number n.

If an atom is situated in an external electric or magnetic field there is an interaction between the orbital electron and the applied field. The interaction between the electron and a uniform magnetic field, with a consequent splitting of energy levels is related to the Zeeman effect. This level splitting leads to a new fine structure in the spectral lines of atoms radiating in a magnetic field.

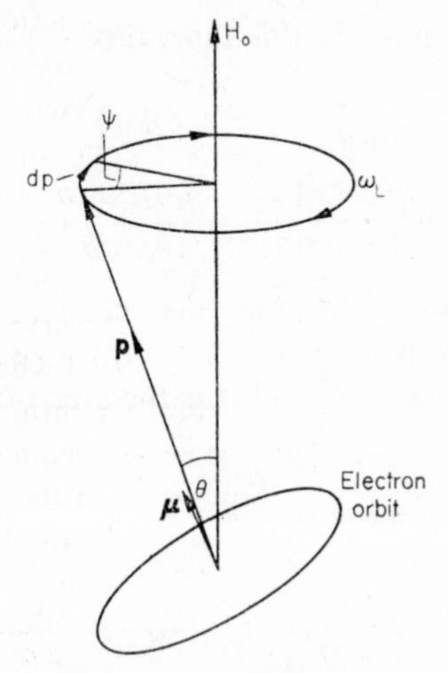

FIG. 8. Larmor precession of an electron orbit in a magnetic field H_0.

Consider the interaction between the equivalent magnetic dipole moment μ of an orbital electron and a uniform magnetic field H_0.

μ is proportional to the angular momentum p of the electron

$$\therefore \mu = \gamma p \tag{38}$$

where γ, a scalar, is known as the gyromagnetic ratio. The vectors μ and p are normal to the plane of the electron orbit. Suppose μ and p are inclined at an angle θ to the field H_0 (Fig. 8), then there is a torque T acting on the dipole μ, tending to align the dipole in the field direction. As the magnetic dipole is associated with the orbital electron current, the dipole precesses

† The state $l = 0$, an s-state, signifies the absence of any orbital angular momentum of the electron, and would be inadmissible according to the Bohr–Sommerfeld theory. In the new mechanics an s-state describes a spherically symmetric electron charge distribution.

at a definite angular velocity ω_L (Larmor precession) around the field direction like a quantized gyroscope.

The torque $\boldsymbol{T}$ is given by the vector product

$$\boldsymbol{T} = \boldsymbol{\mu} \times \boldsymbol{H}_0 = \mu H_0 \sin\theta \times \text{unit vector normal} \tag{39}$$

to the plane defined by $\boldsymbol{\mu}$ and $\boldsymbol{H}_0$.

By Newton's second law of motion

$$\boldsymbol{T} = \frac{d\boldsymbol{p}}{dt} \tag{40}$$

and $d\boldsymbol{p}$, the increase in $\boldsymbol{p}$ in a short time dt, is normal to the plane of $\boldsymbol{p}$ and $\boldsymbol{H}_0$.

The angle of precession $d\psi$ in this short time is given by

$$d\psi = \frac{dp}{p \sin\theta} \qquad \text{(Fig. 8)} \tag{41}$$

$$\therefore \omega_L = \frac{d\psi}{dt} = \frac{dp}{dt} \cdot \frac{1}{p \sin\theta} = \frac{\mu H_0 \sin\theta}{p \sin\theta} = \frac{\mu}{p} H_0 = \gamma H_0 \tag{42}$$

Using Ampère's circuital theorem, the magnetic dipole moment μ of a circulating charge e is given by $\mu = i \times A$, where i is the current $= e\nu$,† where ν is the orbital frequency, and A is the area of the orbit $= \pi r^2$

$$\therefore |\mu| = e \nu \pi \cdot r^2 \tag{43}$$

Using the Bohr quantization rule $p = m v r = n \hbar$, and inserting $\nu = v/(2\pi r)$ in eqn. (43), we find

$$\mu = e \frac{v}{2\pi r} \pi r^2 = \frac{e v r}{2} = \frac{n e \hbar}{2m} \tag{44}$$

For $n = 1$, we obtain the elementary atomic magnetic moment, known as the Bohr magneton μ_B where

$$\mu_B = \frac{e\hbar}{2m} = 9{\cdot}273 \times 10^{-21} \text{ erg oersted}^{-1} \tag{45}$$

Combining eqn. (44) with eqn. (42)

$$\omega_L = \frac{\mu}{p} \cdot H_0 = \frac{n e \hbar}{2 m n \hbar} H_0 = \frac{e}{2m} \cdot H_0 \tag{46}$$

The normal to the electron orbit rotates around the field H_0 keeping the inclination θ constant. The Larmor frequency is independent of θ.

In 1920, Pauli put forward the hypothesis that only certain discrete inclinations of an orbit are possible. For a given orbital quantum number l,

† In this equation, e is measured in e.m.u. and is equal to the electron charge in e.s.u. divided by the velocity of light c measured in cm sec^{-1}.

quantum mechanics predicts that the projection of the angular momentum vector $\sqrt{[l(l+1)]}\hbar$ must be given by $m\hbar$, where m can assume the values l, $l-1, l-2, \ldots, 1, 0, -1, -2, \ldots, -l$. m is known as the magnetic quantum number. Thus for a given value of l there are $(2l+1)$ possible magnetic sub-states (Fig. 9). There exists ample experimental confirmation of the spatial quantization rule.

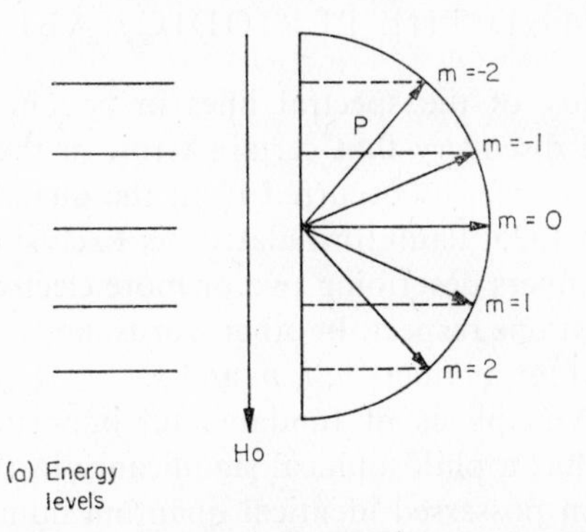

FIG. 9. Zeeman splitting of energy levels of the hydrogen atom in a magnetic field H_0, for $l = 2$ state. There are five possible orientations of the orbital angular momentum $\boldsymbol{p}$.

Electron Spin

The problem of predicting the spectral frequencies of atoms in general is formidable due to the mutual interactions of the Z electrons. However, in the case of the alkali metals, the problem can be tackled by assuming that the valency electron moves outside a closed core of filled electron shells and it is possible to make approximate predictions concerning the light emitted by transitions of the valency electron. It was found that the Bohr–Sommerfeld theory failed to account for the well-known doublet structure of the optical spectra of the alkali metals. The best known example is the relatively large spacing of 6 Å for the yellow sodium D lines.

In 1925, Uhlenbeck and Goudsmit resolved the discrepancy by postulating an extra degree of freedom for each electron. Each electron has a permanent magnetic dipole moment of one Bohr magneton associated with an intrinsic angular momentum or spin. According to quantum mechanics the magnitude of this spin angular momentum $\boldsymbol{p}_s$ is

$$\sqrt{[s(s+1)]}\,\hbar$$

where the quantum number s describing the electron spin has the value $s = \pm\frac{1}{2}$.

In an applied magnetic field, there are two possible spin components: $\frac{1}{2}\hbar$ in the direction of the field, $-\frac{1}{2}\hbar$ antiparallel to the field. The couplings of orbital and spin angular momenta of the electrons in an atom is a complex problem and will not be discussed here. The total angular momentum of an electron representing the vector sum of $\boldsymbol{l}$ and $\boldsymbol{s}$ is described by the quantum number $\boldsymbol{j} = \boldsymbol{l} + \boldsymbol{s}$.†

2.4. PAULI EXCLUSION PRINCIPLE AND THE PERIODIC TABLE

A systematic study of the spectral lines in helium and other elements by Pauli led to the discovery that certain terms in the energy states were missing. These missing terms occurred if all the quantum numbers of the electrons agreed. In 1925, Pauli formulated his Exclusion Principle.

The quantum numbers describing two or more electrons in a single atom must differ in at least one respect. In other words, no two electrons can have the same four quantum numbers n, l, m and s.

The Exclusion Principle is of fundamental importance in atomic and nuclear physics. It has a philosophical significance in the sense that if two electrons in an atom possessed identical quantum numbers they would be physically indistinguishable and we could not count them. The principle determines an upper limit to the number of electrons that can move in a definite volume of space. This limits the amount of matter in space and fixes the order of magnitude of the density of ordinary matter. The scope of the principle is now much wider than this.†† It applies to the conduction electrons in a metal crystal and to the nucleons in an atomic nucleus.

The first great success of Pauli's principle was the correlation of the order of elements in the Periodic Table with the electronic shell structure deduced from the Exclusion Principle. Consider the progressive building of heavier atoms starting with the lightest, hydrogen. The nuclear charge Z is increased one unit at a time by adding one proton and the new atom is neutralized by the addition of one electron, which is bound in the lowest available

† For the majority of atoms, except very heavy ones, one finds that the orbital angular momenta vectors of the electrons couple to give a resultant $\boldsymbol{L} = \sum \boldsymbol{l}$, the spin vectors couple to give a resultant spin vector $\boldsymbol{S}$, where $\boldsymbol{S} = \sum \boldsymbol{s}$. The resultant orbital and spin angular momentum vectors then combine to give a resultant angular momentum vector $\boldsymbol{J} = \boldsymbol{L} + \boldsymbol{S}$. For nucleons, in nuclei, except for very light nuclei, one finds that the spin and orbital angular momentum vectors of a given nucleon couple to give a resultant vector $\boldsymbol{j} = \boldsymbol{l} + \boldsymbol{s}$. Then the resultant vectors of the nucleons couple to give a resultant for the nucleus $\boldsymbol{J} = \sum \boldsymbol{j}$.

†† One of the most interesting and controversial extensions of the Exclusion Principle is due to Eddington, who in a systematic attempt to link the fundamental constants of atomic physics (such as the fine structure constant α) with cosmological constants, contended that the principle is a quantum mechanical aspect of the phenomenon of gravitation. Eddington regarded gravitation and the principle of exclusion as different aspects of the indistinguishability of elementary particles. See *From Euclid to Eddington*, by Sir E. WHITTAKER.

energy state. The electrons are arranged in definite groups or shells around the nucleus. The electrons in the inner shell (K shell) have principal quantum number $n = 1$, and they are the most firmly bound electrons in the atom. The next shell (L shell), moving out from the nucleus, has principal quantum number $n = 2$ and so on.

For each orbital quantum number l there are $2\,(2l + 1)$ possible states for an electron. [$(2l + 1)$ magnetic sub-states and each sub-state has two possible values for the spin quantum number s.] The maximum occupation number of electrons in different l orbitals are:

Orbital Type	s,	p,	d,	f,	g
l	0,	1,	2,	3,	4
Maximum occupation, number of electrons.	2,	6,	10,	14,	18

For a given value of n, l can assume the integral values $0, 1, 2, \ldots, n - 1$ The great chemical stability of the rare gas atoms can be explained. Helium for example, has two electrons with quantum numbers $n = 1, l = 0, m = 0, s = +\frac{1}{2}$ and $n = 1, l = 0, m = 0, s = -\frac{1}{2}$, which just completes the K shell. A closed shell atom is expected to have marked chemical stability. The addition of a third electron to form the alkali metal lithium is only possible if it enters a new shell, the L shell. This electron is much less firmly bound than the K shell electrons and it is responsible for the chemical activity of the atom. Adding protons and electrons one at a time we reach element number 10 (neon) and find that the second shell is now full. The ten orbital electrons in neon have the following quantum numbers.

K shell	$n = 2$,	$l = 0$,	$m = 0$,	$s = \pm\frac{1}{2}$	2 electrons
L shell	$n = 2$,	$l = 0$,	$m = 0$,	$s = \pm\frac{1}{2}$	2 electrons
	$n = 2$,	$l = 1$,	$m = 1$,	$s = \pm\frac{1}{2}$	2 electrons
	$n = 2$,	$l = 1$,	$m = 0$,	$s = \pm\frac{1}{2}$	2 electrons
	$n = 2$,	$l = 1$,	$m = -1$,	$s = \pm\frac{1}{2}$	2 electrons
				Total	10 electrons

Adding one more proton and electron, the alkali metal sodium is formed, the new electron enters a $3s$ state ($n = 3$, $l = 0$) and it is this electron which is responsible for the chemical activity and optical spectrum of the element.

At certain places in the Periodic Table, the addition of the next electron may begin the formation of the next electron shell before the previous one is completely filled. This happens with the element potassium ($Z = 19$), the first eighteen electrons fill the K shell, the L shell, and the $3s$ and $3p$ sub-shells of the M shell. The last electron to be added prefers to enter a

$4s$ orbital (an N shell state) rather than a $3d$ orbital. This occurs because the $4s$ orbital is more tightly bound than the $3d$ orbital. The rule that n determines to a high degree the energy of a bound electron for a one electron atom or ion does not always apply to a multi-electron atom. A useful rough rule is that the electron orbital with the lowest value of $n + l$ is the tightest bound when the two states differ in n by one unit. For the $4s$ orbital, $n + l = 4$, for the $3d$ orbital, $n + l = 5$. Calcium ($Z = 20$) also prefers to bind the last two electrons in $4s$ states (with opposite spins) outside the inert gas atom structure of argon ($Z = 18$). With the next element scandium ($Z = 21$), the last electron begins to fill the $3d$ M sub-shell. (N.B. if the last electron went into the N shell it would have to be in a $4p$ state and $n + l = 5$ is not smaller than $n + l$ for the $3d$ state.) A convenient way of describing the electronic structure of an atom is illustrated for the element scandium, Sc:

$$1s^2 \quad 2s^2 \quad 2p^6 \quad 3s^2 \quad 3p^6 \quad 3d^1 \quad 4s^2,$$

where the exponents represent the number of electrons in the respective orbital states. The occupation numbers of electrons in the $3d$, $4s$ and $4p$ states, from potassium ($Z = 19$) to krypton ($Z = 36$), where the M shell is finally complete, are set out in Table 2.

Notice that in going from element 23, vanadium, to element 24, chromium, only one electron occupies the $4s$ state in the element with the greater nuclear charge. There is no element in its ground state with 4 or 9 electrons

TABLE 2

Element		Z	Occupation number of electrons in the orbitals		
			$3d$	$4s$	$4p$
Potassium	K	19	0	1	0
Calcium	Ca	20	0	2	0
Scandium	Sc	21	1	2	0
Titanium	Ti	22	2	2	0
Vanadium	V	23	3	2	0
Chromium	Cr	24	5	1	0
Manganese	Mn	25	5	2	0
Iron	Fe	26	6	2	0
Cobalt	Co	27	7	2	0
Nickel	Ni	28	8	2	0
Copper	Cu	29	10	1	0
Zinc	Zn	30	10	2	0
Gallium	Ga	31	10	2	1
Germanium	Ge	32	10	2	2
Arsenic	As	33	10	2	3
Selenium	Se	34	10	2	4
Bromine	Br	35	10	2	5
Krypton	Kr	36	10	2	6

in the $3d$ state. With element number 36, krypton, the M shell is filled and the sub-shells $4s$ and $4p$ of the N shell are also completely filled. This represents a chemically inactive atom like argon. The abrupt change in chemical activity of an atom on passing a closed electron shell structure is reflected in the sharp drop in the first ionization energy. (The first ionization energy is the minimum amount of energy to detach the least tightly bound electron from an atom or molecule). This effect is shown in Table 3.

TABLE 3

Element		First ionization energy (eV)
Helium	He	24·6
Lithium	Li	5·39
Neon	Ne	21·6
Sodium	Na	5·14
Argon	Ar	15·8
Potassium	K	4·34

2.5. EXPERIMENTAL DETERMINATIONS OF ATOMIC ENERGY STATES

The energy level concept developed by Bohr and Sommerfeld explained in a satisfactory way the spectra of hydrogen. Nevertheless, an extensive investigation was made at the time to obtain direct evidence for the existence of atomic and molecular energy levels. In particular the phenomena of excitation and ionization of atoms in a gas by electron impact has been studied in great detail. The pioneer experiments of Franck and Hertz (1914) established the existence of "Critical Potentials". This meant that electrons accelerated through known voltages had just sufficient kinetic energy to excite an atom to a higher energy state. Experiments of this type confirmed the energy level scheme and later developments led to the measurement of the cross sections for excitation or ionization of atoms by electron impact. It is important to realise that even if a moving electron has sufficient kinetic energy to excite a valency electron of an atom during a collision this will not necessarily occur. In general the probability of excitation in a collision is of the order of 1% or less. The probability is zero at the threshold energy for the process; it increases with the excess energy of the bombarding electron and passes through a maximum (sometimes a sharp one, sometimes a very broad one) and then decreases as the kinetic energy of the bombarding electron increases. During a collision, angular momentum of the electron–atom system must be conserved and if excitation of the atom occurs the angular momentum of the excited orbital electron changes by an integral multiple of $\hbar$. This quantum restriction has a marked effect on the excitation probability during a collision.

One of the best of the "early" critical potential experiments was carried out by Davis and Goucher in 1917. This was the first experiment to distinguish between the excitation and ionization potentials. A diagram of the apparatus is shown in Fig. 10. Electrons from a hot metal filament F, mounted inside a glass envelope a few inches long, are accelerated by a small variable potential difference V_1 of a few volts applied between F and a platinum wire grid G_1. Mercury vapour at a pressure of the order of 10^{-2} mm Hg fills the vessel. At this pressure the electron collision mean ree path is roughly equal to the distance between the grid G_1 and a second opper grid G_2 a few centimetres away. Throughout the experiment a

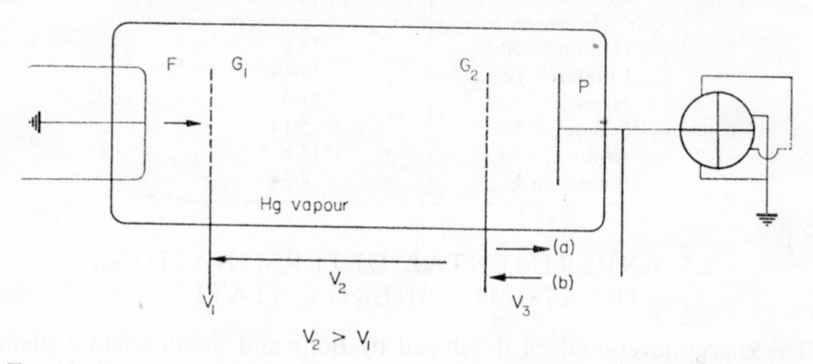

FIG. 10. Apparatus of Davis and Goucher. (Arrows indicate direction of electric field forces on the electrons.)

retarding voltage V_2 is applied between G_1 and G_2 so that $V_2 > V_1$ and $V_2 - V_1$ is kept constant. This means that the electrons from the filament F which pass through the grid G_1 will not have enough energy to overcome the retarding field and reach G_2. An aluminium plate P is mounted a short distance beyond G_2 and is connected to a sensitive quadrant electrometer or electrometer valve to measure a small current (less than 10^{-9} A).

In the first experiment (a) a small potential difference of the order of one volt is applied between G_2 and P so that any electrons between G_2 and P will be attracted to P. The plate current i is observed as the accelerating voltage V_1 between F and G_1 is gradually increased. At first no plate current is observed because the few electrons which collide with atoms of mercury in the region between F and G_1 experience elastic collisions (i.e. the mercury atom is not excited and the electron transfers a fraction of its energy of the order of 10^{-5} to the heavy mercury atom). When V_1 is increased beyond 4·9 V plate current is first observed. This potential is known as the first critical or the *resonance potential* of the mercury atom. Electrons of kinetic energy greater than 4·9 eV may excite a valency electron of a mercury atom to its first excited state. This process will first occur in the vicinity of the grid G_1. Within about 10^{-8} sec the excited atom will return to its normal state by radiating a photon (in the U-V region). If this photon strikes the grid G_2 or the plate P, a photo electron *may* be emitted (the probability is less than 10^{-2}) and such an electron in the space between G_2 and P will be attracted to the plate P and recorded. It is not difficult to understand why the plate current is small when it is realised that several events of low probability must occur in order that an electron reaches the plate P. Increasing V_1 beyond 4·9 V increases the number of excited atoms and the detection current rises. At 6·7 V there is a sharp increase in the slope of the i–V_1 curve due to the onset of a second process of excitation, i.e.

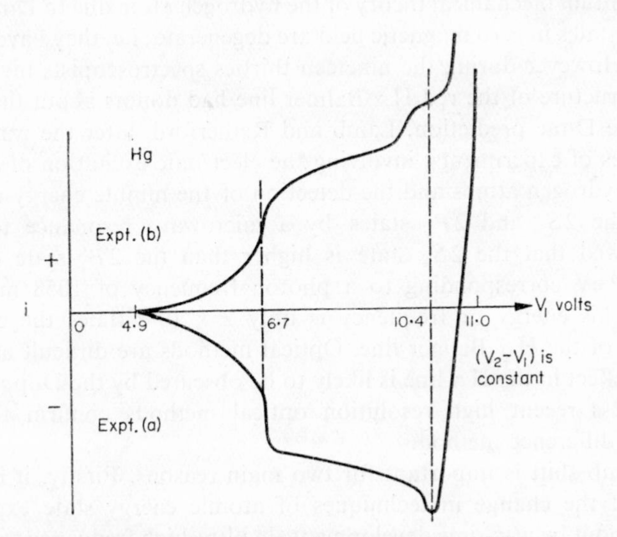

FIG. 11. Plate current as a function of voltage V_1 (Davis and Goucher experiment).

there is a second excited state for the mercury atom 6·7 eV above the ground state. Eventually when V_1 reaches 10·4 V, the *ionization potential* of mercury, electrons colliding with mercury atoms near G_1 ionize a few of them. These positive ions are *attracted* by the voltage V_2 to the grid G_2 and they gain sufficient energy to overcome the retarding field between G_2 and P. At this stage the plate current is ambipolar: positive ions flow to P and photo electrons released from G_2 travel to P. The resultant plate current decreases rapidly as V_1 is increased beyond 10·4 as the positive ion contribution increases rapidly and before V_1 reaches 11 V this component completely swamps the photo-electric component (Fig. 11 (a)).

A second experiment (b) can be performed with the polarity of the voltage V_3 reversed, so that photoelectrons emitted from G_2 and P by the ultraviolet radiation from excited mercury atoms will be attracted to G_2. The plate current flows in the opposite direction to that observed in the first experiment (Fig. 11b). In this case the positive ion current which occurs when V_1 is greater than 10·4 V augments the photoelectric current and there is no reversal in the resultant plate current as V_1 is increased beyond 11 V.

Lamb Shift

To conclude this section we select a recent outstanding atomic energy state experiment. This is the Lamb shift experiment in which W. E. Lamb and R. C. Retherford measured with high precision the minute energy difference between the $2S_{\frac{1}{2}}$ and $2P_{\frac{1}{2}}$ states† of atomic hydrogen. According to the quantum mechanical theory of the hydrogen atom due to Dirac (1928), these two states in zero magnetic field are degenerate; i.e. they have identical energies. However during the nineteen thirties spectroscopists investigating the fine structure of the red Hα Balmer line had doubts about the correctness of the Dirac prediction. Lamb and Retherford, after the war, carried out a series of experiments, involving the electronic excitation of a moving beam of hydrogen atoms and the detection of the minute energy difference between the $2S_{\frac{1}{2}}$ and $2P_{\frac{1}{2}}$ states by a microwave resonance technique. They showed that the $2S_{\frac{1}{2}}$ state is higher than the $2P_{\frac{1}{2}}$ state by about $6{\cdot}4 \times 10^{-6}$ eV corresponding to a photon frequency of 1058 megacycles per sec. This energy or frequency is only 2×10^{-6} times the energy or frequency of the Hα Balmer line. Optical methods are difficult as the fine structure effect in the Hα line is likely to be obscured by the Doppler effect. Nevertheless recent high resolution optical methods confirm the direct frequency difference method.

The Lamb shift is important for two main reasons. Firstly, it is an illustration of the change in techniques of atomic energy state experiments brought about by war-time developments in ultra-high frequency techniques. Secondly, the failure of the Dirac theory to account for this energy shift led to an intense period of theoretical activity in quantum electrodynamics. This resulted not only in the close agreement of the new theory with the experiment but to the prediction that the magnetic moment of the electron should differ by a small amount from the Dirac value of exactly one Bohr magneton. This prediction has been confirmed.

The main features and principles of the experiment of Lamb and Retherford are

(1) The production of a beam of hydrogen atoms in a vacuum with a mean speed of 8×10^5 cm per sec, by the thermal dissociation of molecular hydrogen in an oven at a temperature of 2500°K. (About 64% of the molecules are dissociated into atoms.)

(2) The definition of the atomic beam by suitable slits.

† The $2S_{\frac{1}{2}}$ state corresponds to $n = 2$, $l = 0$ (S electron). $j = l + s = \frac{1}{2}$ (subscript). The $2P_{\frac{1}{2}}$ state corresponds to $n = 2$, $l = 1$ (P state), $j = l - s = \frac{1}{2}$ (subscript).

(3) The excitation of hydrogen atoms to the $2S_{\frac{1}{2}}$ state and $2P_{\frac{1}{2}}$ states by transverse electron bombardment with electron energies of 10·8 eV (i.e. above the 10·2 eV resonance potential of the $2S_{\frac{1}{2}}$ state).

(4) The realization that the $2S_{\frac{1}{2}}$ state is metastable,† if the excited atom is in a region free from distorting electric fields. The necessity of reducing to very low values electric fields along the atomic beam is of paramount importance. The mean lifetime of the metastable $2S_{\frac{1}{2}}$ state is uncertain but it is probably of the order of 10^{-4} sec; whereas atoms in the $2P$ states decay to the $1S$ state emitting a photon of wavelenght 1216 Å (the first line of the Lyman series) with a mean life of about $1{\cdot}6 \times 10^{-9}$ sec. Thus an atom in a $2P$ state travelling with a speed of 8×10^{5} cm per sec will decay after a flight of about $1{\cdot}3 \times 10^{-3}$ cm.

(5) The success of the experiment depends on a detector which will respond to the impact of hydrogen atoms in the metastable state but not to that of a hydrogen atom in the ground state. Unfortunately this detector is also sensitive to ultraviolet photons which are produced by hydrogen atoms and residual hydrogen molecules. It is possible to discriminate between the "signal" current at the detector and the "background" current.

(6) The atomic beam after passing through the transverse beam of electrons passes through a region containing an r.f. field. The atoms are perturbed throughout their flight by a uniform magnetic field whose flux density can be varied up to about 3000 gauss. This results in Zeeman splitting of the $2S$ and $2P$ energy states into different magnetic sub-states. If the frequency ν of the R/F field is related to the energy difference ΔE of one of the $2S_{\frac{1}{2}}$ and one of the $2P_{\frac{1}{2}}$ magnetic sub-states by the quantum equation $\Delta E = h\nu$, a resonance effect is observed in the sense that atoms in the higher state ($2S_{\frac{1}{2}}$) are *stimulated* to emit a very low energy photon (in the microwave region) and jump to the non-metastable $2P_{\frac{1}{2}}$ state. The atom promptly decays to the ground state. The resonance condition is observed by the reduction in the number of metastable atoms reaching the detector plate.

(7) It is much easier to vary the applied magnetic field, which alters the energy difference ΔE, to obtain resonance at one of several set frequencies rather than to attempt the technically difficult task of continuously varying the frequency ν. The theory of the Zeeman splitting of atomic hydrogen enables the energy difference ΔE between the $2S_{\frac{1}{2}}$ and $2P_{\frac{1}{2}}$ states in zero magnetic field to be deduced by extrapolating the results in finite fields. According to the Dirac theory ΔE should tend to zero. This is not observed and the limiting value of ΔE in zero field corresponds to a high radio frequency of 1058 Mc/s.

A schematic diagram of the apparatus is shown in Fig. 12.

† A metastable state is an excited state of exceptionally long lifetime.

O is a small tungsten oven in which hydrogen gas admitted through a valve is heated to about 2500°K. The gas pressure is of the order of 10^{-3} atm. Atoms emerging from a slit in the oven pass through a slit B in a plate with a mean speed of 8×10^5 cm per sec.

Electrons emitted from a hot cathode K are accelerated through a potential difference of about 10·8 V to a grid electrode C. They pass through the grid and cross the atomic beam and are collected by the anode A. The space between C and A is an equipotential volume so there are no perturbing electric fields to distort the charge distribution of the atoms excited to the $2S_{\frac{1}{2}}$ metastable state. Atoms recoil under the electron impact with a spread

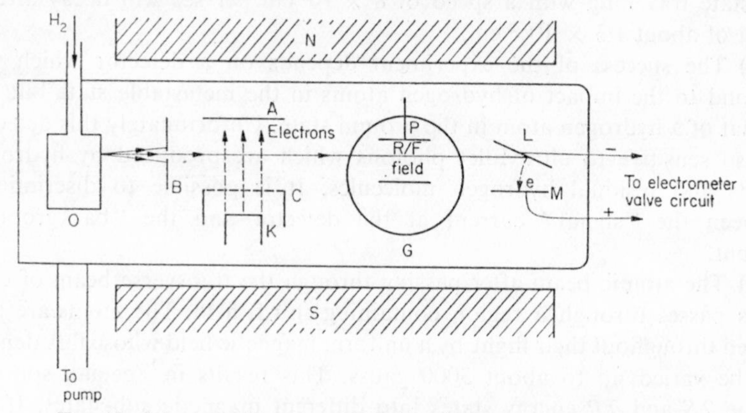

FIG. 12. Schematic diagram of Lamb and Retherford's experiment.

in recoil angle and some of them pass through two slots in G the r.f. interaction space. The plate P in this space can be raised to a potential of 100 V or more relative to the atomic beam. This electric field quenches the metastable nature of the $2S_{\frac{1}{2}}$ state. It is very useful for detecting the background photoelectric current flowing from L to M due to ultraviolet photons reaching L. Metastable atoms striking the tungsten plate L may transfer their excitation energy of 10·2 eV to an electron in the plate and eject it from the plate. The electron is collected by the tungsten plate M which is 3 or 4 V positive with respect to L. The detector current is measured with an electrometer valve circuit of input resistance about 7×10^{10} ohms.

It is instructive to list the factors which determine the expected detector current. Some of these are very uncertain but it is obvious that in this type of experiment careful consideration of the possibility of being able to detect a current is essential. The following factors influence the detector current.

(1) The number of hydrogen atoms escaping per second from the oven at an angle θ with respect to the wall normal into a solid angle Ω is

$$\frac{n_0 \, a \, v \, \Omega \, X \cos\theta}{4\pi}$$

where n_0 is the number of atoms and molecules per unit volume, X is the fractional dissociation, a is the area of the opening in the oven and v is the average speed of the atoms in the oven.

(2) Ignoring recoil due to electron impact, a value of A/R^2 for Ω the solid angle subtended by a detector L of area A distance R from the oven would apply. Also $\cos\theta = 1$.

(3) A fraction δ of the metastable atoms would reach the detector as their recoil allows them to pass through G.

(4) f the fraction of atoms excited to the $2\,S_{\frac{1}{2}}$ state.

(5) μ the fraction of metastable atoms which survive any residual quenching electric fields between the electron excitation region and the detector.

(6) η the efficiency of the detector for metastable atoms. The factor f is estimated as follows. Let I be the electron bombarding current in electrons per sec and let the electron stream be of width w and height h. An atom has a time of flight across this stream of w/v. If σ is the excitation cross section for the $2s$ state, the transition rate is I/wh, as wh is the area of the electron beam. The probability of excitation in crossing the stream is then given by

$$f = \frac{I\sigma}{wh} \times \frac{w}{v} = \frac{I\sigma}{hv} = 2{\cdot}3 \times 10^{-8}$$

put $I = 200\,\mu\text{A} = 1{\cdot}24 \times 10^{15}$ electrons per sec.
$h = 1$ cm
$v = 8 \times 10^5$ cm per sec.

The theoretical estimate of σ for the $2S$ state is uncertain but for electrons of energy about 10·8 eV it is probably not less than 10^{-17} cm² (σ rises steeply from the threshold energy of 10·2 eV to a maximum value of about 2×10^{-17} cm² at 14·8 eV then it falls away more slowly on the high energy side, falling to 1×10^{-17} cm² around 50 eV).

A reasonable estimate for σ is 1×10^{-17} cm².

About one in forty million atoms is excited to the $2S$ state.

The detector signal is given by the expression

$$S = \frac{n_0\,a\,X\,A\,I\,\sigma\,\delta\,\mu\,\eta}{4\pi\,R^2\,h} \quad \text{electrons per sec.}$$

Inserting the following values
$n_0 = 2{\cdot}94 \times 10^{15}$ cm^{-3} (10^{-3} atm, 2500°K)
$a = 3{\cdot}1 \times 10^{-3}$ cm², $A = 1{\cdot}21$ cm², $R = 6{\cdot}35$ cm; $h = 1$ cm
$\sigma = 1 \times 10^{-17}$ cm²
$I = 1{\cdot}87 \times 10^{15}$ electrons per sec (300 μ A).
$X = 0{\cdot}64$
$\delta = 0{\cdot}5$
$\mu = 0{\cdot}5$
$\eta = 0{\cdot}5$

The last three estimates are very rough. It emerged that the detector efficiency η of 0·5 was probably much too high.

These values predict a signal current of

$$S = 3{\cdot}26 \times 10^7 \text{ electrons per sec} = 5{\cdot}2 \times 10^{-12} \text{ A}$$

This is about 10^4 times the minimum detectable current using an electrometer circuit and a sensitive galvanometer. The observed current was about forty times smaller than this, probably due to stray electric fields and low detector efficiency. Various ways of feeding r.f. power into the interaction region were considered. A coaxial transmission line enters at the top of

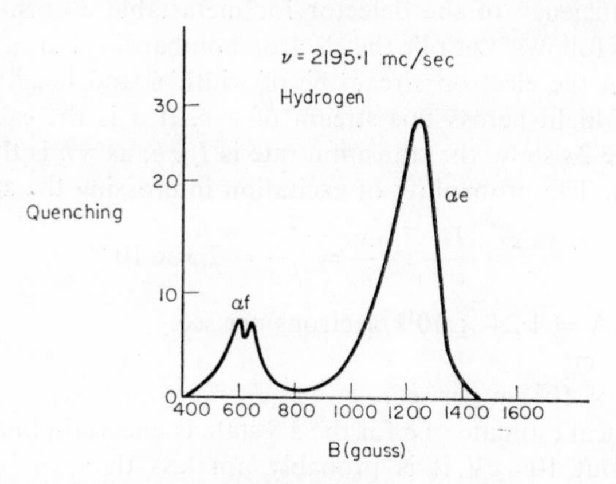

FIG. 13. Resonance curves in Lamb–Retherford experiment. (*Phys. Rev.* **81**, 228, 1951.)

the apparatus and is terminated at the bottom end by an unmatched crystal. The crystal current indicates the r.f. power. An auxiliary electrode P in the interaction space can be raised to a potential of more than 100 V to quench (i.e. greatly reduce the lifetime of) the metastable atoms. Resonance curves are plotted by observing the galvanometer current in the detector circuit when the r.f. power is interrupted for different Zeeman magnetic fields. An observed resonance curve at a frequency of 2195·1 Mc per sec is shown in Fig. 13. The resonance peak αf corresponds to transitions between the $2S_{\frac{1}{2}}$ magnetic sub-state $m = \frac{1}{2}$ and the $2P_{\frac{1}{2}}$ sub-state $m = -\frac{1}{2}$; the peak αe to the transitions from the $2S_{\frac{1}{2}}$, $m = \frac{1}{2}$ magnetic sub-state to the $2P_{\frac{1}{2}}$, $m = \frac{1}{2}$ sub-state. A hyperfine structure of the αf resonance curve is clearly shown.

A full account of the Lamb shift experiments, including a detailed discussion of the reasons for choosing the final design of the apparatus, is given in a series of papers listed in the bibliography.

BIBLIOGRAPHY

M. BORN, *Atomic Physics*, 7th Ed., Blackie, London 1962.

F. K. RICHTMEYER, E. H. KENNARD and T. LAURITSEN, *Introduction to Modern Physics*, 5th Ed., McGraw-Hill, New York 1955.

A. SOMMERFELD, *Atomic Structure and Spectral Lines*, Methuen, 1930.

R. C. JOHNSON, *Atomic Spectra*, Methuen, London 1946.

G. P. HARNWELL and W. E. STEPHENS, *Atomic Physics*, McGraw-Hill, New York 1955.

F. L. ARNOT, *Collision Processes in Gases*, 3rd Ed., Methuen, 1943.

N. Bohr's original papers on the origin of spectral lines are in *Phil. Mag.* **6**, 1, 476, 857, 1913.

The "Lamb" Shift experiments are discussed in the book by G. W. SERIES, *The Spectra of Atomic Hydrogen*, Oxford University Press, 1957, and in the following papers:

W. E. LAMB and R. C. RETHERFORD, *Phys. Rev.* **79**, 549, 1950; **81**, 222, 1951; **86**, 1014, 1952; **89**, 98, 106, 1953.

EXAMPLES

1. A metal has a threshold wavelength of 5200 Å. Calculate the photoelectric work function of the surface in eV. What is the maximum velocity of emission of photoelectrons if the surface is illuminated with light of wavelength 4500 Å?
2. The saturation photoelectric current from a high vacuum photo emission cell is 400 microamps. per watt of incident monochromatic radiation (5500 Å). What is the probability of an incident photon ejecting an electron?
3. Calculate the energy, speed and radius of an electron in the first Bohr orbit of atomic hydrogen and singly ionized helium. It is possible to capture negative mu mesons (mass 207 times electron mass) in Bohr orbits. What is the radius and speed of such a meson in the first Bohr orbit around a carbon nucleus ($Z = 6$)?
4. Calculate the difference between the ionization potentials of atomic hydrogen and deuterium and atomic hydrogen and tritium. The masses of the deuteron and the triton can be taken as two and three times the proton mass respectively. (Use the standard values for e, h and c.)
5. The Rydberg constants for atomic hydrogen and singly ionized helium are 109,677·58 cm^{-1} and 109,722·26 cm^{-1} respectively. The slight difference is a result of the different values of the reduced electron mass. Determine the ratio of the electron to the proton mass, given that the masses of atomic hydrogen and helium are 1·0081 and 4·0039 respectively. Hence find the value of e/m for the electron, if the Faraday is 96,520 coulombs.g.equiv.$^{-1}$.
6. In an experiment of Cario and Franck (1923), mercury and thallium vapour at a temperature of 800°C in a quartz tube is irradiated with the intense spectral line of the mercury spectrum of wavelength 2536 Å. A spectroscopic examination of the fluorescent radiation revealed the presence of the 2768 Å and 3776 Å lines of thallium. The thallium atoms had been excited by "collisions of the second kind" with excited mercury atoms which had absorbed the 2536 Å radiation (resonance absorption). The energy difference in a collision of the second kind appears as kinetic energy of the recoiling atoms. Calculate the recoil velocities of the mercury and the thallium atoms after a collision of the second kind (a) in which the excited thallium atom emits the 2768 Å line in returning to its ground state, (b) in which the 3776 Å line is emitted. Why is the 3776 line less strongly absorbed than the 2768 line? (Atomic weights: Hg, 201; Tl, 204.)

CHAPTER 3

THE THEORY OF RELATIVITY

3.1. INTRODUCTION

It is a commonplace statement that scientific knowledge is acquired by observation and experiment. Yet it is true to say that prior to the development of the theory of relativity by Einstein, the implications of the relation of the observer describing phenomena to the phenomena themselves were not fully realized. The concept of relative velocity in the history of mechanics is not new; nevertheless it was always assumed that the concepts of absolute velocity, absolute rest and absolute time are meaningful. Newton postulated the existence of a unique "even-flowing" universal time. His well-known laws of motion make no reference to the state of motion of the observer describing the motion of bodies. The first law of motion, for instance, states that

"Every body continues in its state of rest or of uniform motion in a straight line, except in so far as it is compelled by impressed forces to change that state".

The point of view of relativity with regard to this type of statement is that it is wrong to say that the motion of a given body satisfies Newton's first law of motion. What one can say is—that for a certain special class of observers known as *inertial observers*, a given body may move with constant rectilinear motion. However, for observers who move with an acceleration relative to the inertial group of observers, the body in question will have an acceleration and therefore be under the influence of impressed forces. The assumption that it is possible to assign absolute motion or rest to one particular observer is unjustified.

Relativity is concerned with the relations between the measurements of lengths and time intervals by different groups of observers. One special group, described in the preceding paragraph is the inertial group. These observers move with uniform relative velocity with respect to each other but there is no relative acceleration between them. The special theory of relativity is restricted to the relations between the description of events given by inertial observers. The general theory relaxes this restriction, and is especially concerned with the description of events given by observers in relative acceleration. In this chapter, we are primarily interested in the special theory, and several of the important formulae obtained are required in atomic and nuclear physics. A very brief account of the general theory concludes the chapter. The recent discovery of the existence of a few highly monochromatic gamma ray sources by R. Mössbauer has been responsible for a number of new experiments to test the Einstein relativity principle of equivalence.

The special theory of relativity is based on the hypothesis that it is impossible to assign absolute velocity to the motion of any material particle or object. The velocity of light in free space, however, is an absolute velocity. This special property of electromagnetic waves has a number of important implications in the theory. The most important property of this velocity c is that it represents the upper limit to the velocity of propagation of any form of energy or signal. The concept of "cause and effect" in scientific thinking would be meaningless if signals could travel instantaneously. Starting from the fundamental hypotheses, it is then possible to deduce the mathematical relations existing between the descriptions of lengths and time intervals according to different inertial observers. Two startling conclusions are reached. The first is that the length of an object relative to a moving observer is less than the length relative to an observer who is at rest with respect to the object. The second is that the time interval between two events which occur at the same place relative to one observer is less than the time interval relative to an observer moving with respect to the pair of events. It is found that two events occurring simultaneously, but at different places, for one observer, will not be judged as simultaneous events by another observer. Thus the concepts of length, time interval and simultaneity lose their absolute character.

The recognition of the relative nature of length and time and the discovery of the transformation equations linking the measurements of inertial observers has had repercussions throughout the whole of physics. It has been found that in order to retain the law of conservation of momentum it is necessary to introduce the law that the mass of an object is a function of its speed relative to the observer. The mass increases with the velocity relative to the observer and approaches an infinite value as the velocity approaches the upper limit c. Combining this new law with the familiar definitions of energy and work the important conclusion is reached that to every quantity of energy E there is an associated mass $m = E/c^2$. The laws of conservation of mass and energy are no longer separate conservation laws; they are fused together in a single energy–mass conservation law.

We must now turn to a more detailed discussion of the evidence and arguments in support of the two fundamental postulates of the special theory of relativity.

3.2. THE POSTULATES OF SPECIAL RELATIVITY

The special theory of relativity is based on two fundamental postulates. The first postulate is a denial of the concept of absolute velocity. The second postulate, however, claims there is one exception to this rule, namely the velocity of light. On the wave theory, the velocity of light is independent of the motion of the source but the velocity relative to an observer should depend on the velocity of the medium responsible for carrying the wave (the aether). There is now good evidence for the corpuscular (photon) nature of radiation, but we find that the velocity of a moving source is not added vectorially to the velocity of propagation of the wave from a stationary source.

The first postulate can be expressed in the following way: "It is impossible to detect or measure the uniform rectilinear velocity of a body through space, or through any aether assumed to fill all space and matter".

As a corollary of the first postulate we can state that "The laws of physics must be identical in form for all inertial observers". If this were not so, any difference in form could be interpreted as signifying that there is a difference in the absolute motion of the system of coordinates used by different observers. The expression of the laws of physics in a form which is independent of the coordinate system used to describe them is known as the principle of covariance. The principle does not, of course, state that there is no change in the coordinate values describing phenomena when we change from one coordinate system to another. The principle of covariance is a consequence of the relativity of motion, and in developing the laws of physics great care must be taken to exclude unsuspected assumptions that are the result of using one particular coordinate system.

The rejection of the concept of absolute motion as physically meaningless would be contradicted if it were possible to detect the motion of any body whatsoever relative to the aether. It is natural to assume that if the universal aether theory is true, the laws of physics would take on a specially fundamental form when described in a coordinate system at rest in the aether. The aether would, in fact, replace the earlier idea of a unique space filling the whole of the universe. The aether concept seemed to be a necessity of thought to the mechanically-minded scientists of the nineteenth century. It was impossible to conceive of a wave motion propagated through space without the existence of a medium throughout that space. The aether, so essential to the comfort of the physicist's mind, nevertheless, possessed a number of curious properties. The aether would have to be extremely tenuous in order that it should not impede the motion of the stars and planets. However, by analogy with the known factors determining the velocity of propagation of acoustic vibrations through solids and fluids, the aether would require an extremely high modulus of elasticity in order that the velocity of electromagnetic waves should be as high as 3×10^8 m per sec. In addition, the transverse nature of electromagnetic waves, demonstrated most clearly by their polarization properties, means that the aether is more like a solid than a liquid or gas.

The first attempt to detect the relative motion of the earth and the aether was made in 1881 by Michelson, using his celebrated interferometer. Six years later, in 1887, Michelson was joined by Morley, and they, within the limits of their experiment, did not detect any motion of the earth through the aether at any time of the year. This is difficult to understand on the aether theory, as the earth moves round the sun at a speed of 30 km per sec, and even if, by chance, the earth is at rest in the aether at one time of the year it would not be later in the year. The belief that the earth occupies a position of special significance in the universe is alien to the spirit of modern physics. The best modern repetitions of the Michelson–Morley experiment set the velocity of the earth relative to the hypothetical aether at less than one thousandth part of the earth's orbital speed. Thus it is reasonable to reject the principle of absolute velocity, an idea first expressed by Mach and Poincaré, who did not accept the reality of the aether hypothesis.

The Michelson–Morley Experiment

This famous experiment was carried out to determine the velocity of the earth through the aether. The method is an application of the Michelson interferometer. A beam of light from an extended monochromatic source S is divided into two perpendicular beams I and II by partial reflection at

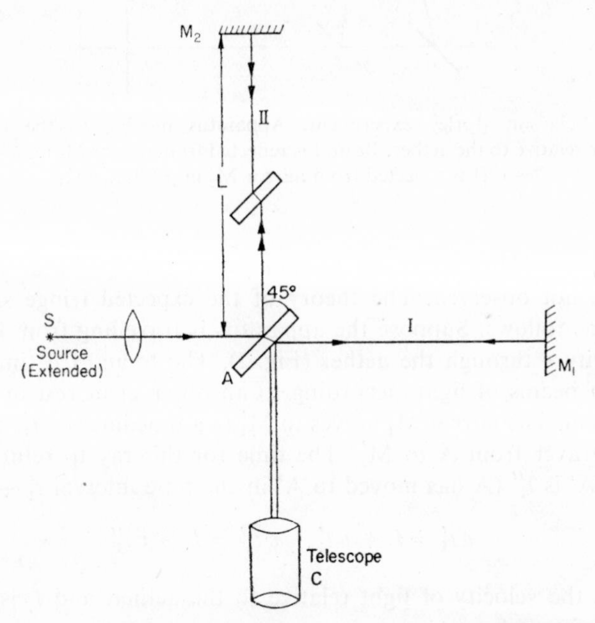

Fig. 1. Michelson Interferometer. Light is split into two perpendicular beams by reflection from semi-silvered surface A inclined at 45°. The path lengths of each of the two beams is equal to 2 L. The two beams reunite and produce interference fringes viewed through the telescope C.

a semi-silvered optical flat A, inclined at 45° to the two divided beams (Fig. 1). The beams, after reflection from the plane mirrors M_1 and M_2 respectively, retrace their paths and recombine in the telescope C. If the mirrors M_1 and M_2 are exactly perpendicular, interference fringes consisting of concentric circles are seen through C. These are the well-known "fringes of constant inclination" (the light beam incident on A from the source is not strictly collimated). The path lengths of the two beams are adjusted to be exactly equal and the whole apparatus, which floats on mercury, is rotated through 90°. A finite velocity of the earth (and with it the interferometer) through the aether should produce, on the aether theory, a shift of the interference pattern across the cross-hairs of the telescope eye-piece.

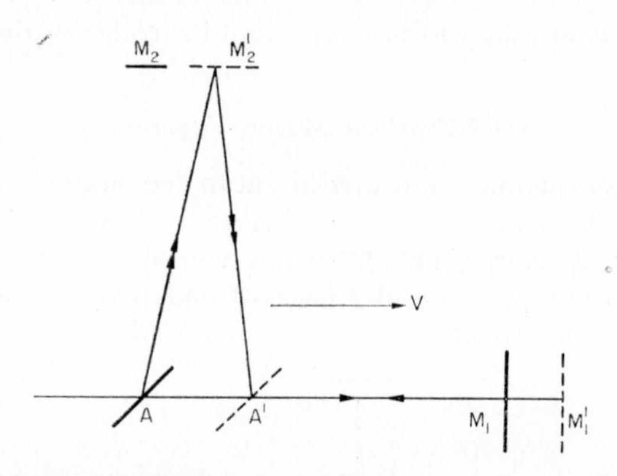

FIG. 2. Michelson–Morley experiment. Apparatus moving to the right with velocity v relative to the aether. Beam I is reflected from mirror M_1 in position M_1'. Beam II is reflected from mirror M_2 in position M_2'.

This shift, no matter what the orientation of the apparatus or the time of year, is not observed. The theory of the expected fringe shift can be described as follows. Suppose the apparatus is travelling from left to right with velocity v through the aether (Fig. 2). The to and fro times of flight of the two beams of light, according to an observer at rest in the aether, are not equal. The mirror M_1 moves to M_1' in a time interval t_1', the time for ray I to travel from A to M_1'. The time for this ray to return from the mirror to A′ is t_1'' (A has moved to A′ in the time interval $t_1' + t_1''$).

$$c\,t_1' = L + v\,t_1', \quad c\,t_1'' = L - v\,t_1'' \tag{1}$$

where c is the velocity of light relative to the aether, and L is the length of the interferometer arm.

$$\therefore\ t_1' = \frac{L}{c - v}, \quad t_1'' = \frac{L}{c + v}$$

The to and fro time of flight of ray I, t_1 is equal to $t_1' + t_1''$

$$\therefore\ t_1 = \frac{2L}{c}\frac{1}{(1-\beta^2)} \quad \text{where} \quad \beta = \frac{v}{c} \tag{2}$$

To determine t_2 the to and fro time of flight of ray II we note that in the interval $t_2/2$, the mirror M_2 has moved to M_2', where $M_2 M_2' = v\,t_2/2$. The triangle A M_2' A' is isosceles and we can write

$$\left(v\frac{t_2}{2}\right)^2 + L^2 = \left(c\frac{t_2}{2}\right)^2 \tag{3}$$

$$\therefore\ t_2 = \frac{2L}{c}\frac{1}{\sqrt{[1-\beta^2]}} \tag{4}$$

The difference in the times t_1 and t_2 is given by

$$\tau = t_1 - t_2 = \frac{2L}{c}\left[\frac{1}{(1-\beta^2)} - \frac{1}{\sqrt{(1-\beta^2)}}\right] \tag{5}$$

If $\beta \ll 1$, then expanding eqn. (5) with the aid of the binomial theorem,

$$\tau = \frac{L\beta^2}{c} \tag{6}$$

Suppose the interferometer is rotated through 90°, so that the directions of the beams I and II are now perpendicular and parallel to the velocity v, respectively. The interference system should be displaced relative to the cross-hairs of the telescope eye-piece by an amount corresponding to the time difference

$$2\tau = \frac{2L\beta^2}{c} \tag{7}$$

The number n of fringes displaced is given by

$$n = \frac{2\tau}{T} = 2\tau\frac{c}{\lambda} = \frac{2L\beta^2}{\lambda} \tag{8}$$

where T and λ are the period and wavelength of the light respectively. To increase the sensitivity of the method, Michelson and Morley increased the path length to 11 m by successive to and fro reflections before combining the light beams in the telescope. For monochromatic light of wavelength 5900 Å, an aether velocity v equal to the orbital velocity of the earth around the sun (30 km per sec), n is 0·37 fringes. Such a shift would have been detected by Michelson and Morley. Later repetitions of the experiment were capable of detecting a shift of 1/100 fringe. No shift has been observed. So deeply embedded in physical thinking was the aether concept in nineteenth century physics, that every attempt, plausible and implausible, was made to account for the null result without abandoning the reality of the aether. Perhaps the most interesting of these attempts was that of Lorentz and independently FitzGerald. They postulated a contraction of the length of every object moving through the aether just sufficient to cancel the time of flight difference of the two beams of light in the Michelson–Morley experiment. Lengths perpendicular to the aether velocity are unaffected. Far-fetched as this explanation may seem, it must be remembered that the length of a material object is determined by the relative density of packing of the constituent atoms, which in turn depends on electrical forces between the atoms. Motion through the medium, which is the seat of all electromagnetic phenomena, is expected to modify these electrical forces and thereby account for the hypothetical contraction. However, an experiment devised by Kennedy, in which the arms of a Michelson interferometer were made as unequal in length as feasible, demonstrated a null effect for the relative motion of the earth and the aether.† The contraction hypothesis mentioned above is not sufficient to explain this null result; in addition a time-dilatation effect is required.

The Absolute Velocity of Light

Direct proof of the independence of the velocity of light to the relative motion of light source and observer is not available. The indirect evidence is very strong. Several years after Einstein's first papers on the special theory of relativity (1905), de Sitter in 1913 gave a convincing argument in terms of the observed periodicities of double stars. Systematic observations of double stars were first carried out by Sir William Herschel at the end of the eighteenth century. A double star is a pair of stars which revolve around a common centre of gravity under their mutual gravitational attraction. If the velocity of the star towards or away from the earth is added vectorially to the velocity of light, a marked eccentricity in the observed double star orbit would result. Consider a binary star system (Fig. 3).

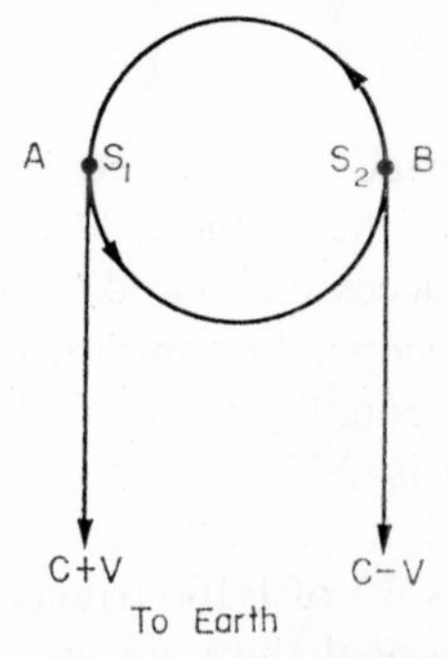

FIG. 3. Double Star Orbit. Star S_1 at A, has velocity v towards the Earth. Star S_2 at B, has velocity v away from the Earth.

† R. J. KENNEDY and E. M. THORNDIKE, *Phys. Rev.* **42**, 400, 1932.

If the star S_1 is at A at time t, then it will be observed in this position at a later time $t + d/(c + v)$ on the earth, (d is the distance from the star to the earth, v the speed of the star towards the earth). If T is the half period of the star S_1, it will reach B at $t + T$ and be observed in this position on earth at a time $t + T + d/(c - v)$ Thus the observed half period of S_1 is

$$T + \frac{d}{c - v} - \frac{d}{c + v}$$

A similar calculation for the other member of the pair, S_2, yields for the half period of S_2 the value

$$T + \frac{d}{c + v} - \frac{d}{c - v}$$

The difference in the observed half periods of S_1 and S_2 is

$$\frac{4vd}{c^2 - v^2} \simeq \frac{4vd}{c^2} \tag{9}$$

de Sitter pointed out that for many binary stars, this time difference is of the order of the half period T. The fact that no discrepancy in the orbit shape (calculated from Newton's gravitational law) has been observed, is convincing proof that the relative velocity of approach of the light from a star is not influenced by the motion of the star towards or away from the observer.

3.3. THE LORENTZ TRANSFORMATION

Consider the relation between the velocities of three particles A, B and C travelling in a straight line (Fig. 4). According to the laws of Newtonian kinematics,

$$u + v + w = 0, \tag{10}$$

where u is the velocity of A relative to C
v is the velocity of C relative to B,
w is the velocity of B relative to A.

If v is the velocity of a photon, $v = c$ and $u = -c$, for all values of w, because the velocity of light has the same value in all frames of reference. Equation (10) cannot be the correct law of addition of velocities. All our terrestial experience supports the classical equation and the new relativity

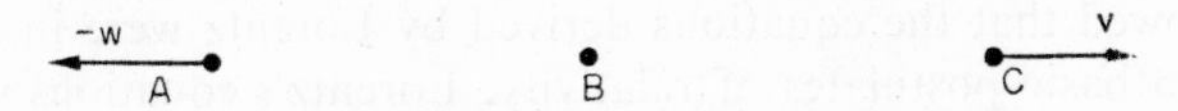

FIG. 4. Three collinear particles A, B, C in a frame of reference in which particle B is at rest. C has velocity v relative to B: A has velocity $-w$ relative to B. The velocity of A relative to C is u.

law will reduce to the classical result when u, v and w are all small compared to the velocity of light. Equation (10) is replaced by a function relation

$$f(u, v, w) = 0 \tag{11}$$

But, in order that the solution of (11) gives a single value for the velocity v and that no special significance is attached to u, v, or w (in accordance with the first relativity postulate), the function can be written

$$l + m(u + v + w) + n(v\,w + w\,u + u\,v) + p \cdot u\,v\,w = 0 \tag{12}$$

where l, m, n, p are undetermined constants.

Now, if $w = 0$, $u = -v$

$$\therefore\ l - n\,u^2 = 0, \text{ for all values of } u$$

$$\therefore\ l = 0 \quad \text{and} \quad n = 0$$

Equation (12) reduces to

$$m(u + v + w) + p\,u\,v\,w = 0$$

If $v = c$, $u = -c$ for all values of w

$$\therefore\ m\,w - p\,c^2\,w = 0$$

$$\therefore\ m = p\,c^2$$

Thus the law of composition of collinear velocities is

$$u + v + w + \frac{u\,v\,w}{c^2} = 0$$

It is more convenient to denote the velocity of C relative to A as u, so replacing u by $-u$, we find that

$$u = \frac{v + w}{1 + \dfrac{v\,w}{c^2}} \tag{13}$$

This important equation replaces the relation $u = v + w$, and in particular it means that two velocities, each less than c, cannot be compounded to exceed the velocity of light. For if $v = c$, $w = c$

$$u = \frac{c + c}{1 + \dfrac{c^2}{c^2}} = c!$$

One of the main objects of the special theory is to find the transformation relations between the space and time measurements of inertial observers. Einstein showed that the equations derived by Lorentz were in agreement with the two basic postulates of relativity. Lorentz's equations were originally derived in relation to electromagnetic phenomena (Maxwell's equations do in fact satisfy this transformation), but they are of wider application than was originally realised.

Consider two inertial observers O and O′ in the systems of Cartesian axes S and S′ (Fig. 5). System S′ is moving to the right, parallel to the x and x'- axes, with constant velocity v. No loss in generality results from having the x and x', the y and y', and the z and z'- axes parallel. At $t = 0 = t'$, O and O′ coincide.

A particle at a single moment (an event) is described by four coordinates in each system (x, y, z, t); (x', y', z', t'); the time measurements are made by clocks at rest in their respective systems. The relations between these coordinates, according to Newtonian physics are

$$x' = x - v\,t, \quad y' = y, \quad z' = z, \quad t' = t. \tag{14}$$

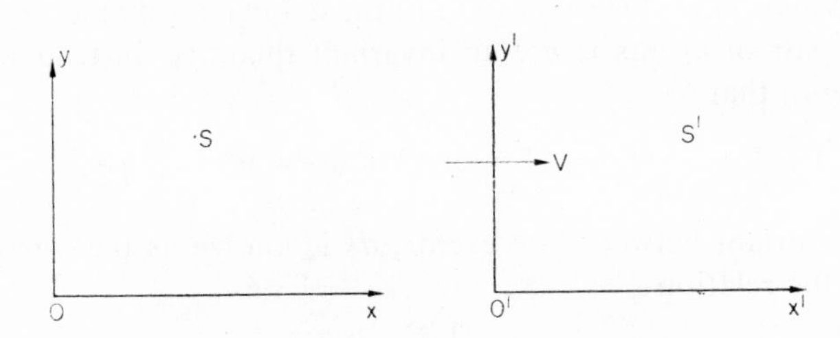

FIG. 5. Two inertial systems S and S′, described from the point of view of system S at rest. At $t = 0 = t'$, O′ coincides with O. S′ moves to right with constant velocity v parallel to the $0\,x$ and $O\,x'$ axes.

These equations are known as the GALILEAN TRANSFORMATION. We anticipate that the new relations will be reduced to these equations in the limit of low velocity ($v \ll c$).

The new relations, the LORENTZ TRANSFORMATION, are

$$x' = \frac{x - v\,t}{\sqrt{\left(1 - \frac{v^2}{c^2}\right)}}, \quad y' = y, \quad z' = z, \quad t' = \frac{t - \frac{v\,x}{c^2}}{\sqrt{\left(1 - \frac{v^2}{c^2}\right)}} \tag{15}$$

To justify these relations, we first note that if v is small compared to c, the equations reduce to the Galilean transformation. Secondly, solving for the unprimed quantities in terms of the primed, we obtain by very simple algebra the relations

$$x = \frac{x' + v\,t'}{\sqrt{\left(1 - \frac{v^2}{c^2}\right)}}, \quad y = y', \quad z = z', \quad t = \frac{t' + \frac{v\,x'}{c^2}}{\sqrt{\left(1 - \frac{v^2}{c^2}\right)}} \tag{16}$$

These relations are in agreement with the first postulate of relativity, as the only possible effect of changing our description from one inertial observer to another is to change the sign of v (replacing v by $-v$, and the primed by the unprimed quantities in eqn. (15) results in eqns. (16)).

In classical physics we are familiar with the idea that the distance between a pair of events is independent of the observer, that is, that the following relation holds

$$(dx)^2 + (dy)^2 + (dz)^2 = (dx')^2 + (dy')^2 + (dz')^2, \tag{17}$$

where dx, dy, dz are the differences in the coordinates of the pair of events measured by O, the corresponding primed quantities referring to observations of the *same* pair of events by O′. In Einsteinian mechanics, the distance between a pair of events is *not* an invariant quantity, instead we find by simple algebra that

$$x^2 + y^2 + z^2 - c^2 t^2 = x'^2 + y'^2 + z'^2 - c^2 t'^2. \tag{18}$$

The new invariant between two events, ds is known as the *interval* and is defined by the relation

$$(ds)^2 = (dt)^2 - \frac{1}{c^2}(dx^2 + dy^2 + dz^2) \tag{19}$$

The simplest example occurs when $ds = 0$; and

$$dx^2 + dy^2 + dz^2 = dr^2 = c^2\,dt^2$$

$$\therefore dr = c\,dt.$$

In words, this means that a pulse of light emitted at $t = 0$, $t' = 0$, would have advanced a distance dr in the time dt. In the same way, $dr' = c\,dt'$, and each observer describes the expanding wave front of the pulse as a sphere of radius $c\,dt$ (or $c\,dt'$) with himself as centre. This result is in agreement with the second postulate of relativity, namely, that all observers obtain the same value for the speed of light. The paradoxical situation arises, contradictory to our intuitive concepts of space and time, that two observers, no longer coincident, regard the same wave front as a sphere with himself as the centre.

The law of composition of velocities (eqn. 13) can be derived from the Lorentz transformation equations. Differentiating eqn. (16) (v is constant), we obtain

$$\frac{dx}{dt'} = \frac{\dfrac{dx'}{dt'} + v}{\sqrt{\left(1 - \dfrac{v^2}{c^2}\right)}}, \quad dy = dy', \quad dz = dz', \qquad \frac{dt}{dt'} = \frac{1 + \dfrac{v}{c^2}\dfrac{dx'}{dt'}}{\sqrt{\left(1 - \dfrac{v^2}{c^2}\right)}} \tag{20}$$

Let $u'_x = dx'/dt'$, be the x'-velocity component of a particle relative to O, let $u_x = dx/dt$, be the x-velocity component of the same particle relative to O′, then, as $dx/dt = (dx/dt') \times (dt'/dt)$ we obtain

$$u_x = \frac{u'_x + v}{1 + \frac{v\,u'_x}{c^2}}, \quad u_y = \frac{u'_y \sqrt{\left(1 - \frac{v^2}{c^2}\right)}}{1 + \frac{v\,u'_x}{c^2}}, \quad u_z = \frac{u'_z \sqrt{\left(1 - \frac{v^2}{c^2}\right)}}{1 + \frac{v\,u'_y}{c^2}} \tag{21}$$

u_y, u_z, u'_y, u'_z are the y and z-components of velocity in the two systems.

$$\text{Also} \quad u^2 = u_x^2 + u_y^2 + u_z^2 \quad \text{and} \quad u'^2 = u_x'^2 + u_y'^2 + u_z'^2. \tag{22}$$

The first equation of (21) is identical with eqn. (13) as $u'_x = w$.

3.4. LORENTZ CONTRACTION AND TIME DILATATION

Two important consequences of the Lorentz transformation equations are easily obtained. The first concerns the effect of the motion of an observer

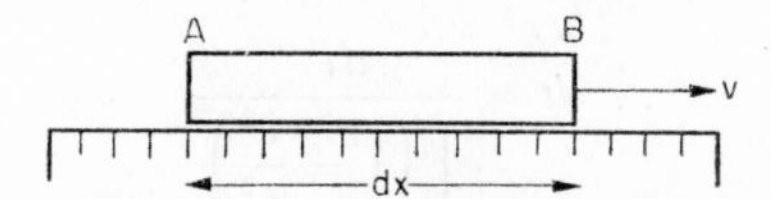

FIG. 6. Rod A B, of length dx' in system S′, moves past measuring rod at rest in system S with velocity v. dx is the observed length of A B in system S.

in measuring the length of an object which is parallel to this motion. Consider two measuring rods parallel to the x and x'-axes, one at rest in S, the other at rest in S′. The rod at rest in S has a length dx according to the observer in this system. The observer at rest in S′ (Fig. 6) judges the coincidence of the ends of this rod with scale divisions on the measuring rod at rest in system S. The separation of these divisions is noted at the same time in system S ($dt = 0$). Hence differentiating the first equation of eqns. (15), and putting $dt = 0$, we obtain

$$dx' = \frac{dx}{\sqrt{\left(1 - \frac{v^2}{c^2}\right)}}$$

$$\therefore\ dx = \sqrt{\left(1 - \frac{v^2}{c^2}\right)}\, dx' \tag{23}$$

The length of the rod measured by O is less than the length dx' measured by O′. Thus an observer, moving parallel to the length of an object, observes a length smaller than the length measured by an observer at rest relative to the object. This effect is known as the Lorentz contraction. It should not be confused with the hypothetical Lorentz–FitzGerald contraction introduced to explain away the null result of the Michelson–Morley experiment. The Lorentz contraction is simply a consequence of the fact that length is not an absolute entity, it is a relation between the object of interest and the observer.

Next consider a pair of events which occur at the same point in S′ (for example, the striking of Big Ben at one and two o'clock). What is the time interval dt of this pair of events for an observer at rest in S?

dt' is the time interval in S′, $(dx' = 0)$.

Differentiating the first relation of eqns. (15) we have, if $dx' = 0$,

$$dx = v\,dt$$

Substituting for dx in the differential of the last relation of eqns. (15) we obtain

$$dt' = \frac{dt\left(1 - \frac{v^2}{c^2}\right)}{\sqrt{\left(1 - \frac{v^2}{c^2}\right)}}$$

$$\therefore\ dt = \frac{dt'}{\sqrt{\left(1 - \frac{v^2}{c^2}\right)}} \tag{24}$$

A time interval dt' in system S′ is observed as a longer time dt in the moving system S. To a moving observer, all clocks go slow. This effect is known as Time Dilatation. There is good experimental evidence in favour of the time dilatation effect. This is provided by the observation of secondary cosmic ray particles which are found at sea level. The particles concerned are known as mu-mesons (muons); they are produced by the decay of pi-mesons (pions) high in the atmosphere, which have been produced by the impact of high energy primary cosmic ray particles with nuclei of nitrogen and oxygen. According to measurements made with muons brought to rest, their mean lifetime is about 2 μsec. Now a particle moving at the speed of light could only pass through 600 m of the atmosphere. Most of the muons in cosmic rays are produced at heights fifty or hundred times 600 m. How is it that so many reach sea level without decaying? The answer is provided by the time dilatation effect. The muons, created by the decay of the pions high in the atmosphere, have speeds close to that of light, thus the mean life to an observer at rest on the earth is increased by the factor η. $\left[\eta = \left(1 - \frac{v^2}{c^2}\right)^{-\frac{1}{2}}\right]$. Laboratory observations on high energy pions (a 70 MeV pion has a dilatation factor η of about 1·5) are in agreement with the time dilatation formula. An alternative, and equally correct explanation of the large flux of muons at sea level is to look at the effect from the point of view of an observer travelling with the muon. The depth of the atmosphere is reduced by the Lorentz contraction factor and it is now possible for many muons of mean lifetime 2 μsec to reach sea level.

3.5. THE DOPPLER EFFECT

The modification of our concepts of space and time measurements has repercussions throughout the whole of physics. One modification in the field of optics, of some interest and importance, is in the formula for the Doppler shift in frequency of a moving light source. In Fig. 7, P is a source of light at rest in the system S′, and therefore moving with a velocity v

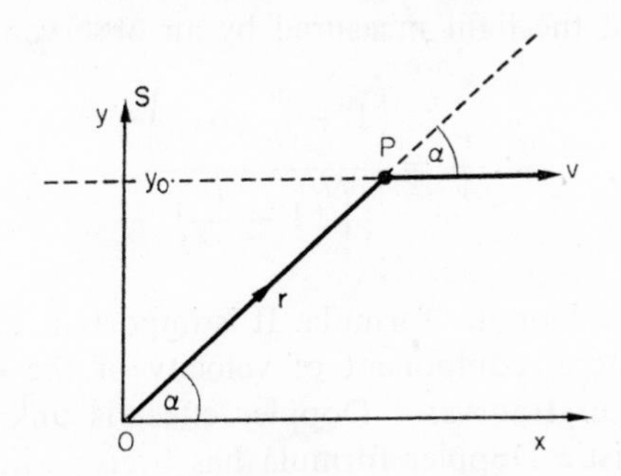

FIG. 7. Moving source of light P emits a signal from P which is observed at O.

with respect to the system S. Suppose the light source crossed the $y\,z$ plane of S at $t = 0$. Then at a later instant t, the coordinates of P in the system S are $(v\,t, y_0, z_0, t)$, where y_0, z_0 are constants. A signal emitted from P at this instant will reach O at a later instant T, where

$$r^2 = x^2 + y_0^2 + z_0^2 = c^2(T - t)^2 \tag{25}$$

Differentiating with respect to time we obtain

$$x\,dx = c^2(T - t)\,(dT - dt)$$

But $x = v\,t$ and $dx = v\,dt$

$$\therefore\; dT = dt\left(1 + \frac{v\,x}{c\,r}\right) \tag{26}$$

If dt' is the period of the wave disturbance emitted by P, measured by an observer at rest relative to the source, then the period dt observed in system S is given by the time dilatation formula

$$dt = \frac{dt'}{\sqrt{\left(1 - \frac{v^2}{c^2}\right)}}$$

Substituting dt' in place of dt in eqn. (26) we obtain

$$dT = \frac{dt'}{\sqrt{\left(1 - \frac{v^2}{c^2}\right)}}\left(1 + \frac{v}{c}\cos\alpha\right) \tag{27}$$

where α is the angle between the radius vector $\boldsymbol{r}$ and the velocity of the source $\boldsymbol{v}$.

dT is the time interval between the reception of successive wave crests at O.

Now
$$\frac{dT}{dt'} = \frac{\nu'}{\nu},$$
where ν' is the frequency of the light measured by an observer in S′ and ν is the frequency of the light measured by an observer in S

$$\therefore \frac{\nu'}{\nu} = \frac{\left(1 + \frac{v}{c}\cos\alpha\right)}{\sqrt{\left(1 - \frac{v^2}{c^2}\right)}} \tag{28}$$

This is the relativistic Doppler formula. It is important to notice that even when there is no radial component of velocity of the source ($\alpha = 90°$), ν is less than ν'. This transverse Doppler effect is unknown in classical physics. The relativistic Doppler formula has been verified by comparing the arithmetic mean of the shift in frequency of two beams of light emitted in opposite directions from canal rays of hydrogen with the frequency of the light emitted by the atoms at rest.†

A recent test of the relativistic Doppler formula has been carried out by J. P. Cedarholm and C. H. Townes.††. They made use of the remarkably high frequency stability of the ammonia beam maser oscillator.‡ An electrostatically focused beam of ammonia molecules, travelling with thermal velocity, enter an aperture in the end of a cavity. The molecules entering the cavity are in the higher of the two energy states corresponding to the inversion frequency of the NH_3 molecule. (Classically we can think of the nitrogen atom oscillating to and fro through the plane of the three hydrogen atoms.) If electromagnetic radiation of frequency 23,870 Mc/c, is fed into the cavity, stimulated emission of radiation at this frequency is observed from the ammonia molecules. For a sufficiently high molecular beam

† H. E. Ives and G. R. Stilwell, *J. Opt. Soc. Am.*, **28**, 215. 1938. Observations were made of the blue green H β line (4861 Å) emitted by singly ionized molecular hydrogen ions travelling with a kinetic energy of 20,000 eV. The light emitted with and against the motion of the particles was observed simultaneously with the aid of a mirror in the canal ray tube.

‡ J. P. Gordon, H. J. Zeiger, C. H. Townes, *Phys. Rev.* **99**, 1264, 1955. A description of the ammonia beam maser.

†† J. P. Cedarholm and C. H. Townes, *Nature*, **184**, 1350, 1959.

strength, the molecules can maintain a very monochromatic oscillation with a frequency stability of 1 in 10^{12} over a few seconds. The relativity experiment compared the frequency of two masers with oppositely directed beams. The masers were mounted on a rack which could be rotated about a vertical axis. When the masers were rotated through 180° from an initial E–W position at noon a frequency difference, observable as a low audio frequency beat oscillation, should be produced if there is a component of the aether's velocity relative to the earth. Over a period of several months no frequency difference was detected. A frequency shift of 1/50 c/s would have been detected, this corresponds to a motion through the aether of less than 10^{-3} of the earth's orbital velocity (30 km per sec). This experiment is a convincing demonstration of the first postulate of relativity.

3.6. RELATIVISTIC DYNAMICS

We have found that the Newtonian law of the composition of velocities is only an approximation, valid for velocities low compared to the velocity of light. The new transformation equations necessitate an alteration in the fundamental conservation laws of mechanics. In order to retain the law of conservation of linear momentum and the definition of force as rate of change of linear momentum, the restriction that the mass of a body is independent of its motion has to be relaxed. To find the relation between mass and velocity we require a result implicit in the velocity transformation equation, eqn. (21).

A particle in system S′ has a velocity $\boldsymbol{u}'$, with components u_x', u_y', u_z' and a velocity $\boldsymbol{u}$ in system S, with components u_x, u_y, u_z.

Let $u_x' = u' \cos\alpha'$; $u_x = u\cos\alpha$.

We have,

$$u_x = \frac{u_x' + v}{1 + \dfrac{v\,u_x'}{c^2}}, \quad u_y = \frac{u_y'\sqrt{\left(1 - \dfrac{v^2}{c^2}\right)}}{1 + \dfrac{v\,u_x'}{c^2}}, \quad u_z = \frac{u_z'\sqrt{\left(1 - \dfrac{v^2}{c^2}\right)}}{1 + \dfrac{v\,u_x'}{c^2}} \tag{21}$$

$$u'^2 = u_x'^2 + u_y'^2 + u_z'^2 \quad \text{and} \quad u^2 = u_x^2 + u_y^2 + u_z^2$$

Squaring and adding, and using the fact that $u_y'^2 + u_z'^2 = u'^2 \sin^2\alpha'$ we get,

$$u = \frac{\left[u'^2 + v^2 + 2u'\,v\cos\alpha' - \dfrac{u'^2\,v^2\sin^2\alpha'}{c^2}\right]^{\frac{1}{2}}}{1 + \dfrac{v\,u'\cos\alpha'}{c^2}} \tag{29}$$

$$1 - \frac{u^2}{c^2} = \frac{\left[1 - \dfrac{v^2}{c^2} - \dfrac{u'^2}{c^2} + \dfrac{v^2\,u'^2}{c^4}\right]}{\left[1 + \dfrac{v\,u'\cos\alpha'}{c^2}\right]^2} \tag{30}$$

Factorizing, we obtain the result

$$\sqrt{\left(1-\frac{u^2}{c^2}\right)} = \frac{\sqrt{\left(1-\frac{v^2}{c^2}\right)}\sqrt{\left(1-\frac{u'^2}{c^2}\right)}}{1+\frac{v\,u'\cos\alpha'}{c^2}} \tag{31}$$

Consider the head-on collision of two identical elastic particles in two inertial systems of coordinates S′ and S. Suppose, in the S′ sytem, the two particles move with velocities u' and $-u'$ parallel to the x-axis so that they meet head-on. After the collision they rebound with the respective velocities $-u'$ and u'. The particles viewed from an observer in the system S, have velocities before the collision u_1 and u_2 and, to allow for the possible variation of mass with speed, we denote their masses by m_1 and m_2 respectively

Equating the total mass and total momentum of the two particles before and at the instant of collision in system S (the two particles are momentarily at rest in system S′ at this moment), we can write

$$m_1 + m_2 = M, \quad m_1 u_1 + m_2 u_2 = MV, \tag{32}$$

where M is the total mass of the two particles at the moment they share a common velocity (zero in S′, V in S).

Using eqns. (21), and writing u_1 for u_x, $u'_x = u'$ ($u'_y = 0 = u'_z$), we have

$$u_1 = \frac{u'+v}{1+\frac{u'v}{c^2}} \quad \text{and} \quad u_2 = \frac{-u'+v}{1-\frac{u'v}{c^2}} \tag{33}$$

Eliminating, M, u_1 and u_2 from (32) and (33) we obtain

$$\frac{m_1}{m_2} = \frac{1+\frac{u'v}{c^2}}{1-\frac{u'v}{c^2}} \tag{34}$$

Using eqn. (31), with $\cos\alpha' = 1$ we finally obtain the result

$$\frac{m_1}{m_2} = \frac{\sqrt{\left(1-\frac{u_2^2}{c^2}\right)}}{\sqrt{\left(1-\frac{u_1^2}{c^2}\right)}} \tag{35}$$

The two particles are identical and therefore have the same mass m_0 to an observer at rest. Equation (35) means that the mass of a moving particle relative to a given observer is inversely proportional to the factor $\sqrt{(1-(u^2/c^2))}$

where u is the relative velocity of the particle. The mass m of a particle depends on its velocity u according to the relation

$$m = \frac{m_0}{\sqrt{\left(1 - \frac{u^2}{c^2}\right)}}, \tag{36}$$

where m_0 is the rest mass of the particle.

This result again demonstrates the upper limit for the velocity of particles. As $u \to c$, $m \to \infty$; thus an infinite force is required to accelerate a particle of *finite* rest mass to the velocity of light.

Bucherer's Experiment

A number of experimental tests has been made of the Einstein mass–velocity law. In an experiment devised by A. H. Bucherer, a point source of β-rays (radium fluoride) is placed at the centre of a parallel plate capacitor, consisting of two silvered glass discs A and B, 0·25 mm apart (Fig. 8). The capacitor is mounted inside a cylindrical vacuum chamber around the inside curved surface of which is located a photographic film. A uniform magnetic field acts throughout the volume of the chamber, with its lines of force horizontal. A suitable voltage is applied to the capacitor. Electrons emitted from the source S, which succeed in emerging from the narrow gap between the capacitor plates, travel with speed v in a direction θ in a horizontal plane (Fig. 9) so that

$$Bev \sin\theta = Ee \tag{37}$$

where e is the electron charge,
E is the vertical electric field between the plates,
B is the flux density of the magnetic field.

$$\therefore\ v \sin\theta = E/B \tag{38}$$

If the ratio E/B† is set equal to $c/2$, electrons moving at the speed of light must be travelling in the direction $\theta = 30°$ or $150°$ to emerge from the

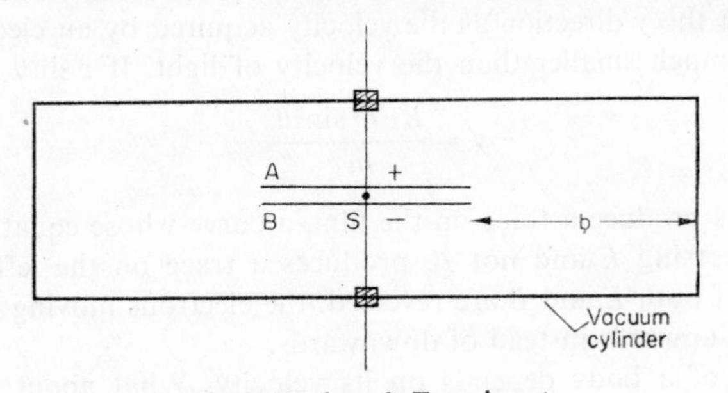

FIG. 8. Bucherer's Experiment.

† In m.k.s. units: E is in V per m, B is in webers per m², v is in m per sec.

capacitor. Electrons travelling at 90° to the magnetic field have a velocity $c/2$, if they are to reach the photographic film.

An electron, which escapes from the capacitor, experiences a vertical acceleration $B\dfrac{e}{m}v\sin\theta$, for a time $t = b/v$, where b is the distance from the edge of the capacitor plate to the photographic film. The vertical displacement y of an electron striking the film is given by

$$y = \frac{1}{2}B\frac{e}{m}v\sin\theta\left(\frac{b}{v}\right)^2 \tag{39}$$

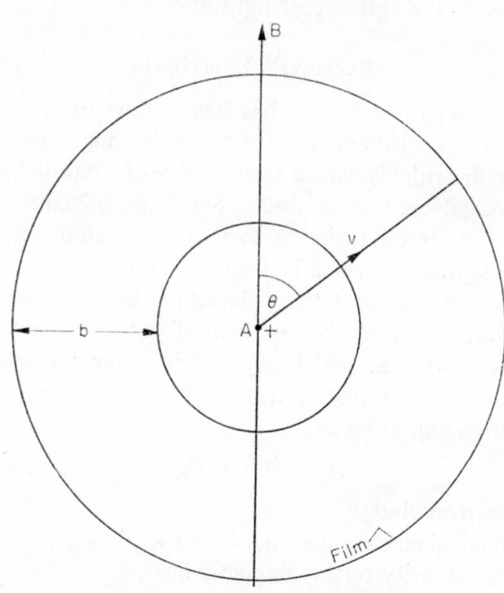

FIG. 9. Plan view of Bucherer's apparatus. Upper disc A is positively charged. Magnetic force is downwards.

It is legitimate to use the equations of constant acceleration of Newtonian mechanics in the y direction as the velocity acquired by an electron in this direction is much smaller than the velocity of light. If $v\sin\theta = c/2$, then

$$y = \frac{Beb^2\sin^2\theta}{mc} \tag{40}$$

The electrons produce a trace on the film, a curve whose equation is given by (40). Reversing $\boldsymbol{E}$ and not $\boldsymbol{B}$, produces a trace on the left-hand side of the film. If both $\boldsymbol{E}$ and $\boldsymbol{B}$ are reversed, the electrons moving to the right are deflected upwards instead of downwards.

The mass of a body depends on its velocity. What about the electric charge of a body? Maxwell's electromagnetic equations obey the Lorentz transformation and one of the consequences of Maxwell's theory is the law of continuity of electric charge. It can be shown that the electric charge e of a particle is an invariant under a Lorentz transformation. The mass m of an electron moving with speed v can be obtained from careful measurements of $2y$ (two traces are obtained by reversing $\boldsymbol{E}$ and $\boldsymbol{B}$) and using eqns. (38) and (40). A series of values of e/m for different velocities v $\left(\beta = \frac{v}{c}\right)$ is given in Table 1.

TABLE 1 BUCHERER'S EXPERIMENT

$\beta = \frac{v}{c}$	$\frac{e}{m\sqrt{(1-\beta^2)}} \times 10^{-11}$ coulomb kg^{-1}
0·3173	1·752
0·3787	1·761
0·4281	1·760
0·5154	1·763
0·6870	1·767

The constancy of $e/(m\sqrt{(1-\beta^2)})$ is convincing proof that, in this range of velocity, the electron mass m is given by the relation

$$m = (m_0/\sqrt{(1-\beta^2)})$$

The Equivalence of Mass and Energy

Classical mechanics makes great use of the laws of conservation of mass and conservation of energy. Einstein showed that these two conservation laws are united into one single law and he considered this to be the most important result of the special theory. Consider the acceleration from rest of a particle, of rest mass m_0, under the action of an impressed force $\boldsymbol{F}$.

$$\boldsymbol{F} = \frac{d(m\boldsymbol{v})}{dt} \tag{41}$$

$$\text{or} \quad \boldsymbol{F} = m\frac{d\boldsymbol{v}}{dt} + \boldsymbol{v}\frac{dm}{dt} \tag{42}$$

allowing for the increase of mass with velocity.

The gain in energy dE for a small displacement $d\boldsymbol{r}$ is given by

$$dE = \boldsymbol{F}\cdot d\boldsymbol{r}$$

$$\therefore\ dE = m\frac{d\boldsymbol{r}}{dt}\cdot d\boldsymbol{v} + dm\,\boldsymbol{v}\cdot\frac{d\boldsymbol{r}}{dt} \tag{43}$$

$$\therefore\ dE = m\,v\,dv + v^2\,dm \tag{44}$$

Differentiating $m = m_0\left(1 - \frac{v^2}{c^2}\right)^{-\frac{1}{2}}$, we obtain

$$dm = \frac{v\,m_0}{c^2}\left(1 - \frac{v^2}{c^2}\right)^{-\frac{3}{2}} dv = \frac{m\,v}{c^2}\left(1 - \frac{v^2}{c^2}\right)^{-1} dv \tag{45}$$

Equation (44) can then be written

$$dE = c^2\left(1 - \frac{v^2}{c^2}\right) dm + v^2\,dm$$

$$\text{or} \quad dE = c^2\,dm \tag{46}$$

Integrating we obtain the kinetic energy T,

$$T = \int_{E_0}^{E} dE = \int_{m_0}^{m} c^2\,dm$$

$$T = E - E_0 = c^2(m - m_0) \tag{47}$$

Thus the kinetic energy of a body is equal to its increase in mass (in virtue of its motion) multiplied by the square of the velocity of light. For low velocities, $\beta \ll 1$, we can expand eqn. (47) as a series

$$T = c^2\,m_0\left[(1 - \beta^2)^{-\frac{1}{2}} - 1\right] = c^2\,m_0\left[\frac{1}{2}\beta^2 + \frac{3}{8}\beta^4 \cdots\right]$$

$$T = \frac{1}{2}m_0\,v^2 + \frac{3}{8}m_0\frac{v^4}{c^2} + \cdots \tag{48}$$

For small velocities, T reduces to the classical formula $T = \frac{1}{2}m_0\,v^2$.

The term $E_0 = m_0c^2$ in eqn. (47) is interpreted as a latent or passive form of energy associated with the rest mass of the particle. Thus 1 kg of matter, no matter what its composition, if it could be annihilated would release 9×10^{16} joules of energy. In the vast majority of chemical and physical energy transformations energy and mass are conserved separately. Usually only a very tiny fraction of the total energy of a system is involved in the transformation process. Relativity theory provides no answer to the problem of why the major portion of the energy of a system remains passive or frozen during a chemical reaction. The answer is provided, not by relativity, but by the laws of quantum physics, in particular by the properties of the elementary particles. Elementary particles can only release their latent energy if they are completely destroyed in a reaction; thus an electron and its antiparticle the positron release all their passive energy $2m_0c^2$ in the form of γ-radiation. There is no process in which a fraction of the rest mass of an electron or nucleon is converted from passive into active energy. The great importance of the Einstein equation $dE = c^2\,dm$ lies in the fact that it is possible to compute the active energy changes of possible nuclear reactions if sufficiently accurate atomic masses are available. Einstein suggested that the law might be tested by the careful determination of the masses of the particles involved in radioactive decay. Langevin in 1913 was the first to suggest that the deviations from integral values of atomic weights, insofar as this is not due to a mixture of isotopes, is a consequence of the equivalent mass decrement of the powerful interaction potential energy of the nucleons in the nucleus.

To illustrate the validity of the Einstein law, we shall consider the evidence provided by a study of the masses and energies of the particles involved in a nuclear reaction. J. D. Cockcroft and G. T. S. Walton studied the nuclear reaction produced by bombarding Li^7 nuclei with monoenergetic protons of kinetic energy ranging from 50 keV to 1 MeV. When an incident proton is captured by a Li^7 nucleus, the "compound nucleus" Be^8 is momentarily formed. This nucleus is highly unstable and immediately breaks into two He^4 nuclei (α-particles)

$$ {}_3Li^7 + {}_1H^1 = {}_2He^4 + {}_2He^4 \dagger $$

The masses of the atoms involved are known with high precision from mass spectrograph determinations. In atomic mass units,†† they are

$$ \begin{array}{rlrl} Li^7 &= 7{\cdot}01823 & He^4 &= 4{\cdot}00387 \\ H^1 &= 1{\cdot}00815 & He^4 &= 4{\cdot}00387 \\ \hline Li^7 + H^1 &= 8{\cdot}02638 & He^4 + He^4 &= 8{\cdot}00774 \\ \hline \end{array} $$

The nuclear reaction involves a decrease in mass of 0·01864 a.m.u. This appears as "active", energy i.e. kinetic energy of the product particles, after the kinetic energy of the incident proton has been added on.

1 a.m.u. $= \dfrac{1}{N}$ kg, where N is Avogadro's number, $6{\cdot}0249 \times 10^{26}$ kg mole^{-1}.

Therefore the energy released is given by $\Delta E = c^2 \Delta m + T_p$, where T_p is the kinetic energy of the incident proton.

$$ \therefore\ E = \left[\frac{(2{\cdot}9979 \times 10^8)^2 \times 0{\cdot}01864}{6{\cdot}0249 \times 10^{26} \times 1{\cdot}6021 \times 10^{-19}} + T_p \right] \text{eV} $$

$$ \therefore\ E = [17{\cdot}35 + T_p]\ \text{MeV} $$

Careful determinations of the range and hence the energies of the two α-particles emitted have confirmed this equation with good accuracy. The best comparisons of energy and mass have verified the energy–mass law to an accuracy of 2 parts in 10,000.

Unfortunately, the much smaller energies involved in chemical reactions preclude the application of the energy–mass relation in computing the heats

† Mass numbers are written as superscripts: charge numbers (Z) as subscripts. These numbers are separately conserved.

†† 1 a.m.u. $\equiv \frac{1}{16} \times$ mass of O^{16} atom.

of reactions. Typical chemical reactions involve "active", i.e. released energies of the order of a few electron volts per molecule.

$$1 \text{ a.m.u.} \equiv \frac{c^2}{N} \text{joules} \equiv \frac{c^2}{eN} eV \equiv 931{\cdot}16 \text{ MeV}. \quad (49)$$

Conversely, 1 MeV $\equiv 1{\cdot}0739 \times 10^{-3}$ a.m.u. (50)

An energy of 1 eV has a mass equivalent of $1{\cdot}0739 \times 10^{-9}$ a.m.u. Thus a chemical reaction involving the release of a few eV per molecule is accompanied by a mass change which is too low to be detected with the aid of a mass spectrograph.

Energy–Momentum Relations

It is often useful to combine a number of the formulae of relativistic mechanics. In particular we can combine the following equations, to obtain a relation between the total energy E, momentum p, and rest mass energy m_0c^2, of a particle.

$$m = \frac{m_0}{\sqrt{\left(1 - \frac{v^2}{c^2}\right)}}, \quad p = \frac{m_0 v}{\sqrt{\left(1 - \frac{v^2}{c^2}\right)}}, \quad E = \frac{m_0 c^2}{\sqrt{\left(1 - \frac{v^2}{c^2}\right)}}$$

$$\therefore p^2 c^2 + m_0^2 c^4 = \frac{m_0^2 v^2 c^4 + m_0^2 c^6 - m_0^2 v^2 c^4}{c^2 - v^2} = \frac{m_0^2 c^4}{1 - \frac{v^2}{c^2}}$$

$$\therefore E = \sqrt{[(p c)^2 + (m_0 c^2)^2]} \quad (51)$$

This useful relation can be represented by the "energy triangle" (Fig. 10).

In many cosmic-ray experiments the momentum of a charged particle is determined by measuring the curvature of the path of the particle crossing

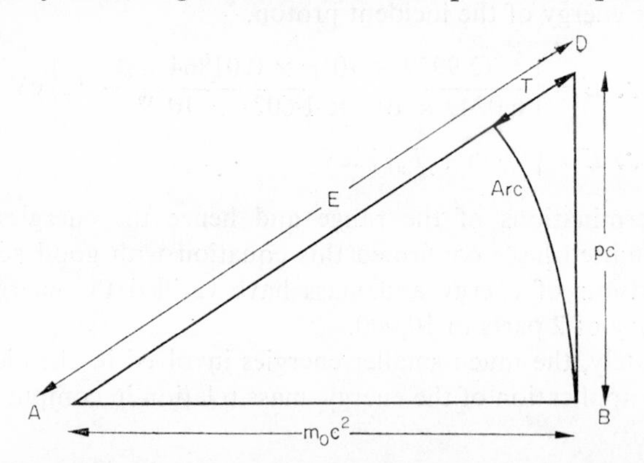

FIG. 10. "Energy Triangle". A B D is a right-angled triangle. The arc of radius A B(m_0c^2) divides the total energy A D(E) into rest mass energy m_0c^2 and kinetic energy T.

a cloud chamber situated in a strong uniform magnetic field. If the trajectory of the particle is normal to the magnetic induction vector $\boldsymbol{B}$ of the field then

$$Bev = \frac{mv^2}{r} \tag{52}$$

where e, m, v and r are the charge,† relativistic mass, speed and radius of curvature of the particle respectively. Dividing by v we can say the particle momentum p is given by

$$p = Bre \tag{53}$$

It is often convenient to express the momentum in units of MeV/c. This is done by multiplying both sides of eqn. (53) by c

$$pc = Brce$$

In m.k.s. units, pc is measured in joules, dividing by e the electron charge (in coulombs) we can write

$$pc = (Brc)\,\mathrm{eV} \tag{54}$$

Thus p is now measured in units of eV/c. A simple example is given to illustrate the use of these units. Suppose a charged muon describes an orbit of 50 cm radius in a magnetic field of flux density 20,000 gauss. What is its kinetic energy?

The rest mass energy of the muon is 207 times the rest mass energy of the electron (0·511 MeV).

$$\therefore\ m_0 c^2 = 207 \times 0{\cdot}511 = 106\ \mathrm{MeV}$$

The momentum p of the muon is given by

$$pc = 2 \times 0{\cdot}5 \times 3 \times 10^8\ \mathrm{eV} = 300\ \mathrm{MeV}$$

as $B = 2$ webers per m², $r = 0{\cdot}5$ m, $c = 3 \times 10^8$ m sec^{-1}.

Inserting the values of pc and $m_0 c^2$ in eqn. (51) we obtain for the total energy E of the muon

$$E = \sqrt{(300^2 + 106^2)} = 318\ \mathrm{MeV}$$

The kinetic energy $T = E - m_0 c^2 = 318 - 106 = 212$ MeV.

The Centre-of-mass System

Nuclear reactions are observed in a system of coordinates in which the target nuclei are at rest. This reference frame is called the "Laboratory" System (L-system). Considerable advantage is gained if the reaction is described in a reference frame which moves with the centre of mass of the particles involved in the reaction. In this frame, the "Centre-of-mass"

† The charge of the particle is the same for all observers, i.e. it is an invariant of the Lorentz transformation.

system (C-system), the centre of mass is at rest, and the total momenta of the particles is zero before and after the reaction.

If sufficient energy is available a nuclear collision may result in the creation of particles. The laws of conservation of momentum and energy, however, normally require that the products of a nuclear reaction have considerable momentum in the forward direction (i.e. the direction of the incoming projectile particle). The minimum energy to create new particles (the threshold energy) has its smallest value in the C-system, for the products of the reaction at threshold will be at rest in this system.

Consider the collision of two particles of rest mass m_1 and m_2 travelling in a straight line with velocities v_1 and v_2 (momenta p_1 and p_2) in the L-system. The total energies of the particles are E_1 and E_2. ($v_1 > v_2$). The corresponding values of these quantities in the C-system are u_1', u_2', p_1', p_2', E_1', E_2'. Let $v = \beta c$, denote the velocity of the centre of mass in the L-system.
In the C-system, we have

$$p_1' = \frac{m_1 u_1'}{\sqrt{(1 - u_1'^2/c^2)}} \tag{55}$$

where u_1' is the velocity of the first particle.
The law of transformation of velocities yields the relation

$$u_1' = \frac{v_1 - v}{1 - \dfrac{v_1 v}{c^2}}$$

Hence, we obtain after some algebra,

$$p_1' = \frac{m_1(v_1 - v)}{\sqrt{(1 - v_1^2/c^2)}\sqrt{(1 - v^2/c^2)}} = \eta\{p_1 - \beta/c\, E_1\} \tag{56}$$

where

$$\eta = (1 - v^2/c^2)^{-\frac{1}{2}} \tag{57}$$

A similar equation applies to the momentum of the second particle.
In the C-system, the total momentum is zero, i.e.

$$p_1' + p_2' = 0 \tag{58}$$

From (56), (57) and (58) we obtain the relation

$$\beta/c(E_1 + E_2) = p_1 + p_2 \tag{59}$$

The energies of the particles in the C-system are obtained by substituting the values of u_1' and u_2' in

$$E_1' = \frac{m_1 c^2}{\sqrt{(1 - u_1'^2/c^2)}}, \quad E_2' = \frac{m_2 c^2}{\sqrt{(1 - u_2'^2/c^2)}} \tag{60}$$

Thus for E_1' we obtain,

$$E_1' = \frac{m_1 c^2 - m\, v_1 v}{\sqrt{(1 - v^2/c^2)}\sqrt{(1 - v_1^2/c^2)}} = \eta(E_1 - \beta\, p_1 c) \tag{61}$$

Thus the total energy in the C-system is given by

$$E_1' + E_2' = \eta[(E_1 + E_2) - \beta c(p_1 + p_2)]$$

$$= \left[1 - \frac{c_2(p_1 + p_2)^2}{(E_1 + E_2)^2}\right]^{-\frac{1}{2}} \left[(E_1 + E_2) - \frac{c^2(p_1 + p_2)^2}{(E_1 + E_1)}\right] \quad (62)$$

where β has been eliminated by using eqn. (59). Squaring eqn. (62) and simplifying we obtain the relation

$$(E_1' + E_2')^2 = (E_1 + E_2)^2 - c^2(p_1 + p_2)^2 \quad (63)$$

Using eqn. (51), we obtain

$$(E_1' + E_2') = [c^4(m_1^2 + m_2^2) + 2(E_1 E_2 - c^2 p_1 p_2)]^{\frac{1}{2}} \quad (64)$$

Apply this equation to the head-on impact of a proton of total energy E_1, momentum p_1, with a proton at rest ($E_2 = m_0c^2$, $p_2 = 0$). Then eqn. (64) becomes

$$(E_1' + E_2') = [2m_0^2 c^4 + 2E_1 m_0 c^2]^{\frac{1}{2}} \quad (65)$$

where m_0c^2 is the rest mass energy of a proton, 938 MeV.

If the kinetic energy of the incident proton T is much greater than m_0c^2 (this would apply to protons accelerated to 25,000 MeV in the CERN synchrotron), eqn. (65) reduces to the approximation $(E_1' + E_2') = [2m_0c^2 E_1]^{\frac{1}{2}}$.

This means that the energy available for the creation of new particles increases as $E_1^{\frac{1}{2}}$, thus increasing E_1 from 25 GeV† to 100 GeV will only double the energy in the C-system. For a value of $E_1 = 25$ GeV, $(E_1' + E_2')$ is about 7 GeV. Unfortunately the technique of bombarding a stationary target with an incident high energy proton beam is wasteful in the sense that in the L-system a considerable portion of the projectile energy is transferred to the recoiling particles to conserve momentum. It is the great hope of the accelerator physicist to produce elementary particles by allowing two high energy proton beams to collide head-on (Chapter 18).

In 1955, O. Chamberlain *et al.* produced and detected the antiproton (the negative proton). A beam of 6·2 GeV protons, in the Berkeley synchrotron, bombarded the nucleons in a copper target. The antiproton $\bar{p}$ is created along with its dual particle, the proton p

$$p + p \rightarrow p + p + (p + \bar{p}) \quad (66)$$

The reaction is represented by eqn. (66), a high energy proton collides with a proton in the copper nucleus and creates a proton–antiproton pair. At the threshold of pair creation, the four particles (three protons and one antiproton) are at rest in the C-system. Equation (65) shows that at the threshold,

$$(E_1' + E_2') = 4\, m_0c^2 = [2m_0c^2(E_1 + m_0\, c^2)]^{\frac{1}{2}}$$

† 1 GeV or 1 BeV = 1000 MeV.

Squaring, we obtain

$$E_1 = 7m_0c^2 = T_1 + m_0c^2$$
$$T_1 = 6m_0c^2 = 5{\cdot}6 \text{ GeV}$$

Thus the incident proton must have a kinetic energy greater than 5·6 GeV to create a proton–antiproton pair. (this is considerably greater than $2m_0c^2$, $\sim$2 GeV. The assumption that the target nucleon is at rest in the L-system is in general not true. The motion of the nucleons in the target nucleus reduces the threshold energy in the L-system to about 4·3 GeV.

3.7 POLARIZED LIGHT

The phenomenon of polarization is a consequence of the transverse nature of electromagnetic wave motion. Fundamentally it is more useful to consider circularly polarized rather than plane polarized light as the more elementary concept.† Electromagnetic wavelengths in the visible region of the spectrum are much longer than the dimensions of the atomic or molecular system emitting the radiation. The radiation pattern corresponds to that of the well-known electric dipole oscillation. The photon radiated by the system carries away an angular momentum equal to $\hbar$. This angular momentum is associated with the polarization properties of the radiation.

There are two independent states of polarization corresponding to right and left circularly polarized photons. In the former case the spin axis is parallel to the velocity of the photon; that is, the photon spins in a clockwise sense as it advances. For left circularly polarized light, the photon spins counter-clockwise as it advances. The two states of polarization can be described by quantum numbers $S = +1$ and $S = -1$. The interesting questions arises as to why the general rule that there are $(2S + 1)$ orientations or states of polarization for elementary particles does not apply to photons.†† The answer to this question lies in the fact that photons travel with the unique velocity c. First, it should be noted that the reason we can describe one photon as left and another as right circularly polarized, is a consequence of the law that it is not possible for a moving observer to overtake a photon and thereby reverse the direction of its relative velocity. If this were possible the sense of spin of the photon would be reversed and a statement to the effect that a given photon is right (or left) circularly polarized would not be a Lorentz–invariant statement.

In Fig. 11 we represent the results of Lorentz transformation calculations concerning the relative orientation of the spin and linear velocity vectors of a particle seen by different inertial observers. Consider first a particle

† Linearly polarized light can always be regarded as the superposition of two states of oppositely circularly polarized light.

†† See the article by E. P. WIGNER, *Rev. Mod. Phys.*, **29**, 255, 1957.

with its spin axis vertical (parallel to the z' axis) and moving with a *small* vertical velocity u' in the system S′. The spin and velocity vectors are parallel in the system S′ (Fig. 11 (a), sketch 1). However, to an observer in a system S, which is moving with a velocity v to the left of S′, the spin and velocity vectors are no longer parallel (Fig. 11 (a), sketches 2 and 3). In sketch 3 the velocity of the system S is greater than in sketch 2. If on the other hand, the vertical velocity u' of the particle in the system S′, which is still parallel to the spin axis, is close to that of light, the spin and velocity vectors are now nearly parallel for the observer in the system S moving leftwards

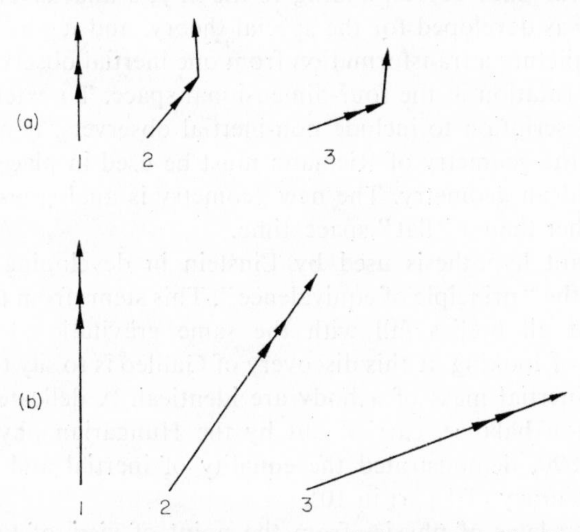

FIG. 11. Spin vector (single arrow). Velocity vector (double arrow). (a) Particle with a small vertical component of velocity u' in S′ is viewed from S moving to the left of S′ with increasing values of v(1, 2, 3); (b) same as (a), except u' is close to c. If $u' = c$, the spin and velocity vectors are parallel to all inertial observers (E. P. WIGNER, *Rev. Mod. Phys.* **29**, 255, 1957).

with respect to S′. Figure 11 (b) illustrates this new state of affairs. These results can be deduced from the Lorentz transformation equations. In the limit as u' approaches c, the spin and velocity vectors appear to be parallel for all observers. This is the case for circularly polarized photons. The velocity vector is always parallel or antiparallel to the spin axis.

Relativity arguments, however, do not inform us why there are two rather than one state of polarization. The concept of reflection symmetry is invoked. Nature exhibits no preference for left rather than right circularly polarized light. Each type of photon is the antiparticle of the other type of photon. A right circularly polarized photon seen in a plane mirror would be described as a left circularly polarized photon and vice versa. The principle of reflection symmetry is intimately related to the quantum mechanical concept of parity (Chapter 6).

3.8 THE GENERAL THEORY OF RELATIVITY

The removal of the restriction that we confine ourselves to observers who do not move with relative accelerations takes us into the realm of general relativity. The general theory must be able to give a satisfactory description of gravitational fields. The extension to general theory involves the concept of the geometry of the "space–time continuum" in which we set up our coordinate systems. Minkowski was the first to use the quasi-geometrical concept of physical events occurring in a four-dimensional continuum with axes corresponding to the x, y, z and ict coordinates of events. This was developed for the special theory, and it was found that it is possible to picture a transformation from one inertial observer to another in terms of a rotation in the four-dimensional space. To extend the quasi-geometrical description to include non-inertial observers, it was shown by Einstein that the geometry of Riemann must be used in place of the more familiar Euclidean geometry. The new geometry is analogous to that of a "curved" rather than a "flat" space–time.

An important hypothesis used by Einstein in developing a theory of gravitation is the "principle of equivalence". This stems from the significant discovery that all bodies fall with the same gravitational acceleration. Another way of looking at this discovery of Galileo is to say that the gravitational and inertial mass of a body are identical. A delicate test using a sensitive torsion balance, carried out by the Hungarian physicist Eötvös in the year 1890, demonstrated the equality of inertial and gravitational mass to an accuracy of 1 part in 10^8.

Consider the laws of physics from the point of view of two observers, one at rest on the surface of the earth, the other in a freely falling lift near the surface. The observers will agree in all respects except one. The man in the lift would be unaware of the existence of gravity. Thus it is possible, in a uniform gravitational field, over a small spatial region, to abolish the effects of gravity by describing the motion of bodies relative to a freely falling observer. As far as is known, no experiment whatsoever can distinguish between the uniform acceleration of the observer and a gravitational field. This is the principle of equivalence. The removal of the local effects of gravitation by transforming to an accelerated system is, of course, only possible in view of the fact that all bodies have the same acceleration in a gravitational field.

The Russian physicist V. Fock† makes out a strong case against the idea that the principle of equivalence is of more than local interest. He contends that it is not possible to remove the effects of gravity over large regions of space (by suitable transformations) and it is always possible to distinguish gravitational forces from other types of force (centrifugal, etc.). Be that

† Page 206 *et seq.* of his book (see Bibliography).

as it may, all the evidence is in favour of the identity of inertial and gravitational mass.

According to the energy–mass law, we can argue that a photon of energy $E\,(h\,\nu)$ should have an inertial mass E/c^2. In a gravitational field the photon should interact with the field as if it were a particle of gravitational mass E/c^2. A photon moving through a gravitational field will gain (or lose) an energy dE given by

$$dE = \frac{E}{c^2}\,d\varphi \tag{67}$$

where $d\varphi$ is the decrease (or increase) in gravitational potential. Thus a photon travelling vertically downwards through a height h, near the surface of the earth, should gain an energy dE given by

$$dE = \frac{E}{c^2}\,g\,h \tag{68}$$

where g is the acceleration due to gravity.

The gain in energy is, in principle, detectable as a frequency shift $d\nu$ given by

$$\frac{d\nu}{\nu} = \frac{dE}{E} = \frac{g\,h}{c^2} \tag{69}$$

This frequency shift, near the surface of the earth, amounts to 1 part in 10^{18} per cm fall!

Estimates of the difference in gravitational potential at the surfaces of the sun and earth predict a wavelength shift (to the red) of the light from atoms in the surface of the sun of value $\delta\,\lambda/\lambda = 2 \times 10^{-6}$

The dense white dwarf companion star to Sirius, is particularly favourable as the expected shift $\delta\,\lambda/\lambda$ is about 6×10^{-5}. The astrophysical observations of these shifts support the theory, but they cannot be considered as entirely convincing. It is very difficult to exclude the possibility of other effects in the stellar atmosphere being responsible for the shifts. However, the recent discovery of R. L. Mössbauer, that a few γ-ray sources emit highly monochromatic γ-radiation, has made possible the first *terrestial* test of eqn. (68) (Chapter 13). It should be clearly understood, however, that this is by no means a complete verification of Einstein's theory of gravitation. Whatever is the final outcome of Einstein's general theory, there is no doubt that it represents one of the greatest intellectual achievements of all time.

BIBLIOGRAPHY

H. Dingle, *The Special Theory of Relativity*, Methuen, London 1940.

W. H. McCrea, *Relativity Physics*, Methuen, London 1935.

P. G. Bergmann, *Introduction to the Theory of Relativity*, Prentice-Hall, Englewood Cliffs, N.J. 1942.

W. Pauli, *The Theory of Relativity* (translated by G. Field), Pergamon Press, London 1959.

C. Møller, *The Theory of Relativity*, Clarendon Press, 1952.
J. Aharoni, *The Special Theory of Relativity*, Clarendon Press, 1959.
V. Fock, *The Theory of Space, Time and Gravitation* (translated by N. Kemmer), Pergamon Press, London 1959.

EXAMPLES

1. Two electrons are emitted in opposite directions from a beta active source. If the kinetic energies of the electrons are 0·51 and 1·02 MeV respectively, calculate the velocity of each electron relative to the source. What is the relative velocity between the electrons? (Rest mass energy of the electron is 0·51 MeV)
2. The half-life of a free neutron is about 12 min. What is the effective half-life of high energy cosmic ray neutrons of 10^{14} eV? (Rest mass energy of the neutron is 939·5 MeV). What distance, in light years, would neutrons of this energy travel before 90% of them decay?
3. An observer sees two supernovae explosions 100 light years apart as simultaneous events. What is the time interval between these events according to an observer moving with a velocity $0{\cdot}01\,c$ relative to the first observer in a direction parallel to the line joining the two exploding stars?
4. A metre rod is orientated at an angle of 30° to the x-axis in a system at rest. What is the length and orientation to the x' axis to an observer in a system moving parallel to the axis with a velocity $0{\cdot}8\,c$?
5. A ray of light from a distant star enters a terrestial telescope at an angle of elevation of 60°. What is the inclination of the ray to an observer travelling horizontally with a velocity of $0{\cdot}6c$? (This is the relativistic aberration of light).
6. The H δ line in the Balmer series has a wavelength of 4101 Å. A distant receding nebula is observed and the H δ line appears at a wavelength of 5023 Å. Calculate the velocity of recession of the nebula. Hubble's law states that the velocity of recession of nebulae is proportional to their distance. If the constant of proportionality is 800 km per sec per 10^6 parsec, what is the distance of the nebula for which the H δ line is displaced to the position of the H α line (6563 Å)?
7. In Bucherer's experiment, a potential difference of 100 V is applied to the capacitor plates, which are 0·25 mm apart. What is the flux density of the magnetic field if the minimum "escape" velocity of the beta particles is $c/2$? What vertical deflection is expected for particles travelling in a horizontal plane at an angle of 60° to the magnetic field, if the distance from the edge of the capacitor to the photographic film is 20 cm. (e/m_0 is $1{\cdot}759 \times 10^{11}$ coulomb kg^{-1})?
8. The production of an electron–positron pair occurs when a gamma ray interacts with the Coulomb field of a nucleus. Show that the threshold energy for pair production is very nearly $2m_0\,c^2$. Show also that if an electron–positron pair is produced by a gamma ray colliding with a stationary electron, the threshold energy is $4m_0\,c^2$.
9. A particle moves in a system of coordinates S′ with velocity u' (components u'_x, u'_y, u'_z). Derive expressions for the components of acceleration $\dot{u}_x$, $\dot{u}_y$, $\dot{u}_z$, in a system S moving to the left of S′ with constant velocity v parallel to the x' axis, in terms of the velocity and acceleration components of the particle in system S′. Electrons emitted from a plane cathode are accelerated, *in vacuo*, by a potential difference of 2000V applied between the cathode and a parallel plate 0·5 cm apart. Calculate the velocity and acceleration of the electrons at the moment they strike the anode. What is the velocity and acceleration of the electrons in a system of coordinates moving parallel to but in the opposite direction to the electron beam with a velocity $0{\cdot}8\,c$?
10. Prove that a photon cannot be absorbed by a free electron at rest.
11. For an electron linear accelerator (total length 70 m) electrons are injected at one end at low energy and they gain kinetic energy linearly along the length, emerging at th, far end with a kinetic energy of 1 GeV. If the electron rest mass energy is 0·51 MeVe calculate the length of the accelerator in the electron rest system.

CHAPTER 4

X-RAYS

4.1 THE CONTINUOUS X-RAY SPECTRUM

X-rays are produced in an X-ray tube by bombarding a metal target with high energy electrons. It has been known for a long time that X-rays are electromagnetic waves of very short wavelength. The radiation generated by electron impact consists of a continuous spectrum and, if the electron energy is high enough, a superimposed series of spectral lines characteristic of the target. The characteristic line spectrum of a material can also be excited by irradiating it with high energy X-rays.

The continuous spectrum, or "Bremsstrahlung", is generated by the rapid deceleration of electrons penetrating the surface of the target. Except for very high energy electrons, only a small fraction of the energy of the incident electrons is converted into X-rays, most of the energy is frittered away by atomic excitation and ionization, and is rapidly degraded to heat energy. Most of the bremsstrahlung ("braking-radiation") is generated in the deflection of a high energy electron by the Coulomb field of an atomic nucleus. Electron scattering is less important as the Coulomb interaction is between two particles of unit charge. An electron passing close to a nucleus of charge $Z e$ will experience an acceleration proportional to $(Z e^2)/(m r^2)$ where m is the electron mass, and r is the distance between the electron and the nucleus. According to classical electromagnetic theory, the electron should emit radiation of intensity proportional to the square of the acceleration. Bremsstrahlung is therefore more copious for targets of high atomic number and is insignificant for charged particles of greater mass (mesons, protons).

It was established by Duane and Hunt in 1915 that there is a sharp short wavelength cut-off to the continuous spectrum given by the equation

$$eV = \frac{h c}{\lambda_0} \tag{1}$$

where eV is the energy gained by an electron falling through a potential difference V, h is Planck's constant, c is the velocity of light, and λ_0 is the minimum bremsstrahlung wavelength. This abrupt cut-off corresponds to the highest photon energy that can be produced, namely that corresponding to the kinetic energy of the bombarding electrons.

The radiation emitted from the target of a conventional X-ray tube is complicated by the fact that X-rays are generated at different depths in the target by electrons of different energies. The X-rays generated beneath the surface of the target also are attenuated by absorption before escaping from the target. To compare theory and experiment, it is desirable to study the radiation generated by electron bombardement of very thin targets. If the target is thin enough, self absorption is negligible and the photons observed are generated by electrons of one energy. A few experiments have

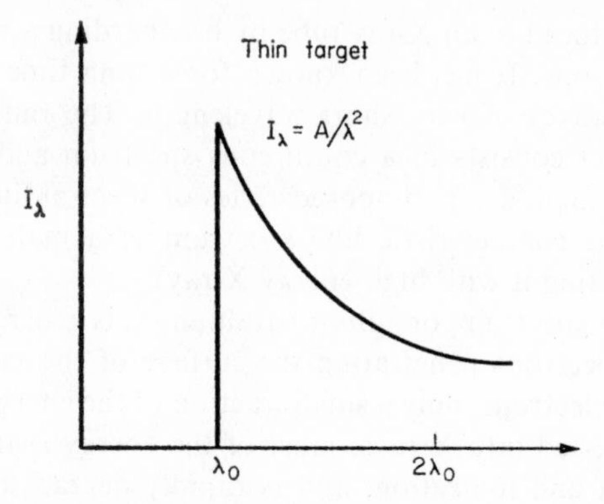

FIG. 1. The X-ray intensity I_λ distribution as a function of λ (λ_0 cut-off wavelength).

been carried out with thin metallic foils, e.g. Al 0·6 microns thick, and with fine vapour streams. The distribution of radiation from a thin target is shown in Fig. 1. It is found that the intensity of radiation I varies inversely as the square of the wavelength λ, with of course, a cut-off at the wavelength λ_0. This distribution is easily shown to follow if it is assumed that the energy radiated per unit frequency interval is uniform up to the maximum frequency ν_0.

The radiation generated in a thick target is effectively the superposition of a series of thin target spectra corresponding to a gradual increase in λ_0 as the electron beam penetrates the target. Typical intensity–wavelength distribution curves for the elements tungsten ($Z = 74$) and molybdenum ($Z = 42$) for an accelerating voltage of 35 kV are shown in Fig. 2. In agreement with the Duane–Hunt law the cut-off wavelength is independent of the atomic number of the target. The peak intensity occurs at a wavelength λ_m which is approximately 1·5 times the cut-off wavelength λ_0. This ratio does, however, vary to some extent with V and Z. The gentle decline in I at long wavelengths exhibits no sharp cut-off and observation is difficult due to

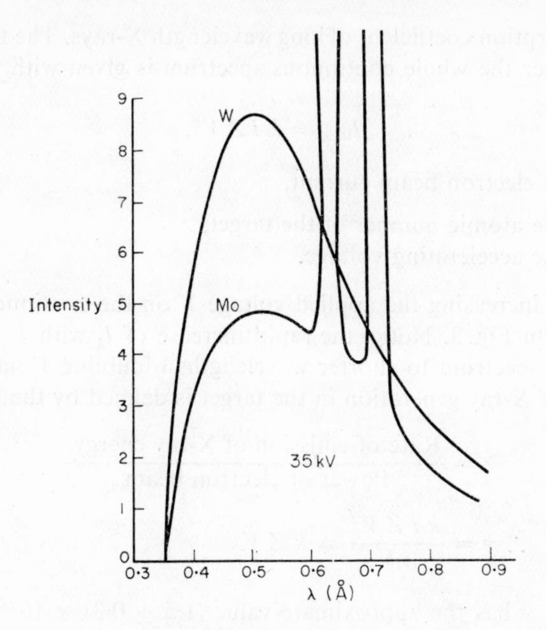

FIG. 2. Spectrum from W and Mo at 35 kV.

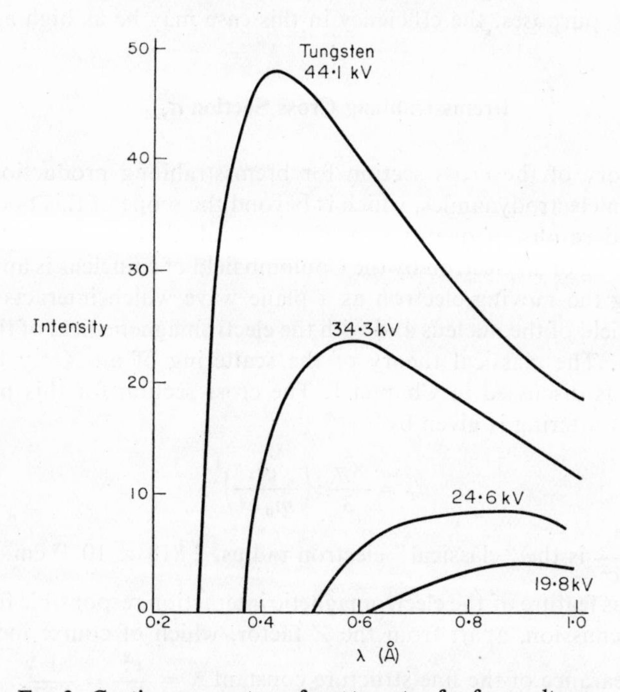

FIG. 3. Continuous spectrum from tungsten for four voltages.

the high absorption coefficient of long wavelength X-rays. The total intensity integrated over the whole continuous spectrum is given with fair accuracy by

$$I_{total} = k\,i\,Z\,V^2, \tag{2}$$

where i is the electron beam current,

Z is the atomic number of the target,
V is the accelerating voltage.

The effect of increasing the applied voltage V on the continuous spectrum is illustrated in Fig. 3. Notice the rapid increase of I_λ with V and the shift of the whole spectrum to shorter wavelengths (doubling V halves λ_0). The efficiency ε of X-ray generation in the target is defined by the ratio

$$\varepsilon = \frac{\text{Rate of emission of X-ray energy}}{\text{Power of electron beam}}$$

$$\therefore\ \varepsilon = \frac{k\,i\,Z\,V^2}{i\,V} = k\,Z\,V \tag{3}$$

The constant k has the approximate value $(1{\cdot}5 \pm 0{\cdot}3) \times 10^{-9}$. Efficiencies of conventional X-ray tubes for X-ray diffraction are less than 1%. Linear electron accelerators generating X-rays up to 20 MeV are now used for therapeutic purposes, the efficiency in this case may be as high as 40%.

Bremsstrahlung Cross Section σ_{rad}

The theory of the cross section for bremsstrahlung production is part of quantum electrodynamics, which is beyond the scope of this book. A few aspects and results of quantum mechanical calculations are listed below. The scattering of an electron by the Coulomb field of a nucleus is approached by treating the moving electron as a plane wave which interacts with the Coulomb field of the nucleus and with the electromagnetic field of the radiated photon. The classical theory of the scattering of an X-ray by a free electron was discussed in Chapter 1. The cross section for this process of Thomson scattering is given by

$$\sigma_T = \frac{8\pi}{3} \cdot \left(\frac{e^2}{m_0\,c^2}\right)^2$$

where $\dfrac{e^2}{m_0\,c^2}$ is the "classical" electron radius, $2{\cdot}818 \times 10^{-13}$ cm.

A curious feature of the electromagnetic interaction responsible for bremsstrahlung emission, apart from the Z factor, which of course increases σ, is the appearance of the fine structure constant $\alpha = \dfrac{e^2}{\hbar\,c} = \dfrac{1}{137}$.

The cross section for radiative emission by an electron σ_{rad} is of the order of

$$Z^2 \frac{1}{137}\left(\frac{e^2}{m_0 c^2}\right)^2 = Z^2 \sigma_0$$

where $\sigma_0 = \frac{1}{137} \times (2{\cdot}818 \times 10^{-13})^2 = 0{\cdot}580 \times 10^{-27}\ \text{cm}^2.$ (4)

For very low Z elements σ_{rad} is much less than σ_T.

The radiation cross section σ_{rad} is defined as the fraction of the total energy $(T + m_0 c^2)$, kinetic plus rest mass energy, which is radiated by an electron as it passes through an absorber 1 atom per cm² thick.

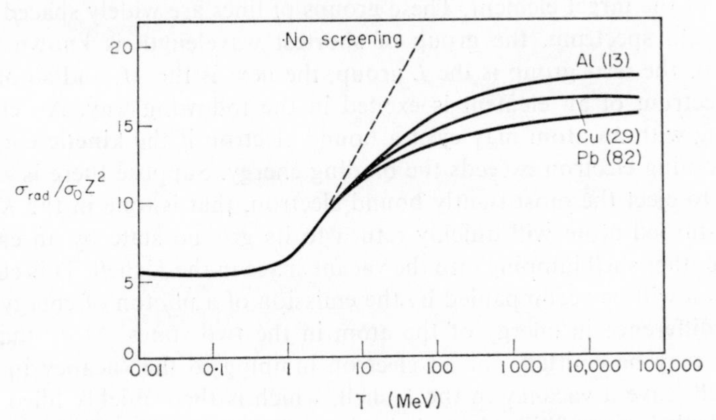

FIG. 4. Variation of σ_{rad} with kinetic energy T of electron in different absorbers.

The following approximations are useful in certain electron energy ranges. There is no simple general mathematical expression for σ_{rad} over the complete range of energy.

(1) For low kinetic energies, $T \ll m_0 c^2$

$$\sigma_{rad} = 5{\cdot}3\sigma_0 Z^2\ \text{cm}^2 \tag{5}$$

This result is derived ignoring the screening effect of bound atomic electrons on the radiative electron–nucleus collision.

(2) For electrons of high kinetic energy, $T \gg m_0 c^2$, two formulae are obtained

$$\sigma_{rad} = 4\sigma_0 Z^2\left[\ln\left\{2\frac{(T + m_0 c^2)}{m_0 c^2}\right\} - \frac{1}{3}\right] \tag{6}$$

if electron screening is neglected; and

$$\sigma_{rad} = 4\sigma_0 Z^2\left[\ln\left(\frac{183}{Z^{\frac{1}{3}}}\right) + \frac{1}{18}\right] \tag{7}$$

if electron screening is taken into consideration.

The variation of σ_{rad} divided by $\sigma_0 Z^2$ over a wide range of electron kinetic energy is shown in Fig. 4. The effect of screening by bound electrons is very important at electron energies above 100 MeV, σ_{rad} tends towards a constant value.

4.2 CHARACTERISTIC LINE SPECTRUM

Let us consider the effect of gradually raising the voltage V applied to an X-ray tube. At low voltages the only radiation observed is bremsstrahlung and this will be of long wavelength and low intensity. As V is increased there appears at a number of critical voltages a series of line spectra characteristic of the target element. These groups of lines are widely spaced in the wavelength spectrum, the group of shortest wavelength is known as the K group, the next group is the L group, the next is the M, and so on. The line spectrum of an element is excited in the following way. An electron colliding with an atom may eject a bound electron if the kinetic energy of the incoming electron exceeds the binding energy. Suppose there is enough energy to eject the most tightly bound electron, that is, one in the K shell. The disturbed atom will quickly return to its ground state by an electron from another shell jumping into the vacant space in the K shell. This electron transition will be accompanied by the emission of a photon of energy equal to the difference in energy of the atom in the two states. More than one photon may be emitted, for an electron jumping to the vacancy in the K shell will leave a vacancy in the L shell, which is then quickly filled by an outer shell electron filling the hole in the L shell. The K lines correspond to electron transitions to a vacancy in the K shell of an atom, the L lines to a vacancy in the L shell and so on. For light elements M lines cannot be produced as there is no M shell of electrons.

The occurrence of critical potentials for the excitation of the line spectra is readily understood. No K lines can be radiated if the incident electron kinetic energy e V is less than E_K, the K shell binding energy. (E_K varies from about 1 keV for neon ($Z = 10$), to 125 keV for thorium ($Z = 90$)). The L lines can, of course, be excited at lower potentials than the K lines as the L shell binding energy E_L is smaller. (E_L varies from about 2·5 keV at $Z = 40$, to 20 keV at $Z = 90$). The intensity of the characteristic lines increases as the voltage is increased, so does the bremsstrahlung, and there is an optimum voltage for X-ray diffraction work when the $K\alpha$ line is to be used (the continuous spectrum is, in general, a nuisance in X-ray diffraction investigations). The line spectrum of an element may be excited by incident X-rays if their photon energy is sufficient to eject a K or L shell electron. The fluorescent radiation characteristic of an element excited in this way has proved to be a valuable method of chemical analysis. Identification of the characteristic fluorescent wavelengths reveals the presence of certain elements. On the other hand, fluorescent X-rays can be inconvenient. Thus the diffraction of the $K\alpha$ X-rays of Cu (1·54 Å) by any iron compound or alloy is confused by the fluorescent $K\alpha$ radiation of Fe (1·94 Å), which is strongly excited as the Cu$K\alpha$ photons have an energy slightly greater than the K shell electron binding energy in Fe. The probability of K shell photo-ionization is relatively high when the photon energy is just greater than E_K.

X-ray line spectra are in marked contrast to optical line spectra. There is no obvious pattern connecting the optical spectra of the elements, whereas there is a definite pattern for X-ray spectra. There is a monotonic steady displacement of the K and L lines to shorter wavelengths as the atomic number Z increases. This simplicity in X-ray spectra was demonstrated by the pioneer researches of Moseley who found a simple relation between the characteristic frequencies of corresponding lines of different elements and their atomic number Z. The frequency ν of the $K\alpha$-lines of the elements can be represented by the approximate formula

$$\sqrt{\nu} = A(Z - \sigma), \quad \text{Moseley's Law,} \tag{8}$$

where A is a constant,

Z is the atomic number,

σ is a small empirical constant.

Moseley's law proved to be of great value in assigning atomic numbers to "new" elements when they were discovered. Thus hafnium was shown to be element number 72, by exciting and measuring its $K\alpha$ wavelength. At the time of Moseley's work (1914), the chemical significance of atomic number rather than that of atomic weight was not fully appreciated. Measurements of X-ray wavelengths can be regarded as another way of determining the number of electrons Z in an atom (see Chapter 1).

A simple modification of the Bohr theory of atomic hydrogen leads to an understanding of Moseley's law. The energy of a K shell electron can be written as

$$E_1 = -\frac{m\,e^4(Z - \sigma)^2}{2\hbar^2} \tag{9}$$

where m is the mass of the electron,

e is the electron charge,

$Z\,e$ is the nuclear charge,

$\hbar$ is Planck's constant divided by 2π,

and σ is a constant, which represents the screening effect on the Coulomb interaction of a K electron and the nucleus by the remaining $(Z - 1)$ atomic electrons. For a K electron ($n = 1$) it is anticipated that the screening correction should be small ($\sigma \ll Z$).

The energy of an L shell electron ($n = 2$) is given by

$$E_2 = -\frac{m\,e^4(Z - \sigma)^2}{2^2\;2\hbar^2} \tag{10}$$

The assumption that σ has the same value for a K and L shell electron is obviously wrong but it does not lead to serious error.

The energy of the $K\alpha$ photon, which is emitted when an electron from the L shell ($n = 2$) jumps to a vacancy in the K shell ($n = 1$) is given by

$$h\,\nu = E_2 - E_1$$

where ν is the Kα line frequency.

$$\therefore\ h\,\nu = \frac{m\,e^4(Z-\sigma)^2}{2\hbar^2}\left(\frac{1}{1^2}-\frac{1}{2^2}\right)$$

$$\therefore\ h\,\nu = \frac{3}{4}h\,c\,R(Z-\sigma)^2$$

where R is the Rydberg constant for hydrogen,

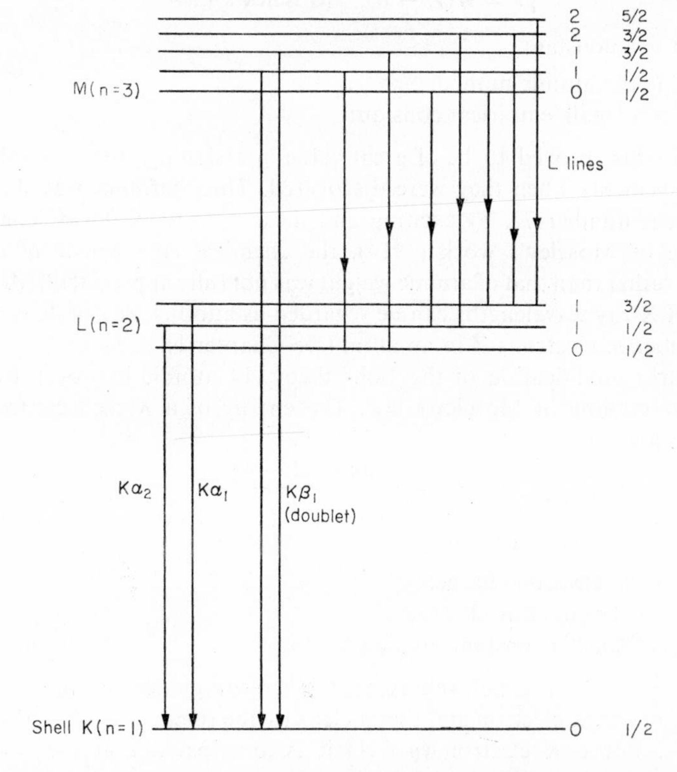

FIG. 5. Some of the allowed electric dipole transitions between L and K shell, M and K shell, and M and L shell. The $K\beta_2$ doublet is not shown as it involves transitions from the N shell ($n = 4$):

viz: $n = 4,\ l = 1,\ j = \frac{1}{2} \rightarrow n = 1,\ l = 0,\ j = \frac{1}{2}$.

$n = 4,\ l = 1,\ j = \frac{3}{2} \rightarrow n = 1,\ l = 0,\ j = \frac{1}{2}$.

$$R = \frac{m e^4}{4\pi c \hbar^3} \quad \text{(eqn. (28), Chapter 2).}$$

$$\therefore \sqrt{\nu} = \frac{\sqrt{3}}{2} (R c)^{\frac{1}{2}} (Z - \sigma) \tag{11}$$

This is Moseley's law, if the constant A in eqn. (8) is identified by the relation

$$A = 0{\cdot}866 \, (R c)^{\frac{1}{2}}$$

Empirically for Z in the range 20 (Ca) to 30 (Zn), the $K\alpha$ frequency ν is given by the formula

$$\sqrt{\nu} = 0{\cdot}874 \, (R c)^{\frac{1}{2}} (Z - 1{\cdot}13) \tag{12}$$

The agreement between eqns. (11) and (12) is good and a screening constant of 1·13 is reasonable.

The scheme of energy levels involved in the X-ray transitions of the K and L lines is shown in Fig. 5. Selection rules limit the number of transitions observed. The emitted radiation corresponds to electric dipole transitions ($E\,1$).†

The selection rules are

$$\Delta l = \pm 1$$

$$\Delta j = 0 \text{ or } \pm 1$$

The j transition $0 \rightarrow 0$ is forbidden.

X-ray lines of lower intensity are sometimes produced which do not obey these rules. They correspond to either electric quadrupole $E\,2$ or magnetic dipole $M\,1$ transitions. The $K\alpha$ is a close doublet and although the lines are longer in wavelength than the $K\beta$ lines, it is much more intense.

4.3 X-RAY ABSORPTION

A collimated X-ray beam is attenuated as it passes through matter according to the exponential law

$$I = I_0 \, e^{-\mu x} \tag{13}$$

where I_0 is the incident intensity,

I is the transmitted intensity,

x the thickness of the absorber.

μ is known as the linear absorption coefficient of the medium. It is convenient to introduce the *mass* absorption coefficient, μ/ϱ, where ϱ is the density of the medium.

Equation (13) can be written

$$I = I_0 \, e^{-(\mu/\varrho)}(\varrho x) \tag{14}$$

† Electric dipole, quadrupole, octopole transitions are known as $E1$, $E2$, $E3$, etc.

ϱx is equal to the mass of unit area of the absorber and is a convenient way of measuring the amount of absorbing material. The mass absorption coefficient μ/ϱ is a more fundamental measure of absorption than the linear coefficient as it is independent of the physical state of the absorber, solid, liquid or gas. The absorption coefficient can be split into two parts

$$\frac{\mu}{\varrho} = \frac{\sigma}{\varrho} + \frac{\tau}{\varrho} \tag{15}$$

where σ/ϱ is the *scattering* coefficient, which is nearly independent of the wavelength and is of the order of 0·2 cm² g⁻¹. The *transformation* coefficient τ/ϱ is a measure of true absorption. In contrast to the scattering coefficient, the transformation coefficient varies rapidly with wavelength and atomic number Z of the absorber. The variation of τ/ϱ with wavelength for platinum ($Z = 78$) is shown in Fig. 6. There are sharp discontinuities at certain wavelengths known as absorption edges. Between absorption edges, the

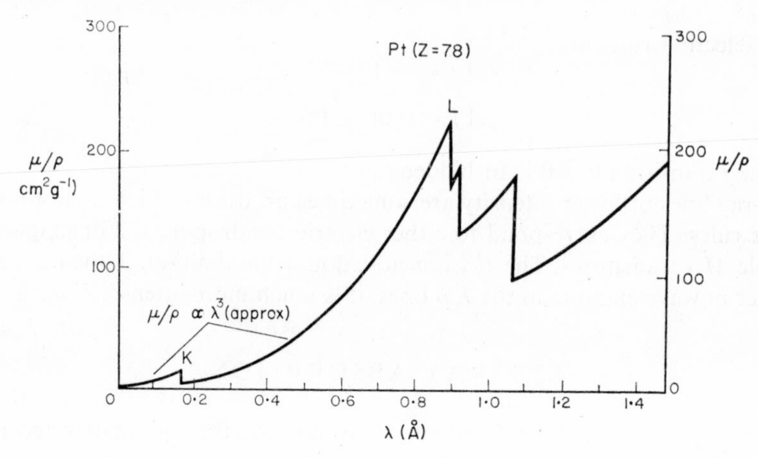

FIG. 6. Variation of mass absorption coefficient μ/ϱ with X-ray wavelength λ for element 78 (Pt). Between absorption edges μ/ϱ is roughly proportional to λ^3.

transformation coefficient varies approximately as the cube of the wavelength. There is also a rapid variation of τ/ϱ with atomic number Z. For the same wavelength, τ/ϱ varies approximately as Z^4.

The existence of absorption edges is explained in the following way. One of the important absorption processes is photoelectric emission. An incident X-ray photon ejects a K or L shell atomic electron. Photons on the long wavelength side of an absorption edge have insufficient energy to free a bound electron from the appropriate shell. There is a one-to-one correspondence between the number of K and L energy states of the absorbing atom

(Fig. 5). The determination of X-ray absorption edge wavelengths enables binding energies of *K*, *L*, *M* electrons to be calculated, e.g.

$$E_K = h\nu_K = \frac{hc}{\lambda_K} \qquad (16)$$

where E_K is the *K*-shell binding energy, and λ_K is the *K*-absorption edge wavelength.

The *K*-emission wavelengths and absorption edge wavelengths of a few elements are given in Table 1.

TABLE 1

Element	Z	Emission wavelength (Å)		
		$K\alpha_1$	$K\alpha_2$	$K\beta_1$
Mo	42	0·709	0·714	0·632
Cu	29	1·540	1·544	1·392
Ni	28	1·658	1·662	1·500
Cr	24	2·290	2·294	2·085

Element	Z	*K*-Absorption edge wavelength (Å)
Zr	40	0·689
Ni	28	1·487

For many diffraction purposes a monochromatic beam of radiation is desirable. The $K\alpha$ components are about six times as intense as any other wavelength and the relative intensity of the $K\alpha$ to the $K\beta$ components can be greatly increased by placing a suitable filter in the beam. For example, nickel foil of thickness 0·021 mm reduces the $K\beta$ intensity of copper radiation to $^1/_{600}$ that of the $K\alpha$. It should be realized that the $K\alpha$-intensity will be reduced by the filter and this is a waste of X-ray energy. The filtering property of the nickel foil can be understood by consulting the data in Table 1. The *K* absorption edge frequency of $_{28}$Ni lies between the $K\beta$ and $K\alpha$ emission wavelengths of $_{29}$Cu. This is not a capricious result for the *K* edge wavelength of any element is shorter than the $K\beta$ emission wavelength (see the values for Ni) and it is to be expected that the *K* edge wavelength of element *Z* will be longer than the $K\beta$ emission wavelength of element $Z + 1$ or $Z + 2$. The mass absorption coefficient of Ni for Cu $K\alpha$ radiation is 49·2 cm² g⁻¹, whereas the value for Cu $K\beta$ radiation is as high as 286 $cm^2\ g^{-1}$. The much greater absorption of Cu $K\beta$ radiation occurs because the $K\beta$ photons have energy greater than the *K* electron binding energies in Ni. A suitable filter for Mo radiation is zirconium foil.

4.4 THE REFRACTION OF X-RAYS

A simple classical explanation of the minute amount of refraction experienced by X-rays in matter is based on the theory of forced vibrations.

Suppose the electrons in an atom are set into forced vibration by an incident X-ray whose electric field is

$$\boldsymbol{E} = \boldsymbol{E}_0 \sin \omega t$$

A bound electron has a natural oscillation frequency

$$\nu_0 = \frac{\omega_0}{2\pi}$$

If the electron is displaced in the x-direction by the electric field of the X-ray the equation of motion is

$$\ddot{\boldsymbol{x}} + \omega_0^2 \boldsymbol{x} = \frac{e}{m} \boldsymbol{E}_0 \sin \omega t \tag{17}$$

This equation neglects any damping term.

After the initial transient motion has subsided the electron motion is given by

$$\boldsymbol{x} = \frac{e\,\boldsymbol{E}}{m(\omega_0^2 - \omega^2)} \tag{18}$$

For X-rays of wavelength about 1 Å, ν_0 is 3×10^{18} sec^{-1} which is about 1000 times the natural frequency of oscillation of a bound electron.

$$\omega_0^2 \ll \omega^2$$

as

$$\boldsymbol{x} = -\frac{e\,\boldsymbol{E}}{m\,\omega^2} \tag{19}$$

The negative sign means that the vibrating electron is 180° out of phase with the incident wave. Consequently an electron scatters the incident wave with a phase change of π.

If there are n electrons per unit volume in a medium, it will acquire an induced dipole moment per unit volume (polarization) P, given by,

$$\boldsymbol{P} = n\,e\,\boldsymbol{x} = -\frac{n\,e^2\,\boldsymbol{E}}{m\,\omega^2} \tag{20}$$

The electric displacement vector $\boldsymbol{D} = K\boldsymbol{E}$, where K is the dielectric constant, is given by

$$\boldsymbol{D} = K\boldsymbol{E} = K_0\,\boldsymbol{E} + 4\pi\,\boldsymbol{P} \tag{21}$$

where K_0, the dielectric constant of free space, is equal to unity,

$$\therefore\; K = 1 + 4\pi\frac{\boldsymbol{P}}{\boldsymbol{E}} \tag{22}$$

Substituting eqn. (20) in eqn. (22) we get

$$K = 1 - \frac{4\pi n e^2}{m \omega^2} \tag{23}$$

According to Maxwell's electromagnetic theory, in a non-ferromagnetic medium $K = \mu^2$, where μ is the refractive index of the medium. Using this relation and the fact that

$$1 \gg \frac{4\pi n e^2}{m \omega^2}$$

we obtain the following expression for the refractive index

$$\mu = 1 - \frac{2\pi n e^2}{m \omega^2} = 1 - \delta \tag{24}$$

where $$\delta = \frac{2\pi n e^2}{m \omega^2} \ll 1$$

substituting typical values: $n \simeq 10^{23}$ electrons per cm^3

$$\omega \simeq 10^{19}\ \text{sec}^{-1}$$

$$e = 4{\cdot}8 \times 10^{-10}\ \text{e.s.u.}$$

$$m = 9 \times 10^{-28}\ \text{g}$$

we find δ is $\simeq 2 \times 10^{-6}$.

In terms of the X-ray wavelength λ, δ can be written as

$$\delta = \frac{n \lambda^2}{2\pi}\left(\frac{e^2}{m c^2}\right) = \frac{n \lambda^2}{2\pi} b \tag{25}$$

using the relation $\omega = 2\pi \nu = 2\pi c/\lambda$

b is the familiar classical electron radius and it is sometimes known as the coherent scattering length or amplitude of an electron for X-rays. Slow neutrons (velocity 2000 m per sec) have a wavelength of the order of 1 Å and it can be shown that the refractive index of a medium for neutrons is given by

$$\mu = 1 - \frac{n \lambda^2 b}{2\pi}$$

where, in this case, n is the number of atomic *nuclei* per cm^3, λ is the neutron wavelength, and b is the nuclear scattering length.

For neutrons, b is of the order of nuclear radii (10^{-13} cm to 10^{-12} cm) but is *not* in general equal to the nuclear radius. Most nuclei have positive scattering lengths, signifying a phase change of π for the nuclear–neutron scattering as in the X-ray case. A few nuclei have negative scattering lengths corresponding to neutron scattering without any phase change. This aspect of "Neutron Optics" is discussed in Chapter 15.

To return to X-ray refraction, we find that the focusing of X-rays by lenses is impracticable in view of the very slight deviation of μ from unity. At very small glancing angles, however, total *external* reflection is possible from very smooth surfaces. An X-ray incident on a plane mirror surface at an angle of incidence $(90-\theta_c)$ is just totally reflected if θ_c is the critical glancing angle

$$\mu = \sin(90-\theta_c) = \cos\theta_c = 1 - \frac{\theta_c^2}{2}\cdots \tag{26}$$

as θ_c is a very small angle and writing μ as $1-\delta$, we get

$$\theta_c = \sqrt{(2\delta)} \tag{27}$$

For lead glass, and radiation of wavelength 1·54 Å (Cu $K\alpha$), θ_c is 18 min of arc!

In spite of the very small critical glancing angle, totally reflected X-rays have been obtained from polished surfaces and also from ruled optical diffraction gratings.

4.5. MEASUREMENT OF X-RAY WAVELENGTHS BY RULED GRATINGS

Following the successful demonstration of the phenomenon of total X-ray reflection, it was realized that X-ray wavelengths might be measured by using a plane ruled grating as a reflection grating. The effective grating

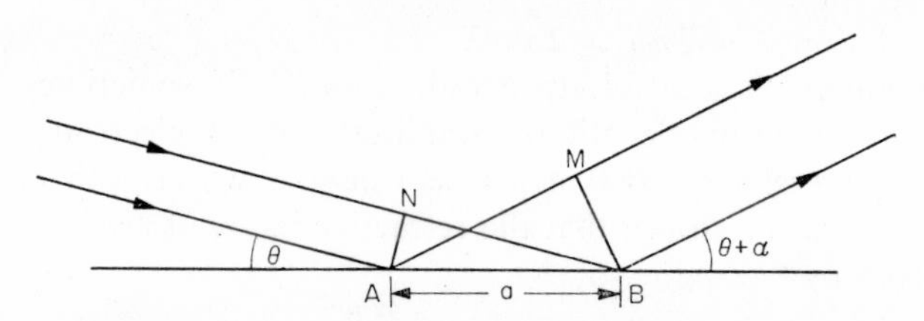

FIG. 7. Reflection of X-rays from a ruled grating.

spacing is greatly fore-shortened for a fine collimated X-ray beam incident at a glancing angle θ of a few minutes of arc. The reflected spectra are reasonably strong if θ is less than the critical value θ_c. Consider a collimated beam (a typical collimation is two slits $\frac{1}{100}$ mm wide, 50 cm apart), incident on a plane grating whose spacing A B = a (Fig. 7).

The path difference of rays scattered from A and B in the direction $(\theta+\alpha)$ is = N B − A M, where A N and B M are perpendiculars

$$N B - A M = a[\cos\theta - \cos(\theta + \alpha)]$$
$$N B - A M = a[\cos\theta(1 - \cos\alpha) + \theta\,\alpha],$$

as θ and α are small angles,

$$\cos\theta \to 1, \quad 1 - \cos\alpha = 2\sin^2\frac{\alpha}{2} = \frac{\alpha^2}{2}$$

Therefore diffracted beams appear if

$$a\left[\frac{\alpha^2}{2} + \theta\,\alpha\right] = n\,\lambda \qquad (28)$$

where n is the order of the spectrum (n is an integer).
Diffraction spectra have been recorded on photographic plates so that the angles θ and α can be determined. In spite of the small values of θ and α this method of X-ray wavelength determination reached a very high degree of precision during the nineteen-thirties, especially in the U.S.A. and Sweden.

4.6. X-RAY DIFFRACTION

X-rays as they travel through matter are scattered and absorbed by electrons. The rays which are scattered without change in wavelength are capable of producing diffraction effects. During the process of coherent scattering the electrons concerned remain in their initial quantum states. When an X-ray photon is scattered *coherently* by an electron in a crystal, momentum is conserved by the recoil of the crystal as a whole. On account of the enormous difference in the mass of the crystal and the mass of the electron, the energy lost by the scattered photon is negligible. In addition to coherent scattering, X-rays are scattered with an increase in wavelength and no interference effects are observed. This incoherent scattering, discovered by A. H. Compton in 1922, is the result of a collision of an X-ray photon with a loosely bound electron, the electron recoiling from the atom. From the point of view of X-ray diffraction experiments, Compton scattering is a nuisance as it adds to the general diffuse background of scattered radiation thereby hindering the observation of weak diffracted beams.

For the moment, let us consider the factors which determine the *directions* of the diffracted rays, without considering at this stage, the *intensities* of the spectra. The only point to note is the phase change of π associated with the Thomson scattering of X-rays.† This is not important if all the electrons in a crystal scatter with a phase shift of π. The history of X-ray diffraction

† The phase shift may differ from π, if the X-ray frequency is close to an absorption edge frequency. An elegant experiment by Coster, Knol and Prins has demonstrated this effect for Zn in a ZnS crystal (see p. 33 *et seq.* of *The Crystalline State* Vol. 2).

began with the idea of von Laue that the regular periodic structure of the atoms in a crystal might function as a three-dimensional grating for X-rays. The necessary conditions for the waves scattered by the electrons in a crystal to reinforce each other at a distant point can be derived as follows.

Consider the scattering of a collimated beam of X-rays by a row of equally spaced scattering points (Fig. 8). The spacing of the points is represented

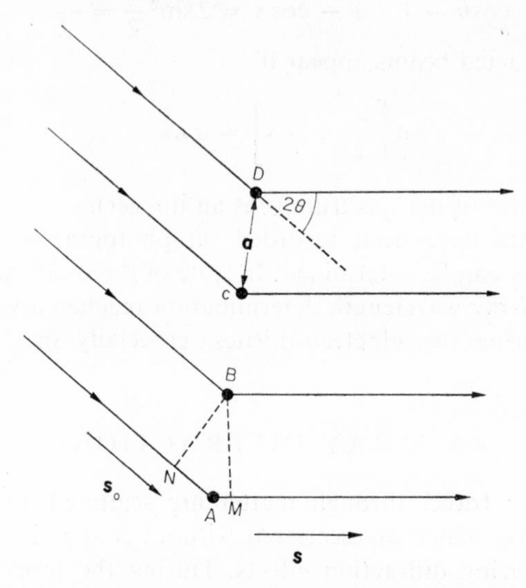

FIG. 8. Parallel beam of radiation scattered by a row of scattering points A, B, C, D, . . . , etc. (Spacing = $\boldsymbol{a}$).

by the vector $\boldsymbol{a}$. The unit vectors $\boldsymbol{s}_0$ and $\boldsymbol{s}$ denote the directions of the incident and scattered rays respectively. The path difference of rays scattered by adjacent points A and B is

$$\mathrm{AM} + \mathrm{AN} = \boldsymbol{a}\cdot\boldsymbol{s} - \boldsymbol{a}\cdot\boldsymbol{s}_0 = \boldsymbol{a}\cdot(\boldsymbol{s}-\boldsymbol{s}_0) = \boldsymbol{a}\cdot\boldsymbol{S} \tag{29}$$

where

$$\boldsymbol{S} = \boldsymbol{s} - \boldsymbol{s}_0 \tag{30}$$

N and M are the feet of the perpendiculars drawn from B to the incident and scattered rays through A.†

The condition for observing a diffracted beam from the one-dimensional lattice is

$$\boldsymbol{a}\cdot\boldsymbol{S} = h\lambda \tag{31}$$

where $h\lambda$ is an integral number of wavelengths; h can be positive or negative.

The magnitude of the vector $\boldsymbol{S} = \boldsymbol{s} - \boldsymbol{s}_0$ is $2\sin\theta$, where 2θ is the angle of scattering (Fig. 9). $\boldsymbol{S}$ is normal to the plane which bisects the angle between the incident and scattered rays. The significance of this "reflecting

† The minus sign in eqns. (29) and (30) occurs because the angle between $\boldsymbol{s}_0$ and $\boldsymbol{AB}$ is obtuse.

plane" will appear when we consider a three-dimensional space lattice of scattering centres. For a given order of diffraction h, the diffracted rays lie on the surface of a cone with the row of lattice points as axis.

A crystal has aptly been described as "three-dimensional wallpaper". A certain unit of pattern, known as the unit cell, is repeated regularly throughout the crystal. The unit cell is a parallelepiped with three adjacent

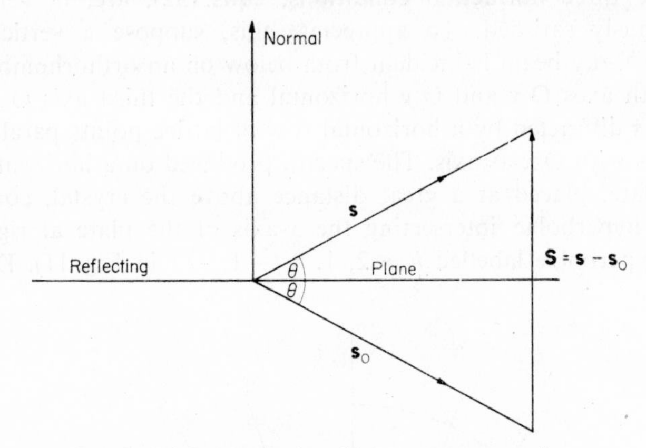

FIG. 9. "Reflecting" plane bisects vectors $\boldsymbol{s}$ and $\boldsymbol{s}_0$.

sides defined by vectors $\boldsymbol{a}$, $\boldsymbol{b}$ and $\boldsymbol{c}$. Choosing a corner of the unit cell as origin, it is customary to choose coordinate axes O x, O y, O z parallel to the respective vectors $\boldsymbol{a}$, $\boldsymbol{b}$, $\boldsymbol{c}$. Three conditions must be satisfied if diffraction spectra are produced by the crystal lattice

$$\begin{aligned} \boldsymbol{a} \cdot \boldsymbol{S} &= h\,\lambda, \\ \boldsymbol{b} \cdot \boldsymbol{S} &= k\,\lambda, \qquad \text{Laue equations} \quad (32) \\ \boldsymbol{c} \cdot \boldsymbol{S} &= l\,\lambda, \end{aligned}$$

where h, k, l are integers positive or negative.

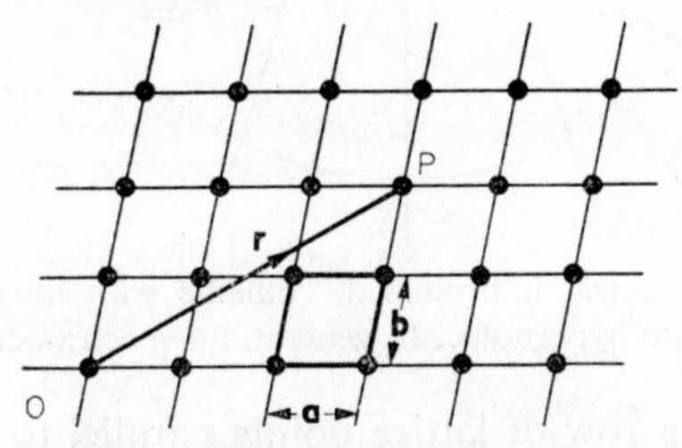

FIG. 10. Three-dimensional network of points. Unit cell described by vectors $\boldsymbol{a}$, $\boldsymbol{b}$, $\boldsymbol{c}$ ($\boldsymbol{c}$ is normal to the plane of the figure).

A point inside the crystal has coordinates u, v, w. If the point lies at the corner of any unit cell, u, v and w are necessarily integers. A lattice point P is described by a position vector $\boldsymbol{r}$ (Fig. 10).

$$\boldsymbol{r} = u\,\boldsymbol{a} + v\,\boldsymbol{b} + w\,\boldsymbol{c}$$

The path difference of rays scattered by lattice points O and P is

$$\boldsymbol{r} \cdot \boldsymbol{S} = (h\,u + k\,v + l\,w)\,\lambda \tag{33}$$

and we see that as u, v, w are integers, the diffraction conditions are satisfied for waves scattered by *all* the lattice points.

When a monochromatic beam of collimated X-rays passes through a crystal the three diffraction conditions, eqns. (32), are, in general, not simultaneously satisfied. To appreciate this, suppose a vertical monochromatic X-ray beam is incident from below on an orthorhombic† space lattice, with axes O x and O y horizontal and the third axis O z vertical. The X-rays diffracted by a horizontal row of lattice points parallel to O x form cones with O x as axis. The spectra produced on a horizontal photographic plate, placed at a great distance above the crystal, consist of a family of hyperbolae intersecting the x-axis of the plate at right angles (see the hyperbolae labelled $h = 2, 1, 0, -1, -2$ in Fig. 11). Diffraction

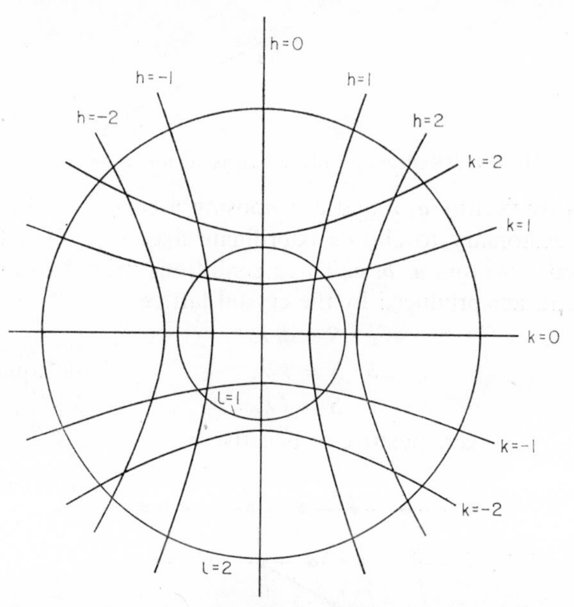

FIG. 11. Diffraction spectra, if produced, coincide with intersection of a circle and two hyperbolae. In general, no spectra occur.

spectra produced by a row of lattice points parallel to O y also appear as a family of hyperbolae crossing the y axis of the photographic plate at right angles. Spectra formed by a horizontal plane of lattice points consist of a number of *points* at the intersections of the hyperbolae. Notice that adding an extra dimension to a line grating reduces the spectra from lines

† For an orthorhombic crystal, the crystallographic axes are mutually perpendicular.

to points. The diffraction cones corresponding to scattering by a vertical row of lattice points have O z as axis. They intersect the photographic plate above the crystal in a series of concentric circles labelled $l = 1$, $l = 2$ (Fig. 11). A three-dimensional space lattice will produce spectra where three curves intersect. It is obvious that, in general, this will not occur. Rotating the crystal or selecting the "correct" wavelength from the continuous spectrum of an X-ray source are possible ways of obtaining spectra.

The Bragg Law

Soon after the first successful X-ray diffraction experiment carried out by Friedrich and Knipping at von Laue's suggestion, W. L. Bragg introduced a simpler way of deriving the diffraction conditions. Each diffracted beam can be regarded as the result of *selective reflection* from an internal set of parallel lattice planes.† The waves scattered from a single lattice plane of points are all in phase in a direction corresponding to the law

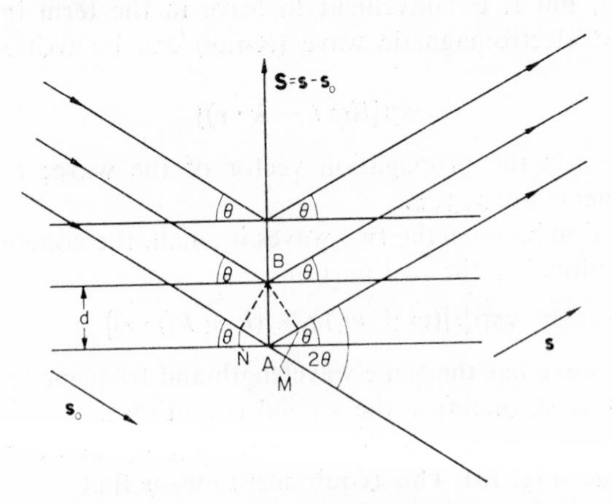

FIG. 12. Bragg concept of X-ray diffraction by selective *reflection* from parallel lattice planes.

of reflection. In addition, if the path difference between waves reflected from adjacent lattice planes is a whole number of wavelengths, *all* the scattered waves will be in phase and give rise to a diffracted beam.

The path difference of X-rays reflected from consecutive lattice planes of spacing d is easily shown (Fig. 12) to be

$$2d \sin\theta$$

† In 1938, J. Laval observed for the first time diffuse diffraction spots or streaks which do not obey Bragg's law and are in fact connected with the thermal vibrations of the atoms in the crystal.

where θ is the glancing angle of the incident rays.

Diffraction occurs if

$$2d \sin\theta = n\lambda \qquad \text{Bragg law} \tag{34}$$

where n is an integer known as the order of reflection. An alternative and very instructive way of deriving the Bragg law, is based on the concept that the spatial distribution of electrons in a crystal can be regarded as a triple Fourier series of scattering material. This point of view was first put forward by W. H. Bragg as early as 1915. The Bragg reflection of X-rays from a given set of lattice planes represents an interaction between the incoming electromagnetic wave of frequency $\omega/(2\pi)$ and the Fourier component of electron charge density in a direction normal to the lattice planes. The latter can be written as the real part of

$$\exp[i(\omega_1 t - \boldsymbol{k}_1 \cdot \boldsymbol{r})] \tag{35}$$

where $\boldsymbol{k}_1 = 2\pi/d$, as d is the periodicity in a direction normal to the lattice planes; the electron charge density component is represented by a standing wave ($\omega_1 = 0$), but it is convenient to leave in the term involving time.

The incident electromagnetic wave (X-ray) can be written as the real part of

$$\exp[i(\omega t - \boldsymbol{k} \cdot \boldsymbol{r})] \tag{36}$$

where $\boldsymbol{k} = 2\pi/\lambda$ is the propagation vector of the wave; $\boldsymbol{r}$ is the vector whose components are x, y, z.

If the interaction between the two waves is small, the coherently scattered wave is proportional to the real part of

$$\exp\{i[(\omega \pm \omega_1)t - (\boldsymbol{k} \pm \boldsymbol{k}_1) \cdot \boldsymbol{r}]\} \tag{37}$$

The diffracted wave has the same wavelength and frequency as the incident wave. Now $\omega_1 = 0$, therefore the second condition is satisfied. To satisfy the first condition the propagation vectors $(\boldsymbol{k} \pm \boldsymbol{k}_1)$ and $\boldsymbol{k}$ must have the same magnitude (Fig. 13). This requirement means that

$$\sin\theta = \frac{|k_1|}{2|k|} = \left(\frac{2\pi}{d}\right)\left(\frac{1}{2}\right)\left(\frac{\lambda}{2\pi}\right)$$

or

$$2d \sin\theta = \lambda \tag{38}$$

This is Bragg's law for the first order reflection from the lattice planes concerned. The absence of n in eqn. (38) signifies the result that a single sinusoidal scattering periodicity produces one and only one order of diffraction. For example, if the density of blackening varies sinusoidally across a glass plate, a beam of light passing through the plate only forms one order of diffraction. The collective thermal motions of the atoms in a crystal can be regarded as a system of thermal waves running through the crystal. These lattice vibrations whose energy must be quantized (the quantum is known as a *phonon*) will interact with the incident electromagnetic wave and produce a scattered wave with a slight frequency shift as ω_1 for a lattice wave is finite but much smaller than ω for the X-ray. In the same way, ultrasonic waves travelling through a liquid function as a diffraction grating for light waves travelling through the liquid.

What is the connection between Bragg's law, eqn. (34), and Laue's diffraction conditions, eqn. (32)? It is not difficult to show that the integers h, k, l (provided they have no common factor n)† in Laue's equation are

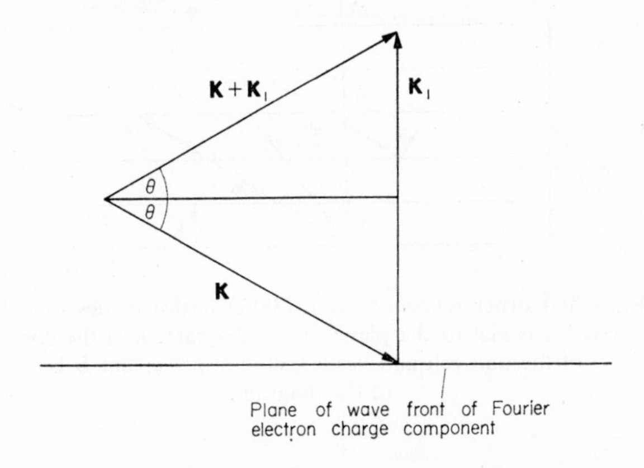

FIG. 13. Wave scattering process.

the *Miller indices* of the reflection planes involved in the Bragg interpretation. The orientation of a particular set of lattice planes relative to the crystal axes are represented in the following way. Consider the plane of the set which is adjacent to the one of the set which passes through the origin of the unit cell. If the intercepts on the x, y, and z axes are a/h, b/k, c/l, respectively, then $(h\,k\,l)$ are the Miller indices of the set of planes. Lattice planes of importance in relation to diffraction have small integers for h, k and l.†† Planes parallel to prominent faces of the crystal have especially simple indices, e.g. (100) (110) (111). To take a simple example, consider the first order reflection from the (302) planes of an orthorhombic crystal (Fig. 14). The vector $\boldsymbol{S} = \boldsymbol{s} - \boldsymbol{s}_0$ is normal to the (302) planes.

We see from eqn. (33) that the path difference of X-rays scattered from opposite corners of the unit cell in the direction $\boldsymbol{s}$ is $(h + k + l)\lambda$, as $u = 1$, $v = 1$, $w = 1$ for the lattice point opposite the origin. For the (302) planes the path difference of X-rays reflected from the lattice plane through O and the lattice plane through B is $(h + k + l)\,\lambda = 5\lambda$. Now there are five

† n is in fact the order in Bragg's equation.

†† Negative intercepts are denoted by negative indices which are written $\bar{h}, \bar{k}$ or $\bar{l}$ etc.

lattice planes of the (302) set between O and B. (N.B. in Fig. 14 there are three planes between O and A as $h = 3$, and two planes between A and B as $l = 2$; $k = 0$, as the lattice planes are parallel to the y axis). Thus the

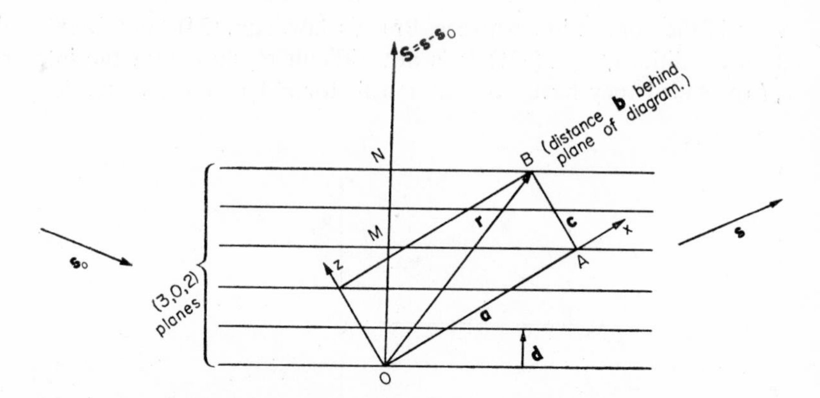

FIG. 14. Bragg first order reflection from (3 0 2) lattice planes of orthorhombic lattice. Oy axis is normal to the plane of the diagram. B is the corner opposite to the origin O of the unit cell and lies a vector displacement $\boldsymbol{b}$ behind the plane of the diagram.

X-rays reflected from *successive* lattice planes have a path difference of one wavelength, which is the condition for a first order reflection. It is in fact often convenient to regard the nth order reflection from the $(h\,k\,l)$ planes as a first order reflection from a parallel set of planes with the smaller interplanar spacing d/n. These planes are described by Miller indices $(nh\,nk\,nl)$. The problem of deducing the interplanar spacing d of a set of planes $(h\,k\,l)$ is purely geometrical and for orthogonal axes it is easy to show that

$$d_{hkl} = \frac{1}{\sqrt{\left[\left(\frac{h}{a}\right)^2 + \left(\frac{k}{b}\right)^2 + \left(\frac{l}{c}\right)^2\right]}} \tag{39}$$

This reduces to

$$d_{hkl} = \frac{a}{\sqrt{(h^2 + k^2 + l^2)}} \tag{40}$$

for cubic crystals as the unit cell has $a = b = c$.

For the crystal systems with non-orthogonal axes more complicated expressions for d occur and they are to be found in many standard books on X-ray crystallography (see the bibliography).

The different orders of Bragg reflection are demonstrated in a convincing way by reflecting a collimated beam of monochromatic X-rays (e.g. Rh $K\alpha$, 0·613 Å) from the lattice planes parallel to the cleavage plane of a crystal of β-corundum (Al_2O_3). This particular lattice spacing is much greater than the X-ray wavelength and nineteen orders of reflection are detectable when the glancing angle θ is increased from one to thirty-six degrees.

It should be noted that if λ is greater than $2d$ for a set of planes, the Bragg law cannot be satisfied for any finite order of reflection, as $|\sin\theta| \gg 1$. In this case the X-ray beam will cross this set of planes without any energy being reflected away.

Finally let us consider the sharpness of the diffraction spectra. Over what range of angle is the Bragg reflection intensity appreciable from a perfect† crystal? To answer this question, consider a perfect crystal m lattice planes thick, i.e. the crystal thickness = $m\,d$. For the nth reflection from these planes the path difference between waves reflected from the first and last lattice plane is $m\,n\,\lambda$. At a slightly different glancing angle $\theta + d\theta$, this path difference will increase to $(m\,n + 1)\lambda$. The waves reflected from the m lattice planes now just annul one another, for we can divide the waves into a series of pairs in the following way. The waves reflected from the 1st and the $(m/2)$th plane are 180° out of phase, so are the waves reflected from the 2nd and $(m/2 + 1)$th plane . . . , etc. Thus there is complete destructive interference in the direction $\theta + d\theta$.

Multiplying the Bragg equation by m

$$2m\,d\sin\theta = n\,m\,\lambda \tag{41}$$

and differentiating, remembering that $d(n\,m) = 1$.

$$2m\,d\cos\theta\,d\theta = \lambda$$

$$\therefore 2d\theta = \frac{\lambda}{m\,d\cos\theta} = \frac{\lambda}{t\cos\theta} \tag{42}$$

where t is the thickness of the crystal, $t = m\,d$.

Now $2d\theta$ is effectively the angular range over which Bragg reflection occurs, i.e. at angle θ, the intensity is a maximum, and at angles $\theta \pm d\theta$, the intensity has fallen to zero. For a perfect crystal, as small as 10^{-4} cm thick, the angular range of reflection for λ about 1 Å is of the order of 1 min of arc. Perfect crystals with linear dimensions of the order of 1/10 mm or more reflect over a very small angular range of the order of seconds of arc. The angular range in practice is more likely to be determined by the slight divergence of the X-rays from the collimator. The intensity of the transmitted beam decreases to zero as the crystal is slowly turned through the reflecting position. The amplitude of the wave train reflected by a single lattice plane at the Bragg setting is about 10^{-4} times the amplitude of the incident wave train. Thus in a flawless crystal, thicker than 10^{-4} cm (i.e. about 10^4 lattice planes thick), no incident radiation will penetrate to a

† A perfect crystal is one free from dislocations, i.e. all the lattice planes of any set are parallel throughout the crystal.

greater depth. This enhanced "absorption" of the primary beam in addition to true absorption (for NaCl crystal, $\mu = 162\ \text{cm}^{-1}$ for Cu $K\alpha$ radiation) is known as *primary extinction.* Only a few crystals, including some white diamonds, are flawless. The other extreme is the ideally imperfect or *mosaic* crystal, which is composed of a number of small crystallites slightly disorientated with respect to each other. The orientation may vary over several minutes from one crystallite to another. Thus a mosaic crystal block will reflect X-rays over several minutes, in some cases as much as half a degree, as it slowly rotates through the Bragg position. The primary extinction in the individual crystallites is not complete as they are very small; nevertheless the crystallites in the lower part of the mosaic block are partially screened from the incident radiation. In addition, some of the lower lying crystallites may be parallel to ones near the surface and selective "absorption" by Bragg reflection will occur in both crystallites at the same setting. The screening of the internal crystallites of a mosaic block from the primary beam is known as *secondary extinction.* In reality, the majority of crystals fall between the ideal flawless and the ideal mosaic types. The extinction effects and the true absorption of X-rays in a crystal are important factors influencing the *intensities* of the diffraction spectra.

Experimental Techniques of X-ray Crystallography

A brief account is given below of some of the experimental methods of X-ray diffraction. The Laue method differs from all other methods in employing the continuous radiation from an X-ray tube. A collimated beam of X-rays passes through a small single crystal and the diffracted beams are recorded on a photographic plate placed a few centimetres beyond the crystal.† The great difficulty in using the Bragg equation is the question of assigning the correct wavelength to each spot. Each Bragg reflection selects the wavelength in the continuous spectrum which satisfies the Bragg law

$$2d \sin\theta = n\lambda$$

In 1913 W. H. Bragg introduced the ionization spectrometer. A collimated X-ray beam is incident on a set of vertical lattice planes of a crystal, which is slowly rotated. The scattered X-rays are detected by a rotating ionization chamber (Fig. 15). The ionization chamber is rotated at twice the rate of the crystal and is therefore in the correct position to detect the Bragg reflections. The intensity of the diffracted beams is determined by measuring the ionization current with a sensitive electrometer. A dense gas such as methyl bromide filling a chamber 15 cm in length will absorb

† Excellent accounts of the events leading to Laue's discovery are given by FRIEDRICH in *Naturwissenschaften* for April 1922, and in Chapter 1 of K. LONSDALE's *Crystals and X-Rays* (G. BELL).

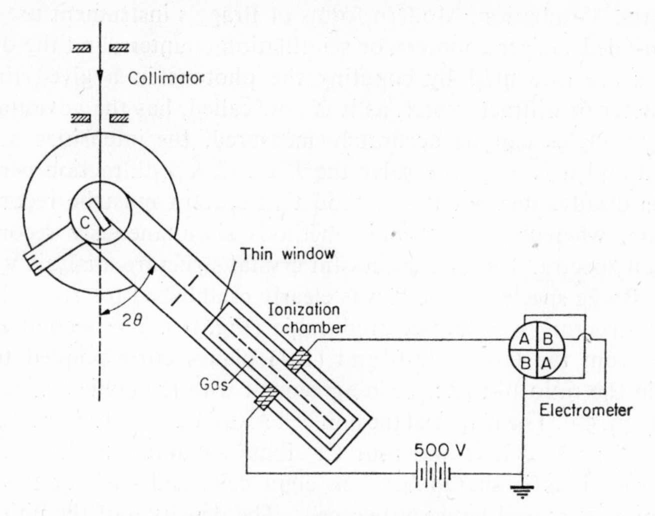

FIG. 15. Bragg ionization spectrometer. X-rays "reflected" from crystal C are detected by ionization chamber.

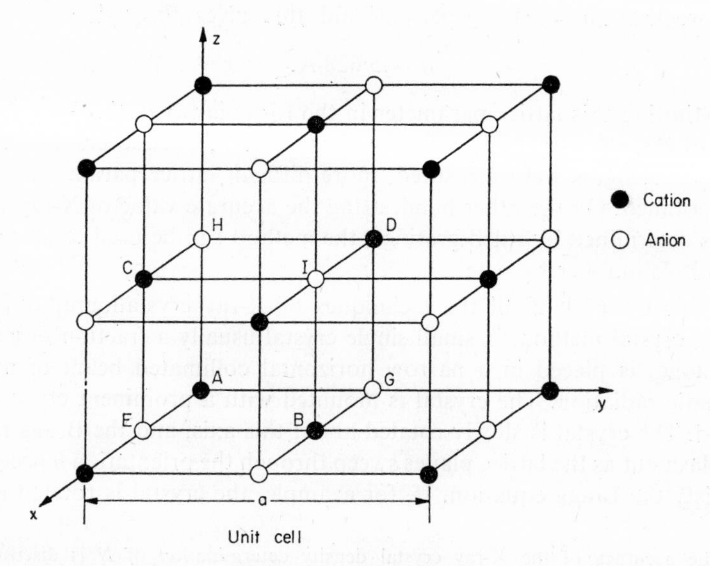

FIG. 16. Rock salt-type face-centred cubic structure A, B, C, D four cations "belonging" to unit cell E, G, H, I four anions "belonging" to unit cell.

most of the X-radiation. Modern forms of Bragg's instrument use krypton or xenon-filled Geiger counters, or scintillation counters, and the diffracted intensities are measured by counting the photons in a given time. The spectrometer or diffractometer, as it is now called, has the advantages that the Bragg angles can be accurately measured, the intensities accurately measured and it is easy to resolve the $K\alpha$ and $K\beta$ diffraction peaks. It is a serious disadvantage of the method that spectra must be recorded one at a time, whereas photographic methods simultaneously record many diffraction spectra. The first successful crystal structure analysis was made with the Bragg spectrometer. It was clearly established for rocksalt (NaCl) that the structure was face-centred cubic (Fig. 16). The second order reflections from the (100), (110) and (111) planes corresponded to values of $\sin\theta$ in the ratio $\sqrt{1} : \sqrt{2} : \sqrt{3}$, in agreement with the cubic lattice formula for d_{hkl} (eqn. 40). The length of the unit cell a was found as follows. Effectively there are four Na^+ ions and four Cl^- ions per unit cell, for each of the eight corner ions is shared between eight cells and each of the six face centred ions is shared between two cells. The density ϱ of the unit cell and consequently of the whole crystal is given by

$$\varrho = \frac{4(A_{Na} + A_{Cl})}{Na^3} \tag{43}$$

where A_{Na} and A_{Cl} are the atomic weights of Na and Cl respectively, N is Avogadro's number, and a^3 is the volume of the unit cell.

For rocksalt, $\varrho = 2{\cdot}163$ g per cm³ and this gives the value

$$a = 5{\cdot}628 \text{ Å}.$$

Substituting this lattice parameter in the formula for d, the X-ray wavelength of 0·586 Å was obtained for Pd $K\alpha$ radiation. Once several prominent X-ray wavelengths were measured, more difficult lattice parameters could be determined. On the other hand, using the accurate value of X-ray wavelengths determined by ruled gratings, the method can be used to determine Avogadro's number.†

The most useful of all the techniques of X-ray crystallography is the *rotating* crystal method. A small single crystal usually a fraction of a millimetre long, is placed in a narrow horizontal collimated beam of monochromatic radiation. The crystal is mounted with a prominent crystal axis vertical. The crystal is slowly rotated about this axis, and the Bragg reflections flash out as the lattice planes sweep through the orientation θ necessary to satisfy the Bragg equation. If, for example, the crystal is rotated about

† The accuracy of the X-ray crystal density determination of N is discussed in detail in *Fundamental Constants of Physics* by COHEN, CROWE, DUMOND (Interscience Publishers).

the z axis (parallel to $\boldsymbol{c}$), then lattice planes parallel to this axis have indices ($h\,k\,0$) and they will produce Bragg reflections in horizontal directions. The reflections from the vertical ($h\,k\,0$) planes intersect a cylindrical photographic film, whose axis coincides with the rotation axis of the crystal, in a horizontal row of spots (Fig. 17). This is the zero layer line. The ($h\,k\,1$)

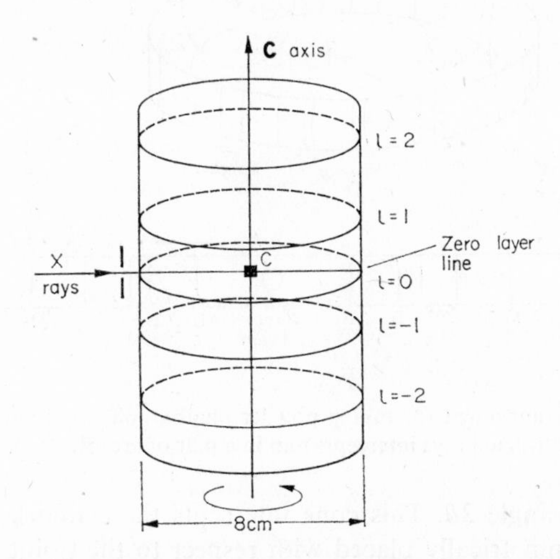

FIG. 17. Recording rotating crystal diffraction spectra on cylindrical film. Spectra consist of rows of horizontal spots known as layer lines. Each layer line corresponds to Bragg reflection from lattice planes with a common l value.

planes are tilted back from the vertical and they reflect the X-rays upwards to form the first layer line, a row of spots lying about the zero layer line. An account of the rather intricate business of allocating indices to all the diffraction spots is outside the scope of this book. In practice, several rotation photographs are taken, the crystal being rotated about various prominent crystal axes.

In contrast to all the methods described above, the *powder* method invented independently by Debye and Scherrer, and by Hull, uses a sample consisting of an aggregate of very small randomly orientated crystallites. The specimen consists of a fine powder of fine crystallites stuck to a fine hair or packed into a very thin glass capillary tube. Metals in bulk are polycrystalline and a fine metal wire is suitable as a "powder" specimen. Sometimes, however, fine metal filings, carefully annealed, are used. A narrow horizontal collimated beam of X-radiation passes through the vertical wire or cylindrical powder and the diffracted beams are recorded on a flat plate on the far side of the specimen or on a cylindrical strip of film surrounding the specimen (Fig. 18). Diffraction spectra are observed because a few of the vast number of tiny crystallites will by chance have the correct orientation θ to reflect the incident beam. The diffracted rays corresponding to the same interplanar spacing d all lie on the surface of

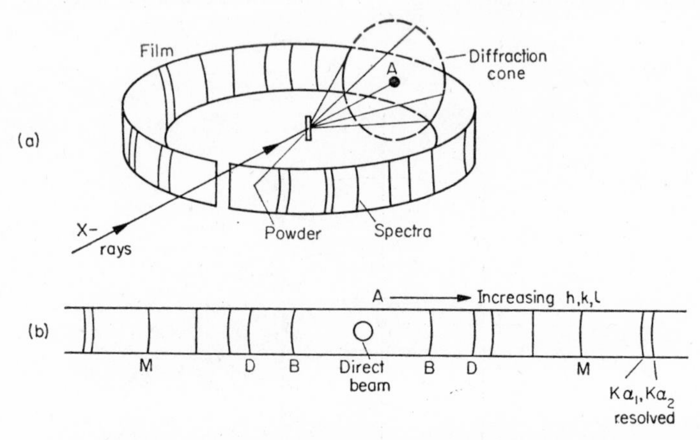

FIG. 18. (a) Arrangement for taking powder photograph; (b) Film flattened out. Each cone of diffracted rays intercepts film in a pair of arcs B, B: D, D: M, M, etc.

a cone of semi-angle 2θ. This cone intercepts the cylindrical strip of film in two arcs symmetrically placed with respect to the point of intersection of the direct beam with the film. The diffraction arcs are usually discontinuous in appearance, but this can be removed by slowly rotating the powder specimen during the exposure. Standard powder diffraction cameras are 9 cm and 19 cm in diameter. A powder specimen is of the order of 0·3 mm wide and it is bathed in a collimated X-ray beam about 0·5 mm wide. The direct transmitted beam is absorbed by a lead disc in front of the film to prevent local fogging of the film due to diffuse scattering in the emulsion. In the case of cubic crystals, (fortunately many metals crystallize in this system) the indices corresponding to the diffraction arcs can easily be assigned. For a cubic crystal we have

$$\frac{2a\sin\theta}{\sqrt{(h^2+k^2+l^2)}} = \lambda \tag{44}$$

the order n has been incorporated in the indices;

$$\therefore \sin^2\theta = \frac{\lambda^2}{4a^2}(h^2+k^2+l^2) \tag{45}$$

The Bragg angle θ is easily found as each diffraction cone has a semi-axial angle of 2θ. Plotting $\sin^2\theta$ against assumed values of $(h^2+k^2+l^2)$ will yield a straight line of slope $\lambda^2/(4a^2)$ if the indices have been correctly assigned. Notice that moving away from the centre of the flattened film,

$(h^2 + k^2 + l^2)$ increases. Another interesting point is the resolution of the $K\alpha_1$ and $K\alpha_2$ spectral line components at high Bragg angles. This is easy to understand for differentiating the Bragg equation: $2d \sin\theta = \lambda$, we get $2d \cos\theta \, d\theta = d\lambda$, and dividing, we obtain

$$d\theta = \frac{d\lambda}{\lambda} \tan\theta \tag{46}$$

For a given pair of spectral lines $K\alpha_1$, and $K\alpha_2$, $2d\theta$, the angular separation of the diffracted rays is observable, as $\tan\theta$ is large for 2θ close to 180°.

Intensity of Diffraction Spectra

A typical X-ray rotation or powder diffraction photograph is characterized by the markedly different intensities of the diffraction spectra. Determinations of the arrangement and positions of the atoms within the unit cell, can, in principle, be carried out from quantitative measurements of the intensities of the diffraction spectra. There are many factors which influence the intensity. First, there is the polarization factor $(1 + \cos^2 2\theta)$, which represents the way in which the amplitude of an unpolarized wave scattered by an electron varies with θ (eqn. (17) Chapter 1). If monochromatic radiation, e.g. the $K\alpha$ line of a source, is selected by Bragg reflection from a suitable crystal (urea nitrate gives a very strong reflection), the radiation is not completely unpolarized and this complicates the angular scattering factor $(1 + \cos^2 2\theta)$ given by the Thomson theory. Angular factors arise in relation to the time a rotating crystal or powder satisfies the Bragg reflection conditions. Also the absorption of X-rays diffracted at small angles in a powder is less than that for the rays diffracted through large angles. This is a result of the greater distance travelled in the specimen by the "back" reflections.

Atomic Scattering Factor (Form Factor)

The two fundamental reasons for different diffraction intensities are, however, connected with the interference of the X-waves scattered by different regions of the electron charge distribution in an atom, and the interference between the resultant waves scattered by all the atoms within the unit cell.

The classical theory of X-ray scattering by electrons is inadequate according to quantum mechanics, as it is not possible to ascribe simultaneously *precise* values to the position and momentum coordinates of an electron. The new mechanics describes the electronic structure of an atom in terms of a *probability* charge distribution surrounding the nucleus. It is more correct to picture the atomic electrons, not as Keplerian planets revolving round the nucleus, but as a cloud of negative charge, dense where one expects to find an electron shell and rarefied between shells and beyond the "surface" of the atom. There is good evidence that in simple crystals the atoms or ions can be treated as separate scattering units.

In spite of the quantum mechanical modification of Thomson's scattering theory it is still convenient to compare the scattering by an atom with that due to a single "classical electron". The *atomic scattering factor f* of an atom is defined as the ratio of the amplitude of the scattered wave from an atom and the amplitude of the wave scattered by a free electron in place of the atom. The two amplitudes, of course, must be compared at the same distant point. The atomic scattering factor f is a function of the ratio $\sin\theta/\lambda$, where 2θ is the angle of scattering and λ is the wavelength. At small values of this ratio, the waves scattered from different regions of the electron

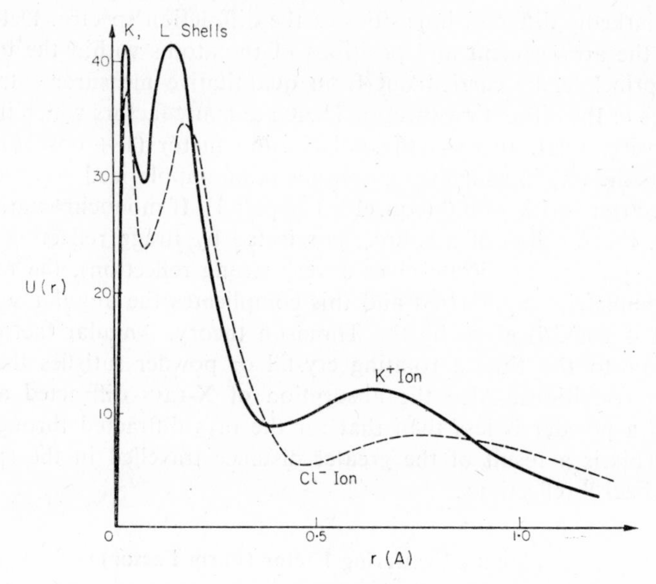

FIG. 19. Radial distribution of electron density function $U(r)$ in electrons per angström, for the potassium and chloride ions. (Hartree self-consistent field calculation.)

cloud are nearly all in phase, thus f is nearly equal to Z, the number of electrons in the atom. At larger scattering angles, f falls away quite rapidly (Fig. 21) as the path difference of waves scattered by different regions of the electron cloud may be a significant fraction of the wavelength. Thus as the ratio $\sin\theta/\lambda$ increases, destructive interference becomes more and more important and f tails away to a low value at large angles.

The main problem in deriving f values as a function of $\sin\theta/\lambda$ is the derivation of the probability distribution of electron charge in the atom. This has been done, in a number of instances, by using approximate numerical methods to solve the Schrödinger equation for the atom (e.g. Hartree's Self-Consistent Field Method). The result of such calculations for the K^+ and Cl^- ions is shown in Fig. 19. Here $U(r)$ is plotted against the distance r from the centre of the atom, where $U(r)\,dr$ is the number of electrons lying been radial distances r and $r + dr$. The atomic scattering factor is then obtained from the $U(r)$ function as follows.

Consider the X-rays scattered from the centre of the atom and a volume element dV at a distance $\boldsymbol{r}$ from the centre. The phase difference δ of the two rays in the direction corresponding to Bragg reflection is given by

$$\delta = \frac{2\pi}{\lambda}\boldsymbol{r}\cdot\boldsymbol{S} \tag{47}$$

Now waves of the same frequency and wavelength but differing in phase and amplitude, can be combined vectorially in a phase-amplitude diagram. Thus for m waves of amplitudes $a_1, a_2, \ldots, a_j, \ldots, a_m$ and phases $\delta_1, \delta_2, \ldots, \delta_j, \ldots, \delta_m$, the resultant disturbance has an amplitude A given by the magnitude of the vector

$$\sum_1^m a_j\, e^{(i\delta_j)} \tag{48}$$

In dealing with a continuous distribution of scattering electrons, the summation above is replaced by the volume integral

$$f = \int_{\substack{\text{vol. of}\\ \text{atom}}} \varrho(r) e^{i\left[\frac{2\pi}{\lambda}\boldsymbol{r}\cdot\boldsymbol{S}\right]} dV \tag{49}$$

where $\varrho(r)\,dV$ is the probability of an electron being found in the volume element dV.

Consider the element dV as a ring of circumference $2\pi r \sin\alpha$ and cross sectional area $dr \cdot r\, d\alpha$ (Fig. 20). Remembering that $|\boldsymbol{S}| = 2\sin\theta$, we see from Fig. 20 that,

$$\frac{2\pi}{\lambda}\boldsymbol{r}\cdot\boldsymbol{S} = \frac{4\pi}{\lambda}\sin\theta\, r\cos\alpha = \mu\, r\cos\alpha \tag{50}$$

where
$$\mu = 4\pi\left(\frac{\sin\theta}{\lambda}\right) \tag{51}$$

$$dV = 2\pi r^2 \cdot dr \sin\alpha\, d\alpha \tag{52}$$

let
$$x = \mu\, r\cos\alpha \tag{53}$$

then
$$dx = -\mu\, r\sin\alpha\, d\alpha$$

and eqn. (49) can be written

$$f = \int_0^\infty \frac{2\pi r^2}{\mu r}\varrho(r)\, dr \int_{-\mu r}^{+\mu r} e^{ix}\, dx \tag{54}$$

$$\therefore f = \int_0^\infty \frac{2\pi r^2}{\mu r} \varrho(r)\, dr \left(\frac{e^{\mu r} - e^{-\mu r}}{i}\right) = \int_0^\infty 4\pi r^2 \varrho(r) \frac{\sin \mu r\, dr}{\mu r} \qquad (55)$$

The function $\sin\mu r/\mu r$ is well known in the theory of Fraunhofer diffraction.† For small values of μ, the function decreases slowly with r, whereas for values of $(\sin\theta)/\lambda$ approaching 1 Å^{-1}, the function decreases fairly quickly

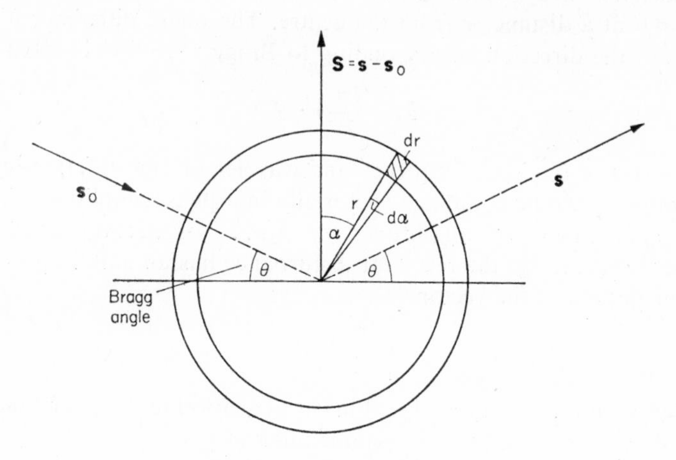

FIG. 20. X-ray scattered by spherically symmetric electron cloud.

from unity at $r = 0$ to zero at a small value of r. The function then becomes negative and oscillates about the r axis but it does not again reach a value near unity. Consequently little contribution is made to the integral f (eqn. 55) by the electron distribution beyond the first zero of the function $(\sin\mu r)/\mu r$. Combining the numerical values of the $U(r)$ function and $(\sin\mu r)/\mu r$ the integral can be evaluated by graphical or numerical methods. The atomic scattering factors of the potassium K^+ and choride Cl^- ions deduced in this way, are shown in Fig. 21. It is interesting to compare these two curves, as both ions contain 18 electrons, and the slightly higher value of f for K^+ is a result of the higher peaks of $U(r)$ corresponding to the K and L shells (Fig. 19).

The atomic scattering factors calculated in the manner indicated above have ignored the thermal vibrations of the atoms about their equilibrium lattice positions. The thermal motion of the atoms in a lattice plane reduce the *intensity* of the reflection in the same way that a poor optical grating ruled with broad diffuse lines gives weak diffraction spectra. However the *sharpness* of the spectra is *not* reduced, the resolving power depending only on the number of reflecting planes or the number of ruled lines. If f_0

† JENKINS and WHITE, *Fundamentals of Optics*, 2nd. Ed, McGraw-Hill, p. 283.

is the value of the atomic scattering factor for an atom at rest, it can be shown† that for the atom in a crystal at temperature T, the value is given by

$$f = f_0 \cdot e^{-M}, \qquad (56)$$

where

$$M = 8\pi^2 \overline{u^2} \left(\frac{\sin\theta}{\lambda}\right)^2 \qquad (57)$$

and $\overline{u^2}$ is the mean square displacement of the atoms at right angles to the reflecting planes at temperature T. At high temperatures, $\overline{u^2}$ is directly proportional to T. Debye and Waller have derived useful expressions for $\overline{u^2}$ in terms of T and the thermal and elastic constants of the crystal.

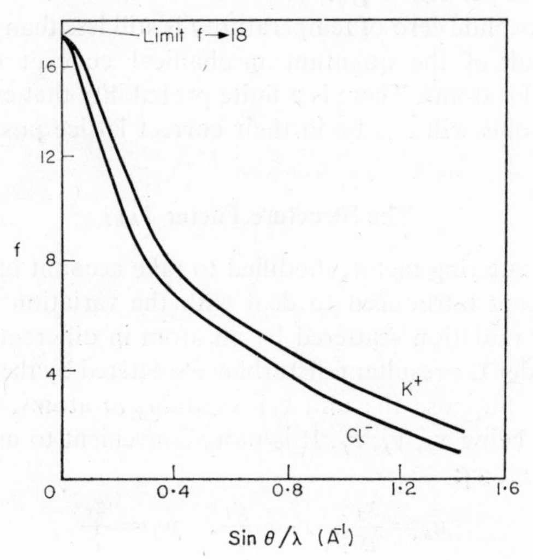

FIG. 21. Atomic scattering factors of K^+ and Cl^- ions, derived from Fig. 15. (There are 18 scattering electrons in each type of ion.)

In soft metals like Na and Pb the constituent atoms are not tightly bound and $\overline{u^2}$ is large and f is significantly less than f_0 except at very low temperatures. For a hard crystal like diamond, however, $\overline{u^2}$ is small and the reduction in f value is small. At large values of $\sin\theta/\lambda$, the temperature effect may be so large that the higher orders of diffraction are very weak. Cooling some crystals to liquid air temperature increases the intensity of these high order spectra by a large amount. To illustrate the temperature effect, the root mean square displacements, $\sqrt{(\overline{u^2})}$, for Na^+ ions and Cl^- ions in rocksalt at 290°K have been estimated as 0·242 Å and 0·218 Å respectively. Sub-

† R. W. JAMES, *The Crystalline State*, Vol. II (G. BELL), 1948, p. 21.

stituting these values in eqns. (56) and (57), we find that for the (111) reflection.

$$\left(\frac{\sin\theta}{\lambda}\right)^2 = \left(\frac{1}{2d_{111}}\right)^2 = \frac{h^2+k^2+l^2}{4a^2} = \frac{3}{(11{\cdot}26)^2}$$

for NaCl, $a = 5{\cdot}628$ Å at 290°K,

$$\therefore\ M_{\mathrm{Na}^+} = 8\pi^2(0{\cdot}242)^2 \times \frac{3}{(11{\cdot}26)^2} = 0{\cdot}1094 \ \therefore\ f_{\mathrm{Na}^+} = f_{0_{\mathrm{Na}^+}}\, e^{-0{\cdot}1094}$$

$$\therefore\ f_{\mathrm{Na}^+} = 0{\cdot}896\, f_{0_{\mathrm{Na}^+}}$$

For a (111) plane of Cl^- ions, $f = f_0\, e^{-0{\cdot}08884} = 0{\cdot}916 f_0$.

For the (400) reflection, the effect of thermal vibration reduces the f value to about 60 per cent of f_0.

Even at the absolute zero of temperature f is still less than f_0. This curious fact is the result of the quantum mechanical concept of "zero-point-oscillation" of the atoms. There is a finite probability that even at the absolute zero the atoms will not be in their correct lattice positions.

The Structure Factor F_{hkl}

The atomic scattering factor, modified to take account of thermal movement, is a concept introduced to deal with the variation in the intensity of the coherent radiation scattered by an atom in different directions. We must now consider the resultant disturbance scattered by the group of atoms in the unit cell. Suppose the unit cell contains m atoms, the coordinates of the jth atom being x_j, y_j, z_j. It is more convenient to use the fractional coordinates u_j, v_j, w_j:

$$u_j = \frac{x_j}{a},\quad v_j = \frac{y_j}{b},\quad w_j = \frac{z_j}{c} \tag{58}$$

The resultant wave scattered by the unit cell, in terms of the wave scattered by a single "Thomson electron" at the origin of the unit cell, is called the structure factor F.

$$F = \sum_{j=1}^{m} f_j\, e^{i\delta_j} \tag{59}$$

where f_j is the atomic scattering factor of the jth atom, including the temperature correction, and δ_j is the phase of the wave scattered by the jth atom relative to the wave scattered by the atom at the origin of the cell. For waves scattered in the direction of Bragg reflection from the $(h\,k\,l)$ planes, δ_j is obtained by multiplying eqn. (33) by $2\pi/\lambda$,

$$\therefore\ \delta_j = 2\pi(h\,u_j + k\,v_j + l\,w_j) \tag{60}$$

$$\therefore\ F_{hkl} = \sum_{j=1}^{m} f_j \exp\,[i2\pi(h\,u_j + k\,v_j + l\,w_j)] \tag{61}$$

The intensity of the wave scattered by the unit cell in a direction corresponding to the $(h\,k\,l)$ reflection is proportional to $|F_{hkl}|^2$.

To demonstrate the use of the structure factor, consider the diffraction of X-rays by a face-centred cubic crystal such as Cu or Ag. Here atoms are located at the corners and the centres of the six faces of the cubic cell. Each corner atom "belongs" to eight unit cells meeting at that corner, and each face-centred atom is shared between two unit cells. To each unit cell there are four atoms ($m = 4$), with fractional coordinates (000), $(\frac{1}{2}\,\frac{1}{2}\,0)$, $(0\,\frac{1}{2}\,\frac{1}{2})$ and $(\frac{1}{2}\,0\,\frac{1}{2})$.

$$\therefore\ F_{hkl} = f e^{0} + f e^{i\pi(h+k)} + f e^{i\pi(k+l)} + f e^{i\pi(h+l)} \qquad (62)$$

where f is the atomic scattering factor of copper. For reflections from planes with h, k, l all even or all odd integers, $F_{hkl} = 4f$, because the sum of any pair of indices is even and each exponential term is unity. This result means that the waves scattered by the four atoms are all in phase. On the contrary, we find that $F_{hkl} = 0$, if the indices are "mixed", i.e. two even, one odd; or two odd, one even. This is because two of the last three terms in eqn. (62) are equal to $-f$. Thus for a face-centred structure, certain reflections are missing. It is easy to see why some of the "simple" reflections are not observed. For instance, the reflection of X-rays from consecutive (110) planes is cancelled by the waves reflected from parallel planes, which interleave these planes exactly halfway (Fig. 22). If the face-centred atoms (open circles)

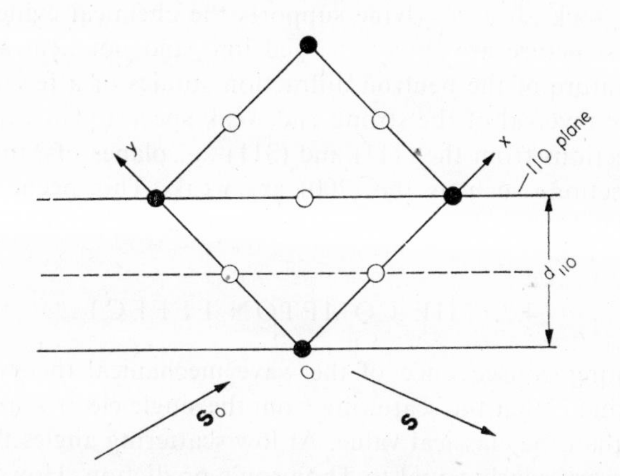

FIG. 22. Bragg reflection from (110) planes of f.c.c. crystal.

were removed, there would be no reflection from interleaving planes to produce waves π out of phase with the reflections from the (110) planes through the corner atoms. Complete annihilation of the first, third, fifth . . . order reflections from the (110) planes occurs because the density of atoms, i.e. number per unit area, in all the planes is the same.

It is a simple matter to prove that for a body-centred structure, i.e. one with atoms at the eight corners and one at the centre of the unit cell, F is zero when $h + k + l$ is odd.

Finally to conclude this section let us consider the diffraction of X-rays by a rocksalt type of structure. The lattice is face-centred cubic with two interpenetrating lattices of cations Na^+ and anions Cl^- (Fig. 16). The sizes of the circles in the figure are *not* meant to represent the diameters of the ions in the unit cell. There are eight ions per unit cell, four of each kind, with fractional coordinates, Na^+: (000), $(\frac{1}{2}\frac{1}{2}0)$, $(\frac{1}{2}0\frac{1}{2})$ and $(0\frac{1}{2}\frac{1}{2})$.

Cl^-: $(\frac{1}{2}00)$, $(0\frac{1}{2}0)$, $(00\frac{1}{2})$ and $(\frac{1}{2}\frac{1}{2}\frac{1}{2})$.

The structure factor F_{hkl} is given by

$$F = f_1[e^0 + e^{i\pi(h+k)} + e^{i\pi(h+l)} + e^{i\pi(k+l)}] + f_2[e^{i\pi h} + e^{i\pi k} + e^{i\pi l} + e^{i\pi(h+k+l)}] \quad (63)$$

where f_1 and f_2 are the atomic scattering factors of Na^+ and Cl^- respectively for $(\sin\theta)/\lambda$ corresponding to the $(h\,k\,l)$ reflection. As before for the simple face-centred cubic structure (Cu) we find that F_{hkl} vanishes for "mixed" indices. In addition, however, the odd order reflections from (111), (311), (511), (531), . . . planes are faint as $F_{hkl} = 4\,(f_1 - f_2)$. For rocksalt this structure factor is small but finite as f_1 is smaller than f_2 (at low Bragg angles f_1 and f_2 are close to 10 and 18 respectively). Sylvine (KCl) has a similar structure to rocksalt but the (111), (311), . . . spectra are too faint to observe as f_1 and f_2 for K^+ and Cl^- are very nearly equal at all values of $(\sin\theta)/\lambda$ (Fig. 21). The careful measurements of the intensities of the spectra from rocksalt and sylvine supports the chemical evidence that the units in the structure are singly charged ions and not neutral atoms. An interesting feature of the neutron diffraction studies of a few rocksalt type crystals is the reversal of the strong and weak spectra. Thus the odd order neutron reflections from the (111) and (311) . . . planes of MnO are strong whereas reflections such as the (200) are weak. This peculiarity and its physical significance is discussed in Chapter 15.

4.7. THE COMPTON EFFECT

An interesting consequence of the wave mechanical theory of coherent X-ray scattering is that the scattering from the single electron in a hydrogen atom is less than the classical value. At low scattering angles the scattering amplitude is very nearly equal to Thomson's prediction. However, at large angles of scattering the interference between the waves scattered by different parts of the electron charge distribution reduces the amplitude of the resultant wave. In other words, f is small compared to Z. It is now known, that as the coherent scattered intensity $|f^2|$ falls away, the incoherent scattered intensity increases as $|(1 - f^2)|$. Thus we find that the total amount of scattered radiation is given by Thomson's classical formula. A. H. Compton in 1922 was the first person to measure spectroscopically the wavelength of the incoherent scattered radiation. He found that the wavelength of the incoherent radiation was always longer than the incident radiation (Fig. 23). The quantitative explanation of the increase in wavelength with increase in

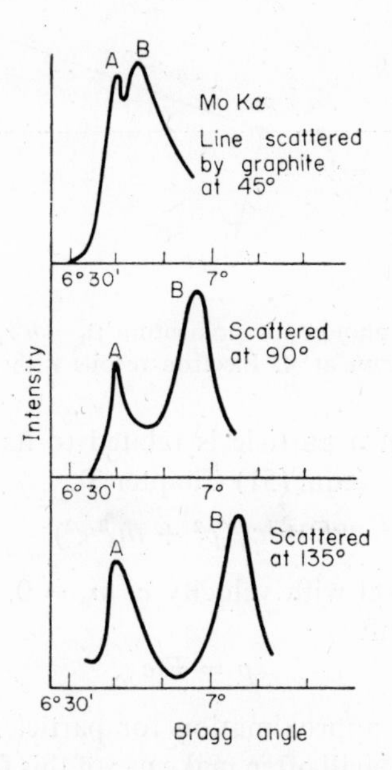

FIG. 23. Compton's measurements of radiation spectra from graphite. Peak A is the coherent line (0·71 Å), Peak B is the Compton line. $\Delta\lambda$ increases as $(1-\cos\varphi)$. Measurements made with an ionization spectrometer.

scattering angle was given independently by A. H. Compton and P. Debye in 1923. The essential idea is that we consider Compton scattering as a direct collision between an incident X-ray photon and a *single* loosely bound atomic electron. The scattered photon is of lower energy and momentum as the electron is ejected from the parent atom, sometimes with a relativistic velocity. Soon after the theory of the scattering process, C. T. R. Wilson and W. Bothe observed short tracks of the Compton recoil electrons in a cloud chamber exposed to an X-ray beam. The tracks of recoil electrons have a marked difference in appearance to those produced by electrons ejected by photoelectric absorption of X-rays. In particular the Compton recoil electrons always have a component of momentum in the direction of the incident X-rays.

Consider the collision between a photon of energy E_1 with an electron of low binding energy (we shall in fact assume it to be at rest). Suppose the photon is scattered through an angle φ, its energy is reduced to E_2. The electron recoils with a kinetic energy $T = E_1 - E_2$ in a direction θ

relative to the incident X-ray (Fig. 24). The vectors $\boldsymbol{p}_1, \boldsymbol{p}_2, \boldsymbol{m}\,\boldsymbol{v}$, representing the momenta of the incident and scattered photons and the recoiling electron must be coplanar.

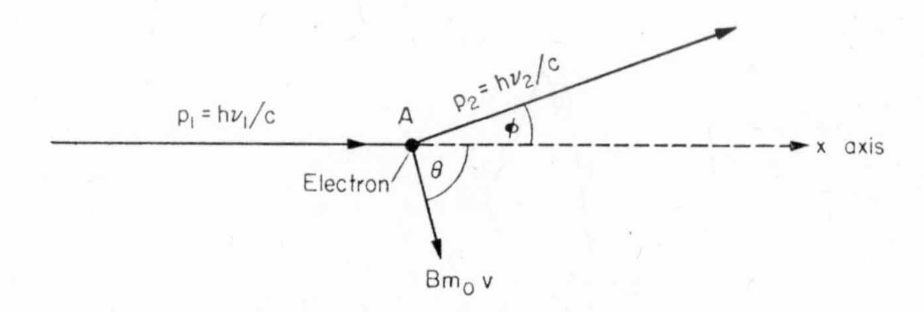

FIG. 24. Incident X-ray photon of momentum $\boldsymbol{p}_1 = h\,\nu_1/c$ is scattered through angle φ by an electron at A. Electron recoils with momentum $B\,m_0\,v$.

The total energy E of a particle is related to its momentum p and rest mass m_0 by the equation (eqn. (51) Chapter 3).

$$E = c\sqrt{(p^2 + m_0^2\,c^2)} \tag{64}$$

For photons which travel with velocity c, $m_0 = 0$, otherwise E is infinite. We have the simple result

$$p = E/c \tag{65}$$

This relation is a good approximation for particles with finite rest mass, when $E \gg m_0\,c^2$, and we shall often make use of this for high energy electrons and mesons.

Denoting the quantity $1\Big/\sqrt{\left(1 - \frac{v^2}{c^2}\right)}$ by B, where v is the recoil velocity of the electron, we can write down the two conditions required to conserve momentum in the collision

$$\left(\frac{E_1}{c}\right) = \left(\frac{E_2}{c}\right)\cos\varphi + B\,m_0\,v\cos\theta \tag{66}$$

where m_0 is the electron rest mass

also,
$$0 = \left(\frac{E_2}{c}\right)\sin\varphi - B\,m_0\,v\sin\theta \tag{67}$$

These equations represent momentum conservation in the x and y directions. Squaring and adding to eliminate θ, we get

$$\left(\frac{E_1}{c}\right)^2 + \left(\frac{E_2}{c}\right)^2 - 2\left(\frac{E_1}{c}\right)\left(\frac{E_2}{c}\right)\cos\varphi = B^2\,m_0^2\,v^2 = \frac{m_0^2\,c^2\,v^2}{c^2 - v^2} \tag{68}$$

dividing by $m_0^2\,c^2$,

$$\left(\frac{E_1}{m_0\,c^2}\right)^2 + \left(\frac{E_2}{m_0\,c^2}\right)^2 - 2\left(\frac{E_1}{m_0\,c^2}\right)\left(\frac{E_2}{m_0\,c^2}\right)\cos\varphi = \frac{v^2}{c^2 - v^2} \tag{69}$$

The conservation of energy condition can be written as

$$E_1 + m_0 c^2 = E_2 + B m_0 c^2 \tag{70}$$

Here we are assuming the electron is at rest before the collision, and that after the collision its mass is increased from m_0 to $B m_0$.

Re-writing eqn. (70) and squaring we get

$$[(E_1 - E_2) + m_0 c^2]^2 = B^2 m_0^2 c^4 \tag{71}$$

$$\therefore (E_1 - E_2)^2 + 2(E_1 - E_2) m_0 c^2 = m_0^2 c^4 (B^2 - 1) = m_0^2 c^4 \frac{v^2}{c^2 - v^2} \tag{72}$$

Dividing by $m_0^2 c^4$,

$$\left(\frac{E_1}{m_0 c^2}\right)^2 + \left(\frac{E_2}{m_0 c^2}\right)^2 - 2\left(\frac{E_1}{m_0 c^2}\right)\left(\frac{E_2}{m_0 c^2}\right) + 2\left(\frac{E_1}{m_0 c^2}\right) - 2\left(\frac{E_2}{m_0 c^2}\right) = \frac{v^2}{c^2 - v^2} \tag{73}$$

From eqns. (69) and (73) we can eliminate the unknown velocity v and write

$$2\left(\frac{E_1}{m_0 c^2}\right)\left(\frac{E_2}{m_0 c^2}\right)(1 - \cos\varphi) = 2\left(\frac{E_1}{m_0 c^2} - \frac{E_2}{m_0 c^2}\right) \tag{74}$$

or

$$\frac{1}{E_2} - \frac{1}{E_1} = \frac{1}{m_0 c^2} \operatorname{vers}\varphi \tag{75}$$

Now

$$E_2 = h\frac{c}{\lambda_2} \quad \text{and} \quad E_1 = h\frac{c}{\lambda_1}$$

where λ_1 and λ_2 are the wavelengths of the incident and scattered X-rays.

Hence we can write

$$\lambda_2 - \lambda_1 = \Delta\lambda = \frac{h}{m_0 c} \operatorname{vers}\varphi \tag{76}$$

The quantity $\frac{h}{m_0 c}$ is known as the electron Compton wavelength λ_c and it has the value 0·02426 Å.

The increase in wavelength on scattering $\Delta\lambda$ is in complete agreement with experiment. For X-rays or γ-rays of high energy (short wavelength) the percentage increase in wavelength is very high at large scattering angles. Notice that $\Delta\lambda$ is independent of λ_1. The maximum wavelength increase occurs when the scattered photon returns along its original path, i.e. $\varphi = \pi$ and $\Delta\lambda = 2\lambda_c$. The electron, in this case, recoils in the forward direction ($\theta = 0$) and it acquires its maximum possible energy. The electron recoil angle θ cannot exceed 90° and in this region the kinetic energy T of the electron is small. To determine the recoil kinetic energy T, we have from eqn. (75)

$$T = E_1 - E_2 = \frac{E_1 E_2}{m_0 c^2} \operatorname{vers}\varphi \tag{77}$$

Also from eqn. (75) we have

$$E_2 = \frac{E_1}{1 + \left(\frac{E_1}{m_0 c^2}\right) \text{vers}\,\varphi} \tag{78}$$

$$\therefore T = \frac{E_1^2 \,\text{vers}\,\varphi}{m_0 c^2 \left[1 + \frac{E_1}{m_0 c^2} \text{vers}\,\varphi\right]} \tag{79}$$

At small scattering angles φ, vers φ is small and T is proportional to E_1^2 or $\frac{1}{\lambda_1^2}$.

If E_1 is $\gg m_0 c^2$, a simpler expression for T_{max} can be obtained

For $T = T_{max}$, $\varphi = \pi$, $\theta = 0$ and vers $\varphi = 2$.

$$\therefore T_{max} = \frac{2E_1^2}{2E_1\left[1 + \frac{m_0 c^2}{2E_1}\right]} = E_1\left\{1 - \frac{m_0 c^2}{2E_1} + \frac{m_0^2 c^4}{2E_1^2} \dots\right\}$$

$$\therefore T_{max} = E_1 - \frac{m_0 c^2}{2} + \frac{(m_0 c^2)^2}{2E_1} \dots \simeq (E_1 - 0{\cdot}25)\ \text{MeV} \tag{80}$$

Further confirmation of the validity of the theory of Compton scattering has been obtained in the last ten years. Using high resolution coincidence electronic circuits, a number of workers have shown that the events involved in the scattering process are simultaneous to within 10^{-9} sec.

BIBLIOGRAPHY

A. H. Compton and S. K. Allison, *X-Rays in Theory and Experiment*; D. Van Nostrand, New York 1933.
This is a standard treatise on X-rays and, in spite of its age, it is strongly recommended as a comprehensive text-book.
G. L. Clark, *Applied X-Rays*, McGraw-Hill, New York 1955.
W. T. Sproull, *X-Rays* in *Practice*, McGraw-Hill, New York 1946.
The above two books are very useful general books on X-rays.
S. T. Stephenson, *The Continuous X-Ray Spectrum*, pp. 337–369, Handbuch der Physik, Vol. XXX, Springer-Verlag, Berlin 1957.
A. E. Sandström, *Experimental Methods of X-Ray Spectroscopy*, pp. 78–240, Handbuch der Physik, Vol. XXX, Springer-Verlag, Berlin 1957.
W. L. Bragg, *The Crystalline State*, Vol. I, G. Bell, London 1933.
R. W. James, *The Crystalline State*, Vol. II, G. Bell, London 1948.
H. Lipson and W. Cochran, *The Crystalline State*, Vol. III, G. Bell, London 1953.
The three published volumes on *The Crystalline State* give a comprehensive background to the study of crystals by X-ray diffraction. Vol. II in particular deals in a very thorough way with the fundamental "optical" theory of X-ray diffraction.
K. Lonsdale, *Crystals and X-Rays*, G. Bell, London 1948. Strongly recommended as a supplement to the more formal textbooks.
R. W. James, *X-Ray Crystallography*, 5th Ed., Methuen, London 1953.

EXAMPLES

1. An X-ray tube with a molybdenum target ($Z = 42$) is operated with an electron beam current of 20 mA at a steady potential of 20 kV. The mean wavelength of the continuous radiation is 1·7 times the cut-off wavelength λ_0. Calculate λ_0 and estimate the number of X-ray quanta emitted from the target in 1 sec. What is the expected counting rate in a Geiger counter, of cross section 2 cm², whose efficiency is 20% for X-rays, placed 2 m from the target (neglect absorption of X-rays)?
   Are the K lines excited? (The K absorption edge wavelength of Mo is 0·6170 Å). Calculate in eV the L shell binding energy of Mo, given that the $K\alpha$ emission wavelength is 0·712 Å.
2. The arcs on a powder photograph of a cubic structure correspond to the following Bragg angles: 25·4°, 29·6°, 44·3°, 55·0°, 58·33°, 81·10°. Assign indices to these reflections and deduce the lattice type. If the wavelength of the radiation used was 1·78 Å, calculate the size of the unit cell (Grad. I. Phys. 1959).
3. A fine aluminium wire is mounted in a 19 cm diameter powder camera. If the temperature of the wire is increased from 20°C to 60°C, the separation of the arcs on the cylindrical film corresponding to the (511) reflection increases by 2·55 mm. The incident radiation is Cu $K\alpha$ (1·540 Å) and the lattice parameter of Al, which is a face centred cubic structure, at 20°C is 4·049 Å. Calculate the coefficient of linear expansion of aluminium.
4. A rotation photograph of a cubic crystal, of cell parameter 7·7 Å, is taken about the c axis using radiation of wavelength 1·54 Å. Which of the planes (103), (104), (204) will have an opportunity of reflecting the X-rays? (Grad. I. Phys. 1957).
5. On a powder photograph of a cubic element taken with unfiltered cobalt K radiation, lines were observed corresponding to the following Bragg angles:
   22° 51′, 25° 24′, 26° 38′, 29° 42′, 39° 21′, 44° 28′, 48° 1′,
   50° 56′, 55° 14′, 59° 6′, 63° 42′, 77° 42′, 81° 46′, 82° 41′.

   Given that the density of the element is 8·90 g cm^{-3}, calculate its atomic weight. (Avogadro's number is $6{\cdot}025 \times 10^{23}$, Co wavelength: $K\alpha_1 = 1{\cdot}78529$ Å, $K\alpha_2 = 1{\cdot}78919$ Å, $K\beta = 1{\cdot}61744$ Å. (Grad. I. Phys. 1956).
6. Accurate determinations of Planck's constant have been made by determining the short wavelength cut-off λ_0 of the continuous radiation from an X-ray tube. In one experiment, the (200) reflection of the minimum wavelength from rocksalt occurred at a Bragg angle of 17° 16′ when the X-ray tube voltage was 7400 V. Derive an expression for, and then evaluate, Planck's constant given:
   density of rocksalt is 2·164 g cm^{-3}, the Faraday F is 96,522 coulomb per g. equiv, c is $2{\cdot}9979 \times 10^{10}$ cm sec^{-1}, electron charge e is $4{\cdot}8029 \times 10^{-10}$ e.s.u.; molecular weight of NaCl is 58·46.
7. A powder photograph of sodium chloride in the form of a cylindrical specimen 0·25 mm diameter is taken at 17° with Cu $K\alpha$ radiation (1·542 Å). For such a specimen, $\mu R = 2$, where μ is the linear absorption coefficient of NaCl for Cu $K\alpha$ radiation and R is the radius of the cylindrical powder. The effect of absorption A on the relative intensities of the diffraction spectra has been calculated by Claasen (θ is the Bragg angle): for $\mu R = 2$.

	0°	22½°	45°	67½°	90°
A (%)	4·79	6·27	9·98	13·58	15·6

The relative intensities of the powder lines recorded on a cylindrical film are proportional to

$$|F_{hkl}|^2\, p\, A \frac{(1+\cos^2 2\theta)}{\sin^2 2\theta} \cos\theta\,,\dagger$$

† See K. Lonsdale, *Crystals and X-Rays*, p. 116 *et seq.*

where F_{hkl} is the structure factor.

p is the multiplicity factor or the number of $(h\,k\,l)$ planes giving coincidence diffraction cones: e.g. there are six sets of planes corresponding to (200) reflection giving the same θ: viz. (200), (020), (002), $(\bar{2}00)$,† $(0\bar{2}0)$, $(00\bar{2})$,

A is the absorption factor

$(1+\cos^2 2\theta)$ is the polarization factor in the Thomson scattering formula. Next a factor $1/\sin 2\theta$ (Lorentz factor) is required to represent the relative *times* for which a given reflection occurs as the specimen is rotated (finite angular range of Bragg reflection). Finally, two factors $\cos\theta$ and $1/\sin 2\theta$ represent the number of tiny crystallites in the proper reflecting position and the relative amounts of energy in unit length of the diffraction rings.

Calculate the relative intensities of the (200) and (222) lines taking into account thermal vibrations:

Lattice parameter $a = 5{\cdot}628$ Å.

$(\sqrt{\overline{u^2}})$ for Na^+ ion is 0·242 Å, $(\sqrt{\overline{u^2}})$ for Cl^- is 0·218 Å

ATOMIC SCATTERING FACTOR f_0

$\frac{\sin\theta}{\lambda}$ (Å)$^{-1}$	0	0·1	0·2	0·3
Na^+	10·0	9·5	8·2	6·7
Cl^-	18·0	15·2	11·5	9·3

8. Show that in a Compton collision, the angles θ and φ are related by the equation, $\cot\theta = \left(1+\frac{E_1}{m_0 c^2}\right)\tan\frac{\varphi}{2}$.
9. An incident γ-ray of 1·02 MeV energy is scattered in a Compton collision through (a) 60°, (b) 90°, (c) 120°, (d) 180°. Find the recoil energy and direction of recoil of the electron in each case ($m_0 c^2 = 0{\cdot}51$ MeV).

† A negative Miller index is written as $\bar{h}$ or $\bar{k}$ or $\bar{l}$.

CHAPTER 5

ELECTRON DIFFRACTION

5.1 THE WAVE NATURE OF MATTER

One of the most significant aspects of the quantum theory is the wave–corpuscular dual nature of light. Whenever we are dealing with the propagation of light through space the wave theory is normally employed, whereas the processes of absorption and emission of radiation are easier to understand in terms of the photon theory. The processes of photoelectric emission and Compton scattering are convincing demonstrations of the corpuscular properties of electromagnetic radiation. We recall that, according, to the special theory of relativity, the energy E, momentum p, and rest mass energy $m_0 c^2$ of a particle are connected by the equation

$$E = \sqrt{[(p c)^2 + (m_0 c^2)^2]} \tag{1}$$

Unless a particle travelling at the speed of light is to have an infinite energy, its rest mass must be zero. In fact, photons travel at speed c or they do not exist. Thus for photons we have the simple relation between the energy and the momentum

$$E = p c \tag{2}$$

According to the quantum theory,

$$E = h \nu \tag{3}$$

where h is Planck's constant of action, and ν is the frequency of the radiation.

Thus
$$p = \frac{h \nu}{c} = \frac{h}{\lambda}$$

or
$$\lambda = \frac{h}{p} \tag{4}$$

In 1924, L. de Broglie† made the important suggestion that particles of matter (electrons, atoms, molecules, etc.) would under certain circumstances exhibit wave properties. Normally the conditions are such that the corpuscular aspects of electrons and atoms are dominant; for instance, we can describe the trajectory of the electrons in a cathode ray tube and accurately predict the deviation produced by deflecting electric or magnetic

† L. de Broglie, *Phil. Mag.*, 47, 446, 1924.

fields. Nevertheless, there are circumstances in which the wave nature of matter is important, and the interpretation of phenomena is made in terms of the familiar principles of wave optics; viz. interference and diffraction. L. de Broglie showed that moving particles of matter should have an associated wavelength λ given by eqn. (4), but it must be emphasized that the momentum p is not equal to E/c, but is given by the relation for a particle of finite rest mass. Thus

$$\lambda = \frac{h}{p} = \frac{h}{m\,v} \tag{5}$$

where v is the velocity of the particle, and m is the mass in a frame of reference in which the wavelength is measured.

De Broglie develops his theory from the assumption that a frequency ν_0, can be associated with the rest mass energy of a particle

$$h\,\nu_0 = m_0\,c^2 \tag{6}$$

The vibration ψ associated with this particle in a system S at rest relative to the particle can be written as

$$\psi = \psi_0 \exp(2\pi\,i\,\nu_0\,t) \tag{7}$$

where ψ_0 is the amplitude of the vibration and t is the time. An observer moving to the right with constant velocity v (system S′) will describe this vibration as a progressive wave. The momentum p' and total energy E' of the particle are given by the relativistic equations

$$p' = -\eta\,m_0\,v, \qquad E' = \eta\,m_0\,c^2 \tag{8}$$

where

$$\eta = (1 - v^2/c^2)^{-\frac{1}{2}}$$

p' is negative in the system S′ as it moves to the *left of* the observer. The wave motion of the particle in the system S is described, with the aid of the Lorentz transformation (Chapter 3), by the equation

$$\psi' = \psi_0' \exp[2\pi\,i\,\nu_0\{\eta(t' + (v/c^2)\,x')\}] \tag{9}$$

The positive sign in the inner bracket represents the fact that to S′ the wave is travelling to the left. The frequency ν' of the wave is given by, (using eqn. 6);

$$\nu' = \nu_0\,\eta = \frac{m_0\,c^2}{h}\,\frac{1}{\sqrt{(1 - v^2/c^2)}} = \frac{m'\,c^2}{h} = \frac{E'}{h} \tag{10}$$

where m' is the mass of the particle relative to an observer in S′. The wavelength λ' of the progressive wave is given by

$$\lambda' = \frac{c^2}{\nu_0\,\eta\,v} = \frac{c^2\sqrt{(1 - v^2/c^2)}}{\nu_0\,v} = \frac{h\sqrt{(1 - v^2/c^2)}}{m_0\,v} = \frac{h}{m'\,v} = \frac{h}{p'} \tag{11}$$

This is the result given in eqn. (5). It is natural, of course, for the observer, in S′ to consider himself at rest and the particle travelling with a momentum p'.

An important aspect of the wave–corpuscular duality is the relation between the velocity of the particles and the velocity of propagation of the waves. It is often important in optics to distinguish between two velocities; the phase velocity and the group velocity. A perfectly monochromatic wave train must be of an infinite length, thus it cannot be used as a signal; there is no start or end to the wave train and there is no distinguishing feature or mark travelling with the wave. The velocity which describes the motion of a pure Fourier component is known as the phase velocity, but it does not represent the rate of flow of energy. Thus there is no restriction on its magnitude and it may exceed c, the velocity of light in free space,† without violating the principle of relativity. In a dispersive medium, i.e. one in which the velocity of propagation varies with the frequency of the Fourier components, the rate of flow of energy is represented by the group velocity. This is the velocity of propagation of a specific condition of amplitude, or the rate of movement of the resultant crest. Consider, for example, the superposition of two waves of equal amplitude and nearly the same frequency and wavelength, (we drop the prime symbols)

$$\psi_1 = \psi_0 \exp\{2\pi i(\nu_1 t - k_1 x)\} \tag{12}$$

$$\psi_2 = \psi_0 \exp\{2\pi i(\nu_2 t - k_2 x)\} \tag{13}$$

where,

$$\nu_2 = \nu_1 + 2d\nu$$

$$k_1 = \frac{1}{\lambda_1}, \quad k_2 = \frac{1}{\lambda_2} \quad \text{and} \quad k_2 = k_1 + 2dk. \tag{14}$$

The resultant wave motion is given by the sum of eqns. (12) and (13), and using the relation

$$\exp(i\alpha) + \exp(i\beta) = \exp i\left(\frac{\alpha+\beta}{2}\right)\cdot 2\cos\left(\frac{\alpha-\beta}{2}\right) \tag{15}$$

we obtain for the resultant wave

$$\psi = \psi_1 + \psi_2 = 2\psi_0 \cos[2\pi(-d\nu\cdot t + dk\cdot x)] \exp[2\pi i\{(\nu_1 + d\nu)t - (k_1 + dk)x\}] \tag{16}$$

This equation represents a wave in which the amplitude varies in space and time and the peak of the resultant disturbance travels with a velocity v_g, the group velocity given by

$$v_g = \frac{d\nu}{dk} = \frac{d\nu}{d(1/\lambda)} \tag{17}$$

Now $E = h\nu$ and $p = \dfrac{h}{\lambda}$.

$$\therefore d\nu = \frac{dE}{h} \quad \text{and} \quad d\left(\frac{1}{\lambda}\right) = \frac{dp}{h}$$

$$\therefore v_g = \frac{dE}{dp}$$

† The refractive index of a medium for X-rays is slightly less than unity; thus the phase velocity, which is given by c divided by the refractive index, is greater than c.

Squaring eqn. (1) and differentiating, we have

$$E\,dE = p\,c^2\,dp$$

$$\therefore\ v_g = \frac{p\,c^2}{E} = \frac{m\,v\,c^2}{m\,c^2} = v \tag{18}$$

That is, the velocity of the particle of matter is equal to the group velocity v_g of the corresponding de Broglie waves. This result is not unexpected, as the particle velocity is the velocity of a signal or the rate of flow of energy. According to relativity v cannot exceed c, and we cannot have a group (signal) velocity greater than c. The phase velocity of the de Broglie wave train is greater than c, for the group and phase velocities v_g and v_p are related by the equation

$$v_g\,v_p = c^2 \tag{19}$$

The most immediate property of a particle that springs to mind is the concept of *location*. But the representation of an electron or atomic beam as a homogeneous wave train gives no idea as to the location of the electron in the length of the wave train. If an aperture in a screen is opened for a very short time to allow a very short wave train to pass through, the wave train is made up of a wide range of Fourier components. Such a wave pulse, or wave packet, has a finite amplitude over a short length so we can say with high confidence that this corresponds to the position of the particle. Outside this region the wave disturbance is very small and the individual Fourier components cancel out by destructive interference. The inherent uncertainty in connection with the precise location of a particle at a given time is an important consequence of wave mechanics (Chapter 6).

5.2 ELECTRON DIFFRACTION

Electrons, accelerated *in vacuo* through a potential difference V, gain a kinetic energy eV. For non-relativistic velocities,

$$eV = \tfrac{1}{2}\,m\,v^2 \tag{20}$$

where m and v are the electron mass and velocity respectively.

Substituting the de Broglie relation $\lambda = h/(m\,v)$, we obtain

$$\lambda = \frac{h}{\sqrt{(2m\,e\,V)}} \tag{21}$$

A useful approximate relation for λ, provided V is less than about 10,000 V is

$$\lambda = \sqrt{\left(\frac{150}{V}\right)}\ \text{Å} \tag{22}$$

Thus electrons of kinetic energy 150 eV have a de Broglie wavelength of 1 Å, which is of the same order as the X-ray wavelengths commonly used in diffraction experiments. Above 10 kV, eqn. (21) becomes unreliable, as it does not take into account the relativistic increase in mass of the electron. Accurate wavelengths are computed using the equation

$$eV = \sqrt{[(p\,c)^2 + (m_0\,c^2)^2]} - m_0\,c^2 \tag{23}$$

where $m_0\,c^2$ is the rest mass energy of the electron, and the momentum p is related to the wavelength by the equation $p = h/\lambda$. Hence we have

$$(eV + m_0\,c^2)^2 = \frac{h^2\,c^2}{\lambda^2} + (m_0\,c^2)^2$$

$$\lambda = \frac{h\,c}{\sqrt{[eV(eV + 2m_0\,c^2)]}} \tag{24}$$

It is useful to remember that $m_0\,c^2 = 510{,}980$ eV, when evaluating λ with the aid of eqn. (24). A table of wavelengths for accelerating potentials in the range 10 to 100 kV is given below.

TABLE 1

V (kV)	λ (Å)	V (kV)	λ (Å)
10·0	0·1227	50·0	0·0534
20·0	0·0857	55·0	0·0512
25·0	0·0764	60·0	0·0486
30·0	0·0695	70·0	0·0447
35·0	0·0643	80·0	0·0417
40·0	0·0599	90·0	0·0391
45·0	0·0564	100·0	0·0361

Some idea of the error involved in calculating wavelengths using the non-relativistic formula, eqn. (22), is obtained by calculating λ at 60 kV using eqn. (22); this gives a value of 0·05 Å, about three per cent too high. The errors increase in magnitude at still higher potentials.

The first conclusive experiments demonstrating the diffraction of electrons were reported by C. Davisson and L. H. Germer in 1927, working at the Bell Telephone laboratories. In one of their experiments, a fine beam of electrons accelerated *in vacuo* through potential differences in the range 30 to 600 V, were incident normally on the (111) face of a *single* nickel crystal. The electrons scattered from the surface lattice planes of the nickel crystal were collected and recorded by an insulated Faraday cylinder connected to a sensitve galvanometer. The potential of the Faraday cylinder was biased so that electrons which had lost more than one tenth of their incident energy were not collected. The (111) face of the crystal could be rotated through 360° about an axis parallel to the incident beam.

The results of this experiment are not easy to interpret, but the observations exhibited strong peaking of the number of scattered electrons in definite directions, which were shown to be related to the symmetry of the crystal. Davisson and Germer were able to show that this anisotropic scattering could be interpreted as the result of interference effects between the electron waves scattered by the surface lattice planes of the crystal. They were also able to show that the scattering was compatible with the de Broglie wavelength equation.

Soon after the experiments of Davisson and Germer, G. P. Thomson, using fast electrons in the range 17 to 64 kV, demonstrated in a convincing way, the diffraction of electrons passing through very thin films. This type of experiment bears a marked resemblance to the Debye–Scherrer X-ray powder method. The electron wavelengths are, however, about twenty times shorter than the typical X-ray diffraction wavelength and consequently the Bragg angles are much smaller. It is essential to employ high voltage electrons and extremely thin films in transmission experiments, in order that the electrons shall pass through the film with a negligible loss of energy. The use of thicker films and lower energy electrons results in a considerable spread in the wavelengths of the transmitted electrons, preventing the possibility of observing coherent diffraction effects.

The apparatus used by G. P. Thomson is illustrated in Fig. 1. A beam of fast electrons is produced in a cold cathode gas discharge tube A; the applied potential difference between cathode and anode is varied between

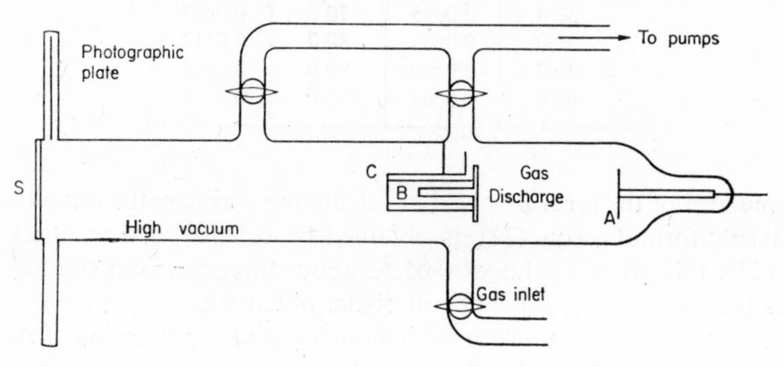

FIG. 1. G. P. THOMSON's electron diffraction apparatus. (From *The Wave Mechanics of Free Electrons*, G. P. THOMSON, McGraw-Hill, 1930 by courtesy of the University of Cornell.)

10 and 60 kV. A beam of electrons from the gas discharge vessel passes through a fine tube B (diameter 0·25 mm, length 6 cm) into the high vacuum part of the apparatus. The tube B is surrounded by a soft iron cylinder which provides magnetic screening. An extremely thin specimen C is mounted on the end of the tube B, and the transmitted electrons are recorded on a fluorescent screen S, or photographic plate, 30 cm beyond the specimen. Film thicknesses suitable for diffraction experiments are in the range 10^{-6} to 10^{-5} cm. Many methods of film preparation are used; one suitable for thin metallic specimens (silver) consists in depositing a thin

layer from the vapour in a high vacuum on a polished plate of rocksalt; the rocksalt is dissolved and the thin film is caught and mounted on a brass sheet pierced with a central hole.

The diffraction patterns observed, consist of a central spot surrounded by a series of diffraction rings. The whole pattern can be deflected sideways by a magnetic field showing that the effect is due to *electron* waves and not X-rays generated in the thin film by the incident electrons. Thomson showed that the diffraction patterns produced by thin films of aluminium, platinum and gold agreed with the X-ray lattice spacings if the electron wavelength is given by the Broglie equation. With thin polycrystalline specimens, the diffracted beams correspond to Bragg reflections from prominent internal lattice planes. All orientations of the normal to a set of planes around the incident beam direction are possible, and diffraction effects are observed (Fig. 2) if

$$2d \sin\theta = n\lambda$$

The "reflected" rays lie on the surface of a cone of semi-vertical angle 2θ For face-centred-cubic crystals, reflections from lattice planes with mixed Miller indices do not occur (Chapter 4). Thus the (111) reflection corresponds

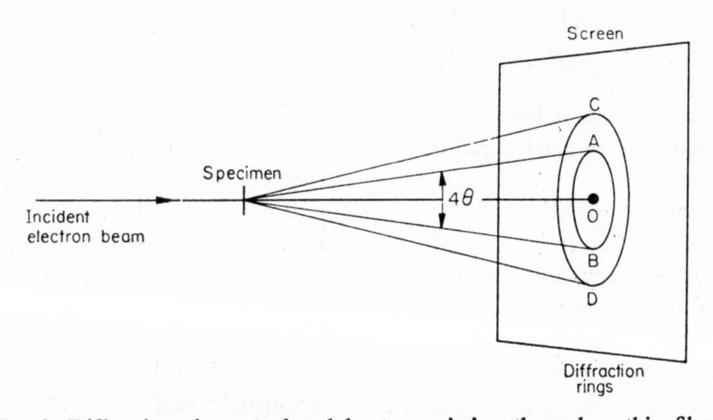

FIG. 2. Diffraction rings produced by transmission through a thin film.

to the smallest Bragg angle. In view of the fact that the electron wavelengths are much shorter than X-ray wavelengths the Bragg angles are small. Thus for the $(h\ k\ l)$ diffraction ring, we can write

$$\frac{2a\theta}{\sqrt{(h^2+k^2+l^2)}} = n\lambda \tag{25}$$

If $2r$ is the diameter of the diffraction ring formed on the screen at a distance b beyond the specimen, we have, as θ is small,

$$2r = b\,4\theta \tag{26}$$

Combining eqns. (25) and (26) the diffraction ring diameters $2r$ are given by

$$2r = \frac{2nb\lambda}{a} \sqrt{(h^2 + k^2 + l^2)} \tag{27}$$

Thomson, using the relation $\lambda = h/(m\,v)$, and calculating the electron velocity from the measured high potential, compared the lattice parameter "a" of the unit cells of Al, Au, Pt, Pb with the X-ray results. Close agreement was obtained for the two sets of parameters (Table 2). This can be considered as a very satisfactory demonstration of the correctness of de Broglie's formula.

TABLE 2. LATTICE PARAMETER "a" (Å)

Metal	X-rays	Electrons
Aluminium	4·046	4·03
Gold	4·06	4·09
Platinum	3·91	3·89
Lead	4·92	4·99

5.3 ACCURATE VERIFICATION OF DE BROGLIE'S EQUATION

The agreement between the results of X-ray and electron diffraction determinations of lattice parameters of simple crystals, is strong evidence in favour of the accuracy of de Broglie's wavelength relation. Nevertheless, the de Broglie equation plays such a fundamental role in wave mechanics (Chapter 6), that it is desirable to check the equation with the greatest possible accuracy. One of the best experimental tests of the de Broglie formula is that carried out by J. G. Tappart for electrons in the energy range from 24 to 64 keV.

The method avoids the measurement of the high accelerating potential difference, a difficult task if it is to be accurately performed. An electron beam is extracted from a cold cathode discharge tube A at a high negative potential (Fig. 3). The beam is collimated by two diaphragms B and C

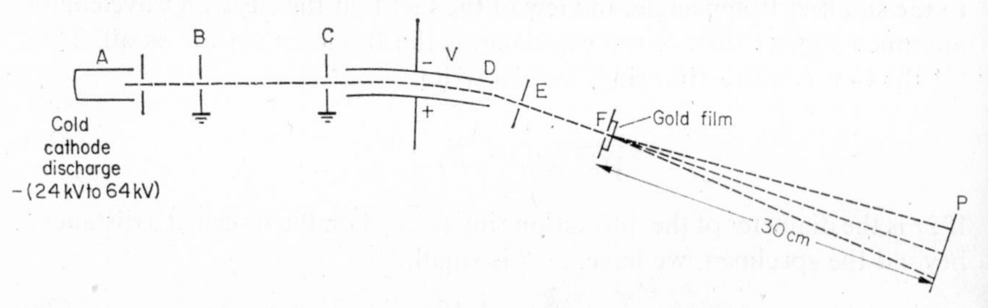

FIG. 3. Tappart's apparatus for verifying de Broglie's equation.

8·9 cm apart, pierced with holes 0·01 cm diameter. Monoenergetic electrons are selected by passing the beam through an electrostatic field set up between the cylindrical deflector plates D, 11·4 cm long, 1·9 cm wide and 2·4 cm apart. Deflecting potentials up to 850 V are applied to the plates and measured with high accuracy. The collimated electron beam is deflected by the field and the selected electrons pass through two diaphragms E and F. The diaphragm E rejects secondary electrons from the deflector plates; the final diaphragm F is 0·01 cm in diameter and directly fastened to the specimen holder. The specimen is a very thin gold foil which scatters the highly monochromatic electron waves and forms a simple diffraction pattern on a photographic plate P, 30 cm beyond the specimen. A magnetic field produced by a steady current in a Helmholtz pair of coils compensates the earth's field in the space between the cold cathode discharge tube and the specimen. A high vacuum, better than 10^{-6} mm of mercury is maintained in the main part of the apparatus, and a baffle mounted midway between the specimen and the photographic plate prevents scattered rays from the walls reaching the plate.

Without considering relativity effects, the electrons selected by the electrostatic filter would have a velocity v given by

$$\frac{V}{d} e = m \frac{v^2}{R} \tag{28}$$

where V is the voltage applied to the deflector plates D, which are spaced a distance d apart. Electrons which have a trajectory of radius R pass through the apertures E and F. If the electron wavelength is given by $\lambda = h/(m\, v)$, the quantity $\lambda^2 V$ should be a constant. The calculations are, however, more involved because of the relativity effects, and Tappart showed that the quantity

$$\lambda^2 V \Big/ \left(1 + \frac{h^2}{m_0^2 \lambda^2 c^2}\right) \tag{29}$$

should be a constant. As V is varied, the wavelength of the selected rays is compared by measuring the diameters of the diffraction rings recorded on the photographic plate. Small errors in the assumed lattice constant of gold and in the measured specimen-to-plate distance are not important as we are primarily interested in the ratio of wavelengths accompanying some measured change in V. The selected electron wavelengths covered the range 0·04713 to 0·07881 Å and the constancy of the expression given in eqn. (29) was established with high precision.

J. V. Hughes† has verified the de Broglie equation for electrons travelling near the velocity of light using a radioactive beta source.

† J. V. Hughes, *Phil. Mag.* **19**, 129, 1935.

5.4 THE ATOMIC SCATTERING FACTOR

The intensities of diffraction spectra are determined by the strength of the interaction between the incident wave and the scattering matter in the crystalline specimen. In Chapter 4 we discussed the coherent scattering of X-rays by the atoms in a crystal and found that the atomic scattering factor f was given by

$$f = \int_0^\infty 4\pi\, r^2\, \varrho(r) \cdot \frac{\sin \mu\, r}{\mu\, r}\, dr \tag{30}$$

where
$$\mu = 4\pi \left(\frac{\sin\theta}{\lambda}\right)$$

Interference occurs between the X-rays scattered by different parts of the electron charge distribution in the atom and f decreases as $(\sin\theta)/\lambda$ increases. Nuclear scattering makes a negligible contribution to the amplitude of the scattered wave. Apart from a polarization term, an X-ray of unit amplitude, scattered by an atom, has an amplitude at distance r equal to

$$f \cdot \frac{1}{r}\, \frac{e^2}{m\, c^2} \tag{31}$$

The corresponding problem of the coherent scattering of electron waves by the electron charge distribution and nucleus of an atom has been calculated by Born and in a more convenient form by Mott. This is a wave-mechanical problem and the incident electron wave of unit amplitude, is written as the real part of

$$\exp\left[2\pi\, i(\nu\, t - k\, x)\right] \tag{32}$$

where ν is the frequency, and k the wave number $(1/\lambda)$. The scattered wave at distance r has the form

$$f_e(\theta, \varphi) \frac{1}{r} \exp\left[2\pi\, i(\nu\, t - k\, r)\right] \tag{33}$$

where $f_e(\theta, \varphi)$ is the amplitude of the scattered wave in a direction specified by the polar angles θ and φ. The scattered wave at r has an amplitude

$$\frac{1}{r}\, \frac{e^2}{2m\, v^2} (Z - f) \cdot \frac{1}{\sin^2\theta} \tag{34}$$

where v is the electron velocity, Z is the atomic number of the atom and f is the X-ray atomic scattering factor, given by eqn. (30). Nuclear scattering is important and it tends to cancel the scattering from the electron cloud. At small Bragg angles, $(Z - f)$ and $\sin^2\theta$ each tend to zero, but the ratio has a finite value. By substituting $\lambda = \dfrac{h}{mv}$, we can re-write eqn. (34) in the form

$$\frac{1}{r} \cdot \frac{e^2 m}{2h^2} (Z - f) \frac{\lambda^2}{\sin^2\theta} \tag{35}$$

Comparing X-ray and electron scattering we obtain, on substituting the appropriate constants, for the ratio of the scattered and incident wave amplitudes, a_r/a_0, at distance r

X-rays:

$$\frac{a_r}{a_0} = \frac{1}{r} \cdot 2{\cdot}82 \times 10^{-13} f \tag{36}$$

Electron waves:

$$\frac{a_r}{a_0} = \frac{1}{r} \cdot 2{\cdot}38 \times 10^{-10} (Z - f) \left(\frac{\lambda}{\sin\theta}\right)^2 \tag{37}$$

where λ is measured in Å.

These equations show that the scattering power of an atom for electron waves is very much greater than that for X-rays. This has the very important practical consequence that exposure times in electron diffraction investigations are very small, sometimes a fraction of a second, compared with many minutes or hours for X-ray studies.

5.5 PRACTICAL APPLICATIONS

The short exposure times for electron diffraction photographs is a grea advantage, but the low penetrating power of electrons limits the specimens suitable for transmission experiments to very thin films. Great use has been made of the diffraction of electron beams incident at small glancing angles on the surface of single crystals or polycrystalline specimens. The electron waves reflected from the surface lattice planes of the specimen produce a diffraction pattern on a distant screen or photographic plate. The very small depth of penetration of the electrons responsible for the diffraction effects provides valuable information about the structure of the first ten or so lattice planes of the specimen. Electron diffraction has proved invaluable for studying surface phenomena, whereas it is not suitable for studying the internal structure of crystals. The X-ray and electron diffraction techniques are essentially complementary. Neutron diffraction, comes into its own, in certain special applications, when neither the X-ray nor electron diffraction methods is useful. Electron diffraction has been of great value in elucidating the internal structure of single organic molecules. Electron waves traversing a stream of vapour molecules are scattered with sufficient power to form diffraction patterns from single molecules. Such methods have provided valuable information about the internal atomic structure of molecules.

BIBLIOGRAPHY

R. BEECHING, *Electron Diffraction*, Methuen, 2nd Ed., London 1946.
Z. G. PINSKER, *Electron Diffraction*, Butterworths, London 1953.

EXAMPLES

1. A beam of 100 keV electrons passes normally through a very thin gold foil in an electron diffraction apparatus. The electrons are recorded on a photographic plate 40 cm beyond the gold film. Calculate the diameters of the first four diffraction rings. Gold is face-centred-cubic with a lattice parameter of 4·078 Å.
2. Calculate the de Broglie wavelength of the following particles;
   (a) an electron of kinetic energy 100 MeV, 500 MeV, 20 GeV
   (b) a "thermal neutron" at room temperature (300°K)
   (c) a 500 MeV pion (pion rest mass is 273 electron mass units).

CHAPTER 6

QUANTUM MECHANICS

6.1. INTRODUCTION

Niels Bohr's theory of stationary atomic energy states and the successful prediction of the spectral frequencies of the hydrogen atom are landmarks in the history of atomic physics. The theory was a brilliant combination of the quantum hypothesis, first introduced by Planck in relation to the theory of black-body radiation, and the nuclear atomic model proposed by Rutherford to explain the large angle scattering of alpha particles passing through thin foils. Bohr's original treatment was confined to circular electron orbits and this was extended by Sommerfeld to include elliptic orbits. Taking into consideration the relativistic variation in mass of an electron with its speed as it describes an elliptic orbit, Sommerfeld showed that this led to an understanding of the fine structure of spectral lines. Another important achievement was the extension, in a semi-quantitative way, to the energy level scheme responsible for the characteristic X-ray line spectra of the elements, and the explanation of Moseley's law. However, certain phenomena, such as the anomalous Zeeman effect and the doublet nature of the alkali metal spectra, defied explanation in terms of electrons with only *three* degrees of freedom. This difficulty was overcome by the introduction of the hypothesis of a fourth degree of freedom, associated with the intrinsic spin angular momentum of the electron. To fit the facts, however, the electron spin angular momentum must be half integral, in terms of $\hbar$ as the fundamental unit of angular momentum. The culmination of the Bohr scheme is the beautiful way the periodicity of the chemical elements falls into place in terms of the filling of electron shells, whose maximum occupation number is strictly governed by the Pauli exclusion principle.

In spite of the great successes of the Bohr–Sommerfeld method it contained a number of unsatisfactory features. First, there was no explanation of why the laws of electromagnetism do not apply to *bound* electrons. Second, the Bohr quantum postulate was introduced in an entirely *ad hoc* way and it is difficult to see any reason for the selective electron orbits. It is important to emphasize that although the theory predicts the correct relations for the spectral frequencies of one-electron atoms or ions, no picture or explanation of the actual radiation mechanism is forthcoming. A general, but by no means trivial criticism of the Bohr atomic model is the highly artificial nature of the concept of a planetary electron–nucleus atom, as there is no *a priori* justification for the picture of discrete sharply localized electrons moving in well-defined Keplerian orbits.

No one was more aware of these flaws in the theory than Bohr. In particular, he realized that the theory provided no indication of the intensities and states of polarization of the spectral lines. Bohr introduced the useful hypothesis known as the *Correspondence Principle*. This principle states that the laws of quantum physics gradually go over into those of classical physics in the limit of large quantum numbers. For example, the frequency of revolution of an electron in a high quantum state of the hydrogen atom (n large) approaches asymptotically the Bohr frequency corresponding to a quantum jump from state $n + 1$ to state n. In terms of a classical model, an atomic electron would radiate a complete spectrum of lines corresponding to the periodic motion of the revolving electron. It is difficult to reconcile the classical model with the quantum view that a given atom at a given time radiates a single monochromatic line.† The only way out of this dilemma is to compare the classical spectral components of a single atom with the *statistical* behaviour of a great number of atoms undergoing quantum energy transitions. It is along these lines that Bohr and others used the correspondence principle to deduce the relative intensities of spectral lines. Possibly the most advanced application of the correspondence principle was the treatment of the phenomenon of the dispersion of light by Kramers and Heisenberg. By this time (1923), it was also known that the Bohr theory failed to account for the spectral frequencies and ionization potential of the helium atom. This is a very difficult mathematical problem as it involves the notorious *three-body* interaction. Nevertheless it was abundantly clear that the Bohr–Sommerfeld theory was in need of drastic revision. To sum up the period 1913–1925, the era of what is now known as the "classical quantum theory"; we can say that, in spite of the introduction of a number of *ad hoc* quantum postulates and rules, microphysics was still essentially classical *in thought*—one still used without qualms the concepts of well-defined electron orbits, and the principle of Laplacian determinism remained unquestioned.

During an amazingly short period of time from 1925 to 1927, a major revolution in thinking about atomic phenomena was introduced and developed into the subject known as *quantum mechanics*. The first developments were due to W. Heisenberg and it was soon realized that the new method made use of the laws of *matrix algebra*.†† An elementary account of *matrix*

† Strictly speaking an atom must radiate for an infinite time in order to produce perfectly monochromatic light (see the Uncertainty Principle).

†† Matrix algebra is the language of linear transformations and the key discovery of the new mechanics is that dynamical variables are represented by linear operators.

mechanics is given at the end of this chapter. A year later, Schrödinger, guided by the ideas of de Broglie on the wave nature of matter, developed the treatment of atomic events known as *wave mechanics*. The two formalisms use quite different mathematical languages; nevertheless it was shown that the two treatments are essentially similar and lead to identical results. Sometimes one language is more useful and fruitful than the other and it is advisable to be familiar with the basic concepts and methods of both methods. On the whole, the Schrödinger method seems to be less abstract than that of Heisenberg, partly because it has its origins in the experimentally verified hypothesis of wave–particle duality, and partly because it involves the use of differential equations instead of the less well-known matrix algebra. For these reasons, we begin with an outline of the principles of wave mechanics, leading to a statement of the "Schrödinger Wave Equation".

6.2. SCHRÖDINGER'S WAVE EQUATION

Our starting point is the well-established de Broglie relation $\lambda = h/p$, connecting the linear momentum p of a moving particle with its associated wavelength λ. This law has been accurately verified in the case of electrons (Chapter 5) and diffraction effects with neutral atoms and thermal neutrons show that it is not confined to electrically charged particles. A vital clue to the setting up of a wave description of atomic states is provided by the realization that the Bohr stationary energy states, selected by the quantization condition $m\,v\,r = n\,[h/(2\pi)]$ correspond to a standing wave pattern for the electron orbit. Thus substituting $m\,v = h/\lambda$ in the Bohr angular momentum rule, we obtain the condition

$$2\pi\,r = n\,\lambda$$

In other words, stationary states are associated with stationary electron wave patterns, just as the modes of vibration of a sonometer string of length l correspond to the "quantum rule" $l = n(\lambda/2)$. Bohr's mysterious quantization rule appears in a more logical and satisfactory way than in the old quantum theory. In addition it is not completely irrational to expect that no radiation is emitted from a stationary electron wave distribution.

The correspondence principle requires that the laws of the new theory should be in complete agreement with classical mechanics in the limit of large quantum numbers. An important analogy in the formulation of wave mechanics is the correspondence between wave optics and geometrical optics in those applications where the size of obstacles, apertures and so on are large compared with the wavelength of light. In the domain of microscopic physics we must not be surprised to find that the classical method of particle mechanics is inadequate, just as we know that geometrical optics fails to give a correct account of many optical phenomena.

The simplest system to describe in terms of the wave language is the motion of an atomic particle of mass m in a straight line with constant momentum p. Such a particle is in field-free space and its energy E (kinetic) is associated with a frequency ν, where

$$E = h\nu \tag{1}$$

also

$$p = h/\lambda = k h \tag{2}$$

If the particle is moving from left to right, parallel to the x-axis a possible wave equation is

$$\psi = \psi_0 \exp\{2\pi i(k x - \nu t)\} \tag{3}$$

For the moment, we ignore the physical meaning of the wave displacement ψ, and simply regard the wave function $\psi(x, t)$ as a mathematical description of the state of the dynamical system. It is characteristic of quantum mechanics in general that the classical concepts of position, momentum, angular momentum, energy . . . are inadmissible in the atomic domain. Clear cut association of a definite momentum at a definite point of a trajectory, or of a definite energy at a definite instant of time are meaningless concepts. We must be careful not to force the phenomena of atomic physics into the framework of concepts built up by the gradual development of classical physics. However it is desirable to retain as much as possible from the realm of macroscopic physics and we still find it useful to retain many of the physical concepts. Nevertheless it is not surprising to find that the dynamical variables are represented by more complex mathematical quantities than numbers. Briefly, it is found necessary to represent the dynamical variables of an atomic system—the position, energy, momentum . . . by *mathematical operators*. These mathematical operators act upon the wave functions or vectors which are our mathematical description of the state of a system. In wave mechanics, great use is made of *differential operators*. To see this, let us obtain the operators associated with the momentum and energy of a moving particle described by the wave function, eqn. (3). Differentiating eqn. (3) partially with respect to x or t we obtain

$$\frac{\partial \psi}{\partial x} = 2\pi i k \psi \quad \text{and} \quad \frac{\partial \psi}{\partial t} = -2\pi i \nu \psi \tag{4}$$

Using relations (1) and (2), we can write eqns. (4)

$$\frac{h}{2\pi i}\,\frac{\partial \psi}{\partial x} = p_x \psi \quad \text{and} \quad -\frac{h}{2\pi i}\cdot\frac{\partial \psi}{\partial t} = E \psi \tag{5}$$

Thus we can represent p_x by the differential operator

$$-i\hbar\frac{\partial}{\partial x}$$

and the energy E by the differential operator

$$i\hbar \frac{\partial}{\partial t}$$

In the case of motion in three dimensions, the vector momentum operator $\boldsymbol{p}$ is

$$-i\hbar \operatorname{grad}$$

These operators are interpreted as operators which act upon the wave function ψ. This is always understood; nevertheless it is possible to build up an operator algebra, without specific use of the wave function.

Let us now write down the classical expression for the kinetic energy E of a particle, $p^2/2m$, in terms of the differential operators.

$$\frac{1}{2m}\left\{-i\hbar\frac{\partial}{\partial x}\left(-i\hbar\frac{\partial}{\partial x}\right)\right\}\psi = i\hbar\frac{\partial\psi}{\partial t} \tag{6}$$

or

$$-\frac{\hbar^2}{2m}\frac{\partial^2\psi}{\partial x^2} = i\hbar\frac{\partial\psi}{\partial t} \tag{7}$$

This equation is of limited interest as it describes the rectilinear motion of a particle in field-free space. Suppose we consider the motion of a particle in a field of force $F(x, t)$ which is derivable from a potential energy function $V(x, t)$

$$\boldsymbol{F} = -\frac{\partial V}{\partial x} \tag{8}$$

Now express the total energy of the system in terms of the position and conjugate momentum coordinates. The energy expressed in this way is called the *Hamiltonian function H*

$$H = \frac{p^2}{2m} + V(x, t) \tag{9}$$

In quantum mechanics, H is the operator which acting on the wave function ψ is equivalent to

$$H\psi = i\hbar\frac{\partial\psi}{\partial t} \tag{10}$$

Substituting eqn. (9) in eqn. (10) and replacing p with its equivalent differential operator, eqn. (10) becomes

$$-\frac{\hbar^2}{2m}\frac{\partial^2\psi}{\partial x^2} + V(x, t)\,\psi = i\hbar\frac{\partial\psi}{\partial t} \tag{11}$$

This is the one-dimensional Schrödinger wave equation.

For three-dimensional motion, the appropriate equation is

$$-\frac{\hbar^2}{2m}\nabla^2\psi + V(x, y, z, t)\psi = i\hbar\frac{\partial\psi}{\partial t} \tag{12}$$

Schrödinger interpreted this equation in the following way. The only possible states of a system are those which correspond to well-behaved solutions. A well-behaved solution is one which, along with its spatial derivatives $\frac{\partial \psi}{\partial x}, \frac{\partial \psi}{\partial y}, \frac{\partial \psi}{\partial z}$, is finite, continuous, and single-valued throughout the complete range of values of x, y and z. The concise statement of the Schrödinger equation (eqn. 12) means that the allowed energy states of a system correspond to the Hamiltonian operator H, which when applied to the wave functions $\psi_1, \psi_2, \psi_3 \ldots$ describing a quantum state, multiplies the wave function by a number $E_1, E_2, E_3 \ldots$ Thus the allowed states or *eigenstates* of the system are given by the relations

$$\begin{aligned} H\,\psi_1 &= E_1\,\psi_1 \\ H\,\psi_2 &= E_2\,\psi_2 \\ &\vdots \end{aligned} \tag{13}$$

The wave functions $\psi_1, \psi_2, \psi_3 \ldots$ are called the *eigenfunctions* of the system and they are said to belong to the *eigenvalues* E_1, E_2, E_3 of the Hamiltonian operator H. $E_1, E_2, E_3 \ldots$ are the energy levels of the system. We have seen in the Bohr theory that other dynamical variables of a system (e.g., angular momentum) are quantized. In certain cases if α is the operator representing the dynamical variable, the quantized values of the variable, $\lambda_1, \lambda_2, \lambda_3 \ldots$ satisfy the operator equations

$$\begin{aligned} \alpha\,\psi_1 &= \lambda_1\,\psi_1 \\ \alpha\,\psi_2 &= \lambda_2\,\psi_2 \end{aligned} \tag{14}$$

Again we say the *numbers* $\lambda_1, \lambda_2 \ldots$ are eigenvalues of the operator α belonging to the eigenfunctions $\psi_1, \psi_2 \ldots$. The operators of quantum mechanics are linear operators, that is, they satisfy the operational identities

$$\alpha(\psi + \varphi) = \alpha\,\psi + \alpha\,\varphi \tag{15}$$

$$\alpha\,c = c\,\alpha \tag{16}$$

where α is the operator, ψ and φ arbitrary wave functions and c is any number. This means that if $\psi_1, \psi_2, \psi_3 \ldots$ are well-behaved solutions of the Schrödinger equation, then so is the wave function

$$\psi = a_1\,\psi_1 + a_2\,\psi_2 + a_3\,\psi_3 + \ldots \tag{17}$$

where $a_1, a_2, a_3 \ldots$ are numerical coefficients, possibly complex. This equation is interpreted in the following way. If one particular coefficient $|a_j| = 1$, and all the other a's are zero, then the system is definitely in the jth eigenstate. If the a's are normalized so that

$$a_1\,a_1^* + a_2\,a_2^* + a_3\,a_3^* + \ldots = 1 \tag{18}$$

where a_j^* is the conjugate complex of a_j, then $a_j\,a_j^*$ is a measure of the probability of finding the system in the jth eigenstate. The composite ψ function represented by eqn. (17) corresponds to the superposition of the various eigenstates. Suppose the system is in the state described by the composite $\psi = \sum_{n} a_n \psi_n$ and the observable is then measured and found to belong to the eigenfunction ψ_m. The act of measurement has interfered with the original composite state and *forced* the system into the eigenstate corresponding to the eigenfunction ψ_m.

6.3. THE PROBABILITY AMPLITUDE

What physical interpretation is to be attached to the wave function ψ in the Schrödinger equation? It describes the state of the system, but it would be helpful if some direct physical interpretation could be obtained. A clue to this interpretation is provided by the way in which the wave and photon theories of light describe the intensity distribution in a diffraction pattern. The intensity is proportional to the square of the wave *amplitude* in the wave description and it is proportional to the *flux* of photons in the particle description. M. Born suggested that this correspondence between amplitude and particle flux allows one to interpret the wave function $\psi(\boldsymbol{r}, t)$ in the following way. The quantity

$$P \equiv |\psi(\boldsymbol{r}, t)|^2 \, d\tau$$

where $d\tau$ is a small volume element centred around the extremity of the position vector $\boldsymbol{r}$, is a measure of the *probability* of observing the particle, described by the wave function $\psi(\boldsymbol{r}, t)$ in the element of volume $d\tau$ at the time t. The wave amplitude ψ is a probability amplitude, the square of which yields the probability P. In order that the square of the wave function, or what is the same thing $\psi^* \psi$, yields the absolute probability, it is necessary to impose the *normalization* condition that the volume integral

$$\int \psi^* \psi \, d\tau$$

extended over the region of space throughout which ψ is finite, is equal to unity. This normalization condition ensures that the particle in question exists, that is, that it must be somewhere. The probability concept is intimately connected with the fundamental principle that the notion of strict determinacy is no longer valid. Under identical conditions, it is not possible to predict with certainty what a particle will do; all we can say is that there is a definite probability that a certain event will happen. The observation of interference effects with very weak beams of light forces us to realize that it is not possible to associate a photon with one definite light beam. In Young's double-slit interference experiment it is not possible, in principle, to *locate* the photon and assert that it has passed through one slit rather than the other. In quantum mechanics, the photon wave function is a composite one taking into account the complete geometrical system responsible for the interference phenomenon. Each photon interferes with itself and not with any other photon!†

It is often useful to extend the probability concept of the electronic wave functions $\psi_1, \psi_2, \psi_3, \ldots$ of a bound atomic electron by visualizing the function $e\,\psi_n^*\,\psi_n\,d\tau$ as a volume distribution of electric charge. The picture of sharp, discrete, localized electrons is abandoned and replaced by a probability "electron cloud" distribution. The new model was discussed in Chapter 4, in connection with the theory of the X-ray atomic scattering factor.

6.4. THE TIME-INDEPENDENT SCHRÖDINGER EQUATION

The solution of the Schrödinger eqn. (12) is simplified if the potential energy function does not depend on the time variable t. Let us see if it is possible to split the wave function $\psi(\boldsymbol{r}, t)$ into the *product* of two simpler functions; $u(\boldsymbol{r})$, which is a function of the position coordinates of the particle, and $f(t)$ a function of t only.

$$\psi(\boldsymbol{r}, t) = u(\boldsymbol{r})\,f(t) \tag{19}$$

Substituting in the Schrödinger eqn. (12), we get

$$-\frac{\hbar^2}{2m} f(t)\,\nabla^2 u(r) + V(\boldsymbol{r})\,f(t)\,u(\boldsymbol{r}) = i\,\hbar\,u(\boldsymbol{r}) \cdot \frac{df}{dt} \tag{20}$$

Dividing throughout by $\psi(\boldsymbol{r}, t) = u(\boldsymbol{r})\,f(t)$, we obtain

$$\frac{1}{u(\boldsymbol{r})}\left\{-\frac{\hbar^2}{2m}\nabla^2 u + V(\boldsymbol{r})\,u(\boldsymbol{r})\right\} = \frac{i\,\hbar}{f}\,\frac{df}{dt} \tag{21}$$

The left hand side of this equation is a function of space coordinates only, whereas the right-hand side depends on the time variable t only. In order that the equation is satisfied for all values of $\boldsymbol{r}$ and t, the two sides of the equation must be equal to some *constant*, E say. We can now write

$$\frac{i\,\hbar}{f}\,\frac{df}{dt} = E \tag{22}$$

and hence

$$f = C \exp\left(-\frac{i\,E\,t}{\hbar}\right) \tag{23}$$

Also we have

$$-\frac{\hbar^2}{2m}\nabla^2 u + V(\boldsymbol{r})\,u = E\,u(\boldsymbol{r}) \tag{24}$$

† See Chapter 1 of DIRAC's *Quantum Mechanics* for a full discussion of these ideas.

This equation is called the time-independent Schrödinger wave equation. Incorporating the constant of integration C in eqn. (23) in the function $u(\boldsymbol{r})$ we can write

$$\psi(\boldsymbol{r}, t) = u(\boldsymbol{r}) \exp\left(-\frac{iEt}{\hbar}\right) \tag{25}$$

An important property of the wave function ψ when V is independent of t is that $\psi^* \psi$ is also independent of t,

for $$\psi^* \psi = u^*(\boldsymbol{r})\, u(r) \exp\left(\frac{iEt}{\hbar}\right) \exp\left(-\frac{iEt}{\hbar}\right) = u^* u$$

The potential energy functions associated with the bound energy states of a system are time independent; thus the probability $\psi^* \psi$ of observing the particle in the vicinity of $\boldsymbol{r}$ does not depend on the time of observation.

6.5. ONE-DIMENSIONAL RECTANGULAR POTENTIAL WELL

A simple application of the time-independent wave eqn. (24) is the motion of a particle of mass m in a straight line parallel to the x-axis in a region where the field of force $\boldsymbol{F}(x)$ acting on the particle is represented by a potential energy function $V(x)$ known as a rectangular or square well (Fig. 1). This is a smoothed out version of the potential function of an electron bound in a metal block. The abrupt rise in V at $x = -a$ and $x = +a$ corresponds to the sudden change in potential energy at the free surface of the metal. Classically an electron bound in the metal block will have a total energy E, less than the well depth V_0. The energy difference $V_0 - E$ is in fact the work function of the metallic surface. According to classical physics, the electron inside the metal is forever bound within the potential well ($E < V_0$) as an electron outside the surface would possess a negative kinetic energy a meaningless concept in classical physics. We shall find

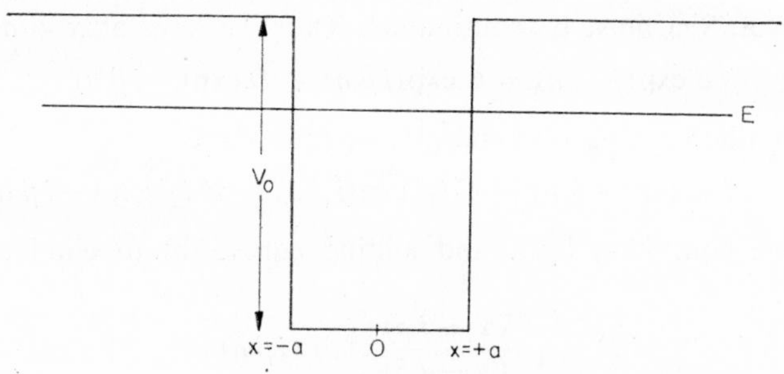

FIG. 1. Potential energy well
$x \leqq -a,\ x \geqq a,\ V = V_0$
$-a \leqq x \leqq a,\quad V = 0$
$V_0 > E$. A "classical" particle of total energy E would remain permanently bound in the well.

that according to wave mechanics, however, there is a small but finite probability of observing the electron outside the potential well. This startling result is a typical quantum mechanical result and illustrates the limited validity of classical concepts. To obtain this result we must obtain the well-behaved solutions of the equation

$$-\frac{\hbar^2}{2m}\frac{d^2u}{dx^2} + V(x)\,u(x) = E\,u(x) \tag{26}$$

where $V(x) = V_0$, for $x \leqq -a$ and $x \geqq a$

$V(x) = 0$, for $-a \leqq x \leqq a$

We have, in fact, two equations to solve

$$\frac{d^2u}{dx^2} + \frac{2m}{\hbar^2}(E - V_0)\,u = 0, \quad \text{for} \quad x \leqq -a \text{ and } x \geqq a \tag{27}$$

and

$$\frac{d^2u}{dx^2} + \frac{2m\,E\,u}{\hbar^2} = 0, \quad \text{for} \quad -a \leqq x \leqq a \tag{28}$$

The solutions for $V_0 > E$ are respectively

$$u = A\exp(\alpha x) + B\exp(-\alpha x), \quad x \leqq -a \text{ and } x \geqq a \tag{29}$$

where

$$\alpha = \sqrt{\frac{2m(V_0 - E)}{\hbar^2}} \tag{30}$$

and

$$u = C\exp(i\beta x) + D\exp(-i\beta x) \quad -a \leqq x \leqq a \tag{31}$$

where

$$\beta = \sqrt{\frac{2m\,E}{\hbar^2}} \tag{32}$$

and A, B, C, D are arbitrary constants.

The well-behaved solutions require that for $x \leqq -a$, B must be zero, otherwise u tends to infinity as x tends to $-\infty$. For $x \geqq a$, A must be zero, otherwise u tends to infinity as x tends to ∞. At $x = \pm a$ where two of the solutions join together there must be a smooth fit, that is, $u(x)$ and its x-derivative $u'(x)$ must be continuous. Thus we have at $x = a$,

$$B\exp(-\alpha a) = C\exp(i\beta a) + D\exp(-i\beta a) \tag{33a}$$

and differentiating eqns. (29) and (31) we must have

$$-B\alpha\exp(-\alpha a) = C\,i\beta\exp(i\beta a) - D\,i\beta\exp(-i\beta a) \tag{33b}$$

Multiplying eqn. (33a) by α and adding eqn. (33b) to eliminate B, we obtain

$$D = -\frac{(\alpha + i\beta)}{(\alpha - i\beta)}\exp(2i\beta a)\,C \tag{34}$$

At $x = -a$, we must have

$$A\exp(-\alpha a) = C\exp(-i\beta a) + D\exp(i\beta a) \tag{35a}$$

$$\alpha A\exp(-\alpha a) = C\,i\beta\exp(-i\beta a) - D\,i\beta\exp(i\beta a) \tag{35b}$$

Multiplying eqn. (35a) by α and subtracting to eliminate A, we obtain

$$D = -\frac{(\alpha - i\beta)}{(\alpha + i\beta)}\exp(-2i\beta a)\,C \tag{36}$$

In general, it is not possible to satisfy eqns. (34) and (36) simultaneously. To do this we find that there is a restriction on the possible energy values E. Equating eqns. (34) and (36) we find that

$$(\alpha + i\beta)^2(\cos 2\beta a + i\sin 2\beta a) = (\alpha - i\beta)^2(\cos 2\beta a - i\sin 2\beta a)$$

or, simplifying

$$(\alpha^2 - \beta^2)\sin 2\beta a = -2\alpha\beta\cos 2\beta a \tag{37}$$

Substituting the relations for α and β, using eqns. (30) and (32) this condition is

$$\tan 2a\sqrt{\frac{2mE}{\hbar^2}} = \frac{2\sqrt{[E(V_0 - E)]}}{2E - V_0} \tag{38}$$

The roots of this equation in E, can be determined by graphical means. It is found that there is a finite number of allowed discrete energies E_1, E_2, E_3, ... These are the quantized energy levels of the bound electron. For convenience we introduce the dimensionless parameter η defined by

$$\eta = \frac{2ma^2V_0}{\hbar^2} \tag{39}$$

If the well depth V_0 is 1 eV ($1{\cdot}602 \times 10^{-12}$ erg) and the width $2a$ is 2 Å (2×10^{-8} cm), η for a bound electron (m equal to $9{\cdot}108 \times 10^{-28}$ g) is equal to 0·2625. Thus if $V_0 = 6$ eV and $2a = 9{\cdot}6$ Å, $\eta = 36$. In this case, the roots of eqn. (38) are approximately equal to

$$E_1 = 0{\cdot}3\text{ eV},\quad E_2 = 1{\cdot}2\text{ eV},\quad E_3 = 2{\cdot}64\text{ eV}\quad\text{and}\quad E_4 = 4{\cdot}44\text{ eV}.$$

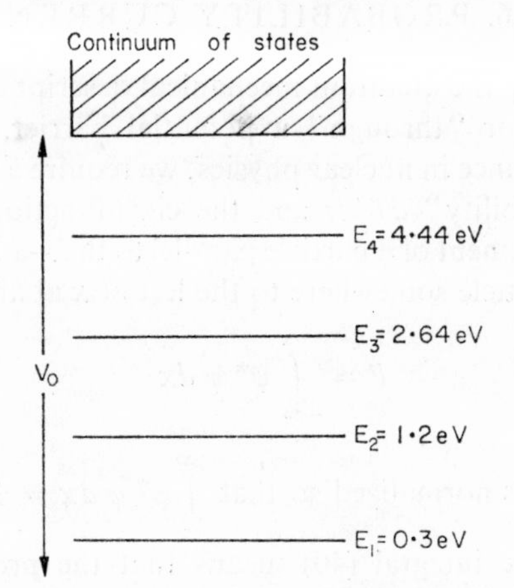

FIG. 2. Energy levels for electron bound in rectangular potential well; $V_0 = 6$ eV, $a = 4{\cdot}8$ A, $\eta = 36$. For $E > V_0$, there is no restriction on possible energies.

There are only four bound states for the electron. The energy level scheme and the corresponding eigenfunctions u_1, u_2, u_3, u_4 are shown in Figs. 2 and 3 respectively.

The novel feature of the eigenfunctions is their finite value *outside* the potential well. This means that there is a finite probability $u^*(x)\,u(x)\,dx$ of finding the electron in the space interval x to $x + dx$ outside the well. The wave function falls away exponentially outside the well and it is a very sensitive function of the particle mass. Thus if $V_0 - E$ is 1 eV, the value of $u^*(x)\,u(x)$ at a distance 2 Å outside the well, in terms of its value at $x = \pm a$ is about 0·1 for a bound electron, whereas for a bound proton (mass 1836 times greater) it is about 10^{-43}!

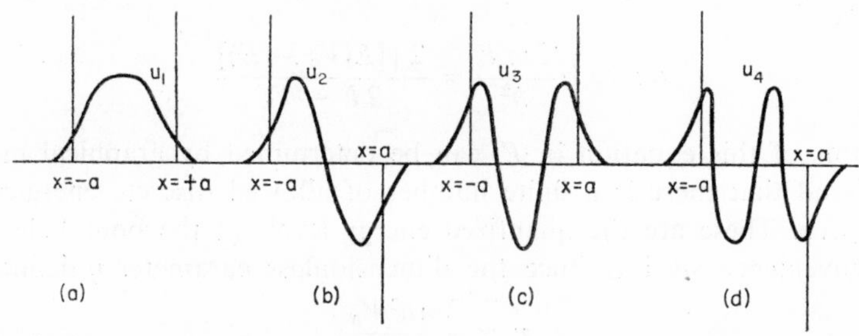

FIG. 3. The four eigenfunctions u_1, u_2, u_3, u_4, corresponding to the energy levels (eigenstates) E_1, E_2, E_3, E_4 of Fig. 2. In each case, a sinusoidal function joins smoothly on to a decaying exponential function at the walls of the barrier ($x = +a$). The finite value of u outside the well corresponds to a finite probability of finding the particle outside the well.

6.6. PROBABILITY CURRENT

Before considering the quantum mechanical description of the movement of particles across or "through" a potential barrier, a phenomenon of considerable importance in nuclear physics, we require a theorem connecting the "flow of probability" dP/dt and the eigenfunctions of a particle.

Consider the movement of a particle parallel to the x-axis. The probability P of observing the particle somewhere to the left of x at an instant of time t is

$$P = \int_{-\infty}^{x} \psi^* \psi \, dx \tag{40}$$

The wave function is normalized so that $\int_{-\infty}^{\infty} \psi^* \psi \, dx = 1$. A decrease in the value of the definite integral (40) means that the probability of finding the particle to the *right* of x has increased. In this event we can legitimately speak of a probability current or flow of probability from left to right, parallel to the x-axis. Thus the rate of increase of the probability of finding the particle to the right of x is given by

$$\frac{dP}{dt} = -\frac{\partial}{\partial t}\int_{-\infty}^{x} \psi^* \psi \, dx \tag{41}$$

The time-dependent Schrödinger equation is

$$i\hbar \frac{\partial \psi}{\partial t} = -\frac{\hbar^2}{2m}\frac{\partial^2 \psi}{\partial x^2} + V\psi \tag{42}$$

The wave function $\psi(x, t)$ is in general complex. Taking the complex conjugate of eqn. (42), we obtain the equation,

$$-i\hbar \frac{\partial \psi^*}{\partial t} = -\frac{\hbar^2}{2m}\frac{\partial^2 \psi^*}{\partial x^2} + V\psi^* \tag{43}$$

Multiplying eqn. (42) by ψ^* and eqn. (43) by ψ and adding, we find tha eqn. (41), which can be written in the form,

$$\frac{dP}{dt} = -\int_{-\infty}^{x} \left\{\psi^* \frac{\partial \psi}{\partial t} + \psi \frac{\partial \psi^*}{\partial t}\right\} dx \tag{44}$$

becomes

$$\frac{dP}{dt} = -\frac{\hbar}{2im}\int_{-\infty}^{x} \left\{\psi \frac{\partial^2 \psi^*}{\partial x^2} - \psi^* \frac{\partial^2 \psi}{\partial x^2}\right\} dx \tag{45}$$

Integrating by parts, we obtain,

$$\frac{dP}{dt} = -\frac{\hbar}{2im}\left\{\left|\frac{\partial \psi^*}{\partial x}\psi\right|_{-\infty}^{x} - \int_{-\infty}^{x} \frac{\partial \psi^*}{\partial x}\frac{\partial \psi}{\partial x} dx\right.$$

$$\left. - \left|\frac{\partial \psi}{\partial x}\psi^*\right|_{-\infty}^{x} + \int_{-\infty}^{x} \frac{\partial \psi}{\partial x}\frac{\partial \psi^*}{\partial x} dx\right\} \tag{46}$$

The two definite integrals cancel and as the wave function $\psi \to 0$ as $x \to -\infty$, thus

$$\frac{dP}{dt} = \frac{\hbar}{2im}\left\{\psi^* \frac{\partial \psi}{\partial x} - \psi \frac{\partial \psi^*}{\partial x}\right\} \tag{47}$$

6.7. ONE-DIMENSIONAL RECTANGULAR POTENTIAL BARRIER

We shall now apply the probability current equation of the last section to the passage of a particle of energy E through a rectangular potential barrier of height V_0 (Fig. 4). We find that even if V_0 is greater than E, there is a finite probability that a particle incident on the barrier, from the left will be found to the right of the barrier, a classically forbidden region. This phenomenon is known as the *tunnel effect*; the particle behaves in a sense as if it "tunnels through" the potential barrier. Using the wave theory, we describe the motion of the particle to the left of the barrier by an incident and superimposed reflected wave (it is expected that a change in the potential energy V at $x = 0$, will reflect part of the incident disturbance). Thus we can write $\psi(x, t) = u(x) \exp\left(-2\pi \frac{iEt}{h}\right)$ and

$$-\frac{\hbar^2}{2m}\frac{d^2u}{dx^2} = Eu \quad \text{for} \quad x \leqq 0 \quad \text{and} \quad x \geqq a$$

To the left of the barrier, the solution of the time-independent wave equation is

$$u = A\exp(i\beta x) + B\exp(-i\beta x), \quad x \leqq 0 \tag{48}$$

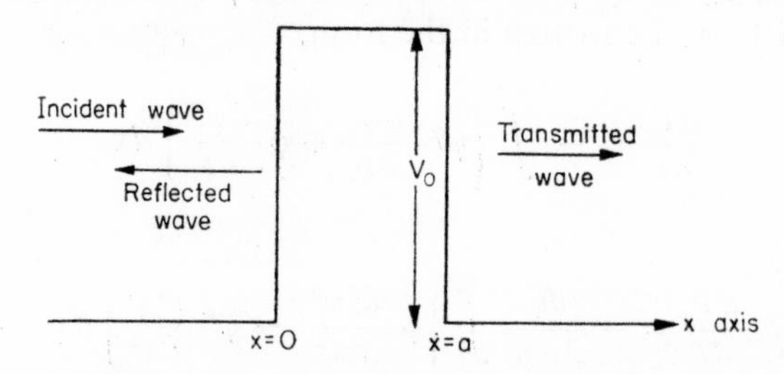

FIG. 4. Rectangular potential barrier. (Particle incident from the left.)

where

$$\beta = \sqrt{\frac{2mE}{\hbar^2}} \tag{49}$$

To the right of the barrier, there is only one wave,

$$u = C\exp(i\beta x)\dagger \qquad x \geqq a \tag{50}$$

The probability current dP/dt is obtained by using eqns. (47) and (48), and eqns. (47) and (50). Omitting the time factors, we have for $x \leqq 0$.

$$\frac{dP}{dt} = \frac{\hbar}{2im}[i\beta(A\exp\{-i\beta x\}+B\exp\{i\beta x\})(A\exp\{i\beta x\}-B\exp\{-i\beta x\})$$
$$+ i\beta(A\exp\{i\beta x\} + B\exp\{-i\beta x\})(A\exp\{-i\beta x\} - B\exp\{i\beta x\})]$$

This simplifies to

$$\frac{dP}{dt} = \frac{\hbar}{m}\beta[|A|^2 - |B|^2], \quad \text{for} \quad x \leqq 0 \tag{51}$$

† The complete wave function $\psi(x, t) = C\exp i(\beta x - \omega t)$, where $\omega = \frac{2\pi E}{h}$, represents a plane wave travelling from left to right.

Substituting for β and inserting $(mv^2)/2$ for the energy E, we obtain

$$\frac{dP}{dt} = v[|A|^2 - |B|^2] \qquad x \leqq 0 \tag{52}$$

where v is the velocity of the particle.

It is easy to show that for $x \geqq a$,

$$\frac{dP}{dt} = v\,|C|^2 \tag{53}$$

Inside the potential barrier, the wave equation is

$$-\frac{\hbar^2}{2m}\frac{d^2 u}{dx^2} + V_0 u = E u \qquad 0 \leqq x \leqq a$$

First consider the case when $E > V_0$; then the solution of the wave equation is

$$u = D\exp(i\alpha x) + E\exp(-i\alpha x) \qquad 0 \leqq x \leqq a \tag{54}$$

where

$$\alpha = \sqrt{\frac{2m(E - V_0)}{\hbar^2}}. \tag{55}$$

The continuity conditions at $x = 0$ and $x = a$ yield four relations.

$$\text{At } x = 0, \quad A + B = D + E \tag{56}$$

$$i\beta(A - B) = i\alpha(D - E) \tag{57}$$

At $x = a$,

$$C\exp(i\beta a) = D\exp(i\alpha a) + E\exp(-i\alpha a) \tag{58}$$

$$i\beta C\exp(i\beta a) = i\alpha D\exp(i\alpha a) - i\alpha E\exp(-i\alpha a) \tag{59}$$

From eqns. (56) and (57) we obtain

$$2D = A(1 + \beta/\alpha) + B(1 - \beta/\alpha) \tag{60}$$

and

$$2E = A(1 - \beta/\alpha) + B(1 + \beta/\alpha) \tag{61}$$

Adding eqns. (58) and (59) and substituting for $2D$, using eqn. (60) we obtain

$$C\left(1 + \frac{\beta}{\alpha}\right)\exp[i\beta a] = \left\{A\left(1 + \frac{\beta}{\alpha}\right) + B\left(1 - \frac{\beta}{\alpha}\right)\right\}\exp[i\alpha a] \tag{62}$$

Subtracting eqn. (59) from eqn. (58) and substituting for $2E$, using eqn. (61), we obtain

$$C\left(1 - \frac{\beta}{\alpha}\right)\exp[i\beta a] = \left\{A\left(1 - \frac{\beta}{\alpha}\right) + B\left(1 + \frac{\beta}{\alpha}\right)\right\}\exp[-i\alpha a] \tag{63}$$

Dividing eqn. (62) by eqn. (63), and cross multiplying, we obtain

$$\frac{B}{A} = \frac{(\beta^2 - \alpha^2)(1 - \exp[2i\alpha a]}{(\beta + \alpha)^2 - (\beta - \alpha)^2\exp[2i\alpha a]} \tag{64}$$

Eliminating B, we find

$$\frac{C}{A} = \frac{4\beta\alpha\exp[i(\alpha - \beta)a]}{(\beta + \alpha)^2 - (\beta - \alpha)^2\exp[2i\alpha a]} \tag{65}$$

The probability current relations, expressed by eqns. (52) and (53) can be interpreted as defining a reflection coefficient $R = |B/A|^2$ for the incident wave coming from the left, and a transmission coefficient $T = |C/A|^2$. T is the probability of the incident particle crossing the potential barrier. Multiplying eqns. (64) and (65) by their complex conjugates, we find that,

$$R = \left|\frac{B}{A}\right|^2 = \left[1 + \frac{4\beta^2\alpha^2}{(\beta^2 - \alpha^2)^2 \sin^2\alpha a}\right]^{-1} \tag{66}$$

$$T = \left|\frac{C}{A}\right|^2 = \left[1 + \frac{(\beta^2 - \alpha^2)^2 \sin^2\alpha a}{4\beta^2\alpha^2}\right]^{-1} \tag{67}$$

We find that $R + T = 1$, a result to be expected, as the particle is either reflected or transmitted by the barrier.

Substituting for β and α, using eqns. (49) and (55) we obtain

$$R = \left[1 + \frac{4E(E - V_0)}{V_0^2 \sin^2\alpha a}\right]^{-1} \qquad E > V_0 \tag{68}$$

$$T = \left[1 + \frac{V_0^2 \sin^2\alpha a}{4E(E - V_0)}\right]^{-1} \qquad E > V_0 \tag{69}$$

If E is just greater than V_0, α is very small, and eqn. (67) tends towards

$$T = \left[1 + \frac{\beta^2 a^2}{4}\right]^{-1} \doteq \left[1 + \frac{m V_0 a^2}{2\hbar^2}\right]^{-1} \tag{70}$$

The transmission coefficient oscillates as E rises above V_0 (Fig. 5). When $\alpha a = n\pi$, $T = 1$, this is an example of constructive interference. This condition is equivalent to the relation

$$2a = n\lambda$$

where λ is the de Broglie wavelength of the particle crossing the barrier $0 \leqq x \leqq a$. This means that the waves reflected to and fro between the discontinuities at $x = 0$ and $x = a$ are in phase at $x = a$ and out of phase at $x = 0$ (hence $R = 0$).

The important problem of transmission through, rather than over the barrier, that is when $V_0 > E$, can be solved by replacing α in eqns. (66) and (67) by $i\gamma$ where

$$\gamma = \sqrt{\frac{2m(V_0 - E)}{\hbar^2}} \tag{71}$$

We find for T, when $V_0 > E$

$$T = \left[1 + \frac{V_0^2 \sinh^2\gamma a}{4E(V_0 - E)}\right]^{-1} \tag{72}$$

T decreases monotonically from $\left(1 + \frac{m V_0 a^2}{2\hbar^2}\right)^{-1}$ at $E = V_0$ to zero at $E = 0$.

A good approximation for T, at low energy E, and for a barrier such that the dimensionless ratio $\eta = \frac{2ma^2 V_0}{\hbar^2} \gg 1$, is

$$T = \frac{16E(V_0 - E)}{V_0^2} \exp(-2\gamma a) \tag{73}$$

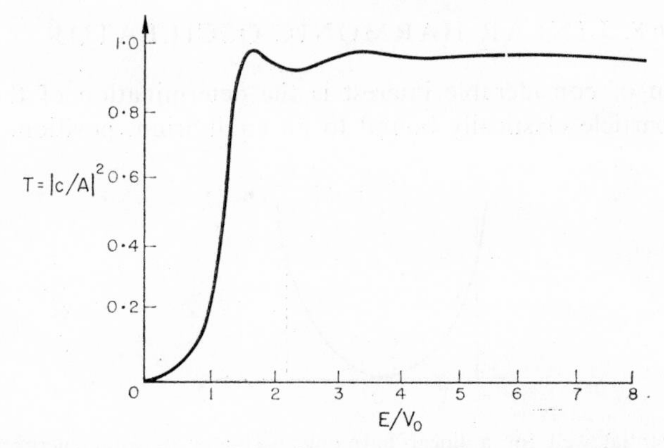

FIG. 5. Transmission coefficient of a rectangular potential barrier for

$$\eta = \frac{2ma^2 V_0}{\hbar^2} = 16.$$

(From L. I. SCHIFF, *Quantum Mechanics*, 2nd Edition, McGraw-Hill, 1955. Used by permission of the publishers.)

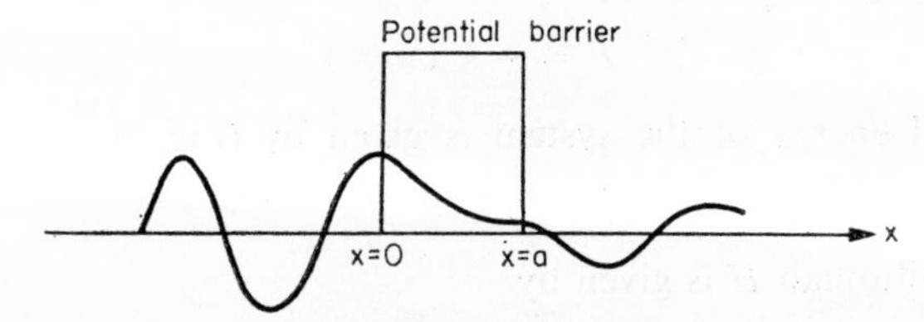

FIG. 6. Wave function $u(x)$ for wave incident on potential barrier from left (Tunnel effect).

The wave function $u(x)$ for a particle incident on the barrier from the left, with an energy E less than the barrier height V_0, is shown in Fig. 6. The wave function beyond the barrier $x > a$ has a small amplitude, representing the small transparency of the barrier. Nevertheless, there is a finite chance of the incident particle passing through the barrier into the classically forbidden region. The wave mechanical tunnel effect plays a vital role in a number of phenomena in the atomic and nuclear domain. Electrons, for example, may pass through a potential barrier at the common surface of two metals, provided the barrier is only a few electron volts high and a few angström units thick. We shall see (Chapter 9) that the phenomenon of natural alpha particle radioactivity is an example of the tunnel effect through the Coulomb potential barrier surrounding the atomic nucleus. The rectangular potential barrier is a highly artificial well shape. However, the general conclusions of barrier transparency are applicable in practical cases.

6.8. LINEAR HARMONIC OSCILLATOR

A problem of considerable interest is the determination of the energy levels of a particle elastically bound to an equilibrium position. Suppose

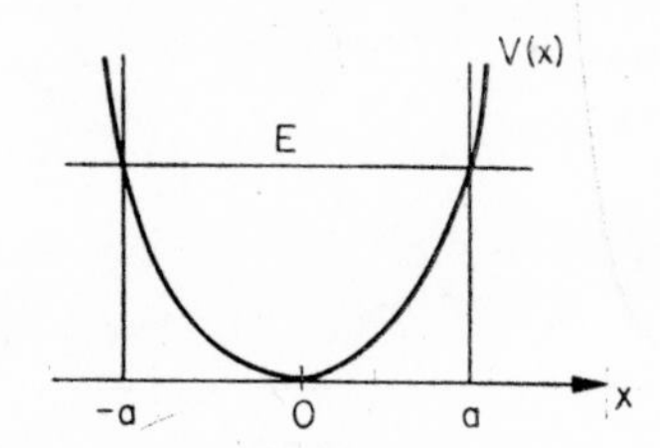

FIG. 7. Potential well for a linear harmonic oscillator of total energy E and classical amplitude a. $V(x) = \frac{1}{2} k x^2$. Classically the region outside $|x| > a$ is forbidden, but there is a finite chance of finding the particle in this region according to wave mechanics.

the particle is free to vibrate in one direction only (along the x-axis); we can write for the restoring force F,

$$F = -k x$$

The potential energy of the system is given by (Fig. 7)

$$V = \tfrac{1}{2} k x^2 \tag{74}$$

and the Hamiltonian H is given by

$$H = \frac{p^2}{2m} + \frac{1}{2} k x^2 \tag{75}$$

The time-independent Schrödinger equation is

$$-\frac{\hbar^2}{2m} \frac{d^2 u}{dx^2} + \frac{1}{2} k x^2 u = E u \tag{76}$$

where

$$\psi = u(x) \exp\left(-2\pi i \frac{E}{h} t\right)$$

To solve eqn. (76) it is convenient to change the variable from x to s by the substitution

$$s = x/a, \quad \text{where } a \text{ is an undetermined constant.} \tag{77}$$

Substituting in eqn. (76) we obtain

$$-\frac{\hbar^2}{2m\,a^2}\frac{d^2 u}{ds^2}+\frac{1}{2}k\,a^2\,s^2\,u = E\,u \tag{78}$$

or

$$-\frac{d^2u}{ds^2}+\frac{k\,m\,a^4\,s^2}{\hbar^2}u = \frac{2m\,a^2}{\hbar^2}E\,u \tag{79}$$

Put

$$a^4 = \frac{\hbar^2}{k\,m}, \quad \text{and} \quad \lambda = \frac{2m\,a^2\,E}{\hbar^2} = \frac{2E}{\hbar}\sqrt{\frac{m}{k}} \tag{80}$$

The wave equation becomes

$$-\frac{d^2u}{ds^2}+s^2\,u = \lambda\,u \tag{81}$$

The solution of eqn. (81) can be found by writing $u(s)$ in the form†

$$u(s) = v(s)\exp(-\tfrac{1}{2}s^2) \tag{82}$$

where $v(s)$ is a polynomial of finite order in s.

Substituting eqn. (82) in eqn. (81) we obtain the equation

$$\frac{d^2v}{ds^2}-2s\frac{dv}{ds}+(\lambda-1)\,v = 0 \tag{83}$$

Express v as a power series in s

$$v(s) = a_r\,s^r + a_{r+1}\,s^{r+1} + a_{r+2}\,s^{r+2} + \cdots \qquad a_r \neq 0 \tag{84}$$

Substituting eqn. (84) in eqn. (83) we obtain

$$\textstyle\sum_m \{a_m\,m(m-1)\,s^{m-2} + a_m(\lambda-1-2m)\,s^m\} = 0 \tag{85}$$

The coefficients of each power of s in eqn. (85) must vanish. Terms in s^k in eqn. (85) are obtained from the first term in eqn. (85) when $m = k+2$, and from the second term in eqn. (85) when $m = k$. Thus the coefficient of s^k in eqn. (85) is

$$(k+2)\,(k+1)\,a_{k+2} + (\lambda-1-2k)\,a_k \tag{86}$$

The coefficient of s^k must vanish for every value of k; thus

$$\frac{a_{k+2}}{a_k} = \frac{2k+1-\lambda}{(k+1)\,(k+2)} \tag{87}$$

The coefficient of the lowest power of s, that is, of s^{r-2} in eqn. (85) is $a_r\,r(r-1) = 0$

$$\therefore\ r = 0 \quad \text{or} \quad 1$$

If $r = 0$, putting $a_0 = 1$ and omitting the odd powers of s, as eqn. (87) is a relation involving alternate coefficients, we can write

$$v_0(s) = 1 + a_2\,s^2 + a_4\,s^4 + \cdots$$

† An instructive account of the mathematical reasoning leading to this assumption is given by V. Rojansky, *Introductory Quantum Mechanics*, pp. 16–22.

If $r = 1$, putting $a_1 = 1$, we can write

$$v_1(s) = s + a_3 s^3 + a_5 s^5 + \cdots$$

The general solution of eqn. (83) can be written as

$$v = A\, v_0(s) + B\, v_1(s) \tag{88}$$

where A and B are arbitrary constant.

If the series for $v_0(s)$ and $v_1(s)$ terminate, $v_0 \exp(-\frac{1}{2}s^2)$ and $v_1 \exp(-\frac{1}{2}s^2)$ approach zero when $|x| \to \infty$. On the other hand, if v_0 and v_1 are infinite series, the function $u(s)$ is not well-behaved. For one of the series to terminate for some value of k, the numerator of eqn. (87) must be zero. The constant A or B in eqn. (88) for the other series must be zero

$$\therefore\ 2k + 1 = \lambda, \quad \text{where } k \text{ is a positive integer.} \tag{89}$$

Substituting the possible values of λ, given by eqn. (89), in eqn. (80), and denoting the integer k by n, we have

$$\frac{2E}{\hbar}\sqrt{\frac{m}{k}} = 2n + 1$$

$$E = \left(n + \frac{1}{2}\right)\hbar\sqrt{\frac{k}{m}} = \left(n + \frac{1}{2}\right)h\,\nu_c \tag{90}$$

where $\nu_c = \dfrac{1}{2\pi}\sqrt{(k/m)}$, is the classical frequency of oscillation (91)

Thus the energy levels of the linear harmonic oscillator consist of a series of equally spaced levels $h\,\nu_c$ apart. An unexpected feature is the prediction of a finite energy $\frac{1}{2}\,h\,\nu_c$ in the ground state ($n = 0$). This means that an atom in a crystal at the absolute zero of temperature would still possess a *zero-point energy* of oscillation. We shall see, later in this chapter, that this result is a consequence of the Heisenberg uncertainty principle, whereby it is inherently impossible exactly to specify the energy of a system at some definite instant of time. In discussing the coherent scattering of X-rays by atoms in Chapter 4, it was pointed out that the effect of zero-point vibration of the atoms in a crystal is borne out by experiment.

6.9. SPHERICALLY SYMMETRIC POTENTIAL

There is a number of problems of interest in atomic physics in which the potential energy is spherically symmetrical about some centre. Coulomb potential of the proton–electron interaction in the hydrogen atom is a good example. The Laplacian operator ∇^2 is then more conveniently expressed in spherical polar coordinates r, θ, φ, instead of Cartesian coordinates x, y, z. The transformation relations for the coordinates are (Fig. 8),

$$x = r\sin\theta\cos\varphi$$
$$y = r\sin\theta\sin\varphi$$
$$z = r\cos\theta$$

The time-independent wave equation is then given by

$$-\frac{\hbar^2}{2m}\left[\frac{1}{r^2}\frac{\partial}{\partial r}\left(r^2\frac{\partial}{\partial r}\right)+\frac{1}{r^2\sin\theta}\frac{\partial}{\partial\theta}\left(\sin\theta\frac{\partial}{\partial\theta}\right)+\frac{1}{r^2\sin^2\theta}\frac{\partial^2}{\partial\varphi^2}\right]u+V(r)\,u=E\,u \tag{92}$$

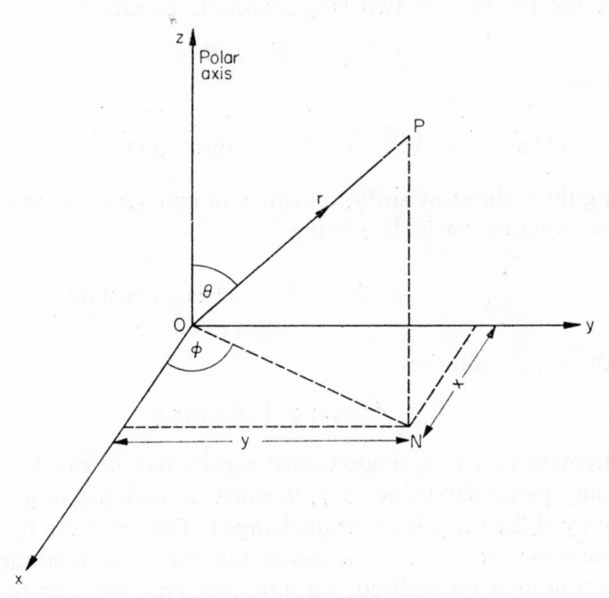

FIG. 8. Relationship between spherical polar coordinates r, θ, φ and Cartesian coordinates x, y, z of point P.

The potential energy function $V(r)$ is independent of the angles θ and φ. The equation can be solved by expressing $u(r, \theta, \varphi)$ as the product of two functions $R(r)$, and $Y(\theta, \varphi)$

$$u(r, \theta, \varphi) = R(r)\,Y(\theta, \varphi).$$

Substituting in eqn. (92) and dividing throughout by u, we obtain

$$\frac{1}{R}\frac{d}{dr}\cdot\left(r^2\frac{dR}{dr}\right)+\frac{2mr^2}{\hbar^2}(E-V)=-\frac{1}{Y}\left[\frac{1}{\sin\theta}\frac{\partial}{\partial\theta}\left(\sin\theta\frac{\partial Y}{\partial\theta}\right)+\frac{1}{\sin^2\theta}\frac{\partial^2 Y}{\partial\varphi^2}\right] \tag{93}$$

The left-hand side is a function of the variable r, and the right-hand side depends on θ and φ and not on r. The two sides of the equation must be equal for all values or r, θ, and φ. Thus each side must be equal to the same constant, which we shall denote by λ. Dealing with the right-hand side of eqn. (93) first, we then have the equation

$$\frac{1}{\sin\theta}\,\frac{\partial}{\partial\theta}\cdot\left(\sin\theta\,\frac{\partial Y}{\partial\theta}\right)+\frac{1}{\sin^2\theta}\,\frac{\partial^2 Y}{\partial\varphi^2}+\lambda\,Y=0 \tag{94}$$

We can now proceed to split eqn. (94) into two equations by expressing $Y(\theta, \varphi)$ as the product of two single-variable functions,

$$Y(\theta,\varphi)=\Theta(\theta)\cdot\Phi(\varphi) \tag{95}$$

This leads to

$$\frac{1}{\Theta\sin\theta}\,\frac{d}{d\theta}\cdot\left(\sin\theta\,\frac{d\Theta}{d\theta}\right)+\frac{1}{\Phi\sin^2\theta}\,\frac{d^2\Phi}{d\varphi^2}+\lambda=0 \tag{96}$$

Multiplying throughout by $\sin^2\theta$, we can split eqn. (96) into two equations, the one involving the variable φ being

$$\frac{d^2\Phi}{d\varphi^2}=-m^2\,\Phi \qquad \text{where } m^2 \text{ is a constant} \tag{97}$$

This has the simple solution

$$\Phi=A\cos m\,\varphi+B\sin m\,\varphi \tag{98}$$

The requirement that ψ is single-valued means that Φ can have only one value for any particular value of φ. Φ must be periodic in φ, that is, increasing φ by $\pm 2\pi$ must leave Φ unchanged. Thus m must be an integer, positive, negative or zero. m is called the magnetic quantum number. If the function Φ is normalized, we note that eqn. (98) can be written in the equivalent form

$$\Phi=C\exp(\pm im\varphi)$$

Hence

$$\oint\Phi^*\,\Phi\,d\varphi=1$$

or

$$C^2\,2\pi=1$$

$$C=\frac{1}{\sqrt{2\pi}}$$

The equation involving the variable θ is

$$\frac{1}{\sin\theta}\,\frac{d}{d\theta}\left(\sin\theta\,\frac{d\Theta}{d\theta}\right)+\left(\lambda-\frac{m^2}{\sin^2\theta}\right)\Theta=0 \tag{99}$$

This is a well-known differential equation know as *Legendre's equation.* It is simplified by introducing the variable $\mu=\cos\theta$, where $-1\leqq\mu\leqq 1$. As $d\mu=-\sin\theta\,d\theta$, we find that eqn. (99) becomes

$$\frac{d}{d\mu}\left[(1-\mu^2)\frac{d\Theta}{d\mu}\right]+\left[\lambda-\frac{m^2}{1-\mu^2}\right]\Theta=0 \tag{100}$$

Let us consider the special case when the magnetic quantum m is equal to zero; then (100) becomes

$$\frac{d^2\Theta}{d\mu^2} - \mu^2\frac{d^2\Theta}{d\mu^2} - 2\mu\frac{d\Theta}{d\mu} + \lambda\,\Theta = 0 \tag{101}$$

This can be solved by expressing Θ as a power series in μ,

$$\Theta = a_0 + a_1\,\mu + a_2\,\mu^2 + \cdots a_j\,\mu^j + \cdots \tag{102}$$

Differentiating we obtain

$$\frac{d\Theta}{d\mu} = a_1 + 2a_2\,\mu + \qquad + j\,a_j\,\mu^{j-1} + \cdots \tag{103}$$

$$\frac{d^2\Theta}{d\mu^2} = 2.1a_2 + 3.2a_3\,\mu + \qquad + j(j-1)\,a_j\,\mu^{j-2} \tag{104}$$

Substituting eqns. (102), (103) and (104) in eqn. (101), we obtain

$$\begin{array}{ll} 2.1a_2 + 3.2a_3\,\mu + \cdots & +j(j-1)\,a_j\,\mu^{j-2} + \cdots \\ -2.1a_2\,\mu^2 - 3.2a_3\,\mu^3 - \cdots & -j(j-1)\,a_j\,\mu^j - \cdots \\ -2a_1\,\mu - 2.2a_2\,\mu^2 - \cdots & -2j\,a_j\,\mu^j - \cdots \\ +\lambda\,a_0 + \lambda\,a_1\,\mu + \cdots & +\lambda\,a_j\,\mu^j = 0 \end{array} \tag{105}$$

This series must vanish for all values of μ; hence the coefficient of each power of μ must be zero. Thus we have the following relations

$$\begin{array}{l} 2.1a_2 + \lambda\,a_0 = 0 \\ 3.2a_3 - 2a_1 + \lambda\,a_1 = 0 \\ \cdots\cdots\cdots\cdots\cdots\cdots \\ (j+2)(j+1)\,a_{j+2} + [\lambda - 2j - j(j-1)]\,a_j = 0 \end{array} \tag{106}$$

From this set of equations we obtain the recurrence formula

$$\frac{a_{j+2}}{a_j} = \frac{j(j+1) - \lambda}{(j+1)(j+2)} \tag{107}$$

If a_0 is known, we can use eqn. (107) to determine $a_2, a_4, a_6, \ldots$ etc., and if a_1 is known, we can determine the odd coefficients $a_3, a_5, a_7, \ldots$ As $j \to \infty$, we note that $a_{j+2}/a_j \to 1$. Thus an infinite power series will diverge if $|\mu| = 1$. Well-behaved solutions of the Legendre equation can be obtained by setting either the even or odd coefficients of the power series to zero and terminating the series at some particular value of j. Thus if

$$j(j+1) = \lambda \tag{108}$$

a_{j+2} and all succeeding coefficients will be zero. The polynomials can be derived using eqn. (107), if a_0 and a_1 are known. The Legendre polynomials $P_n(\mu)$ correspond to $a_0 = 1$ and $a_1 = \mu$. Thus we find that

$$\begin{array}{l} P_0(\mu) = 1, \quad P_1(\mu) = \cos\theta \\ P_2(\mu) = \tfrac{1}{2}(3\cos^2\theta - 1), \quad P_3(\mu) = \tfrac{1}{2}(5\cos^3\theta - 3\cos\theta) \\ P_4(\mu) = \tfrac{1}{8}(35\cos^4\theta - 30\cos^2\theta + 3) \quad \text{etc.} \end{array} \tag{109}$$

If the magnetic quantum number m is finite, we find that

$$\lambda = l(l+1)$$

where

$$l = j + |m| \tag{110}$$

We shall see that l corresponds to the quantization of angular momentum of the system and it is known as the azimuthal quantum number. When m is finite and $l \geqq |m|$, the solutions of Legendre's equation are called the *associated Legendre functions,* $P_l^m(\cos\theta)$. The $P_l^m(\mu)$ and the Legendre polynomials $P\theta(\mu)$ are linked by the equation

$$P_l^m(\mu) = (1-\mu^2)^{\frac{|m|}{2}} \frac{d^{|m|}}{d\mu^{|m|}} P_l(\mu) \tag{111}$$

The complete angular part $Y(\theta, \varphi)$ of the wave function $\psi(r, \theta, \varphi)$ is then given by

$$Y_{lm}(\theta, \varphi) = N_{lm} P_l^m(\mu) \exp(im\varphi) \tag{112}$$

where N is the normalizing constant. This solution is called a *spherical harmonic*. For each value of l, there are $(2l+1)$ values of m, namely, $m = l, (l-1), \ldots 0, \ldots -(l-1), -l$. The normalized spherical harmonics are given by

$$Y_{lm}(\theta, \varphi) = \left[\frac{(2l+1)}{4\pi} \frac{(l-|m|)!}{(l+|m|)!}\right]^{\frac{1}{2}} P_l^m(\mu) \exp(im\varphi) \tag{113}$$

The first few spherical harmonics Y_{lm} or Y_l^m are

$$\begin{aligned}
&Y_{0,0} = \frac{1}{\sqrt{(4\pi)}}, \quad Y_{1,1} = -\sqrt{\frac{3}{8\pi}} \sin\theta \exp(i\varphi) \\
&Y_{1,0} = \sqrt{\frac{3}{4\pi}} \cos\theta, \quad Y_{1,-1} = \sqrt{\frac{3}{8\pi}} \sin\theta \exp(-i\varphi) \\
&Y_{2,0} = \sqrt{\frac{5}{16\pi}} (3\cos^2\theta - 1), \quad Y_{2,1} = \sqrt{\frac{15}{8\pi}} \sin\theta \cos\theta \exp(i\varphi) \\
&Y_{2,2} = \sqrt{\frac{15}{32\pi}} \sin^2\theta \exp(2i\varphi) \qquad Y_{3,0} = \sqrt{\frac{7}{16\pi}} (5\cos^3\theta - 3\cos\theta) \quad \text{etc.}
\end{aligned} \tag{114}$$

Spherical harmonic functions are associated with many important quantum phenomena including the radiation field pattern produced by the emission of photons from an excited atom or nucleus, which carries away a total angular momentum of l units (in terms of $\hbar$) and m units parallel to some special direction.

We are now in a position to return to the radial wave function $R(r)$. Thus in eqn. (93) equating the left-hand side to the constant $\lambda = l(l+1)$, we get

$$\frac{1}{r^2}\frac{d}{dr}\left(r^2 \frac{dR}{dr}\right) + \frac{2m}{\hbar^2}\left[E - V(r) - \frac{l(l+1)\hbar^2}{2mr^2}\right] R = 0 \tag{115}$$

This equation can be expressed more conveniently by introducing the function $G(r)$ defined by

$$R(r) = \frac{G(r)}{r}$$

Equation (115) is now replaced by

$$\frac{d^2G}{dr^2} + \frac{2m}{\hbar^2}\left[E - V(r) - \frac{l(l+1)\,\hbar^2}{2m\,r^2}\right] G = 0 \qquad (116)$$

An instructive classical analogy can be found for the last term inside the brackets. $m\,r^2$ is the instantaneous moment of inertia I of the particle about the centre of the force-field and $l(l+1)\,\hbar^2$ is the square of its angular momentum about this centre. Thus the term $\frac{l(l+1)\,\hbar^2}{2m\,r^2}$ is the quantum analogue of the rotational energy of the system. The negative sign indicates that this term corresponds to a repulsive force corresponding to a "centrifugal barrier".

The normalization condition for the new radial function $G(r)$ is

$$\int_0^\infty \frac{1}{r^2}\, G^*(r)\, G(r)\, dr = 1 \qquad (117)$$

In order that the original wave function $R(r)$ is well-behaved at the origin, $G(0)$ must be equal to zero.

6.10. THE HYDROGEN ATOM

The spherically symmetric potential energy function of the electron–nucleus Coulomb interaction is

$$V(r) = -\frac{Z\,e^2}{r}$$

It is advantageous to introduce the dimensionless parameters ϱ and ε in eqn. (116) where

$$\varrho = r/a \qquad (118)$$

and a is the radius of the first Bohr orbit

$$a = \frac{\hbar^2}{m\,e^2\,Z} \qquad (119)$$

$$\varepsilon_E^2 = \frac{-E}{E_0} = \frac{-E}{(\hbar^2/2m\,a^2)} \qquad (120)$$

E_0 is the ground state energy of the hydrogen atom according to the Bohr theory.

The potential energy can be expressed in terms of $\varepsilon^2(\varrho)$, where

$$\varepsilon^2(\varrho) = -\frac{V(r)}{E_0} = -\frac{V(r)}{(\hbar^2/2ma^2)} \tag{121}$$

The radial wave eqn. (116) now becomes

$$\frac{d^2G}{d\varrho^2} + \left[\varepsilon^2(\varrho) - \frac{l(l+1)}{\varrho^2} - \varepsilon_E^2\right] G = 0 \tag{122}$$

Restricting the solution of eqn. (122) to the states for which the orbital angular momentum is zero, $l = 0$, (s states), we require the well-behaved solutions of

$$\frac{d^2G}{d\varrho^2} + \left(\frac{2}{\varrho} - \varepsilon_E^2\right) G = 0 \tag{123}$$

First we note that for large values of r and therefore ϱ, the first term inside the brackets is negligible and eqn. (123) has the solution

$$G(\varrho) = C\exp(-\varepsilon_E\,\varrho) \quad \text{for} \quad \varrho \to \infty \tag{124}$$

Now as $G(0)$ must be zero, we try to express the solution of eqn. (123) for all values of ϱ by

$$G(\varrho) = \varrho\,[\exp(-\varepsilon_E\,\varrho)]\,F(\varrho) \tag{125}$$

where $F(\varrho)$ is a power series in ϱ

$$F(\varrho) = a_0 + a_1\varrho + a_2\varrho^2 + \cdots + a_j\varrho^j + \cdots \tag{126}$$

Differentiating eqn. (125) twice and substituting in eqn. (123) we obtain

$$\varrho\frac{d^2F}{d\varrho^2} + 2(1 - \varepsilon_E\,\varrho)\frac{dF}{d\varrho} + 2(1 - \varepsilon_E)\,F = 0 \tag{127}$$

Writing out the power series for F in eqn. (127) each term must be identically zero, and the coefficient of ϱ^j is

$$[j(j+1) + 2(j+1)]\,a_{j+1} + 2[1 - \varepsilon_E(j+1)]\,a_j = 0 \tag{128}$$

It can be shown that well-behaved solutions correspond to a finite number of terms. In order that this condition applies

$$\varepsilon_E = \frac{1}{j+1} = \frac{1}{n}, \quad \text{where} \quad n = 1, 2, 3, \ldots$$

Now $$\varepsilon_E^2 = -\frac{E}{E_0}$$

Hence $$E = -\frac{E_0}{n^2} = -\frac{\hbar^2}{2m\,a^2\,n^2} = -\frac{Z^2\,e^4\,m}{2\hbar^2\,n^2} \tag{129}$$

These quantized values of E, given by eqn. (129), are identical with the Bohr energy level values.

For the ground state, $n = 1$, the radial wave function $G_1(\varrho)$ is given by

$$G_1(\varrho) = a_0\,\varrho\exp(-\varepsilon_E\,\varrho) \tag{130}$$

$G_1(\varrho)$ tends to zero as $\varrho \to 0$ and $\varrho \to \infty$ but is finite for all values of ϱ between 0 and ∞.

For the second state, $n = 2$, $a_1 = -a_{0/2}$ and we have

$$G_2(\varrho) = a_0\varrho(1 - \varrho/2)\exp(-\varepsilon_E\varrho) \tag{131}$$

$G_2(\varrho)$ vanishes for $\varrho = 0$, $\varrho = 2$ and $\varrho = \infty$

Thus the wave function has one intermediate node between $\varrho = 0$ and $\varrho = \infty$. In the same way, it can be shown that the $3s$, $4s$, $5s$, ... state wave functions $G_3(\varrho)$, $G_4(\varrho)$, $G_5(\varrho)$, ... have 2, 3, 4 ... nodes respectively.

Solutions of the radial wave equation for $l = 1$, $l = 2$, ... can be found. We shall merely state the result that the energy eigenvalues are found to depend on n and not on l. For each value of n, l can assume the values 0, 1, 2, ..., $n - 1$. Also for each value of l there are $2l + 1$ possible values of the magnetic quantum number m. Therefore the number of eigenstates with the same energy, the total degeneracy as it is called, is equal to

$$\sum_{l=0}^{n-1}(2l + 1) = \frac{2n(n-1)}{2} + n = n^2$$

The degeneracy associated with the different magnetic sub-states is a consequence of the spherical symmetry of the potential energy function. On the other hand, the degeneracy with respect to the quantum number l, is a characteristic feature of the Coulomb potential. Thus if we consider the energy levels of the valency electron of an alkali metal atom, the potential energy is not strictly Coulomb and consequently the nth level is split into l sub-levels. The spherical symmetry of $V(r)$ is destroyed by the application of an external magnetic field and we now find that each magnetic sub-state has a different energy. This is the familiar Zeeman level splitting.

The Two-body Problem

It will be recalled that the Bohr theory of the hydrogen atom was able to take into consideration the motion of the nucleus by replacing the electron mass m in the energy level formula by the *reduced mass* $\mu = (m\,M)/(m + M)$, where M is the mass of the nucleus. We will now see how the reduced mass is introduced into the wave mechanical method.

The Schrödinger wave function ψ of a two-body system (electron plus nucleus) is a function of the spatial coordinates of both bodies as well as the time t

$$\psi = \psi(x_1, y_1, z_1, x_2, y_2, z_2, t)$$

where (x_1, y_1, z_1) are the position coordinates of the electron of mass m_1 and (x_2, y_2, z_2) are the position coordinates of the nucleus of mass m_2.

The Schrödinger equation can be written

$$\left(-\frac{\hbar^2}{2m_1}\nabla_1^2 - \frac{\hbar^2}{2m_2}\nabla_2^2 + V\right)\psi = i\hbar\frac{\partial\psi}{\partial t} \tag{132}$$

where $\nabla_1^2 \equiv \frac{\partial^2}{\partial x_1^2} + \frac{\partial^2}{\partial y_1^2} + \frac{\partial^2}{\partial z_1^2}$ and $\nabla_2^2 \equiv \frac{\partial^2}{\partial x_2^2} + \frac{\partial^2}{\partial y_2^2} + \frac{\partial^2}{\partial z_2^2}$

For the hydrogen atom, the function V depends only on the difference of the coordinates of the two interacting particles; writing

$$x = x_1 - x_2, \quad y = y_1 - y_2, \quad z = z_1 - z_2$$

we can say that V is a function of x, y, z.

Denoting the coordinates of the centre of mass of the system by X, Y and Z, we have

$$X = \frac{m_1 x_1 + m_2 x_2}{M}, \quad Y = \frac{m_1 y_1 + m_2 y_2}{M}, \quad Z = \frac{m_1 z_1 + m_2 z_2}{M}$$

where $M = m_1 + m_2$.
Hence we obtain

$$\frac{\partial}{\partial x_1} = \frac{m_1}{M}\frac{\partial}{\partial X} + \frac{\partial}{\partial x}, \quad \text{etc.}$$

and

$$\frac{\partial^2}{\partial x_1^2} = \left(\frac{m_1}{M}\right)^2 \cdot \frac{\partial^2}{\partial X^2} - \left(\frac{2m_1}{M}\right)\frac{\partial^2}{\partial X\,\partial x} + \frac{\partial^2}{\partial x^2}$$

$$\frac{\partial^2}{\partial x_2^2} = \left(\frac{m_2}{M}\right)^2 \cdot \frac{\partial^2}{\partial X^2} + \left(\frac{2m_2}{M}\right)\frac{\partial^2}{\partial X\,\partial x} + \frac{\partial^2}{\partial x^2}$$

Thus

$$\frac{1}{m_1}\frac{\partial^2}{\partial x_1^2} + \frac{1}{m_2}\frac{\partial^2}{\partial x_2^2} = \frac{1}{M}\frac{\partial^2}{\partial X^2} + \frac{1}{\mu}\frac{\partial^2}{\partial x^2}$$

where

$$\mu = \frac{m_1 m_2}{m_1 + m_2}$$

Equation (132) transforms to

$$\left\{-\frac{\hbar^2}{2M}\nabla_{X,Y,Z}^2 - \frac{\hbar^2}{2\mu}\nabla_{x,y,z}^2 + V(x, y, z)\right\}\psi = i\hbar\frac{\partial\psi}{\partial t} \tag{133}$$

where the suffixes in the ∇^2 symbols refer to the variables of differentiation. The form of eqn. (133) suggests that it might be possible to express $\psi(x, y, z, X, Y, Z, t)$ as the product of three functions

$$\psi = u(x, y, z)\, U(X, Y, Z) \exp\left(-\frac{i(E + E')\,t}{\hbar}\right) \tag{134}$$

Substituting in eqn. (133) we obtain the equations

$$-\frac{\hbar^2}{2\mu}\nabla^2 u + V u = E u \tag{135}$$

$$-\frac{\hbar^2}{2M}\nabla^2 U = E' U \tag{136}$$

Equation (136) is of minor interest; it describes the free motion of the centre of mass of the atom. The first eqn. (135), on the other hand, expresses the important result that the two-body interaction is effectively transformed into a one-body problem, provided the electron mass m_1 is replaced by μ the reduced mass of the system.

6.11. PARITY

We now turn to a number of general quantum mechanical concepts. The first of these is the idea of the *parity* of a particle or system. Suppose we consider the wave function $\psi(\boldsymbol{r}, t)$ of a particle or system and consider the effect on ψ of reflecting the position coordinates x, y, z, through the origin: $x \to -x$, $y \to -y$, $z \to -z$. This inversion or parity operation as it is called, is equivalent to changing from a right-handed system of Cartesian axes to a left-handed system. Now the probability function $\psi^* \psi$ cannot depend on the arbitrary choice of a left-handed or right-handed set of axes. Thus

$$|\psi(\boldsymbol{r}, t)|^2 = |\psi(-\boldsymbol{r}, t)|^2$$

The invariance of $\psi^* \psi$ under the parity operation leaves two possibilities for the behaviour of the wave function.

If
$$\psi(x, y, z) = \psi(-x, -y, -z)$$

the system is said to have *even* parity. A convenient notation for an eigen-state of known spin I and even parity is I^+, the plus sign denoting even parity.

If
$$\psi(x, y, z) = -\psi(-x, -y, -z)$$

the system is said to have *odd* parity, and this is indicated by a minus sign attached as a superscript to the spin of the state, i.e., I^-.

The concept of parity does not appear directly in classical physics, but it is intimately related to the reflection-symmetry properties of space. The operators of quantum mechanics possess parity characteristics. The position vector $\boldsymbol{r}$ of a particle obviously has odd parity, as do the momentum operators $-i\hbar\frac{\partial}{\partial x}$, $-i\hbar\frac{\partial}{\partial y}$, $-i\hbar\frac{\partial}{\partial z}$. Operators such as p_x^2, p_y^2, p_z^2 have even parity. A more complicated example is the angular momentum of a system. Thus a particle of mass dm at (x, y, z), which is rotating about the axis Oz, has an angular momentum

$$dG = dm\left(x \cdot \frac{\partial y}{\partial t} - y \cdot \frac{\partial x}{\partial t}\right)$$

The parity operation changes the sign of x and y on reflection through the origin, but also changes the sign of the velocity components $\frac{\partial x}{\partial t}$, $\frac{\partial y}{\partial t}$.

Thus dG has even parity. Angular momentum is an example, of what is known as an *axial vector*, whereas the position vector $\boldsymbol{r}$ is a *polar vector*. Polar vectors reflected through the origin change sign, whereas axial vectors reflected through the origin do not change sign.

In Section 6.8 we considered the wave mechanical treatment of the linear harmonic oscillator, without going as far as evaluating the eigenfunctions.† The first three eigenfunctions, for states with $n = 0, 1, 2$ respectively, are, apart from normalization factors, given by

$$u_0(x) \sim \exp\left(-\frac{x^2}{2a^2}\right), \quad a^4 = \frac{\hbar^2}{km} \quad \text{(see eqn. 80)}$$

$$u_1(x) \sim x \exp\left(-\frac{x^2}{2a^2}\right) \tag{137}$$

$$u_2(x) \sim \left(\frac{4x^2}{a^2} - 2\right) \exp\left(-\frac{x^2}{2a^2}\right)$$

Under the parity operation, it is easy to see that for the linear harmonic oscillator, the wave functions $u_0(x)$, $u_2(x)$, $u_4(x)$, ... of the states for n even have even parity. The parity of the states for which n is odd have odd parity.

Elementary particles possess an intrinsic parity. The particle must not have acceleration of any kind in order that we can assign an *intrinsic* parity. It is conventional to define the intrinsic parity of the electron, proton and neutron as even. The parity of other elementary particles must be determined by experiment and it has been established that the parity of the pion is odd.

The parity concept can be extended to include a group or system of particles such as an atom or atomic nucleus. At the outset it is important to understand that the parity of such a system is a property of its *state*; different excited states of a given nucleus may, and often do, possess different parities. Thus if the system contains n particles (nucleons say), the parity operation reflects all the position vectors $\boldsymbol{r}_1, \boldsymbol{r}_2, \ldots, \boldsymbol{r}_n$ through the origin. The system has even parity if

$$\psi(\boldsymbol{r}_1, \boldsymbol{r}_2, \ldots, \boldsymbol{r}_n) = \psi(-\boldsymbol{r}_1, -\boldsymbol{r}_2, \ldots, -\boldsymbol{r}_n).$$

and odd parity if

$$\psi(\boldsymbol{r}_1, \boldsymbol{r}_2, \ldots, \boldsymbol{r}_n) = -\psi(-\boldsymbol{r}_1, -\boldsymbol{r}_2, \ldots, -\boldsymbol{r}_n).$$

The inversion through the origin of the point whose spherical polar coordinates are (r, θ, φ) is equivalent to the rotation transformations:

$$\theta \to \pi - \theta; \quad \varphi \to \pi + \varphi$$

† See L. Pauling and E. B. Wilson, *Introduction to Quantum Mechanics*, McGraw-Hill, New York, 1935.

There is an important connection between the angular momentum l of a central-field system and its parity. This comes about as follows. The angular part of the wave function of the system is proportional to

$$\Theta_l^{|m|} \exp(i\, m\, \varphi)$$

where $\Theta_l^{|m|}$ is the associated Legendre function, given by

$$P_l^{|m|}(\cos\theta) \sin^{|m|}\theta$$

The transformation $\theta \rightarrow \pi - \theta$ leaves $\sin^{|m|}\theta$ unchanged, but if $l + m$ is odd, $P_l^{|m|}$ changes sign because it is an odd polynomial in $\cos\theta$.
Hence

$$P_l^{|m|}(\pi - \theta) = (-1)^{l+m} P_l^{|m|}(\theta)$$

The inversion operation $\varphi \rightarrow \pi + \varphi$ multiplies $\exp(i\, m\, \varphi)$ by $\exp(i\, m\, \pi)$. If m is even, $\exp(i\, m\, \pi) = +1$; if m is odd, $\exp(i\, m\, \pi) = -1$. Combining these results, we find that if l is even so is the parity of the system; whereas if l is odd so is the parity. This is true for all allowed values of m.

Parity is related to the symmetry properties of fundamental phenomena in physics. Long after the establishment of the important conservation laws of physics it was realized that these were essentially equivalent to certain symmetry properties of space and time. For example, it is assumed that the fundamental phenomena of physics are the same if they are observed at different places and different times; this is known as the principle of translational space–time symmetry. The laws of conservation of energy and conservation of linear momentum are in agreement with this symmetry principle. It is also assumed that the results of a fundamental experiment in physics are independent of the spatial orientation of the apparatus. This principle of rotation symmetry is related to the law of conservation of angular momentum. Symmetry concepts have played a great part in the history of art and science.† Leibniz expressed the view that Nature shows no preference for right-handed objects over left-handed objects. It may be argued that the existence of left-handed and right-handed spiral-like sugar molecules contradicts this view. Any preference in Nature for one type rather than the other is believed to be some accident of biological evolution, just as we find human beings with hearts on the left-hand side. The laws of physics are assumed to be invariant with respect to reflection; that is, a mirror image world would leave the laws of physics unchanged. This reflection symmetry principle is equivalent to the statement that:

"The parity of a closed system cannot change".

The law of conservation of parity has been of great value in nuclear physics, as it is possible to make important predictions concerning nuclear reactions and decays, without detailed knowledge of the nuclear wave functions. Recently (1957), however, it was suggested by T. D. Lee and C. N. Yang

† H. Weyl, *Symmetry*, Princeton University Press, 1932.

that in the so-called "weak interactions" responsible for beta decay, muon decay, Nature discriminates strongly between left and right-handed systems. The non-conservation of parity in "weak interactions" has been confirmed by many experiments and has led to a marked advance in our knowledge of "weak interactions".†

6.12. QUANTUM STATISTICS

In dealing with the collective behaviour of a number of *identical* particles it is necessary to employ statistical methods. The system may be the molecules of a gas, the photons in equilibrium with the walls of a cavity at a constant temperature, the conduction electrons in a metal, the atomic nuclei in a crystal . . . etc. Suppose we consider a system of n identical particles. The complete wave function ψ of the system will depend on the space (and spin) coordinates of the n particles; $\boldsymbol{r}_1, \boldsymbol{r}_2, \ldots, \boldsymbol{r}_n$. Interchanging the position (and spin) coordinates of any two of the n *indistinguishable* particles has no effect on the probability function $\psi^* \psi$, as there is no *observable* change in the system. Symbolically, we can express this by considering the interchange of particles 1 and 2, and writing

$$|\psi(\boldsymbol{r}_1, \boldsymbol{r}_2, \boldsymbol{r}_3, \ldots, \boldsymbol{r}_n)|^2 \equiv |\psi(\boldsymbol{r}_2, \boldsymbol{r}_1, \boldsymbol{r}_3, \ldots, \boldsymbol{r}_n)|^2$$

The identity holds for the interchange of any pair (or pairs) of particles. There is still, however, an ambiguity regarding the wave functions. If the interchange of any two particles leaves the wave function of the complete system unchanged it is called a *symmetric wavefunction*

$$\psi(\boldsymbol{r}_1, \boldsymbol{r}_2, \boldsymbol{r}_3, \ldots, \boldsymbol{r}_n) = \psi(\boldsymbol{r}_2, \boldsymbol{r}_1, \boldsymbol{r}_3, \ldots, \boldsymbol{r}_n)$$

If, on the other hand, the interchange of any two particles changes the sign of the wave function it is called an *antisymmetric wavefunction.*

$$\psi(\boldsymbol{r}_1, \boldsymbol{r}_2, \boldsymbol{r}_3, \ldots, \boldsymbol{r}_n) = -\psi(\boldsymbol{r}_2, \boldsymbol{r}_1, \boldsymbol{r}_3, \ldots, \boldsymbol{r}_n)$$

It is important not to confuse the parity operation with the operation involving the interchange of two particles (there are special systems where the operations are identical; see below).

An important experimental law connecting the statistical behaviour of a system of particles and their intrinsic spin is that a system of particles of integral spin (in terms of the unit $\hbar$) has a symmetric wavefunction, whereas a system of particles of half-integral spin has an antisymmetric wavefunction. A system with a symmetric wavefunction obeys the statistical laws of *Bose–Einstein*. The individual particles are called *bosons*: examples are photons, pions, deuterons, alpha particles, N^{14} nuclei. A system described by an antisymmetric wavefunction obeys the laws of *Fermi–Dirac*

† See Chapter 14, Section 7.

statistics. The individual particles are known as *fermions*: examples are electrons, protons, neutrons, neutrinos. The antisymmetry property of a collection of fermions can be shown to lead to the Pauli Exclusion Principle, a remarkable result.

Let us consider a system of two bosons; the complete wave function ψ of the system must be symmetric. This wave function can be written as the product of a spatial wave function φ and a spin wave function α,

$$\psi = \varphi\,\alpha$$

If the boson spin is not zero, the spin function can be either symmetric or antisymmetric depending on the relative orientation of the spin axes of the two bosons. Thus if α is antisymmetric, φ is antisymmetric; if α is symmetric, φ is symmetric. There is no restriction on the allowed values of orbital angular momenta. Suppose however the two bosons have zero spin; then there is no spin direction to orient the particles and α must be a symmetric function. Hence φ is a symmetric funtion. The O_2^{16} molecule is an example of two bosons (O^{16} nuclei) of zero spin. Interchanging the two nuclei is equivalent to the parity inversion operation. Therefore the parity of the molecule is the same as the symmetry property of interchanging the two O^{16} nuclei. Hence all states of the O_2^{16} molecule have even parity and we saw in the last section that even parity corresponds to even values of the orbital angular momentum quantum number l. This prediction is borne out by observations of the rotational band spectra of the O_2^{16} molecule as alternate lines, corresponding to odd values of l, are missing.

Destroying the symmetry by substituting an O^{17} nucleus for one of the O^{16} nuclei in the O_2^{16} molecule, the restriction on l is removed and the alternate lines of the band spectrum appear. Thus we see that the symmetry properties of the nuclei have a profound influence on the *electronic* behaviour of the molecule.

6.13. THE COMMUTATION LAWS

The representation of dynamical variables by linear operators leads to the general conclusion that such operators do not always obey the commutative law of algebra. Thus if α and β are two operators

$$\alpha\beta - \beta\alpha \neq 0$$

Using the Schrödinger differential operators for a position coordinate $q = x$ of a particle and its corresponding momentum coordinate $p = m\dot{x}$, we can evaluate the operator relation

$$qp - pq$$

where p is represented by the differential operator $-i\hbar\dfrac{\partial}{\partial x}$.

Thus we can write

$$(q\,p - p\,q)\,\psi = q\left(-\,i\hbar\frac{\partial\psi}{\partial x}\right) + i\hbar\frac{\partial}{\partial x}(q\,\psi)$$

$$= -\,i\hbar\,q\frac{\partial\psi}{\partial x} + i\hbar\,q\frac{\partial\psi}{\partial x} + i\hbar\,\psi = i\hbar\,\psi$$

or

$$q\,p - p\,q = i\hbar \tag{138}$$

The value of $\alpha\,\beta - \beta\,\alpha$ is known as the commutator of the operators α and β. Equation (138) is a special case of the general quantum mechanical law

$$\alpha\,\beta - \beta\,\alpha = i\hbar[\alpha, \beta] \tag{139}$$

where $[\alpha, \beta]$ is the operator associated with the Poisson bracket of the dynamical variables α and β. For a system with one degree of freedom the Poisson bracket $[\alpha, \beta]$ is given by

$$[\alpha, \beta] = \frac{\partial\alpha}{\partial q}\cdot\frac{\partial\beta}{\partial p} - \frac{\partial\alpha}{\partial p}\cdot\frac{\partial\beta}{\partial q} \tag{140}$$

Equation (138) follows from eqns. (139) and (140) as $[q, p] = 1$.

Not all dynamical variables fail to obey the commutative law of algebra. The breakdown of the commutation law is intimately connected with the quantum uncertainty principle (see next section). Observables which obey the law $\alpha\,\beta = \beta\,\alpha$ are said to commute and they are essentially non-interfering in the sense that the operation of measuring one of the variables α does not disturb the simultaneous measurement of the other variable β. The failure of the commutative law is a recognition of the discovery that it is often impossible *in principle* to determine simultaneously the precise values of the variables α and β.

6.14. THE HEISENBERG UNCERTAINTY PRINCIPLE

It was indicated in the last section that the breakdown of the commutative law of quantum mechanical operators is related to the fundamental impossibility of precise simultaneous measurement of certain dynamical variables. Thus it is possible to prove using the operator formalism, as was first done by Heisenberg, that the simultaneous measurement of the canonically conjugate variables x and p of a particle, where x is a position coordinate and p the corresponding momentum coordinate, cannot be done with a precision better than that implied by the relation

$$\Delta x \cdot \Delta p \geqq \hbar/2 \tag{141}$$

Δx and Δp are the uncertainties in our knowledge of the variables x and p

However it is possibly more instructive to consider the argument o Heisenberg concerning a "thought experiment" to measure x and p Suppose we attempted to measure simultaneously the x position coordinat and momentum of an electron by scattering light into a high power microscope. Thus in order to "see" and locate the electron we must scatter at least one photon into the microscope objective (Fig. 9). An electron in the vicinity of O scattering incident light from the left into the microscope produces a diffraction pattern image, so that, at best, we can locate the electron with a precision given by the well-known formula in wave optics

$$\Delta x \sim \frac{\lambda}{2 \sin u} \tag{142}$$

where λ is the wavelength of the scattered light and $2u$ is the angle subtended at O by the aperture of the microscope objective. The uncertainty Δx can be made small by using short wavelength radiation ("hard" gamma rays)

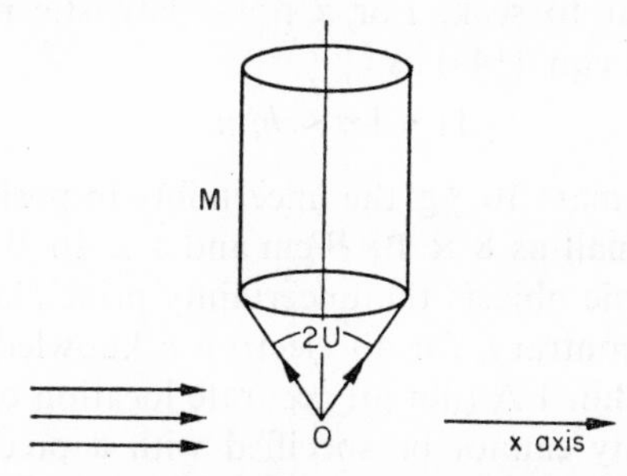

FIG. 9. Light scattered by a particle into the high power microscope M. Extreme rays subtend angle $2u$ at O.

and a large aperture angle u. Unfortunately these conditions interfere with the accurate determination of the electron's x-component of momentum. The electron recoils under the impact of the incident photon (Compton effect) and this disturbs the momentum of the electron. The fact that the act of measuring a physical quantity alters its magnitude is of course not a new discovery! The new discovery is that in the realm of quantum physics it is not possible *in principle* to determine the precise extent of the disturbance involved. Thus we cannot evaluate the change in the electron's momentum as we cannot say what is the precise scattering angle of a photon which passes through the microscope. If the photon is scattered through an angle $(90 - u)$ the change in the x-component of the electron's momentum is approximately equal to

$$\frac{h}{\lambda}(1 - \sin u)$$

On the other hand, if the photon is scattered through the angle $(90 + u)$ the corresponding momentum change is

$$\frac{h}{\lambda}(1 + \sin u)$$

Thus the uncertainty in the disturbance and hence the uncertainty in our knowledge of p, just prior to the scattering event is given by the difference in these extremes,

$$\Delta p \sim \frac{2h}{\lambda} \sin u \tag{143}$$

Closing up the aperture and using long wavelength radiation will reduce this uncertainty in the electron's momentum determination. These requirements are however just the ones to reduce the resolving power of the microscope. Combining eqns. (142) and (143) we find that

$$\Delta p \, \Delta x \sim h \tag{144}$$

Why have we not stumbled across this uncertainty in macroscopic physics? The answer is not far to seek. For a non-relativistic moving particle of mass m, we can write eqn. (144) as

$$\Delta v \cdot \Delta x \sim h/m$$

and for a particle of mass 10^{-6} g, the uncertainty in position Δx and velocity Δv could be as small as 8×10^{-11} cm and 8×10^{-11} cm per sec respectively. For macroscopic objects the uncertainty principle is of no practical importance. On the contrary, for an electron a knowledge of the location of the particle to within 1 Å (not an accurate location on an atomic scale) means that its velocity cannot be specified with a precision greater than 6×10^8 cm per sec! We now begin to understand Heisenberg's lack of confidence in the precise classical-like electron orbits of the Bohr atomic model.

A second uncertainty relation of prime importance is concerned with the simultaneous attempt to specify the energy of a system at a particular time. Thus if ΔE and Δt are the uncertainties in the energy E and time t

$$\Delta E \cdot \Delta t \geqq \frac{\hbar}{2} \tag{145}$$

To illustrate this consider an attempt to determine the energy of a photon within a short epoch dt by opening for this time a shutter in a screen which is illuminated with a parallel beam of monochromatic light (Fig. 10). The wave train passing through the opening is cut short to a length of the order $c\,dt$, where c is the velocity of light. This short wave train is no longer monochromatic and a Fourier analysis shows that there is a continuous distribution of spectral components over a frequency band $d\nu$ of the order of $1/(dt)$. This frequency spread means that the photon's energy E is undetermined to an extent $dE = h\,d\nu$. Combining this uncertainty with our ignorance dt in the time of transit of the photon through the shutter we obtain

$$dE \cdot dt \sim h\,d\nu \cdot dt \sim h$$

The energy–time uncertainty relation has an important bearing on the natural widths of atomic and nuclear energy states. Suppose at $t = 0$, n_0 nuclei are in an excited energy state. The decay of the excited nuclei from this state is governed by the law of radioactive decay; that is, after time t, n, the number of nuclei remaining in the excited state is given by

$$n = n_0 \exp(-\lambda t)$$

or

$$n = n_0 \exp\left(-\frac{t}{\tau}\right) \tag{146}$$

where λ is the decay constant, and $1/\lambda = \tau$ is the mean lifetime of a nucleus in this state. In specifying the energy of the excited state we insist that it has this energy with a time uncertainty of the order of τ. This in conjunction

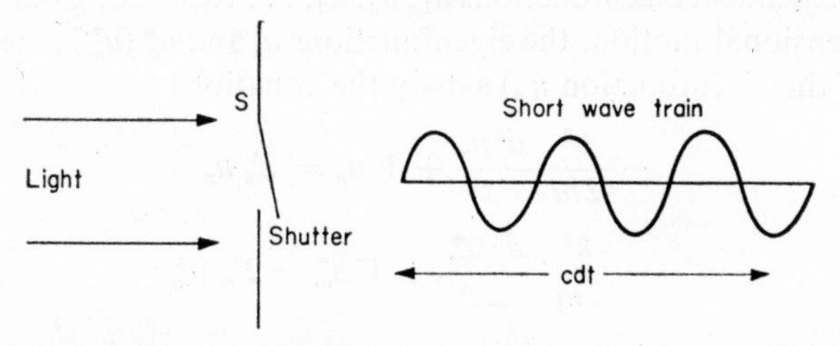

FIG. 10. Shutter in screen S open for a short time dt allows a short wave train of length $c\,dt$ to pass through.

with eqn. (145) means that the energy of the state has a natural spread or width ΔE given by

$$\Delta E \cdot \tau \sim \hbar \tag{147}$$

If the width ΔE is measured in electron volts, eqn. (147) becomes

$$\Delta E \cdot \tau \sim 6 \times 10^{-16} \text{ eV-sec} \tag{148}$$

Thus a state with a lifetime of 6×10^{-16} sec has a width of 1 eV.†

One of the most interesting applications of the energy–time uncertainty relation is the discovery of "virtual" particles. Recent theoretical developments in the quantum theory of radiation, including the theory of the Lamb frequency shift (see Chapter 2), have made great use of the concept of "virtual" photons. These virtual photons are physically unobservable but are exchanged to and fro between electrically charged particles and are responsible for the Coulomb interaction. They have a fleeting existence and they are created in apparent contradiction to the law of conservation of energy. The uncertainty principle comes to the rescue in the sense that it

† An interesting analogy is discussed in relation to the band-width and signal duration in a "communication system" by D. GABOR, Theory of Communication, *J. Inst. Elec. Engs.* **93**, Part III, 429, 1946.

is possible for a system to "borrow" an amount of energy ΔE provided it is "repaid" within the time interval Δt, where $\Delta E \, \Delta t \sim \hbar$. This startling idea has proved to be of great importance in extending the range of quantum field theory. It is not surprising to find that if sufficient energy is available to a system of electric charges, real (observable) photons are created, that is, light is emitted. In an analogous way the short-range nuclear force between two nucleons is pictured in terms of the exchange of virtual mesons. If sufficient energy is supplied real mesons are created and can be observed.

6.15. ORTHOGONAL PROPERTY OF EIGENFUNCTIONS

Consider a system with a series of discrete energy states described by the time-independent eigenfunctions $u_1, u_2, u_3, \ldots$ Restricting our discussion to one dimensional motion, the eigenfunctions u_n and u_m^* (u_m^* is the conjugate complex of the eigenfunction u_m) satisfy the equations

$$-\frac{\hbar^2}{2m}\frac{d^2 u_n}{dx^2} + V u_n = E_n u_n \tag{149}$$

$$-\frac{\hbar^2}{2m}\frac{d^2 u_m^*}{dx^2} + V u_m^* = E_m u_m^* \tag{150}$$

where E_n and E_m are the eigenvalues associated with states n and m. Multiplying eqn. (149) by u_m^* and eqn. (150) by u_n and subtracting, we obtain

$$u_m^* \frac{d^2 u_n}{dx^2} - u_n \frac{d^2 u_m^*}{dx^2} = \frac{2m}{\hbar^2}(E_m - E_n)\, u_m^* u_n$$

$$\therefore \quad \int_{-\infty}^{\infty} \frac{d}{dx}\left(u_m^* \frac{d u_n}{dx} - u_n \frac{d u_m^*}{dx}\right) dx = \int_{-\infty}^{\infty} \frac{2m}{\hbar^2}(E_m - E_n)\, u_m^* u_n \, dx$$

Now

$$\left[u_m^* \frac{d u_n}{dx} - u_n \frac{d u_m^*}{dx}\right]_{-\infty}^{\infty}$$

is zero, because the wave functions u_m^* and u_n must tend to zero at $\pm\infty$. Thus we find that

$$\frac{2\pi}{\hbar^2}(E_m - E_n) \int_{-\infty}^{\infty} u_m^* u_n \, dx = 0 \tag{151}$$

Hence $$\int_{-\infty}^{\infty} u_m^* u_n \, dx = 0, \quad \text{unless} \quad n = m$$

This theorem applies to the complete wavefunctions ψ_m^*, ψ_n and it can be shown to be true for motion in three dimensions. Thus we can express the orthogonality of wave functions belonging to different eigenstates by the relation

$$\int \psi_m^* \psi_n \, d\tau = \delta_{mn}, \quad \text{where} \quad \delta_{mn} = 0 \quad \text{if} \quad m \neq n\dagger$$
$$\delta_{mn} = 1 \quad \text{if} \quad m = n \tag{152}$$

The term orthogonal is used because of the similarity to the vanishing of the scalar product of two orthogonal vectors.

6.16. ELEMENTARY PERTURBATION THEORY

It frequently happens in quantum mechanics that certain problems can be treated in terms of the effect of a small perturbing interaction on a system of well-defined eigenfunctions and eigenvalues. Examples of this method of approach include the interaction of an external magnetic field with the energy states of an atom (Zeeman splitting) and the phenomena of stimulated emission and absorption of electromagnetic radiation. A simple approximate perturbation treatment of this type of problem is to represent the state of the disturbed system in terms of an expansion of the *unperturbed energy eigenfunctions.* Suppose H_0 is the Hamiltonian function of the undisturbed system; then we can write for this *undisturbed* system

$$H_0 \psi = i \hbar \frac{\partial \psi}{\partial t} \tag{153}$$

The general solution is

$$\psi = a_1 \psi_1 + a_2 \psi_2 + \cdots + a_n \psi_n \tag{154}$$

where

$$\sum_{i=1}^{n} |a_j^2| = 1$$

If the interaction is switched on, we can write the new Hamiltonian in the form $H_0 + \mathscr{V}$. Remember the perturbing potential is small compared with H_0. The modified Schrödinger equation is

$$(H_0 + \mathscr{V}) \psi = i \hbar \frac{\partial \psi}{\partial t} \tag{155}$$

As the eigenfunctions $\psi_1, \psi_2, \ldots \psi_n$ form a complete set we can express the solution of the modified Schrödinger equation, eqn. (155), as a series in $\psi_1, \psi_2, \ldots \psi_n$. We now regard the coefficients $a_1, a_2, a_3 \ldots$ as *variables in time,* representing the possibility that the interaction potential $\mathscr{V}$ may cause a transition from one state to another. This method of "variation of coefficients", first introduced by Dirac, allows us to follow the changes that result from the perturbing potential as we are dealing with quasi-stationary

† δ_{mn} is known as the Kronecker delta symbol.

energy states. Writing $b_1, b_2, \ldots b_n$ for the new coefficients, which may vary with time, we have

$$\psi = b_1 \psi_1 + b_2 \psi_2 + \cdots + b_n \psi_n$$

Substituting in eqn. (155)

$$\sum_i b_i H_0 \psi_i + \sum_i b_i \mathscr{V} \psi_i = i\hbar \sum_i \left\{ \frac{db_i}{dt} \psi_i + b_i \frac{\partial \psi_i}{\partial t} \right\} \tag{156}$$

Using eqns. (153) and (154) we obtain

$$\sum_i \frac{db_i}{dt} \psi_i = -\frac{i}{\hbar} \sum_i b_i \mathscr{V} \psi_i \tag{157}$$

Multiplying by ψ_n^* and integrating over all space, we obtain with the aid of the orthogonality theorem (eqn. (152)),

$$\frac{db_n}{dt} = -\frac{i}{\hbar} \sum b_i \int \psi_n^* \mathscr{V} \psi_i \, d\tau \tag{158}$$

This equation expresses the rate at which the coefficient a_n varies with time after the perturbation is switched on. Suppose, for example, the unperturbed system was originally in the eigenstate m, so that $a_m = 1$ and all the other a's are zero. After the perturbing potential is applied at $t = 0$, the magnitudes of the various coefficients $b_1, b_2, \ldots$ begin to increase and b_m will begin to decrease. This effect represents the possibility that the perturbing potential $\mathscr{V}$ will induce a transition of the system from the original state m to one of the other states. If the interaction is weak, we can assume that the rate of decrease of b_m is small, and b_m remains nearly equal to unity, at least for a short time t. The rate of increase of b_n at the expense of b_m($\sum |b_i|^2$ must always equal unity), can be written

$$\frac{db_{mn}}{dt} = -\frac{i}{\hbar} \int \psi_n^* \mathscr{V} \psi_m \, d\tau \tag{159}$$

or

$$b_{mn} = -\frac{i}{\hbar} \int_0^t \int \psi_n^* \mathscr{V} \psi_m \, d\tau \, dt \tag{160}$$

The coefficient has been written as b_{mn} because $|b_{mn}|^2$ measures the probability of finding the system at time t in the nth state as the result of a transition from the mth state. Integrals of the type $\int \psi_n^* \mathscr{V} \psi_m \, d\tau$ are of great importance in quantum mechanics and they are closely related to the mathematical language of matrix mechanics. Integrals of this type are known as matrix elements of the operator $\mathscr{V}$ and are conveniently abbreviated to $(n|\mathscr{V}|m)$. Notice that they are concerned with the transition probabilities from state m to state n.

To illustrate the application of these results we now consider the phenomenon of radiation. The function $e\,\psi_n^* \psi_n$ describes the electron charge distribution of an electron in an atom in the state n. The electric dipole moment $\boldsymbol{\mu}$ is assumed to be given by the integral†

$$e \int \psi_n^* \boldsymbol{r} \psi_n \, d\tau \tag{161}$$

where $\boldsymbol{r}$ is the position vector from the origin to the point where the wave function is evaluated. Classical radiation theory predicts that radiation is emitted if the dipole moment oscillates. The power of the radiation is given by

$$I = \frac{2}{3c^3} |\ddot{\mu}|^2 \tag{162}$$

It is found that the dipole moment integral, expression (161), vanishes for all the eigenstates of the atom; thus expression (162) also vanishes and we now have a justification for Bohr's assumption that the allowed energy states of an atom are stationary and do not emit radiation. This in effect means that the different radiation contributions from the electron cloud distribution in the atom completely cancel by destructive interference. We know that radiation is emitted in transitions between eigenstates, so it seems reasonable to associate a dipole moment $\boldsymbol{\mu}_{mn}$ with a quantum jump from state m to state n, where

$$\boldsymbol{\mu}_{mn} = e \int \psi_n^* \boldsymbol{r} \psi_m \, d\tau \tag{163}$$

Introducing the time-independent wave functions u_n^*, u_m,

$$\psi_n^* = u_n^* \exp\left(\frac{i E_n t}{\hbar}\right)$$

$$\psi_m = u_m \exp\left(-\frac{i E_m t}{\hbar}\right)$$

$\boldsymbol{\mu}_{mn}$ can be written

$$\boldsymbol{\mu}_{mn} = e \exp(-2\pi i \nu_{mn} t) \int u_n^* \boldsymbol{r} u_m \, d\tau \tag{164}$$

where

$$\nu_{mn} = \frac{E_m - E_n}{h} \tag{165}$$

The integral $\int u_n^* \boldsymbol{r} u_m \, d\tau$ is a permanent property of the atom and is a matrix element of the position coordinate $\boldsymbol{r}$, which is sometimes written in the form $\boldsymbol{r}_{mn}$. Substituting the expression (164) for $\boldsymbol{\mu}_{mn}$ in the classical radiation formula (162) we obtain for the energy radiated per unit time

$$I = \frac{2e^2}{3c^3} (2\pi \nu_{mn})^4 |\boldsymbol{r}_{mn}|^2 \tag{166}$$

If the matrix elements $\boldsymbol{r}_{mn}$ vanish for any pair of eigenstates no radiation is emitted. It can be shown that this happens unless $\Delta l = \pm 1, \Delta m = 0, \pm 1$.

† This is intimately related to the expectation value of the operator μ.

In this way, quantum mechanics makes sense of the empirical selection rules introduced in the old quantum theory.

The absorption of radiation can be treated in the following way. Consider an atom initially in the state m (not necessarily the ground state) and at $t = 0$ the atom is bathed in monochromatic polarized light for a short time t'. The incident beam of polarized light can be described by the equation

$$E_x = 2E_{0x} \cos 2\pi \nu t = E_{0x}\{\exp(2\pi i \nu t) + \exp(-2\pi i \nu t)\} \quad (167)$$

The electric field of the radiation sweeping over the atom perturbs the eigenstates and as the wavelength of the radiation is long compared to the diameter of the atom, the interaction potential energy can be written as

$$\mathscr{V} = E_x e x \quad (168)$$

Substituting eqn. (167) in eqn. (168) and then in eqn. (160) we get

$$b_{mn} = -\frac{i e E_{0x}}{\hbar} \int_0^{t'} \{\exp[2\pi i(\nu - \nu_{mn}) t]$$

$$+ \exp[-2\pi i(\nu + \nu_{mn}) t]\} \, dt \int u_n^* x \, u_m \, d\tau \quad (169)$$

Writing x_{mn} for the matrix element $\int u_n^* x \, u_m \, d\tau$, and evaluating the integral involving t we obtain,

$$b_{mn} = \frac{e x_{mn} E_{0x}}{\hbar} \left[\frac{1 - \exp[2\pi i(\nu - \nu_{mn}) t']}{\nu - \nu_{mn}} - \frac{1 - \exp[-2\pi i(\nu + \nu_{mn}) t']}{\nu + \nu_{mn}} \right] \quad (170)$$

If ν_{mn} is positive and ν is very close to ν_{mn} the first term inside the brackets is very large compared with the second term and the high value of b_{mn} signifies the resonant process of the incident radiation inducing *stimulated emission* of radiation from the initial state m to the lower state n. On the other hand, if ν_{mn} is negative and ν is very close to ν_{mn}, the second term inside the brackets is very large compared with the first term and we have the phenomenon of *resonant absorption* involving a transition of the atom from state m to a higher state n.

6.17. MATRIX MECHANICS

The first approach to the formulation of a new quantum mechanics was conceived by W. Heisenberg in 1925. The guiding principle of his method was to free the fundamental theory of atomic phenomena from the introduction of entities which were essentially unobservable. In a sense there are many quantities still directly unobservable, Schrödinger's wave function ψ is one, but observables such as the probability function $\psi^* \psi$ are directly related to this type of unobservable. On the other hand, any attempt to locate the precise position of an orbital atomic electron would only succeed in ejecting it from the orbit; thus exact location is a meaningless concept.

Accepting the notion of stationary energy states from the Bohr theory, Heisenberg retains those aspects of the theory directly related to the observed spectral radiations. These are the frequencies and intensities of the atomic spectral lines. A natural way of setting out the observed frequencies is to arrange them in rows and columns. Such an array is known as a *matrix*.

$$\begin{matrix} \nu_{00} & \nu_{01} & \nu_{02} & \nu_{03} & \cdots \\ \nu_{10} & \nu_{11} & \nu_{12} & \nu_{13} & \cdots \\ \nu_{20} & \nu_{21} & \nu_{22} & \nu_{23} & \cdots \end{matrix}$$

The matrix element ν_{mn} corresponds to the frequency emitted when the atom makes a transition from state m to state n and ν_{mn} is given by the Bohr relation

$$\nu_{mn} = \frac{E_m - E_n}{h}$$

It follows that the matrix elements $\nu_{00}, \nu_{11}, \nu_{22}, \ldots$ are all zero and $\nu_{mn} = -\nu_{nm}$.

In a similar way we can set up an *amplitude matrix*, where the matrix element a_{mn} has the property that $|a_{mn}|^2$ is the intensity of the radiation associated with the spectral frequency ν_{mn}.

Thus we find that in matrix mechanics the linear operators representing the dynamical variables are arrays of numbers known as matrices. These arrays obey the laws of matrix algebra and a concise summary of the basic laws and definitions are given in the next section. The Schrödinger equation

$$H\psi = E\psi$$

is still valid and useful, but different mathematical entities are introduced to represent H and ψ. The Hamiltonian function is now represented by a matrix and the eigenfunction ψ is represented by a special type of matrix, a single row of numbers; each number can be regarded as the component of a vector in a fictitious space (possibly of infinite dimensions). The equation $H\psi = E\psi$ still has the significance that the stationary energy states of a system are those for which the Hamiltonian operator (matrix) acting on the eigenfunction ψ_n (eigenvector) simply multiplies the eigenvector ψ_n by a number E_n. The number E_n is one of the energy eigenvalues. This operator equation also applies to other dynamical variables besides the Hamiltonian, such as the angular momentum of the system. Thus if α is the matrix representing the dynamical variable α, eigenvalues of α correspond to the numbers λ which satisfy the operator equation

$$\alpha\psi = \lambda\psi$$

Matrix Algebra

The concept of a matrix arises when we consider linear transformations. Consider the transformation produced by rotating two rigid Cartesian axes O x, O y, counter-clockwise in the plane of O x y through an angle θ. The new axes are O x' and O y' (Fig. 11). The transformation equations connecting the position coordinates of any point P are

$$\begin{aligned} x' &= \cos\theta \cdot x + \sin\theta \cdot y \\ y' &= -\sin\theta \cdot x + \cos\theta \cdot y \end{aligned} \tag{171}$$

Extending the rotation of axes to a rigid set of three cartesian axes and denoting x by x_1, y by x_2, z by x_3 and x' by x'_1, y' by x'_2, z' by x'_3, we can express the transformation equations in the form

$$\begin{aligned} x'_1 &= \alpha_{11} x_1 + \alpha_{12} x_2 + \alpha_{13} x_3 \\ x'_2 &= \alpha_{21} x_1 + \alpha_{22} x_2 + \alpha_{23} x_3 \\ x'_3 &= \alpha_{31} x_1 + \alpha_{32} x_2 + \alpha_{33} x_3 \end{aligned} \tag{172}$$

where the quantities α_{ij} are the direction cosines of the ith axis in the primed system with respect to the jth axis in the unprimed system. It is convenient to abbreviate this set of transformation equations and tabulate the *rotation matrix* α

$$\begin{pmatrix} \alpha_{11} & \alpha_{12} & \alpha_{13} \\ \alpha_{21} & \alpha_{22} & \alpha_{23} \\ \alpha_{31} & \alpha_{32} & \alpha_{33} \end{pmatrix}$$

(a) A matrix of this type with the same number of rows and columns is called a *square matrix*. It is possible to have matrices with more rows than columns and vice versa. The notation shown above for labelling the individual matrix elements means that α_{ij} is the element occurring in the ith row and jth column.

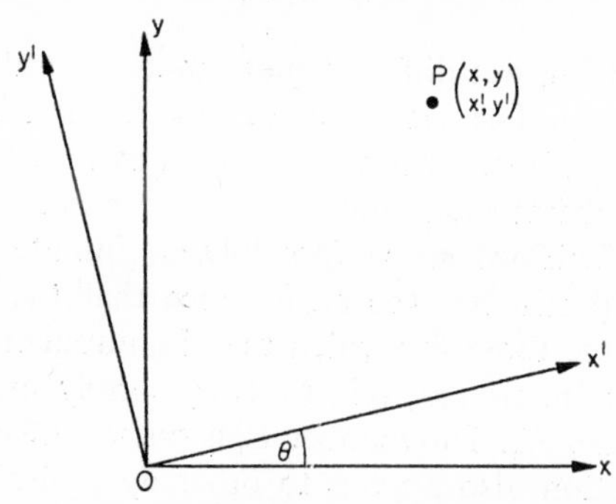

FIG. 11. Rotation of axes through angle θ.

† A lucid and concise summary of the basic properties of matrix algebra is given in E. P. WIGNER, *Group Theory* (translated by J. J. GRIFFIN), Academic Press, New York, 1959, Chap. 1.

(b) Two matrices are equal if, and only if, they contain the same number of rows p, the same number of columns q (p not necessarily equal to q) and if corresponding elements α_{ij} are equal for all values of i and j.

(c) Two matrices α and β can be added if they have the same number of rows p and the same number of columns q (p not necessarily equal to q). The resultant matrix is obtained by adding corresponding elements. Thus the element in the ith row and jth column of the matrix $(\alpha + \beta)$ is equal to

$$\alpha_{ij} + \beta_{ij}$$

Thus
$$\begin{pmatrix} 3 & 2 \\ -4 & 1 \\ 2 & 5 \end{pmatrix} + \begin{pmatrix} -1 & 3 \\ 2 & 4 \\ 3 & 3 \end{pmatrix} = \begin{pmatrix} 2 & 5 \\ -2 & 5 \\ 5 & 8 \end{pmatrix}$$

(d) The difference of two matrices α and β is defined so that the element in the ith row, jth column of $(\alpha - \beta)$ is equal to

$$\alpha_{ij} - \beta_{ij}$$

(e) Multiplying a matrix by a number c multiplies every element of the matrix by c.

Thus
$$3 \times \begin{pmatrix} 2 & 1 \\ 3 & -2 \end{pmatrix} = \begin{pmatrix} 6 & 3 \\ 9 & -6 \end{pmatrix}$$

(f) The most important law of matrix algebra is the law of matrix multiplication. Suppose we return to the rotation matrix α and consider the effect of a second rotation operation β following the first rotation operation α The combined effect is represented by the rotation matrix $\beta\alpha$. (The order of rotations must be maintained as $\alpha\beta$ does not produce the same effect as $\beta\alpha$.) It can be shown that the *product matrix* $\beta\alpha$ is formed by the rule that the element in the ith row, jth column of $\beta\alpha$ is given by the sum rule

$$(\beta\alpha)_{ij} = \sum_k \beta_{ik}\alpha_{kj} \tag{173}$$

In words this rules states that to obtain the element in the ith row jth column of the product matrix $\beta\alpha$, multiply each element in the ith row of β by the corresponding element in the jth column of α and sum the products. An example of this rule is

$$\begin{pmatrix} 2 & 1 & 3 \\ 3 & 1 & -2 \\ -1 & 0 & 2 \end{pmatrix} \times \begin{pmatrix} 1 & 4 & -2 \\ 0 & 2 & 1 \\ 3 & 1 & 1 \end{pmatrix} =$$

$$= \begin{pmatrix} 2.1 + 1.0 + 3.3 & 2.4 + 1.2 + 3.1 & 2(-2) + 1.1 + 3.1 \\ 3.1 + 1.0 - 2.3 & 3.4 + 1.2 - 2.1 & 3(-2) + 1.1 - 2.1 \\ -1.1 + 0.0 + 2.3 & -1.4 + 0.2 + 2.1 & -1(-2) + 0.1 + 2.1 \end{pmatrix} =$$

$$= \begin{pmatrix} 11 & 13 & 0 \\ -3 & 12 & -7 \\ 5 & -2 & 4 \end{pmatrix}$$

If the order of multiplication is reversed we do *not* get the same result. Thus we find

$$\begin{pmatrix} 1 & 4 & -2 \\ 0 & 2 & 1 \\ 3 & 1 & 1 \end{pmatrix} \times \begin{pmatrix} 2 & 1 & 3 \\ 3 & 1 & -2 \\ -1 & 0 & 2 \end{pmatrix} = \begin{pmatrix} 16 & 5 & -9 \\ 5 & 2 & -2 \\ 8 & 4 & 9 \end{pmatrix}$$

(g) The failure of the commutative law $\alpha\beta = \beta\alpha$ is an important property of matrix algebra. However, the distributive and associative laws of algebra are valid. Thus if α, β and γ are any matrices

$$\alpha(\beta + \gamma) = \alpha\beta + \alpha\gamma$$

and

$$\alpha(\beta\gamma) = (\alpha\beta)\gamma$$

(h) Matrices of special significance in quantum mechanics are *diagonal matrices.* These are square matrices with all the elements $\alpha_{ij} = 0$ unles $i = j$. The elements α_{jj} lie along a diagonal line and are called diagonal elements. The *unit matrix* is a special diagonal matrix in which all the diagonal elements are equal to unity

$$\begin{pmatrix} 1 & 0 & 0 & 0 & \dots \\ 0 & 1 & 0 & 0 & \dots \\ 0 & 0 & 1 & 0 & \dots \\ 0 & 0 & 0 & 1 & \dots \end{pmatrix}$$

It is easy to show that multiplying any matrix α by the unit matrix produces the matrix α.

$$\alpha.1 = \alpha \quad \text{or} \quad 1.\alpha = \alpha$$

The sum of the diagonal elements of a square matrix is known as the *trace* or *spur* of the matrix. $\text{tr}\,\alpha = \alpha_{11} + \alpha_{22} + \alpha_{33} + \dots$

(i) One column matrices

$$u = \begin{pmatrix} u_1 \\ u_2 \\ u_3 \\ \cdot \\ \cdot \\ \cdot \end{pmatrix}$$

are used to denote vectors, where u_1, u_2, u_3 are the components of the vector u. It is important to realize that the components u_1, u_2, ... refer to a particular set of axes in the vector-space. In quantum mechanics the eigenstates of a system can be represented by special vectors u where $\alpha\, u = \lambda\, u$. An example of a matrix α multiplying a vector u is

$$\begin{pmatrix} 11 & -6 & 2 \\ -6 & 10 & -4 \\ 2 & -4 & 6 \end{pmatrix} \times \begin{pmatrix} 1 \\ 2 \\ 2 \end{pmatrix} = \begin{pmatrix} 11.1 - 6.2 + 2.2 \\ -6.1 + 10.2 - 4.2 \\ 2.1 - 4.2 + 6.2 \end{pmatrix} = \begin{pmatrix} 3 \\ 6 \\ 6 \end{pmatrix}$$

Now in this special case the product vector $\begin{pmatrix}3\\6\\6\end{pmatrix}$ can be written $3 \times \begin{pmatrix}1\\2\\2\end{pmatrix}$, which is just three times the original vector u. Here we have an example of the eigenvalue equation $\alpha\, u = \lambda\, u$ being satisfied, where the operation of multiplying the vector u by the matrix operator α simply multiplies the vector by the number 3. This number is an eigenvalue of the operator α belonging to the eigenvector u.

(j) The transpose β of a matrix α is obtained by interchanging rows and columns

$$\beta_{ij} = \alpha_{ji}$$

Thus the transpose of

$$\begin{pmatrix}2 & 1 & -3\\0 & 4 & 5\\3 & 7 & -2\end{pmatrix} \quad \text{is} \quad \begin{pmatrix}2 & 0 & 3\\1 & 4 & 7\\-3 & 5 & -2\end{pmatrix}$$

The Hermitian adjoint matrix of the matrix α, denoted by α^*, is formed by taking the transpose of α and then taking the complex conjugate of each element. Thus if β is the Hermitian adjoint of α

$$\beta_{ij} = \alpha^*_{ji}$$

The Hermitian adjoint of

$$\begin{pmatrix}3 & 2-i & 3i\\3+i & 4 & 3\\2 & 1-i & 2+i\end{pmatrix} \quad \text{is} \quad \begin{pmatrix}3 & 3-i & 2\\2+i & 4 & 1+i\\-3i & 3 & 2-i\end{pmatrix}$$

Matrices which are equal to their Hermitian adjoint, i.e. $\alpha_{ij} = \alpha^*_{ji}$, are called Hermitian matrices and they play an important role in quantum mechanics. Observables can only be represented by Hermitian matrices. An example of a Hermitian matrix is

$$\begin{pmatrix}2 & 2+i & 3-2i\\2-i & 4 & 1+i\\3+2i & 1-i & 5\end{pmatrix}$$

The diagonal elements of a Hermitian matrix must be real as $\alpha_{ii} = \alpha^*_{ii}$.

(k) The *reciprocal* of a matrix may or may not exist. The reciprocal of a matrix α is denoted by the symbol α^{-1}. It is defined by the relation

$$\alpha\,\alpha^{-1} = 1 = \alpha^{-1}\alpha$$

It can be proved that the elements of α^{-1} are given by

$$(\alpha^{-1})_{ij} = \frac{1}{\det\alpha}\,\frac{\partial \det\alpha}{\partial \alpha_{ij}},$$

where det α is the determinant

$$\begin{vmatrix} \alpha_{11} & \alpha_{12} \cdots & \alpha_{1n} \\ \alpha_{21} & \alpha_{22} & \alpha_{2n} \\ \cdot & & \\ \cdot & & \\ \cdot & & \\ \alpha_{n1} & \alpha_{n2} \cdots & \alpha_{nn} \end{vmatrix}$$

The partial derivative $\dfrac{\partial \det \alpha}{\partial \alpha_{ij}}$ is called the *cofactor* of the element α_{ij}.

(l) A matrix α is a *unitary matrix* if its Hermitain adjoint is equal to its reciprocal α^{-1}.

$$\alpha^* = \alpha^{-1} \quad \text{or} \quad \alpha^* \alpha = 1 \quad \text{or} \quad \alpha \alpha^* = 1$$

6.18. THE LINEAR HARMONIC OSCILLATOR

We have already considered the Schrödinger method of evaluating the energy levels of a charged particle of mass m capable of executing simple harmonic motion in one dimension (Section 8). We shall now obtain the same result using the methods of matrix mechanics and it will be seen that the mathematical methods are quite different.

The basic dynamical variables of the linear oscillator are the position coordinate $q = x$ and the linear momentum $p = m\dot{x}$. At some stage it is necessary to introduce a fundamental quantum postulate to replace the commutation law $\alpha\beta = \beta\alpha$. The equation we require has been given in Section 13, eqn. (138)

$$qp - pq = i\hbar$$

The position matrix q (or x), by analogy with classical mechanics, is expected to satisfy the set of relations

$$\ddot{x}_{nm} + \omega_0^2 x_{nm} = 0 \tag{174}$$

where

$$x_{nm} = x_{nm}^0 \exp(i\,\omega_{nm}\,t) \tag{175}$$

and x_{mn}^0 is the amplitude of the transition between states n and m. Thus eqns. (174) have solutions given by

$$(\omega_0^2 - \omega_{nm}^2)\,x_{nm} = 0 \tag{176}$$

Either

$$x_{nm} = 0 \quad \text{or} \quad \omega_{nm} = \pm\,\omega_0 \tag{177}$$

It is natural to identify the solution $\omega_{nm} = +\omega_0$ with the emission of radiation† due to a transition from state n to the adjacent lower state $n - 1$. The solution $\omega_{nm} = -\omega_0$ is associated with the absorption of radiation corresponding to the transition from state n to the state $n + 1$. The quantum selection rule that transitions between states differing in n by more than

† This, of course, is a consequence of the harmonic oscillation of a *charged* particle.

unity are forbidden is implied in eqn. (177). This means that x_{nm} is zero unless n and m differ by unity. We can write out the position matrix x as follows.

$$x = \begin{pmatrix} 0 & x_{01} & 0 & 0 & \cdots & \\ x_{10} & 0 & x_{12} & 0 & \cdots & \\ 0 & x_{21} & 0 & x_{23} \cdots & & \\ 0 & 0 & x_{32} & 0 & & x_{34} \cdots \end{pmatrix} \tag{178}$$

It is convenient to label the first element x_{00} so that we can label the eigen-solutions starting with $n = 0$.

We now want to form the Hamiltonian matrix of the oscillator. This is given by

$$H = \frac{p^2}{2m} + \frac{1}{2} k x^2 \tag{179}$$

where
$$k = m\omega_0^2 \quad \text{or} \quad \nu_0 = \frac{\omega_0}{2\pi} = \frac{1}{2\pi}\sqrt{\frac{k}{m}} \tag{180}$$

To find the matrix for p, we make use of the relation $p_x = m\dot{x}$, and eqn. (175)

$$p = im \begin{pmatrix} 0 & \omega_{01} x_{01} & 0 & 0 & \cdots \\ \omega_{10} x_{10} & 0 & \omega_{12} x_{12} & 0 & \cdots \\ 0 & \omega_{21} x_{21} & 0 & \omega_{23} x_{23} & \cdots \\ \vdots & & & & \end{pmatrix} \tag{181}$$

Now
$$\omega_{01} = \omega_{12} = \omega_{23} = \cdots = -\omega_0$$
and
$$\omega_{10} = \omega_{21} = \omega_{32} = \cdots = +\omega_0$$
Hence we obtain

$$p = im\omega_0 \begin{pmatrix} 0 & -x_{01} & 0 & 0 & \cdots \\ x_{10} & 0 & -x_{12} & 0 & \cdots \\ 0 & x_{21} & 0 & -x_{23} & \cdots \\ \vdots & & & & \end{pmatrix} \tag{182}$$

To write down the Hamiltonian matrix H, given by eqn. (179), we square the x and p matrices using the laws of matrix multiplication eqn. (173). Thus x^2 is given by

$$x^2 = \begin{pmatrix} 0 & x_{01} & 0 & 0 & \cdots \\ x_{10} & 0 & x_{12} & 0 & \cdots \\ 0 & x_{21} & 0 & x_{23} & \cdots \\ \vdots & & & & \end{pmatrix} \times \begin{pmatrix} 0 & x_{01} & 0 & 0 & \cdots \\ x_{10} & 0 & x_{12} & 0 & \cdots \\ 0 & x_{21} & 0 & x_{23} & \cdots \\ \vdots & & & & \end{pmatrix}$$

$$\therefore x^2 = \begin{pmatrix} x_{01} x_{10} & 0 & x_{01} x_{12} & \cdots \\ 0 & x_{10} x_{01} + x_{12} x_{21} & 0 & \cdots \\ x_{21} x_{10} & 0 & x_{21} x_{12} + x_{23} x_{32} & \cdots \\ \vdots & & & \end{pmatrix} \tag{183}$$

Squaring the p matrix we get

$$p^2 = m^2 \omega_0^2 \begin{pmatrix} x_{01}x_{10} & 0 & -x_{01}x_{12} & 0 \cdots \\ 0 & x_{10}x_{01} + x_{12}x_{21} & 0 & \cdots \\ -x_{21}x_{10} & 0 & x_{21}x_{12} + x_{23}x_{32} & \cdots \\ \vdots & & & \end{pmatrix} \tag{184}$$

Using the relation $k = m\,\omega_0^2$ and adding $\dfrac{p^2}{2m}$ to $\frac{1}{2}m\,\omega_0^2\,x^2$ we obtain the matrix for H

$$H = m\,\omega_0^2 \begin{pmatrix} x_{01}\,x_{10} & 0 & 0 & \cdots \\ 0 & x_{10}x_{01} + x_{12}x_{21} & 0 & \cdots \\ 0 & 0 & x_{21}x_{12} + x_{23}x_{32} & \cdots \\ \vdots & & & \end{pmatrix} \tag{185}$$

Two striking features of the Hamiltonian matrix are that it is a diagonal matrix and that the diagonal matrix elements are not time dependent. For example,

$$x_{10}\,x_{01} = x_{10}^0\,x_{01}^0 \exp(i\,\omega_0 t)\exp(-\,i\,\omega_0\,t) = x_{10}^0\,x_{01}^0, \text{ etc.}$$

The elements H_{nn} of the diagonal Hamiltonian matrix are the energy eigenvalues E_n of the system. We can write eqn. (185) in the form

$$H = \begin{pmatrix} E_0 & 0 & 0 & \cdots \\ 0 & E_1 & 0 & \cdots \\ 0 & 0 & E_2 & \cdots \\ \vdots & & & \end{pmatrix} \tag{186}$$

where
$$E_n = m\,\omega_0^2(x_{n,n-1}\,x_{n-1,n} + x_{n,n+1}\,x_{n+1,n}) \tag{187}$$

This is as far as we can go without introducing the quantum rule, $(x = q)$

$$x\,p - p\,x = i\,\hbar$$

Inserting the matrices for x and p, eqns. (178) and (182), in this rule we obtain the matrix equation

$$2i\,m\,\omega_0 \begin{pmatrix} x_{01}\,x_{10} & 0 & 0 & \cdots \\ 0 & x_{12}\,x_{21} - x_{10}\,x_{01} & 0 & \cdots \\ 0 & 0 & x_{23}\,x_{32} - x_{21}\,x_{12} & \cdots \\ \vdots & & & \end{pmatrix}$$

$$= i\,\hbar \begin{pmatrix} 1 & 0 & 0 \\ 0 & 1 & 0 \\ 0 & 0 & 1 \\ \vdots & & \end{pmatrix} \tag{188}$$

Corresponding elements of the two sides of this matrix equation must be equal. Hence we obtain the set of equations

$$
\begin{aligned}
x_{01}x_{10} &= \frac{\hbar}{2m\,\omega_0} \\
x_{12}x_{21} - x_{10}x_{01} &= \frac{\hbar}{2m\,\omega_0} \\
x_{23}x_{32} - x_{21}x_{12} &= \frac{\hbar}{2m\,\omega_0}
\end{aligned}
\tag{189}
$$

Solving these equations in turn we obtain

$$
\begin{aligned}
x_{01}x_{10} &= \frac{\hbar}{2m\,\omega_0} \\
x_{12}x_{21} &= \frac{2\hbar}{2m\,\omega_0} \\
x_{23}x_{32} &= \frac{3\hbar}{2m\,\omega_0} \\
&\vdots
\end{aligned}
\tag{190}
$$

Inserting these results in eqn. (187) we obtain the energy eigenvalues

$$E_n = m\,\omega_0^2\left\{\frac{(n+1)\hbar}{2m\,\omega_0} + \frac{n\hbar}{2m\,\omega_0}\right\}$$

or

$$E_n = \frac{\hbar\,\omega_0}{2}(2n+1) = \hbar\,\omega_0(n+\tfrac{1}{2})$$

or

$$E_n = \hbar\sqrt{\frac{k}{m}}(n+\tfrac{1}{2}) \tag{191}$$

Thus we obtain the same results as the Schrödinger method and in particular the zero-point energy term $\frac{1}{2}\hbar\,\omega_0$ occurs as before. It is interesting to contrast the wave and matrix mechanical approaches to the problem and to notice that the matrix method stays much closer to the classical description.

6.19. ANGULAR MOMENTUM

The concept of angular momentum of a system is of fundamental importance in quantum mechanics. We shall discuss in an elementary way how the concept is developed in matrix mechanics. We begin with the classical definition of the angular momentum vector $\boldsymbol{M}$ of a particle about a point

$$\boldsymbol{M} = \boldsymbol{r} \times \boldsymbol{p} \tag{192}$$

where $\boldsymbol{r}$ is the position vector of the particle with respect to the point and $\boldsymbol{p}$ is the linear momentum of the particle. The three Cartesian components of $\boldsymbol{M}$, M_x, M_y and M_z are given by

$$\begin{aligned} M_x &= y\,p_z - z\,p_y \\ M_y &= z\,p_x - x\,p_z \\ M_z &= x\,p_y - y\,p_x \end{aligned} \tag{193}$$

The commutator of the angular momentum components M_x, M_y is †

$$\begin{aligned} M_x\,M_y - M_y\,M_x &= (y\,p_z - z\,p_y)(z\,p_x - x\,p_z) - (z\,p_x - x\,p_z)(y\,p_z - z\,p_y) \\ &= y\,p_x(p_z\,z - z\,p_z) + x\,p_y(z\,p_z - p_z\,z) \end{aligned} \tag{194}$$

Using the quantum mechanical commutator rule, eqn. (138), we have

$$z\,p_z - p_z\,z = i\,\hbar$$

Hence eqn. (194) becomes

$$M_x\,M_y - M_y\,M_x = i\hbar(x\,p_y - y\,p_x) \quad = i\,\hbar\,M_z$$

Similarly

$$\begin{aligned} M_y\,M_z - M_z\,M_y &= i\,\hbar\,M_x \\ M_z\,M_x - M_x\,M_z &= i\,\hbar\,M_y \end{aligned} \tag{195}$$

The relations (195) give us some information concerning the operators representing components of angular momentum. First we note that no two of the three components M_x, M_y, M_z commute with each other. It is not possible in principle to measure simultaneously two components without mutual interference.

Introducing the operator

$$M^2 = M_x^2 + M_y^2 + M_z^2$$

it is easy to prove that M^2 commutes with M_x, M_y, and M_z. Thus selecting the operators M^2 and M_x,

$$\begin{aligned} M^2\,M_x - M_x\,M^2 &= (M_x^2 + M_y^2 + M_z^2)\,M_x - M_x(M_x^2 + M_y^2 + M_z^2) \\ &= (M_y^2\,M_x - M_x\,M_y^2) + (M_z^2\,M_x - M_x\,M_z^2) \\ &= M_y(M_y\,M_x - M_x\,M_y) + (M_y\,M_x - M_x\,M_y)\,M_y \\ &\quad + M_z(M_z\,M_x - M_x\,M_z) + (M_z\,M_x - M_x\,M_z)M_z \end{aligned}$$

Using the relations (195) we can now write

$$M^2\,M_x - M_x\,M^2 = -i\,\hbar\,M_y\,M_z - i\hbar\,M_z\,M_y + i\,\hbar\,M_z\,M_y + i\,\hbar\,M_y\,M_z = 0$$

This result means that it is possible to measure simultaneously the total angular momentum and its component in one selected direction.

Another important set of relations is

$$\begin{aligned} (M_x + i\,M_y)\,M_z &= (M_z - \hbar)(M_x + i\,M_y) \\ (M_y + i\,M_z)\,M_x &= (M_x - \hbar)(M_y + i\,M_z) \\ (M_z + i\,M_x)\,M_y &= (M_y - \hbar)(M_z + i\,M_x) \end{aligned} \tag{196}$$

† The order of multiplication of the operators, x, p_x, M_x etc. must be strictly observed.

To prove the first relation:

$$(M_x + i\,M_y)\,M_z = (M_x\,M_z - M_z\,M_x) + i(M_y\,M_z - M_z\,M_y) + M_z\,M_x + i\,M_z\,M_y$$
$$= -i\hbar\,M_y - \hbar\,M_x + M_z\,M_x + i\,M_z\,M_y$$
$$= (M_z - \hbar)(M_x + i\,M_y).$$

The operators M_x, M_y, M_z appear symmetrically in the equations we have derived so that they all possess the same set of eigenvalues. Now as M_z and M^2 commute, it is possible to find a wave function ψ which is a simultaneous eigenfunction of M_z and M^2

$$M_z\,\psi = a\,\psi \tag{197}$$

M_z operating on ψ multiplies it by the number (eigenvalue) a;

and

$$M^2\,\psi = b^2\,\psi \tag{198}$$

M^2 operating on the same wave function ψ multiplies it by the number (eigenvalue) b^2.

Equation (197) can be written

$$(M_x + i\,M_y)\,M_z\,\psi = a(M_x + i\,M_y)\,\psi$$

substituting the first relation of eqn. (196), we obtain

$$(M_z - \hbar)(M_x + i\,M_y)\,\psi = a(M_x + i\,M_y)\,\psi$$

or, re-arranging the terms

$$M_z\,\{(M_x + i\,M_y)\,\psi\} = (a + \hbar)\,\{(M_x + i\,M_y)\,\psi\} \tag{199}$$

This result means that if a is an eigenvalue of M_z, so is $(a + \hbar)$, provided, of course, the operand $(M_x + i\,M_y)\,\psi$ does not vanish.

As M^2 commutes with both M_x and M_y, we have (using eqn. (198))

$$M^2\{(M_x + i\,M_y)\,\psi\} = (M_x + i\,M_y)\,M^2\,\psi$$
$$= (M_x + i\,M_y)\,b^2\,\psi$$
$$= b^2\{(M_x + i\,M_y)\,\psi\}$$

This means that the operand $(M_x + i\,M_y)\,\psi$, unless it vanishes, is an eigenfunction of the operator M^2 belonging to the eigenvalue b^2 of M^2. Thus b^2 is simultaneously an eigenvalue of ψ and $(M_x + i\,M_y)\,\psi$. Repeating the above argument we can say that if a is an eigenvalue of M_z, so is the series

$$a,\ a + \hbar,\quad a + 2\hbar,\quad a + 3\hbar,\ \ldots$$

The eigenfunctions of M_z corresponding to this series of eigenvalues are all eigenfunctions of M^2 belonging to the eigenvalue b^2.

If we had multiplied $M_z\,\psi = a\,\psi$ by $(M_x - i\,M_y)$, instead of by $(M_x + i\,M_y)$, we would have proved that if a is an eigenvalue of M_z so is the series

$$a,\ a - \hbar,\quad a - 2\hbar,\quad a - 3\hbar,\ \ldots$$

Now we can say that for any state,

$$\langle M^2 \rangle_{av} = \langle M_x^2 \rangle_{av} + \langle M_y^2 \rangle_{av} + \langle M_z^2 \rangle_{av}$$

Hence the square of the eigenvalue of M_z cannot exceed the value of the eigenvalue of M^2 belonging to the same eigenfunction. The series of eigenvalues of M_z must terminate. Denote the highest eigenvalue of M_z by A and the simultaneous eigenfunction of M_z and M^2 by ψ_A. Equation (199) for the highest eigenvalue of M_z can be written

$$M_z \{(M_x + i\,M_y)\,\psi_A\} = (A + \hbar)\,\{(M_x + i\,M_y)\,\psi_A\}$$

If A is the greatest eigenvalue, $(A + \hbar)$ cannot be an eigenvalue of M_z; thus the operand

$$(M_x + i\,M_y)\,\psi_A = 0 \tag{200}$$

Multiply by $(M_x - i\,M_y)$

$$\{M_x^2 + M_y^2 + i(M_x M_y - M_y M_x)\}\,\psi_A = 0$$

or

$$(M^2 - M_z^2 - \hbar\,M_z)\,\psi_A = 0 \tag{201}$$

Now $\quad M^2\,\psi_A = b^2\,\psi_A, \quad M_z^2\,\psi_A = A^2\,\psi_A$

Hence eqn. (201) becomes

$$(b^2 - A^2 - \hbar\,A)\,\psi_A = 0$$

or

$$A^2 + \hbar\,A - b^2 = 0, \quad \text{as} \quad \psi_A \neq 0 \tag{202}$$

A similar argument concerning the lowest eigenvalue A' of M_z yields the corresponding equation

$$A'^2 - \hbar\,A' - b^2 = 0 \tag{203}$$

Comparing eqns. (202) and (203), A' must be equal to $-A$. From this, we deduce the important result that the possible values of M_z range in steps of magnitude $\hbar$ from $-A$ to $+A$.

Hence $\quad A - (-A) = 2A = m'\,\hbar,$

where m' is a positive integer

$$A = \frac{m'}{2}\,\hbar$$

Hence A is an integral or half-integral multiple of $\hbar$.

$A = j\,\hbar$, where j is an integer or half-integer. Inserting this expression for the eigenvalue j in eqn. (202) we obtain

$$j^2\,\hbar^2 + j\,\hbar^2 = b^2$$

thus M^2 has eigenvalues $j(j + 1)\,\hbar^2$ and M_z can assume any one of the integrally spaced values from $-j\hbar$ to $+j\hbar$.

The possibility of half-integral values for j does not arise naturally in the Bohr theory. The half integral quantum numbers were originally introduced in connection with the concept of electron spin. The way in which the electron spin concept is grafted on to the original Bohr–Sommerfeld theory is not aesthetically satisfying. Classical mechanics can be regarded as the limit of quantum mechanics as $\hbar$ tends to zero. The concept of orbital angular momentum $l\hbar$, is still meaningful as $\hbar \to 0$, for there is no limitation on the magnitude of l. With electron spin, however, s has two eigenvalues $\pm\frac{1}{2}$; therefore in the limit as $\hbar \to 0$, $s\hbar \to 0$. Thus there is no true classical analogue to the quantum mechanical concept of electron spin. It was first shown by Dirac that the concept of electron spin arose in a natural way if a wave equation, invariant under Lorentz transformations, is used to describe electrons.

6.20. THE RELATIVISTIC WAVE EQUATION

In Chapter 3 we discussed the Lorentz transformation and showed that it was compatible with the principle that the velocity of light in free space c is the same for all observers. The quantity $x^2 + y^2 + z^2 - c^2 t^2$ is invariant under a Lorentz transformation. If we introduce the coordinate $T = i\,c\,t$, the invariant quantity is $x^2 + y^2 + z^2 + T^2$. In classical physics, a rotation of the Cartesian spatial axes, leaves the quantity $x^2 + y^2 + z^2$ unchanged. The similarity of the two invariant quantities suggests that the Lorentz transformation is associated with a rotation in a four-dimensional space whose axes are $x, y, z, i\,c\,t$. The Lorentz transformation equations (Chapter 3, eqn. (16)), can be written

$$x = \frac{x'}{\sqrt{(1-\beta^2)}} - \frac{i\beta T'}{\sqrt{(1-\beta^2)}} = x'\cos\theta - T'\sin\theta \tag{204}$$

$$T = \frac{i\beta x'}{\sqrt{(1-\beta^2)}} + \frac{T'}{\sqrt{(1-\beta^2)}} = x'\sin\theta + T'\cos\theta \tag{205}$$

where $T = i\,c\,t,\quad T' = i\,c\,t',\quad \beta = \frac{v}{c}\quad$ and $\quad\tan\theta = i\beta.$

The expression of the Lorentz transformation in this form can be pictured as a *rotation* in the x–T plane through an angle θ. Two successive Lorentz transformations are equivalent to two successive rotations and it is easy to show that the product of two Lorentz transformations is itself a Lorentz transformation.

The introduction of the variable $T = i\,c\,t$, allows one to treat special relativity by quasi-geometrical methods. For example, it is useful to introduce the four-vector $\boldsymbol{p}$ to represent the momentum of a particle. The components of $\boldsymbol{p}$ are p_1, p_2, p_3, p_4 where

$$p_1 = p_x,\quad p_2 = p_y,\quad p_3 = p_z,\quad p_4 = \frac{iE}{c} \tag{206}$$

and E is the energy of the particle.

$$\Sigma p_\mu p_\mu = p_x^2 + p_y^2 + p_z^2 - \frac{E^2}{c^2} = - m^2 c^2, \qquad (207)$$

where m is the rest mass of the particle.

The wave function ψ of a relativistic particle must satisfy the wave equation

$$\{\Sigma p_\mu p_\mu + m^2 c^2\} \psi = 0 \qquad (208)$$

As before, components of momentum are represented by linear differential operators

$$p_\mu = - i \hbar \frac{\partial}{\partial \mu}$$

so that

$$p_\mu^2 = - \hbar^2 \frac{\partial^2}{\partial \mu^2}$$

Equation (208) becomes

$$- \hbar^2 \left[\frac{\partial^2}{\partial x^2} + \frac{\partial^2}{\partial y^2} + \frac{\partial^2}{\partial z^2} + \frac{1}{(i c)^2} \frac{\partial^2}{\partial t^2}\right] \psi + m^2 c^2 \psi = 0$$

or

$$- \hbar^2 \left[\frac{\partial^2}{\partial x^2} + \frac{\partial^2}{\partial y^2} + \frac{\partial^2}{\partial z^2} - \frac{1}{c^2} \frac{\partial^2}{\partial t^2}\right] \psi + m^2 c^2 \psi = 0 \qquad (209)$$

Now this equation as it stands cannot be considered to be of the correct form. The state of a quantum mechanical system is specified by its wave function $\psi(\boldsymbol{r}, t)$. Equation (209) contains the *second* partial derivative of ψ with respect to t. This means that $\psi(\boldsymbol{r}, t)$ is determined, if $\psi(\boldsymbol{r}, t)$ and $(\partial \psi)/(\partial t)$ at $t = 0$ are known. The extra boundary condition involving the value of $(\partial \psi)/(\partial t)$ at $t = 0$ should not be necessary. This difficulty is avoided if the assumption is made that eqn. (208) can be *factorized*:

$$(\gamma_1 p_1 + \gamma_2 p_2 + \gamma_3 p_3 + \gamma_4 p_4 + i m c)$$
$$(\gamma_1 p_1 + \gamma_2 p_2 + \gamma_3 p_3 + \gamma_4 p_4 - i m c) \psi = 0 \qquad (210)$$

where the operators γ_μ satisfy ($\mu = 1, 2, 3, 4$)

$$\gamma_\mu^2 = 1. \quad \gamma_\mu \gamma_\nu = - \gamma_\nu \gamma_\mu \quad \text{for} \quad \mu \neq \nu$$

In addition, γ_μ commutes with the p_ν.

The wave equation for a relativistic particle, first derived by Dirac in 1928, is assumed to be of the form

$$(\gamma_1 p_1 + \gamma_2 p_2 + \gamma_3 p_3 + \gamma_4 p_4 - i m c) \psi = 0 \qquad (211)$$

The Dirac eqn. (211) is symmetrical in the space coordinates x, y, z and the coordinate $i c t$. Dirac succeeded in showing that, as a direct consequence of the Lorentz invariance of the relativistic wave equation, the electron has a new degree of freedom. In a magnetic field $\boldsymbol{H}$, the electron has a potential energy $\left(\frac{e\hbar}{2mc}\right)\boldsymbol{\sigma}\cdot\boldsymbol{H}$ associated with this degree of freedom. The operator $\boldsymbol{\sigma}$ is related to the electron spin operator $\boldsymbol{s}$ by the equation

$$\boldsymbol{s} = \tfrac{1}{2}\hbar\,\boldsymbol{\sigma}$$

The way in which the electron spin is derived from the relativistic equations is one of the most satisfactory features of the Dirac theory. Nevertheless, recent developments in the quantum theory of radiation led to the prediction that the electron spin magnetic moment is slightly greater than one Bohr magneton, namely, 1·001167 units. This prediction is in excellent agreement with experiment.

The second major triumph of the Dirac electron theory is concerned with the discovery of "particle–antiparticle" symmetry. The energy of a relativistic particle is given by the relation

$$E = \pm\sqrt{(p_1^2 c^2 + p_2^2 c^2 + p_3^2 c^2 + m^2 c^4)}$$

At first sight, it seems nonsensical to consider the negative root o\ the equation. Dirac explored the possible physical meaning of a negative energy solution. A particle of negative energy is not directly observable. Moreover, the difference in energy between a positive and negative energy electron must exceed $2mc^2$. If we assume that all the negative energy states are normally filled, then the exclusion principle forbids the transition of a real (i.e. positive energy) electron to a negative energy state. Under special circumstances, a negative energy electron may absorb sufficient energy ($\geqq 2mc^2$) and make a transition to an empty positive energy state. This particle is observed as a real, negatively charged, positive energy electron. What about the vacancy or hole left in the negative energy band of states? This hole can, under the action of a field of force, move. It will, however, in an electric field respond like a *positively* charged particle. Moreover the moving hole has a *positive* energy and can therefore be observed. The hole has all the properties of a positive electron or *positron.* The positron was first observed by Anderson in 1932, through the absorption of an energetic gamma ray in the walls of a cloud chamber and the creation of an electron–positron pair:

$$\gamma \rightarrow e^+ + e^-, \quad \text{if} \quad E_\gamma > 2mc^2.$$

If this particle–antiparticle symmetry property is extended to the proton, the Dirac electron theory is not completely adequate to predict the behaviour of protons. The proton is not a "Dirac"-type particle; it has an anomalous magnetic moment, and it interacts strongly with protons and neutrons at short distances. The proton is subject to both nuclear and electromagnetic interactions. The anomalous magnetic moment is ascribed to the creation and absorption of a virtual meson cloud surrounding the core of the proton. Dirac's hole theory of positrons originally did not predict that the holes must have the same mass as that of the electron.† Following Anderson's discovery of the positron, and the determination of the positron momentum and rest mass, the theorem that—"to every particle there is an antiparticle" —became firmly established as one of Nature's symmetry laws. The successful production and identification of the negative proton (antiproton) in 1955 confirmed this symmetry law. The present view of the general particle–antiparticle relations are that they have:

(a) Equal but opposite electric charges.
(b) Same rest mass.
(c) Same spin angular momentum.
(d) Equal but opposite magnetic dipole moments.
(e) Same half-life (if unstable).
(f) They are created in pairs, e.g. $\gamma \rightarrow e^{+} + e^{-}$, or, $p + p \rightarrow p + p + (p + \bar{p})$, where $\bar{p}$ denotes the antiproton.
(g) They are annihilated in pairs $e^{+} + e^{-} \rightarrow 2\gamma$; the annihilation of an electron and positron nearly at rest is accompanied by the emission of two oppositely directed gamma quanta to conserve momentum.

BIBLIOGRAPHY

R. H. DICKE and J. P. WITTKE, *Introduction to Quantum Mechanics*, Addison-Wesley, 1960.
R. W. GURNEY, *Elemetary Quantum Mechanics*, Cambridge University Press, 1940.
This is a lucid introduction to elementary wave mechanics. Matrix mechanics is not included.
V. ROJANSKY, *Introductory Quantum Mechanics*, Prentice Hall, Englewood Cliffs, N.J. 1938.
This is one of the most comprehensive introductions to wave and matrix mechanics. Strongly recommended for the beginner.
L. I. SCHIFF, *Quantum Mechanics*, 2nd Ed., McGraw-Hill, New York 1955.
L. LANDAU and E. M. LIFSHITZ, *Quantum Mechanics* (Translated from the Russian), Pergamon Press, London 1958.
P. A. M. DIRAC, *The Principles of Quantum Mechanics*, 4th Ed., Clarendon Press, Oxford 1958.
The above three volumes are more advanced treatments and are not suitable as an introduction to Quantum Mechanics.
V. HEINE, *Group Theory in Quantum Mechanics*, Pergamon Press, London 1960.
A useful introduction to Group Theory methods in Quantum Mechanics.

EXAMPLES

1. Consider the following one-dimensional potential well for an electron. When $x < -b$ and $x > b$, $V = \infty$; for $-b < x < -a$ and $a < x < b$, $V = 0$; for $-a < x < a$, $V = V_0$. Solve the wave equation for this well. If $b = 3{\cdot}065$ Å, $a = 0{\cdot}836$ Å, $V_0 = 50$eV, determine the first three energy levels of the system. In each case determine and plot the wave function and its square throughout the region $-b < x < b$. Comment on the parity of the wave functions.

† Dirac at first associated the hole in the "sea" of filled negative energy states with the proton!

2. Consider the following one-dimensional triangular barrier for an electron. $V = 0$, when $x < -V_0/a$ and when $x > V_0/a$; $V = V_0 + a\,x$, for $-V_0/a < x < 0$, $V = V_0 - a\,x$, for $0 < x < V_0/a$ (a is a constant). For a total energy $E < V_0$, show that the wave equation can be reduced to the form $\frac{d^2\psi}{d\xi^2} = \xi\,\psi$, in the region $-V_0/a \leqq x \leqq 0$.

If $V_0 = 16$ eV, $E = V_0/2$, and $a = 1$ eV per Å, calculate the transparency of the barrier. (Hint: look up the properties of the Airy integral, e.g. in H. Jeffreys and B. S. Jeffreys, *Methods of Mathematical Physics*).

3. Show that the Pauli spin matrices defined by eqns. (2) in Appendix B satisfy the commutation rules of eqns. (1) in Appendix B.

CHAPTER 7

THE DETERMINATION OF ATOMIC MASSES

7.1. INTRODUCTION

The most important result of the special theory of relativity is the law $E = m c^2$, expressing the equivalence of mass and energy. One consequence of this law is that the mass of an atom is less than the sum of the masses of its constituent electrons and nucleons. This mass decrement is a measure of the total binding energy of the atom, the major fraction of which is contributed by the binding of the nucleons (protons and neutrons) in the nucleus. Let us denote the mass of a neutral atom of atomic number Z (proton number) and mass number A (nucleon number) by the symbol ${}_Z M^A$. Imagine that the atom is pulled apart into Z electrons, Z protons and $(A - Z)$ neutrons so that the interaction energy between any pair of the particles is vanishingly small. It is assumed that the constituent particles are at rest in the frame of reference in which the original atom was at rest. The total work to pull the atom apart, the so-called binding energy B, is given by the equation

$$B = [Z M_{\mathrm{H}} + (A - Z) M_n - {}_Z M^A] c^2 \tag{1}$$

where, M_{H} is the mass of the neutral hydrogen atom,

M_n is the mass of the free neutron.

In view of the fact that even in the heaviest atoms ($A > 200$), where the electron binding energy is most important, the contribution to B of the electrons is never in excess of 1 MeV, eqn. (1) can be taken as a very good representation of the *nuclear binding energy*. It is found that the mean binding energy per nucleon B/A, is of the order of 8 MeV per nucleon throughout the range of the periodic table, thus justifying the neglect of the electron binding energy. A knowledge of the binding energy of nuclei and the way in which the mean binding energy per nucleon varies throughout the periodic table, is invaluable in throwing light on trends and variations in nuclear stability. In this chapter we shall be concerned with some of the experimental methods of determining atomic masses and not with the interpretation of nuclear binding energies.

The accurate determination of atomic masses began in 1919 with the invention of the *mass spectrograph* by F. W. Aston. In addition to the determination of a number of atomic masses, Aston was able to confirm

Soddy's prediction that many stable elements posses isotopes. About the same time, A. J. Dempster in the U.S.A. developed a mass spectrometer especially suitable for isotope analysis. From the beginning, it was realized that the O^{16} atom was the most suitable standard and it is defined to have an atomic mass of exactly 16 atomic mass units† (natural oxygen has a small fraction of the heavier isotopes O^{17} and O^{18}). Strictly speaking, the mass spectroscope compares the ratio or difference of the charge-to-mass ratio $n\,e/M$ of ions of the atomic species of interest with that of O^{16}. The number n of electron charges carried by the ion must be identified and in the most accurate modern determinations due allowance is made for the difference between the ionic and atomic mass. Tables of atomic mass invariably quote the mass of the neutral atom. During the last forty years, mass determinations have improved in accuracy by many orders of magnitude; the best modern determinations have an accuracy better than 1 part in 10^7.

In the last ten years, several novel "time-of-flight" instruments have been introduced which in some cases have yielded mass values as accurate as the best conventional mass spectrographic determination. We include a description of one of these methods, the "Mass Synchrometer" invented by L. G. Smith at the Brookhaven National Laboratory, New York. The introduction of new methods of precise mass determination is important because it provides a valuable check on the existence of unsuspected systematic errors inherent in one particular type of determination.

A different approach to the problem of mass differences is through the determination of the "heat of nuclear reactions" or the reaction Q value as it is called. This is a measure of the net energy change (positive or negative) in a nuclear reaction. Suppose for example, a beam of particles (protons, deuterons, neutrons, . . .) of rest mass M_1 and kinetic energy E_1, strikes a thin target containing nuclei of rest mass M_0, kinetic energy E_0 (this is the thermal energy and is usually small) and initiates a nuclear reaction producing two particles with rest masses M_2 and M_3 and kinetic energies E_2 and E_3. The Q of this reaction is given by the equation

$$(M_0 + M_1)\,c^2 = (M_2 + M_3)\,c^2 + Q \tag{2}$$

or as
$$M_0\,c^2 + E_0 + M_1\,c^2 + E_1 = M_2\,c^2 + E_2 + M_3\,c^2 + E_3$$

$$Q = (E_2 + E_3) - (E_0 + E_1) \tag{3}$$

If the energy and direction of emission (with respect to the direction of the beam of initiating particles) of *one* of the product particles is measured, then using the principle of conservation of momentum the Q of the reaction can be determined, assuming the incident particle kinetic energy E_1 is known. In recent years, extensive measurements have been made involving the analysis of the particle energies with deflecting electric and magnetic

† Recently a new standard based on the C^{12} atom having exactly 12 atomic mass units has been adopted.

fields. Related to this type of approach, is the accurate measurement of *total* disintegration energies (the recoil energy of the heavy particle is included) in alpha and beta transformations. This enables the mass difference of the parent and daughter nucleus to be calculated. This is very useful for the heavy alpha emitters, as this is the region where mass spectroscope measurements are most difficult. However, the accuracy of these results does not compare with the best mass spectroscopic determinations.

7.2. BASIC COMPONENTS OF MASS SPECTROSCOPES

Ion Sources

Mass spectroscopes fall into two main divisions. First there is the high precision *mass spectrograph* for the accurate determination of atomic masses. Instruments designed for the accurate comparison of relative isotopic abundances of stable elements have a moderate precision ($\pm$ 100 millimass units m.m.u.); they are known as *mass spectrometers*. Closely related to the latter are the instruments designed to separate and collect *weighable* quantities of the isotopes of an element. The design of the ion source is influenced by the ion beam current required. Much greater beam currents are desirable in the isotope collection instruments than in the mass spectrograph. Many different modes of ion production have been used, partly because of the wide variety in chemical and physical properties of the element or compound producing the ions. It is much easier to produce ions directly from a gas like CO_2 than it is from a refractory metal such as Pt, Au or U. To list a few of the methods used, we have

(a) High voltage–low current electric discharge in a gas at low pressure. The positive ions produced in a 20 kV discharge tube have a wide spread in energy; this is a decided disadvantage of this method.

(b) Low voltage–high current source. Gas or vapour admitted through a leak valve into a small box is bombarded with low (100 eV) energy electrons emitted from an electron gun. Some of the gas molecules are ionized by electron collisions and large increases in ion beam intensity are achieved in some sources by causing the electrons to follow a helical path through the ionizing region by means of a magnetic field (500 to 1000 gauss). The ions are extracted from the source through a slit system to which is applied a suitable potential difference.

(c) In a few rare cases ions are easily produced by coating a metal filament with a suitable salt (Li salt for example). The ions are liberated when the filament is heated.

(d) Ions of refractory elements such as Pt, Au and U are best obtained by passing an oscillatory spark discharge (*in vacuo*) between electrodes of the metal.

A detailed discussion of the techniques involved in the design of ion sources for mass spectroscopes, accelerating machines (Van de Graaff, cyclotron, etc.) is out of place in this book but it is important to realize that this is a vital part of the complete device.

Energy Filters

The ions emerging from the exit slit of the ion source may have charges, e, $2e$, $3e$, ..., a wide range of energy (depending on the type of source), and a range of masses depending on the isotopes present. The mass spectroscope must be able to *focus* ions of the same mass at the same place on the detector (photographic plate or electrical detector). It is vital that the instrument is capable of focusing ions of different energies ("velocity focusing") and different initial directions of motion ("space focusing") at the same point (or line) on the detector. This combination of "double focusing" is a characteristic of all the best instruments but it is not possible to achieve good focusing for a *wide* range in ionic energies and directions.

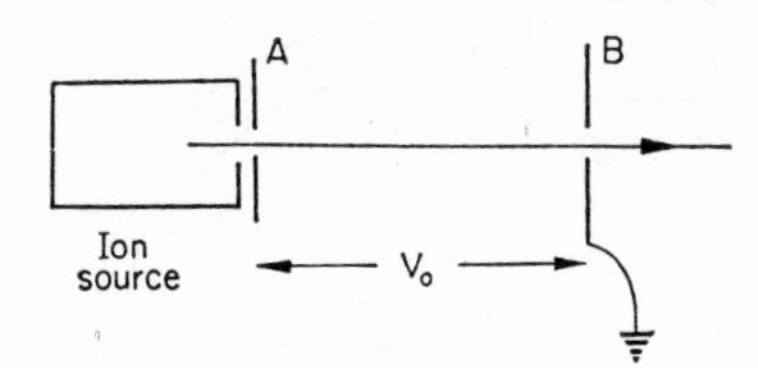

FIG. 1. Ions from low energy ion source accelerated by a high potential V_0.

The ions from the source are often given nearly the same energy by accelerating them through a high potential difference V_0 (Fig. 1). This method is suitable for a low voltage ion source and we can then say that the ions emerging from the second slit B all nearly have the same energy. This constitutes a crude *energy filter*. Thus ions emerge from slit B with a kinetic energy given by†

$$\tfrac{1}{2} M v^2 = n e V_0 \tag{4}$$

To improve the focusing achieved by the arrangement depicted in Fig. 1, the emerging ion beam enters the electrostatic cylindrical energy filter shown in Fig. 2. This device consists of a pair of cylindrical plates A and B of large radius of curvature R in comparison to the spacing of the plates d. A potential difference V is applied to the plates, symmetrically with respect to the potential of the exit slit of the preceding filter (Fig. 1). Most of the ions entering the second filter will, in general, collide with either plates A or B and be lost. In order that an ion entering the filter along the central axis (shown dotted in Fig. 2) will emerge from the exit slit of the filter

† In this chapter we use m.k.s. units. (e in coulombs, V in V, v in msec^{-1}, B in weber m^{-2}.)

it must satisfy the equation

$$n\,e \cdot \frac{V}{d} = M \frac{v^2}{R} \tag{5}$$

or

$$\frac{1}{2} M\,v^2 = \frac{n\,e\,V\,R}{2d} \tag{6}$$

Thus the filter will select ions of one definite kinetic energy. Ions of different mass transmitted by the filter must, of course, have different velocities v and therefore different momenta. It has also been shown that ions entering the filter with the correct energy, but inclined at a small angle to the direction of the central ray emerge very close to the central ray, if the angular aperture P O Q of the cylinder is set equal to $\pi/\sqrt{2}$ (127° 17′). This is a form of direction focusing. An ion entering the filter inclined at an angle of 2° with respect to the central ray will emerge displaced laterally about 0·5 mm with respect to the central ray for a value of R equal to 30 cm.

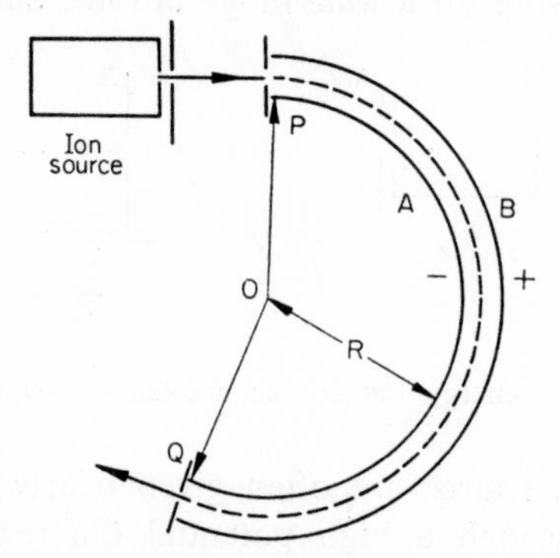

FIG. 2. Ions accelerated through high potential V_0, enter cylindrical electrostatic energy filter. The potentials applied to the cylindrical plates A and B are symmetrical with respect to the potential (earth) of the beam at P. Angular aperture $\widehat{POQ}$ for optimum "space focusing" is $\pi/\sqrt{2}$.

Momentum (Magnetic) Filter

We have seen that the ions emerging from the cylindrical energy filter (Fig. 2) all have the same kinetic energy, but ions of different mass will have different momenta. To disperse and focus ions of the same mass the beam emerging from the exit slit of the cylindrical energy filter is passed through a *sectorial magnetic field.* Optimum space focusing is obtained if the entrance slit S_1 (Fig. 3) the apex of the boundaries of the magnetic field O, and the exit slit S_2 of the momentum filter lie on the same straight line. Ions entering the magnetic field region normal to the wedge-shaped boundary follow a circular path, centre O, radius R, in the magnetic field region, where

$$B\,n\,e\,v = \frac{M\,v^2}{R} \tag{7}$$

B is the flux density of the field, and it is normal to the plane of the particle trajectory. For a given charge $n\,e$, R is proportional to the particle's momentum

$$M\,v = B\,R\,n\,e \tag{8}$$

The central ray leaves the magnetic field normal to the field boundary. Particles of the same momentum, but inclined at a small angle $\pm\alpha$ to the central ray, are brought to a focus at B which lies closer to O than the point A where the central ray crosses the line S_1 O S_2. The dotted line indicates the trajectory of a central ray particle which has a momentum slightly greater than the value Mv satisfying eq. (8).

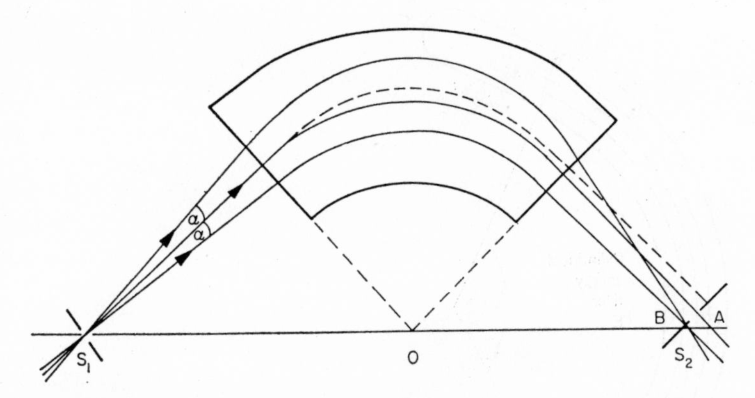

FIG. 3. Momentum (Magnetic) Filter. Entrance slit S_1, field apex O, and exit slit S_2 are collinear.

7.3. MASS SPECTROSCOPES

Bainbridge and Jordan Mass Spectrograph (1936)

One of the best pre-war precision mass spectrographs is the instrument invented by Bainbridge and Jordan. A schematic diagram to illustrate the main components and layout of the instrument is shown in Fig. 4. This is an example of a double focusing instrument. Ions from a high voltage–low current gas discharge tube emerge with a fairly broad energy spread into a cylindrical electrostatic energy filter E (see last section). The whole of the apparatus, apart from the low pressure ion source, is maintained at a good high vacuum pressure (10^{-6} mm Hg). The ions emerging from the energy filter are then analysed by the magnetic filter M into different mass species M_1, M_2, etc. and each component is focused as a line trace on the photographic plate. Optimum focusing is obtained by choosing the sectorial angle of the magnetic field to be equal to 60°. Notice also that the exit slit of the energy filter, the apex of the boundaries of the edges of the magnetic pole pieces, and the photographic plate lie in the same horizontal plane.

An important property of all mass spectroscopes is the *mass resolving power* δ, defined by the ratio

$$\delta = \frac{M}{\Delta M}$$

Here ΔM is the smallest difference in ionic mass that can be resolved at the detector for ions of mass M. Thus with photographic recording, ΔM corresponds to the width of the spectral line produced on the plate by ions

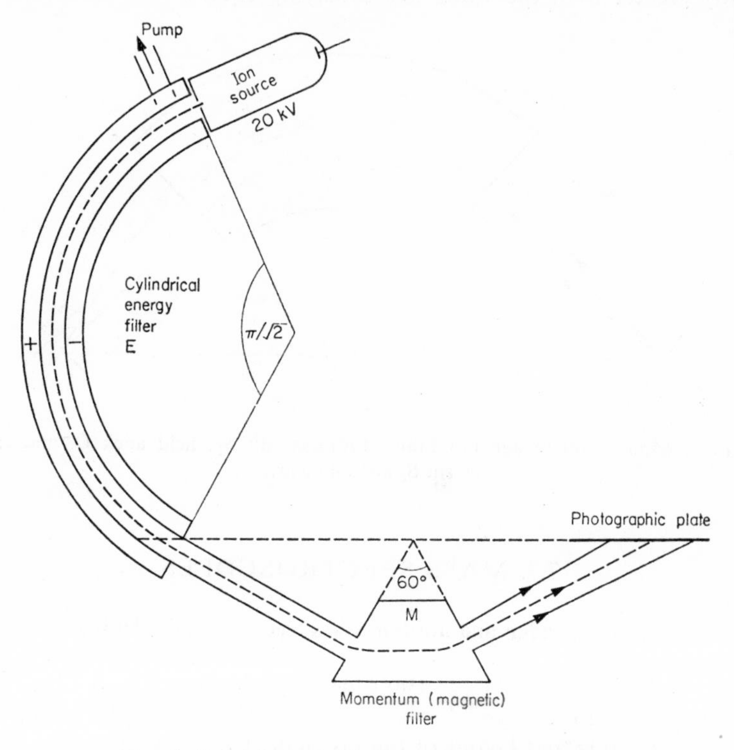

FIG. 4. Bainbridge and Jordan mass spectrograph.

of mass M. It is usual to measure the width of the line from the half amplitude positions on each side of the maximum. The Bainbridge–Jordan instrument, with R approximately equal to 25 cm for each filter, has a resolving power of the order of 10,000. This correspond to a *dispersion* on the photographic plate of about 5 mm between spectral lines produced by ions differing in mass by 1 per cent. This spectrograph has the advantage that the mass displacement scale across the photographic plate is very nearly linear. It is important to understand that no attempt is made to deduce the mass of an ion from the electron optics of the spectrograph. The position of one spectral line is carefully compared with the position of known mass reference lines. Once the dispersion factor $\Delta M/\Delta x$ across the detector is known, M is determined from a careful measurement of the line spacing Δx.

The Mass Doublet Method

Invaluable in the accurate measurement of atomic masses is the use of the technique known as the mass doublet method. Ions with the same value of $n\,e/A$, where A is the nearest integer to the precise mass M, will be recorded at nearly the same position on the detector. Thus ions of methane $C^{12}H^1_4$ carrying a single charge have a mass number 16 and will be focused close to but not exactly on top of singly charged ions of the mass standard O^{16}. The mass difference between the O^{16} and $C^{12}H^1_4$ ions is directly determined. A small error in the dispersion ratio $\Delta M/\Delta x$ is unimportant as it has a very small effect on the *actual* mass value of the $C^{12}H^1_4$ ion. The mass dispersion ratio itself is determined by recording traces on the photographic plate corresponding to a series of ions differing in mass by unit mass number: C (12), CH (13), CH_2 (14), CH_3 (15), CH_4(16); O ≡ 16; OH (17), OH_2 (18). It is difficult to measure doublet spacings accurately unless the intensities of the line components are nearly equal.

A number of important fundamental mass doublets are of great practical value. For example consider the three doublets

$$(C^{12}H^1_4)^+ \quad \text{and} \quad (O^{16})^+$$
$$(H^2_3)^+ \quad \text{and} \quad (C^{12})^{++}$$
$$(H^1_2)^+ \quad \text{and} \quad (H^2)^+$$

Denoting the *exact* masses of the above atoms by the symbols:

$$H^1 \equiv H, \quad H^2 \equiv D, \quad C^{12} \equiv C, \quad O^{16} \equiv O,$$

three empirical equations can be obtained:

$$2H - D = a$$
$$3D - C = b$$
$$C + 4H - O = c$$

where a, b, c are the measured doublet separations.

Solving the three equations and substituting the mass value $O^{16} \equiv 16$, we obtain the masses of the three unknowns

$$H^1 = 1 + \tfrac{1}{16}(6a + 2b + c)$$
$$H^2 = 2 + \tfrac{1}{8}(-2a + 2b + c)$$
$$C^{12} = 12 + \tfrac{1}{4}(-6a - 2b + 3c)$$

In this way, the masses of H^1, H^2 and C^{12} have been determined with sufficient accuracy to warrant their use as secondary standards of mass.

A problem of major importance in mass spectroscopy, which has begun to be tackled in the last few years, is the question of determining the masses of certain of the *heavier* atoms with sufficient accuracy relative to O^{16} to warrant designating them as secondary standards.

Mass Spectrograph of Quisenberry, Scolman and Nier (1956)

A number of mass spectroscopes has been constructed in the last few years which have succeeded in pushing the limits of accuracy beyond 1 part in 10^7. One example is the intrument of A. O. Nier and his group at the University of Minnesota. The improved accuracy is the result of several important principles and design features in mass spectroscopy. First, the actual physical size of the apparatus is much greater than that employed in earlier instruments. For example, the radius of the magnetic momentum analyser is ~ 40 cm, about three times the value of previous models. The

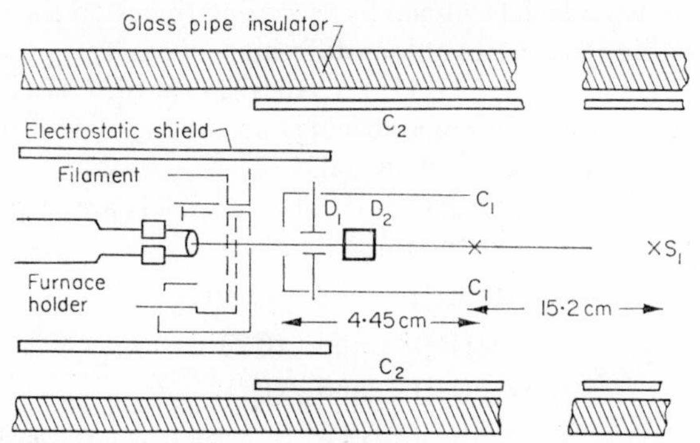

FIG. 5. Ion source of "Quisenberry, Scolman and Nier" Spectrometer.

cylindrical electrostatic energy filter has a radius of curvature as large as 50 cm. The photographic recording of mass spectra is ultimately limited by the finite grain size. The Nier instrument makes use of an ingenious form of *electrical* recording in which the mass spectra of the components of a doublet are superimposed on the screen of a cathode ray oscilloscope. The new spectrometer incorporates important principles of electron-optical design, so that ions of a given mass are focused correct to first-order aberration theory regarding energy spread, and correct to the second-order regarding direction focusing.

The Nier mass spectrometer consists of an ion source, (shown in detail in Fig. 5) a cylindrical electrostatic energy analyser E, a magnetic momentum analyser M, and a detector in the form of a multi-stage electron multiplier tube. A schematic diagram of the instrument is given in Fig. 6. Positive ions formed in the ion source are accelerated through a potential drop of about 40 kV and are focused on the fine slit S_1 (0·0008 cm wide). The second slit S_2 (0·020 cm wide) limits the angular divergence of the ion beam entering the 90° electrostatic energy analyser E. The energy analyser has cylindrical plates 2 cm apart with a radius of curvature of the order of 50 cm. A symmetric potential of the order of 3000 V is applied to the plates (Fig. 7). An exit slit S_3 (0·040 cm wide) of the energy analyser is mounted in line with the apex O of the magnetic momentum analyser M and the entry slit S_4 (0·0008 cm wide) to the electron multiplier tube.

The ion source (Fig. 5) produces ions by the bombardment of vapour molecules, emerging from a small furnace, with electrons emitted from a hot filament. The electron stream, indicated by the dotted lines, is confined to a narrow beam by an applied magnetic field. The ions produced are accelerated and focused at the slit S_1 by a large voltage applied between two cylinders.

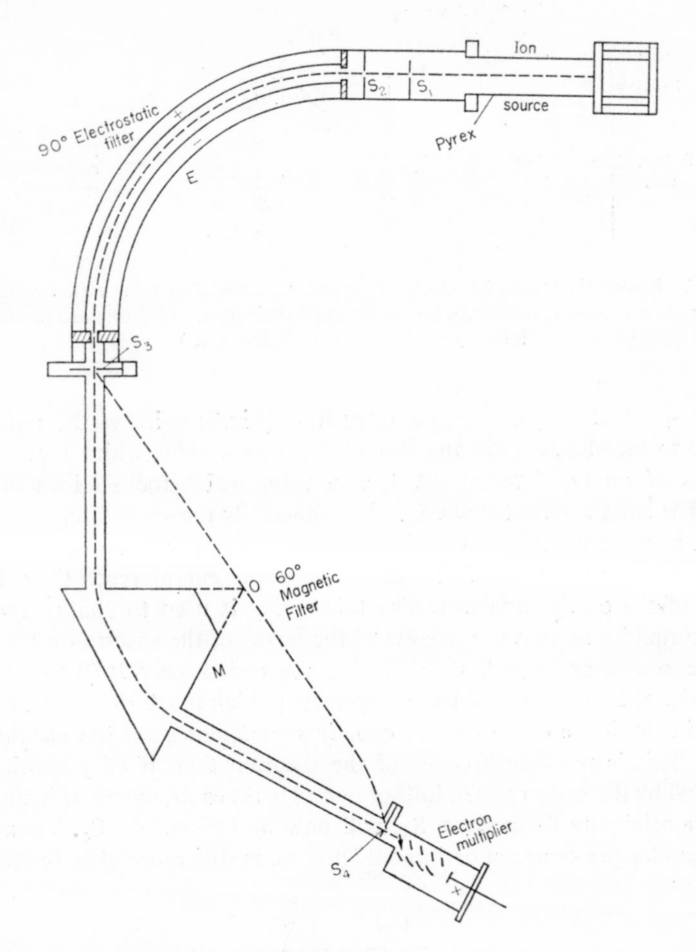

FIG. 6. Mass spectrograph of Quisenberry, Scolman and Nier. The slits S_3 and S_4 and apex O of the magnetic field lie in the same straight line. Ions travel about 3 m from S_1 to S_4.

An ingenious peak matching method for mass doublets is employed. This works in the following way. The sawtooth time base voltage of low frequency (~ 30 c/s) of an oscilloscope is used as a signal to modulate the magnetic field of the magnetic analyser M. This sweeps the focused beams of ions of neighbouring mass doublets across the fine slit S_4. The beam current reaching the electron multiplier, which is in the range 10^{-12} to 10^{-9} A, is amplified by the multiplier and after further amplification is displayed as a vertical deflection on the oscilloscope screen. The sawtooth waveform is synchronized with a pulse which simultaneously actuates three high-speed

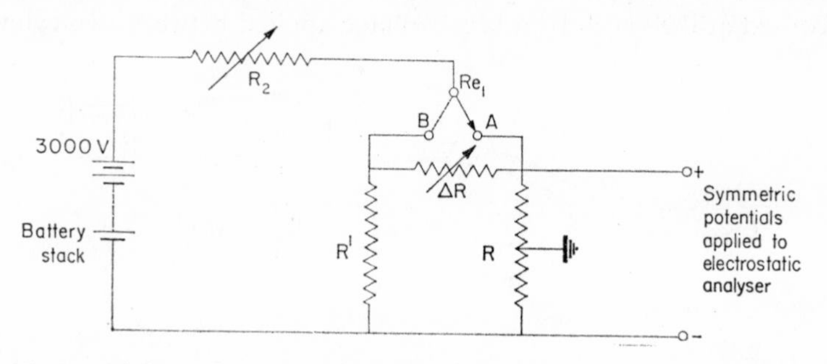

FIG. 7. Potential supplies for electrostatic analyser. Re_1, fast relay which switches from A to B in synchronism with oscilloscope time base. (Resistors are mounted inside a temperature controlled box.)

mercury-contact relays. The first relay Re_1, (Fig. 7) switches the potentials applied to the electrostatic analyser plates from a value which focuses ions of mass M on the detector slit S_4 to a value which focuses ions of mass $M + \Delta M$ on the detector slit S_4. Simultaneously the second relay operates so that a corresponding change in the ion accelerating voltage is produced. This is necessary in order that ions of the proper energy reach the entrance slit S_2 of the energy analyser. The third relay is used to change the gain of the amplifier so that the heights of the peaks of the spectra on the oscilloscope screen are equal. By adjusting the resistance ΔR (0 to 100 kΩ), the peaks of two mass doublet components (which must, of course, be produced in the ion source) can be *exactly superimposed* on the oscilloscope screen. This is possible because of the theorem that, if all potentials are increased by the same ratio α, ions of mass $1/\alpha$ times M, where M is the mass of ions originally focused on S_4, will now be focused on S_4. Thus when two doublet peaks are superimposed the mass difference ΔM is obtained from

$$\frac{\Delta M}{M} = \frac{\Delta R}{R}$$

where M is the mass of the lighter component.

The superposition technique means an improvement in measuring mass doublet separations of about ten-fold over the photographic method as it depends on the great efficiency of the human eye in judging any lack of coincidence of the two peaks. The potential supply for the cylindrical electrostatic analyser is derived from a 3 kV battery stack. All the resistors, except R_2, are high quality wire wound components and R and R' are matched to within 0·01% ($R' = R = 3{\cdot}3\ \mathrm{M}\Omega$). Resolving powers as high as 60,000 are common with this instrument and values exceeding 75,000 have been obtained. One source of confusion in mass spectroscopy is connected with the existence of the second isotope of carbon, C^{13}. Many important ions are obtained from hydrocarbon vapours and the contamination of a beam of hydrocarbon ions with ions in which *one* of the C^{12} atoms is replaced by a C^{13} atom is likely to lead to false results. High resolving power instruments can separate the satellite component corresponding to the C^{13} atom and avoid this source of error. One of the most important tasks of the Nier spectrometer and others of the same class is the establishment of accurate secondary mass standard such as H^1, H^2, C^{12}, S^{32} etc.

The Mass Synchrometer

A mass spectrometer of unusual design is the mass synchrometer of L. G. Smith. This essentially determines the masses of ions in terms of a *high harmonic frequency* of their cyclotron frequency of revolution in a magnetic field. This instrument, like the Nier spectrometer described above, employs electrical recording with the mass doublet components brought into sharp coincidence on an oscilloscope screen. However in Smith's case, the circuit parameter which is adjusted to produce synchronism is a frequency and not a resistance.

Figure 8 is a schematic diagram of the mass synchrometer. Ions formed by electron bombardment currents of 10 to 20 mA in the ion source, after passing through suitable "focusing" slits, emerge from the earthed slit S_1 with a kinetic energy of the order of 2500 eV. A uniform magnetic field of flux density B (in the range 0 to 7000 gauss) deflects the ions into a circular trajectory of the correct radius to enter the slits S_2, S_3, S_4. The two outer slits S_2 and S_4 are earthed and a r.f. alternating potential is applied to the "modulator" slit S_3. This modulation voltage causes the ion beam velocity to vary approximately harmonically. Let us suppose that an ion after describing one half-turn, from the source slit S_1 to the slit S_2, passes through the modulator slit system S_2, S_3, S_4, so that the energy of the ion is reduced by the right amount to enable it to pass through the fine slit S_5. After a further half revolution it again enters the modulator slit system and, if it does so when the r.f. voltage has the same value, it will again lose energy so that it passes through the slit S_6. On the next revolution through the modulator slit system it loses the same amount of energy and after another half-turn enters the electrical detector (a Faraday cylinder) mounted behind the slit S_7. The principle of mass determination is based on the well-known fact that for non-relativistic charged particles, the angular frequency of rotation ω around the magnetic field axis is independent of the speed of the ions

$$\omega = \frac{B\,e}{M}.$$

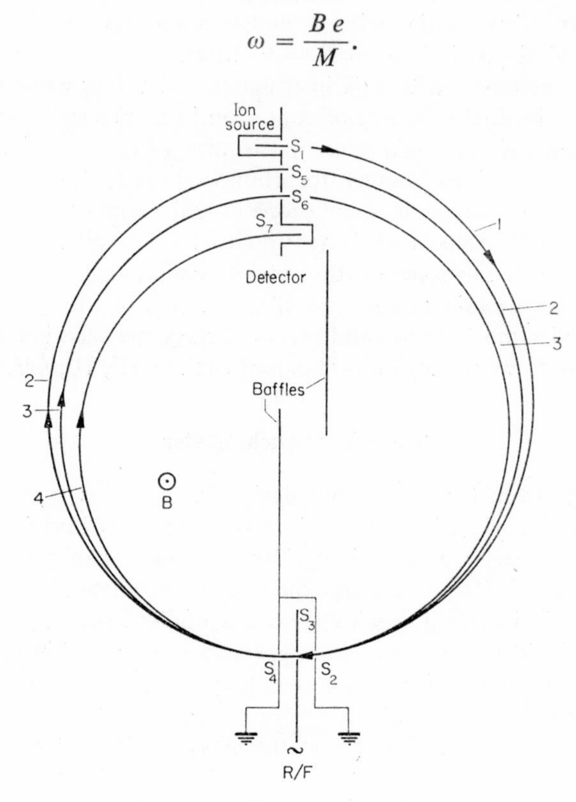

FIG. 8. Mass synchrometer of L. G. Smith and C. C. Damm. Ions revolve with the "cyclotron" angular frequency $\omega = B\,e/m$ around the magnetic field direction, losing energy each time they pass through the "modulator" slit system S_2, S_3, S_4 Ions are collected in a Faraday cylinder placed behind the slit S_1. (Redrawn from *Rev. Sci. Instr.*, **27**, 639, 1956, by kind permission of American Institute of Physics.)

If the frequency f of the r.f. field applied to the slit system S_2–S_3–S_4 is an exact multiple n of $\omega/2\pi$, ions will always experience the same loss in energy. In a typical mass determination we have $f \sim 15$ Mc/s for $n \sim 100$. The cyclotron rotation frequency is inversely proportional to the mass of the ions; hence it is possible to use the instrument as a spectrometer and focus ions of one particular mass value so they succeed in passing through the slits S_5, S_6 and S_7 on successive revolutions. The diameter of the outer ion orbit is 11 in. and the last orbit (S_4 to S_7) is just under 9 in., so that the inter-slit distances between S_1 and S_5, S_5 and S_6, S_6 and S_7 are about 2/3 in.

The difference in mass Δm of the two components of a doublet is determined in terms of the frequency difference Δf of the r.f. voltages, applied to the ion energy modulator, required to superimpose the signal peaks on the screen of an oscilloscope. This is achieved in the following way. The sawtooth time base of the oscilloscope operates at low audio frequency ($\sim$ 30 c/s). On alternate sweeps of the sawtooth voltage, a sinusoidal voltage of resonant frequency f ($f = n\,\omega/2\pi$, for one of the doublet components) is applied to the modulator slits. The other doublet component, corresponding to the resonant frequency $f + \Delta f$, is displayed on the other alternate sweeps of the sawtooth voltage. Following the argument outlined in the last section in relation to the Nier spectrometer, both types of ion will follow identical orbits, if the accelerating voltage is shifted between sweeps by a fractional amount equal to $\Delta M/M$.

The resonant frequency difference Δf of the two mass components is determined with high accuracy. A stable variable audio-frequency oscillator, which can be set at any frequency between 20 and 20,000 c/s, locks the frequency difference of two r.f. oscillators (one a 3 Mc/s crystal controlled oscillator) at a frequency Δf equal to the audio oscillator frequency. The correct operation of the lock-in device is continuously checked by showing an elliptic Lissajous pattern on an oscilloscope. The outputs of the two r.f. oscillators are alternately fed, by a relay circuit actuated by the sweep voltage of the time base, to a mixer, which is also fed with the output of a third r.f. oscillator, adjustable in frequency from 4 to 5 Mc/s. The output signal from this mixer is alternately of frequency f (f will have a value in the range 1 to 2 Mc/s) and frequency $f + \Delta f$. This is then fed into a frequency multiplier and amplifier, which multiplies the frequency by a factor of 4, 8, 16 or 32, producing signals anywhere in the range 4 to 64 Mc/s. The output is applied to the modulator slits. Thus on alternate sweeps of the sawtooth voltage ($\sim$ 30 c/s), a signal of frequency $m\,f$ and then $m(f+\Delta f)$ is used to modulate the ion beam energy (m is the multiplication factor selected, 4, 8, 16 or 32).

After the appropriate value of Δf has been selected, by setting the frequency of the audio oscillator, for exact matching on the oscilloscope screen of the doublet components, Δf is measured with high precision by first scaling down by a factor of two the modulator voltage of frequency $m\,f$, and then counting cycles on a 7 decade scaler, for a time interval exactly equal (to within $\frac{1}{100}$ audio cycle) to either 200 or 2000 audio cycles. Then the frequency $m(f + \Delta f)$ is measured in the same way. Thus in a few seconds the frequency f and frequency difference Δf is read off. The mass difference ΔM is obtained from either of the relations

$$\frac{\Delta f}{f_2} = \frac{\Delta M}{M_1} \quad \text{or} \quad \frac{\Delta f}{f_1} = \frac{\Delta M}{M_2}$$

where f_1, corresponds to the resonant frequency of ions of mass M_1, and similarly for f_2 and M_2.

The mass synchrometer is capable of covering a range of mass numbers from 2 to 250 at ion energies of 2500 eV. The instrument is capable of a precision of the order of 1 in 10^7 and it is proving a very useful complement to the more orthodox type of mass spectroscope. It is always an advantage to have several methods of determination based on different principles in order that unsuspected systematic errors may be revealed.

BIBLIOGRAPHY

H. E. DUCKWORTH, *Mass Spectroscopy*, Cambridge University Press, 1960.

F. W. ASTON, *Mass Spectra and Isotopes*, Arnold, London 1942.

K. T. BAINBRIDGE, Part V of Vol. I of *Experimental Nuclear Physics*, E. Segrè (Editor), Wiley, New York 1953.

Nuclear Masses and their Determination, Ed. by H. Hintenberger, Pergamon Press, London 1957.

A number of review articles dealing with precise mass determinations and the separation of stable isotopes is to be found in *Progress in Nuclear Physics*, Vol. 6, Ed. by O. R. FRISCH, Pergamon Press, London 1957.

L. G. SMITH and C. C. DAMM, *Mass synchrometer*, *Rev. Sci. Instr.* **27**, 639, 1956.

EXAMPLES

1. In a mass spectrograph, monoenergetic singly charged atomic oxygen ions and singly charged methane ions are selected by a cylindrical electrostatic filter of radius 30·0 cm. The filter consists of two curved plates 0·50 cm apart, one plate is at a potential of +416·7 V, the other at −416·7 V. After selection by the electrostatic filter, the ions enter a uniform magnetic field of 5000 gauss and describe semicircular orbits before striking a photographic plate. Calculate the diameter of the orbit for the oxygen ions. The separation of the traces on the plate due to the oxygen and methane ions is 0·414 mm. Calculate the exact mass of the neutral H^1 atom. The mass of the neutral C^{12} atom is 12·003803 a.m.u.
2. In a mass synchrometer of the Smith type, Ag^+ ions of mass 106·9 a.m.u. circulate in a magnetic field of 6500 gauss. They succeed in reaching the detector when the radio frequency is 11·21 Mc/s. The distance between the slits S_1 and S_2 is 27·94 cm. The difference in the inter-slit distances S_1–S_2 and S_4–S_5 (Fig. 8) is 1·692 cm. Calculate
   (a) the kinetic energy of the Ag^+ ions entering S_2,
   (b) the kinetic energy of the ions leaving S_4. What is the smallest percent change in the radio frequency to again collect the Ag^+ ions?

CHAPTER 8

GENERAL PROPERTIES OF ATOMIC NUCLEI

8.1. CHARGE, MASS, SIZE AND CONSTITUTION

The atomic nucleus was discovered in 1911 by Rutherford in interpreting the large angle scattering of alpha particles passing through very thin metal foils. Rutherford showed that the scattering was compatible with a purely electrostatic interaction between the positive charge of the alpha particle and a concentrated positively nucleus of diameter of the order of 10^{-12} cm. The atomic nucleus occupies a very small fraction of the total volume of an atom.

Some of the well-established properties of atomic nuclei are:

(1) All nuclei are positively charged and the magnitude of the electric charge is an integral multiple Z of the proton (hydrogen nucleus) charge e.† In a neutral atom, Z is equal to the number of orbital electrons; Z is known as the atomic number of the atom.

(2) More than 99·9 per cent of the mass of an atom is concentrated inside the tiny volume of the nucleus.

(3) Nuclei are spherical or nearly spherical in shape (there are a few important exceptions). The determination of nuclear radii is discussed in detail in Chapter 9. An important approximate rule for nuclear radii r is

$$r = r_0 A^{1/3} \tag{1}$$

where A is the mass number of the nucleus and r_0 is a constant equal to about 1·2 fermi (1 fermi $\equiv 10^{-13}$ cm).

The striking correlation between r and A suggests that there is a universal density for nuclear matter

$$\varrho = A\Big/\frac{4}{3}\pi r^3 = \frac{3}{4\pi}\,\frac{1}{r_0^3} \sim 10^{14} \text{ g per cm}^3$$

There is no simple law connecting atomic size and mass. The high density of nuclear matter $\sim 10^{38}$ nucleons per cm³ is a direct result of the close

† For evidence concerning the exact equality of the magnitude of the electron and proton charges see, HALLAS and CRANSHAW, *Nature*, **184**, 892, 1959, and H. BONDI and R. LYTTLETON, *Nature*, **184**, 974, 1959.

packing of neutrons and protons within the nucleus. In contrast, the electron distribution throughout the volume of the atom is very diffuse.

The nucleus is a tightly bound system of particles with a large potential energy which offsets the kinetic energy of the nucleons (the nucleons move with a speed of the order of a tenth of the velocity of light).

Before the discovery of the neutron in 1932, it was assumed that the nucleus was a collection of tightly bound protons and electrons. This hypothesis seemed very reasonable as a number of unstable isotopes emit electrons in the process known as beta decay. The nucleus of the common nitrogen isotope N^{14}, in terms of the proton–electron model, consists of 14 protons and 7 electrons. The electrons make no significant contribution to the nuclear mass but they annul the charge of seven of the protons. However, there is a number of strong reasons why electrons cannot exist as semi-permanent nuclear particles.

First, we cite the important rule of quantum statistics that nuclei containing an even number of nucleons obey the Bose–Einstein statistics. Now, an examination of the intensity pattern of the rotational spectrum of molecular nitrogen N_2^{14} gives unambiguous evidence that the N^{14} *nuclear* spin is one unit (in terms of $\hbar$). Nuclei containing an even number of nucleons have integral spin in contrast to odd mass number nuclei with half integral spins. Thus the spectroscopic evidence favours an even number of nucleons for the N^{14} nucleus. On the proton–electron model of N^{14} there would be 21 nucleons, an odd number. If, on the other hand, the nucleus consists of seven protons and seven neutrons, there is no contradiction as there are 14 nucleons, an even number.

A second strong argument against the *p–e* model is based on Heisenberg's uncertainty principle. If an electron is confined to a sphere of diameter $\sim 10^{-12}$ cm, the momentum of the electron is indeterminate to an extent Δp, given by

$$\Delta p \, \Delta x \sim \hbar \sim 10^{-27} \text{ ergs-secs.}$$

The energy of the electron may be as large as ΔE, where

$$\Delta E = c\,\Delta p, \text{ for a relativistic electron}$$

$$\Delta E = \frac{c\,\hbar}{\Delta x} = \frac{3 \times 10^{10} \times 10^{-27}}{10^{-12}} = 3 \times 10^{-5} \text{ ergs} \sim 20 \text{ MeV}$$

It seems unlikely that the nuclear-electron potential energy is > 20 MeV which it must be if electrons exist inside the nucleus. The large mass of the proton and the neutron compared with the electron mass do not lead to excessively large kinetic energies for bound neutrons and protons.

The small magnetic dipole moments of atomic nuclei would be difficult to understand if electrons were permanent constituents of nuclear matter. The large magnetic moments of the electrons should swamp the moments of the protons, if we assume that the proton moment is of the order of one nuclear magneton

$$\mu_n = \frac{e\hbar}{2Mc}$$

where M is the proton mass.

In addition to the arguments outlined above, there is now considerable evidence that apart from the Coulomb interaction between electrons and protons, the residual interaction is very small. The electron–neutron interaction is very small. The electron–neutron interaction is discussed in Chapter 15; this is so small, however, that one cannot detect neutrons moving through matter by the ionization due to neutron–electron collisions. Again in the beta decay process known as *orbital electron* capture (Chapter 14), an atomic electron (usually one from the K shell) which spends a small part ot its time inside the nuclear volume interacts with a proton to form a neutron. This interaction is very weak, about 10^{-12} times as strong as the nucleon–nucleon short range interactions.

We can therefore take it as well established that a nucleus can be described by three integers: Z the proton number (atomic number), N the neutron number, and $A = Z + N$, the mass number equal to the total number of nucleons (neutrons and protons) inside the nucleus.

A number of important nuclear terms and their definitions are listed below.

Word or Symbol	*Definition*
Nucleon	Proton or Neutron.
Nuclide	A given species of atom characterized by the charge number Z and mass number A.
$_zM^A$	This is the symbol for the exact mass of an atom of the nuclide (Z, A). It is usually given in atomic units (Chapter 7).
Isotopes	Nuclides with the same Z but different A (e.g. H^1, H^2, H^3 and Ne^{20}, Ne^{22}).
Isobar	Nuclides with the same A but different Z (e.g. $_{40}Zr^{96}$, $_{42}Mo^{96}$, $_{44}Ru^{96}$).
Isotones	Nuclides with the same N, $(A - Z)$, e.g. $_{38}Sr^{88}$, $_{42}Mo^{92}$).
Isodiapheres	Nuclides with the same "neutron excess" number $N - Z$ (e.g. $_{10}Ne^{22}$, $_8O^{18}$).

8.2. NUCLEAR STABILITY, BINDING ENERGY

The existence of many stable nuclei which require large amounts of energy to break them up is a direct consequence of the great strength of nuclear forces. However, the quantitative measurement of the nuclear force, even between a pair of nucleons, is very difficult. It has been mainly studied by observing the angular scattering cross sections of high energy protons and neutrons by protons. A satisfactory theory of the nucleon–nucleon force is still in its infancy. Even if a detailed theory of the nucleon–nucleon interaction became available, it would still be a hopeless task to calculate

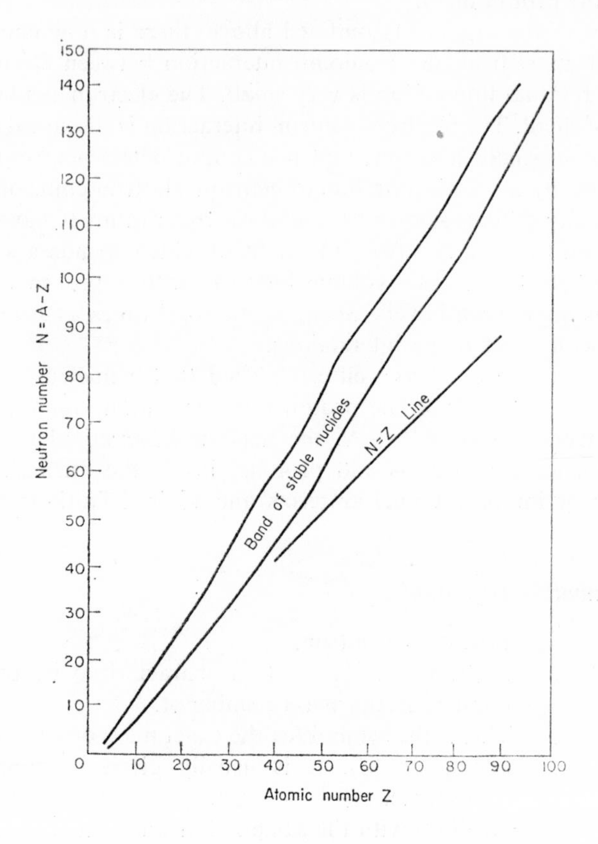

FIG. 1. N–Z chart for stable nuclides.

the resultant interaction of all the nucleons in a medium or heavy nucleus. This is the well-known problem of solving a many-body interaction.

The problem of nuclear stability can, however, be approached in a semi-empirical way. Thus important stability trends are observed if a plot of the nuclides is made with Z as abscissa and N as the ordinate (Fig. 1). For low mass nuclides, there is a strong tendency for the most stable nuclides to have $N = Z$. This suggests that there is some property of nuclear forces associated with equal numbers of protons and neutrons (this is the symmetry effect). For large A, however, N exceeds Z by a large number;

this is a reflection of the necessity for extra neutrons to compensate the increasing Coulomb repulsion of the Z protons. Excess neutrons are required to overcome the Coulomb repulsion.

Amongst the heavy elements, several are found which are unstable and decay by the radioactive process known as beta decay. This class of nuclides lies above the narrow band of stable nuclides in the $N-Z$ chart. They are neutron-rich, and become stable by converting a neutron into a proton, an electron and a massless neutral particle (the antineutrino $\bar{\nu}$) being emitted from the transforming nucleus.

$$\beta^- \text{ decay: } n \rightarrow p + e^- + \bar{\nu}$$

Many artificial beta-active nuclides can be produced by irradiating a sample of a stable nuclide with neutrons; e.g.

$$_{49}\text{In}^{115} + n \rightarrow {}_{49}\text{In}^{116} + \gamma$$

$$_{49}\text{In}^{116} \rightarrow {}_{50}\text{Sn}^{116}$$

A second class of unstable nuclides found amongst the heavier elemente is the alpha emitters. These transform by the emission of an alpha particle (helium nucleus). The reduction in nuclear charge reduces the disruptivs Coulomb energy. All the natural alpha emitters are derived from the three very long lived elements: uranium, thorium and actinium. These nuclides and their radioactive descendants are found today because the half life of the parent element is comparable with the age of the earth ($\sim 10^{10}$ years).

Proton-rich nuclei can be formed by bombarding suitable nuclide samples with charged particles accelerated in a machine (Van de Graaff, cyclotron). There are many examples of (d, n) reactions, in which an incident deuteron (kinetic energy a few MeV) is captured† by a nucleus and a neutron is emitted. The resultant effect is to add a proton to the target nucleus. The product nucleus may be unstable against positive electron decay—the decay process corresponding to the transformation of a proton into a neutron, a positron and a massless neutral particle (the neutrino ν) being emitted. Positron emitters are confined to light and medium light nuclides and are represented by points below the stability band.

$$\beta^+ \text{ decay: } p \rightarrow n + e^+ + \nu$$

e.g.

$$_{5}\text{B}^{10}\,(d, n)\,{}_{6}\text{C}^{11}$$

$$_{6}\text{C}^{11} \xrightarrow[\text{decay}]{\beta+} {}_{5}\text{B}^{11}$$

A new form of instability has recently been discovered. Uranium and especially many of the new artificially produced transuranic nuclides are

† It is immaterial in this context to discuss the mechanism of (d, n) stripping reactions in which the deuteron as a unit is not captured by the nucleus. Effectively a proton is added to the nucleus and produces a proton rich nuclide.

unstable against *spontaneous fission.* In this process the unstable nucleus breaks up into two nuclei of roughly equal mass. The effect is strongly related to the disruptive Coulomb energy and is dependent on the ratio Z^2/A.

In the preceding chapter an account is given of the experimental methods of determining precise values of atomic masses. The motivation behind mass spectroscopy is the calculation of nuclear binding energies B. The binding energy B of a nucleus whose atomic mass is ${}_ZM^A$ is given by the formula

$$B = [Z\, M_H + (A - Z)\, M_n - {}_ZM^A]\, c^2$$

where M_H is the mass of the neutral hydrogen atom,
M_n is the mass of the neutron,
and ${}_ZM^A$ is the mass of the atom (Z, A).
The binding energy B and mean binding energy B/A per nucleon for the lightest nuclei are given in Table 1.

TABLE 1

Nucleus	B (MeV)	B/A (MeV per nucleon)
${}_1H^2$	2·226	1·113
${}_1H^3$	8·485	2·828
${}_2He^3$	7·720	2·573
${}_2He^4$	28·30	7·075
${}_3Li^6$	31·99	5·332
${}_3Li^7$	39·25	5·607
${}_4Be^9$	58·16	6·462
${}_5B^{10}$	64·75	6·475

The values of B/A vary in an erratic manner from nucleus to nucleus for the very light nuclides. Nevertheless, two prominent features stand out in Table 1. First, we note the very low value of 1·113 MeV per nucleon for the ${}_1H^2$ nucleus (the deuteron). This is a result of the relatively large separation of the neutron and proton in the deuteron; the potential energy of the n–p interaction in the nucleus just overcomes the kinetic energy of the nucleons. The second outstanding feature is the very high value of B/A, 7·075 MeV per nucleon, for the ${}_2He^4$ nucleus (the alpha particle). The great stability of the alpha particle is mainly a consequence of the pairing off of the two protons and two neutrons with opposite spins. The resultant angular momentum of the alpha particle is zero; the spins of the four nucleons cancel and the internal orbital angular momentum must be zero. This state of affairs corresponds to a very stable system.

A plot of B/A against mass number A of the most beta stable isobars is given in Fig. 2. Up to $A \sim 20$, B/A varies in a haphazard way. (Table 1 shows this effect up to $A = 10$). Above $A \sim 20$, the binding energy per nucleon B/A is remarkably constant (to $\sim 10\%$). This must reflect an important property of nuclear forces. If all the A nucleons inside the nucleus interacted with all the remaining $A - 1$ nucleons with the same strength one would except B to increase as $A(A - 1)$, or approximately as A^2 for the heavy nuclei. This is not the case. Agreement with observations is obtained if it is postulated that nuclear forces *saturate* in the sense that the interaction between two nucleons may be such that there is little interaction with a third nucleon. This is known to be the case for certain types of chemical force. The two hydrogen atoms in the hydrogen molecule interact

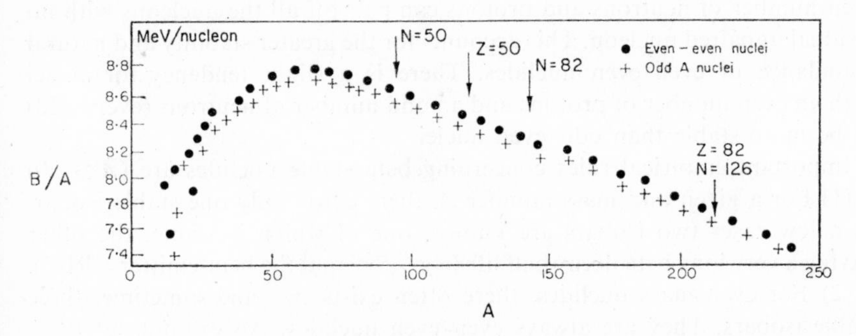

FIG. 2. Graph of mean binding energy per nucleon, B/A, against A.

through the exchange of two electrons between the atoms. A third hydrogen atom has only a very weak interaction with the hydrogen molecule and there is no stable H_3 molecule. It is interesting to compare the theory of the force of the chemical *homopolar* bond with the theory that nucleons interact through the exchange of pions. An atomic nucleus is sometimes compared to a drop of liquid; the binding energy of a drop of liquid hydrogen is proportional to the number of pairs of atoms; the molecular forces (van der Waals) are much weaker than the forces holding the hydrogen molecule together. Nucleons in the surface of the nucleus are less firmly bound, as are the surface molecules in a liquid. It is possible to use the idea of surface tension in discussing the surface oscillations of a vibrating nucleus in the liquid drop theory of fission (Chapter 17). The constancy of the density of nuclear matter is interpreted in terms of an incompressible nuclear fluid.

The binding energy curve exhibits important trends. B/A increases to a maximum of about 8·8 MeV per nucleon around mass number 60 and then decreases slowly and monotonically to about 7·6 MeV per nucleon in the vicinity of $A = 240$. One can appreciate that commercial attempts to release large amounts of nuclear energy correspond to the fission of heavy elements or the fusion of light elements. A study of the binding energy curve shows that nuclides with an even number of protons and an even number of neutrons (even–even nuclides) have consistently higher values of B/A than neighbouring odd mass nuclides. It is a striking fact that there are only four stable odd–odd nuclides: $_1H^2$, $_3Li^6$, $_5B^{10}$ and $_7N^{14}$. These are all nuclides of low mass number and correspond to the low mass number stability rule $Z = N$. The greater stability of even–even nuclides in comparison with those of odd mass number (even–odd or odd–even) is roughly the same as that of the odd A nuclides over the rare odd–odd nuclides. It is a characteristic feature of nuclear forces that nuclear states, with paired off nucleon spins tend to be more firmly bound. Nuclei composed of an even number of neutrons and protons can pair off all the nucleons with no residual unpaired nucleon. This accounts for the greater stability and natural abundance of even–even nuclides. There is a slight tendency for nuclei with an even number of protons and an odd number of neutrons (even–odd) to be more stable than odd–even nuclei.

Important empirical rules concerning beta stable nuclides are ($A > 20$)

(1) For a given odd mass number A, there exists only one stable isobar. In a few cases two isobars are known, one of which is stable, the other having a very long beta decay half life (e.g. $_{38}Sr^{87}$ and the beta-emitter $_{37}Rb^{87}$).

(2) For even mass nuclides, there often exists two and sometimes three stable isobars. They are always even–even nuclides. An example of three stable isobars is $_{40}Zr^{96}$, $_{42}Mo^{96}$ and $_{44}Ru^{96}$.

(3) If isotopes (or isotones) with masses $A + 2$ and $A - 2$ are stable, so is the isotope (or isotone) with mass A.

(4) If a nuclide of mass number $2n + 1$ and containing an even number of neutrons (protons) is stable, its isotones (isotopes) with masses $2n$ and $2n + 2$ are stable.

8.3. SEMI-EMPIRICAL MASS FORMULA

Von Weizsäcker in 1935 obtained a formula for expressing the atomic mass of a nuclide, in terms of a series of binding energy "correction terms" to the main mass contribution from protons and neutrons. This formula has been modified in the light of more recent knowledge, but in its main outline it remains unchanged. The mass of an atom $_ZM^A$ is primarily determined by the term

$$M_0 = Z\,M_H + (A - Z)\,M_n$$

The nearly constant value of B/A for all but the lightest nuclides means that the main correction term to be added to M_0 is the volume binding energy term

$$M_1 = -a_1 A$$

The volume binding energy corresponds to a negative mass term. This term, however, exaggerates the binding energy of nucleons in the surface of the nucleus. These nucleons are not so firmly bound as those well inside the surface. The surface area of the nucleus varies as r^2 and therefore as $A^{2/3}$. The reduced binding of the surface nucleons can be taken into account by a positive mass correction term

$$M_2 = a_2 A^{2/3}$$

The next correction term is the negative binding associated with the mutual Coulomb repulsion of the Z protons. On the assumption that the Z protons are uniformly distributed throughout the nuclear volume, a simple classical argument† using Gauss' theorem shows that the Coulomb self-energy E_c of the nucleus is given by

$$E_c = \frac{3}{5} \frac{Z^2 e^2}{r}$$

For light nuclei, we must recognize the discrete nature of the protons and replace Z by $Z(Z - 1)$. Caution is needed in accepting the value of the numerical coefficient of $^3/_5$. The assumption that the volume distribution of protons is uniform is probably incorrect. Protons obey the Pauli principle and two of them cannot occupy the same place and this effect must be considered in a more realistic estimate of E_c. Nevertheless the effect of the Coulomb self-energy on the mass formula is to increase the mass by an amount

$$M_3 = +a_3 \frac{Z^2}{A^{\frac{1}{3}}}$$

At first sight it is difficult to see why all stable nuclei do not consist of neutrons alone. Observation, however, emphasizes the result that when the Coulomb self-energy is unimportant (light nuclei), there is a marked tendency for Z and N to be equal. This important feature of nuclear binding is called the *symmetry effect*. The origin of this effect will not be discussed here, except to say that it is a reflection of the symmetric nature of the wave function describing the exchange forces between nucleons.†† From the point of view of the mass formula, any deviation from $N = Z$, reduces the binding; this suggests that a term involving the square of $(N - Z)$ or $(A/2 - Z)$ is required. A more detailed argument‡ yield a symmetry mass correction term of the form

$$M_4 = +a_4 \frac{(A/2 - Z)^2}{A}$$

† A similar argument is given for the gravitational self-energy of a star (Chap. 22).

†† J. M. Blatt and V. F. Weisskopf, *Theoretical Nuclear Physics*, Wiley, New York 1952, p. 213.

‡ E. Fermi, *Nuclear Physics*, University of Chicago Press, 1949, p. 22.

Finally the tendency for the most stable nuclei to be even–even nuclei must be allowed for. A mass correction term δ has been suggested where

$$\delta = + a_5 A^{-\frac{3}{4}} \quad \text{for odd–odd nuclides (the least stable);}$$

$$\delta = 0 \quad \text{for even–odd or odd-even nuclides;}$$

$$\delta = - a_5 A^{-\frac{3}{4}} \quad \text{for even–even nuclides (the most stable).}$$

Collecting together the different stability or mass correction terms we can write for the exact mass of an atom (Z, A)

$$_{Z}M^{A} = Z\,M_{\mathrm{H}} + (A - Z)\,M_n - a_1 A + a_2 A^{\frac{2}{3}} + a_3 Z^2 A^{-\frac{1}{3}} + a_4 \frac{(A/2 - Z)^2}{A} + \delta \qquad (2)$$

The empirical values of the coefficients which give a good fit to the observed masses are $a_1 = 16{\cdot}92$, $a_2 = 19{\cdot}1$, $a_3 = 0{\cdot}763$, $a_4 = 101{\cdot}8$, $a_5 = 36{\cdot}5$. (The coefficients are given in $m\,m\,u$ ($10^{-3}\,a\,m\,u$).)

The most stable isobar for a given mass number A corresponds to a minimum value of $_{Z}M^{A}$

$$\left(\frac{\partial M}{\partial Z}\right)_A = 0 = M_{\mathrm{H}} - M_n + 2a_3 Z A^{-\frac{1}{3}} - 2a_4 \frac{(A/2 - Z)}{A}$$

or

$$Z = \frac{M_n - M_{\mathrm{H}} + a_4}{2a_3 A^{-\frac{1}{3}} + 2a_4 A^{-1}} \qquad (3)$$

The empirical value of the constant a_4, or rather the ratio a_3/a_4, for the most stable isobars, is found by obtaining the best fit with the experimental curve of Z versus A. The constants $a_1, a_2 \ldots$ are not calculated theoretically but are found by substituting several *measured* mass values in the formula and solving simultaneous equations. The problem is over-determined in the sense that more mass values can be substituted than is necessary to determine the constants. It is not possible to find an empirical formula which is a very good fit for a very wide range in mass number A. This is not surprising in view of the assumptions made in obtaining the correction terms. Over a limited range of A, however, the formula is remarkably successful.

An important property of the mass formula is that the mass $_{Z}M^{A}$ is a quadratic function of Z for a given mass number A. The $_{Z}M^{A}$ versus Z curve is a *parabola*. Experimentally it is known that for odd-A nuclides, there is only one stable isobar; this corresponds to the Z value nearest to the minimum of the mass parabola. There are often two and sometimes three stable isobars for even–A nuclides.

8.4. NUCLEAR SPIN

W. Pauli in 1924 suggested that some atomic nuclei may possess an intrinsic spin angular momentum. Intimately associated with the nuclear spin is a magnetic dipole moment. This is understandable classically because nuclei have an electric charge and a finite size, and a spinning charged sphere generates a magnetic field. Pauli's suggestion was prompted by the discovery that many optical spectral lines exhibit a hyperfine structure of the order of 1 cm^{-1}. Such splittings are much smaller than the fine structure effects and they have two origins. The first, called the *isotope shift*, is attributed to the variation in the reduced mass of the electron reponsible for the optical transition between isotopes of the element in question. There is also an isotope effect connected with the shift in the Coulomb energies of the atomic electrons due to the variation in nuclear size between isotopes of the same element. In monoisotopic elements (e.g. bismuth) these effects are absent and the hyperfine structure is solely due to the magnetic interaction between the magnetic moment of the nucleus and the magnetic moment of the valency electron responsible for the optical line.

The intrinsic angular momentum of a nucleus is a vector $\boldsymbol{I}$, which is the sum of contributions from the spin and orbital angular momenta of the individual nucleons within the nucleus. The nuclear shell model (Chapter 20) shows that it is fruitful to consider the nucleons moving in quasi-stationary orbits within the nuclear volume (at least in the ground or low lying excited states). It is unfortunate that the term nuclear spin is used to describe the resultant angular momentum of the nucleus.

The nuclear spin vector $\boldsymbol{I}$ has a magnitude $[I(I+1)]^{\frac{1}{2}}$, but the maximum observable component of $\boldsymbol{I}$ is I (in terms of the fundamental unit $\hbar$). This has important consequences, for it means that in a uniform magnetic field for example, the vector $\boldsymbol{I}$ cannot be aligned parallel to the field, as otherwise its component in the field direction would be greater than I.

Parallel to the nuclear spin vector $\boldsymbol{I}$ is the nuclear magnetic dipole moment vector $\boldsymbol{\mu}$. The two vectors are related by the equation

$$\boldsymbol{\mu} = g_n \mu_n \boldsymbol{I} \tag{4}$$

where g_n is the nuclear g factor

$\mu_n = \dfrac{e\hbar}{2Mc}$ is the *nuclear magneton* (M is the proton rest mass).

Unfortunately it is not possible at present, as it is with electronic magnetic moments to predict nuclear g factors.

The maximum observable component of $\boldsymbol{\mu}$ (for example, the component parallel to a uniform magnetic field) is denoted by μ and is simply known as the magnetic moment of the nucleus

$$\mu = g_n \mu_n I$$

We now consider the interaction between the magnetic moment of a nucleus and its surrounding electrons. Let $\boldsymbol{H}_J$ denote the magnetic field produced at the site of the nucleus by the surrounding electrons, and $\boldsymbol{J}$ the vector sum of the resultant orbital angular momenta of the atomic electrons $\boldsymbol{L}$ and the resultant electronic spin $\boldsymbol{S}$. As the nucleus does not respond to the rapid motion of the electronic magnetic fields, it is permissible to take the time average of these fields and express the potential energy of the interaction between $\boldsymbol{\mu}$ and $\boldsymbol{H}_J$ by

$$V = -\boldsymbol{\mu}\cdot\boldsymbol{H}_J = -\left(\frac{\mu H_J}{IJ}\right)\boldsymbol{I}\cdot\boldsymbol{J}$$

or

$$V = A_J\,\boldsymbol{I}\cdot\boldsymbol{J},$$

where the constant A_J, which is called the interval factor, is given by

$$A_J = -\frac{\mu H_J}{IJ}$$

The total angular momentum of the atom is the vector

$$\boldsymbol{F} = \boldsymbol{I} + \boldsymbol{J}$$

The observable components of $\boldsymbol{F}$ are $I + J, I + J - 1, \ldots |I - J|$.

If $J \geqq I$, there are $2I + 1$ values of F.

If $I \geqq J$, there are $2J + 1$ values of F.

To obtain the scalar product $\boldsymbol{I}\cdot\boldsymbol{J}$ we write

$$\boldsymbol{F}^2 = (\boldsymbol{I} + \boldsymbol{J})^2 = \boldsymbol{I}^2 + \boldsymbol{J}^2 + 2\boldsymbol{I}\cdot\boldsymbol{J}$$

Hence

$$\boldsymbol{I}\cdot\boldsymbol{J} = \tfrac{1}{2}[\boldsymbol{F}^2 - \boldsymbol{I}^2 - \boldsymbol{J}^2]$$

Using the quantum mechanical rule that $\boldsymbol{F}^2$ is equal to $F(F + 1)$, etc. . . . (replacing operators by eigenvalues), the magnetic potential energy V is given by

$$V = \tfrac{1}{2}A_J\,C$$

where C is a function of F.

Thus each atomic energy level, with total angular momentum J, is split into a group of sub-states corresponding to the different values of F. Two adjacent sub-states differ in F values by unity; thus the energy gap between these sub-states is

$$\tfrac{1}{2}[\{F(F + 1) - I(I + 1) - J(J + 1)\} - \{(F - 1)\,F - I(I + 1) - J(J + 1)\}]\,A_J = A_J\,F$$

where F is the greater of the two F values for the two adjacent sub-states.

Determination of Nuclear Spin

In the preceding paragraph it was pointed out that the magnetic hyperfine splitting of *atomic* energy states produces $2I + 1$ or $2J + 1$ sub-states. If it is established that $J > I$, then careful counting of the number of hyperfine states yields the value $2I + 1$, and hence I.

As an example of this method, it has been observed, with the aid of a large optical grating spectrograph, that optical lines in the spectra of the transuranic element americium (Am^{241} and Am^{243}) have a maximum of six hyperfine components. It is believed that the atomic levels responsible have a large value of J, $J > I$, so $2I + 1 = 6$, $I = {}^5/_2$ (for both isotopes). Least ambiguity occurs in interpretation when the optical transitions are between one level with relatively large splittings and another with negligible splitting. For an optical line of wave number 2×10^4 cm^{-1} ($\lambda \sim 5000$ Å), the hyperfine splitting observed is typically 2 cm^{-1}, that is 0·01 per cent.

A second method of nuclear spin determination makes use of the interval rule above. Consider three adjacent sub-states with F values of F, $F-1$, and $F-2$. Then the intervals between the middle state and the other two states will be in the ratio

$$\frac{A_J F}{A_J(F-1)} = \frac{F}{F-1}$$

If J is known, I can be found from F and J.

Nuclear spins can be found by observing the hyperfine splitting associated with a nuclear *Paschen–Back* effect. In a weak magnetic field the total angular momentum vector $\boldsymbol{F}$ of the atom orientates itself in the magnetic field (magnetic quantum number m_F) and precesses around the field direction. This is analogous to the well-known atomic Zeeman effect. In a stronger field, however, the coupling between the vectors $\boldsymbol{I}$ and $\boldsymbol{J}$ is broken up by the field and $\boldsymbol{I}$ and $\boldsymbol{J}$ orientate and precess independently of each other. F is no longer a "good quantum number". We now have two magnetic quantum numbers m_J and m_I. This corresponds to the atomic Paschen–Back effect, but in the nuclear case it is more easily achieved as the coupling between $\boldsymbol{I}$ and $\boldsymbol{J}$ is about 2000 times smaller than that between the electron angular momentum vectors $\boldsymbol{L}$ and $\boldsymbol{S}$. Each level corresponding to a given value of m_J is split into $2I + 1$ hyperfine sub-levels. The selection rules for transitions between levels are

$$\Delta m_I = 0$$
$$\Delta m_J = \pm 1, 0$$

If the number of hyperfine components can be counted, the nuclear spin I is obtained. An example of this method is the determination of the spin of the nucleus Na^{23}. The resonant absorption of the sodium D line, of wavelength 5890 Å, in a magnetic field in the range 1000 to 3000 gauss revealed two groups of four hyperfine components corresponding to $\Delta m_J = 0$. Thus the spin of the nucleus of Na^{23} is ${}^3/_2$.†

† D. A. Jackson and H. Kuhn, *Proc. Roy. Soc.*, A **167**, 205, 1938.

The symmetry and parity properties of homonuclear diatomic molecules with zero nuclear spin have been discussed in Chapter 6, Section 12. In the rotational spectrum of molecular oxygen O_2^{16}, alternate lines of the band spectrum are missing. This is a consequence of the zero spin of the O^{16} nucleus. A more extensive argument shows that for nuclei following either Bose–Einstein ox Fermi–Dirac statistics, the ratio of statistical weights of alternate rotational states is $I + 1 : I$. Thus for nuclei with spins I equal to $\frac{1}{2}$ and 1, the ratios of the intensities of alternate spectral lines in the rotational spectrum of the molecules are 3 : 1 and 2 : 1 respectively. For $I = 0$, we have the special case discussed above with alternate lines in the spectrum missing. Photometric observations of the lines in the band spectrum (usually the Raman spectrum) can distinguish clearly between low spin values. Unfortunately for higher values of I, it is more difficult to determine I as the ratio $I + 1 : I$ is close to unity.

8.5. NUCLEAR MOMENTS

Atomic nuclei in general possess electric and magnetic moments. The distribution of electric charge throughout the finite nuclear volume is responsible for the electric moments. Internal electric currents associated with the intrinsic angular momentum of the nucleus are responsible for the magnetic moments. External electric and magnetic fields are too weak to perturb the charge distribution and currents within the nuclear volume. It is important to realise that atomic nuclei are normally situated in electric and magnetic fields set up by the surrounding atomic or molecular electrons.

Electric Dipole Moment

It is a fundamental rule that atomic nuclei do not possess electric dipole moments. This follows if there is a plane of symmetry passing through the centre of mass of the nucleus (nuclei are never "pear-shaped"). An important theorem of quantum mechanical systems is that in stationary states there are no permanent electric dipole moments. The total electric charge of the nucleus Ze can be written

$$Ze = \int \mathrm{e}(x, y, z)\, d\tau$$

where $\varrho(x, y, z)$ is the volume density of charge, $d\tau$ is an element of volume. The z-component of the electric dipole moment D_z is given by

$$D_z = \int z\, \mathrm{e}(x, y, z)\, d\tau \tag{5}$$

z is measured from the centre of mass of the charge distribution.

In terms of the nuclear wave function $\psi(\boldsymbol{r}_1, \boldsymbol{r}_2, \ldots, \boldsymbol{r}_Z, \boldsymbol{r}_{Z+1}, \ldots, \boldsymbol{r}_A)$, where the first Z coordinates refer to the position vectors of the protons, measured from the centre of mass and the remaining $A - Z$ vectors refer to the neutrons, the electric dipole moment D_z is given by the quantum mechanical expression

$$D_z = e \sum_{i=1}^{z} \int z_i |\Psi(\boldsymbol{r}_1, \ldots, \boldsymbol{r}_A)|^2 \, d\tau \tag{6}$$

The integration is over all coordinates and the sum is over the first Z particles (protons only). Now stationary states of the nucleus have even or odd parity wave functions ψ. $|\psi^2|$ however has even parity. The position coordinate z_i has odd parity. Thus the integrals

$$\int z_i |\psi(\boldsymbol{r}_1, \ldots, \boldsymbol{r}_A)|^2 \, d\tau$$

vanish, as we have the product of an even and odd function integrated over a region where $|\psi^2|$ has a plane of symmetry. Hence the absence of electric dipole moments.

Electric Quadrupole Moment

Consider now the nucleus in an electric field $\boldsymbol{E}$ which varies over the nuclear dimensions. Apart from a constant component, we can write the z-component E_z in the form

$$E_z = \left(\frac{\partial E_z}{\partial z}\right)_0 \cdot z = F z$$

The subscript zero denotes the field gradient at the centre of the nucleus. Assume the electric field $\boldsymbol{E}$ has cylindrical symmetry about the z-axis, and we also have

$$\operatorname{div} \boldsymbol{E} = \frac{\partial E_x}{\partial x} + \frac{\partial E_y}{\partial y} + \frac{\partial E_z}{\partial z} = 0$$

(the electric charges responsible for $\boldsymbol{E}$ are outside the nucleus).

$$\therefore E_x = -\tfrac{1}{2} F x, \quad E_y = -\tfrac{1}{2} F y$$

The potential $\varphi(x, y, z)$ of the field $\boldsymbol{E}$ satisfies the relations

$$E_x = -\frac{\partial \varphi}{\partial x}, \quad E_y = -\frac{\partial \varphi}{\partial y}, \quad E_z = -\frac{\partial \varphi}{\partial z}$$

Hence $$\varphi = -\frac{1}{4} F(2z^2 - x^2 - y^2)$$

or $$\varphi = -\frac{1}{4} F(3z^2 - r^2)$$

using $$r^2 = x^2 + y^2 + z^2$$

Electrostatic theory shows that the potential energy W of the nucleus in this electric field is given by

$$W = \int \varphi(x, y, z) \varrho(x, y, z) \, d\tau \tag{7}$$

or $$W = -\frac{1}{4} F e \int (3z^2 - r^2) \, |\psi(x, y, z)|^2 \, d\tau$$

$$\therefore \; W = -\frac{1}{4} \left(\frac{\partial E_z}{\partial z} \right)_0 \cdot Q e \tag{8}$$

where $$Q = \int (3z^2 - r^2) \, |\Psi(x, y, z)|^2 \, d\tau \tag{9}$$

Q is called the electric quadrupole moment and is measured in units of cm^2. The wave function $\psi(x, y, z)$ is normalized for protons only.

For a spherically symmetric distribution of charge the mean values of x^2, y^2 and z^2 are equal:

$$\langle x^2 \rangle = \langle y^2 \rangle = \langle z^2 \rangle = \frac{1}{3} r^2$$

and the integral (9) vanishes. Spherical nuclei have zero electric quadrupole moment. For nuclei with zero spin there is no preferred axis and the average in time of the nuclear charge is spherically symmetric. It can also be proved, using quantum mechanics, that Q is zero for the case $I = \frac{1}{2}$.† Thus a nucleus can only have a spectroscopic electric quadrupole moment if its spin quantum number I is greater than or equal to unity. For a prolate spheroid, $3\langle z^2 \rangle > \langle r^2 \rangle$ and Q is positive; whereas for an oblate spheroid, $3\langle z^2 \rangle < \langle r^2 \rangle$ and Q is negative. If the three semi-axes of a spheroidal nucleus are a, a, and c we obtain, assuming a uniform charge distribution, by integration

$$Q = \frac{\varrho V}{e} \frac{2}{5} (c^2 - a^2) = \frac{2}{5} Z (c^2 - a^2)$$

where the volume of the nucleus $V = \frac{4}{3} \pi a^2 c = \frac{4}{3} \pi R^3$ approximately. This assumes that the departure from spherical shape is slight.

Taking the mean radius R as $(c + a)/2$ and introducing the eccentricity η, defined by

$$\eta = (c - a)/R$$

we obtain

$$Q = \frac{4}{5} \eta Z R^2$$

and if $\eta \ll 1$, $$\frac{c}{a} = 1 + \eta$$

It is not possible to determine electric quadrupole moments with high accuracy. Most methods are based on the measurement of the hyperfine structure in an atom, a molecule, or a crystalline solid, produced by the interaction energy (eqn. (8)) between the quadrupole moment Q and the

† E. Fermi, *Nuclear Physics*, University of Chicago Press, 1949, p. 15.

electric field gradient $\left(\frac{\partial E_z}{\partial z}\right)_0$ at the nucleus. It is difficult to estimate the *gradient* of the field at the position of the nucleus. One can estimate the order of magnitude of the hyperfine splitting associated with the energy term

$$W = -\frac{1}{4}\left(\frac{\partial E_z}{\partial z}\right)_0 \cdot Q\, e$$

Let us assume that the electric field gradient is produced by an atomic electron at a distance r_e ($\sim 10^{-8}$ cm) from the nucleus.

$$\left|\frac{\partial E_z}{\partial z}\right| \sim \frac{d}{dr}\left(\frac{e}{r_e^2}\right) \sim \frac{e}{r_e^3}$$

Values of Q are of the order of $Z\, r_n^2$, where r_n is the nuclear radius. Thus W is roughly equal to

$$\frac{Z\, e^2\, r_n^2}{r_e^3}$$

Comparing this with the potential energy V_e of the electron in the Coulomb field of the nucleus,

$$|V_e| \sim \frac{Z\, e^2}{r_e}$$

The ratio of the quadrupole to the Coulomb energy is seen to be $\sim\left(\frac{r_n}{r_e}\right)^2 \sim 10^{-8}$. Optical line frequencies correspond to wave numbers in the region of 10^5 cm^{-1}, so we expect the hyperfine structure associated with the electric quadrupole moment to be about 10^{-3} cm^{-1}. This is in the radio-frequency spectrum at about 30 Mc/s. The majority of quadrupole moments have been determined by measuring the energy associated with the orientation of the nucleus in an atomic or molecular system. The first determination of a quadrupole moment was made by Schüler and Schmidt in 1935 from the hyperfine structure of the atomic spectrum of Eu. Since the 1939–1945 war, many determinations using high resolution radio-frequency or microwave spectroscopy have been successfully carried out. Historically, the establishment and determination of the quadrupole moment of the *deuteron*† in a molecular beam experiment was of prime importance. This discovery showed that the nuclear force between the neutron and proton of the deuteron is not a central force, as otherwise Q would vanish. The nuclear force between the two nucleons depends on the relative direction of the nuclear spins and the position vector joining the nucleons.

The departure from a spherical charge distribution for the majority of nuclei is not marked. In general η lies in the range 0·01 to 0·03. There are exceptions; the rare earth nuclei have large positive quadrupole moments. There are, in fact, more nuclei with positive rather than negative quadrupole

† Chapter 16.

moments. The record for a high quadrupole moment is that of the nucleus Lu^{176} with a Q of 7×10^{-24} cm², corresponding to a strongly deformed nucleus ($\eta = 0{\cdot}35$). Lu^{176} also has the highest nuclear spin value known ($I \geqq 7$). The spins and quadrupole moments Q of some nuclei are given in Table 2.

TABLE 2

Nucleus	Spin I	Q (10^{-24} cm²)
$_1H^2$	1	0·00274
$_3Li^7$	3/2	−0·02
$_7N^{14}$	1	0·02
$_{13}Al^{27}$	5/2	0·15
$_{27}Co^{59}$	7/2	0·5
$_{53}I^{127}$	5/2	−0·8 ± 0·05
$_{63}Eu^{151}$	5/2	1·2
$_{63}Eu^{153}$	5/2	2·5
$_{70}Yb^{173}$	5/2	3·9 ± 0·4
$_{71}Lu^{175}$	7/2	5·1 ± 0·3
$_{71}Lu^{176}$	>/7	7 ± 1
$_{95}Am^{243}$	5/2	4·9

Magnetic Moments

All atomic nuclei with a finite spin quantum number I possess a magnetic dipole moment μ_I. The quantum mechanical parity arguments which explain the absence of nuclear electric dipole moments do not apply to magnetic moments. It has already been pointed out that nuclear magnetic dipole moments are expected to be roughly equal to one nuclear magneton μ_n, where

$$\mu_n = \frac{e\hbar}{2Mc}$$

and M is the proton rest mass.

The experimental methods of determining the magnetic moments of nuclei are described in Chapt. 16. At this stage, we note that nuclear magnetic moments can be measured with high precision (accuracy 1 part in 50,000), but they are not understood theoretically to the first decimal place! It is interesting to compare the magnetic moments of the proton, neutron and deuteron:

TABLE 3

Nucleus	Spin	Magnetic moment (μ_n)
Proton H^1	$\frac{1}{2}$	2·7927
Neutron	$\frac{1}{2}$	−1·9131
Deuteron H^2	1	0·8576

The nuclear moments are given in nuclear magnetons. First, we find that the magnetic moment of the proton is 2·79 times the value we anticipate by analogy with the electron magnetic moment $e\hbar/2m_e c$. More startling than this, however, was the discovery that the *neutral* elementary particle—the neutron—has a magnetic moment. The negative sign denotes that the spin axis of the neutron is related to the magnetic dipole axis as if the effect is due to a rotating negatively charged sphere. The negative magnetic moment of the neutron may arise if the neutron has a charge distribution which is negative near the surface and positive near the centre (the resultant charge must, of course, be zero). A naive argument might expect that the magnetic moment of the deuteron would be the sum of the magnetic moments of the proton and neutron as the nucleon spins are parallel ($I = 1$) in the deuteron. However μ_p plus μ_N is 0·02 nuclear magnetons greater than μ_d. This 2 per cent difference is much greater than the experimental errors and therefore denotes a real difference. This discrepancy is important as it is one of the facts involved in discussing the structure of the deuteron (Chapt. 19).

There is definite evidence in certain nuclei of the existence of higher magnetic moments. For instance, very accurate measurements of the hyperfine structure of the $^2P_{3/2}$ ground level of In^{115} and I^{127} have shown that the observed splitting cannot be explained in terms of nuclear magnetic dipole and electric quadrupole moments alone but requires the assumption of a nuclear magnetic *octupole moment.*

8.6. NUCLEAR FORCES

The theory of the atomic nucleus as we know it today began with Heisenberg's conjecture that the nuclear particles are protons and neutrons. Immediately one is confronted with the key problem of nuclear physics: what is the nature of the nuclear force? The Coulomb interaction of the protons represents a *negative* binding energy and there must exist an attractive interaction between the nucleons which is much stronger than the Coulomb repulsion. The gravitational attraction between the nucleons is 10^{-38} times too small to account for the nuclear forces. The electrical interaction is of the wrong sign, and attempts to account for the nuclear stability in terms of magnetic forces, associated with the internal electric currents of the nucleus, have proved to be hopeless. There is no doubt of one fact; that is, the nuclear force, even between two nucleons, is far more complicated than the familiar electromagnetic force. The study of nuclear forces has proved to be one of the most difficult problems attempted in the history of physics. In the last decade, considerable progress has been made in measuring the nuclear force between two nucleons. These experiments are mainly based on the study of proton–proton or neutron–proton collisions.

The interaction between nucleons is complex in the sense that it depends not only on the separation of the nucleons but on their relative spin directions and orbital angular momentum. The interaction is of very short range and beyond a separation of a few fermis the nuclear force is exceedingly small. At the other extreme, the inter-nucleon force becomes strongly repulsive, probably at a separation less than about 0·5 fermis. To compare the Coulomb and nuclear forces we find that at a separation of about 1 fermi, the nuclear force between two protons is 30 or 40 times the strength of the Coulomb repulsion. At a separation of 4 fermis, the nuclear and Coulomb forces are approximately equal; whereas at 25 fermis the short range nuclear force has decreased to 10^{-6} times the electrical force. The onset of a nuclear repulsive force at very short separations prevents the complete collapse of nuclear matter.

Two principles of great importance concerning nuclear interactions are those known as "Charge Symmetry" and "Charge Independence". The first principle maintains that the nuclear interaction between a pair of neutrons, *n–n* force, is the same as the interaction between a pair of protons, *p–p* force, when due allowance is made for the Coulomb force in the proton case. The second principle goes beyond this and assumes that the *n–p*, *n–n*, and *p–p* interactions are effectively equal, after correcting for the Coulomb repulsion in the *p–p* interaction. It is, of course, implicit in the above laws that the inter-nucleon interactions are compared under identical conditions of separation, spin orientation, etc.

It is not easy to obtain accurate measurements of the nuclear force between two nucleons. Understanding the nuclear force is even more difficult. Ideas on nuclear forces stem from the bold hypothesis put forward by the Japanese physicist, H. Yukawa, in 1935, that the nuclear force between two nucleons may arise from the continuous exchange of mesons between the particles. Just as the Coulomb interaction is conceived in terms of the exchange of virtual photons between electric charges so the inter-nucleon interaction is believed to occur through the exchange of a particle of mass intermediate between that of the electron and the proton. Yukawa explained the finite range of the nuclear force by showing that mesons of rest mass about 200 times the electron rest mass would set the range at about 10^{-13} cm. The mesons are electrically charged and thus the transfer of a charged meson between a neutron and proton would result in the exchange of identity for the nucleons. Thus a proton absorbing a negative meson emitted by a neutron would be changed into a neutron and the neutron emitting the meson would become a proton. At a later date, N. Kemmer suggested the existence of a neutral meson responsible for the nuclear *p–p* interaction. In 1938, it seemed that Yukawa's ideas were supported by the reported discovery of charged particles of mass about 200 m_e in the cosmic radiation. These particles however, were found to have a very weak interaction with nuclei. This did not agree with the Yukawa theory that mesons have a strong nuclear interaction. The dilemma was solved in 1947 by the discovery by C. F. Powell, G. P. S. Occhialini and C. M. G. Lattes, of a heavier meson of mass nearer 300 m_e, than 200 m_e in the cosmic radiation. These particles, known as π mesons (pions) were detected by flying the new emulsion photographic plates in high altitude balloons. The pions were found to have a strong interaction with nuclei and they are believed to be the Yukawa particle. The lower mass meson, discovered first, is known as the μ meson (muon) and it is produced by the spontaneous decay of the pion after about 10^{-8} sec.

A simple argument shows that the mass of the pion, now known to be close to 273 m_e, accounts for the finite range of the nuclear force. The rest mass energy of the pion is 273 times that of the electron and is thus about 135 MeV. When a nucleon spontaneously emits a virtual pion, at least 135 MeV of energy is "borrowed". By the uncertainty principle we find that the energy must be "repaid" within a short time Δt given by

$$\Delta E \Delta t \sim \hbar$$

if $\Delta E \sim 135$ MeV, then $\Delta t \sim 5 \times 10^{-24}$ sec.

This means that the pion must be absorbed by another nucleon before the pion has travelled a distance greater than $5 \times 10^{-24} \times 3 \times 10^{10} \sim 1{\cdot}5 \times 10^{-13}$ cm, assuming the pion is travelling with a speed $\sim c$. This distance of 1·5 fermis is equal to the observed order of the range of nuclear forces. In sharp contrast, the Coulomb interaction is of infinite range and this agrees with the zero rest mass of the exchange particles, the virtual photons. It is not surprising that observable pions are created when high energy protons bombard nuclear targets.

BIBLIOGRAPHY

R. D. EVANS, *The Atomic Nucleus*, McGraw-Hill, New York 1955.

E. FERMI, *Nuclear Physics*, The University of Chicago Press, 1950.

A. E. S.GREEN, *Nuclear Physics*, McGraw-Hill, New York 1955.

A. H. WAPSTRA, Atomic Masses of Nuclides, in *Handbuch der Physik*, Vol. XXXVIII/1, Springer-Verlag, Berlin 1958.

F. M. KELLY, Determination of Nuclear Spins and Magnetic Moments by Spectroscopic Methods, in *Handbuch der Physik*, Vol. XXXVIII/1, Springer-Verlag, Berlin 1958.

CHAPTER 9

DETERMINATIONS OF NUCLEAR SIZE

9.1. INTRODUCTION

The majority of atomic nuclei are spherical or nearly spherical in shape. A few nuclei exhibit high electric quadrupole moments, an indication that the electric charge distribution is non-spherical. For the spherical nuclei, the nuclear radius r is given by the rough rule

$$r = r_0 A^{\frac{1}{3}} \qquad (1)$$

where A is the number of nucleons in the nucleus (mass number) and r_0 is a constant of the order of 1·2 to 1·3 fermis. This formula must not be interpreted too literally. First it should be emphasized that there is no sharp boundary defining the surface of the nucleus. High energy electron scattering experiments have clearly demonstrated that the electric charge distribution decreases gradually near the surface of the nucleus. The formula for the nuclear radius also ignores completely the individual structure of nuclei. The success of the shell model of the nucleus shows that it is useful to regard the nucleons inside the nucleus as bound in definite orbits. For certain nuclei, a particularly stable structure is found corresponding to the filling of a nucleon shell (compare the marked stability of atoms with closed electron shell structure). Closed shell nuclei are expected to show a slightly smaller radius than other nuclei of approximately the same mass number.

A question of considerable importance is whether or not the electric charge distribution is the same as the nuclear matter distribution within the nucleus. A few years ago it was argued, that contrary to Coulomb repulsion considerations, there should be an excess of neutrons near the nuclear surface† and this would reveal itself in larger nuclear radii based on nuclear force experiments compared with determinations based on Coulomb interactions with the nucleus. At the present time, the weight of evidence suggests that the electrical radius of a nucleus is not significantly less than the nuclear matter radius.

Historically, the first estimates of nuclear size were made about fifty years ago. These were based on the study of high angle α-particle scattering. The Rutherford cross section formula is derived (Chapt. 1) on the assumption

† M. H. Johnson and E. Teller, *Phys.. Rev.*, **93**, 357, 1953.

that the α-particle–nucleus interaction is given by Coulomb's inverse square law. For high energy α-particles, which closely approach a nucleus, it is found that the scattering cross section is larger than expected. This "anomalous" scattering is interpreted as evidence that the α-particle has come within range of the nuclear forces of the scattering nucleus. Observations of the onset of anomalous scattering enable an upper limit for the nuclear radius to be calculated. The separation of the α-particle and scattering nucleus is equal to the sum of the radii of the nucleus and alpha particle added on to the range of the nuclear force. For heavy nuclei this is not much greater than the radius of the nucleus in question.

It is convenient to classify the methods of investigating nuclear size and charge distribution into two main categories. One group of methods is based on the study of the range of nuclear forces; the nucleus is probed by a nucleon or light nucleus. The interaction involves the specific nuclear forces. The other group of methods studies the electric field and charge distribution of the nucleus. The probing particle is an electron or muon (the latter seems to behave simply like a "heavy electron"). This type of study has the important advantage that the theory of electrical interactions is well-known, in contrast to our ignorance about the theory of nuclear forces. The electrical methods have also provided detailed information concerning the distribution of electric charge within the nucleus. Studies have also been made of the charge distribution of the proton and neutron. Apart from the intrinsic interest of nuclear size determinations, there are problems involving the probability of charged particles penetrating the Coulomb barrier surrounding a nucleus whose radius is required. In this chapter, we shall not discuss in detail all the methods that have been employed in determining nuclear radii. Detailed reviews of the subject are listed in the bibliography at the end of the chapter. The more accurate methods are described and the appropriate background theory is given in sufficient detail for the principle of the method to be understood. The methods are not given in historical order and we consider first the recent electrical methods. The electrical determinations of r_0 gave values considerably smaller than the earlier results ($r_0 \sim 1{\cdot}2$ in place of $1{\cdot}5$ fermis) and a close examination of the earlier methods led to the conclusion that the all earlier methods overestimated the value of r_0.

9.2. ELECTRICAL METHODS

Mesonic X-Rays

Large fluxes of mesons can be produced with the aid of the new particle accelerators developed since the war. Many experimental studies of pions and muons have been performed with mesons produced in this way. The first experimental determinations of nuclear radii using muons, clearly demonstrated that the radius constant r_0 is about 20 per cent less than the previously accepted value.† The experiments were conducted using a beam of 385 MeV protons to produce negative pions of kinetic energy 110 MeV. The beam of pions of the required energy and charge were selected by a magnetic analyser. Charged pions have a mean lifetime of about 10^{-8} sec and decay into muons and neutrinos. The pion beam becomes mixed with muons by this decay process. The mesons can be slowed down by a suitable thickness of absorber so that muons are brought to rest in the target material.

Fermi and Teller in 1947†† predicted the possibility of the existence of *mesonic atoms*. Mesons traversing matter lose energy by excitation and ionization processes. When they reach thermal energies, negative (not positive) mesons may be captured into Bohr-type orbits. The mesons then jump from orbit to orbit moving closer to the nucleus. In the last few orbit transitions, X-rays are radiated. The time for a negative meson to slow down from about 2 keV and be captured into a $1s$ atomic orbital has been estimated to be about 10^{-13} sec in graphite. The lifetimes of pions (10^{-8} sec) or muons (10^{-6} sec) is much longer than this "capture time", so many mesons may be capable of forming mesonic atoms. The mesons describe Bohr-orbits much closer to the nucleus than the electrons of the atom, due to the much greater mass of the meson compared with that of the electron. For a one-electron atom, the radius r and energy E of the stationary states are given by (Eqns. 25 and 26, Chapter 2).

$$r = \frac{n^2 \hbar^2}{m Z e^2} \tag{2}$$

$$E = -\frac{m Z^2 e^4}{2n^2 \hbar^2} \tag{3}$$

The Bohr orbit of a muon, for a given value of n and Z, has a radius about 207 times less than that of an electron (the mass of a muon is 207 times the electron mass). The energy of the bound muon, on the other hand, is 207 times that of the corresponding bound electron. These formulae are derived assuming the Coulomb field of the nucleus is due to a point charge. The muon orbits, for low n values, are well inside the K electron shell and the perturbing effects of the electrons on the bound moun are negligible.

There is strong evidence that the interaction between muons and the nucleus is essentially Coulomb in character. A recent determination of the magnetic moment of the muon confirms the belief that it is a "Dirac particle" of spin$\frac{1}{2}$.‡ The de Broglie wavelength of the bound muon is much shorter than the wavelength of a bound electron; hence it can be localized more sharply than an electron.

† V. L. Fitch and J. Rainwater, *Phys. Rev.*, **92**, 789, 1953.

†† E. Fermi and E. Teller, *Phys. Rev.*, **72**, 399, 1947.

‡ A "Dirac particle" is one that satisfies the relativistic wave equation of Dirac (Chapter 6, Section 20).

This means that the muon is a suitable particle for probing the nucleus. The estimated energy of a muon in a $1s$ orbit around the nucleus of a lead atom ($Z = 82$), using formula (3) is ~ 20 MeV. The experimental evidence shows that this is about twice the correct value! The explanation of the large discrepancy is connected with the finite size of the lead nucleus. The Bohr radius of the muon in the $1s$ state in the lead atom according to eqn. (2) is 3·1 fermis. This is less than the radius of the nucleus of the lead atom! In other words, the formulae based on a point charge nucleus are seriously in error for the $1s$ muon state. For nuclei of low Z ($Z < 20$) and $n \geqq 3$, the energies of the bound mesonic states given by eqn. (3) are in good agreement with experiment. This is because the mesonic orbit radius is well outside the nucleus. For the $1s$ state in a lead mesonic atom, it is calculated that the muon spends about 50% of its time inside the nuclear volume. Inside the nucleus, the effective Coulomb field acting on the muon is reduced below the value appropriate to the nuclear charge Ze. (In the same way, the gravitational intensity inside the earth is reduced below the surface value.) The reduction in the Coulomb force reduces the binding of the mesonic states; all the energy levels are raised, but the effect is most pronounced for the innermost orbit ($1s$).

It is essential to think about the meson orbits in terms of a probability distribution. Thus in every state, the muons spend part of their time inside the nuclear volume.

The hardest mesonic X-rays are produced in transitions to the $1s$ state. In the experiment of Fitch and Rainwater, the X-rays emitted in a muon transition from the $2P$ to the $1S$ state were detected with a scintillation counter.

The X-ray energies were measured with an accuracy of about 1%. Theoretical calculations based on different assumed nuclear radii, for the mesonic X-ray energies, were compared with the experimental values. The

TABLE 1. MESONIC X-RAYS: $2\,P_{3/2} \rightarrow 1\,S_{1/2}$ TRANSITIONS (energies in MeV)

Element (Z)	Calculated energy (point nucleus)	Observed X-ray energy	"Best fit" value of r_0 (fermis)
Al 13	0·363	0·35	—
Si 14	0·421	0·41	—
Ti 22	1·045	0·955	1·17
Cu 29	1·826	1·55	1·21
Zn 30	1·954	1·6	—
Sb 51	5·83	3·5	1·22
Hg 80	15·51	5·8	—
Pb 82	16·41	6·02	1·17
Bi 83	16·88	6·0	—

observed energies and the energies calculated on the basis of a point nucleus and a finite nucleus of radius $r = r_0 A^{1/3}$ are shown in Table 1. The last column gives the best estimated value of r_0 which fits the observed X-ray energies.

Fitch and Rainwater believed they could just detect the fine structure splitting in the mesonic spectrum corresponding to the estimate that the $2P_{3/2}$ level is 0·2 MeV higher than the $2P_{1/2}$ level.

The constant r_0 determined by the muon X-ray observations is equal to $1{\cdot}20 \pm 0{\cdot}03$ fermi.

The finite nuclear size modifies the electron energy levels of atoms. Studies have been made of the shifts in levels responsible for the *L*-lines in the X-ray spectra of heavy elements, and also the shifts in the optical spectra. These shifts are much smaller than those involved in the mesonic levels and are not capable of yielding the same degree of accuracy in determining nuclear radii. However, the results do not disagree with the mesonic X-ray determinations.

Electron Scattering

The most powerful method of studying the electric charge distributions of atomic nuclei is based on the *elastic scattering* of high energy electrons. Estimates of nuclear size have been made using electron scattering at energies below 50 MeV, but the most significant contributions have been made with electron energies in the range 100 to 900 MeV. The outstanding contributions have been made by R. Hofstadter and his group at Stanford University, using the high energy electron linear accelerator.

The amount of information that can be extracted from high energy electron scattering depends on the magnitude of the de Broglie wavelength of the incident electrons compared with the radius of the scattering nucleus. When the two lengths are of the same order, electron scattering by the nuclear charge is closely analogous to electron diffraction at wavelengths of about 0·1 Å by the electron charge distribution of an atom. The reduced de Broglie wavelengths $\bar{\lambda} = (\lambda/2\pi)$ for electrons of kinetic energy T in the range 50 to 500 MeV are given in Table 2. These wavelengths are easily calculated for highly relativistic electrons.

The total electron energy $E = T + m_0 c^2$

But
$$T \gg m_0 c^2$$
$$E = T = cp$$

where p is the electron momentum

$$\bar{\lambda} = \frac{\lambda}{2\pi} = \frac{\hbar}{p} = \frac{\hbar c}{E}$$

Before discussing the quantum mechanical theory of electron–nuclear scattering, we must consider the recoil of the nucleus during the scattering process. By elastic scattering, we mean the process whereby the nucleus is not excited to levels above its ground state, no mesons are emitted, and the electron does not radiate bremsstrahlung. Theoretically it is more convenient to discuss the scattering event in a system of coordinates in which the centre

TABLE 2

Kinetic energy (MeV)	50	100	200	300	400	500
λ (fermi)	3·9	2·0	1·0	0·67	0·5	0·4

of mass of the electron–nucleus system is at rest. The centre of mass system has the advantage that the kinetic energy of the electron remains the same before and after the collision. In the system in which the nucleus before the collision is considered to be at rest (the laboratory system), the electron loses kinetic energy in an elastic collision and the nucleus recoils. It is a simple matter to calculate the energy of the recoiling nucleus E_n. For highly relativistic electrons, $E = c\,p$; we can treat the electron–nucleus collision as a process similar to a photon–electron Compton collision. The energy of the recoiling nucleus E_n, when the incident electron of energy E is scattered through an angle θ is given by

$$E_n = \frac{E^2}{M\,c^2}\,\frac{1 - \cos\theta}{1 + \dfrac{E}{M\,c^2}(1 - \cos\theta)} \tag{4}$$

where M is the mass of the nucleus.

The energy of the scattered electron E' is thus obtained from

$$E' = E - E_n$$

The energy of elastically scattered electrons from protons as a function of scattering angle (in the laboratory system) is shown in Fig. 1. The incident electrons had an energy close to 187 MeV.

Experimentally, inelastically scattered electrons must be separated from those elastically scattered. For example, in studying the scattering of 187 MeV electrons by carbon nuclei at an angle of 80°, the elastically scattered electrons have an energy of 185·1 MeV and an inelastic group is observed at 180·7 MeV. This group arises from the excitation of the C^{12} nucleus to the 4·43 MeV level by the incident electrons. The different groups of scattered electrons are resolved using a semicircular magnetic momentum analyser. For high energy electrons, this requires a powerful magnetic analyser. The Stanford analyser for 550 MeV electrons has a central radius of curvature

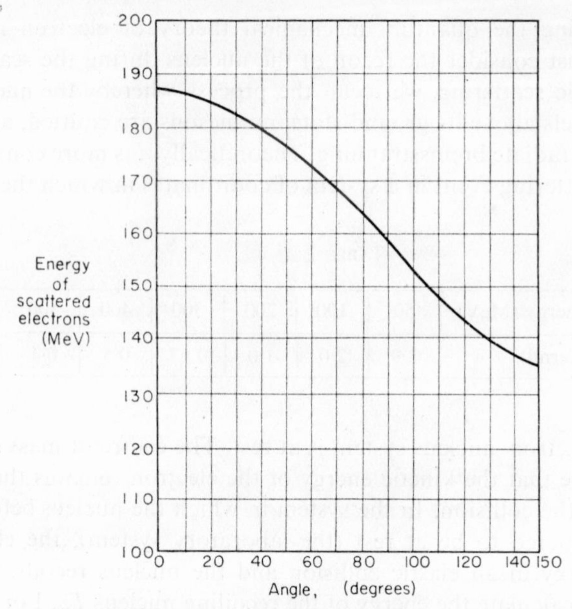

FIG. 1. Energy of elastically scattered electrons as a function of lab. angle. (Incident energy is 187 MeV.)

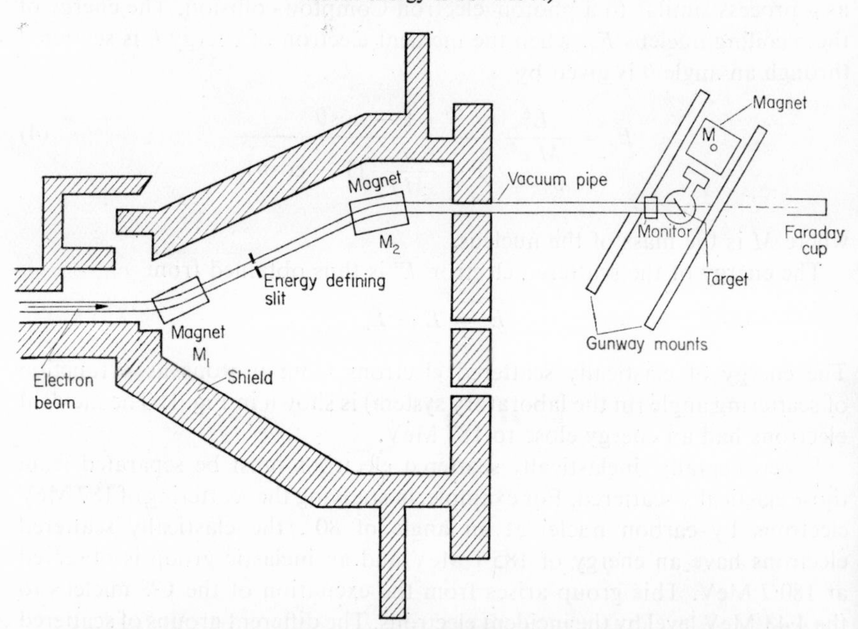

FIG. 2. Experimental layout for observing electron scattering at 550 MeV, electron beam from linear accelerator is deflected by magnets M_1 and M_2. Electrons scattered by target are focused on to a detector (not shown) by magnet M. Monitor records the total number of electrons incident on the target.

of 36 in. and the complete magnetic spectrometer weighs 30 tons. The selected electrons have an energy spread less than 1 MeV at 500 MeV and they are detected by counting the Cherenkov light† flashes produced in a Perspex cylinder with a photomultiplier tube. The experimental arrangement for studying the scattering of 550 MeV electrons is illustrated in Fig. 2. The targets used are often in the form of thin metal foil (e.g. gold 0·002 in. thick). Sometimes gas targets are used (hydrogen or helium) and a gas target chamber is filled with gas up to pressure of 2000 lb per in.^{2}

The observed elastic scattering of high energy electrons is compared with theoretical predictions based on different nuclear charge models. The scattering at different energies and angles is expressed in terms of the *differential scattering cross section*, $\sigma(\theta)$.

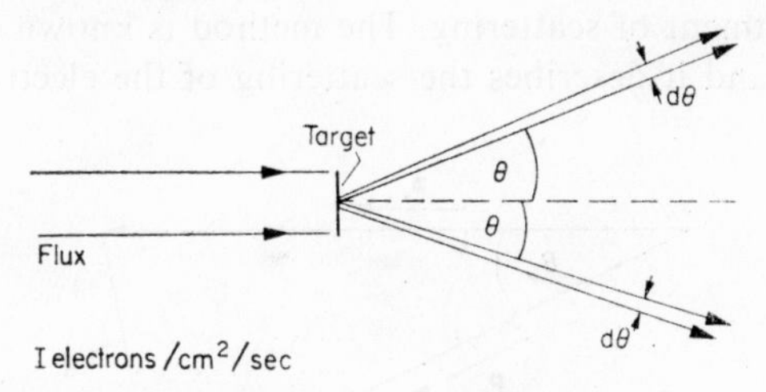

FIG. 3. Electron scattering at angle θ. Solid angle $d\Omega = 2\pi \sin\theta\, d\theta$.

If a collimated beam of I electrons crosses unit area of a "thin"†† target containing N nuclei per unit volume, then the number of electrons scattered through an angle θ into an elementary solid angle $d\Omega$ per unit time is given by

$$n_\theta = \sigma(\theta)\, I\, d\Omega \tag{5}$$

where

$$d\Omega = 2\pi \sin\theta\, d\theta$$

The scattering of relativistic electrons by atomic nuclei was first discussed theoretically by N. F. Mott in 1929. For elastic scattering of an electron of velocity $v = \beta c$, from a point nucleus of zero spin, taking into account its spin and magnetic moment, Mott obtained the following formula‡ for the differential cross section

$$\sigma_M(\theta) = \left(\frac{Ze^2}{2mc^2}\right)^2 \left(\frac{1-\beta^2}{\beta^4}\right) \frac{1}{\sin^4 \frac{1}{2}\theta} (1 - \beta^2 \sin^2 \tfrac{1}{2}\theta) \tag{6}$$

where Ze is the charge of the nucleus,
mc^2 is the electron rest mass energy,

† Cherenkov radiation and detectors are discussed in Chapter 11.

†† A "thin" target is one in which the fraction of incident electrons scattered is very small.

‡ N. F. MOTT and H. S. W. MASSEY, *The Theory of Atomic Collisions*, Clarendon Press, Oxford 1949.

and θ is the polar angle of scattering (Fig. 3), (measured in the centre of mass system).

For high energy electrons ($T > 100$ MeV), β is very close to unity and we can put

$$\beta^4 = 1$$

$$E = \frac{m c^2}{(1 - \beta^2)^{\frac{1}{2}}}$$

Then we obtain

$$\sigma_M(\theta) = \left(\frac{Ze^2}{2E}\right)^2 \frac{\cos^2 \frac{1}{2}\theta}{\sin^4 \frac{1}{2}\theta} \tag{7}$$

This formula is derived by a perturbation approximation of the wave mechanical treatment of scattering. The method is known as the first Born approximation and it describes the scattering of the electron waves by the

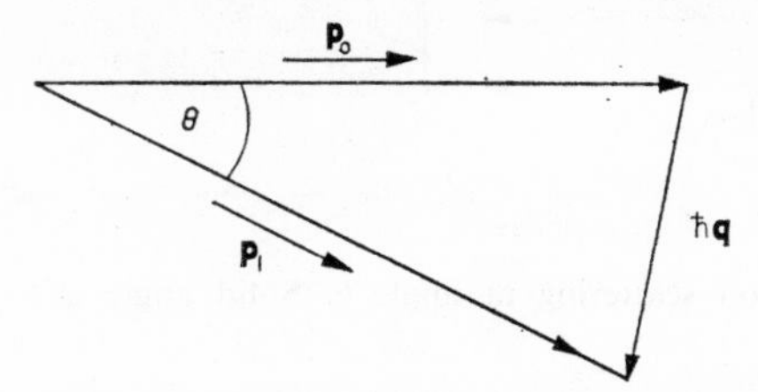

FIG. 4. Momentum transfer diagram. $|p_0| = |p_1|$ (centre-of-mass system). $\hbar\, \boldsymbol{q} = \boldsymbol{p}_1 - \boldsymbol{p}_0$.

Coulomb potential of the point nucleus in terms of plane waves. This is wrong, as the wave front of the electron wave train is distorted by the strong Coulomb field in the vicinity of the nucleus. The Born approximation is a good one provided

$$Z\alpha = \frac{Ze^2}{\hbar c} = \frac{Z}{137} \ll 1 \tag{8}$$

where $\alpha = e^2/\hbar\, c = \frac{1}{137}$; α is the dimensionless fine-structure constant. The Mott formula is valid for light nuclei ($Z \leqq 137$), but it is seriously in error for heavy nuclei as it predicts too low a scattering cross section $\sigma(\theta)$, especially at high scattering angles.

The observed scattering of high energy electrons by a nucleus of finite size is less than that predicted for a point nucleus. This effect can be considered as an interference phenomenon between electron waves scattered by different regions of the nuclear charge distribution. The scattering cross section $\sigma_s(\theta)$ is equal to the Mott formula (eqn. 7) multiplied by a new factor

$$\sigma_s(\theta) = \sigma_M(\theta) \left| \int \varrho(r) \exp(i\, \boldsymbol{q} \cdot \boldsymbol{r})\, d\tau \right|^2 \tag{9}$$

where $\varrho(r)$ is the nuclear charge density as a function of the distance from the centre of the nucleus: $\boldsymbol{q}$ is a vector defined by the equation.

$$\hbar \boldsymbol{q} = \boldsymbol{p}_1 - \boldsymbol{p}_0 \tag{10}$$

where $\boldsymbol{p}_0$ and $\boldsymbol{p}_1$ are the momentum vectors of the electron before and after the scattering respectively. These momenta are in the centre of mass system and thus for elastic scattering

$$|p_0| = |p_1|$$

$\hbar \boldsymbol{q}$ is known as the momentum transfer vector.

From the vector diagram (Fig. 4), we see that

$$\hbar q = 2p_0 \sin\tfrac{1}{2}\theta$$

$$p_0 = \frac{E}{c} = \frac{\hbar}{\lambda}$$

Thus

$$q = \frac{2}{\lambda} \sin\frac{1}{2}\theta \tag{11}$$

We note that $\boldsymbol{q} \cdot \boldsymbol{r}$ is a dimensionless product. The volume integral in eqn. (9), ($d\tau$ is an element of nuclear volume) is taken over the whole nuclear charge distribution. This type of integral arises in connection with the coherent scattering of X-rays or electron waves by the electron charge distribution of an atom. The integral in eqn. (9) can be written in a more convenient form

$$F = \int_0^\infty \varrho(r) \frac{\sin q\,r}{q\,r} 4\pi\, r^2\, dr \tag{12}$$

or

$$F = \frac{4\pi}{q} \int_0^\infty \varrho(r) \sin q\, r \cdot r\, dr \tag{13}$$

F, by analogy with X-ray and electron diffraction theory, is called the *form factor*.

The scattering cross section eqn. (9) can be written

$$\sigma_s(\theta) = \sigma_M(\theta)\, |F|^2$$

At low electron energies and small scattering angles F is nearly equal to unity and

$$\sigma_s(\theta) \doteqdot \sigma_M(\theta)$$

For higher energies and large scattering angles (say 150°), F is much smaller than unity and

$$\sigma_s(\theta) \ll \sigma_M(\theta)$$

Thus the effects of finite nuclear size are most clearly revealed by comparing the elastic scattering of high energy electrons at large angles with the point nucleus, Mott formula. This method is available for light nuclei but cannot be expected to give valuable results for heavy nuclei as the Born approximation is invalid. Theoretical calculations of elastic scattering cross sections for heavy nuclei have been carried out using the method of "partial wave phase shift analysis."† Various nuclear charge distributions are considered in turn, and the scattering cross sections for different electron energies E, and scattering angles θ are computed. In Fig. 5, the results of phase shift

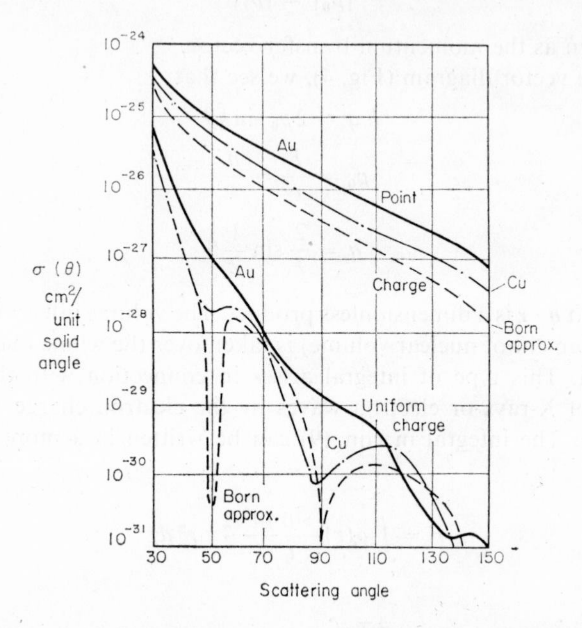

FIG. 5. Theoretical scattering cross sections for Au (79) and Cu (29) by phase shift analyses. Also shown is the Born approximation. Two sets of curves are shown: point nucleus and uniform charge model.

analyses for gold ($Z = 79$) and copper ($Z = 29$), assuming a uniform nuclear charge distribution, are shown. In the same figure, the curves for a point nucleus and the Born approximation calculations are also shown. It is interesting to see that the Born approximation predicts diffraction minima of zero cross section at certain angles. These minima are nearly washed out in the more accurate phase shift calculations.

The model of the nuclear charge distribution which is the best fit to the experimental scattering observations for nuclei over a wide range of mass number, $40 < A < 238$, is shown in Fig. 6. The theoretical cross section curve for gold ($Z = 79$), calculated on the basis of the model shown in

† D. R. YENNIE, G. D. RAVENHALL and R. N. WILSON, *Phys. Rev.*, **95**, 500, 1954.

Fig. 6, is shown in Fig. 7. The different curves correspond to different electron energies. The agreement between the theoretical and experimental curves is remarkably good. The theoretical model shown in Fig. 6, is known as the Fermi model and is represented by the equation

$$\varrho(r) = \frac{\varrho_1}{1 + \exp[K(r - c)]} \tag{14}$$

where ϱ_1 and K are constants, and c is the distance from the centre of the nucleus to the point where $\varrho(r)$ has fallen to half its central value. This dis-

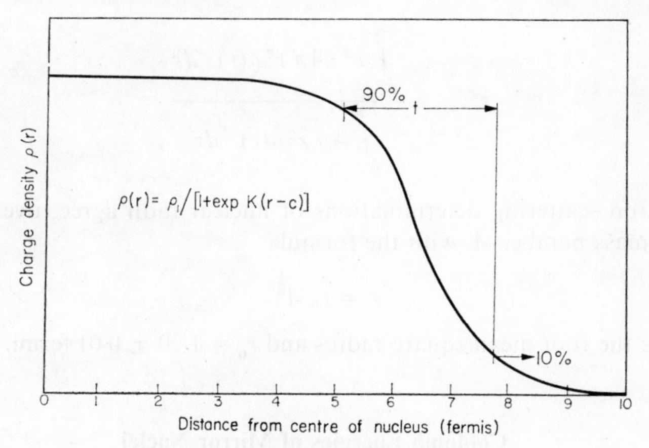

FIG. 6. Model of gold nucleus.

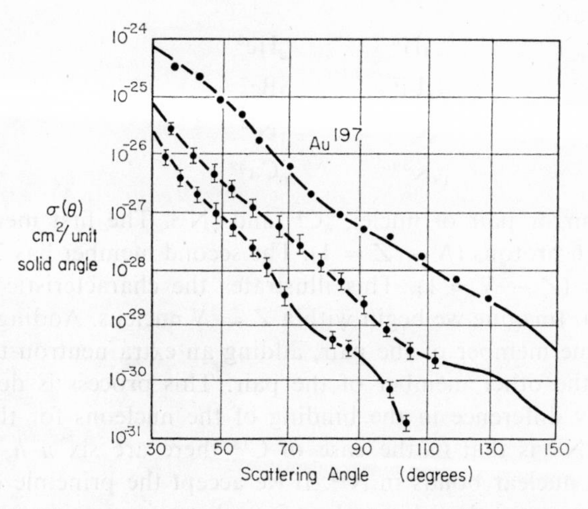

FIG. 7. Theoretical curves based on model of gold nucleus (Fig. 6) and experimental points for three different electron energies.

tance c can be considered as a measure of the nuclear radius. The concept of a sharply defined nuclear radius is much less definite than was formerly believed. The fall away of charge density near the nuclear surface can be measured in terms of the "*skin-thickness*" t, the distance between points corresponding to $\varrho(r)$ equal to 90% and 10% of the central density. An important result of the electron scattering studies is that the "skin-thickness" t, over a wide range of mass number, is nearly constant with $t = 2{\cdot}3$ fermi. The best way of representing nuclear charge radii, when the charge density $\varrho(r)$ is non-uniform, is to give the root mean square radius. This is defined as the square root of

$$\langle r^2 \rangle_{av} = \frac{\int_0^\infty r^2 \cdot 4\pi r^2 \varrho(r) \cdot dr}{\int_0^\infty 4\pi r^2 \varrho(r) \cdot dr} \tag{15}$$

The electron scattering determinations of nuclear radii agree, over a wide range of mass number A, with the formula

$$r = r_0 A^{\frac{1}{3}}$$

where r is the root mean square radius and $r_0 = 1{\cdot}20 \pm 0{\cdot}01$ fermi.

Coulomb Energies of Mirror Nuclei

Certain pairs of isobars are known as mirror nuclides. A few examples of mirror pairs are

$_1H^3$	$_2He^3$
$_3Li^7$	$_4Be^7$
$_6C^{13}$	$_7N^{13}$
$_{19}K^{39}$	$_{20}Ca^{39}$

Consider the mirror pair of nuclei, $_6C^{13}$ and $_7N^{13}$. The first member has 7 neutrons and 6 protons ($N - Z = 1$). The second member has 7 protons and 6 neutrons ($Z - N = 1$). This illustrates the characteristic property of mirror nuclei. Imagine we begin with a $Z = N$ nucleus. Adding an extra proton forms one member of the pair, adding an extra neutron to $Z = N$ nucleus forms the other member of the pair. This process is depicted in Fig. 8. The only difference in the binding of the nucleons for the mirror nuclei C^{13} and N^{13} is that in the case of C^{13} there are six n–n bonds in place of six p–p nuclear bonds in N^{13}. If we accept the principle of charge symmetry, which states that the nuclear force between a pair of protons is the same as the nuclear force between a pair of neutrons in the same state, then there should be no difference in the nuclear binding forces of a pair of mirror nuclei. The total binding energy of the two nuclei will not be the same however, because of the difference in the Coulomb self energy.

The Coulomb energy of a spherical nucleus with a uniform charge distribution is (see Chapter 8)

$$E_c = \frac{3}{5} Z(Z-1)\frac{e^2}{r} \tag{16}$$

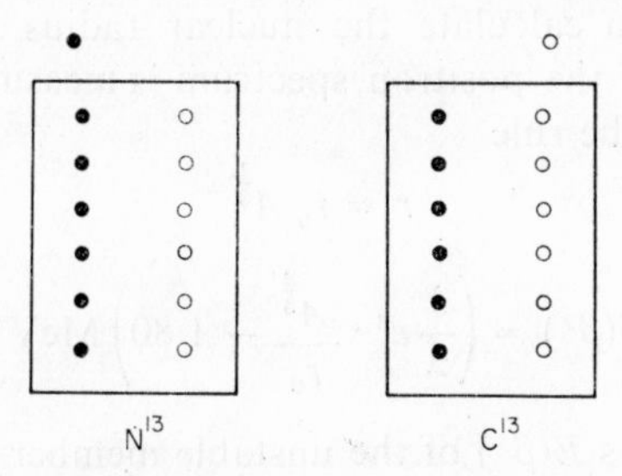

FIG. 8. Mirror nuclei N^{13} and C^{13}. Protons • neutrons ○ The "extra" proton or neutron is shown outside the $Z = N$ configuration.

For a pair of mirror nuclei of radius r, charges Ze and $(Z+1)e$, the *difference* in Coulomb energy is

$$\Delta E_c = \frac{6}{5}\frac{Ze^2}{r} \tag{17}$$

In many cases of mirror nuclei, the member with charge $(Z+1)e$ is unstable against positron decay. This is the beta decay process (Chapter 14), in which a proton in the unstable nucleus changes into a neutron, a positive electron (positron e^+), and a massless particle, the neutrino (ν). The disintegration energy is shared between the emitted positron and neutrino (a very small fraction is given to the recoiling daughter nucleus). The nucleus formed after the decay process (the daughter nucleus) is, of course, the mirror nucleus of the parent nucleus.

For example N^{13} is unstable and decays according to the equation

$$_7N^{13} \to {}_6C^{13} + e^+ + \nu$$

Suppose the maximum kinetic energy carried away by the emitted positron is $E(\beta^+)$ (the neutrino energy is negligible in this case). The positron energy, if the daughter nucleus is formed in the ground state, is given by

$$E(\beta^+) = \frac{6}{5}\frac{Ze^2}{r} - m_0 c^2 - (m_n - m_p)c^2 \tag{18}$$

The whole of the change in the Coulomb energy is not available. An energy equal to $m_0 c^2$, the rest mass energy of the positron, is absorbed in *creating* the positron, and an energy equal to $(m_n - m_p)c^2$ is absorbed in transforming a proton (mass m_p) into a neutron (mass m_n). For mirror nuclei $A = 2Z + 1$, where Z is the atomic number of the daughter nucleus.

$$m_0 c^2 = 0{\cdot}51 \text{ MeV}, \quad (m_n - m_p) c^2 = 1{\cdot}29 \text{ MeV}$$

Hence,
$$E(\beta^+) = \frac{3}{5}\frac{e^2}{r}(A - 1) - 1{\cdot}80, \text{ MeV} \tag{19}$$

Thus it is possible to calculate the nuclear radius r, if the end point (maximum energy) of the positron spectrum is measured. Provided A ≧ 1 we should get, using the rule

$$r = r_0 A^{\frac{1}{3}}$$

$$E(\beta^+) = \left(\frac{3}{5} e^2 \cdot \frac{A^{\frac{2}{3}}}{r_0} - 1{\cdot}80\right) \text{MeV} \tag{20}$$

If the positron energies $E(\beta^+)$ of the unstable member of a range of mirror nuclides is plotted against $A^{2/3}$, a linear graph should be obtained, with an intercept of $-1{\cdot}80$ MeV on the energy axis. This agrees tolerably well with the experimental data, giving a value for r_0 of about 1·45 fermi. This radius constant is about 20% higher than the high energy electron scattering value. The discrepancy is a consequence of the neglect of quantum mechanical effects in calculating the Coulomb energy E_c. Specific account must be taken of the correlation between the positions of any pair of protons within the nucleus. The Pauli principle prevents two protons occupying the same region of space. This effectively reduces the probability of finding two protons close together and consequently reduces the Coulomb energy. The correlation effect has been calculated and when this is included, the Coulomb energy of a nucleus of charge $Z e$ is

$$E_c = \frac{3}{5}\frac{e^2}{r}\left[Z(Z - 1) - 0{\cdot}77 Z^{\frac{4}{3}}\right] \tag{21}$$

Nuclear radii calculated, using the corrected Coulomb energy formula, eqn. (21), are about 20% smaller than the earlier estimates.

The values of r_0 for several nuclei, determined in this way, are given in Table 3.

TABLE 3

Nucleus	B^{11}	C^{13}	N^{15}	O^{17}	F^{19}	Ne^{21}	Na^{23}	Mg^{25}	Al^{27}
r_0 (fermi)	1·28	1·34	1·31	1·26	1·26	1·25	1·22	1·23	1·20

There is a considerable variation in the nuclear radius constant r_0. The first three nuclei yield high values of r_0. This is not surprising as the theory of Coulomb energy is most uncertain for light nuclei. Excluding the first three values of r_0 in Table 3, the mean value of r_0 for the remaining mirror nuclei is given by $r_0 = 1{\cdot}23 \pm 0{\cdot}3$ fermi.

In view of the assumptions and uncertainties in the theory of the binding energies of mirror pairs, nuclear radii determined by this method should be treated with caution.

9.3. NUCLEAR FORCE METHODS

Fast Neutron Cross Sections

The total cross sections of elements for neutrons in the energy range 10 to 50 MeV is expected to be equal to

$$\sigma_t = 2\pi r^2 \tag{22}$$

For neutrons in this energy range, the nucleus should behave as a "black disc" of area πr^2. This measures the absorption cross section for the incident neutrons. There is also a scattering cross section of πr^2 which can be explained in the following way. For fast neutrons, the de Broglie wavelength λ is small compared with the nuclear radius. The nuclear obstacle, a "black disc" of radius r throws a shadow behind it. The incident neutron waves are diffracted round the disc (Fig. 9). This shadow scattering is analogous to the diffraction of light waves at the edge of an opaque disc. At a certain distance L beyond the obstacle the shadow has disappeared. This corresponds to a diffraction angle at the edge of the obstacle of the order of $\bar{\lambda}/r$. Hence the distance L is of the order of

$$\frac{r^2}{\bar{\lambda}}$$

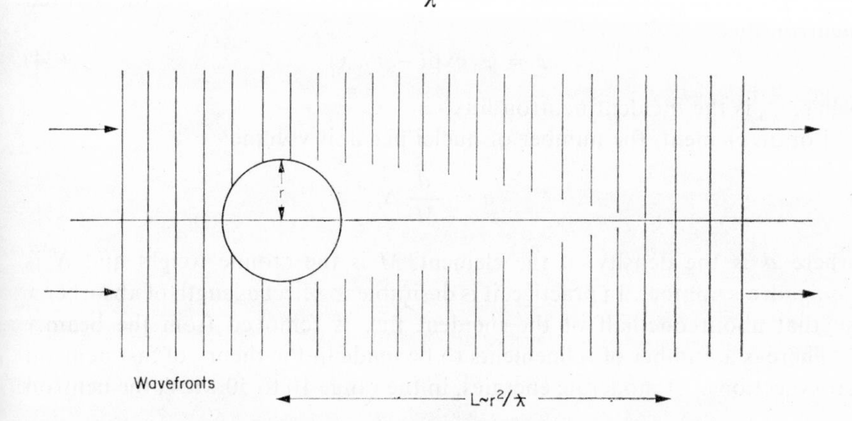

FIG. 9. Shadow scattering by "black" nucleus.

In optics for discs of the order of 1 cm radius, this is a large distance ($\sim$ 1 km), and thus we normally observe sharp geometrical shadows. For high energy neutrons, say > 10 MeV, the distance L is only a few nuclear radii. This must mean that some neutrons are diffracted away from the original direction. Thus if the neutron detector is a considerable distance behind the absorber, these diffracted or scattered neutrons will not reach the detector. To estimate how many neutrons are removed in this way we can represent the shadow behind the nucleus as an interference effect between the incident neutron wave train and a neutron source of area πr^2 in place of the nucleus, emitting waves with the same intensity as the incident beam, but with a phase difference of π. The waves emitted from such a source would have diverged at a distance $r^2/\lambda\!\!\!^-$ beyond the nucleus. In order to reproduce the shadow behind the opaque nucleus, the number of neutrons emitted from the source must be equal to the number of neutrons incident on the nucleus. Thus the shadow scattering cross section must also be equal to πr^2.

Nuclear radii can be calculated by determining the fraction of neutrons in a collimated beam removed by absorption and scattering in an absorber. The detector is placed well beyond the absorber and great care must be taken so that scattered neutrons are not recorded. Consider a cylindrical absorber of length x, containing n nuclei per unit volume. Then if the cross sectional area of the cylinder is A, the probability of a neutron being removed in traversing a very short length dx of the cylinder is equal to the effective target area of the nuclei in this slice ($\sigma\, n\, A\, dx$) divided by the area A. Thus the decrease in neutron flux, $-d\varphi$, in traversing this slice, is given by

$$-\frac{d\varphi}{\varphi} = \sigma\, n\, dx \tag{23}$$

where φ is the number of neutrons incident on unit area of the slice per unit time. Integrating we obtain the well known formula for the transmitted neutron flux

$$\varphi = \varphi_0 \exp(-\sigma\, n\, x) \tag{24}$$

where φ_0 is the incident neutron flux.

For an element, the number of nuclei per unit volume

$$n = \frac{d}{M} N$$

where d is the density of the element, M is the atomic weight and N is Avogadro's number. In practice, it is desirable to select a length of absorber x so that about one-half of the incident flux is removed from the beam.†

There is a number of refinements to be made in the theory of fast neutron cross sections. At moderate energies, in the range 10 to 50 MeV, the neutron

† Methods of producing and detecting high energy neutrons are discussed in Chapter 15.

wavelength is not negligible in comparison with the nuclear radius. Feshbach and Weisskopf have considered this effect for a "black" spherical nucleus, and obtained a total cross section.

$$\sigma_t = 2\pi(r + \lambda\!\!\!^{-})^2 \qquad (25)$$

At neutron energies above 100 MeV, the cross section decreases. This is a result of the high energy nuclear transparency effect. The neutron wavelength is so small, that it is possible for an incident neutron to pass through the nucleus without interacting with any of the nucleons. There is evidence that the transparency effect is found at lower energies. The most successful nuclear model for interpreting neutron cross sections is the *optical model* of the nucleus.† The nucleus is pictured as a "cloudy crystal ball", that is, as a homogeneous medium of complex refractive index. The imaginary part of the refractive index determines the non-elastic processes; absorption, reaction and inelastic scattering. The incident neutrons move in a nuclear field of force when they reach the surface of the nucleus, represented by a complex potential well:

$$V = -(V_0 + i\,W_0) \qquad \text{inside the nucleus}$$

and

$$V = 0 \qquad \text{outside the nucleus}$$

The term $-V_0$ represents a rectangular well and the incident neutron waves are refracted when they cross the nuclear surface. The imaginary term $-i\,W_0$ is introduced to represent the absorption processes. Optical model calculations have been applied to a wide energy range of neutron cross section phenomena. The well depth V_0 selected depends on the neutron energy. For 14 MeV neutrons $-V_0 \sim 45$ MeV, and $-W_0 \sim 11$ MeV.

Unfortunately the calculated values of nuclear radii depend on the exact assumptions made concerning the complex potential. Nevertheless, high energy neutron scattering data, interpreted in terms of the optical model, fit reasonably well with the $r = r_0 A^{1/3}$ law, with $r_0 = 1{\cdot}23 \pm 0{\cdot}03$ fermi.

This value for r_0 is about 15% lower than previous estimates by this method. Thus there is no justification for the view that the electric charge distribution is smaller than the effective nuclear potential well region.

Theory of Alpha Radioactivity††

An important correlation between the half-life of radioactive elements, which decay by α-particle emission, and the kinetic energy E of the emitted

† A. E. Glassgold, pp. 123–162, in *Progress in Nuclear Physics*, Vol. 7 (Editor: O. R. Frisch), Pergamon Press, London 1959.

†† See Chapter 13, Section 3.

α-particle, was first noticed by Geiger and Nuttall in 1911. In terms of the decay constant λ, the Geiger–Nuttall law is

$$\log\lambda = a + b\log E \tag{25}$$

where a and b are constants.

This is an approximate empirical law, but it is remarkable as it covers a range in λ of 10^{25} or more, corresponding to a range in E from about 2 to 9 MeV. The decay constant, that is, the probability of a nucleus decaying in unit time, is an enormously sensitive function of the energy of the emitted particle.

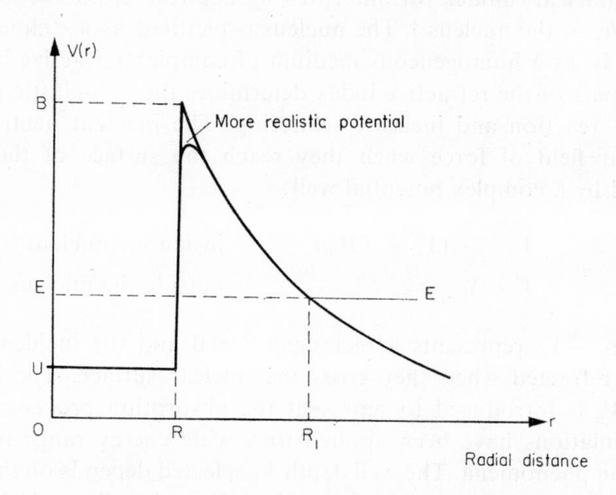

FIG. 10. Idealized potential well for α-decay. B height of Coulomb barrier. $R < r < R_1$ ... classically forbidden region.

The first successful attempt to explain the Geiger–Nuttall law was made independently in 1928 by Gamow and by Condon and Gurney. The explanation is based on the wave mechanical theory of "barrier penetration" (the "tunnel effect"). The potential energy diagram illustrating the interaction between the α-particle and the daughter nucleus of the decay process is shown in Fig. 10. In the simplest theory the α-particle is assumed to exist as an α-particle prior to emission from the unstable nucleus. The gradient of the potential energy $V(r)$ graph represents the resultant force acting on the α-particle. At the surface of the nucleus where $r = R$, the nuclear force between the daughter nucleus and the particle is not known in detail. However, this is known to be much stronger than the Coulomb repulsive force, and we represent this by a steeply descending potential curve. The nuclear force is short-range and the simplest assumption to make is that it abruptly vanishes at the surface of the nucleus. Thus for $r > R$, the interaction is purely Coulombic.

$$r > R \quad V(r) = \frac{(Z-2)\, e \cdot 2e}{r} = \frac{A}{r} \tag{26}$$

where $Z - 2$ is the atomic number of the daughter nucleus, and $2e$ is the charge of the α-particle.

The α-particle is assumed to be in some definite energy state represented by the level E inside the nucleus. This energy is less than the maximum potential energy

$$B = \frac{A}{R} \tag{27}$$

B is called the height of the Coulomb barrier. According to classical mechanics, it is impossible for the bound α-particle to escape from the nucleus as $E < B$. Nevertheless there is, according to wave mechanics, a very small but finite probability of the particle penetrating the potential barrier. If the α-particle reaches the point $r = R_1$, it has escaped from the nucleus and it will acquire a kinetic energy equal to E under the influence of the Coulomb repulsion.

The probability of emission in unit time, λ, can be expressed as the product of two factors

$$\lambda = n \cdot P \tag{28}$$

n is the number of collisions the α-particle inside the nucleus makes with the steep wall of the barrier, at $r = R$, in unit time: p is the penetration factor, the probability of an incident α-particle passing through the potential barrier. Sometimes a third factor is introduced in the theory to remove the artificial assumption that the α-particle exists as a discrete unit inside the nucleus. This extra factor represents the probability of two protons and two neutrons pre-forming an α-particle near the nuclear surface. In view of the fact that estimates of this pre-formation probability are very uncertain, we shall not take it into consideration.

The collision frequency factor n can be estimated as follows. Confining the α-particle of mass m to a region of space of radial extent R, means that we can associate a momentum of the order of $m\,v$ with the particle. Using the uncertainty principle we have

$$m\,v\,R \sim \hbar$$

$$v \sim \frac{\hbar}{m\,R}$$

The number of collisions the α-particle makes with the surface of the nucleus in unit time is given by

$$n \sim \frac{v}{R}$$

or

$$n \sim \frac{\hbar}{m\,R^2} \tag{29}$$

For the natural α-emitters (all heavy nuclides), n is roughly 10^{20} or 10^{21} collisions per sec. If there was no Coulomb barrier, the particle would escape from the nucleus within 10^{-20} sec. The correct way of looking at the problem of α-decay is not to ask why the particle is emitted, but why the α-particle is held back (in some cases it may be held back for 10^{18} secs or more). For a nucleus to be unstable against α-emission, the sum of the binding energies of the "last" two protons and "last" two neutrons in the nucleus must be less than the binding energy of the α-particle (28 MeV). Amongst the heavy elements this condition is often satisfied. However, if the energy excess is too small, the half-life of the process is so high, that the instability of the isotope may elude observation.

The penetration factor P of the Coulomb barrier is obtained by solving the Schrödinger equation of the α-particle in the region $R < r < R_1$. In view of the low rate of decay of the nucleus (the natural unit to fix the time scale of the process is 10^{-21} sec), we can use the time-independent Schrödinger equation

$$-\frac{\hbar^2}{2m}\frac{d^2u}{dr^2} + V(r)\,u(r) = E\,u(r) \tag{30}$$

If we make the simplification that in the region $R < r < R_1$, $V(r)$ is purely Coulombic, we can write eqn. (30) as

$$\frac{-\hbar^2}{2m}\frac{d^2u}{dr^2} + \left(\frac{A}{r} - E\right)u(r) = 0 \tag{31}$$

To solve eqn. (31), try the exponentially decaying function,

$$u(r) = \exp\left(-\frac{1}{\hbar}y(r)\right) \tag{32}$$

Differentiating $u(r)$ twice with respect to r and substituting in eqn. (30) we obtain

$$\frac{\hbar}{2m}\frac{d^2y}{dr^2} - \frac{1}{2m}\left(\frac{dy}{dr}\right)^2 + \left(\frac{A}{r} - E\right) = 0 \tag{33}$$

This equation can be solved by a method of successive approximations. The first approximate solution is obtained by noticing that the coefficient of d^2y/dr^2 is much smaller than that of $(dy/dr)^2$. Neglecting the first term in eqn. (33)† an approximate solution of the equation is

$$y = \int \sqrt{\left[2m\left(\frac{A}{r} - E\right)\right]}\,dr \tag{34}$$

The penetration factor P is, according to the probability interpretation of the wave function $u(r)$, given by

$$P = \left|\frac{u(R_1)}{u(R)}\right|^2 \tag{35}$$

† A detailed discussion of this approximation is given in G. Gamow and C. L. Critchfield, *Theory of Atomic Nucleus and Nuclear Energy Sources*, Clarendon Press, Oxford, 1949, page 160.

From (32) we have $$|u(r)|^2 = \exp\left(-\frac{2y(r)}{\hbar}\right) \qquad (36)$$

Hence combining eqns. (34), (35) and (36)

$$P = \exp\left\{-\frac{2}{\hbar}\int_R^{R_1} \sqrt{\left[2m\left(\frac{A}{r} - E\right)\right]}\, dr\right\} \qquad (37)$$

The integral can be evaluated by using the substitution

$$r = \frac{A}{E}\cos^2\theta$$

when $r = R_1, \theta_1 = 0$; when $r = R, \theta = \theta_0$, where $\cos^2\theta_0 = E/B$.

For the natural α-emitters, the Coulomb barrier B is about 25 MeV high. For a typical α-energy E of 5 MeV,

$$\cos^2\theta_0 \sim \tfrac{1}{5}$$

Writing $\theta_0 = \pi/2 - \varepsilon$ where ε is a fairly small angle, $\cos\theta_0 = \sin\varepsilon = \varepsilon$. Using this approximation, the solution of eqn. (37) is

$$P \simeq \exp\left[-\frac{2\pi\sqrt{(2m)}\,(Z-2)\,e^2}{\hbar\sqrt{E}} + \frac{8e\sqrt{[(Z-2)\,m\,R]}}{\hbar}\right] \qquad (38)$$

Combining eqns. (28), (29) and (30),

$$\ln\lambda = \ln\left(\frac{\hbar}{m\,R^2}\right) + \left[\frac{8e\sqrt{[(Z-2)\,m\,R]}}{\hbar} - \frac{2\pi\sqrt{(2m)}\,(Z-2)\,e^2}{\hbar\sqrt{E}}\right] \qquad (39)$$

It should be emphasized that this expression for λ is an approximate one, and that a number of rather unrealistic assumptions has been made. Nevertheless the equation does represent the enormous variation of λ with the energy E. We have assumed that the mass of the nucleus M is much greater than the mass m of the α-particle. The recoil of the nucleus can easily be taken into consideration by replacing m by the reduced mass M of the system:

$$M = \frac{m\,m_r}{m + m_r}$$

where m_r is the mass of the recoil nucleus.

Theoretical expressions for the α-decay constant λ are not sufficiently accurate to calculate λ with any degree of accuracy. However, they can be used to determine the nuclear radius R, if the observed decay constant and α-particle energy are substituted in eqn. (39) or a more accurate solution of the barrier penetration equation.

Determinations of the radii of nuclei by this method have been made during the last thirty years and apparently lead to large values of the radius constant r_0 ($\sim 1{\cdot}5$ fermi). A close examination of the method, however, reveals a number of arbitrary and uncertain features. The estimate of n is vexed by the problem of what factor should be included to represent the formation of the α-particle near the nuclear surface. The calculation of the barrier penetration probability P, based on the assumption of a pure Coulomb potential from R_1 to R is obviously wrong. The shape of the potential well just outside the nuclear surface is not known. However, it is possible to say that the value of P calculated assuming a pure Coulomb potential is too low, as the nuclear potential will round off the barrier and reduce its height. This means that radii calculated using eqn. (39) will be too big. The finite size of the α-particle should be subtracted from the nuclear radius R. When several refinements of the theory of α-radioactivity are included, the calculated nuclear radius constant is given by $r_0 = 1{\cdot}2 \pm 0{\cdot}1$ fermi.

Alpha Particle Scattering†

When the α-particles emitted in radioactive decay are scattered by medium and heavy nuclei the observed elastic differential scattering cross section agrees closely with the well-known Rutherford formula

$$\frac{d\sigma}{d\Omega} = \left(\frac{2Z\,e^2}{4E}\right)^2 \frac{1}{\sin^4 \frac{1}{2}\theta}$$

where $Z\,e$ is the nuclear charge, E is the kinetic energy of the α-particle and θ the scattering angle.

The α-particles emitted in radioactive decay have energies in the range 4 to 9 MeV—too low to reach the surface of the majority of nuclei. During the past decade there has been a marked revival in the study of the scattering of α-particles by nuclei, using cyclotron-accelerated He^{++} ions. Alpha-particles in the energy range 20 to 50 MeV behave as sensitive probes to the intensity and spatial extent of the α–nuclear interaction in the surface regions of the nucleus. The elastic scattering experiments have been successfully interpreted in terms of the *nuclear optical model.* In this model the nuclear scattering of α-particles is described through the interaction of the incident wave with a complex potential well with a diffuse edge. A simple analytic expression for such a complex potential is that suggested by Woods and Saxon†† (Fig. 11)

$$V = -\left[\frac{V_0 + i\,W_0}{1 + \exp\left(\dfrac{r - R}{d}\right)}\right] \tag{40}$$

† A comprehensive review of alpha-particle scattering is that of R. M. Eisberg and C. E. Porter, *Revs. Mod. Phys.* **33**, 190, 1961.

†† R. W. Woods and D. S. Saxon, *Phys. Rev.* **95**, 577, 1954.

The imaginary term in the potential corresponds to the absorption part of the interaction. r is the radial distance from the centre of the nucleus, R is the nuclear radius and d is a parameter representing the diffuseness of the spatial extent of the interaction potential in the nuclear surface.

The elastic scattering of 40 MeV α-particles by several nuclei in the range of atomic number 29 (Cu) to 90 (Th) closely fits the Woods–Saxon potential with the following values for the four parameters:

$$R = (1{\cdot}35\, A^{\frac{1}{3}} + 1{\cdot}3) \text{ fermi},$$
$$d = 0{\cdot}5 \text{ fermi},$$
$$V_0 = 45^{+6}_{-7} \text{ MeV},$$
$$W_0 = 10^{+1\cdot5}_{-3\cdot5} \text{ MeV}.$$

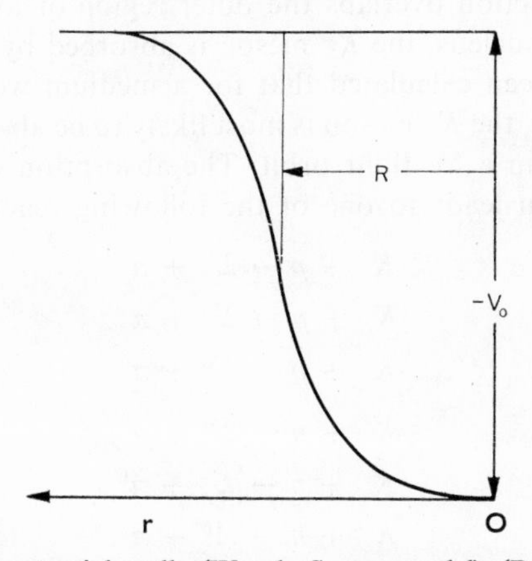

FIG. 11. Nuclear potential well. (Woods–Saxon model) (Real part only.)

The constant term in the expression for R corresponds to the finite size of the α-particle involved in the nuclear scattering.

9.4. NEUTRON AND PROTON SURFACE DISTRIBUTION

It is very difficult to obtain quantitative information about the difference in the radial density distribution $\varrho(r)$ of protons and neutrons in nuclei. Nevertheless, the present weight of evidence supports the view that there is little significant difference in the neutron and proton density in the surface skin where the density is less than 10% of the central value. The low density regions of the nuclear surface can be studied by observations of the absorption of slow negative K mesons (kaons)†.

† P. B. JONES, *Phil. Mag.*, **3**, 33, 1958.

K mesons are heavier than the π mesons; they have a rest mass energy of about 500 MeV and they are unstable with a mean life of about 10^{-8} secs. Copious beams of the K mesons are produced by bombarding nuclei with protons accelerated to the GeV region in a proton synchrotron. A beam of K^- mesons entering a nuclear emulsion stack† loses energy by ionization. Some of the K^- mesons when they reach low energies are captured into Bohr orbits around nuclei of the nuclear emulsion. The theory of the formation of K-mesonic atoms shows that for medium weight nuclei (e.g. Ag, Br, I in the emulsion), the K^- particles cascade down from orbits of high principal quantum number, emitting radiation. One can picture the K^- particle circulating and slowly approaching the nuclear surface during these Bohr orbit transitions. In marked contrast to the behaviour of muons, K mesons interact strongly with nuclear matter. As soon as the approaching K^- meson wave function overlaps the outer region of low nucleon density distribution of the nucleus, the K^- meson is absorbed by a surface neutron or proton. It has been calculated that for a medium weight nucleus with $Z = 41$ and $A = 94$, the K^- meson is most likely to be absorbed by a surface nucleon when it is in a $5g$ Bohr orbit. The absorption of a K^- meson by a proton or neutron leads to one of the following reactions:

$$K^- + p \rightarrow \Sigma^+ + \pi^-$$
$$K^- + p \rightarrow \Sigma^- + \pi^+$$
$$K^- + p \rightarrow \Sigma^0 + \pi^0$$
$$K^- + n \rightarrow \Sigma^0 + \pi^-$$
$$K^- + n \rightarrow \Sigma^- + \pi^0$$
$$K^- + n \rightarrow \Lambda^0 + \pi^-$$

The symbols Σ and Λ^0 stand for the unstable particles known as *hyperons* of rest mass energy 1·19 and 1·12 GeV respectively. Theoretical values for the ratio of π^+/π^-, the number of π^+ to the number of π^- mesons produced by surface absorption of a K^- meson in light and medium weight nuclei have been calculated as functions of the neutron excess in the nuclear surface. Similar calculations have been carried out for the ratio of the number of Σ^- hyperons produced by the reaction $K^- + n \rightarrow \Sigma^- + \pi^0$ and the number produced in the reaction $K^- + p \rightarrow \Sigma^- + \pi^+$. Experimental values of these ratios have been obtained from observations of K^- absorption by Ag, Br and I in nuclear emulsions. A comparison of the theoretical and observational ratios shows that there is no substantial difference in the surface neutron and proton densities. A possible breakdown of the reasoning involved in the K^- absorption process occurs if the K^- meson experiences a scattering collision in the surface of the nucleus and is absorbed deep

† Nuclear emulsion plates are described in Chapter 11.

inside the nucleus. The probability of this process seriously competing with surface absorption is believed to be very small.

Conclusion

The wide variety of the methods of determining nuclear radii indicates that nuclear radii are approximately given by the formula $r = 1{\cdot}20\ A^{1/3}$ fermi. The electrical methods are to be preferred as they involve the better known electromagnetic forces. Searching and detailed criticism of the older methods of determining nuclear radii has revealed important corrections and refinements which were not given sufficient attention. The older determinations gave nuclear radii corresponding to the formula $r = 1{\cdot}45\ A^{1/3}$. It is probable that these larger values of radii are a result of the neglect of important corrections. Perhaps the most important conclusion that can be drawn from the different determinations is that the nuclear force and electrical radii do not differ by a significant amount. The method based on the elastic scattering of electrons has revealed details of the gradual decrease in charge density near the nuclear surface. The startling conclusion is drawn that in light nuclei, $A < 20$, the nucleus is nearly all "surface" in the sense that there is no region where the nuclear density is essentially constant. Finally there is some evidence that the distribution of proton and neutron density is nearly the same in the surface of the nucleus, a conclusion contradicting the arguments of Johnson and Teller that the neutron density extends about one fermi beyond the proton density in the nuclear surface.

BIBLIOGRAPHY

L. R. B. Elton, *Nuclear Sizes*, Oxford University Press, 1961.

M. J. C. Scott, The Radius of a Nucleus, in *Progress in Nuclear Physics*, Vol. 5 (Ed.: O. R. Frisch), Pergamon Press, London 1956.

D. L. Hill, Matter and Charge Distribution Within Atomic Nuclei in Vol. XXXIX, *Handbuch der Physik* (Editor: S. Flügge), Springer-Verlag, Berlin 1957.

International Congress on Nuclear Size and Density Distributions, *Revs. Mod. Phys.* **30**, 412, 1958.

Recent experiments on the charge and magnetic moment distribution of the proton are described in, *Proceedings of the* 1960 *International Conference on High Energy Physics at Rochester*, Interscience, p. 757 "Scattering of 1·3 GeV electrons by Protons", and p. 762 "Splitting of the Proton Form Factors and Diffraction in the Proton".

EXAMPLES

1. The following nuclei are positron unstable. The half-life T is in seconds, the maximum kinetic energy E of the positrons is in MeV.

	O^{15}	F^{17}	Na^{21}	Ar^{35}	Sc^{41}
T	124	66	22·8	1·88	0·873
E	1·723	1·748	2·50	4·96	4·94

Ignoring quantum mechanical effects, obtain graphically the best value of the nuclear radius constant r_0 for the five positron unstable nuclei.

2. Radon ($Z = 86$, $A = 222$) emits monoenergetic α-particles of kinetic energy 5·488 MeV. The half-life of radon is 3·285 d. Using a simple Coulomb barrier model, calculate the nuclear radius of radon.
3. An incident electron of total energy 250 MeV (lab) is scattered elastically through 45° by a He^4 nucleus initially at rest in the lab-system. Calculate the energy of the scattered electron, the kinetic energy and recoil direction of the α-particle.

Suppose the charge distribution of the He^4 nucleus is Gaussian:

$$\frac{4}{3}\pi a^3 \varrho(r) = \left(\frac{6}{\pi}\right)^{\frac{1}{2}} \exp\left(-1\cdot 5\frac{r^2}{a^2}\right)$$

where a is the root-mean-square radius = 1·68 fermi. Calculate $q\,a$ for the above collision and evaluate the form factor $F(q\,a)$.

Calculate the differential elastic scattering cross section for 250 MeV electrons at 45° (a) for a point nucleus (b) for the Gaussian charge distribution given above.

CHAPTER 10

RADIOACTIVE DECAY

10.1. FUNDAMENTAL LAWS OF DECAY

The basic law of radioactivity is that enunciated by Rutherford and Soddy† in 1902. The rate of spontaneous transformation of a radioactive nuclide is proportional to the number of atoms of the nuclide

$$\frac{dn}{dt} = -\lambda n \tag{1}$$

where n is the number of atoms of the nuclide at time t, and λ is the decay constant of the nuclide.

There is indirect evidence that the decay constant of a given nuclide remains constant over geological time epochs ($> 10^9$ years). There is much stronger evidence that λ is uninfluenced by changes in pressure, temperature, and chemical state. The decay constant λ is essentially a nuclear property and the nucleus is shielded from the effects of normal chemical and physical changes.

The fundamental decay law can be interpreted as a statement that the probability of decay of a given atom in a short time interval $dt(\lambda\, dt \ll 1)$ is equal to $\lambda\, dt$, which is independent of the age of the atom. This law does not apply to human decay and it is not the basis of the calculation of life insurance premiums! To emphasize this aspect of radioactive decay, consider two atoms A and B of Ra^{226} produced by the α-decay of Th^{230}. Suppose atom A was born 1000 years ago and has not yet decayed and atom B was born today. Then the chance that atom A and atom B will decay sometime during tomorrow is the same for each atom.

The activity of a radioactive nuclide is defined by the relation

$$A = \left|\frac{dn}{dt}\right| = \lambda n \tag{2}$$

The unit of activity is the *curie*. Originally, this was defined as the activity of radon in secular equilibrium with one gram of radium. In 1950, the unit was re-defined as the activity of any nuclide which disintegrated at the rate of $3{\cdot}7 \times 10^{10}$ disintegrations per sec. This is close to the value of the original

† E. Rutherford and F. Soddy, *Phil. Mag.*, **4**, 370, 569, 1902; **5**, 77, 441, 561, 576, 1903.

unit, but it is a better definition as it will not be altered by any future change in the "best" value of the decay constant of radium (the parent nuclide of radon). Thus

$$1 \text{ curie} \equiv 3{\cdot}700 \times 10^{10} \text{ disintegrations per sec.}$$
$$1 \text{ millicurie (mc)} \equiv 10^{-3} \text{ curie.}$$
$$1 \text{ microcurie } (\mu c) \equiv 10^{-6} \text{ curie.}$$

Integrating eqn. (1) we obtain

$$n = n_0 \, e^{-\lambda t} \tag{3}$$

where n_0 is the number of atoms of the radioactive nuclide at $t = 0$.

Substituting eqn. (3) in eqn. (1) gives

$$A = \left|\frac{dn}{dt}\right| = \lambda \, n = \lambda \, n_0 \, e^{-\lambda t} \tag{4}$$

or

$$A = A_0 \, e^{-\lambda t}$$

where $A_0 = \lambda \, n_0$ is the activity at $t = 0$.

Notice that the activity and the number of atoms of the radioactive nuclide both decay at the same rate.

The Half-life T and the Mean-life τ

The time scale of radioactive decay is conveniently described by the half-life T of the nuclide. T is defined as the time interval for the number of atoms (or the activity) to fall by a factor of two,

$$\text{for} \quad t = T, \quad n = n_0/2 \quad \text{and}$$

$$\frac{n_0}{n} = 2 = e^{\lambda T}$$

$$\lambda \, T = \ln 2 = 0{\cdot}693147 \tag{5}$$

The value of T is independent of the choice of a zero time $t = 0$. After m half-lives, the activity is $(\frac{1}{2})^m$ times the initial activity. For example, one would have to wait for about 5000 years for the activity of Co^{60} ($T \sim 5{\cdot}2$ years) to decay to 0·1% of its initial value. ($(\frac{1}{2})^{10} \sim \frac{1}{1000}$.)

Perhaps a more fundamental parameter of the radioactive decay is the mean-life τ. First, we can show, however, that the exponential transformation law can be derived if we assume that λ is characteristic of the nuclide and is independent of the age. The probability that a given atom will decay during a short time interval dt is

$$\lambda \, dt, \quad \text{if } (\lambda \, dt \ll 1)$$

The probability that a given atom survives the short time interval is

$$(1 - \lambda \, dt)$$

If we now consider a much longer period t, subdivided for convenience into m sub-intervals each of short duration Δt, such that

$$t = m \Delta t_s \quad m \gg 1$$

then, we can write down the probability of a given atom surviving the long period t as the product of the independent probabilities of surviving m short intervals. This probability is

$$(1 - \lambda \Delta t)^m = (1 - \lambda \Delta t)^{t/\Delta t}$$

In the limit as $\Delta t/t \to 0$, we can expand this expression, using the binomial theorem and notice that it is the same as the series for $\exp(-\lambda t)$:

$$(1 - \lambda \Delta t)^{t/\Delta t} = \left\{1 - \frac{\lambda t}{1!} + \frac{(\lambda t)^2}{2!} - \cdots\right\} = e^{-\lambda t} \tag{6}$$

Thus if at an arbitrary zero of time measurement, we have a *large* number n_0 of atoms of a radioisotope then on average we can expect n of them to survive a time interval t, where

$$n = n_0 e^{-\lambda t}$$

The mean-life of a radioisotope is derived in terms of the decay constant λ as follows.† The probability of an atom surviving a time interval t is given by eqn. (6); that is, $e^{-\lambda t}$. The probability that it will decay during the succeeding short interval dt is $\lambda\, dt$. Thus the probability that the value of the life of an atom of a radioelement lies between t and $t + dt$ is

$$e^{-\lambda t} \lambda\, dt \tag{7}$$

Multiplying every possible life value of an atom, t, $(0 < t < \infty)$ by the probability of its occurrence, and summing over all values of t we obtain the mean-life,

$$\tau = \int_0^\infty t\, e^{-\lambda t} \lambda\, dt = \frac{1}{\lambda} \tag{8}$$

Combining eqns. (5) and (8) we obtain the relation

$$T = \tau \ln 2 = 0{\cdot}6931\, \tau \tag{9}$$

(τ is analogous to the "time constant" of a capacitive–resistance network).

The activity of a radioelement at some arbitrary zero of time, $t = 0$, is equal to λn_0 or n_0/τ. Thus if the activity of the element remained *constant* at this initial value for a period of time τ, all the n_0 atoms would decay. In other words, the tangent to the exponential decay curve $n = n_0 e^{-\lambda t}$, at the origin, $t = 0$, $n = n_0$, intersects the time axis at $t = \tau$.

† A similar argument can be used to show that the mean free path of a photon before absorption in a homogeneous medium is equal to the reciprocal of the linear absorption coefficient μ. This follows whenever we have an exponential attenuation or decay law. For X-rays, the intensity I decreases with penetration distance according to the law $I = I_0 \exp(-\mu x)$.

10.2. DECAY OF A MIXTURE OF TWO UNSTABLE ISOTOPES

The most practical method of determining the half-life T of a single radioactive element, which is of the order of several minutes or a few hours, is to measure the rate of emission of the particles emitted by the radioelement. If we can count the number of particles (α or β say) emitted in a time interval t_0 which is $\ll T$, and the number of recorded particles N is large (10^4 or more), then N/t_0 is the average activity during the counting period t_0. In practice, a definite fraction of the emitted particles is recorded, which depends on the solid angle subtended by the detector at the source, the fraction of particles which enter the sensitive volume of the detector, the efficiency of detection of the detector, etc. A plot of the logarithm of the counting rate $C(t)$ as a function of time t, should be a straight line of slope $-\lambda$.

Sometimes we meet the problem of determining λ for a low activity source with a half-life of a few minutes. To obtain a significant number of recorded counts the counting period t_0 is no longer small in comparison with the half-life T. The observed counting rate during the counting period t_0 is the average value

$$\bar{C} = \frac{N}{t_0} \tag{10}$$

During the period t_0, the activity and therefore the counting rate C decays with time from an initial value C_0, to a value

$$C = C_0\, e^{-\lambda t_0}$$

The total number of recorded particles in the counting period is given by

$$N = \int_0^{t_0} C_0\, e^{-\lambda t}\, dt = \frac{C_0}{\lambda}(1 - e^{-\lambda t_0}) \tag{11}$$

$$\bar{C} = \frac{N}{t_0} = \frac{C_0}{\lambda\, t_0}(1 - e^{-\lambda t_0}) \tag{12}$$

$$C_0 = \bar{C}\frac{\lambda\, t_0}{1 - e^{-\lambda t_0}} \tag{13}$$

If an *approximate* value of λ is first determined, then the counting rate C_0 at the beginning of the counting period can be estimated from the observed value $\bar{C}$, using eqn. (13). A plot of $\log C_0$ against time t should yield a linear graph. If the counting period t_0 is the same for all the counting observations there is no need to make the correction using eqn. (13). This is because C_0 is a constant multiple of $\bar{C}$ and the only difference between the semi-logarithmic plots of C_0 and $\bar{C}$ is in the two intercepts on the axis. However, with the decline in activity with time, it is often necessary to obtain approximately the same number of total counts N in a single counting period.

A useful practical rule to remember is that a suitable measure of the statistical fluctuation in N is of the order of $\sqrt{N}$; thus for $N \sim 10{,}000$, the "statistical error" in N is ~ 100 or $\sim 1\%$. The percentage differences between C_0 and $\bar{C}$, expressed in terms of the ratio t_0/T are given in Table 1.

TABLE 1

$\left(\frac{t_0}{T}\right)\%$	$\left(\frac{C_0 - \bar{C}}{C_0}\right)\%$
0·5	0·17
1·0	0·34
1·5	0·52
2·0	0·69
5·0	1·73
10·0	3·57

Thus the correction for a counting period of 1·1 min for C^{11} (11 min half-life), is 3·57%. In view of the statistical fluctuations in radioactive decay, it is not worthwhile making this correction if t_0/T is less than 0·5%.

The *background* counting rate C_B, due to cosmic rays and radioactive impurities near the detector, should be subtracted from the observed counting rate $\bar{C}$, *before* the correction given by eqn. (13) is made (assuming that all the radioactive impurities in materials near to the detector have a very long half-life).

A problem of some interest concerns the determination of the decay constants λ_1 and λ_2 when two separate activities are present. It may, of course, be possible to discriminate with the detector and the associated electronic circuits† between the radiations emitted by the two sources. It is then easy to determine the decay constants of the two activities. However, it is possible to determine the two decay constants, without analysing the radiation. Consider the simplest example, which occurs when $\lambda_1 \gg \lambda_2$.

The decay of radioactive bromine, Br^{80}, produced by the irradiation of a suitable bromine compound (ethyl bromide)†† with thermal neutrons is

† If the two radiations are relatively "hard" and "soft", radiation could be removed with a suitable absorber, the observed activity corresponding to the "hard" radiation source.

†† The specific activity (activity per gram of radioactive source) of the Br^{80} can be greatly increased by using the Szilard–Chalmers effect. The recoil momentum of the bromine nucleus from the ethyl bromide molecule on emitting a γ-ray when it captures a neutron, is sufficient to break the chemical bond. If a small amount of inactive bromine is added to the solution, the radioactive bromine can be extracted with the inactive bromine (carrier) in a concentrated form. The bromine may, for example, appear in a precipitate of AgBr.

illustrated in Fig. 1. There are two activities present, one of 17·6 min half-life, and one of 4·4 hr associated with an *isomeric transition* from a low-lying excited state of the Br^{80} nucleus. A plot of the logarithm of the decay rate of the radioactive bromine against time is non-linear for t less than about 2 hr. After this period, the shorter lived activity has effectively disappeared and the slope of the linear portion of the graph is equal to $-\lambda_2$, where λ_2 is the decay constant corresponding to the 4·4 hr activity. By extrapolation (see dotted line in Fig. 1), the activity of the longer-lived

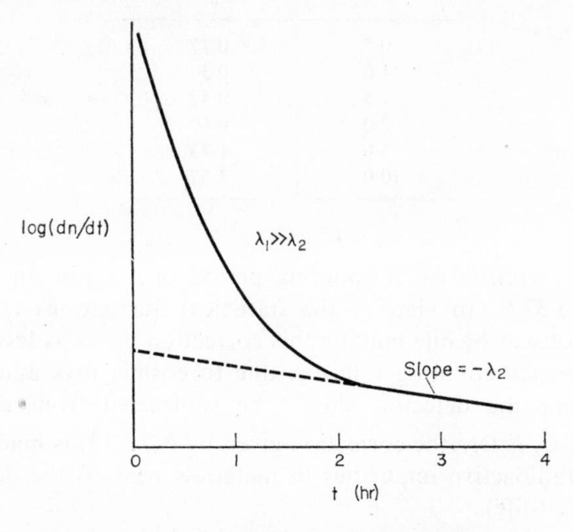

FIG. 1. Decay of mixture of two activities ($\lambda_1 \gg \lambda_2$).

component at earlier instants of time ($0 < t < 2$ hr) can be determined. The activity of the short lived activity can then be found by subtraction. A semi-logarithmic plot of the short lived activity against time is found to be linear with a slope equal to $-\lambda_1$ (λ_1 corresponds to a half-life value of 17·6 min). It is left as a problem for the reader to decide how the correction for decay during the counting period t_0 should be made. In general the analysis of superimposed radioactive decay rates is more complex as there may be more than two activities present and λ_1, λ_2, λ_3 may cover a wide range of relative values.

10.3. RADIOACTIVE SERIES

Apart from a few very long-lived natural radioactive isotopes including K^{40} ($1{\cdot}25 \times 10^9$ y, 0·012%), Rb^{87} (5×10^{10} y, 27·9%) and Sm^{147} ($1{\cdot}3 \times 10^{11}$ y, 15·1%), the naturally occurring radioactive elements belong to one of three radioactive series. The half-lives and percentage abundances of the radioactive isotopes given above are given in the parentheses.

Consider as an example the U^{238} series. The head of the series, U^{238}, has a much longer half-life ($4{\cdot}51 \times 10^9$ y) than any subsequent member of the series. We can represent such a series by the chain

$$P \rightarrow Q \rightarrow R \rightarrow S \rightarrow \cdots$$

P is the radioelement at the head of the series, which transforms with a characteristic decay constant λ_1 into its daughter element Q, which in turn transforms with a decay constant λ_2 into its daughter element R, which in turn transforms with a decay constant λ_3 and so on. The series is eventually terminated by the production of a stable end product RaG(Pb^{206}). The equations representing the net rate of increase of the number of atoms of each member of the series are

$$\frac{dP}{dt} = -\lambda_1 P \tag{14}$$

$$\frac{dQ}{dt} = \lambda_1 P - \lambda_2 Q \tag{15}$$

$$\frac{dR}{dt} = \lambda_2 Q - \lambda_3 R \tag{16}$$

etc.

where the symbols $P, Q, R, \ldots$ are here used to denote the number of atoms of each member of the series, and $\lambda_1, \lambda_2, \lambda_3, \ldots$ are the decay constants of the elements $P, Q, R, \ldots$ etc. For the last member of the series there is no second term on the right-hand side of the differential equation, as the decay constant is zero (stable element). Equation (15) is a statement of the fact that, the net rate of growth of the element Q is the difference between the rate of production of Q by the decay of its parent element P, and the spontaneous rate of decay of Q into its daughter element R. It is important to realise that, apart from the first series member P, dQ/dt, dR/dt, ... do *not* represent the activities of the elements $Q, R, \ldots$ The activities of the elements $Q, R, \ldots$ at any instant of time t are equal to

$$\lambda_2 Q, \quad \lambda_3 R, \ldots$$

The family of differential eqns. (14), (15), (16), ... etc., can be solved by the following substitutions

$$P = A_{11}\, e^{-\lambda_1 t} \tag{17}$$

$$Q = A_{21}\, e^{-\lambda_1 t} + A_{22}\, e^{-\lambda_2 t} \tag{18}$$

$$R = A_{31}\, e^{-\lambda_1 t} + A_{32}\, e^{-\lambda_2 t} + A_{33}\, e^{-\lambda_3 t} \tag{19}$$

$A_{11}, A_{21}, A_{22}, \ldots$ etc. are constants, which can be found by successive substitution. Thus to determine A_{21}, substitute the expression for Q (eqn. 18) in eqn. (15), using the solution of eqn. (14), that is eqn. (17).

$$-\lambda_1 A_{21} e^{-\lambda_1 t} - \lambda_2 A_{22} e^{-\lambda_2 t} \equiv \lambda_1 A_{11} e^{-\lambda_1 t} - \lambda_2 A_{21} e^{-\lambda_1 t} - \lambda_2 A_{22} e^{-\lambda_2 t}$$

or

$$A_{21} = A_{11} \frac{\lambda_1}{\lambda_2 - \lambda_1}$$

Let us consider the special case for which, at $t = 0$, the only element present is the head of the series

at $$t = 0, \quad P = P_0; \quad Q = 0, \quad R = 0, \ldots$$

To find the constant A_{22}, put $t = 0$ in eqn. (18)

$$0 = A_{21} + A_{22}$$

Hence,

$$Q = P_0 \frac{\lambda_1}{\lambda_2 - \lambda_1} (e^{-\lambda_1 t} - e^{-\lambda_2 t}) \tag{20}$$

In a similar way, it is easy to show that

$$R = P_0 \lambda_1 \lambda_2 \left[\frac{e^{-\lambda_1 t}}{(\lambda_2 - \lambda_1)(\lambda_3 - \lambda_1)} + \frac{e^{-\lambda_2 t}}{(\lambda_3 - \lambda_2)(\lambda_1 - \lambda_2)} + \frac{e^{-\lambda_3 t}}{(\lambda_1 - \lambda_3)(\lambda_2 - \lambda_3)} \right]$$

and (21)

$$S = P_0 \lambda_1 \lambda_2 \lambda_3 \left[\frac{e^{-\lambda_1 t}}{(\lambda_2 - \lambda_1)(\lambda_3 - \lambda_1)(\lambda_4 - \lambda_1)} + \frac{e^{-\lambda_2 t}}{(\lambda_1 - \lambda_2)(\lambda_3 - \lambda_2)(\lambda_4 - \lambda_2)} + \frac{e^{-\lambda_3 t}}{(\lambda_1 - \lambda_3)(\lambda_2 - \lambda_3)(\lambda_4 - \lambda_3)} + \frac{e^{-\lambda_4 t}}{(\lambda_1 - \lambda_4)(\lambda_2 - \lambda_4)(\lambda_3 - \lambda_4)} \right] \tag{22}$$

To illustrate these results let us consider the growth and decay of the members of the U^{238} series; RaA (Po^{218}, half-life 3·05 min), RaB (Pb^{214}, 26·8 min), RaC (Bi^{214}, 19·7 min) and RaD (Pb^{210}, 19·4 y).† A suitable deposit of RaA can be produced by inserting a needle into a tube filled with radon gas (half-life 3·8 d) for a few seconds. The nuclide RaD, with its relatively long half-life of 19·4 y can be considered to be stable over a time span of several weeks. The rates of growth illustrated in Fig. 2 are obtained by plotting the equations for P (RaA), Q (RaB), R (RaC) and S (RaD), assuming that at $t = 0$, $P = P_0$ (100 units) and $Q = R = S = 0$. A few general conclusions can be made

(1) At any time t, the sum of the number of atoms of all the members of the series, $P + Q + R + \ldots = P_0$.

(2) Radio-element P has its maximum activity at $t = 0$; this occurs before element Q reaches its maximum activity, which in turn occurs before R reaches its maximum, ...

† All half-life values given in this chapter are obtained from the Table of Isotopes compiled by D. Strominger, J. M. Hollander, and G. T. Seaborg, in *Revs. Mod. Phys.*, **30**, 585, 1958.

(3) It is easy to show that the maximum activity of P must be greater than the maximum activity of Q, and that the maximum activity of Q must be greater than the maximum activity of R . . . etc.

(4) If the maximum activity of Q occurs at the instant t_Q, (corresponding to the peak of the curve), the ratio of the maximum activity of Q and the maximum activity of P is $e^{-\lambda_1 t_Q}$.

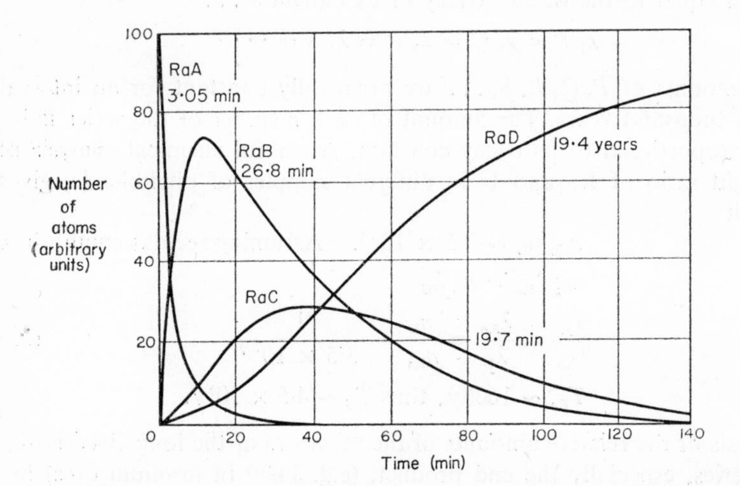

FIG. 2. Relative growth and decay of radio-elements in a radioactive chain. The respective half-lives are indicated on each curve. (Redrawn from RUTHEFRORD, CHADWICK and ELLIS, *Radiations from Radioactive Substances*, Cambridge University Press.)

(5) The initial rate of growth of Q is complementary to the decay curve of P. Initially, for small t, $e^{-\lambda_1 t} \sim 1 - \lambda_1 t$ and Q increases linearly; $Q = P_0 \lambda_1 t$.

(6) For small values of t, R grows quadratically

$$R = P_0 \lambda_1 \lambda_2 \left(\frac{t^2}{2!}\right) \tag{23}$$

and S grows cubically

$$S = P_0 \lambda_1 \lambda_2 \lambda_3 \left(\frac{t^3}{3!}\right) \tag{24}$$

Studying these initial modes of growth, it is, in some cases, possible to deduce that there are one or two intermediate products between P and Q or P and S, although the radiations accompanying the intermediate transformations are undetectable.

A great simplification in the radioactive chain occurs when one of the members has a much longer half-life than any other member of the series and provided we are only interested in the relative amounts of members during a time small compared to the very long half-life. Over a period of a few thousand years, these conditions apply to the members of the uranium series found in uranium bearing ores, which have been undisturbed for geological lengths of time. A condition of *secular equilibrium* applies when the rate of decay of the head of the series (U^{238}) is practically constant and equal to the rate of decay of its daughter ...

Thus $$\lambda_1 P = \lambda_2 Q = \lambda_3 R = \lambda_4 S = \cdots$$

The amounts of $P, Q, R, S, \ldots$ are practically constant for an interval of a few thousand years. The amount of each member of the series is inversely proportional to its decay constant. A careful chemical analysis of the weight ratio of Ra and U in different samples of pitchblende, gives the result

$n_{Ra}/n_U \sim 3\cdot 5 \times 10^{-7}$. Assuming secular equilibrium

$$n_{Ra}\,\lambda_{Ra} = n_U\,\lambda_U$$

or
$$\frac{T_U}{T_{Ra}} = \frac{\lambda_{Ra}}{\lambda_U} = \frac{n_U}{n_{Ra}} = \frac{1}{3\cdot 5 \times 10^{-7}} \tag{25}$$

$$T_{Ra} \sim 1600\text{y}, \text{ thus } T_U \sim 4\cdot 5 \times 10^9\text{y}.$$

Analysis of the relative amounts of the members of the long–lived radioactive series, especially the end product, (e.g. Pb^{206} in uranium ores) has proved to be of great value in establishing the ages of rocks.† An important advance in mineral dating has been associated with the increased sensitivity of modern mass spectrometers in analysing the lead content of minerals into the isotopic components Pb^{204}, Pb^{206}, Pb^{207}, Pb^{208}.

10.4. RADIOACTIVE BRANCHING

The majority of radioactive substances decay by a single mechanism; an α or a β-particle is emitted giving rise to one atom of the daughter element. In a few cases, however, two or even three different modes of decay compete with one another. This phenomenon is known as *Branching*.†† The first examples of branching were found in the natural radioactive series. The "C" products, in the decay chains of uranium, thorium, and actinium, all break up in two or more ways. Consider the $\alpha - \beta$ branching of RaC

† An excellent account of the radioactive methods of Geochronology is given in J. A. Jacobs, R. D. Russell, J. T. Wilson, *Physics and Geology*, McGraw-Hill, New York 1959, pp. 174–199.

†† There are numerous examples of the daughter nucleus, (formed in an excited state) quickly decaying (10^{-13} sec) to the ground state and emitting one or more gamma rays. These are effectively in time coincidence with the α or β-emission. This must not be confused with the branching process of the parent nuclide.

($_{83}Bi^{214}$). The probability of α-emission by one atom in a short time interval dt is $\lambda_\alpha\, dt$. The total decay probability can be written in the form

$$(\lambda_\alpha + \lambda_\beta)\, dt$$

Thus the rate of decay of the number of atoms of RaC is

$$\frac{dN}{dt} = -(\lambda_\alpha + \lambda_\beta) N = -\lambda N; \tag{26}$$

the mean-life τ is equal to $1/\lambda$, where $\lambda = \lambda_\alpha + \lambda_\beta$. The branching ratio R, of the process, is defined by the equation

$$R = \frac{\lambda_\alpha}{\lambda_\alpha + \lambda_\beta}$$

In the case of RaC, R is 0·04%; that is, 0·04% of the disintegrations are by α-decay

$$\mathrm{RaC}({}_{83}\mathrm{Bi}^{214}) \xrightarrow[0{\cdot}04\,\%]{T=19{\cdot}7\,\mathrm{min}\;\;\alpha} \mathrm{RaC''}({}_{81}\mathrm{Tl}^{210})$$

or

$$\mathrm{RaC}({}_{83}\mathrm{Bi}^{214}) \xrightarrow[99{\cdot}96\,\%]{T=19{\cdot}7\,\mathrm{min}\;\;\beta^-} \mathrm{RaC'}({}_{84}\mathrm{Po}^{214})$$

The RaC″ can be collected by recoil from a metal plate covered with a very thin deposit of RaC. (The recoil of the daughter nucleus is much more energetic following α-decay than β-decay.) The RaC″ ($_{81}Tl^{210}$) does not undergo branching but decays by β-emission with a half-life of about 1·5 min. The RaC′ ($_{84}Po^{214}$) decays by α-emission with a very short half-life. Jacobsen estimated the half-life to be $\sim 10^{-6}$ sec by measuring the distance a recoiling RaC′ atom travels before α-particle emission.† Modern delayed coincidence methods give a half-life value of 160 microseconds. The decay products of RaC′ and RaC″ are the same; the two branches in the decay chain join again at RaD ($_{82}Pb^{210}$)

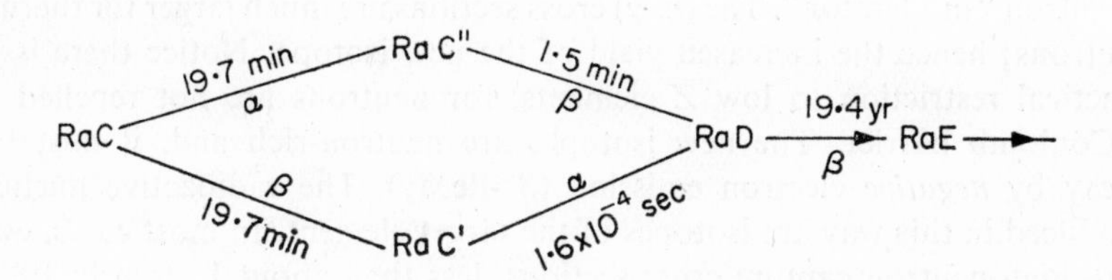

† J. C. Jacobsen, *Phil. Mag.*, **47**, 23, 1924.

The terms mean-life for α- or β-decay are sometimes used. This is the mean-life corresponding to the "switching off" of all other forms of decay. Denoting these "partial" mean-lives by τ_α and τ_β we have

$$\tau_\alpha = \frac{1}{\lambda_\alpha} \quad \text{and} \quad \tau_\beta = \frac{1}{\lambda_\beta} \tag{27}$$

Hence

$$\frac{1}{\tau} = \frac{1}{\tau_\alpha} + \frac{1}{\tau_\beta}$$

10.5. ARTIFICIAL PRODUCTION OF RADIOACTIVE ISOTOPES

A great impetus in the applications of radioactive isotopes arose with the discovery of methods of producing artificial radioactive isotopes.† We shall not concern ourselves with the applications of radioisotopes.

The first artificially produced radioactive substances were discovered by F. Joliot and I. Curie in 1934. They irradiated many of the light elements (low nuclear Coulomb barrier) with α particles (fairly strong, ~ 100 mc, Po α-sources were used). Aluminium foil, for example, exposed to the Po α-particles (5·3 MeV energy) for a few minutes was found to be radioactive, decaying with a half-life of 2·5 min by *positive* electron emission (positron). The activity is due to the production of the radioactive isotope of phosphorus, P^{30} by the nuclear reaction

$$_{13}\text{Al}^{27}(\alpha, n)_{15}\text{P}^{30}$$

$$_{15}\text{P}^{30} \xrightarrow{2\cdot5\text{ min}} {}_{14}\text{Si}^{30} + e^+ + \nu$$

Shortly afterwards, E. Fermi made the discovery that many radioactive isotopes of elements were produced by *neutron* bombardment. The activity of the new isotope, produced by a (n, γ) reaction, was greatly increased by surrounding the neutron source (typically a tube containing beryllium powder filled with radon gas) with hydrogenous material (water, or better still paraffin wax). The fast neutrons from the source are reduced to thermal velocities (~ 2000 m per sec) in the hydrogenous material, which acts as a neutron "moderator". The (n, γ) cross sections are much larger for thermal neutrons; hence the increased yield of the new isotope. Notice there is no practical restriction to low Z elements, for neutrons are not repelled by a Coulomb barrier. The new isotopes are neutron-rich and, if unstable, decay by *negative* electron emission (β^--decay). The radioactive nuclides produced in this way are isotopes of the target element. In most cases, even with high neutron capture cross sections, less than about 1 atom in 10^8 of

† An interesting survey of the early days of radiochemistry at Berkeley is given by W. F. Libby, *Amer. J. Phys.* **26**, 524, 1958.

the target element is converted into the heavier radioactive isotope.† The "active" material cannot be chemically separated from the inactive target material; thus the activity per gram, the so-called *specific activity* of the sample, is likely to be small. There are many applications where it is desirable that the specific activity should be high. It is much easier to do this, if the activity is the result of an (n, p), (n, α), (d, n), (α, n), ... (not (d, p)) reaction. The radioactive product is a *different* element and can be separated chemically from the irradiated target material.

Another important production method is based on the irradiation of suitable targets placed to intercept a beam of accelerated charged particles in a cyclotron. Activities are usually smaller than those corresponding to neutron irradiation near the centre of a high flux reactor, but certain isotopes cannot be made with neutrons. An important example is the production of the radioactive nuclide Co^{57}, by the deuteron bombardment of iron

$$_{26}Fe^{56}(d, n)_{27}Co^{57}$$

Co^{57} decays by the β-process known as orbital electron capture with a half-life of 270 d. The daughter nucleus, Fe^{57} is stable, but it may be formed in one of two excited states. The low energy state decays to the ground state with a mean-life of $\sim 10^{-7}$ sec, emitting a low energy γ-ray (14·4 keV). This gamma transition was one of the first known "recoilless" Mössbauer transitions. (See Chapter 13, Section 11.)

All the above methods of inducing radioactivity are susceptible to the same general theory regarding the calculation of radioactive yield. Provided the neutron flux, or charged particle beam current (and energy), remains constant during the irradiation period, the rate of production k of the active material is constant. We are assuming negligible depletion of the target material, which is the usual case. The net rate of increase of the number of atoms of the radioactive substance is given by

$$\frac{dn}{dt} = k - \lambda n \tag{28}$$

when λn is the induced activity at time t. Solving the equation, and putting $n = 0$ at $t = 0$, we obtain for the induced activity

$$A = \lambda n = k(1 - e^{-\lambda t}) \tag{29}$$

If the irradiation period t exceeds six or seven half-life periods the activity will be close to its *saturation* value A_0 (Fig. 3). The induced activity cannot exceed the saturation value $A_0 = k$. This condition is reached when

† There are exceptions. Prolonged irradiation of uranium in a high neutron flux ($\sim 10^{14}$ neutrons per cm^2 per sec) reactor, to produce Pu, will seriously deplete the amount of uranium in the fuel rod:

$$_{92}U^{238}(n, \gamma)_{92}U^{239} \xrightarrow[23\text{ min}]{\beta^-} {}_{93}Np^{239} \xrightarrow[2\cdot3\text{ d}]{\beta^-} {}_{94}Pu^{239}$$

the rate of production of activity, k, is equal to the spontaneous rate of decay, λn. After removal of the target from the neutron or deuteron flux, the activity of the sample will, of course, decay at its natural rate;

$$A = A_0 e^{-\lambda t} \tag{30}$$

If σ is the reaction cross section leading to the production of the radioactive nuclide, then, for a thin target, the production rate k is given by

$$k = \varphi \sigma N \tag{31}$$

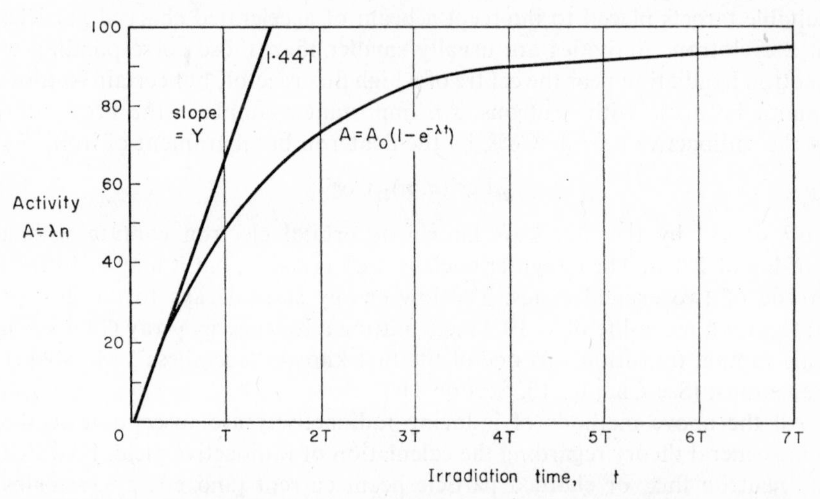

FIG. 3. Growth of induced activity of a radioactive isotope produced at a constant rate k (saturation activity $A_0 = \lambda n$, is represented by 100 units: time scale in terms of half-life T of the isotope). Initial slope of graph measures the yield Y. N.B. $A_0 = YT/\ln 2 = 1{\cdot}44\, YT$.

where φ is the incident flux (particles per cm² per sec), and N is the number of nuclei in the target. For a thick target the flux φ would be attenuated as it passed through the target, and σ would vary with the particle energy.

Sometimes it is more useful to quote the *yield* Y. This is defined as the rate of increase of activity at the beginning of the bombardment period. Differentiating eqn. (29) we get,

$$\frac{dA}{dt} = \lambda k \cdot e^{-\lambda t} \tag{32}$$

$$Y = \left(\frac{dA}{dt}\right)_{t=0} = \lambda k \tag{33}$$

The growth of induced activity in the target is illustrated in Fig. 3. Here the irradiation time is expressed in terms of the half-life T of the induced activity. The slope of the activity curve at the origin represents the yield Y.

10.6. STATISTICAL FLUCTUATIONS IN RADIOACTIVE DECAY

The treatment of radioactive decay described in the preceding sections is based on the assumption that n the number of atoms of a radio-element is a continuous variable. This is satisfactory for highly active sources, but for weak activities, there occur marked fluctuations in decay rate relative to the "continuum" theory.

An important problem is this. What is the probability $P(n)$ that exactly n atoms of a radio-element will decay during a given counting interval, if $\bar{n}$ is the average number of disintegrations occurring in the given time interval?†

Divide the counting interval into a large number (N) of equal sub-intervals. Let p denote the probability of a disintegration occurring in any one of the sub-intervals. Then $1 - p$ is the probability that *no* disintegration occurs in any specified sub-interval. The probability that disintegrations occur in n *specified* sub-intervals is given by the product of the independent probabilities p^n and $(1 - p)^{N-n}$

$$p^n(1 - p)^{N-n} \tag{34}$$

Here it is assumed that $p \ll 1$, and that the probability of two or more disintegrations occurring in a specified sub-interval is negligible. The condition that the n disintegrations occur during n specified sub-intervals must be relaxed. All we are interested in is that the n disintegrations occur sometime during the counting interval. The number of ways of arranging n events in N sub-intervals is the number of combinations:

$$\frac{N(N-1)(N-2)\cdots(N-n+1)}{n!} = \frac{N!}{n!\,(N-n)!} \tag{35}$$

The probability that just n disintegrations occur during the counting interval is the product of eqns. (34) and (35)

$$P(n) = p^n(1 - p)^{N-n}\frac{N!}{n!\,(N-n)!} \tag{36}$$

This is the *Binomial Distribution* first studied by Bernoulli. Notice that the binomial expansion of $(q + p)^N$, where $q = 1 - p$, can be written

$$(q + p)^N = \sum_{n=0}^{N} P(n) \tag{37}$$

A few of the properties of this distribution are required.

As $$q = 1 - p, \quad (q + p)^N = 1$$

or $$\sum_{n=0}^{N} P(n) = 1 \tag{38}$$

In other words, some result must occur.

† This is virtually the same problem as the determination of the probability that exactly n sixes are thrown in N successive throws of a die.

The average number of disintegrations $\bar{n}$ using eqns. (36) and (38) is given by

$$\bar{n} = \sum_{n=0}^{N} n\,P(n) = \sum_{n=1}^{N} n\,P(n)$$

$$\bar{n} = p\,N \sum_{m=0}^{M} p^m (1-p)^{M-m} \frac{M!}{m!(M-m)!} = p\,N \qquad (39)$$

where $m = n - 1$, and $M = N - 1$.

This gives the expected result $p = \bar{n}/N$ for observing one disintegration in a specified sub-interval.

The average of n^2 is defined by the relation

$$\overline{n^2} = \sum_{n=0}^{N} n^2\,P(n) = \sum_{n=1}^{N} n^2\,P(n)$$

$$\overline{n^2} = N p \sum_{m=0}^{M} (m+1)\,p^m (1-p)^{M-m} \frac{M!}{m!(M-m)!}$$

$$\overline{n^2} = N p \left[1 + M p \sum_{s=0}^{S} p^s \frac{S!}{s!(S-s)!}\right] = N p(1 + M p) \qquad (40)$$

where $s = m - 1$, and $S = M - 1$.
Substituting $M = N - 1$ in eqn. (40), we get

$$\overline{n^2} = N p[N p + (1-p)] \qquad (41)$$

The *variance* of the distribution is defined as the average of $(n - \bar{n})^2 = (n - p\,N)^2$.

The square root of the variance, the root-mean-square deviation, more commonly known as the "*standard deviation*" σ is given by

$$\sigma^2 = \overline{(n-\bar{n})^2} = \overline{(n - p\,N)^2} = \overline{n^2} + p^2 N^2 - \overline{2p\,N n} = \overline{n^2} + p^2 N^2 - 2p\,N\bar{n}$$

$$\sigma^2 = \overline{n^2} - p^2 N^2 = \overline{n^2} - \bar{n}^2 \qquad (42)$$

Combining eqns. (41) and (42), we obtain the important result

$$\sigma^2 = \bar{n}[\bar{n} + (1-p)] - \bar{n}^2 = \bar{n}(1-p) \qquad (43)$$

In most examples,† $p \ll 1$, and we have

$$\sigma = \sqrt{\bar{n}} \qquad (44)$$

This is the justification for the previous statement that if n counts are recorded during a counting period the fluctuation in n is expected to be of the order of $\sqrt{n}$. (The most probable value of n is $\bar{n}$.)

† For a short lived radioelement, for which the counting period extends over several half-life periods, p is close to unity and σ will be $\ll \sqrt{\bar{n}}$.

Poisson Distribution

In the limit of small p, and N very large, so that $N \gg n$, the binomial distribution $P(n)$ can be transformed by the approximations

$$\frac{N!}{n!(N-n)!} = \frac{N(N-1)(N-2)\cdots(N-n+1)}{n!} \simeq \frac{N^n}{n!}$$

and $$(1-p)^{N-n} \simeq (1-p)^N \simeq e^{-pN}$$

With these modifications, the probability distribution eqn. (36) becomes

$$P(n) = \frac{(Np)^n\, e^{-pN}}{n!}$$

or $$P(n) = \frac{\bar{n}^n\, e^{-\bar{n}}}{n!} \tag{45}$$

This is known as the *Poisson Distribution.* $P(n)$ reaches a maximum fo $n = \bar{n} - 1$, and $n = \bar{n}$. For large $\bar{n}$, the maximum of the distribution is sharp, and the distribution closely agrees with the Gaussian or *normal* distribution. To show this, expand $\ln P(n)$ as a power series around $n = \bar{n}$

$$\ln P(n) = \ln P(\bar{n}) + \frac{(n-\bar{n})^2}{2!}\left[\frac{d^2}{dn^2}\cdot \ln P(n)\right]_{n=\bar{n}} \tag{46}$$

Using Stirling's approximation

$$\ln(x!) = x\ln x - x + \tfrac{1}{2}\ln 2\pi x \tag{47}$$

and writing, using eqn. (45),

$$\ln P(n) = n\ln\bar{n} - \bar{n} - n\ln n + n - \tfrac{1}{2}\ln 2\pi n \tag{48}$$

$$\left[\frac{d^2}{dn^2}\ln P(n)\right]_{n=\bar{n}} = -\frac{1}{\bar{n}} + \frac{1}{2\bar{n}^2} = -\frac{1}{\bar{n}}, \quad \text{if } \bar{n} \ll 1. \tag{49}$$

Combining eqns. (48) and (49) with eqn. (46), and putting $n = \bar{n}$, we obtain

$$P(n) = -\tfrac{1}{2}\ln 2\pi\bar{n} - \frac{(n-\bar{n})^2}{2\bar{n}}$$

or $$P(n) = \frac{\exp\left\{-\dfrac{(n-\bar{n})^2}{2\bar{n}}\right\}}{(2\pi\bar{n})^{\frac{1}{2}}} \tag{50}$$

This is the Gauss distribution, well-known in the theory of random errors.

The Poisson and Gauss distributions for $\bar{n} = 15$ are shown in Fig. 4. In the Gauss distribution, n is treated as a continous variable and a smooth curve is drawn through the points; n, however, is essentially an integer in the Poisson distribution and no continuous curve is shown. The Gauss curve is symmetrical about its maximum at $n = \bar{n}$, whereas the Poisson distribution is asymmetric. For $\bar{n}$ as low as 15, there is never more than 10% difference between the two values of $P(n)$. The maximum probability for the Poisson distribution has the value 0·1025 at $n = 14$ and $n = 15$, which is slightly below the maximum value of 0·103 for the Gauss distribution. An important feature of both distributions, for $\bar{n}$ as small as 15, is the relatively low value of $P(n)$ at the maximum probability.

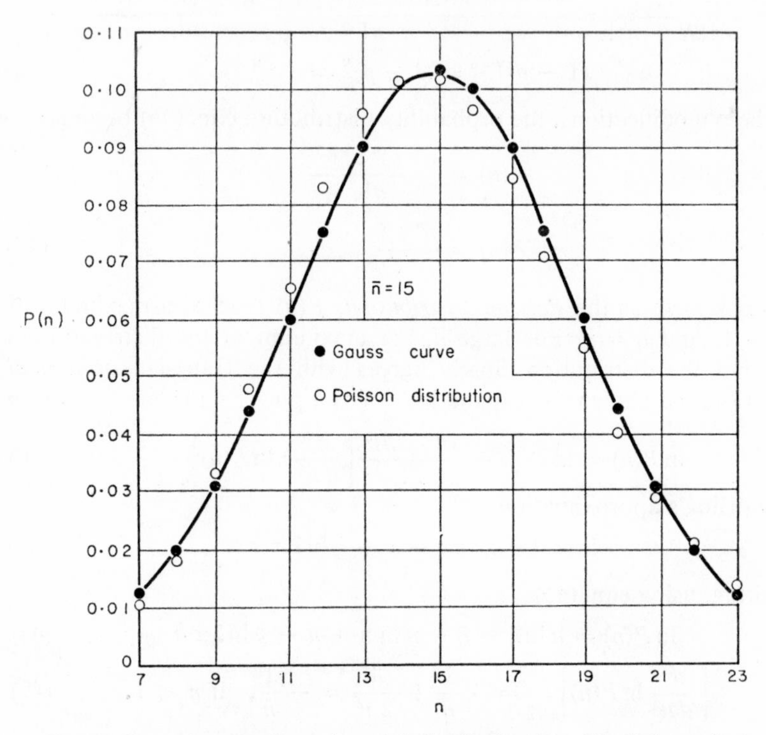

FIG. 4. Curve showing Gauss (normal) distribution ($\bar{n} = 15$). Points refer to $P(n)$ values for Poisson distribution ($\bar{n} = 15$).

The probability of a value of $|n - \bar{n}|$ exceeding $k\,\sigma$, for different values of k is given in Table 2.

TABLE 2

k	0	0·6745	1·0000	1·6449	1·9600
Probability	1·0000	0·5000	0·3173	0·1000	0·0500

In about 32% of the observed counts, n will differ from $\bar{n}$ by more than σ. For a value of n differing from $\bar{n}$ by more than 2σ, however, this occurs in less than 5% of the observed counts.

In practical counting observations, n not $\bar{n}$ is the directly determined quantity. The question arises: "For an observed count n, what is the chance that the mean count lies between the neighbouring values $\bar{n}$ and $\bar{n} + d\bar{n}$?" The question assumes that the same experiment can be repeated a very large number of times, so that $\bar{n}$ can be obtained with any desired degree of accuracy. The answer to this question is also given by the Poisson distribution.

$$P(\bar{n})\,d\bar{n} = \frac{\bar{n}^n e^{-\bar{n}}\,d\bar{n}}{n!} \tag{51}$$

In contrast to the Poisson distribution $P(n)$, given by eqn. (45), n is fixed and $\bar{n}$ is the variable ($\bar{n}$, unlike n, is of course non-integral). The following properties of the distribution $P(\bar{n})$ are important.

$$\int_0^\infty P(\bar{n})\,d\bar{n} = \frac{1}{n!}\int_0^\infty \bar{n}^n e^{-\bar{n}}\,d\bar{n} = \frac{n!}{n!} = 1\dagger \tag{52}$$

In other words, $\bar{n}$ has certainly some value.

The average value of the mean value $\bar{n}$ is given by

$$(n)_{av} = \int_0^\infty \bar{n}\,P(\bar{n})\,d\bar{n} = \frac{1}{n!}\int_0^\infty \bar{n}^{n+1} e^{-\bar{n}}\,d\bar{n} = \frac{(n+1)!}{n!} = (n+1) \tag{53}$$

Differentiating $P(\bar{n})$ with respect to $\bar{n}$, it is easy to show that the most probable value of $\bar{n}$ is n.

The average value of $\bar{n}^2$ is given by

$$(\bar{n})^2{}_{av} = \int_0^\infty \bar{n}^2\,P(\bar{n})\,d\bar{n} = \frac{(n+2)!}{n!} = (\bar{n})_{av}(\bar{n}_{av} + 1) \tag{54}$$

Also

$$\sigma^2 = (\bar{n})_{av} = (n+1)$$

$$\therefore \sigma = \sqrt{[n+1]} \tag{55}$$

The most frequent application of the statistical theory is the determination of the standard deviation of the counting rate of an active source in the presence of background radiation. The observed quantities are the background count, n_2 counts in a time interval t_2, the total count n_1 (source plus background) in a time interval t_1. The time intervals t_1 and t_2 are measured without error. The background counting rate C_2 and its standard deviation are given by

$$C_2 = \frac{n_2}{t_2} \pm \frac{n_2^{\frac{1}{2}}}{t_2} \tag{56}$$

Similarly,

$$C_1 = \frac{n_1}{t_1} \pm \frac{n_1^{\frac{1}{2}}}{t_1} \tag{57}$$

† The definite integral $\int_0^\infty x^n e^{-x}\,dx$ which is easily evaluated by successive integration by parts, can be regarded as a definition of $n!$ for all values of n.

The counting rate associated with the source is $C = C_1 - C_2$. To determine the standard deviation of C, we use the important result that the standard deviation of the sum or difference of two quantities is equal to the square root of the sum of the squares of the standard deviations of the two quantities.

Thus:

$$\sigma(n_1 \pm n_2) = (\sigma_1^2 + \sigma_2^2)^{\frac{1}{2}} \tag{58}$$

Hence,

$$C = (C_1 - C_2) \pm \left(\frac{n_1}{t_1^2} + \frac{n_2}{t_2^2}\right)^{\frac{1}{2}}$$

or

$$C = (C_1 - C_2) \pm \left(\frac{C_1}{t_1} + \frac{C_2}{t_2}\right)^{\frac{1}{2}} \tag{59}$$

Suppose that a fixed time interval t_0 is available for counting. What is the best way to divide t_0 so that the standard deviation σ of C is a minimum? As $t_0 = t_1 + t_2$, we can write

$$\sigma^2 = \left(\frac{C_1}{t_1} + \frac{C_2}{t_0 - t_1}\right)^2$$

Equating $d\sigma^2/dt_1$ to zero, it is easy to show that at the minimum

$$\frac{C_1}{C_2} = \frac{t_1^2}{t_2^2} \tag{60}$$

The Interval Distribution

A distribution of some importance in nuclear physics concerns the distribution in time of successive events which occur randomly. Observations of the times of arrival of cosmic ray bursts agree closely with this assumption of randomness.

Consider the process of radioactive decay. The mean number of disintegrations per unit time is λN. The probability that there will be no disintegrations in unit time is given by the Poisson formula for $P(0)$.

$$P(0) = \frac{(\lambda N)^0 e^{-\lambda N}}{0!} = e^{-\lambda N}\dagger \tag{61}$$

In Section 1, we derived an expression for the mean lifetime against radioactive decay (eqn. 8). We used the fact that the probability of a given atom disintegrating between t and $t + dt$ is equal to

$$P(t)\,dt = \lambda\, e^{-\lambda t}\,dt \tag{62}$$

† In a similar way, the probability that a moving charged particle does not produce any ions along a path length x, is $\exp(-s\,x)$, where s is the average specific ionization (number of ion-pairs formed per unit path length). This factor is important in relation to the sensitivity of charged particle detectors (see Chapter 11).

This formula also applies to the probability of observing random events during the interval t to $t + dt$. From eqn. (62), we see that small time intervals between successive random events are more likely than long time intervals. Out of a large number of events $N + 1$, (N intervals), the number of intervals n lying between the values t_1 and t_2 is given by

$$n = N \int_{t_1}^{t_2} \lambda\, e^{-\lambda t}\, dt = N(e^{-\lambda t_1} - e^{-\lambda t_2}) \tag{63}$$

Consider the time distribution associated with the successive decays of the pion and daughter muon.

$$\pi^{\pm} \rightarrow \mu^{\pm} + \nu(\bar{\nu}) \qquad \text{decay constant } \lambda_1 = \frac{1}{2{\cdot}56 \times 10^{-8}} \text{ sec}^{-1}.$$

$$\mu^{\pm} \rightarrow e^{\pm} + \bar{\nu} + \nu \qquad \text{decay constant } \lambda_2 = \frac{1}{2{\cdot}22 \times 10^{-6}} \text{ sec}^{-1}.$$

Suppose at $t = 0$, the pion produces a pulse (e.g. a light flash in a scintillator) in a detector. The pion is brought to rest in the detector and at a later instant θ, a pulse is produced due to the decay of the pion. At a later instant than θ, a third pulse is produced by the decay of the muon.

The probability that the pion decays in the short time interval between θ and $\theta + d\theta$ is

$$P(\theta)\, d\theta = \lambda_1\, e^{-\lambda_1 \theta}\, d\theta \tag{64}$$

The probability that the pion decays between θ and $\theta + d\theta$, and the daughter muon decays between t and $t + dt$, ($t \geqq \theta$) is the product of two terms.

$$P(\theta)\, d\theta\, P(t)\, dt = \lambda_1 \lambda_2\, e^{-\lambda_1 \theta}\, e^{-\lambda_2 (t-\theta)}\, d\theta\, dt$$

or

$$P(\theta)\, d\theta\, P(t)\, dt = \lambda_1 \lambda_2\, e^{-\lambda_2 t}\, e^{-(\lambda_1 - \lambda_2)\theta}\, d\theta\, dt \tag{65}$$

Relaxing the condition that the pion decays during a *specified* short interval θ to $\theta + d\theta$, we obtain the probability that the muon decays at a time between t and $t + dt$, after the arrival pulse of the pion, by summing over possible values of θ

$$P(t)\, dt = \lambda_1 \lambda_2\, e^{-\lambda_2 t}\, dt \int_0^t e^{-(\lambda_1 - \lambda_2)\theta}\, d\theta$$

$$P(t) = \frac{\lambda_1 \lambda_2}{\lambda_1 - \lambda_2} (e^{-\lambda_2 t} - e^{-\lambda_1 t}) \tag{66}$$

Equation (66) can be derived by realising that the $\pi \rightarrow \mu \rightarrow e$ decay is a special case of the radioactive chain $P, Q, R \ldots$ discussed in Section 3. Thus the probability of an atom Q decaying between time t and $t + dt$ is obtained from eqn. (20), by putting $P_0 = 1$ and multiplying the expression for Q by $\lambda_2\, dt$. This is the same result as eqn. (66). The most probable decay time of the muon occurs when the function $P(t)$ reaches its maximum value.

(This corresponds to the peak of the curve for Q, illustrated in Fig. 2.) Differentiating $P(t)$ with respect to t and equating to zero, it is easy to show that the most probable decay time of the muon is

$$t_\mu = \frac{\ln \lambda_1 - \ln \lambda_2}{\lambda_1 - \lambda_2} = \frac{t_1 t_2 (\ln t_2 - \ln t_1)}{t_2 - t_1} \tag{67}$$

where t_1, t_2 are the mean-lives of the pion and muon, respectively.

10.7. MEASUREMENT OF DECAY CONSTANTS

Radioactive decay is a nuclear process. It is not surprising that many attempts to observe the influence of high pressure, temperature, concentration, electric and magnetic fields,† etc., have failed to detect any change of the decay constant.

There has been observed an interesting exception to the above rule. In the β-decay process known as orbital electron capture, an orbital atomic electron (usually a K shell electron) interacts with a proton inside the nucleus, changing the proton into a neutron. Most of the released energy is carried away by a neutrino (ν).

$$p + e^- \rightarrow n + \nu$$

One of the factors influencing the rate of this process, is the probability of the orbital electron being found inside the nucleus

$$|\psi_e(0)|^2$$

This factor is small, but it is greatest for the K shell electrons. Hence K electron capture is much more likely than L electron capture. In a light isotope, such as Be^7, the interaction of the valence electrons responsible for the chemical bonds in beryllium compounds might have a small effect on the K electron wave function at the nucleus. This effect should produce a small change in the decay constant λ of the $Be^7 - K$ capture process. Experiments have shown that there is a small difference in the decay constants of Be, BeO and BeF_2.

The differences between the decay constants have been measured by the differential ionization current technique first invented by Rutherford. The principle of the method is illustrated in Fig. 5. The two Be^7 sources, produced by the proton bombardment of lithium in a cyclotron, in the form of Be and BeO, were mounted inside two identical ionization chambers A and B respectively. The polarizing potentials applied to the two chambers are equal, but opposite in sign, so that the ionization currents I_A and I_B are opposite in sign. If at time $t = 0$, the activities of the two sources are the

† The isotropic emission of β- and γ-rays can be disturbed by polarizing the nuclei. At low temperatures, $\sim 0{\cdot}01^\circ$K, strong magnetic fields tend to align the spin axes of all the nuclei in a sample.

same, the net ionization current $I = I_A + I_B$ is zero. (The ionization is produced by the 0·48 MeV gamma rays emitted in the decay of an excited state of the Li^7 daughter nucleus). However, if λ (Be) and λ (BeO) differ in magnitude, the net ionization current will change with time. The half-life of Be^7 is 53 d; thus if λ (Be) and λ (BeO) differ by a few parts times 10^{-4},

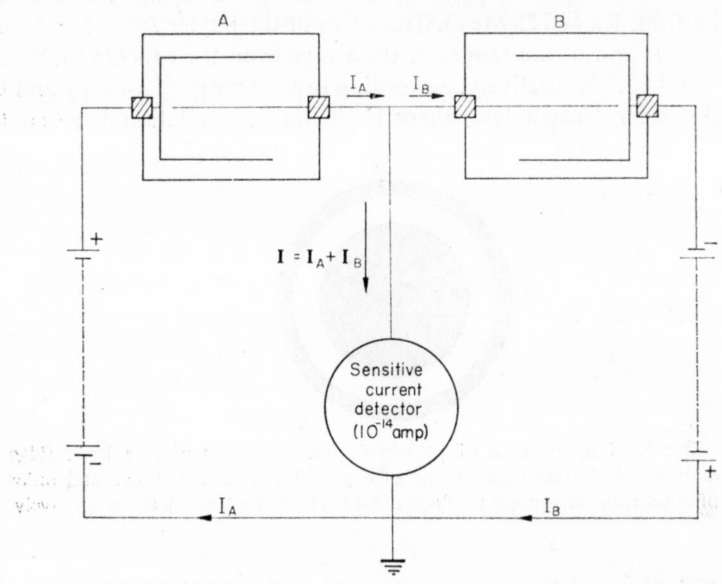

FIG. 5. Differential ionization current method of determining the difference between the decay constants of Be and BeO.

an observable effect should be produced in a few minutes. The results of J. I. Kraushaar, E. D. Wilson and K. T. Bainbridge† were

$$\lambda\,(\text{Be}) \quad - \lambda\,(\text{BeF}_2) = (7{\cdot}41 \pm 0{\cdot}47) \times 10^{-4}\,\lambda$$
$$\lambda\,(\text{BeO}) - \lambda\,(\text{BeF}_2) = (6{\cdot}09 \pm 0{\cdot}05) \times 10^{-4}\,\lambda$$
$$\lambda\,(\text{Be}) \quad - \lambda\,(\text{BeO}) = (1{\cdot}31 \pm 0{\cdot}51) \times 10^{-4}\,\lambda$$

These results are smaller than those found by E. Segrè and C. Wiegand,†† but both experiments clearly demonstrate the influence of chemical bonds on the K capture rate for Be^7.

What is the evidence that the decay constants of the radioelements do not alter over very long periods of time? There is some indirect evidence that the decay constants of the natural α-radioactive elements have remained constant over geological epochs. Certain mineral specimens, for example,

† J. I. KRAUSHAAR, E. D. WILSON and K. T. BAINBRIDGE, *Phys. Rev.* **90**, 610, 1953.
†† E. SEGRÈ and C. WIEGAND, *Phys. Rev.* **75**, 39, 1949; **81**, 284, 1951.

some plates of mica, are found to be darkly coloured. This effect is due to the α-rays emitted by uranium and its decay products in a "uranium mica". A typical "pleochroic halo", (as observed through a polarizing microscope), is sketched in Fig. 6. The central dark ring is produced by the action of all the α-particles (apart from RaA and RaC′) emitted by the uranium and its descendants. The edge of the inner dark circle marks the range of the α-particles from Ra (4·775 MeV). The edges of the lighter second and third rings mark the end of the ranges of the α-rays from RaA (5·998 MeV) and RaC′ (7·680 MeV) respectively. According to the theory of α-decay and the empirical Geiger–Nuttall law, there is an intimate relation between the

FIG. 6. Sketch of appearance of pleochroic haloes in "uranium mica". Edge of dark inner circle represents range of α-particles from Ra. Inner and outer edges of outer ring correspond to range of α-rays from RaA and RaC′ respectively.

decay constant λ and the energy (or range) of the emitted α-particles. The sharp edges to the darkened rings of the mineral haloes produced over thousands of millions of years, support the view that at least the α-decay constants have remained unchanged.

In the case of β-decay we have no corresponding evidence. Dirac and independently Jordan have suggested that the "weak interaction" constants vary with time. According to this theory, the gravitational "constant" G decreases so that the product of G and the age of the Universe remains constant.† The interactions reponsible for β-decay, pion and muon decay, are very weak compared with the strong nuclear forces. Although the strength of the beta decay interaction is much greater than the gravitational interaction, it is nevertheless considered to be very weak. It is possible that the so called Fermi constant†† in β-decay decreases as the Universe ages. In principle, this might be tested by comparing the ages of minerals by the

† See the article by R. H. DICKE, The Principle of Equivalence and the Weak Interactions, *Revs. Mod. Phys.* **29**, 355, 1957. If the gravitational constant G was higher in the past than its present day value, the surface temperature of the earth must be slowly decreasing. A slow decrease in G with age might be responsible for the cracks found in the ocean floor, which some geologists believe are of recent origin.

†† See Chapter 14.

uranium–lead and rubidium–strontium dating methods. The former technique is based on the constancy of the α-decay rate of uranium (a strong interaction process). The strontium dating method is based on determining the amount of Sr^{87} produced by the β-decay of Rb^{87} (half-life 5×10^{10} y) in certain types of mica. If the β-decay "constant" of Rb^{87} has been decreasing over the past 10^9 y, the strontium dating estimate should be about 10 per cent greater than the α-decay rate estimates. Unfortunately, the dating techniques are not reliable enough to prove or disprove this hypothesis.

There is no one method which is suitable for the determination of radioactive decay constants. This is a consequence of the enormous range of the value of decay constants. An indication of this range is given in Table 3.

TABLE 3

Nuclide	Half-life T
Be^8	$1{\cdot}4 \times 10^{-16}$ sec $< T < 4 \times 10^{-15}$ sec
RaC′(Po^{214})	$1{\cdot}6 \times 10^{-4}$ sec
He^6	0·82 sec
Free neutron	$12{\cdot}0 \pm 1{\cdot}5$ min
P^{32}	14·3 days
Co^{60}	5·2 years
C^{14}	5570 years
Sm^{146}	5×10^7 years
U^{238}	$4{\cdot}51 \times 10^9$ years
Sm^{147}	$1{\cdot}3 \times 10^{11}$ years
Bi^{209}	2×10^{18} years

It has been estimated that all β stable nuclides of mass number greater than about 140 are α unstable. The majority of the α-decay half-lives are too long to detect. The upper limit of estimation seems to be about 10^{18} years. At the other extreme, it is difficult to estimate lifetimes of excited nuclear states shorter than 10^{-15} sec. We shall now consider some of the experimental techniques of determining decay constants.

(1) For half-lives in the range of a few seconds to about 10 y, the direct method of determining the activity of the source as a function of time is suitable. A definite fraction of the emitted radiation should enter the detector and be recorded. The accuracy of the direct method decreases at the upper and lower time limits, especially for weak sources.

(2) For half-lives in the range 10 to 10^{18} y the "Weighing method" is often used. From the decay formula,

$$\frac{dN}{dt} = -\lambda N$$

the decay constant can be determined if the number of atoms N in the source is known (by weighing and using the atomic weight and Avogadro's number) and the absolute activity dN/dt is measured. This means that the fraction of emitted particles entering the detector, and the detector efficiency must be known. It is advantageous if the radioactive nuclide can be obtained in the gaseous state and introduced into a gas proportional counter. C^{14} activity is often measured by introducing in it the form of high pressure, CO_2, or acetylene, into a proportional counter (the soft β rays, 0·155 MeV, are completely absorbed in the filling-gas of the counter).

(3) A few half-life ratios have been determined by measuring the relative proportions of radio-elements in minerals which are believed to be in secular equilibrium (the ratio for Ra and U^{238} has been estimated in this way).

(4) For alpha emitters it is possible to estimate half-lives using the empirical "decay constant-range" formula,

$$\log\lambda = a + b\log R$$

All the α-emitters however do not lie on a single line, and some of them are well off any of the linear plots. Estimation of the order of magnitude of λ from the range of the α-particle (in the gas of a cloud chamber, for example) is possible, but no great trust can be placed in the accuracy of the result.

(5) Some of the very long lived activities have been investigated by impregnating the emulsion of a "nuclear emulsion" photographic plate with a known amount of active solution. The plate is then stored (well screened from cosmic rays) for several months. After developing the plate, the number of α-tracks of the "correct" range are carefully counted. An estimate of the activity of the source can thus be made.

(6) When the half-life is of the order of one second, various "mechanical" methods are used. Radioactive isotopes produced by neutron irradiation inside a reactor are sometimes quickly transferred by a blast of compressed air from the interior of the reactor to an external counter. For gaseous sources, the ratio in the count rate recorded by two identical counters separated by a distance l along a tube through which the gas is flowing with a velocity v, enables λ to be found. The count rate recorded by the "down-stream" detector is $\exp(-\lambda\, l/v)$ times that of the "up-stream" detector.

The half-life of B^{12} (0·02 sec), produced by the deuteron bombardment of a boron oxide target attached to an aluminium disc, has been measured by investigating the variation in count rate as the angular velocity of the disc is varied. A β-counter is mounted near the edge of the rotating disc. A similar method has been used to determine the half-life of He^6.† The details and theory of the method are as follows (Fig. 7).

He^6 is produced by the bombardment of Be^9 with *fast* neutrons: $Be^9(n, \alpha)$ He^6, an endoergic reaction. 50 g of powdered beryllium is held in place by cellophane tape against the inner surface of a rotating metal hoop A

† J. E. R. Holmes, *Proc. Phys. Soc.* **62** A, 293, 1949.

of diameter 45 cm. The hoop is rotated at an angular velocity ω. Neutrons form a 230 mc Ra–Be neutron source S bombard an arc length of the hoop corresponding to an aperture angle α. At the opposite side of the hoop, the β-rays accompanying the decay of the induced activity He^6 (occluded in the thin beryllium layer) are counted by the detector D. The angular aperture cut in the lead shielding which screens D from radiation from the source S, subtends an angle β at the centre of the hoop. The average counting rate C recorded by the detector D depends on the angular velocity ω and decay constant λ. The relation is derived as follows.

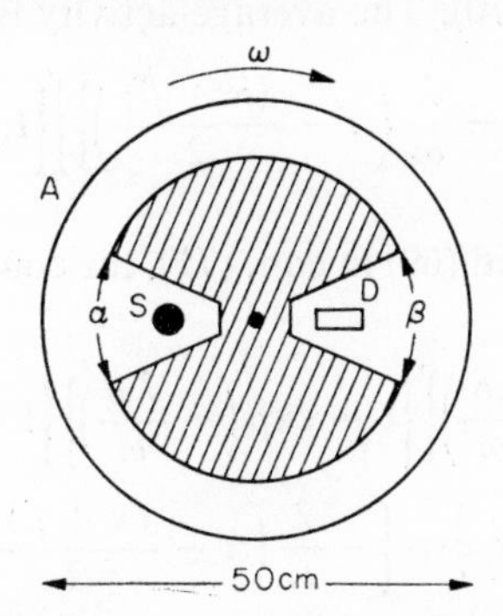

FIG. 7. Determination of half-life of He^6 (0·8 sec). Wheel A, with thin beryllium layer on the inner rim, rotates with angular velocity ω. S . . . neutron source, D . . . β-ray counter. Angular apertures are α and β. (Shading represents lead shielding.) (J. E. R. HOLMES, *Proc. Phys. Soc.* **62**A, 293, 1949.)

The Be target is exposed to the neutron flux for a time α/ω as it passes the source for the first time. The induced activity at the end of this time is given by eqn. (29)

$$A = k\left\{1 - \exp\left(-\lambda\frac{\alpha}{\omega}\right)\right\} \tag{68}$$

After one complete revolution, this activity has decayed to the value $A \exp(-2\pi\lambda/\omega)$; however an extra increment of activity A is added to the beryllium as it has now passed the source aperture twice. After a time, a steady state activity corresponding to the sum of an infinite series is achieved. Thus the resultant activity, at the position corresponding to the Be leaving the aperture of angle α, is equal to

$$A_\infty = A\left\{1 + \exp\left(-\frac{2\pi\lambda}{\omega}\right) + \exp\left(-\frac{4\pi\lambda}{\omega}\right) + \cdots\right\}$$

This is a geometrical progression; hence

$$A_\infty = \frac{A}{\left\{1 - \exp\left(-\frac{2\pi\lambda}{\omega}\right)\right\}} \tag{69}$$

The resultant activity at the entrance to the detetector aperture, at an angle, $\pi - \frac{(\alpha + \beta)}{2}$, beyond the exit of the neutron source aperture is equal to

$$A_\infty \exp\left\{-\frac{\lambda}{\omega}\left(\pi - \frac{(\alpha + \beta)}{2}\right)\right\} \tag{70}$$

The moving He^6 source takes a time interval β/ω to pass the detector aperture. Thus the quantity of interest is the average activity of the He^6 during the time interval β/ω, where the activity at the beginning of this period is given by eqn. (70). The average activity is given by eqn. (12)

$$\bar{A} = \frac{\omega A_\infty}{\lambda \beta}\left[\exp\left\{-\frac{\lambda}{\omega}\left(\pi - \frac{(\alpha + \beta)}{2}\right)\right\}\right]\left\{1 - \exp\left(-\frac{\lambda\beta}{\omega}\right)\right\} \tag{71}$$

Substituting eqns. (68) and (69) in eqn. (71), the counting rate at the detector is given by:

$$C = K\frac{\omega}{\lambda}\left\{1 - \exp\left(-\frac{\lambda\alpha}{\omega}\right)\right\}\left\{1 - \exp\left(-\frac{\lambda\beta}{\omega}\right)\right\}\left\{1 - \exp\left(-\frac{2\pi\lambda}{\omega}\right)\right\}^{-1}$$
$$\times \exp\left\{-\frac{\lambda}{\omega}\left(\pi - \frac{(\alpha + \beta)}{2}\right)\right\} \tag{72}$$

where K is a constant.

If $\lambda\alpha \ll \omega$ and $\lambda\beta \ll \omega$, and $2\pi \gg \alpha + \beta$, eqn. (72) becomes

$$C = \frac{K\omega}{\lambda}\,\frac{\lambda\alpha}{\omega}\,\frac{\lambda\beta}{\omega}\left[\exp\left(-\frac{\lambda\pi}{\omega}\right)\right]\left\{1 - \exp\left(-\frac{2\pi\lambda}{\omega}\right)\right\}^{-1} \tag{73}$$

which may be written in the form

$$C = C_0\frac{x}{\sinh x} \tag{74}$$

where $$x = \frac{\pi\lambda}{\omega}$$

C_0 is the "saturation" counting rate observed when $\omega \gg \pi\lambda$. The variation of C/C_0 as the angular velocity ω is varied is shown in Fig. 8. When the angular velocity of the hoop exceeds 10 revs per sec, the count rate is within 0·1 per cent of the saturation value C_0. In the experiment of Holmes, C_0 was about 60 counts per min, with a steady background from the neutron source of 80 counts per min. For a period of rotation equal to 6·3 times the half-life T, C falls to one half the value of C_0. Thus it is possible from the observed curve (Fig. 8) to determine the half-life T. The half-life value was found to be $T = 0{\cdot}823 \pm 0{\cdot}013$ sec.

(7) In a few cases, half-lives of the order of several thousend years have been determined by calorimetry. The rate of emission of α-radiation by a known weight of Pu^{239} has been determined by measuring the rate of

production of heat due to the self absorption of the α-particles.† The half-life can then be computed.

(8) An important post-war development is based on fast electronic techniques;‡ lifetimes of excited nuclear states which are not less than $\sim 10^{-10}$ second have been determined by the method of "delayed coincidences". To illustrate the principle, consider the determination†† of the decay constant λ of the 0·197 MeV excited state of F^{19}. A teflon disc was irradiated for one minute with fast neutrons, producing the radioactive isotope O^{19} (30 sec half-life). The teflon disc was then placed between two scintillation

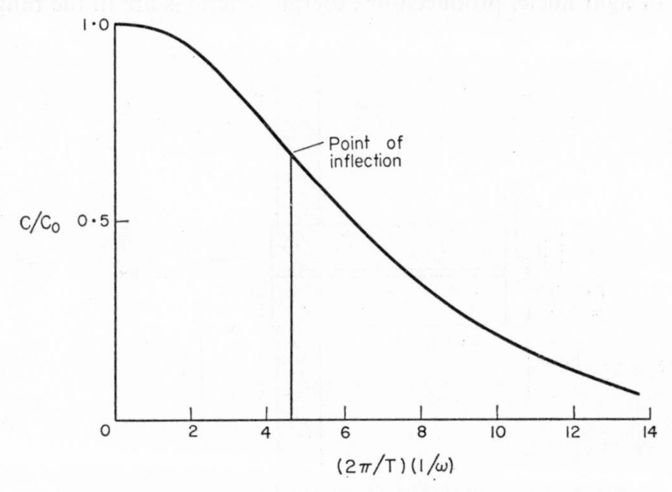

FIG. 8. Variation of counting rate as a function of $(2\pi/T)\,1/\omega$.

detectors, A and B, each consisting of a crystal and a photomultiplier tube. The β-rays from the decay of O^{19} were recorded by A. In about 30 per cent of the decays of O^{19}, the daughter nucleus F^{19} is formed in the 0·197 MeV excited state. The 0·197 MeV γ-rays emitted when the F^{19} nucleus decays to the ground state were detected by B. The output pulse from the β-detector could be delayed by a variable time t with the aid of a variable length of delay cable. This delayed pulse and the output pulse from the γ-detector were fed into a fast coincidence circuit of very short resolving time $d\tau$ ($d\tau$ is the time interval during which two input pulses are recorded as "simultaneous"). The counting rate of the output of the coincidence circuit was measured as a function of the delay time t. The number of delayed coincidences $n(t)\,dt$, provided $\lambda\,d\tau \ll 1$, is proportional to

$$\lambda\,d\tau\,e^{-\lambda t}$$

† J. W. STOUT and W. M. JONES, *Phys. Rev.* **71**, 582, 1947.
‡ Coincidence circuits are discussed in Chapter 12.
†† C. M. P. JOHNSON, *Phil. Mag.* **1**, 573, 1956.

A semi-logarithmic plot of the delayed coincidence count rate and delay time t enables λ to be determined. For the 0·197 MeV state of F^{19} a value of T equal to $8{\cdot}7 \times 10^{-8}$ sec was obtained.

(9) The majority of the half-life values of excited nuclear states are too small to be measured by electronic methods ($T < 10^{-9}$ or 10^{-10} sec). Indirect methods are possible in some cases. These include use of the recoil motion of the radiating excited nucleus and the measurement of the cross section of the resonance scattering of the emitted γ-radiation.†

Two variations of the recoil technique are described.†† Typical recoil velocities of light nuclei produced in exoergic reactions are in the range 10^8

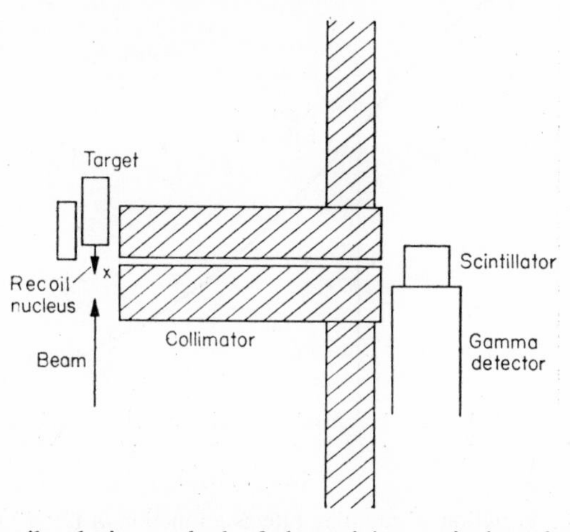

FIG. 9. Recoil velocity method of determining excited nuclear lifetime.

to 10^9 cm/sec. The half-life of the 6·13 MeV excited state of O^{16} has been estimated in the following way (Fig. 9). A very thin F^{19} target in the form of a CaF_2 layer, 10^{-5} cm thick, was deposited on a very flat backing support. This support could be displaced accurately in the direction of the incident proton beam and its position determined to an accuracy of better than 10^{-3} cm. The 6·13 MeV excited state of O^{16} was formed by bombarding the target with 873 keV protons.

$$_9F^{19}\ (p, \alpha)_8\ O^{16*}$$

Just over 2 MeV of kinetic energy is shared between the excited O^{16} nucleus and the α-particle. Conservation of momentum ensures that the O^{16} excited nucleus recoils with about one-fifth of this energy. In some cases, the excited O^{16} nucleus will recoil in the opposite direction to that of the incident

† Resonant fluorescence scattering by nuclei is discussed in Chapter 13, Section 10.

†† S. DEVONS, G. MANNING and D. ST. P. BUNBURY, *Proc. Phys. Soc. (London)* A **68**, 18, 1955.

proton beam. If the recoiling excited nucleus emits a γ-ray when it has recoiled a distance x, where x is the distance from the thin CaF_2 target to the entrance slit of the collimator in front of the γ-scintillation counter, the γ-ray may be recorded by the detector. The counting rate of the γ-counter was measured as a function of the distance x. The observations were found to fit a theoretical curve (Fig. 10) corresponding to a half-life of 10^{-11} sec or less. (A recoiling excited O^{16} nucleus travels a few times 10^{-3} cm in 10^{-11} sec.)

The second method is based on the observation of the Doppler shift in the γ-ray energy of the radiation emitted by the excited nucleus as it is

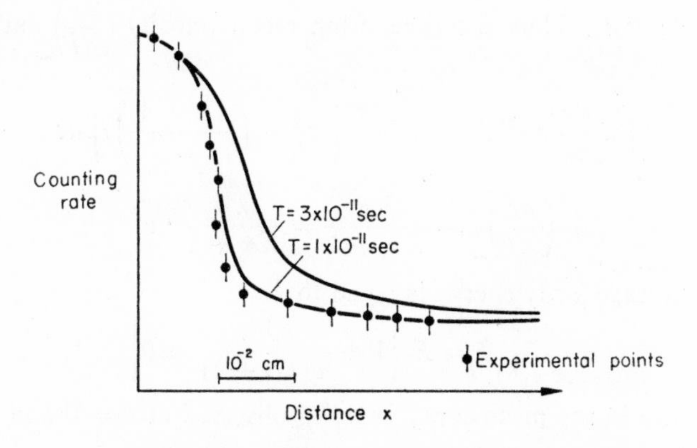

FIG. 10. Experimental results and theoretical curves for 6·13 MeV state of O^{16} produced from $F^{19}(p, \alpha)O^{16*}$ reaction.

slowed down in matter. In solid matter a recoiling nucleus produced in a nuclear reaction is slowed down, losing energy by atomic excitation and ionization, in a time of about 10^{-13} sec. Suppose the excited nucleus produced in a nuclear reaction recoils in the direction of incidence of the particle responsible for the reaction. Let the initial recoil velocity of the excited nucleus be v and suppose the γ-ray emitted by the nucleus is observed at an angle θ relative to the direction of v. The decay constant of the excited state is λ, and E_0 is the γ-ray energy emitted by the nucleus at rest (the very small energy carried away by the nucleus is in this case unimportant); then the average energy E of the γ-radiation in the θ direction is derived as follows. It is found that the residual range of a recoil nucleus is, approximately, proportional to its velocity:

$$(R - r) = \alpha \frac{dr}{dt} \tag{75}$$

R is the total range of the recoil nucleus, $(R - r)$ is the residual range, and α is a constant. For $r = 0$, we have $R = \alpha v$.

Integrating eqn. (75), we obtain

$$r = R(1 - e^{-t/\alpha})$$

Hence

$$\frac{dr}{dt} = \frac{R}{\alpha} e^{-t/\alpha} \tag{76}$$

From the theory of the Doppler effect, a γ-ray emitted by the recoiling nucleus at time t, in the θ direction, has an energy equal to

$$E_0 \left[1 + \frac{1}{c} \frac{dr}{dt} \cos\theta\right] \tag{77}$$

The probability of decay of the recoiling excited nucleus between t and $t + dt$ is $\lambda e^{-\lambda t} dt$. Thus the time–mean recoil velocity $\left(\frac{dr}{dt}\right)_{av}$ at decay is given by

$$\int_0^\infty \lambda \frac{dr}{dt} e^{-\lambda t} dt = \int_0^\infty \lambda \frac{R}{\alpha} \left\{\exp - \left(\frac{\lambda \alpha + 1}{\alpha}\right) t\right\} dt$$

$$\left(\frac{dr}{dt}\right)_{av} = \frac{\lambda R}{\lambda \alpha + 1} = \frac{\lambda \alpha}{\lambda \alpha + 1} \cdot v \tag{78}$$

Thus, the average γ-ray energy is equal to

$$E = E_0 \left[1 + \frac{v \lambda \alpha}{c(\lambda \alpha + 1)} \cos\theta\right] \tag{79}$$

The difference in the mean γ-ray energies observed at $\theta = 0$ and $\theta = \pi$ is given by

$$\Delta E = 2 E_0 \frac{v}{c} \frac{\lambda \alpha}{\lambda \alpha + 1} \tag{80}$$

If ΔE can be measured, the product $\lambda \alpha$ can be obtained. In a typical case $\Delta E / E_0$ is of the order of 1 per cent. If the half-life T of the excited state is $\ll \alpha$, the full Doppler shift $2 E_0 v/c$ is observed. At the other extreme $T \gg \alpha$, the Doppler shift is negligible. Limits of the half-life of a number of excited nuclear states have been obtained in this way. The above analysis considers the case in which the recoil motion of the excited nucleus is derived from the particle initiating the nuclear reaction. The experiments are not easy and a more exact theory takes into consideration the detailed range–velocity relation in the stopping medium. Some degree of variation of α (the slowing down time corresponds to six or seven times the time constant α) can be obtained by mounting a very thin target on different backing materials. Full details of the variations of the method are given in the article by S. Devons *et al.* (*loc. cit.*).

BIBLIOGRAPHY

Sir E. Rutherford, J. Chadwick and C. D. Ellis, *Radiations from Radioactive Substances* (Chapt. 1), Cambridge University Press, 1930.

Article by E. Segrè in *Experimental Nuclear Physics,* Vol. 3 (Ed. by E. Segrè), John Wiley, New York 1959.

R. D. EVANS, *The Atomic Nucleus*, McGraw-Hill, New York 1955, especially Chapt. 15, 26.
W. J. WHITEHOUSE and J. L. PUTMAN, *Radioactive Isotopes*, Oxford University Press, 1953.
D. TAYLOR, *The Measurement of Radioisotopes*, Methuen, 2nd Ed., 1957.
An extensive collection of data and references is given by D. STROMINGER, J. M. HOLLANDER and G. T. SEABORG, in *Revs. Mod. Phys.* **30**, 585, 1958.

EXAMPLES

1. A radio-element P has a half-life of 20 y, and the succeeding products Q and R have half-life values of 19·5 d and 11·4 d respectively. A quantity of the element P is left in a closed vessel for several months so that radioactive equilibrium is attained. Calculate the relative numbers of atoms of P, Q and R present.
2. In an accident with an atomic reactor, Te^{131} a radioactive fission product of uranium escapes to the atmosphere. When will the activity of the daughter product, I^{131}, reach its maximum value and what is the iodine activity in terms of the initial activity of the escaping Te^{131}? (Half-lives of Te^{131} and I^{131} are 1·25 and 8·0 d respectively.)
3. The half-life of Pu^{239} has been determined by immersing a sphere of Pu^{239} of mass 120·1 g in liquid nitrogen and measuring the rate of evaporation of the liquid. The evaporation rate corresponded to a power supply of 0·231 W. Calculate, to the nearest hundred years, the half-life of Pu^{239}, given that the energy of its decay alpha particles is 5·144 MeV. (Take into account the recoil energy of the product nucleus.)
4. One gram of silver foil is exposed to a thermal neutron flux of 10^4 neutrons per cm^2 per sec for 5 min. The natural abundance of Ag^{107} is 51·9 per cent and its (n, γ) cross-section is 45 barns. If the half-life of Ag^{108} is 2·3 min, calculate the activity of the Ag^{108} isotope when it is removed from the neutron flux.
5. In a specimen of pitchblende the lead–uranium weight ratio is 0·225 to 1·000. Calculate the age of the mineral, assuming there is no lead of non-radioactive origin present. The half-life of uranium is $4{\cdot}1 \times 10^9$ y and the atomic weights of Pb and U are 206·0 and 238·4 respectively.
6. The C^{14} activity of living carbon compounds is 15 disintegrations per g of carbon per min. The half-life of C^{14} is 5570 y. What is the fraction of C^{14} atoms in living matter?
7. The average energy of the γ-rays emitted by tritium is 5·68 keV. What is the rate of production of heat if the beta radiation from 10 cm^3 of pure tritium gas at S.T.P. is absorbed? The half-life of tritium is 12·46 y. What is the total energy produced in 20 y, taking into account the decay of the tritium activity?
8. The helium content of a uranium bearing mineral can be used to determine the age of the mineral. A sample of mineral contains $5{\cdot}1 \times 10^{-5}$ cm^3 of helium (at S.T.P.) per g of mineral and $1{\cdot}05 \times 10^{-13}$ g of radium per g of mineral. Estimate the age of the mineral. The half-life values of U^{238} and Ra^{226} are $4{\cdot}51 \times 10^9$ y and 1620 y respectively. (Grad. I. Phys.)
9. The following observations were made to determine the activity of a weak source.

Counting interval (min)	No. of counts with source	No. of counts without source
30	—	472
30	527	—
180	—	2734
180	3175	—

What is the count rate attributable to the source and what is its statistical uncertainty? For how long would counting have to be carried out in order to determine the source count rate to an accuracy of 1 per cent? (Grad. I Phys.)

CHAPTER 11

THE DETECTION OF NUCLEAR RADIATION

11.1. INTRODUCTION

One of the most important aspects of experimental nuclear physics is the problem of the detection, identification, and energy determination of the radiations emitted in nuclear reactions and decay. Charged particles differ from neutral ones as the former ionize and excite molecules as they travel through matter. This is the basic process involved in the detection of charged particles. The detection of neutral particles such as neutrons, neutrinos and high energy photons is achieved through an intermediate interaction releasing a charged particle which is then recorded. Slow neutrons, for example, are usually detected through the ionizing properties of the α-particle and lithium nucleus released in the nuclear reaction, $B^{10}(n, \alpha)\,Li^7$.

In this section we consider the phenomenon of the transfer of energy from a moving charged particle to the electrons of the surrounding medium. Consider a particle of charge $z\,e$ moving with a velocity v so that its closest distance of approach to a stationary electron is b. The particle mass M is much greater than the mass of the electron (m). The transfer of momentum p to the electron is obtained by integrating the Coulomb force acting on the electron during the collision.

$$p = \int_{-\infty}^{\infty} \frac{z\,e^2}{r^2} \sin\theta \, dt \tag{1}$$

By symmetry, there is no component of momentum transferred parallel to the particle velocity. From Fig. 1 we see that

$$-v\,t = b \cot\theta$$

$$v\,dt = b \operatorname{cosec}^2\theta \; d\theta$$

Eliminating dt and r^2 from eqn. (1), we obtain

$$p = \frac{z\,e^2}{b\,v} \int_0^{\pi} \sin\theta \, d\theta = \frac{2z\,e^2}{b\,v} \tag{2}$$

The change in the speed of the charged particle during the collision with a single electron is very small compared to v; thus v may be put outside the integral sign in eqn. (2).

The kinetic energy T transferred to the electron is given by

$$T = \frac{p^2}{2m} = \frac{2z^2 e^4}{m\, b^2 v^2} \tag{3}$$

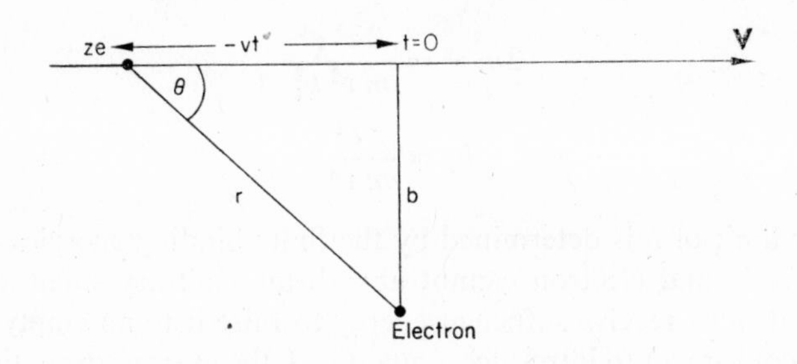

FIG. 1. Moving charged particle (ze) passes stationary electron. The "impact parameter" is b.

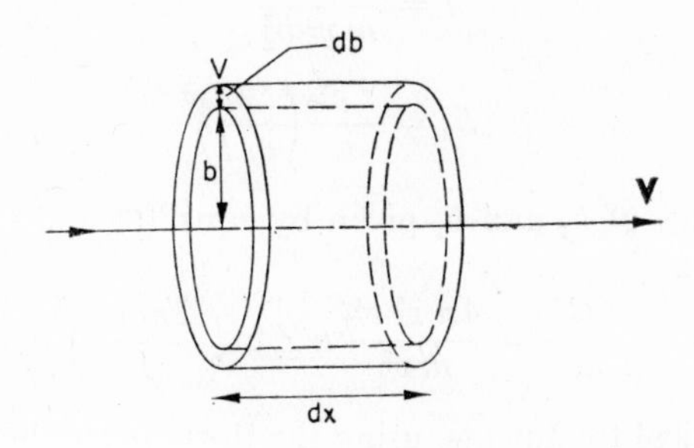

FIG. 2. Electrons lying within cylindrical shell of radii b and $b + d\,b$. The path of the particle is along the axis of the shell.

Now consider the transfer of energy from a charged particle in moving a short distance dx to a cylindrical shell of electrons lying within a distance b to $b + db$ of the path of the particle (Fig. 2). The number of electrons within the shell is $n\, Z\, 2\pi\, b\, d\, b$, where n is the number of atoms per unit volume and Z is the atomic number of the medium. The energy transferred is given by

$$dE = T\, n\, Z\, 2\pi\, b\, db\, dx \tag{4}$$

Thus the energy loss per unit path length of the particle is

$$-\frac{dE}{dx} = \frac{4\pi\, z^2 e^4\, Z\, n}{m\, v^2} \int_{b_1}^{b_2} \frac{db}{b} = \frac{4\pi\, z^2 e^4\, Z\, n}{m\, v^2} \ln \frac{b_2}{b_1} \tag{5}$$

where b_1 and b_2 are the lower and upper limits of the impact parameter b. It seems natural to put $b_1 = 0$ and $b_2 = \infty$; this leads to the result that the rate of loss of energy is infinite! Some finite limits must be found for b in order to obtain a sensible result. The lower limit $b_1 = 0$ is obviously wrong because in a head-on collision eqn. (1) does not apply. In a head-on elastic collision the recoil velocity of the electron is $2v$; thus $T = 2m\,v^2$. It seems plausible to set the lower limit of b by writing

$$2m\,v^2 = \frac{2z^2\,e^4}{m\,v^2\,b_1^2}$$

$$b_1 = \frac{z\,e^2}{m\,v^2} \tag{6}$$

The upper limit of b is determined by the finite binding energies of atomic electrons. A bound electron cannot absorb an arbitrary small amount of energy, as it must receive sufficient energy to raise it to an empty quantum state. It is convenient to introduce a quantity I, the average excitation energy of the atomic electrons of the medium, so that if $T < I$ no energy is transferred. Thus

$$I = \frac{2z^2\,e^4}{m\,v^2\,b_2^2}$$

$$b_2 = \frac{z\,e^2}{v}\left(\frac{2}{m\,I}\right)^{\frac{1}{2}} \tag{7}$$

Inserting the values of b_1 and b_2 given by eqns. (6) and (7) in eqn. (5) we obtain the formula

$$-\frac{dE}{dx} = \frac{4\pi\,z^2\,e^4}{m\,v^2}\,n\,Z\ln\left(\frac{2m\,v^2}{I}\right)^{\frac{1}{2}} \tag{8}$$

Quantum mechanical treatments, using the Born approximation, have been given by H. Bethe (1930) and F. Bloch (1933). The Bethe formula†, taking into account relativistic effects at high particle speeds, is

$$-\frac{dE}{dx} = \frac{4\pi\,z^2\,e^4}{m\,v^2}\,n\,Z\left[\ln\left(\frac{2m\,v^2}{I}\right) - \ln\left(1 - \frac{v^2}{c^2}\right) - \frac{v^2}{c^2}\right] \tag{9}$$

The quantity $-dE/dx$, measured in ergs per cm, is known as the "Stopping power" of the slowing down medium. It is often convenient to divide the stopping power given by eqn. (9) by the density of the medium, thus converting the units of stopping power to ergs per g/cm². In these units the stopping power does not vary much from one medium to another. Values of

† The Born approximation is only valid when $v \gg v_K$, where v_K is the speed of the K shell electrons in the absorbing atoms. Paradoxically the Bethe formula agrees with experiments, even when v is not a lot greater than v_K. A detailed discussion of the slowing down of charged particles is given by J. Ashkin and H. Bethe, in *Experimental Nuclear Physics*, Vol. 1, edited by E. Segrè, pp. 166–357, Wiley, New York 1953.

dE/dx measured in MeV/g/cm² for protons in air over a wide range o kinetic energy E are given in Table 1, and shown graphically in Fig. 3. To obtain $-dE/dx$ in MeV/cm in air at 15°C, 760 mm Hg pressure multiply the figures in column two of the table by the density of air (0·00123 g·cm^{-3}).

The stopping power decreases rapidly (roughly as $1/v^2$) in the particle energy range 1 to 10 MeV. There is a broad minimum in the stopping power at high energies (see Table 1 and Fig. 3). For protons of kinetic energy above 10,000 MeV (10 GeV), the stopping power slowly increases. This increase is associated with the relativistic terms $-\ln(1 - v^2/c^2) - v^2/c^2$ in eqn. (9). Part of this increase arises because the electrical lines of force

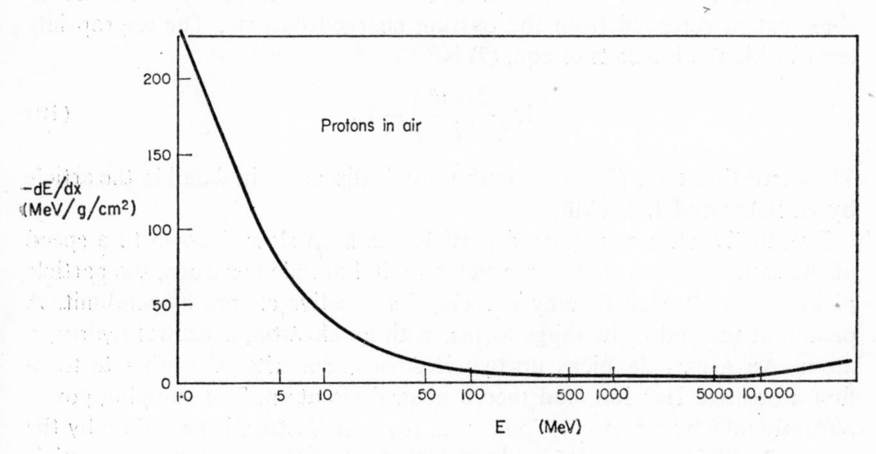

FIG. 3. Plot of Bethe formula for protons ($z = 1$) over a wide energy range (note the logarithmic scale of E).

TABLE 1

E (MeV)	$-dE/dx$ MeV/g/cm²
1·0	238
2·0	145
3·0	107
5·0	74
10·0	42
25	19·3
50	11·0
100	6·4
500	2·45
1000	2·0
2000	1·7
8000	2·0
10,000	2·1

from a high speed charged particle are strongly anisotropic; they concentrate mainly in the transverse direction and thereby increase the strength of the ionizing action of the particle. At very high energies, however, a new effect, not considered by Bethe must be considered. This new effect is connected with the polarization of the atoms of a dielectric stopping medium when the velocity of the charged particle exceeds the phase velocity of light.† Fermi and independently Halpern and Hall have studied the polarization effect quantitatively and shown that it decreases the stopping power below the value predicted by the Bethe formula. For non-relativistic particles, i.e., proton kinetic energy < 10 MeV, the relativistic terms are negligible. In this region, however, the K shell electrons of the stopping atoms are to some extent screened from the passing charged particle. The appropriate term inside the brackets of eqn. (9) is

$$\ln\left(\frac{2m\,v^2}{I}\right) - C_k \tag{10}$$

The correction term C_k and its evaluation is discussed in detail in the article by H. Bethe and J. Ashkin.

Eventually when the charged particle has been slowed down to a speed of the same order as that of the outer orbital atomic electrons, the particle picks up an electron thereby reducing its effective charge by one unit. A proton at the end of its range forms, with an electron, a neutral hydrogen atom. An α-particle picks up two electrons, one after the other to form first a positive He^+ ion, and then a neutral He atom. The stopping power abruptly falls by a factor of four when the first electron is picked up by the α-particle. This is very noticeable near the end of the range of an α-particle in a cloud chamber.

To use the Bethe formula, it is necessary to know the value of the average excitation energy I of all the electrons in an atom of the stopping medium. F. Bloch has shown that a rough rule for calculating I is

$$I = 13{\cdot}5\,Z\ \text{eV}\dagger\dagger \tag{11}$$

Although I does increase with Z, the linear law is an over-simplification of the experimental results. A certain degree of error in the value of I is not very serious as I appears in a logarithmic form in the stopping power formula.

Heavy charged particles, fission fragments, α-particles, deuterons, protons, mesons, rarely experience Rutherford-type nuclear collisions. They travel in straight lines, losing energy discontinuously, but because of the very

† A. Bohr has discussed the close relation between this effect and the emission of Cherenkov radiation. The extra loss of energy due to the emission of Cherenkov radiation by the charged particle is negligible in comparison with the effect of the polarization on the stopping power.

†† It is usual to take a mean value of $Z = 7{\cdot}22$ for an "air" atom (averaged over nitrogen and oxygen).

large number of ions they produce, the process can be regarded as continuous. A heavy charged particle of a given initial kinetic energy E has therefore a well defined straight path length of range R in the stopping medium. Strictly speaking, there are fluctuations in the range about a mean value, as the ionization process is discontinuous (the observed ranges for a given E exhibit a Gaussian distribution around the mean range R). It is very useful in nuclear physics to have empirical formulae or tables of "Range–Energy" relations for different charged particles in various stopping media. It has been shown, for example, that the ranges $R_p(v)$ for protons and $R_\alpha(v)$ for alpha particles, travelling with the same velocity v, in air at 15°C and 760 mm Hg pressure, are related by the formula

$$R_p(v) = 1{\cdot}0072\, R_\alpha(v) - (0{\cdot}30 \pm 0{\cdot}06)\text{ cm} \qquad (12)$$

A useful approximate range–energy formula for protons in the range from a few MeV to about 200 MeV is that due to Brobeck and R. Wilson

$$R = \left(\frac{E}{9{\cdot}3}\right)^{1{\cdot}8} \qquad (13)$$

where R is the range in metres of air at normal temperature and pressure, and E is the kinetic energy of the proton in MeV. At energies below about 2 MeV, the exponent in eqn. (13) is close to 1·5. For α-particles, Geiger as early as 1910, had discovered that in air

$$R = k\, E^{1{\cdot}5} \qquad (14)$$

If an ionizing particle dissipates the whole of its energy E in the gas of an ionization chamber or counter, is it possible to determine the energy of the particle from a measurement of the total number of ion-pairs† formed? The answer is yes, provided the energy W required to produce an ion-pair in the gas is known. Fortunately the value of W is nearly independent of the kinetic energy E of the ionizing particle. For α-particles it is especially constant in argon (variation in W is not greater than 1 per cent). The value of W for Po α-particles (E = 5·3 MeV) is about 28 eV in argon and about 35·5 eV in air. Comparisons of W for fast protons, α-particles, and electrons moving in air, are found to be in the ratio 1·04 : 1 : 0·91. If all the ions set free in an argon-filled counter are collected on the electrodes, a 5·3 MeV α-particle, provided it dissipates all its kinetic energy in the sensitive volume of the counter, will give rise to a charge

$$Q = \frac{E\,e}{W} = \frac{5{\cdot}3 \times 10^{6}}{28} \times 1{\cdot}6 \times 10^{-19}\text{ coulombs} \qquad (15)$$

$$\text{i.e. } Q = 3 \times 10^{-14}\text{ coulombs}$$

† The term ion-pairs refers to an ionization event resulting in the creation of a free electron and a positive ion.

The problem of the energy loss of moving electrons in matter is more complicated than that of heavy charged particles. Moving electrons in matter do *not* move in straight lines; they experience the cumulative effect of a large number of scattering collisions with the atomic electrons. The Bethe formula is modified for electrons on two counts. First, the moving electrons (if non-relativistic) have the same mass as the atomic orbital electrons. The reduced mass of the moving electron is therefore $m/2$. This means that in the first term in the brackets of eqn. (9) we replace $2m\,v^2$ by $m\,v^2$ (for electrons $z = 1$). The second modification was first discussed by Mott, and it is concerned with the fact that in an electron–electron collision, two spin $\frac{1}{2}$ particles, which are *indistinguishable*, interact. For non-relativistic electrons, the stopping power is given by

$$-\frac{dE}{dx} = \frac{4\pi\, e^4\, n\, Z}{m\, v^2} \ln\left[\frac{m\, v^2}{2I}\sqrt{\frac{\varepsilon}{2}}\right] \tag{16}$$

where ε is the base of natural logarithms.

There is little difference in the numerical values given by eqns. (16) and (9) for non-relativistic electrons and protons travelling with the same speed v. The relativistic terms in the electron stopping power formula are more complicated than those in eqn. (9).

At high energies, in addition to the excitation and ionization losses in matter, electrons radiate bremsstrahlung in nuclear collisions. The rate of loss of energy due to radiation is equal to

$$-\left(\frac{dE}{dx}\right)_{\text{rad}} = K\, n\, Z^2\, E \tag{17}$$

where k is a constant, n is the number of atoms per unit volume, Z is the atomic number of the medium, and E is the kinetic energy of the electron. In lead, for example, a 10 MeV electron loses as much energy by radiation as it does by ionization. The corresponding energy for electrons in water is about 100 MeV. Radiative losses for the heavy charged particles are negligble even at the highest laboratory energies.

The function $-\frac{dE}{dx}\Big/W$ for moving charged particles is a measure of the specific ionization s, that is, the number of ion-pairs formed per unit track length. It is sometimes important to distinguish between the primary, s_p, and the total s_t, specific ionizations. The former is defined as the ionization per unit path produced directly by the charged particle. In the majority of ionizing collisions, the ejected electron has a low kinetic energy; occasionally, however, the secondary electron may carry away a kinetic energy as high as $4\left(\frac{m}{M}\right)E$ (in a head-on collision). In a head-on collision between a 20 MeV proton and an electron, the latter recoils with a kinetic energy of 40 keV. This secondary electron, or delta ray, has sufficient energy to produce appreciable ionization. The tracks of delta rays are often seen near the high energy end of the tracks of protons and alpha particles in cloud chamber photographs. A typical delta track in air at S.T.P. is 1 or 2 mm long. The total specific ionization s_t includes the ionization produced by the delta rays. Table 2 gives the approximate values of s_p and s_t for electrons in air at S.T.P. over an energy range 0·02 to 10 MeV.

TABLE 2

E (MeV)	s_p (ion-pairs/cm)	s_t (ion-pairs/cm)
0·02	100	520
0·05	60	250
0·10	44	165
0·20	33	95
0·50	25	55
1·0	22	44
5·0	22	44
10·0	23	46

At high energies, the ratio of s_t and s_p decreases to a constant value of about 2·0.

11.2. THE IONIZATION CHAMBER

The ionization produced by charged particles moving through a gas may be detected as individual voltage pulses in the *pulse ionization chamber*, or as an integrated effect in the *current ionization chamber*. In both instruments, however, it is desirable that all the ions produced by the ionizing radiation are collected on suitable electrodes without significant losses due to recombination of the ions or thermal diffusion out of the sensitive volume of the chamber. The ions are swept to the electrodes by an electric field X. The ratio X/p, where p is the gas pressure (in mm Hg), is *not* high enough in ionization chambers for the liberated electrons to gain sufficient kinetic energy from the applied field to produce additional ion-pairs in travelling to the positively charged electrode.

Charged particles with an initial kinetic energy of a few MeV are brought to "rest" (i.e. to thermal velocities) in condensed media in about 10^{-13} sec. In gases at S.T.P., the slowing down time is of the order of 10^{-9} to 10^{-8} sec. Nevertheless, the ionization track in a gas chamber may be considered to be formed instantaneously. After the primary ionization events, about 10^{-7} sec elapses before all the ionization electrons have kinetic energies less than 10 eV.

Positive ions and heavy negative ions (not electrons), acquire a drift component of velocity $v_\pm$ along the lines of force of the electric field X, which is directly proportional to X/p over a wide range.

$$v_\pm = \mu_\pm \frac{760}{p} X \tag{18}$$

The *ionic mobility* of the ions is defined as the drift velocity in cm per sec in a field of 1 V per cm, at 760 mm Hg pressure and 15°C. Values of $\mu_\pm$ for a few common gases are listed in Table 3.

TABLE 3

Gas	μ_+	μ_-
Air	1·37	1·8
Ar	1·37	1·7
H_2	5·7	8·6
He	5.1	6.3
O_2	1·33	1·80
N_2	1·29	1·82
CO_2	0·79	0·95
CH_3I	0·23	0·23

The mobilities of positive and negative ions are of the same order of magnitude. In electric fields of the order of 1000 V per cm, heavy ions reach the collection electrode in a typical ionization chamber in about 10^{-3} sec. The linear law connecting the drift velocity v and the electric field X is a reflection of the fact that the energy gained by a heavy ion from the electric field is small compared to the thermal agitation energy kT ($X e \lambda \ll k T$, where λ is the collision mean free path of an ion in the gas).

The mobility of free electrons is complicated by the fact that in an elastic collision with a gas molecule an electron loses a very small fraction of its kinetic energy. The electrons drifting in the electric field X may acquire energies which are a lot greater than the thermal energy of the gas molecules. No simple analytic expression is available for the electron drift velocity v_e. At low values of X/p ($X/p < 1$), the drift velocity is proportional to the square root of X/p.

$$v_e = k\left(\frac{X}{p}\right)^{\frac{1}{2}} \tag{19}$$

At high values of X/p, v_e increases more rapidly than the parabolic law. The electron drift velocities are about a thousand times greater than the heavy ion velocities. An important feature of all mobilities is the marked effect of impurity gases or vapours. The addition of 5 per cent of CO_2 to argon increases the electron drift velocity tenfold.† The electron drift velocity in pure argon and in a mixture of 95 per cent argon and 5 per cent carbon dioxide, is given in Table 4 for several values of X/p (the drift velocities are given in units of 10^6 cm per sec).

TABLE 4

Pure Argon		Mixture of Argon (95%) CO_2 (5%)	
X/p	v_e	X/p	v_e
0·05	0·2	0·05	1·0
0·20	0·3	0·20	3.3
0·50	0·4	0·50	5·5
1·0	5	1·0	4·4
1·5	6	1·5	5·5
3·0	10	3·0	4·6

The electrons liberated by the ionizing particle reach the positive electrode of the ionization chamber in about 10^{-6} sec, provided they are not captured during molecular collisions, forming heavy negative ions. Certain gases, the electronegative gases, should not be used if electron capture is to be avoided. Oxygen, water vapour, ammonia and chlorine†† are examples of electronegative gases. The probability of an electron attaching itself to an oxygen molecule at a single collision to form a negative ion varies with kinetic energy of the electron, reaching a maximum probability of 10^{-3}: on average an electron is captured after about a thousand collisions; this will occur in a time much shorter than the electron collection time of 10^{-6} sec.

The individual ionizing particles are recorded as distinct voltage pulses at the electrodes of a pulse ionization chamber. Let us consider the theory in a simple case when a track of n ion-pairs is formed parallel to, and at a distance x_0 from the electron collection electrode (Fig. 4). The electrodes are parallel plates distance d apart, and the chamber gas contains no electronegative components. A voltage V_0 is applied to the electrodes, so that electrons and positive ions drift in opposite directions in a uniform field

† The marked increase in electron drift velocity is a result of the large fall in "electron temperature" on adding a small amount of a polyatomic vapour to the noble gas. The CO_2 molecule, unlike the argon atom, has a number of low-lying electronic energy states which can be excited by electrons moving with an energy of a few eV. This effect reduces the mean kinetic energy of the electrons. The electron mean free path and the time interval between successive molecular collisions increases. Both of these changes contribute to the increase in v_e.

†† The use of the halogen Geiger counter seems to contradict this principle of counter design. However the partial pressure of the electronegative gas is so small that the electron capture process is not serious.

of intensity V_0/d V per cm. The ionization current flowing through the high resistance R (10^8 ohms, say) produces a negative potential pulse $V(t)$ which is amplified by a high gain linear amplifier. The time constant $C R$, where C is the capacitance of the chamber plus the input capacitance of the amplifier, is a lot greater than the electron collection time. It is important to realise that the current through R begins as soon as the electrons and positive ions move apart under the influence of the field X. It can be shown, with

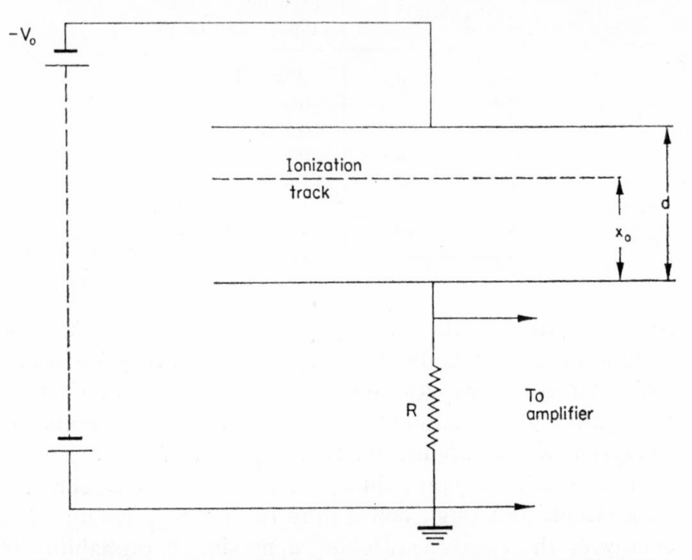

FIG. 4. Parallel plate pulse ionization chamber. Ionization track formed parallel to and at a distance x_0 from the positive electrode.

the aid of Green's theorem in electrostatics, that a single electron induces a charge $q_-(t)$ on the positive electrode at time t, where

$$q_-(t) = -e \times \left[\frac{\text{Potential drop between the electron at time } t \text{ and the } \textit{negative} \text{ electrode}}{\text{Potential drop between the electrodes}}\right] \tag{20}$$

Similarly the charge induced at time t by a single positive ion is given by,

$$q_+(t) = +e \times \left[\frac{\text{Potential drop between ion at time } t \text{ and the } \textit{negative} \text{ electrode}}{\text{Potential drop between the electrodes}}\right] \tag{21}$$

These equations express the result that a charge $\pm e$ induces a charge $\pm f e$ on the positive electrode, where f is the fraction of the number of lines of force from the charge which falls on the positive electrode. The change of potential at the positive electrode at the time t, due to a track of n ion-pairs formed at time $t = 0$, is given by

$$V(t) = n\left[\frac{q_-(t) + q_+(t)}{C}\right] \tag{22}$$

This result is independent of the shape of the potential gradient between the electrodes. In the case of parallel plate geometry, the potential gradient is uniform and eqn. (22) takes the simple form

$$V(t) = \frac{-n\,e\{d - (x_0 - v_e\,t)\} + n\,e(d - x_0)}{C\,d} \tag{23}$$

$$V(t) = -\frac{n\,e\,v_e\,t}{C\,d}, \quad 0 < t < t_e \tag{24}$$

The positive ion drift velocity v_+ is so small compared to the electron drift velocity v_e that during the period 0 to t_e, where t_e is the electron collection time ($x_0 = v_e\,t_e$), the movement of the positive ions is negligible. Hence the appearance of x_0 in the last bracket of the numerator of eqn. (23). For $t > t_e$, there is an abrupt decrease in the rate of rise of potential, the new rate being v_+/v_e times the original rate. The positive ions reach the negative electrode at time $t = t_+$. The potential change at the positive electrode is depicted in Fig. 5. In practice, the time constant $C\,R$, typically 3 or 4 msec ($C = 30$ pF, $R = 100$ MΩ) is not much greater than the ion collection time t_+. This means than an appreciable fraction of the collected charge

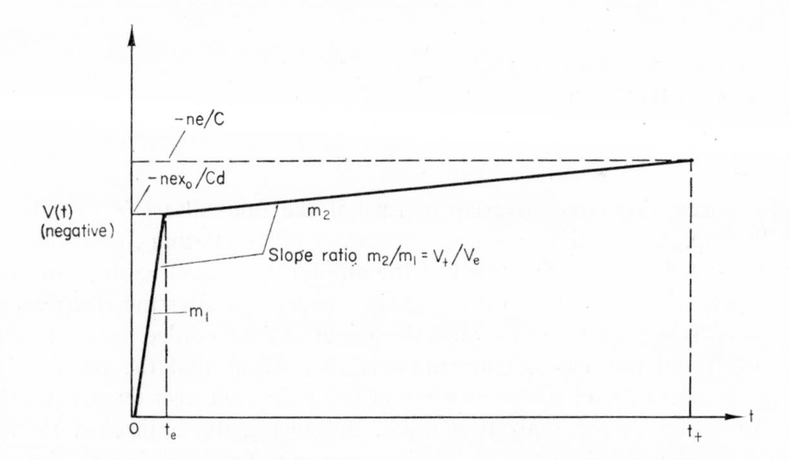

FIG. 5. Shape of potential pulse $V(t)$, for $C\,R \gg t_+$. At $t = t_e$, the electrons reach the collector and the pulse height is $V(t_e) = -\dfrac{n\,e\,x_0}{C\,d}$. At time $t = t_+$, the positive ions reach the negative electrode and V reaches its maximum value of $-n\,e/C$.

on the capacitance will leak away in the time interval t_+. The pulse waveform in Fig. 5 has been drawn, on the assumption that $CR \gg t_+$. An important feature of the voltage pulse $V(t)$ is the dependence of the pulse height $V(t_e)$ on the distance x_0.

$$V(t_e) = -\frac{n e v_e t_e}{C d} = -\frac{n e x_0}{C d} \tag{25}$$

Thus $V(t_e)$ is very small, if the ionization track is produced near the positive electrode. In the event of counting and recording a high flux of ionizing par-

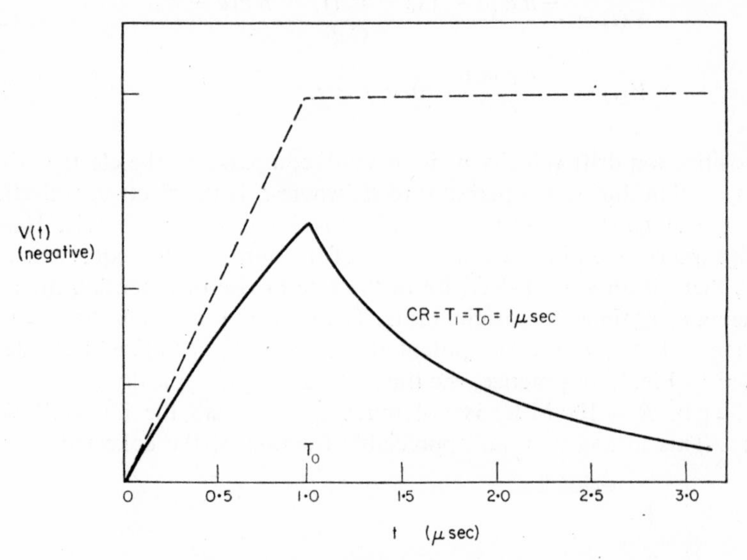

FIG. 6. Ionization chamber pulse "clipped" by short time constant network ($CR = T$).

ticles, succeeding pulses overlap in time if the full pulse $V(t_+)$ is allowed to develop. A short time constant network (a differentiating circuit), usually incorporated in the early stages of the amplifier attached to the ionization chamber, clips the pulse so that the slow linear rise after the electrons are collected is removed (Fig. 6). Thus the height of the recorded pulses depends on $V(t_e)$ and not $V(t_+)$. Unfortunately this means that the pulse height depends not only on n, the number of ion-pairs, but also on the position of formation of the ionization track. In general, the ionization track is not formed parallel to the electrodes. The initial rate of change of potential is given by the derivative of eqn. (24)

$$\frac{dV}{dt} = -\frac{nev_e}{Cd}, \quad 0 < t < t_e \tag{26}$$

If the ionization track is not parallel to the electrodes, eqn. (26) is valid until the *first* electron is collected. After this time the growth of the pulse is no longer linear.

An important modification of the simple parallel plate chamber is achieved by inserting a grid electrode between the original electrodes (Fig. 7). In a typical "gridded-chamber" a grid of many fine wires (0·2 mm diameter), spaced 2 mm apart is mounted about one third of the distance d from the positive electrode. The grid electrode is maintained at a potential of about $-V_0/2$, so that the field between the grid and the high voltage negative

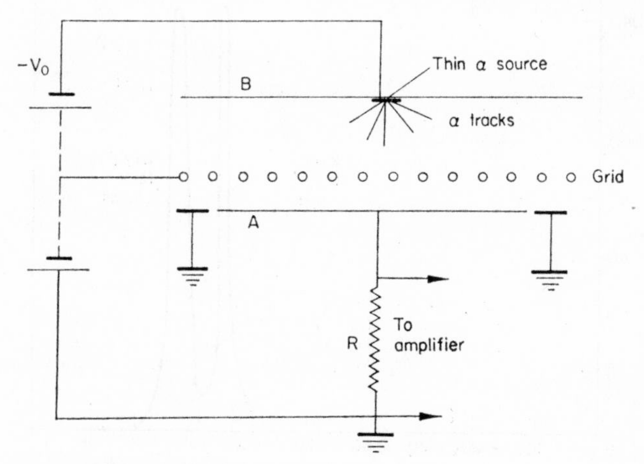

FIG. 7. Grid ionization chamber. Guard ring shown. α source is mounted on the high voltage electrode B. (Gas-tight chamber is not shown.)

electrode is weaker than the field between the grid and the positive electrode. If the complete range of an ionizing particle is confined to the region between the grid and the negative electrode, the grid electrode effectively screens the positive electrode from the electrons and ions. The lines of force from the electrons and ions terminate on the negative and grid electrodes. However, as soon as the electrons have drifted through the grid electrode they induce a change of potential at the positive electrode. Meanwhile, the positive ions slowly drifting towards the negative electrode have no effect as they are screened from the other electrode by the grid. The height of the pulse due to the induction effect of the moving electrons increases to a maximum value when all the electrons are collected. The maximum pulse height is

$$V_{max} = -\frac{ne}{C} \tag{27}$$

The gridded ionization chamber has the marked advantage that the maximum pulse height is independent of the position and orientation of the ionization track, provided the ionizing track is formed above the grid electrode. The advantages of the gridded pulse ionization chamber are shown in the good resolution achieved in discriminating between the pulses produced by the α-particles of U^{234} (4·74 MeV) and U^{238} (4·18 MeV). Figure 8 depicts the distribution in height of the pulses obtained with a gridded ionization chamber designed by Staub and Nicodemus. The electrodes are circular discs of diameter about 2 in.; an annular guard ring is

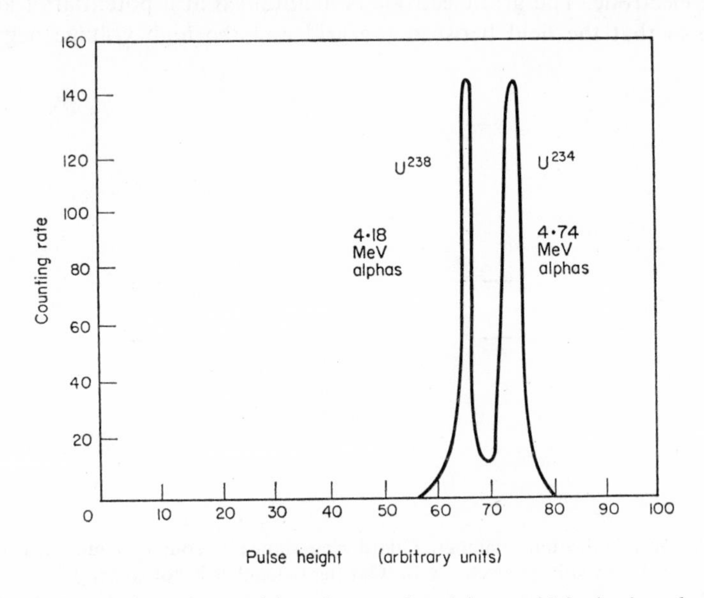

FIG. 8. Resolution of α-particle pulses produced in a grid ionization chamber.

used to produce a uniform field. The chamber is filled with argon at a pressure of 7·5 atm so that the ranges of the α-particles, emitted by a thin uranium source mounted on the high voltage (negative) electrode, are less than the distance between this electrode and the grid (0·5 in.). The grid is located 0·25 in. from the positive electrode. The height of the amplified pulses from an ionization chamber is given by

$$V = \frac{A E e}{W C} \tag{13}$$

where A is the voltage gain of the electronic amplifier (typically 10^5 to 10^6), E is the energy of the ionizing particle, W is the mean energy to produce an ion-pair in the gas of the chamber. Unfortunately, for ionizing particles of low energy, for example soft β-rays of energy less than 50 keV, the pulse developed across the high resistance R is masked by the noise pulses at the input stage to the amplifier. A useful figure to remember is that the ionizing particle must produce about 2000 or more ion-pairs in the gas of the chamber in order to produce pulses detectable against the noise background.

11.3. THE PROPORTIONAL COUNTER

The problem of detecting low energy ionizing particles with the ionization chamber becomes very difficult when the pulse height is less than about 30 μV. A great improvement in the signal-to-noise ratio at the input stage of the electronic amplifier is obtained if *gas amplification* of the ionization produced inside the gas counter occurs.

It has been known since the time of the pioneer work of J. S. Townsend at the beginning of this century that electrons drifting through a gas under the influence of a strong electric field produce ionization by collision with molecules of the gas. The effect is represented by the *first Townsend coefficient* α. This is defined as the average number of ion-pairs formed by an electron drifting unit length in the direction of the electric field. The experimental values of α at different pressures and field strengths are most conveniently represented graphically by plotting α/p against X/p. An approximate empirical formula given by Townsend† is

$$\frac{\alpha}{p} = A\,p \exp\left(-\frac{B\,p}{X}\right) \tag{14}$$

where A and B are constants.

For values of X/p less than about one, α/p is very small for all gases. In pure argon α/p rises slowly at low values of X/p and reaches values of 0·8, 2·1, 4·5, at X/p values of 50, 100, and 200, respectively.

The electrons ejected from molecules by the ionizing particle, including those set free by δ-rays, drift towards the positive electrode. If they move in a region where X/p is high, they will produce additional ionization by collisions with molecules of the gas. In drifting a short distance dx, n electrons will increase the number of electrons to $n + dn$ where

$$dn = \alpha\, n\, dx$$

Thus if n_0 is the number of electrons set free by the ionizing particle and they *all* drift a distance x to the positive electrode, the number of electrons reaching this electrode is

$$n = n_0 \exp\left[\int_0^x \alpha\, dx\right] \tag{15}$$

The ratio n/n_0 is called the *gas amplification A*. To achieve a useful degree of gas amplification with parallel plate geometry, excessively high voltage

† A simple derivation of this approximate formula is given p. 59–60 in J. M. Meek and J. D. Craggs, *Electrical Breakdown of Gases*, Oxford 1953.

gradients (greater than 3000 V per cm at 760 mm Hg) are required. For this reason, coaxial cylinder geometry of the electrodes is preferred. The electric field X is given by

$$X = \frac{V_0}{x \ln\left(\frac{b}{a}\right)} \tag{16}$$

where V_0 is the potential difference between the electrodes, b and a are the radii of the cathode and anode respectively, and x is the distance from the central axis of symmetry. In contrast to the parallel plate counter, the field strength increases from the cathode to the anode. If the anode is a fine wire so that $b \gg a$ (b is usually 1000 a), a very strong field exists close to the anode wire without V_0 being excessive. This means that most of the gas amplification occurs close to the anode, usually within the last 0·1 mm of the electron's path. The difficulty of calculating the gas amplification, with the aid of eqn. (15), lies in the complicated dependence of α on x in the region of interest. Nevertheless, by making reasonable assumptions and averages, Rose and Korff† obtained the following expression for the gas amplification.

$$A = \exp\left[2\left\{\frac{f N a V_0}{\ln\left(\frac{b}{a}\right)}\right\}^{\frac{1}{2}}\left\{\left(\frac{V_0}{V_p}\right)^{\frac{1}{2}} - 1\right\}\right] \tag{17}$$

where N is the number of molecules per unit volume,

V_0 is the voltage between the electrodes,

V_p is the threshold voltage for proportional counting, i.e. if $V_0 < V_p$ no gas amplification is produced. The parameter f, a property of the molecules of the filling gas, is the rate of increase of the ionization cross section with electron kinetic energy ε. The theory assumes that in the range of ε of interest, the ionization cross section σ increases linearly with ε, once ε has risen above the ionization energy of the gas. Values of f for a few important gases are given in Table 5. A high value of f in a proportional counter is useful as large gas amplification can be obtained with moderate operating voltage (1 kV). Argon and methane have this desirable property.

The equation of Rose and Korff was derived assuming that the only source of gas amplification is the ionizing collisions of electrons with molecules of the gas. At very low values of A (< 10) the formula is not very useful as it neglects the statistical fluctuations inherent in the electron avalanche process. For moderate values of A, in the range 100 to 1000, the formula agrees reasonably well with experiment. However, at higher values of A ($\sim 10^4$), in gases of simple structure (argon, neon, hydrogen),

† M. E. Rose and S. A. Korff, *Phys. Rev.* **59**, 850, 1941.

the observed gas amplification is found to be considerably greater than the theoretical value given by eqn. (17). This increase is associated with photons of ultraviolet radiation emitted by excited atoms. A small fraction of these

TABLE 5

Gas	f (cm^2/V)
Helium	$0{\cdot}11 \times 10^{-17}$
Neon	$0{\cdot}14 \times 10^{-17}$
Argon	$1{\cdot}81 \times 10^{-17}$
Hydrogen	$0{\cdot}46 \times 10^{-17}$
Methane	$1{\cdot}24 \times 10^{-17}$

photons release electrons by the photoelectric effect at the cathode. The photoelectrons move towards the central wire and produce fresh Townsend avalanches close to the wire. This effect is undesirable and tends to produce unstable operation of counters filled with pure noble gases at gas amplifications above 1000. The addition of a polyatomic gas or vapour, e.g. methane, to neon or argon prevents the instability associated with the cathode photoelectric effect. The majority of the photons emitted by the atoms excited close to the anode wire will be absorbed by the methane before reaching the cathode.

The voltage pulse developed at the central wire of a proportional counter is closely related to the motion of the positive ions, the majority of which are formed within a fraction of a millimetre of the anode. The electrons collected on the wire do not immediately produce a large potential pulse, as the induced charge of the positive ions effectively annuls the collected negative charge. The initial rise of the pulse is determined by the drift velocity of the positive ions as they recede from the anode. This velocity is at first high, as the ions are in a region of very strong electric field, and the pulse quickly reaches its half-value amplitude (Fig. 9). However, over most of their drift path, the positive ions move in a weak field and may take as long as 10^{-3} sec to reach the cathode. It is important that no electrons should be released when the positive ions reach the cathode otherwise new avalanches would occur. Again, a counter filled with a pure noble gas is unsatisfactory. A positive ion of argon, for example, becomes neutralized close to the cathode surface by pulling an electron out of the surface,

$$Ar^+ + e^- \rightarrow Ar + (I - W)$$

the energy liberated $(I - W)$, the ionization energy I minus the work function W of the surface†, is radiated as light. If a photon of this

† W is usually of the order of 4 or 5 eV.

recombination radiation has sufficient energy it may eject an electron from the cathode. Obviously the process is impossible, if $I < 2W$. Unfortunately for most gases, $I > 2W$. With a mixture of 90 per cent argon and 10 per cent ethyl alcohol vapour or methane, each argon ion experiences a thousand or more collisions with neutral complex molecules before reaching the cathode. This means that no argon ions reach the cathode. They exchange charge with an alcohol molecule during one of the collisions:

$$Ar^+ + C_2H_5\,OH \rightarrow Ar + C_2H_5\,OH^+ + (I_1 - I_2)$$

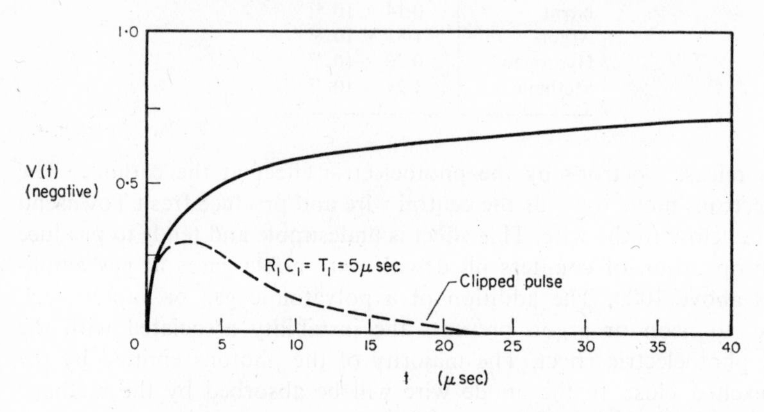

FIG. 9. Typical pulse at the anode wire of a proportional counter. Notice the initial rapid rise to about half the pulse height in a few microseconds, followed by the slow rise as the positive ions drift slowly to the cathode.

The excess energy $(I_1 - I_2)$ is the difference in the ionization potential of argon (15·7 V) and ethyl alcohol (11·3 V) and appears as light or kinetic energy of the colliding bodies. Notice that the reverse process is energetically impossible. The neutralization of the alcohol ions at the cathode is associated, not with radiation, but with the dissociation of the complex molecule into two or more atomic fragments.

The proportional counter has proved to be a versatile detector. The great advantage over the gridded ion chamber is the possibility of measuring the energy of very soft radiations (e.g. the low energy β-rays of tritium, 18 keV maximum). The gas amplification is sufficient to offset the low ionization in the counter. With well-stabilized voltage supplies and carefully designed counters, the pulse size from the counter should be proportional to the energy dissipated by the ionizing particle in the gas of the counter. Successful counters have been operated over a wide range of pressure and temperature; from 1 cm of Hg up to 50 atm, and up to 800°C. End effects in the geometry of counters can be greatly reduced by suitable guard electrodes. One method is illustrated in Fig. 10. Guard tubes at earth potential are insulated from the surrounding field tubes which are held at the correct potential to minimize distortion of the radial electric field.

Large proportional tubes have been used in the study of radioactive samples of low specific activity. Internal sources are prepared by evaporating the radioactive material on to very thin films cemented on to rectangular frames mounted inside the counter. Counters as long as 3 ft and 1 ft in diameter filled with an argon–methane mixture to a pressure of two atmospheres have been used. The counter is mounted in an axial magnetic field of a few thousand gauss to constrain the β-rays to helical paths. This ensures that moderate energy β-rays (500 keV) produce all their ionization within the sensitive volume of the chamber. In spite of the low stopping

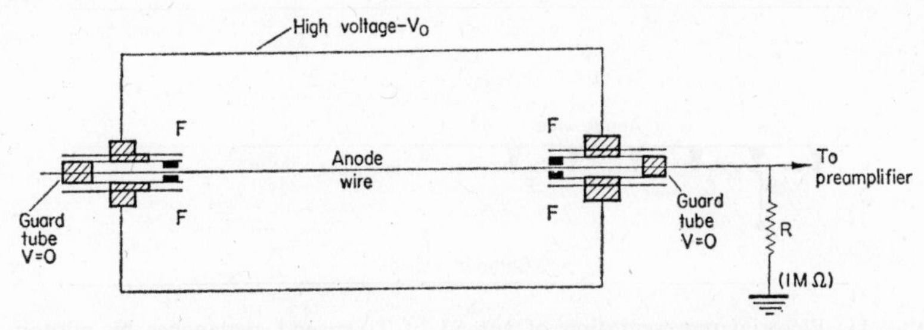

FIG. 10. Cylindrical proportional counter, fitted with guard tubes at earth potential and field tubes at a potential $V = -V_0[\log(r/a)/\log(b/a)]$, where r is the radius of the field tubes.

power of gases, the gas proportional counter has a much better energy resolution, especially for low energy radiation, than the scintillation counter.

11.4. THE GEIGER COUNTER

The Geiger or Geiger–Müller counter is a development of the point counter invented by Geiger in 1908. In its modern form it consists of a fine wire (usually tungsten) mounted along the axis of a cylindrical cathode mounted inside a glass or metal envelope filled with a suitable gas mixture. The applied voltage, with the wire potential positive, is high enough for extensive gas amplification to occur close to the wire. The essential difference between the proportional and Geiger counter is that in the latter the charge collected on the central wire is *independent* of the initial ionization produced by the ionizing particle. The voltage pulse developed across the resistor (typically a few megohms) connected between the anode wire and the high voltage supply may be as large as ten volts. Little or no amplification of the output pulse is required for operating a recording or scaling unit. When it is realized that the formation of only one ion-pair in the sensitive volume of the counter may give rise to an output pulse of 10 V or more amplitude, the high sensitivity of the device is obvious. This, in many applications, is a disadvantage, as the Geiger tube cannot discriminate between particles of different ionizing power, and the output pulse amplitude is not proportional to the energy of the particle detected.

What is the difference in the mode of operation of the proportional and Geiger tubes? The difference lies in the higher gas amplification in the Geiger tube, to such a degree, that the electron (Townsend) avalanches formed close to the anode wire produce new avalanches close to the original ones. These in turn produce new avalanches so that in a very short time a dense positive ion sheath is formed around the whole length of the central wire.

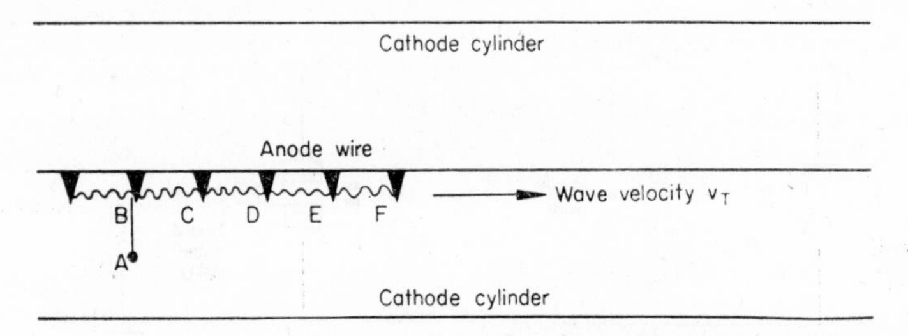

FIG. 11. Pictorial representation of spread of Townsend avalanches by photon emission and absorption. One ion-pair formed at A is responsible for initial avalanche. Wave velocity is about 10 cm/μsec.

The propagation of photoelectric avalanches occurs through the emission and subsequent photoelectric absorption of photons by molecules of the gas. A typical velocity of propagation of the avalanche formation parallel to the anode wire is 10^7 cm/sec. Nearly all modern counters take advantage of the important discovery made in 1937 by Trost† that the addition of a certain proportion of polyatomic vapour such as ethyl alcohol or ethyl acetate produces a *self-quenching* counter. The advantage of adding the polyatomic vapour has been discussed in the previous section with reference to the operation of the proportional counter. The polyatomic vapour exhibits very strong absorption in the short ultraviolet region of the spectrum. This means that ultraviolet photons emitted by excited atoms and molecules in a Townsend avalanche are not likely to travel more than a millimetre through the gas before being absorbed by the photoelectric process. No ultraviolet photons succeed in reaching the cathode and the Townsend avalanches propagate close to the anode wire. A pictorial representation of the spread of the discharge in a Geiger counter is given in Fig. 11. The process of charge exchange during collisions prevents any argon ion reaching

† A. TROST, *Z. Physik* **105**, 399, 1937.

the cathode, thereby preventing the release of any electrons from the cathode, which would trigger off a second discharge. The original Townsend avalanches occurring all along the length of the central wire are quenched by the considerable reduction in field strength close to the wire by the dense positive ion space charge†. The growth of the potential pulse at the anode is determined by the motion of the positive ion sheath as it is repelled away from the high field region. If a second ionizing event occurs before the first positive ion sheath has travelled more than about halfway across the counter, no second pulse is recorded. This is because the field close to the anode wire is still below the Geiger threshold. The time during which the counter is completely insensitive is known as the *dead time* and is typically two hundred or more microseconds. Even after the dead time is over, there is an additional *recovery time* during which a smaller output pulse is produced by an ionizing particle. The dead time plus recovery time may be as long as five hundred microseconds and corresponds to the time it takes the positive ion sheath to reach the cathode. Very high counting speeds are not possible with Geiger counters and it is standard practice to reduce the high potential supply to the counter by two hundred volts or so for a definite time interval τ—the paralysis time—immediately following the initial rise of the Geiger pulse. This is usually achieved by means of a relaxation oscillator triggered by the steep rise of the Geiger pulse. Thus if n_0 is the observed counting rate of a Geiger counter, with paralysis time circuit incorporated, the true counting period is reduced by $n_0 \tau$ units. Thus the "true" counting rate is given by

$$n = \frac{n_0}{1 - n_0 \tau} \tag{18}$$

where τ is the paralysis time, typically 500 μsec.

An important feature of the Geiger counter is the shape and slope of its "plateau curve". This is a plot of the recorded counting rate in a constant flux of radiation, when the voltage applied to the Geiger tube is varied. A typical plateau is shown in Fig. 12. V_G represents the threshold of the Geiger region, below this voltage the size of the output pulses show a considerable spread in size and some of them are not recorded. It should be emphasized that the precise shape of the knee of the plateau curve is partly a property of the associated recording circuit. A good Geiger tube has a plateau extending two hundred or more volts and the slope of the plateau may increase by less than 1 per cent in counting rate, per hundred volt increase.

Geiger counter tubes have a limited life. This is associated with the gradual decomposition of the organic vapour when the positive ions become

† It is in fact the reduction in field strength due to space charge at high gas amplifications that leads to the breakdown of the "proportional counting region".

neutralized at the cathode and dissociate into molecular fragments. Many counters have a maximum useful life of about 10^{10} counts. Towards the end of the useful life of a counter the gas pressure slowly increases due to the increase in molecular fragments; this pushes up the Geiger threshold voltage and in some cases the flatness of the plateau curve is greatly reduced. This may occur with counters which use ethyl alcohol as the quenching agent; OH fragments produced by dissociation may attract electrons in the gas discharge and form heavy negative ions OH^-. The presence of heavy negative ions gives rise to steep plateau curves. One advantage of

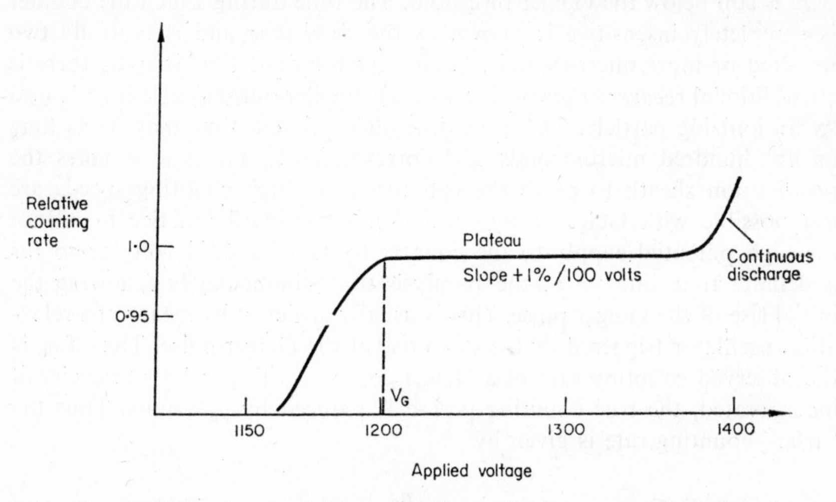

FIG. 12. Geiger counter "plateau curve". Counter is never used in region of continuous discharge.

ethyl acetate as a quenching agent is that its decomposition products are less likely to capture electrons and form heavy negative ions. Certain organic compounds including methane and propane tend to polymerize and should be avoided as quenching agents.

Geiger counters have a very low intrinsic efficiency for detecting gamma radiation. The probability of no ion-pairs being formed in the gas of the counter is equal to

$$\exp(-s\,l\,p)$$

where s is the specific ionization at one atmosphere, p the pressure in atmospheres, and l the path length of the radiation through the sensitive volume of the chamber. With counters filled with argon as the main constituent at a typical pressure of $^1/_5$ atm, the efficiency of detection of a small counter for electrons at their minimum specific ionization is greater than 99·5 per cent. For photons, however, there is only a very small probability ($<1\%$) that an ion-pair is produced directly in the filling gas.

Detection of the photon is more likely to occur through the ejection of a photoelectron from the cathode cylinder into the sensitive volume of the gas. The probability of photoelectric absorption increases as Z^4, where Z is the atomic number of the cathode. Counters using bismuth or lead cathodes have been used for gamma detection but the efficiency is usually not greater than 1 or 2 per cent. To detect radiation of very small penetrating power, counters with very thin end windows are used. Thin end windows of mica, cellophane, or glass only 1 or 2 mg/cm^2 thick will allow α-particles to pass into the sensitive volume of the counter (Fig. 13a). For detecting beta radiation end window counters are used as well as thin walled glass counters which allow the entry of β-rays from all directions. In the latter

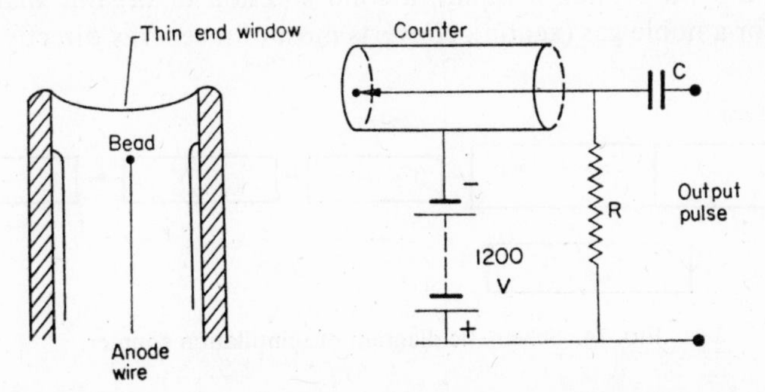

FIG. 13. (a) Thin end window (alpha) counter. Bead on end of anode wire and flare at the end of the cathode cylinder. (b) Basic circuit of Geiger counter.

type of counter, the cathode is often a thin layer of colloidal carbon deposited on the inner wall of the glass envelope. For detecting cosmic rays more robust counters sometimes two or three feet long are used.

There are applications where the use of low voltage counters is a great advantage due to the considerable saving in weight (e.g. in rocket borne counter experiments). The normal argon–ethyl alcohol counter operates at a voltage in the range 1000 to 1400 V. Successful counters have been produced which require a voltage supply as low as 300 or 400 V. A typical filling is 0·05 mm of chlorine, 0·20 mm of argon, and 10 cm of neon. Although the halogens are electronegative and tend to form heavy negative ions the effect is not serious at such low partial pressures. Much thicker anode wires (up to 0·03 in.) can be used and stainless steel cathode cylinders, instead of the usual copper, are used so corrosion does not occur.

11.5. THE SCINTILLATION COUNTER

The early α-particle scattering experiments carried out by Rutherford, Geiger, and Marsden made use of the property of individual α-particles to excite visible luminescence in a zinc sulphide screen. The observations of scintillations through low power microscopes are very tedious, and are severely limited to relatively low counting rates (a hundred a min). For this reason more attention was paid to the development of gas counters and the early form of scintillation counter soon became obsolete.

Soon after 1945 a great revival of interest in the possibilities of scintillation counting came about through the invention of the photomultiplier tube and the intensive study of the luminescent properties of many inorganic and organic crystals. Today it is fair to say that the scintillation counter is the most versatile and widely used detector in nuclear physics. A purely schematic diagram of a scintillation detection unit is shown in Fig. 14. A charged particle moving through a suitable luminescent material, which may be a solid crystal, a liquid, a solid solution of organic material in a plastic, or a noble gas (xenon), converts most of its energy directly into heat.

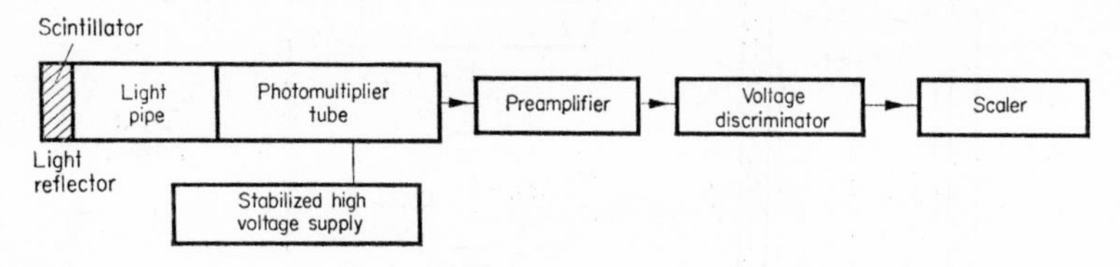

FIG. 14. Schematic diagram of scintillation counter.

A certain fraction C of the energy lost, the conversion efficiency, appears as luminescent radiation emitted in the visible and near ultraviolet spectral regions by excited molecules of the scintillator. The emission of luminescence continues for some time after the stopping or passage of the charged particle. The light intensity of this *phosphorescent* radiation decays exponentially with a mean lifetime T which is an important property of the luminescent material from the viewpoint of suitability as a nuclear radiation detector. A certain fraction of the luminescent photons succeeds in reaching the semi-transparent light sensitive cathode of the photomultiplier tube. Sometimes it is necessary to separate the scintillator from the photomultiplier tube by several feet. A suitable Perspex block guides the light by total internal reflection from the scintillator to the cathode of the photomultiplier.

There are several types of photomultiplier construction in common use in scintillation counting. One of the commonest types is illustrated in Fig. 15. A semi-transparent Cs–Sb cathode is deposited on the inside of the end of a high vacuum envelope. Cathodes of this type have a maximum response to light at the blue end of the spectrum. Photoelectrons ejected from the thin cathode surface are accelerated towards the first *dynode* electrode D_1. This has a venetian blind structure and the surface of the electrode is covered with a layer of material with a high secondary emission coefficient m. Common deposits used to coat the dynodes are Cs–Sb or Ag–Mg. A photomultiplier tube may have as many as thirteen dynodes, each one being maintained at a positive potential of a hundred volts with respect to the previous one. The electron beam current is multiplied by the secondary emission factor at each dynode so that typically the number of electrons reaching the final anode is a million or more times the number of electrons reaching the first dynode.

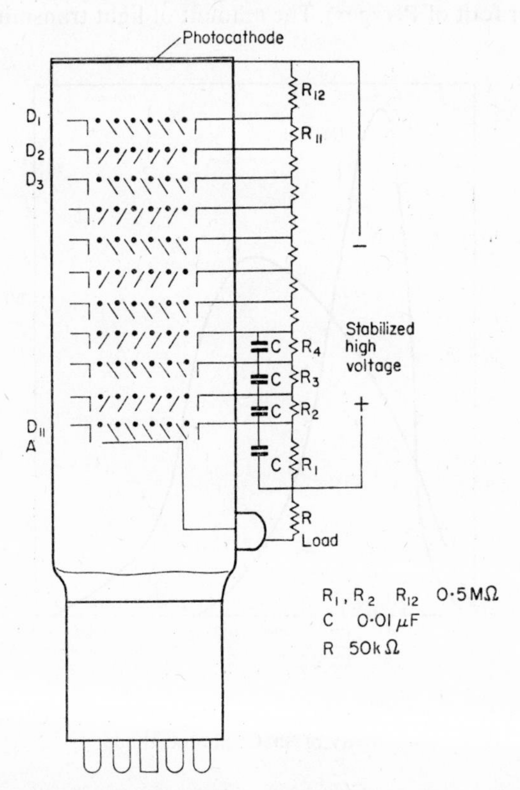

FIG. 15. Photomultiplier tube with eleven dynodes ("venetian blind" type). Wire grids above dynodes act as electrostatic screens. Potential divider chain of resistors $R_1, R_2, \ldots R_{12}$ supplies d.c. voltage to dynodes. R is the anode load. Note the 0·01 μF decoupling capacitors in the last few stages.

The pulse of charge q arriving at the final anode of the photomultiplier tube, due to the stopping of a charged particle of kinetic energy E in the scintillator, is given by

$$q = \left(\frac{E\,C}{W}\right)(T\,G)\;S\,F\,M\,e \qquad (19)$$

C is the conversion efficiency of the scintillator, that is the fraction of the energy lost by the charged particle which is converted into luminescent radiation. W is the mean photon energy of the luminescent radiation (for a sodium iodide–thallium activated crystal at room temperature W corresponds to a wavelength of 4200 Å, i.e. $W \sim 3$ eV). Thus the three factors in the first parentheses of eq. (19) represent the mean number of photons of luminescent radiation produced in the scintillator. Some of this radiation is absorbed in the scintillator (and light pipe if attached—typically 40 per cent is absorbed per foot of Perspex). The amount of light transmitted is denoted

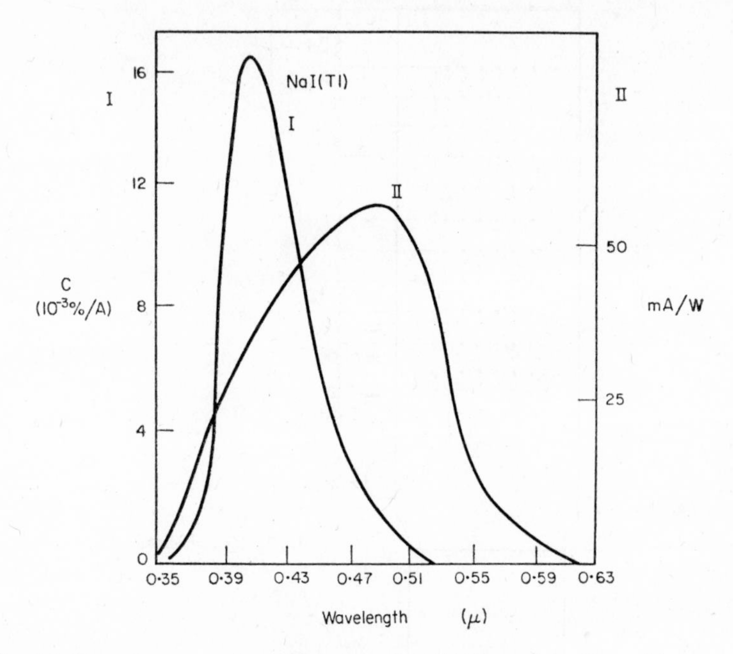

FIG. 16. Curve I: conversion efficiency of NaI(Tl) crystal; Curve II: spectral sensitivity of Sb–Cs photocathode.

by the transparency factor T. G is a geometrical factor which represents the fraction of photons which should reach the cathode of the photomultiplier if $T = 1$. G can be enhanced by surrounding the crystal with aluminium foil to reflect light originally travelling away from the cathode of the tube. The crystal or light pipe should be in good optical contact with the end window of the photomultiplier tube. A fraction S of the photons reaching the cathode eject electrons into the space between the cathode and the dynode D_1. This factor depends on the degree of overlap of the luminescent spectrum and the spectral response curve of the photocathode (Fig. 16). Some of the photoelectrons are not collected by the first dynode which is at a positive potential with respect to the cathode. F, represents the fraction of the photoelectrons reaching the first dynode. This factor is very susceptible to the influence of magnetic fields and for this reason the photomultiplier tube, in its light-tight box, is mounted inside a mu-metal screen. One of the practical reasons for using an intermediate light pipe is to remove the photomultiplier from stray magnetic fields which may be present near the scintillator. If there are N dynodes and the secondary emission coefficient m is the same for all dynodes (this assumes a constant inter-dynode voltage) then the gain of the tube is

$$M = m^N \tag{20}$$

Values of M as high as a million are typical. The gain M is very sensitive to changes in the supply voltage to the potential divider chain of resistors connected to the dynodes (M increases roughly as V^7, where V is the applied voltage). Multiplying the number of electrons reaching the anode by the electron charge e we obtain the expression (19) for the pulse of charge arriving at the anode. The pulse of electrons arriving at the anode charges the capacitance C between anode and earth to a potential difference

$$V = \frac{q}{C}$$

The charge then leaks away through the anode load resistance R at an exponential rate determined by the time constant CR (if C = 20 pF and R = 25 kΩ, CR = 0·5 μsec.). The spread in the arrival time of the electrons at the anode of the photomultiplier tube is partly due to the variation in transit time of the electrons through the tube† but is mainly determined by the decay time of the luminescent radiation (the 10^{-13} sec or so during which the charged particle slows down to rest in the scintillator is negligible in this context). With organic scintillators the decay time $\tau \ll 10^{-6}$ sec; and the output capacitance C charges in a time of the order of 10^{-8} sec or less. Substituting typical values for the factors in eqn. (19), for example, C = 0·10 for a 1 MeV β-ray in NaI(Tl), W = 3 eV, T = 0·5, G = 0·5, S = 0·02, F = 0·50, $M = 10^6$, a potential pulse of amplitude 0·7 V is produced across the capacitance C (20 pF) by a 1 MeV β-ray. The size of the output pulse is, in principle, proportional to the energy dissipated by the charged particle in the scintillator. It is found, however, that some crystals, especially organic ones, give a non-linear relation between particle energy and pulse height for low energy particles (electrons below 100 keV in stilbene). In addition, however, to the behaviour of the scintillator the various factors in eqn. (19) are all subject to statistical fluctuations,

† This variation is most marked in the venetian blind type of tube. The electrons emitted from each dynode move at first in a weak field which is responsible for the major part of the transit time. It is interesting to note that E. Bergstrand attributes the significant difference in Anderson's determination of the velocity of light (1941) and his own determination (1949) to the variation in transit time of photoelectrons released from different regions of the cathode of the photomultiplier tube.

and the height of the output pulse V exhibits variations about the mean value for a given particle energy E. For low energy radiation the resolution of the scintillation spectrometer is poorer than that of a well-designed gas proportional counter. The resolution R of a scintillation counter is defined by the relation

$$\frac{1}{R} = \frac{\overline{q^2} - (\bar{q})^2}{(\bar{q})^2} \tag{21}$$

where $\bar{q}$ is the mean charge collected at the anode and $\overline{q^2}$ is the mean squared charge collected at the anode. Finite resolution arises due to variation in

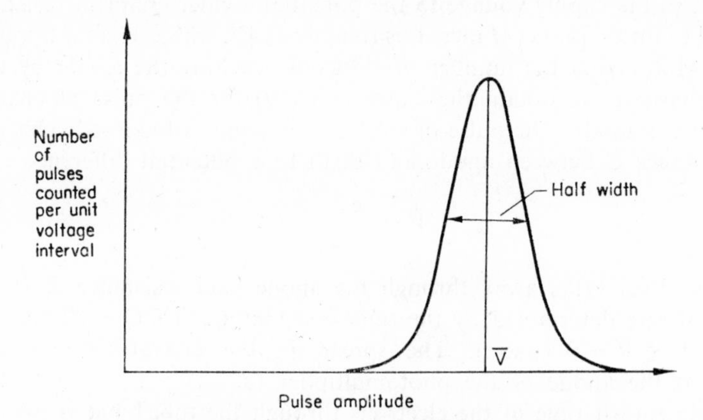

FIG. 17. Diagram illustrating finite energy resolution of scintillation spectrometer. Variation in pulse amplitude for monoenergetic beta particles. The smaller the halfwidth the higher the energy resolution R.

the number of photons emitted in the scintillator, variations in the positions of origin of these photons, and hence in the factors T and G. An important variation in q is associated with the photoelectric emission from the cathode, which follows Poisson's distribution law. Effects due to variation in sensitivity over the surface of the cathode and thermionic emission may be important. The latter effect is sometimes reduced by cooling the photomultiplier tube. Fluctuations in the number of secondary electrons released per incident primary electron on a dynode are less serious the higher the value of m. There is a limit set by the total voltage that can be applied to the photomultiplier tube. One of the best ways of obtaining the best resolution possible is to make sure that the number of electrons reaching the first dynode is as high as possible. The spread in pulse amplitude for monoenergetic α-particles is illustrated in Fig. 17.

Two marked advantages of the scintillation over the gas proportional counter arise from the shorter duration pulse of the former with the possibilities of faster counting rates and much higher resolution coincidence experiments. The stopping power of solid and liquid scintillators is much higher than that of a gas. This is important in the detection of gamma radiation where detection efficiencies as high as 20 per cent have been achieved in sharp contrast to the low efficiencies of gas counters. Sodium iodide crystals activated with a trace of thallium have been proved to be efficient detectors of gamma radiation. The high atomic number of iodine, 53, is associated with large photoelectric absorption and electron–positron pair production cross sections for gamma photons. The spectrum of pulse amplitudes produced in a scintillation spectrometer with a NaI(Tl) crystal

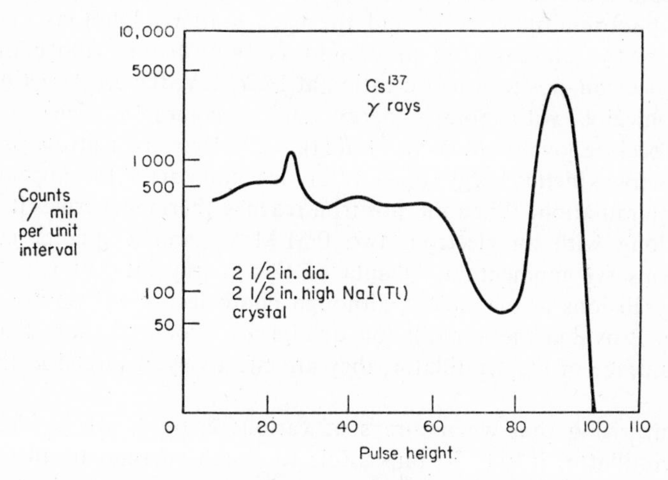

FIG. 18. Pulse height distribution for 662 keV Cs^{137} γ-rays incident on NaI(Tl) crystal.

bombarded with Cs^{137} gamma rays is shown in Fig. 18. The distribution of pulse amplitudes for monoenergetic γ-rays is complicated by the various interaction processes of the gamma quanta, and the finite size of the crystal. Gamma quanta interact with electrons and the Coulomb field of the nuclei in the crystal by photoelectric absorption, Compton scattering, and, for $E_\gamma > 2mc^2$ (1·02 MeV), by electron–positron creation. If the bound atomic electron, usually a K electron, ejected in the photoelectric absorption of a γ-ray does not escape from the surface of the scintillator before dissipating its kinetic energy, the light output from the crystal corresponds to the full γ-ray energy. This *photopeak* in the pulse height distribution of the light pulses due to 662 keV gamma rays absorbed in a NaI(Tl) crystal is clearly shown in Fig. 18. The 30 keV X-ray emitted by an iodine atom following the photoelectric ejection of a K shell electron is easily absorbed in the crystal and the light energy is not sufficiently delayed to be resolved in time from the initial light flash. For photons of energy less than 250 keV photoelectric absorption is more likely than Compton scattering in NaI(Tl). Above this energy, until E_γ exceeds 70 MeV, when pair creation is the dominant process, Compton scattering is the most important process. The important aspect of a Compton photon-electron interaction in gamma spectroscopy is the variable amount of energy transferred to the recoiling electron. Unfortunately, this means that, if the scattered photon escapes from the scintillator, the light pulse produced by the recoiling electron can vary in energy from a low value up to a value corresponding to the maximum recoil kinetic energy of the electron. Sometimes a Compton collision will occur in nearby material, for instance in the window of a photomultiplier tube, and the back scattered photons may be absorbed by the photoelectric process in the scintillator. Above the threshold for electron–positron pair creation at 1·02 MeV, the cross section rises monotonically with γ-ray energy and becomes a significant absorption process above 50 MeV in NaI(Tl). The electron–positron pair share the available kinetic energy (E_γ − 1·02) MeV and part of this appears as luminescent radiation. When the positron reaches thermal energies it is annihilated along with an electron, two 0·51 MeV gamma quanta are radiated to conserve momentum. Quanta of this energy interact mainly by Compton collisions in the crystal, although photoelectric absorption is not negligible. Provided the annihilation quanta are produced more than 1 cm from a surface of the scintillator, they are effectively absorbed in the crystal.

It is not surprising that when γ-rays of various energies are incident on a small scintillator, it may be impossible to assign energies to all the incident γ-rays, especially if the Compton continuum of electron energies of one ray overlaps the photopeak of a weak lower energy ray. If the gamma source is mounted at the centre of a large NaI(Tl) crystal, 5 in. in diameter, 5 in. long, at the bottom of a 0·25 diam. hole, the majority of pulses represent the entire γ-ray energy and a clearly defined photopeak is obtained. Sometimes, at the expense of a large reduction in counting rate, two or more small scintillators are operated in coincidence; the pulses produced by Compton recoil electrons at a certain angle in the first scintillator are recorded if they are accompanied by a coincident pulse due to the absorption in the second scintillator of a photon scattered through a definite angle (135°) in the first scintillator. The efficiency of the arrangement can be increased by demanding that only one of a ring of scintillators mounted to receive the back scattered photons produces a coincident pulse.

Alpha particles are conveniently detected by absorbing them in zinc sulphide activated with a trace of silver in the form of a thin polycrystalline layer 5 to 10 mg/cm^2 thick. Some light is absorbed in the powder but with thin layers this is not serious. The conversion efficiency for typical α-particles is high; the long decay time of 0·25 μsec means that it is not suitable for fast coincidence experiments.

Neutrons can be detected through the emission of a suitable charged particle resulting from a nuclear reaction initiated by the incident neutron. For intermediate and low energy neutrons, lithium iodide crystals, activated with a trace of the rare earth europium, are efficient detectors for neutron energies below 50 keV. The nuclear reaction involved is Li^6 (n, α) H^3 and the cross section is increased if the crystal is grown from a lithium salt enriched in Li^6. Moderate energy neutrons of kinetic energy less than 500 keV have been detected with fair efficiency by using a scintillator which is a gaseous mixture of He^3 and Xe (the Xe is responsible for the luminescence). The reaction induced by the intermediate energy neutrons is ${}_2He^3(n, p){}_1H^3$, and the proton and the triton produce light in the gas. This mode of detection has the important advantage that the scintillator has a low sensitivity to γ-rays. The detection efficiency is increased by employing quaterphenyl as a *wavelength shifter* for the luminescent radiation. A wavelength shifter is a fluorescent material which absorbs and re-emits the luminescent radiation at a longer wavelength which corresponds to a more sensitive region of the spectral response curve of the cathode of the photomultiplier tube.

A list of a few of the commonly used scintillators, together with the properties relevant to scintillation detection are given in Table 6.

The inorganic and organic scintillators differ in two important properties; the former have the higher density and stopping power for gamma rays, the latter have much shorter luminescent decay times. Thus in fast coincidence experiments organic scintillators are to be preferred. Included in the organic scintillators are a wide range of liquid and solid solutions. There is a wide range of liquid organic solutions suitable for scintillation counting and they have the great advantage in certain experiments of being available in large volumes.

Some studies have been made of gaseous scintillators, especially the noble gases, e.g. xenon. The luminescence is in the ultraviolet region of the spectrum and a suitable wavelength shifter is required. Xenon in solid and liquid forms has also proved to be a useful scintillator.

11.6. CHERENKOV COUNTERS

A charged particle moving through a transparent dielectric medium with a velocity greater than the phase velocity of light in the medium emits Cherenkov radiation. As early as 1910, Pierre and Marie Curie had noticed a faint blue light emitted by concentrated solutions of radium. Cherenkov, in 1934, carried out intensive investigations of this radiation and a classical electromagnetic theory of the phenomenon was outlined by Frank and Tamm.

TABLE 6

Scintillator	Density g/cm³	Wavelength of maximum emission. Å	Relative beta-ray pulse height	Alpha–beta pulse-height ratio %	Decay time sec	General remarks
ZnS(Ag)	4·10	4500	200	100	10^{-5}	Generally used in thin layers 10 mg/cm² to detect α-particles
NaI(Tl)	3·67	4200	210	44	$2{\cdot}5 \times 10^{-7}$	Mainly used as γ-detector. Hygroscopic
CsI(Tl)	4·51	–	60	50	$5{\cdot}5 \times 10^{-7}$	Large absorption coefficient for γ-rays. Non-hygroscopic
LiI(Eu)		~4400	74	–	$1{\cdot}5 \times 10^{-6}$	Mainly used as slow neutron detector
Anthracence $C_{14}H_{10}$	1·25	4400	100	9	3×10^{-8}	Commonly used for β-detection
Trans-Stilbene $C_{14}H_{12}$	1·16	3900	60	9	3 to 8×10^{-9}	Commonly used for β-detection
Solution of 5 g/litre of terphenyl + 0·01 g/litre of diphenyl hexatriene dissolved in xylene		4500	48	9	–	Very useful for detecting soft β-rays
Solid solution of tetraphenyl butadiene dissolved in polystyrene	1·1	4450	36	–	$4{\cdot}6 \times 10^{-9}$	Useful high energy β-detector in fast coincidence expects.

Consider a charged particle moving with velocity v in a transparent dielectric medium (Fig. 19). A B is a short length of the path of the particle (v is essentially constant over this length). As the charged particle moves past nearby atoms or molecules in the medium they become momentarily polarized by the Coulomb field of the particle. Each of these atoms, in turn, radiates like a damped oscillating dipole moment. Light is only observed, however, if the elementary wave trains emitted by all the atoms are in phase at a distant point. The Huygens construction of elementary wave optics shows that Cherenkov radiation is only observed at a particular

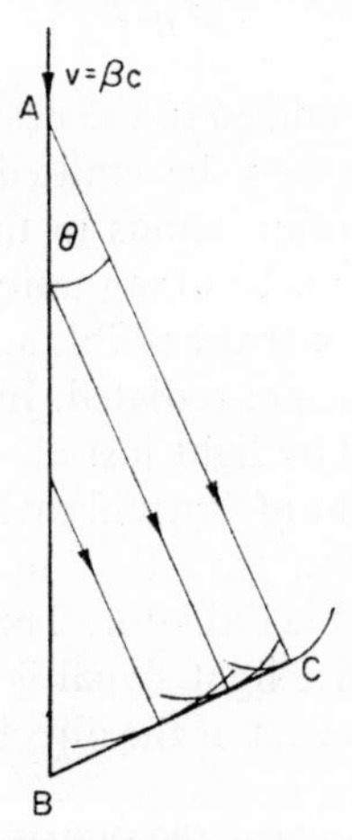

FIG. 19. Huygens construction illustrating the production of coherent wavefront BC of Cherenkov light. There is axial symmetry about AB. Rotate diagram about AB to obtain Cherenkov light cone.

angle θ with respect to the direction of motion of the particle. In Fig. 19 we note that if the time the particle takes to travel from A to B is equal to the time the light takes to travel from A to C, all the light waves emitted by the atoms along the line A B are in phase in the θ direction. Equating these times we obtain

$$\frac{\mathrm{AB}}{\beta c} = \frac{\mathrm{AC}}{c/n}$$

$$\cos\theta = \frac{\mathrm{AC}}{\mathrm{AB}} = \frac{1}{\beta n} \tag{22}$$

The velocity v of the particle is written in the form βc. The Cherenkov light is not, of course, confined to one plane, but is propagated along the surface of a cone, whose axis coincides with the particle and whose semi-vertical angle is θ. Important conclusions can be drawn from eqn. (22). If $\beta < 1/n$, no Cherenkov radiation is observed. This limits the use of

Cherenkov light in nuclear physics to the detection of high velocity charged particles. At the threshold of the production of radiation, $\cos\theta = 1$ and the light is emitted in the direction of movement of the particle. For a high energy particle, whose kinetic energy is a lot greater than its rest mass energy, β is close to unity and there is a maximum angle of emission corresponding to $\cos\theta_{max} = 1/n$.

A useful expression for I, the number of photons emitted per centimetre of path of a charged particle $(z\,e)$ in the frequency interval $\Delta\nu$ is,

$$I = \left(\frac{2\pi z e}{c}\right)^2 \frac{1}{h}\left(1 - \frac{1}{\beta^2 n^2}\right)\Delta\nu = \frac{2\pi z^2}{137\,c}\sin^2\theta\,\Delta\nu \qquad (23)$$

The Cherenkov radiation is confined to the near ultraviolet and visible parts of the spectrum. Some light may be emitted in the infrared, but many dielectrics have strong absorption bands in this region. No radiation can occur in the X-ray region as n is less than unity. For charged particles with $z = 1$, eqn. (23) predicts that over the visible spectrum ($\Delta\nu = 3 \times 10^{14}\,\text{sec}^{-1}$), about $450\sin^2\theta$ photons per cm are radiated. In practice, it is therefore very difficult to detect the Cherenkov light just above the threshold velocity, as $\sin^2\theta$ is very small. The amount of Cherenkov light radiated by a relativistic particle is small in comparison with the luminescent radiation produced by absorbing the particle in a scintillator. The use of Cherenkov counters is only warranted if the smaller light signal is offset by special advantages connected with the threshold effect or the directional properties of the radiation.

One of the first applications of the Cherenkov effect in nuclear physics was the determination of the energy of the external proton beam of the 184 in.

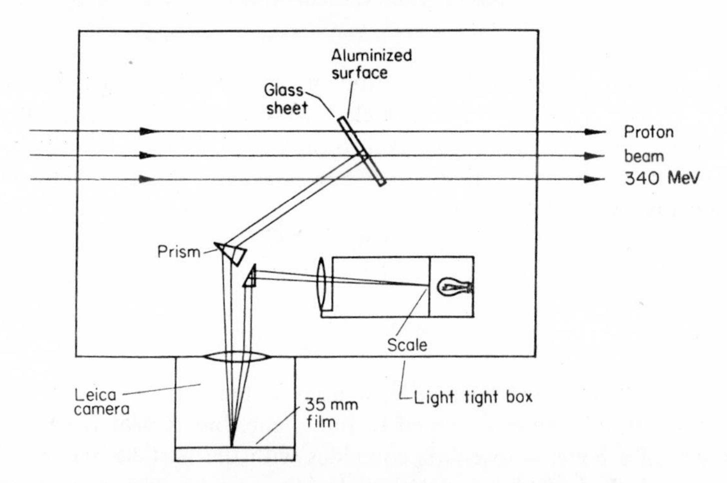

FIG. 20. Mather's determination of velocity of high energy protons by photographing Cherenkov light produced in a glass sheet.

synchrocyclotron at Berkeley.† Mather recorded the Cherenkov light radiated by a collimated beam of protons passing through a thin sheet of glass ($n = 1{\cdot}88$) with a 35 mm Leica camera (Fig. 20). The rear surface of the optically flat glass sheet is aluminized. The sheet is tilted with respect to the proton beam so that part of the Cherenkov light cone radiated in the glass is incident normally on the aluminium surface and reflected so that no refraction occurs at the front surface of the glass. Unfortunately, the angle of emission of the Cherenkov light varies with wavelength λ because the refractive index n depends on λ. Mather introduced a prism so that this dispersion effect was nearly absent. The illuminated scale and collimator, shown in Fig. 20, enabled the measurements of the Cherenkov images to be accurately determined. The recorded Cherenkov light on the camera film corresponded to a θ value of 38·5°. Substituting this value of θ and $n = 1{\cdot}88$ in eqn. (22), $\beta = 0{\cdot}697$. The kinetic energy T of the protons is obtained from the relation,

$$\frac{T + 938}{938} = \frac{1}{\sqrt{(1 - \beta^2)}}$$

where the rest mass energy of the proton is equal to 938 MeV. The kinetic energy T of the protons was found to be 340 MeV with an error less than 1 per cent.

The majority of Cherenkov detecting systems record the emitted light with photomultiplier tubes. The Cherenkov light pulse produced by a fast charged particle is of shorter duration than that produced in any scintillator; there is no parallel to the decay period of luminescence. For this reason, the Cherenkov counters are capable of the highest possible time resolution in coincidence circuits. The small number of photoelectrons released from the cathode of the photomultiplier tube gives rise to a small voltage pulse which may not be distinguished from noise pulses due to thermionic emission from the cathode. However, the use of two or more photomultiplier tubes in coincidence greatly increases the probability of recording genuine Cherenkov light flashes.

A good example of a detector in which the Cherenkov light is focused on to the cathode of two photomultiplier tubes is that designed by Marshall for recording high energy π mesons.† A collimated beam of mesons passes along the axis of a large hemispherical Perspex lens (Fig. 21). The Cherenkov light radiated in this lens is reflected by a surrounding cylindrical mirror M_1 on to one of the plane mirrors M_2, M_3, and then on to the cathodes of the 1 P28 photomultiplier tubes. The phototubes are operated in coincidence and the position of the radiator-lens is adjusted so that the coincidence counting rate is a maximum. This occurs when the Cherenkov light cone is correctly focused on to the phototubes. For pions with a kinetic energy

† R. L. MATHER, *Phys. Rev.* **84**, 181, 1951.
† J. MARSHALL, *Phys. Rev.* **86**, 685, 1952.

of 145 MeV the energy resolution of the detector (full width at one half the maximum counting rate) is ~ 19 MeV (13%).

Cherenkov counters have been designed which only respond to charged particles in a narrow velocity range. The discovery of the antiproton made use of focusing Cherenkov counters of this type. This experiment is described in Chapter 21, Section 7.

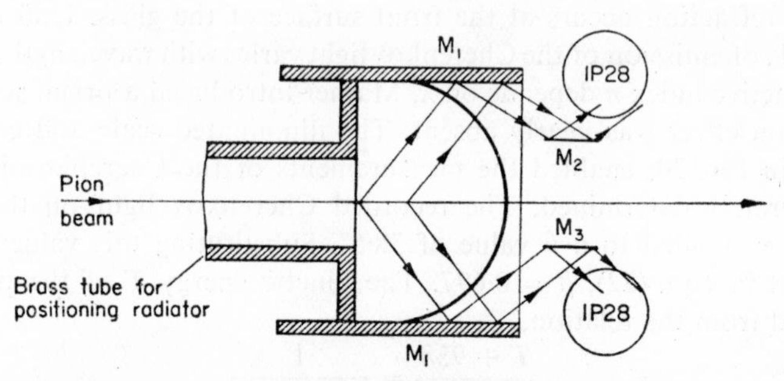

FIG. 21. Marshall's focusing Cherenkov detector using two photomultiplier tubes in coincidence.

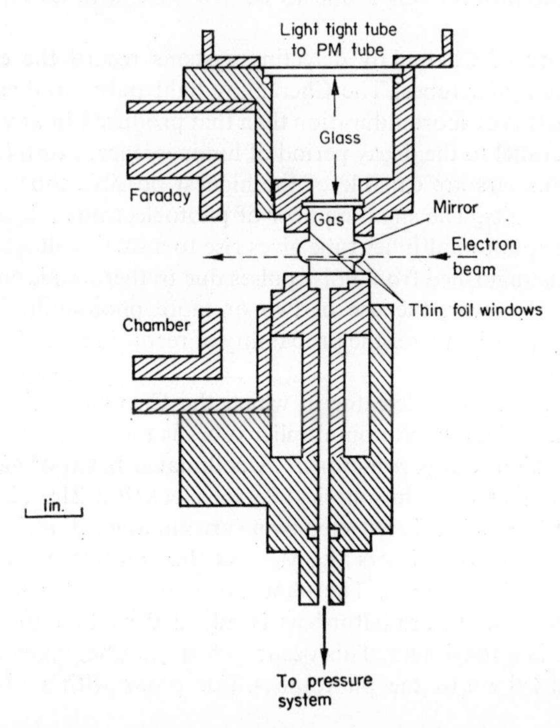

FIG. 22. Schematic diagram of Jennings and Kalmus threshold monitor (CO_2 radiator).

For highly relativistic charged particles (β very close to unity), Cherenkov detectors in which the light is radiated by a gas have been used. The energy of the electrons in a high flux beam of 4·5 MeV electrons has been measured to an accuracy of better than $\pm$ 0·25 per cent using carbon dioxide gas as the radiator (Fig. 22).† The pressure of the CO_2 in the small steel cell is variable in the range 0 to 20 atm. In this way, the refractive index n of the gas can be varied so that the threshold velocity of the detector is adjustable over narrow limits. A thin aluminium foil, mounted at 45° to the electron beam, reflects the Cherenkov light produced by electrons just above the threshold velocity through a glass window on to the photomultiplier tube. The electron beam enters and leaves the gas chamber by very thin foil windows (0·002 in. thick). The pressure of the gas is measured directly by using a Jamin interferometer.

11.7. SEMICONDUCTOR COUNTERS‡

The possibility of using semiconductors for detecting heavy charged particles (protons, deuterons, fission fragments, heavy ions, etc.) has recently been investigated with very promising results. Pure crystals of silicon and germanium have a small electrical conductivity at room temperature. This intrinsic conductivity is due to the thermal excitation of electrons from the filled valence band of the crystal to the vacant conduction band, which in the case of germanium is separated from the top energy level of the conduction band by an energy gap of 0·72 eV. The electrical conductivity of the tetravalent Ge crystal is considerably increased by the deliberate addition of a minute trace of a pentavalent element (As) during manufacture. An n-type semiconductor is produced, in which the increased conductivity is due to one electron donated by each pentavalent atom to the conduction band. A p-type semiconductor, on the other hand, is produced by adding a trace of a trivalent element (In) to the Ge. The missing electron in the conduction band, or "hole" as it is called, behaves like a positive electron and moves through the crystal under the action of an applied electric field.

In 1949, K. G. McKay at the Bell Telephone Laboratories††, demonstrated that α-particles could be detected with an n–p germanium junction (Fig. 23). A bar of germanium is exposed to a very narrow collimated beam of α-particles so that they are absorbed in the n–p junction layer. A potential difference of a few volts is applied to electrodes at the ends of the crystal. The conduction electrons in the n-part of the crystal, and the holes in the p-part, move away from the n–p boundary producing a high resistance junction. The junction thickness is of the order of 10^{-4} to 10^{-3} cm,

† R. E. Jennings and P. I. P. Kalmus, *Nucl. Instr. and Methods* **6**, 209, 1960.

†† G. Dearnaley and D. C. Northrop, *Semiconductor Counters for Nuclear Radiations*, E & F. Spon, London 1963.

‡ K. G. McKay, *Phys. Rev.* **84**, 829, 1951.

and an electric field of about 10,000 V per cm is developed across the junction. McKay showed that the α-particles absorbed in the n–p junction lose nearly all their energy in producing electron–hole pairs. The average energy required to produce one electron–hole pair is about 3 eV. Thus a Po α-particle (5·3 MeV) creates $5{\cdot}3 \times 10^6/3$, that is $1{\cdot}77 \times 10^6$ electron–hole pairs. In the intense electric field in the n–p junction, the electrons and holes move away from the junction, with drift velocities of $\sim 10^7$ cm per sec. A

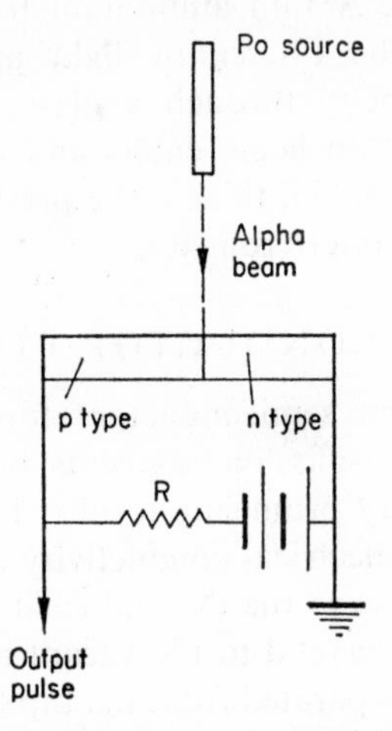

FIG. 23. McKay's experiment. Fine beam of α-particles is absorbed in p–n Ge junction.

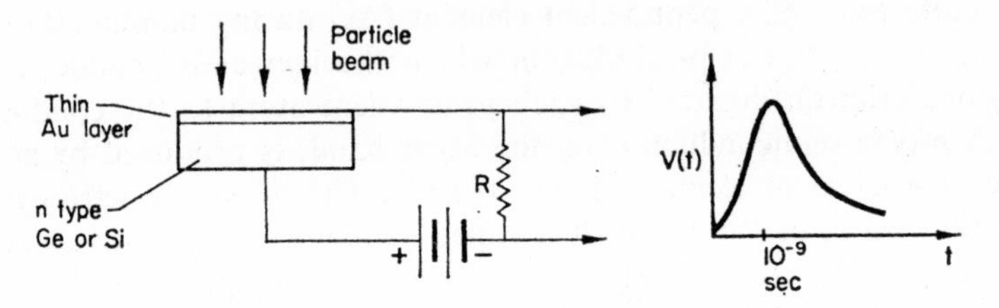

FIG. 24. (a) Surface barrier counter; (b) output pulse developed across load R.

very fast rising potential pulse of the order of a millivolt is produced with a rise time of the order of 10^{-9} or 10^{-10} sec.

The majority of semi conductor counters are of the surface barrier type. A thin gold film about a third of a micron thick is deposited on the flat surface of a small disc of n-type germanium or silicon (Fig. 24). Considerable reduction in the size of noise pulses from the detector is achieved by cooling the semiconductor to liquid nitrogen temperatures. Gold–germanium barrier counters of surface area 1 cm², 1 mm thick, at 77°K have an energy resolution for 5·5 MeV α-particles of about 6 per cent and a pulse height of about 0·3 mV.

Semiconductor barrier layer counters are very insensitive to gamma rays, as the probability of producing a significant number of electron–hole pairs in the very narrow barrier junctions is very small. Covering the front of the counter with a thin layer of B^{10} enables low energy neutrons to be detected through the α-particles produced in the B^{10} (n, α) Li^7 reaction.

The advantages of semiconductor counters are the following:

(1) Low sensitivity to gamma background radiation.

(2) Pulse height is proportional to the kinetic energy of the incident protons, deuterons, α-particles, provided the particle range is less than the junction thickness.

(3) High counting rates are possible. No trouble is experienced up to counting rates as high as 5×10^4 counts per sec.

(4) Very good energy resolution is possible. Energy resolution as high as 2 per cent for Pu^{240} α-particles has been obtained.

(5) Very fast pulse rise time means that the semiconductor counter is more suitable than the grid ionization chamber in coincidence experiments.

(6) The elimination of windows and the low applied voltage needed to operate the counter are advantages over the gas counters.

11.8. NUCLEAR EMULSIONS

Becquerel in 1896 discovered the radioactivity of uranium by observing that it had the curious property of fogging a photographic plate wrapped in black paper. Charged particles passing through the emulsion of a photographic plate interact with the tiny silver halide crystals producing a line of latent images along their paths.† Niépce de St. Victor as early as 1867 observed the fogging of photographic plates by uranium salts but he attributed the effect to the luminescence of the salts.

Reinganum, in 1911, was the first to recognize that individual α-particles traversing a photographic emulsion produce separate tracks. Kinoshita made the important discovery that every silver halide grain traversed by an α-particle is rendered developable.

After these early discoveries the photographic plate was not extensively used as a detector until the post 1945 period. Miss Blau and Wambacher††, however, had made the important discovery in 1937 that a high energy cosmic ray may collide with an atomic nucleus in the emulsion and produce a "star". The nucleus breaks up into several high energy fragments.

The "optical" photographic emulsion is not suitable for quantitative work with nuclear radiations. The sensitivity is low and the tracks due to charged particles have an ill defined range because the developed crystal

† The theory of the photographic process is outside the scope of this book. Important contributions to the subject are due to R. W. Gurney and N. F. Mott, *Proc. Roy. Soc.* (A) **164**, 151, 1938; J. Mitchell, *Rep. Prog. Phys.* **20**, 433, 1957.

†† Blau and Wambacher, *Nature* **140**, 585, 1937.

grains are large and widely spaced. The "optical" emulsion is "noisy" in the sense that background radiation produces a large fog of individual grains. The great improvement in the design for recording nuclear radiations is due to the enterprise of Powell and his group at Bristol, and the researches of the commercial firms of Ilford and Kodak. Special mention should be made of the work of P. Demers, one of the experimenters outside an industrial laboratory, who has succeeded in producing fine grained sensitive emulsions for nuclear research.†

The nuclear emulsions differ from the optical emulsions in two main respects. The former have a much higher ratio of AgBr to gelatine, and the silver halide grains are as small as 0·1 to 0·2 microns in diameter. The thickness usually is in the range 25 to 1000 microns. This great thickness in comparison with the optical emulsion introduces the problem of uniform development. One method is to soak the exposed emulsion plate in the developer at a low temperature for a time long enough for the developer to diffuse into the emulsion. The rate of development, at this termperature is very small. The emulsion is then uniformly developed by raising the temperature. About 1953 an important development in technique was introduced. This was the invention of the *emulsion stack*. The emulsions from scores of nuclear plates are stripped from their glass backings and stacked together. After exposure of the stack, the emulsion layers are separated and mounted on glass plates for chemical processing. Large emulsion stacks have been exposed to cosmic radiation in high flying balloons. An excellent example is the "G–Stack Collaboration Experiment"†† of 1954, in which scientists from five countries collaborated in studying the properties of the *K*-mesons by exposing a stack of volume 15 l. at an altitude of 80,000 ft.

A series of nuclear emulsions has been developed for detecting particles of different specific ionization. A landmark in the history of new emulsions was the invention of the NT 4 emulsion in 1948 by R. W. Berriman†††, which is sensitive enough to record the track of an electron at its minimum specific ionization. The characteristics of the main nuclear emulsions manufactured by Ilford and Kodak (England) are given in Table 7.

For detecting fission fragments, the D 1 emulsion is the most suitable type; the only other particles recorded by this emulsion are α-particles and their tracks are quite different in appearance to those produced by fission fragments. The C 2 Ilford emulsion is a useful general purpose emulsion suitable for recording mesons, protons, and heavier charged particles. The properties of the Ilford G 5 are similar to those of the Kodak NT 4 and this type of emulsion is used to record high energy electrons.

† P. Demers, *Canadian J. Phys.* **32**, 538, 1954.

†† *G–Stack Collaboration, Nuovo Cim.* **2**, 1063, 1955, see also *Antiproton Collaboration, Phys. Rev.* **105**, 1037, 1957.

††† R. W. Berriman, *Nature* **162**, 992, 1948.

High quality microscopes are required for scanning the developed plates. In particular, instruments with a small depth of view, accurate depth gauge, and attached devices for measuring track lengths and angles are desirable. Unfortunately the nuclear emulsions with their high silver halide concentration shrink during the fixation process. The thickness of the processed

TABLE 7

Emulsion	Ilford (Essex)					Kodak (Harrow)		
	D 1	E 1	C 2	B 2	G 5	NT 1a	NT 2a	NT 4
Mean silver halide grain diameter (microns)	0·12	0·14	0·16	0·21	0·18	0·19	0·22	0·39
Highest detectable speed β, $v = \beta c$		0·2	0·31	0·46	All	0·2	0·55	All
Highest detectable energy of electrons (MeV)	–	–	0·03	0·07	All	–	0·1	All
Highest detectable energy of muons (MeV)	–	2	5·5	0·14	All	2	20	All
Highest detectable energy of protons (MeV)	–	20	50	120	All	20	200	All
Highest detectable energy of α-particles (MeV)	Low energy	500	1500	All	All	500	All	All
Highest detectable energy of fission fragments (MeV)	All	All	All	All	All	All	All	All

emulsion is usually about 35 per cent of the original thickness. A knowledge of this shrinkage factor is necessary when the angle of dip of a track in the emulsion is being determined.

The scope of the nuclear emulsion as a detector can be increased by loading the emulsion with suitable compounds. Slow neutrons can be detected using emulsions impregnated with lithium, boron, or uranium Fast neutrons can be detected by the knock-on protons in unloaded emulsions. Loading emulsions with deuterium compounds enable gamma rays of energy above about 3 MeV to be detected through the track of the proton released in the photodisintegration reaction $H^2 + \gamma \rightarrow H^1 + n - 2{\cdot}23$ MeV.

Under favourable conditions, it is possible to determine the charge, mass, and incident kinetic energy of a charged particle brought to rest in a nuclear emulsion. Measurements of the range of the particle in the emulsion, the grain density along its track (i.e. the number of developed grains per unit track length), and cumulative angular deflections due to scattering are all relevant to these determinations. One disadvantage of the nuclear emulsion compared to the cloud chamber is the difficulty in determining the sign of the charge and the momentum of a particle from observations of the curvature of the path in a strong magnetic field. The actual path length in the emulsion is small compared to that in a cloud chamber, and multiple

Coulomb scattering in the emulsion simulates the curvature produced by a magnetic field. With the advent of particle accelerators in the GeV range, producing pulsed beams of high energy particles, the possibilities of producing pulsed intense magnetic fields synchronized with the time of arrival of particles at the surface of a nuclear emulsion plate or stack have been explored. Magnetic fields as high as 650,000 gauss for 1 to 10 msec have been produced by discharging a bank of capacitors through a pair of Helmholtz coils. The accuracy of the determination of the momentum of high energy charged particles in nuclear emulsion stacks is improved by the longer track length available for observation.

The density of a nuclear emulsion is about 4 g cm^{-3}. Consequently the stopping power of an emulsion is more than a thousand times that of air at S.T.P. A particle with a range of more than a metre in air is stopped by a millimetre of emulsion. A 40 MeV proton has a range of 6 mm in a C 2 emulsion and is slowed down to rest in about 10^{-10} sec. The short stopping times of energetic particles in emulsions means that unstable mesons with half-lives of the order of 10^{-10} sec are often brought to rest before the decay products are emitted. Useful range–energy relations for protons, deuterons, α-particles, etc. in nuclear emulsions have been tabulated during the last ten years. One method of obtaining an R–E relation is to measure the range of a homogeneous group of charged particles (of known energy from an accelerator) entering a nuclear emulsion at a small glancing angle. Empirical formulae have been obtained on the assumption that the rate of loss of energy $-dE/dR$ of a particle along its track depends only on its speed v and charge $z\,e$ and is independent of its mass (see Bethe's formula, eqn. (9) in Section 1 of this chapter). The following set of formulae apply to the R–E relations of protons, muons (207 m_e), pions (273 m_e), K-mesons (966 m_e), Σ-hyperons (2327 m_e), deuterons and tritons:

$$\left.\begin{aligned} E_p &= 0{\cdot}251\ R^{0{\cdot}581} \\ E_\mu &= 0{\cdot}101\ R^{0{\cdot}581} \\ E_\pi &= 0{\cdot}113\ R^{0{\cdot}581} \\ E_K &= 0{\cdot}192\ R^{0{\cdot}581} \\ E_\Sigma &= 0{\cdot}277\ R^{0{\cdot}581} \\ E_D &= 0{\cdot}336\ R^{0{\cdot}581} \\ E_T &= 0{\cdot}398\ R^{0{\cdot}581} \end{aligned}\right\} \tag{24}$$

The kinetic energy E is measured in MeV and the range R in the emulsion in microns.

In some applications more accurate R–E relations are required. One example is concerned with the determination of the small mass difference, if any, of the positive K mesons which decay in different ways. The K^+ meson has a mean lifetime of $1{\cdot}22 \times 10^{-8}$ sec and there are six competing decay modes. Three of these are; $K^+ \rightarrow \pi^+ + \pi^+ + \pi^-$ (τ mode), $K^+ \rightarrow \pi^+ + \pi^0$ (θ mode) and $K^+ \rightarrow \mu^+ + \nu$. Careful determinations of the total energy of the decay particles of the different modes allow the mass of the parent meson to be determined.

There is a considerable variation in the stopping power from one emulsion to another, mainly due to the different amounts of water absorbed in the emulsion. Even with emulsions kept in an atmosphere of constant relative humidity there is still a variation in stopping power of the order of 0·5 per cent. A way of overcoming this uncertainty in the *R–E* relation of a given emulsion is to measure the total range of the 8·776 MeV ThC′ (Po^{212}) α-particles in the emulsion (there is a small trace of thorium contamination in all emulsions). Alternatively, the range of a μ^+ meson emitted from a π^+ meson at rest in the emulsion can be used to calibrate the emulsion.

A striking property of elementary charged particles, electrons, mesons, protons and hyperons, is that they all have the fundamental electric charge $\pm e$; thus there is no problem, apart from determining the sign of the charge, in determining the magnitude of the charge. One of the most important discoveries made with nuclear emulsion plates flown in high altitude balloons is that the primary cosmic radiation consists of high energy nuclei in the range of $Z = 1$ to $Z = 30$. It is not easy to determine the charge number Z of a cosmic ray particle which may be as high as 20 or 30. One method of determining Z is to count the frequency of δ-ray tracks spraying out from the dense track of the high energy cosmic ray. Mott has calculated that the number of δ-tracks, produced by secondary electrons in a certainenergy interval, per unit primary particle path length, is given by $N_\delta = KZ^2/\beta^2$. The constant K has to be found by determining N_δ for α-particles of known energy. The speed of the particle ($\beta = v/c$) is obtained by measuring its range. A check on the estimated value of Z is based on observing the "thin-down" length of the particle near the end of its range. The width of the emulsion track gradually decreases near the end of the range as the specific ionization of the charged particle abruptly decreases each time the particle picks up an electron. It is possible to relate the "thin-down" length to the initial charge of the particle.

Some of the advantages of the nuclear emulsion detector are

(1) It produces a visible track with the great advantage of following the complete trajectory of a charged particle. Particles of different ionizing power produce tracks which are quite different in appearance.

(2) The emulsion produces a continuous record. There is a great saving in time, if for example, the angular distribution of the products of nuclear reactions initiated by artificially accelerated charged particles are simultaneously recorded by an angular array of nuclear emulsion plates. The energy of the product particles can be determined from their range in the emulsion, and the differential scattering cross section from counts of the number of tracks formed in each emulsion.

(3) The emulsion is relatively cheap and light.† This makes it ideal for high altitude cosmic ray experiments.

(4) High stopping power. Many short-lived particles are brought to rest in the emulsion before they decay. This greatly increases the probability of recording important decay phenomena. The measurement of the ranges of muons emitted from stopped pions before they decay into electrons ($\pi \rightarrow \mu \rightarrow e$ decay) enables the mean lifetime of the muon to be found.

The most important applications of the emulsion technique are in cosmic ray physics. An outstanding discovery was that of the pion, of rest mass 273 m_e, by the Bristol group, and the establishment of the $\pi \rightarrow \mu \rightarrow e$ decay chain.†† The K mesons were also discovered with nuclear emulsions, the K^+ through its K_{π_3} decay mode, $K^+ \rightarrow \pi^+ + \pi^+ + \pi^-$. The anti-lambda hyperon $\bar{\Lambda}^0$ was first discovered by observing the tracks produced by the decay products; $\bar{\Lambda}^0 \rightarrow \bar{p} + \pi^+$ ($\bar{p}$ is the symbol for the negative or anti-proton).

11.9. THE CLOUD CHAMBER

Lord Rutherford described the cloud chamber as the most beautiful instrument ever invented. Is was developed as a result of the fundamental researches of Coulier (1875), Aitken (1881), and C. T. R. Wilson (1897), on the subject of condensation in supersaturated vapours. The condensation of a vapour into observable liquid droplets occurs if the vapour pressure is higher than the saturated (equilbrium) value for the temperature of the system, provided small condensation nuclei.††† (e.g. fine dust particles) are present.

The saturated vapour pressure P_r over the surface of a liquid droplet of radius r is greater than that over a flat surface (P_∞).
Lord Kelvin showed that

$$\frac{P_r}{P_\infty} = \frac{M}{RT\varrho}\left[\frac{2\theta}{r} + \frac{d\theta}{dr}\right] \tag{25}$$

where θ is the surface tension of the liquid, R is the molar gas constant, M is the gram molecular weight of the liquid, T the absolute temperature of the liquid and vapour and ϱ the density of the liquid. P_r/P_∞ increases rapidly as r is reduced below 10 Å; for a water drop at 291°K P_r/P_∞ is approximately 10 for $r = 5$ Å. For such a small droplet, containing about 20 molecules, the classical theory of a continuous medium is suspect. Nevertheless, very small droplets tend to evaporate very rapidly. If, however,

† Large emulsion stacks, however, cost several hundred pounds, and they may weigh as much as 60 kg.

†† Lattes, Occhialini, and C. F. Powell, *Nature* **159**, 694, 1947.

††† The context should indicate whether the word "nuclei" refers to condensation or atomic nuclei.

the liquid droplet carries an electric charge e, the stability eqn. (25) is modified by the introduction of an electrostatic energy term. J. J. Thomson derived the equation

$$\frac{P_r}{P_\infty} = \frac{M}{RT\varrho}\left[\frac{2\theta}{r} - \frac{(ze)^2}{8\pi\varepsilon r^4}\right] \tag{26}$$

where $z\,e$ is the charge of the drop, ε is the dielectric constant of the surrounding medium and the term $d\theta/dr$ is assumed to be negligible. The effect of

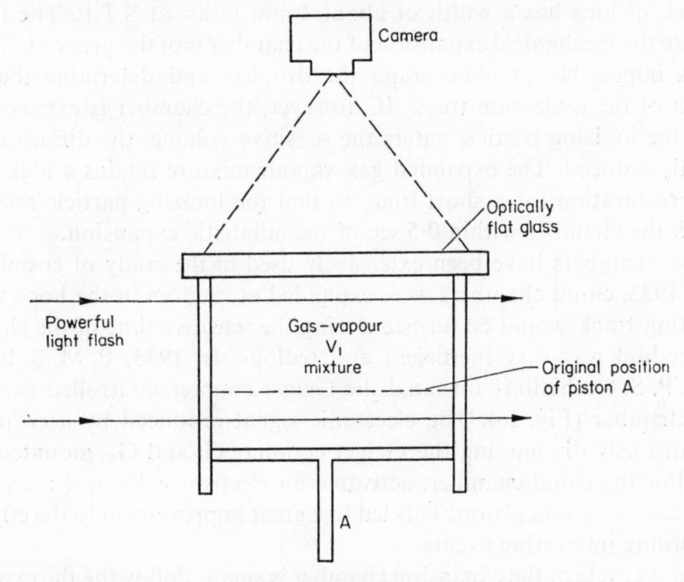

FIG. 25. Schematic diagram of Wilson expansion cloud chamber. Piston A suddenly moves a pre-determined distance increasing the volume of the gas–vapour-mixture from V_1 to V_2.

Condensation tracks are photographed through optically flat glass plate at the top of the chamber.

the electrostatic energy term is to reduce the value of P_r, especially for very small droplets ($r < 6$ Å). Thus a supersaturated vapour in a clean gas will condense round gaseous ions if they are present. C. T. R. Wilson discovered that a supersaturated vapour, produced by the adiabatic expansion of a gas saturated with the vapour of a suitable liquid, will condense in a row of liquid droplets around the trail of ions produced in the wake of a moving charged particle. The principle of the Wilson expansion cloud chamber is illustrated in Fig. 25. A gas enclosed in a vessel of volume V_1 is saturated with the vapours of water or a water–ethyl alcohol mixture at room temperature T_1. The gas–vapour mixture is expanded adiabatically by the sudden controlled movement of the piston to a volume V_2. The expansion ratio V_2/V_1 must exceed 1·31 for positive ions to act as condensation centres in an air–water vapour mixture. For slightly greater expansion ratios a dense background cloud of droplets is formed.

The timing sequence of events in an expansion cloud chamber is important. The liquid droplets grow at a finite rate (a typical value for dr/dt is 25 micron/sec), and they should be allowed to grow to a size which allows them to be photographed. If the droplets are too small insufficient light is scattered for photographic recording. As soon as a trail of ions is produced in the sensitive volume of the chamber they will diffuse and after about 15 msec the track of ions has a width of about 1 mm in air at S.T.P. The time to complete the mechanical expansion of the chamber is of the order of 15 msec, so it is impossible to photograph the droplets and determine the exact position of the ionization track. If, however, the chamber is expanded just before the ionizing particle enters the sensitive volume, the diffusion effect is greatly reduced. The expanded gas–vapour mixture retains a high degree of supersaturation for a short time, so that the ionizing particle must pass through the chamber within 0·5 sec of the adiabatic expansion.

Cloud chambers have been extensively used in the study of cosmic rays. Before 1933, cloud chambers were expanded at random in the hope that an interesting track would be formed during the sensitive time of the chamber. This method was very inefficient and tedious. In 1933, P. M. S. Blackett and G. P. S. Occhialini† invented the Geiger counter–controlled expansion cloud chamber (Fig. 26). The electronic signal produced by a cosmic ray simultaneously discharging the Geiger counters G_1 and G_2, mounted above and below the cloud chamber, activated an electro-mechanical relay which moved the expansion piston. This led to a great improvement in the efficiency of recording interesting events.

The duty cycle of the expansion chamber is small. Following the expansion and photographing of the droplets, which is usually done with a brilliant light flash and a pair of stereoscopic cameras, a number of cleaning expansions to remove condensation centres are carried out. The ions are swept to the walls of the chamber by an electrostatic field. The gas–vapour mixture is allowed to stand for a few seconds, for full saturation to be attained and gas turbulence to die out, before the next expansion occurs.

Important measurements with the cloud chamber include the determination of the variation of specific ionization along the track of a charged particle, and the range of the particle (the stopping power of the device is increased by mounting a number of thin lead plates across the chamber; if the particle is absorbed in one of the plates an effective range can be approximately determined). The sign of the electric charge and the momentum p of the particle can be determined if the chamber is placed in a strong magnetic field. In order to count the individual droplets in an ionizing track, it is necessary to allow the ions to diffuse for at least 0·1 sec before

† P. M. S. Blackett and G. P. S. Occhialini, *Proc. Roy. Soc.* **139**, 699, 1933.

expanding the chamber. Unfortunately, the long time delay necessary for the ions to diffuse apart introduces severe distortion in track position due to convection currents. Hence a simultaneous accurate determination of the momentum of the charged particle by measuring its radius of curvature in a magnetic field is incompatible with an accurate determination of ionization. A marked improvement was introduced by E. W. Cowan†, following a suggestion of J. G. Wilson; Cowan uses an expansion chamber with an argon–helium gas mixture. The diffusion of ions in helium is large, and

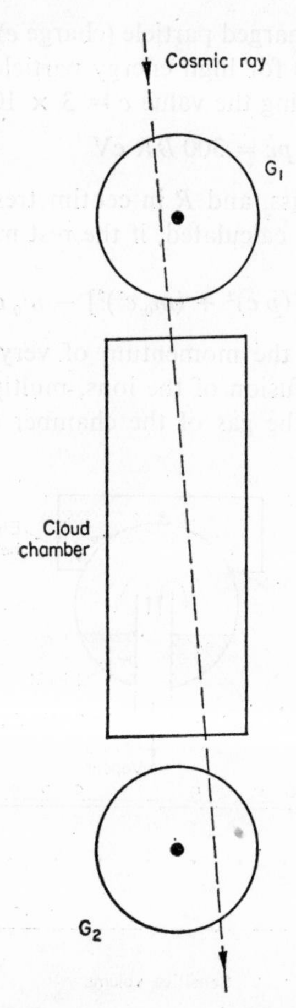

FIG. 26. Counter controlled expansion cloud chamber. Output pulses of Geiger counters G_1 and G_2 are fed into a coincidence unit, the output signal operates an electro-mechanical device which expands the cloud chamber. With a wide chamber, G_1 and G_2 represent several counters.

† E. W. COWAN, *Phys. Rev.* **94**, 161, 1954. Photographs showing the individual droplets are reproduced on pp. 296–297, in the *Handbuch der Physik*. Vol. XLV, 1958.

successful droplet counts have been obtained by expanding the chamber without any delay.

The momentum p of a charged particle can, in principle, be determined from a measurement of its radius of curvature R in a magnetic field B normal to the plane of its trajectory:

$$B e v = \frac{m v^2}{R}$$

$$p = m v = B R e \tag{26}$$

where v is the speed of the charged particle (charge e). It is common practice to quote momentum values for high energy particles in eV/c units, where c is the velocity of light. Using the value $c = 3 \times 10^8$ m per sec, we get

$$pc = 300\, BR \text{ eV} \tag{27}$$

where B is measured in gauss, and R in centimetres. The kinetic energy T of the particle can be easily calculated, if the rest mass energy $m_0 c^2$ of the particle is known:

$$T = \sqrt{[(p\,c)^2 + (m_0\,c^2)^2]} - m_0\,c^2 \tag{28}$$

It is difficult to determine the momentum of very high energy particles. Track distortion due to diffusion of the ions, multiple Coulomb scattering of the charged particle in the gas of the chamber (more severe in a high

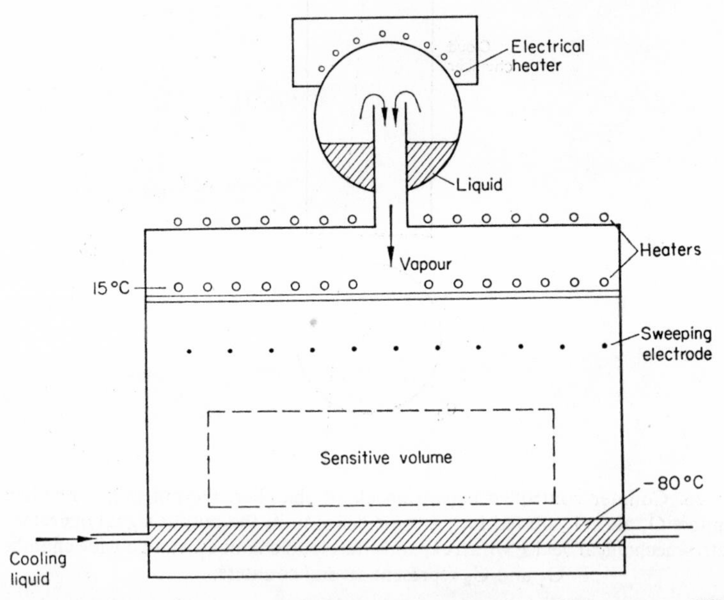

FIG. 27. Schematic diagram of diffusion cloud chamber. Light vapour diffuses downwards into a heavy gas. Vertical temperature gradient is maintained between two horizontal surfaces.

pressure chamber), all mitigate against accurate measurements of the radius R; with fields of the order of $B = 10{,}000$ gauss, momenta of the order of 1000 MeV/c can be readily measured.

The low duty cycle of the expansion chamber is a disadvantage in many applications. The *diffusion cloud chamber* has the advantage that it is continuously sensitive. A light vapour diffuses downwards into a chamber filled with a heavy gas, throughout the volume of which a vertical temperature gradient is maintained (Fig. 27). As the vapour diffuses into the colder regions of the gas, the saturation vapour pressure decreases rapidly and there is a volume near the cold base of the chamber where the supersaturation ratio is high enough for condensation around ions to take place. There is a number of difficulties concerned with the temperature stability of the diffusion chamber. The supply of vapour near the vertical walls of the chamber is low and the sensitive volume does not extend beyond the central regions of the chamber. Wide chambers in comparison with their height are preferred. An interesting application of the diffusion cloud chamber is the determination of the half-life of the free neutron as described in Chapter 15.

Some of the important discoveries made with the cloud chamber are

(1) The discovery of the positron†. High energy γ-rays absorbed in a Pb plate mounted inside the gas of the chamber produced high energy electron–positron pairs; $\gamma \rightarrow e^- + e^+$. The electron and positron emerge from the plate and produce tracks of opposite curvatures in a strong magnetic field.

(2) The muons in secondary cosmic radiation were first observed in a Wilson cloud chamber.

(3) The K^0 meson was discovered by observing the decay in flight into pions: $K^0 \rightarrow \pi^+ + \pi^-$.

(4) The hyperon Λ^0 was also discovered by the observation of the decay in flight $\Lambda^0 \rightarrow p^+ + \pi^-$.

(5) The first reasonably accurate determination of the rest mass of the muon was made by W. B. Fretter††, by combining a simultaneous measurement of the range of a cosmic ray muon in a cloud chamber containing many lead plates, and a momentum determination in a strong magnetic field.

11.10. THE BUBBLE CHAMBER

The Bubble Chamber was invented in 1952 by D. Glaser.‡ The invention was timely as it has proved to be an ideal detector for studying many of the high energy reactions produced by the pulsed proton beams from the

† C. D. Anderson, *Phys. Rev.* **43**, 491, 1933.
†† W. B. Fretter, *Phys. Rev.* **70**, 625, 1946.
‡ D. Glaser, *Phys. Rev.* **87**, 665, 1952.

proton synchrotrons. The Bubble Chamber combines the high stopping of the nuclear emulsion, an almost complete absence of background tracks, freedom from track distortion, and a rapid cycling time.

The bubble chamber operates on the principle that the ions left in the wake of a moving charged particle in a *superheated liquid* act as condensation centres for the formation of vapour bubbles. The vapour bubbles grow at a rapid rate and attain a visible size in a time of the order of 10 to 100 μsec. The string of vapour bubbles is then photographed.

The unstable superheated state of the liquid is produced as follows. The liquid is subjected to a high pressure P_1 at a temperature T_1 only slightly below its boiling point at the pressure P_1 .The applied pressure is suddenly removed and the pressure falls from P_1 to a much lower pressure P_2 after a time of 2 to 10 msec, depending on the volume of the chamber. The liquid is now in an unstable thermodynamic condition as the temperature is considerably higher than the boiling point at the pressure P_2. It has been known for a long time, however, that a superheated liquid in a clean vessel with very smooth walls may not start to boil for several minutes! If a charged particle passes through the unstable liquid during this period, the ions created act as condensation centres for the growth of vapour bubbles. The theory of this nucleation process is not perfectly understood.

Glaser originally attributed the phenomenon to the electrostatic energy associated with the newly formed vapour bubbles. Incredibly large values of n, the number of elementary charges per bubble, are sometimes required to explain the bubble growth. A more likely explanation is that local heating, produced by the short range delta rays along the track of the ionizing particle, is sufficient to initiate bubble growth. The majority of practical bubble chambers do not have perfectly smooth walls. The chamber is usually made of metal and is fitted with thick glass windows sealed to the walls with suitable gaskets. In this type of "dirty" chamber, bubble growth around the gaskets begins immediately the liquid pressure is reduced. However, the central volume of the liquid is still sensitive for the purpose of recording ionizing particles for a period of 10 or 20 msec. The liquid is then rapidly recompressed before the bubbles at the walls grow too large and rise to the top of the chamber. The time sequence of events for a typical chamber is shown in Fig. 28. At the instant A, the high pressure P_1 applied to the bubble chamber liquid is suddenly reduced from a value of 400 (arbitrary units) to 100 units (P_2). The pressure then starts to rise due to bubble formation at the walls. The liquid is recompressed at C and the chamber returns to its initial condition at A′. The time interval between A and A′, about 20 or 30 msec, determines the maximum cycling rate of the chamber. This may be as high as 40 c/s, a marked improvement on the slow cycling rate of a typical cloud chamber. If the bubble chamber is used in conjunction with a pulsed particle accelerator, the expansion is timed so that a group of particles enters the chamber at X, the vapour bubbles are illuminated by a brilliant light flash and photographed at the moment Y.

A large number of liquids are suitable as the working substance of a bubble chamber. The initial high pressure P_1 is chosen to be one-half to three-quarters of the critical pressure. If the latter is high, for example, the critical pressure of water is about 200 atm, the liquid is unsuitable. Initial pressures are seldom greater than 30 atm. Liquids which have been used include; pentane, diethyl ether, propane, xenon, hydrogen, deuterium, and

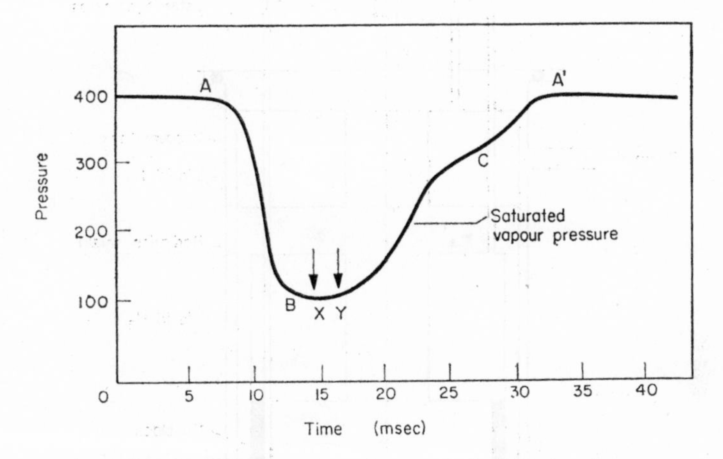

FIG. 28. Time sequence of events in bubble chamber.

helium. Substances with critical temperatures well below room temperature must be cooled by standard low temperature techniques. Liquid hydrogen is an ideal substance for studying high energy interactions with protons; the hydrogen is a pure proton target. The Coulomb scattering of the incident charged particles is very small in hydrogen.

A schematic diagram of a hydrogen bubble chamber, operating a at temperature of 27°K and between pressures P_1 and P_2 of 6 and 2 atm respectively, is illustrated in Fig. 29. There is a wide range in the size of bubble chambers. Liquid hydrogen chambers as long as 6 ft and over a square foot in cross section are now in operation.

Liquid helium chambers operating at 4°K and 1 atm have been used for studying high energy interactions with the nucleons in the He^4 nucleus. Propane has the great advantage that it can be used at a more accessible temperature (57°C). It may not always be possible to decide whether a high energy particle interaction occurs in the carbon or hydrogen target nuclei. Liquid xenon (density 2·3 gcm^{-3}) operating at -14°C is ideal for studying interactions with high energy γ-quanta and neutral pions (π^0);

the pair creation cross section is high in xenon ($Z = 54$). Xenon chambers have the interesting property that satisfactory bubble tracks are produced only if a small amount of ethylene is added, the ethylene quenches the scintillation properties of pure liquid xenon.

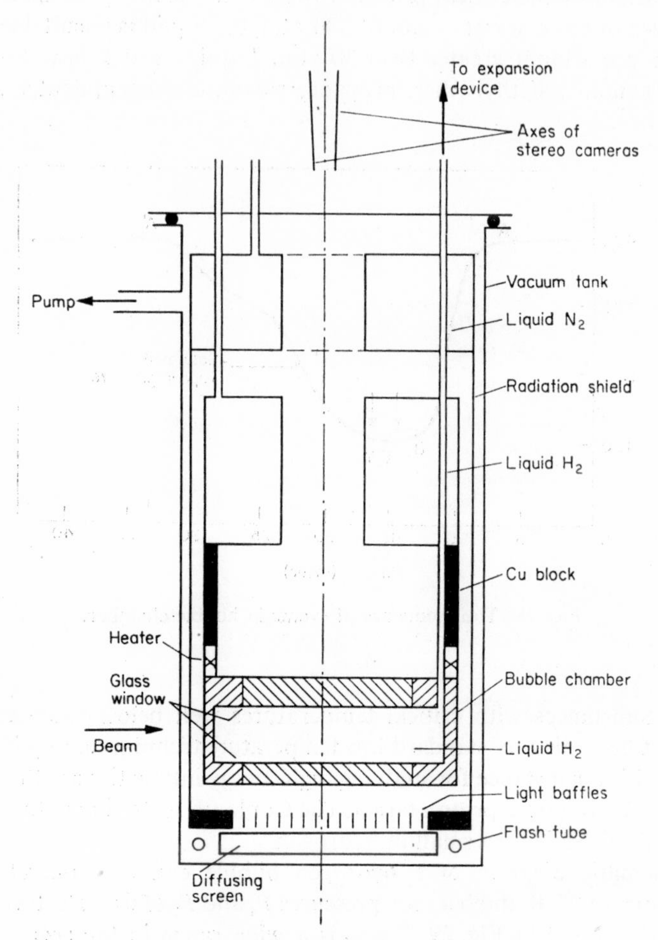

FIG. 29. Liquid hydrogen bubble chamber. (Vacuum tank is made of stainless steel.)

The effects of diffusion on track distortion in a bubble chamber are very small. More serious is the distortion in photographing the bubble tracks due to optical inhomogeneity in the liquid produced by temperature gradients set up by the rapid expansion. Multiple Coulomb scattering of a charged particle is large in high Z liquids (Xe) and the resulting track curvature interferes with momentum determinations by the strong magnetic field deflection method. In liquid hydrogen, the determination of the momentum of a relativistic charged particle from a measurement of 5 cm of track is accurate to 10 per cent if B exceeds 7000 gauss. The same degree of accuracy in a xenon bubble chamber requires a field of 140,000 gauss! The velocity of charged particles can be determined to an accuracy of 5 per cent by counting the number of bubbles formed per unit track length. The method is analogous to droplet counting in a cloud chamber or silver grain counting in a nuclear emulsion.

It is interesting to compare the different stopping powers of the media of "visual detectors" by calculating the number of rare events of cross section 10^{-6} barns per nucleon occurring in the detector, during an 8 hr exposure to a pulsed particle beam of 50 particles passing through the detector every 5 sec. The number of observable events in an 8 hr "working" day are given in Table 8.

TABLE 8

Type of "Visual" Detector	Density gcm^{-3}	Stopping Power of a 50 cm chamber, gcm^{-2}	Events for 8 hr 'day' $\sigma = 10^{-6}$ barns per nucleon
1 atmosphere argon expansion cloud chamber	0·0017	0·085	0·015
20 atmosphere hydrogen diffusion cloud chamber	0·0019	0·095	0·016
Liquid helium bubble chamber	~0·10	5·0	0·86
Liquid propane (C_3H_8) bubble chamber	0·44	22	3·7
Liquid xenon bubble chamber	2·3	115	20
Nuclear emulsion (AgBr)	4.0	200	34

11.11. THE SPARK CHAMBER

A recent development which looks like being very useful in the high energy field is the so-called spark chamber. Briefly it consists of a series of parallel metal plates (aluminium) spaced about 1 cm apart in a vessel containing a gas such as neon at atmospheric pressure. Alternate plates are connected to the positive terminal of a voltage supply, the other plates are connected to the negative terminal.

If the potential difference between adjacent plates is of the order of 10 kV no spark discharge occurs unless a trail of ions is formed in the gas between the plates. A high energy charged particle traversing the spark chamber is observed by photographing (with two cameras to reconstruct the three-dimensional trajectory) the sparks between successive plates. An electric field of a few hundred volts per cm sweeps the ions from the field between observed discharges. The space resolution of the track of the particle is inferior to that of the bubble chamber. However, if the high inter-plate voltage is applied as a short duration pulse (width about 10^{-7} sec), the time resolution of the device is far superior to that of the bubble chamber. Full advantage of this type of detector is taken if it is operated in time coincidence with a high energy scintillation or Cherenkov counter.

BIBLIOGRAPHY

W. J. PRICE, *Nuclear Radiation Detection*, McGraw-Hill, New York 1958. An excellent general account of the subject.

J. SHARPE, *Nuclear Radiation Detectors*, Methuen, London 1955.

D. H. WILKINSON, *Ionization Chambers and Counters*, Cambridge 1950.

B. B. ROSSI and H. H. STAUB, *Ionization Chambers and Counters*, McGraw-Hill 1949.

D. R. CORSON and R. R. WILSON in *Rev. Sci. Instruments* **19**, 207, 1948. A useful review article on gas counters.

H. H. STAUB, *Detection Methods* in Vol. 1, "Experimental Nuclear Physics". Ed. by E. SEGRÈ, Wiley, New York 1953.

H. A. BETHE and J. ASHKIN *Passage of Radiation through Matter* in Vol. 1. *Experimental Nuclear Physics*, Ed. by E. SEGRÈ, Wiley, New York 1953. A comprehensive survey of stopping power of nuclear radiation.

J. B. BIRKS, *Scintillation Counters*, Pergamon Press, London 1953.

S. C. CURRAN, *Luminescence and the Scintillation Counter*, Butterworths, London 1953.

J. V. JELLEY, *Cherenkov Radiation*, Pergamon Press, London 1958.

G. W. HUTCHINSON, *Cherenkov Detection*, in Vol. 8, "*Progress in Nuclear Physics*", Ed. by O. R. FRISCH, Pergamon Press, London 1960.

C. F. POWELL, P. H. FOWLER, and D. H. PERKINS, *The Study of Elementary Particles by the Photographic Method*, Pergamon Press, London 1959. A beautifully illustrated book of nuclear emulsion photographs with sufficient explanation of their interpretion.

J. ROBLAT, *Photographic Emulsion Technique* in Vol. 1, *Progress in Nuclear Physics*, Ed. by O. R. FRISCH, Pergamon Press, London 1950.

J. G. WILSON, *The Principles of Cloud Chamber Technique*, Cambridge 1951.

M. SNOWDEN, *The Diffusion Cloud Chamber* in Vol. 3, "*Progress in Nuclear Physics*", Ed. by O. R. FRISCH, Pergamon Press, London 1953.

C. DODD, *The Bubble Chamber*, in Vol. 5, *Progress in Nuclear Physics*, Ed. by O. R. FRISCH, Pergamon Press, London 1956.

D. V. BUGG, *The Bubble Chamber* in Vol. 7, *Progress in Nuclear Physics*, Ed. by O. R. FRISCH, Pergamon Press, London 1959.

An excellent account of detectors is given by various authors in Vol. XLV, *Handbuch der Physik*, Springer-Verlag, Berlin 1958.

An excellent survey of the Spark Chamber is given in *Rev. Sci. Instruments*, **30**, pp. 482–531 1961.

EXAMPLES

1. Compute the rate of loss of energy (in MeV per cm) of a proton travelling in air at S.T.P. with kinetic energy (a) 4·0, (b) 3·0, (c) 2·0, (d) 1·0. MeV. (Take $I = 13{\cdot}5Z$ eV in air).
2. Compute the specific ionization in air at S.T.P. due to a proton of kinetic energy (a) 4·0, (b) 3·0, (c) 2·0, (d) 1·0 MeV. Assume $W = 35{\cdot}6$ eV per ion-pair.

3. Consider a coaxial cylinder ionization chamber with electrode radii a and b. ($b > a$) charged to a potential difference V_0. Suppose n ion-pairs are produced at a distance x_0 from the axis of the counter at $t = 0$. Derive an expression for the potential pulse $P(t)$ developed at the central (positive) electrode in terms of C, V_0, a, b, x_0, t and k, where $v = k\,X^{0 \cdot 5}$ (v is the electron drift velocity in the field X) and C is the capacitance of the counter. Also derive an expression for the electron collection time t_1.
4. (a) In Question 3, calculate t_1 for an argon filled chamber in which $x_0 = b/2$, $V_0 = 760$ V, $p = 760$ mm Hg, $b = 5$ cm, $a = 0{\cdot}05$ cm and $k = 5 \times 10^5$ units at 760 mm Hg.
(b) Calculate the pulse height $P(t_1)$ if $n = 5000$. The chamber is 30 cm long and the input capacitance of the attached amplifier is 10 pF. Plot $P(t)$ as a function of t for $0 < t < t_1$.
5. A parallel plate ionization chamber consists of argon at a pressure of 1000 mm of Hg. An alpha particle track forms 10,000 ion-pairs parallel to and distant 3·0 cm from the positive electrode. A potential difference of 2800 V is applied to the chamber via a high resistor. Calculate the initial rate of rise of the pulse, the pulse height at the instant when all the electrons are collected, and the final pulse height. Electron drift velocities v in argon at different X/p values are:

$v \times 10^{-5}$ cm sec^{-1}	2·0	3·0	4·0	4·7	5·0
X/p	0·05	0·20	0·50	0·80	1·0

6. A proportional counter, anode wire diam. 0·075 mm, cathode diam. 1·00 cm, is filled to a pressure of 20 cm Hg with a 90–10 per cent argon–methane mixture. The threshold of the proportional region is 610 V. Using the Rose and Korff formula, plot the gas multiplication A versus applied voltage V graph over the range 800 V to 1200 V. If the voltage is set so that $A = 1000$, what per cent variation in V is allowed if A is to be stable to ± 1 per cent? (Room temperature 15°C) (Use the "f" values in Table 5).
7. A current ionization chamber is filled with hydrogen gas at 20 atmospheres to detect fast neutrons. The sensitive volume of the chamber is 0·5 litre and it is irradiated with a flux of 10^7, 1 MeV, neutrons per cm^2 per sec. Assume that a fast neutron scattered by a proton transfers half its kinetic energy to the proton. Calculate the saturation ionization current, given that $W = 36$ eV per ion-pair and the scattering cross section for 1 MeV neutrons is 4·5 barns per hydrogen atom. (Gas temperature is 17°C.)
8. Observations of the total number of developed grains in an emulsion track in terms of the residual range R (unit is 0·85 microns) are given below for a meson and a proton which enter and come to rest in the emulsion. Plot a graph and estimate the rest mass ratio of the proton and meson.

MESON TRACK

R	N
151	145
200	182
251	219
316	263
398	316
501	380
631	457

PROTON TRACK

R	N
151	190
200	246
251	295
316	363
398	447
501	550
631	661
749	813
1000	977

CHAPTER 12

ELECTRONIC TECHNIQUES

12.1. DIFFERENTIATION AND INTEGRATION

In radio engineering, one is primarily concerned with continuous or quasi-continuous sinusoidal voltages. The concepts of reactance, impedance, and phase, are meaningful and useful. On the other hand, the nuclear physicist is interested in pulses of current or voltage which may occur at random in time. The methods of Fourier analysis can, in principle, be

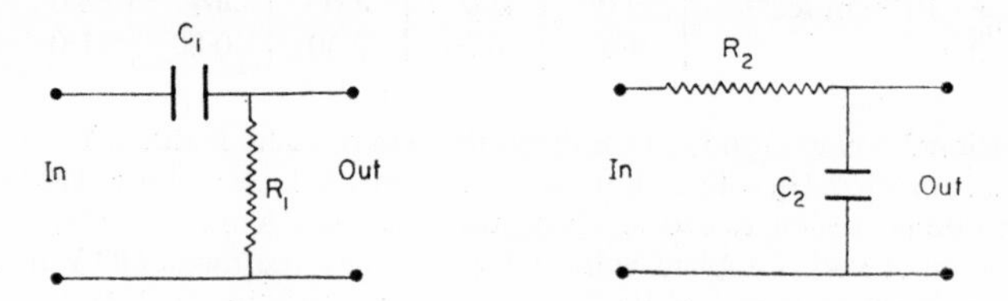

FIG. 1. (a) Differentiating network; (b) integrating network.

applied to electrical pulses, but it is more convenient to discuss the operation of pulse circuits in a more direct way.

A common feature of pulse circuits is the C–R network, and its effect on the size and shape of pulses is of great practical importance. The C–R networks shown in Fig. 1 are (a) a *differentiating* circuit, and (b) an *integrating* circuit. Consider the result of applying a step function potential of height V_0 at time $t = 0$ to the input terminals of the differentiating circuit of time constant $T_1 = C_1 R_1$. The output signal can be derived with the aid of the important principle: "it is impossible to abruptly change the potential difference across a capacitor with a *finite* charging or discharging current". Thus at $t = 0$, the potential difference across R_1 rises immediately from zero to V_0 and then decreases exponentially, $V = V_0 \exp(-t/T_1)$, as the current charging C_1 decreases exponentially from V_0/R_1 to zero. (Fig. 2)

Now consider the transmission of a rectangular voltage pulse of height V_0 and width (duration) T_0 through a differentiating network. The input pulse is equivalent to the sum of two step-function signals (Fig. 3(a)).

(1) $V = 0$ for $t < 0$; $V = V_0$ for $t > 0$.

(2) $V = 0$ for $t < T_0$; $V = -V_0$ for $t > T_0$.

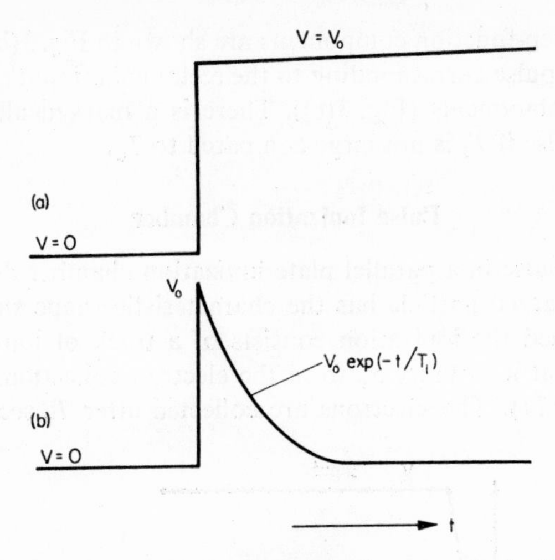

FIG. 2. (a) Step function voltage applied to input terminals of Fig. 1 (a); (b) output pulse.

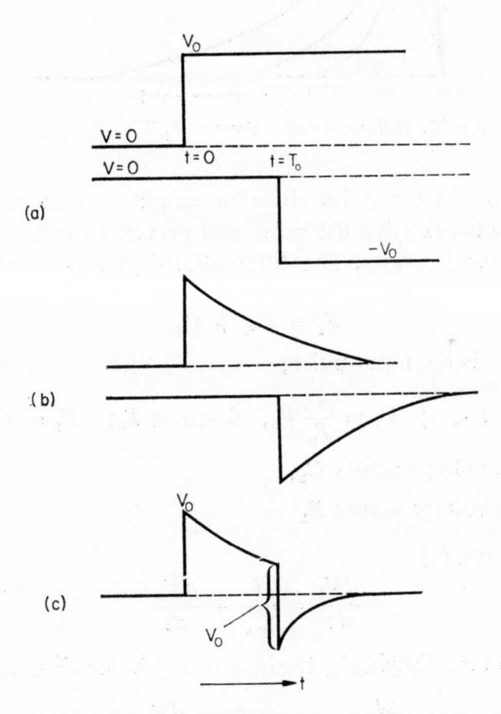

FIG. 3. (a) Rectangular pulse analysed into two step-functions; (b) output components (for $T_1 = T_0$); (c) superposition of output components.

The output step-function components are shown in Fig. 3(b) for $T_0 = T_1$, and the output pulse corresponding to the rectangular input pulse is the sum of these two components (Fig. 3(c)). There is a marked alteration in the shape of the pulse if T_1 is not large compared to T_0.

Pulse Ionization Chamber

The voltage pulse in a parallel plate ionization chamber due to the ionization by a charged particle has the characteristic shape shown in Fig. 4. We have assumed the ionization consists of a track of ion-pairs, formed parallel to and at a distance x_0 from the electron collection electrode (see Fig. 4, Chapter 11). The electrons are collected after T_0 sec ($\sim 10^{-6}$ sec).

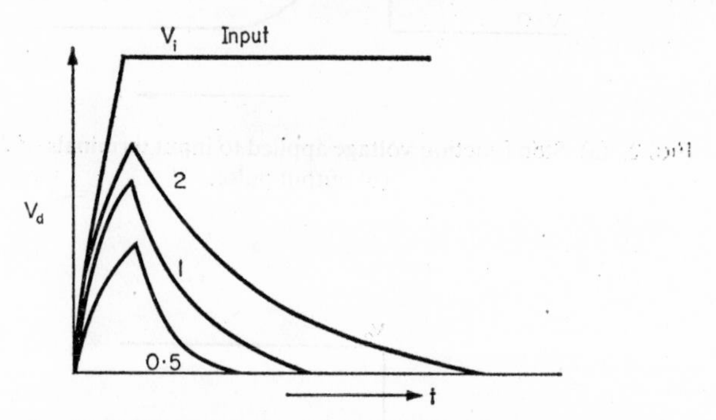

FIG. 4. Input pulse V_i. Differentiated pulse for $T_1/T_0 = 2$, 1, and 0·5.

At an early stage in the pulse chamber amplifier a short time constant differentiating network clips the pulse and prevents overlap of consecutive pulses at high counting rates. The differentiated pulse V_d can be determined as follows:

$$V_i = V_{c_1} + V_d \tag{1}$$

where V_i is the input pulse;

$$V_i = 0, \quad t < 0; \quad V_i = \frac{t}{T_0} V_0, \quad 0 < t < T_0; \quad V_i = V_0, \; t > T_0$$

V_{c_1} is the voltage across C_1,

V_d is the voltage across R_1

Differentiating eqn. (1)

$$\frac{dV_i}{dt} = \frac{i}{C_1} + \frac{dV_d}{dt} \tag{2}$$

Now $i = \dfrac{V_d}{R_1}$ and multiplying by the integrating factor e^{t/T_1}, where $T_1 = C_1 R_1$

(2) becomes
$$\frac{d}{dt}(V_d\, e^{t/T_1}) = e^{t/T_1} \frac{dV_i}{dt} \tag{3}$$

for the interval $0 < t < T_0$, $\dfrac{dV_i}{dt} = \dfrac{V_0}{T_0}$ and integrating eqn. (3) we obtain

$$V_d e^{t/T_1} = \frac{T_1}{T_0} V_0 e^{t/T_1} + A \tag{4}$$

the constant A is found by using the fact that at $t = 0$, $V_d = 0$.

$$\therefore A = -\frac{T_1}{T_0} V_0.$$

Substituting for A in eqn. (4) and re-arranging, we obtain

$$V_d = \frac{T_1}{T_0} V_0(1 - e^{-t/T_1}); \quad 0 < t < T_0 \tag{5}$$

For the interval $t > T_0$, $dV_i/dt = 0$ (strictly this derivative is finite but small and is determined by the positive ion drift velocity).

Hence eqn. (3) becomes

$$\frac{d}{dt}(V_d e^{t/T_1}) = 0 \tag{6}$$

Integrating, we get

$$V_d e^{t/T_1} = B \tag{7}$$

The constant B is obtained by matching the values of V_d at $t = T_0$ given by eqns. (5) and (7).

$$B = \frac{T_1}{T_0} V_0(1 - e^{-T_0/T_1}) e^{T_0/T_1}$$

$$\therefore V_d = \frac{T_1}{T_0} V_0(e^{T_0/T_1} - 1) e^{-t/T_1}, \quad t > T_0 \tag{8}$$

The output pulse V_d from the differentiating network has the shape illustrated in Fig. 4. Three waveforms are shown for three different ratios of T_1/T_0. Notice that severe pulse clipping ($T_1 < T_0$) has a marked effect on the pulse amplitude. The differentiating network sets the low frequency limit of the amplifier; the amplifier does not respond to the slowly increasing part of the input pulse. The gain of the amplifier falls off at high frequencies and the upper frequency limit is determined by the time constant T_2 of the integrating network C_2R_2 (Fig. 1(b)).

Consider the transmission of the output pulse of the network of Fig. 1(a) through an integrating network (Fig. 1(b)). The output pulse of the integrating network is given by

$$V_c = V_d - V_{R_2} = V_d - C_2 R_2 \frac{dV_c}{dt} \tag{9}$$

where V_d is given by the solutions (5) or (8).

For $0 < t < T_0$, the relevant differential equation is

$$\frac{dV_c}{dt} + \frac{V_c}{T_2} = \frac{T_1}{T_0 T_2} V_0(1 - e^{-t/T_1}) \tag{10}$$

Multiplying by $\exp(t/T_2)$, integrating, and using the boundary condition $V_c = 0$ at $t = 0$ it is easy to show that

$$V_c = \frac{T_1}{T_0} V_0(1 - e^{-t/T_2}) - \frac{T_1^2 V_0}{T_0(T_1 - T_2)}(e^{-t/T_1} - e^{-t/T_2}) \tag{11}$$

The solution for the output potential for $t > T_0$ is obtained using eqn. (8) and is given by

$$V_c = \frac{T_1^2 V_0}{T_0(T_1 - T_2)}(e^{T_0/T_1} - 1)\, e^{-t/T_1} - \frac{T_1 T_2 V_0}{T_0(T_1 - T_2)}(e^{T_0/T_2} - 1)\, e^{-t/T_2} \tag{12}$$

One is interested in *when* the output pulse reaches its maximum value, and the height of the pulse at this moment. This maximum always occurs after $t = T_0$, and it is found by differentiating eqn. (12). V_c reaches its maximum value at

$$t_m = \frac{T_1 T_2}{T_1 - T_2} \ln\left[\frac{e^{T_0/T_2} - 1}{e^{T_0/T_1} - 1}\right] \tag{13}$$

and the pulse amplitude at this instant is

$$V_m = \frac{T_1 V_0 [e^{T_0/T_1} - 1]^{\frac{T_1}{T_1 - T_2}}}{T_0 [e^{T_0/T_2} - 1]^{\frac{T_2}{T_1 - T_2}}} \tag{14}$$

For $T_0 = T_1 = T_2$, $V_m = 0{\cdot}35\, V_0$.

The attenuation of the pulse V_0 by the differentiating and integrating networks is a drawback, but it is important to realise that with a pulse ionization chamber it is the signal-to-noise ratio which must be kept as high as possible. It is beyond the scope of this book to discuss sources of electronic noise.† However, there is a range of values for T_1 and T_2 which provides the best signal-to-noise ratios. The choice $T_1 = T_2$ with T_1 a few times T_0 is suitable.

12.2. PULSE AMPLIFIER

The pulse height at the electron collector electrode of an ionization chamber may be as small as 20 or 30 μV. If it is smaller it may be difficult to distinguish it against noise produced in the attached amplifier. In order to amplify pulses with a short rise time of the order of a microsecond or less it is essential that the amplifier should have a high frequency cut off. The rise time of a pulse is usually defined as the time for the pulse to increase from 0·1 to 0·9 of the full pulse height.

If we are only interested in counting the ionization pulses in a gas counter then it is not necessary for the height of the output pulse of the amplifier to be accurately proportional to the height of the counter pulse. In order

† Consult Gillespie's book (see Bibliography).

to determine the energy of the ionizing particle, the height of the counter pulse must be measured and this requires the use of a *linear* pulse amplifier. It is difficult to maintain the voltage gain of an amplifier constant over long periods of time, due to changes in the values of the components. Amplifiers employing negative feedback, in the sense that a certain fraction β of the output voltage is fed-back into the input stage, have a stable gain. Provided the value of β does not change with time and that the fed-back signal is

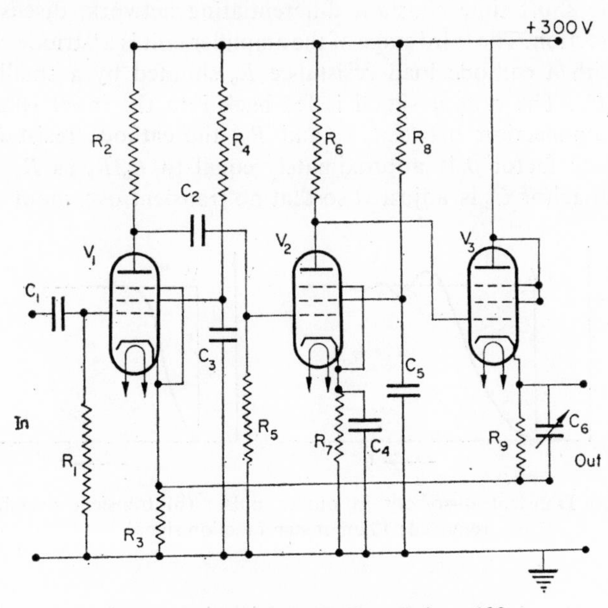

FIG. 5. Linear pulse amplifier. Gain ~ 100.

R_1 500 kΩ	R_5 100 kΩ	R_9 10 kΩ	C_4 0·01 μF
R_2 22 kΩ	R_6 27 kΩ	C_1 100 pF	C_5 0·01 μF
R_3 100 Ω	R_7 220 Ω	C_2 47 pF	C_6 20 pF
R_4 47 kΩ	R_8 47 kΩ	C_3 0·01 μF	V_1, V_2, V_3 6AC7

exactly 180° out of phase with the input signal the gain A' of a feedback amplifier is related to the gain A without feedback by

$$A' = \frac{A}{1 + \beta A}$$

Thus if $A = 1000$ and $\beta = \frac{1}{100}$, $A' \sim 100$. The considerable reduction in gain with feedback is the price we have to pay for increased stability. Variations in A of ± 10 per cent cause variations in A' of $\pm 0 \cdot 3$ per cent.

A pulse linear amplifier frequently consists of three "ring-of-three" units in cascade. A ring-of-three amplifier is shown in Fig. 5. The first unit is the pre-amplifier which is attached to the ionization chamber by a very short cable. The output stage of the pre-amplifier is a cathode follower with its characteristic low output impedance. It is therefore practical to connect the output terimals of the pre-amplifier, by a coaxial screened cable several feet long, to the input terminals of the main amplifier, the latter comprising two ring-of-three units in cascade.

The first two stages of the ring-of-three amplifier are conventional. The coupling network C_2–R_5 between the pentode valves V_1 and V_2 may be used as the short time constant differentiating network, discussed in the preceding section. The third stage of the amplifier unit is a "triode connected" pentode with a cathode load resistance R_9 shunted by a small trimming capacitor C_6. The output signal is fed-back into the input stage through the direct connection between R_9 and R_3, the cathode resistance of V_1. The feedback factor β is approximately equal to R_3/R_9 as $R_9 \gg R_3$. The trimmer capacitor C_6 is adjusted so that no transient overshoot of the type

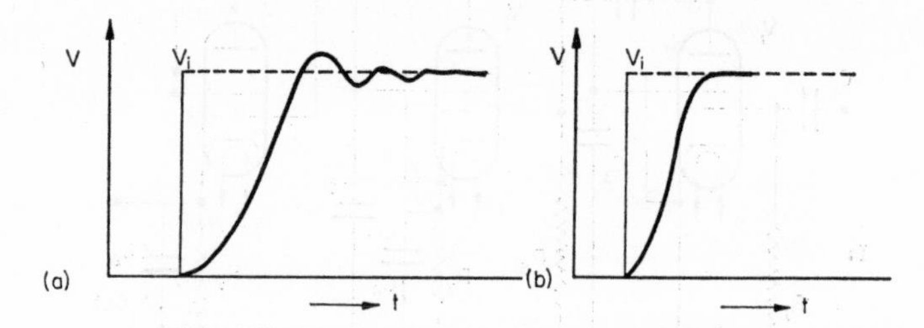

FIG. 6. (a) Transient overshoot in output pulse; (b) transient overshoot just removed; V_i input step function signal.

depicted in Fig. 6 occurs with a fast rising input pulse to the amplifier. Correct choice of the anode load R_6 of V_2 enables a direct connection to be made between the anode of V_2 and the control grid of V_3 without drawing grid current. Full details of pulse ionization chamber amplifiers are given in the book by Elmore and Sands (see bibliography).

12.3. VOLTAGE DISCRIMINATORS

It is often necessary to discriminate between pulses of different amplitude. For instance, a BF_3 proportional counter will respond to gamma rays and neutrons; the neutron pulses associated with the reaction $B^{10}(n, \alpha)\, Li^7$ will be much larger than the gamma ray pulses. A voltage discriminator rejects all voltage pulses below a pre-determined height and produces an output pulse if the selected level is exceeded. An ideal discriminator or pulse height selector (P.H.S.) should satisfy the following requirements:

(1) High stability and the sensitivity to discriminate between input pulses differing in height by a fraction of one volt.

(2) Short rise and recovery times.

(3) Ability to handle a wide range in input pulse height without overloading the circuit.

(4) Generate an output pulse of standard height if the pre-determined level is exceeded.

The Schmitt trigger circuit meets all these requirements. The mode of operation of the circuit is as follows. Suppose the discriminator level potentiometer R_3 of Fig. 7 is set so that the control grid of the pentode V_1 is at earth potential; then V_1 is cut off and V_2 conducts, with the cathode potential ~ 100 V above earth potential. The pentode V_2 and the cathode load resistor R_8 function as a cathode follower with the control grid potential

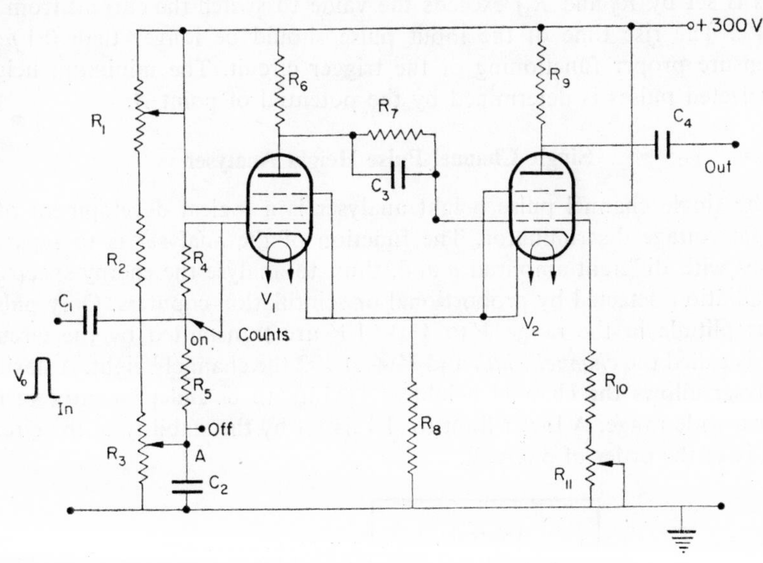

FIG. 7. Voltage discriminator of the Schmitt type.

R_1 50 kΩ	R_5 1 MΩ	R_9 5·6 kΩ	C_2 0·1 μF
R_2 75 kΩ	R_6 3·9 kΩ	R_{10} 40 kΩ	C_3 25 pF
R_3 50 kΩ	R_7 100 kΩ	R_{11} 20 kΩ	C_4 0·01 μF
R_4 2 MΩ	R_8 10 kΩ	C_1 0·01 μF	V_1, V_2 6AC7

a few volts below that of the cathode (N.B. $R_7 - R_{10} + R_{11}$ acts as a d.c. potential divider and effectively determines the common cathode potential). The trigger circuit is in a stable state in this condition. If, however, the potential of the control grid of V_1 is increased to within a few volts of the cathode potential (~ 100 V) V_1 will begin to conduct anode current. A rapid transfer of current from V_2 to V_1 occurs as the falling potential of the anode of V_1 is communicated via R_7 and $R_{10} + R_{11}$ to the control grid of V_2. The signal is fed-back from the second stage to the first stage via the common cathode load resistor (N.B. R_8 is not shunted by a by-pass capacitor). The small capacitance C_3 in parallel with R_7 speeds up the transfer of current from V_2 to V_1. The regeneration process ceases when the control grid potential of V_2 has fallen about 10 V, and V_2 is now cut-off, as the common cathode potential is still $\sim$100 V. The rapid transfer of current produces a positive step function signal at the anode of V_2 of height $\sim$50 V. The circuit is returned to its initial stable state if the control grid potential of V_1 falls a few volts below the potential needed to trigger the circuit into the second stable state (the difference in triggering voltage with a rising and a decreasing potential is known as the hysteresis of the circuit). The circuit shown in Fig. 7 operates with positive input pulses; an output pulse is produced if the amplitude V_0 of the input pulse superimposed on the potential of point A (this is set by R_3 and R_1) exceeds the value to switch the current from V_2 to V_1. The rise time of the input pulse should be longer than 0·1 μsec to ensure proper functioning of the trigger circuit. The minimum height of selected pulses is determined by the potential of point A.

Single Channel Pulse Height Analyser

The single channel pulse height analyser is a logical development of a simple voltage discriminator. The function of the analyser is to separate pulses with different amplitudes and, thus, to analyse the energy spectrum of radiation detected by proportional or scintillation counters. Only pulses of amplitude in the range V to $V + \Delta V$ are transmitted by the circuit. ΔV is called the *channel width* and $V + \Delta V/2$ the channel height. A flexible analyser allows the channel height and width to be independently varied over a wide range. A lower limit to ΔV is set by the stability of the circuit and is of the order of one volt.

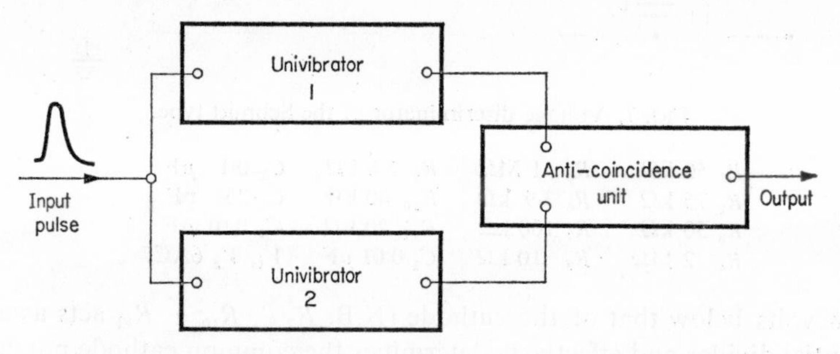

FIG. 8. Block diagram of a single channel pulse height analyser.

The principle of operation of the analyser is easy to understand with the aid of Fig. 8. A positive input pulse V_i is simultaneously applied to two univibrator circuits†, biased differently so that univibrator I delivers a positive output pulse of a constant height V_0 if $V_i > V$, and univibrator II

† The univibrator is discussed in more detail in section 12.4.

delivers a positive output pulse of height V_0 if $V_i > V + \Delta V$. The output pulses of the univibrators are fed to an anticoincidence unit. The function of the latter circuit, is to produce an output pulse of standard height if a suitable positive pulse appears at one of the input channels, provided a simultaneous positive pulse does *not* appear at the other input channel. Thus if univibrator 1 is triggered by V_i but not univibrator 2, the anticoincidence circuit is triggered and an output pulse is transmitted by the complete analyser. Triggering both univibrators ($V_i > V + \Delta V$) will not operate the anticoincidence unit. There is a number of important requirements to be met in the successful operation of an anticoincidence unit. The stability of the pulse height analyser primarily depends on maintaining the triggering potential levels of the two univibrators constant in time, and especially the difference in triggering level, ΔV.

Multi-channel Pulse Height Analyser (Kick-sorter)

When the energy spectrum of some radiation source extends over a wide range it is very tedious to record the spectrum using a single channel pulse height discriminator. Moreover, the mean lifetime of the radiation may be short and it is then highly desirable to record as much information as quickly and efficiently as possible. In the last ten years or so there has been a great deal of ingenuity applied to designing versatile multi-channel pulse height analysers (popularly known as kick-sorters).

The early multi-channel analysers were essentially combinations of $n + 1$ discriminators to define n equal counting-channels. Each of the discriminators has a low and high bias level, the latter corresponding to the lower level of the adjacent discriminator. It is out of place in this book to discuss the elaborate sorting and recording circuits required in a stable multi-channel analyser.†

12.4. THE UNIVIBRATOR

The pulse from a gas or scintillation detector is in many cases not of ideal shape for operating subsequent electronic units. After amplification the counter pulse is shaped by triggering a univibrator circuit. One form of univibrator is depicted in Fig. 9. In the quiescent state, the right-hand triode V_2 is cut-off and the left-hand triode V_1 is conducting, drawing grid current limited by the high resistance R_3. The common cathode potential of the circuit shown in Fig. 9 is of the order of 80 V. A short negative input pulse of a few volts amplitude is sufficient to flip the circuit into its quasi-stationary state, with the potential of the grid of V_1 driven 70 V below cut-off. The anode potential of V_2 is now about 80 V below the H.T. positive line and it will remain stationary until V_1 begins to conduct current; the circuit then quickly returns to its original state with V_2 cut-off. The duration

† A useful survey of the subject is given in the book by R. L. Chase (see bibliography).

of the quasi-stable regime is determined by the rate of charging of C_3 via R_3 whilst V_1 is cut-off. A useful approximate rule of thumb for the duration T of the quasi-stable state is

$$T = \frac{1}{3} R_3 C_3$$

Output rectangular pulses of width T and amplitude ~ 80 V can be obtained from the anode of V_1 (positive) or the anode V_2 (negative). There are limits

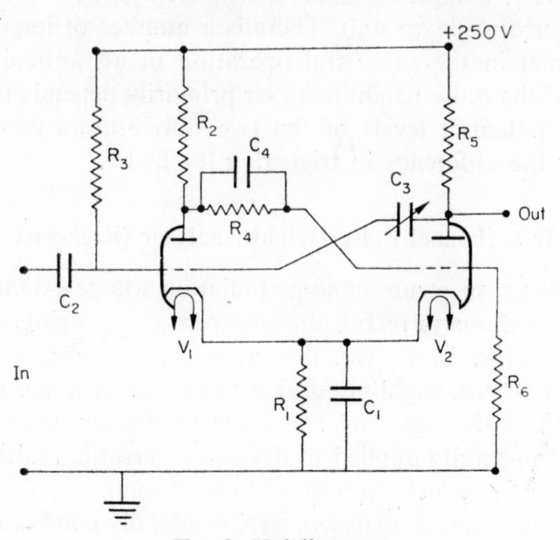

FIG. 9. Univibrator.

R_1	10 kΩ	R_5	10 kΩ	C_3	20–500 pF
R_2	10 kΩ	R_6	150 kΩ	C_4	20 pF
R_3	330 kΩ	C_1	0·01 μF	V_1, V_2	6SN7
R_4	220 kΩ	C_2	20 pF		

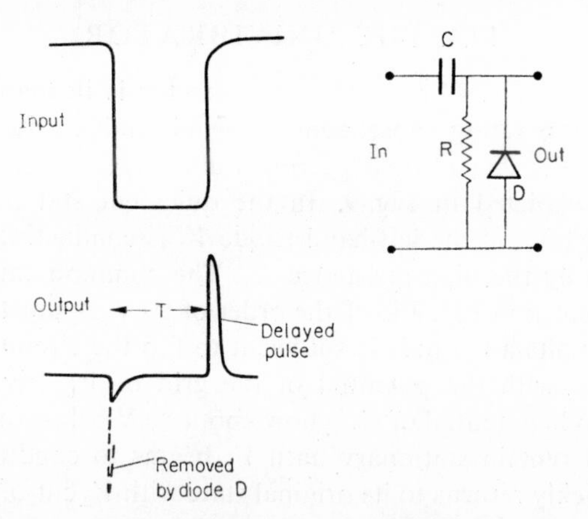

FIG. 10. Production of delayed pulse by sharp differentiation. (A semiconductor diode is suitable for D.)

to the value of T determined by upper and lower practical limits for the values of the components R_3 and C_3.

The univibrator is easily adapted for use in a "delayed coincidence unit". Thus, if the circuit of Fig. 9 is triggered with the fast rise of a negative pulse from a Geiger counter, and the rectangular negative pulse of width T at the anode of V_2 is sharply differentiated, a delayed positive pulse is obtained (Fig. 10). The negative pulse coincident with the triggering pulse is removed by connecting a diode in parallel with R.

12.5. SCALING CIRCUITS

Scaling circuits in nuclear physics are required for the accurate counting and recording of pulses from nuclear radiation detectors. The simplest type of scaler is based on the binary system, dividing the number of input pulses by 2, 4, 8, 16, 32, 64, etc. One of the most reliable "scale-of-two" circuits is shown in Fig. 11.

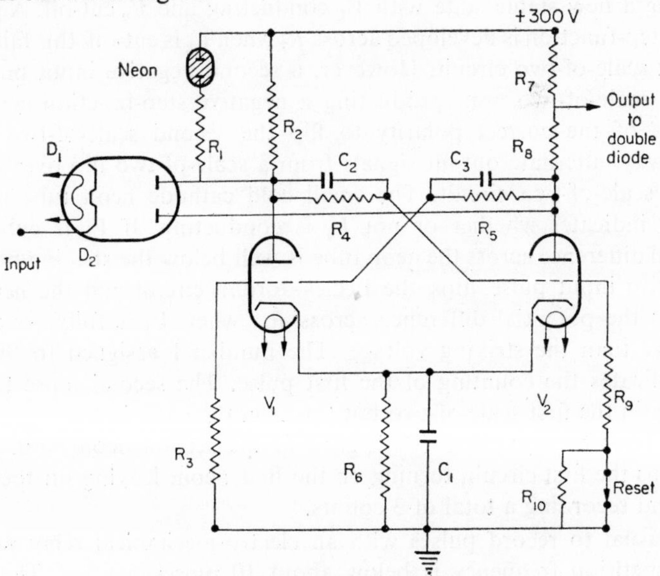

FIG. 11. Scale-of-two, flip–flop circuit.

R_1	1 MΩ	R_6	10 kΩ	C_1	0·01 μF
R_2	20 kΩ	R_7	5·6 kΩ	C_2	50 pF
R_3	100 kΩ	R_8	15 kΩ	C_3	50 pF
R_4	200 kΩ	R_9	100 kΩ	D_1, D_2	6H6
R_5	200 kΩ	R_{10}	50 kΩ	V_1, V_2	6SN7

The heart of this scale-of-two is the Eccles–Jordan "flip-flop" circuit. This consists of a bi-stable double triode arrangement with cross couplings from anode to grid. If the right-hand triode is conducting, with its grid potential a volt or two positive with respect to the common cathode potential, the left-hand triode is well cut-off, because the grid potential is one third of the anode potential of V_2. Typical potentials at various electrodes are: cathodes 80 V; grid of V_2 82 V, grid of V_1 47 V, anode of V_2 140 V, anode of V_1 280 V. The circuit is stable to small fluctuations in the anode and grid potentials.

The "flip-flop" circuit is easily converted into a scale-of-two by coupling two diodes D_1, D_2, directly to the anodes of V_1 and V_2 respectively. The common cathode potential of D_1 and D_2 is normally that of the H.T. positive line, and under these conditions neither diode is conducting. A fast rising negative pulse applied to the input terminal is transmitted via the diode D_1 to the grid of V_2; the rate of fall of the potential is determined primarily by the ratio of the grid-to-earth capacitance and the capacitance of C_2. Regenerative amplification occurs, the anode potential of V_2 rising until it is "caught" by the diode D_2, when the latter becomes conducting. The anode potential of V_2 then follows the input potential, the circuit acquiring a new stable state with V_1 conducting and V_2 cut-off. A positive output step-function is developed across R_7 when V_2 is cut-off, this fails to flip the next scale-of-two circuit. However, a second negative input pulse flips the first scale-of-two unit, producting a negative step-function across R_7, which is of the correct polarity to flip the second scale-of-two circuit. In this way, alternate output signals from a scale-of-two flip over the succeeding scale-of-two circuit. The small cold cathode neon tube in series with R_1 indicates whether or not V_1 is conducting. If V_1 is cut-off, the potential difference across the neon tube is well below the striking potential. A negative input pulse flips the Eccles–Jordan circuit and the neon tube glows as the potential difference across R_2, when V_1 is fully conducting, is greater than the striking voltage. The number 1 assigned to this neon bulb indicates the counting of the first pulse. The second pulse turns off the neon in the first scale-of-two but turns on the neon in the second scale-of-two. Thus the number 2 is assigned to the second neon bulb. A third pulse flips the first circuit, turning on the first neon, leaving on the second neon, and recording a total of 3 counts.

It is usual to record pulses with an electro-mechanical relay when the pulse repetition frequency is below about 10 pulses per sec. The output of the last scale-of-two circuit triggers a univibrator which delivers a rectangular pulse of sufficient amplitude to operate the electro-mechanical relay.

It is more convenient to record the counted pulses using the decimal system. A scale-of-sixteen unit consisting of four scale-of-two circuits in series can easily be modified, with the aid of one extra diode, to function as a scale-of-ten.† However, this modification of a scale-of-sixteen is wasteful of valves and more direct decimal scaling units are to be preferred.

† W. C. Elmore and M. Sands, *Electronics*, McGraw-Hill, New York, pp. 209–212, 1949.

The three currently available types of decimal scaling tube are: the gas filled multi-electrode cold cathode tube, the ribbon beam tube, and the trochotron. The last two are high vacuum tubes and have short resolving times and can therefore be successfully employed at very high counting rates. The gas filled decimal counting tubes are normally limited to counting speeds of a few kc/s but they are ideal for scaling units at low and moderate counting rates.

Gas-filled Counting Tube (Dekatron)

The dekatron† is a neon filled (13 cm Hg pressure) tube containing an anode in the form of a flat disc of diameter ~ 1 cm. Surrounding the anode are thirty symmetrically spaced wire electrodes about 0·02 in. from the anode. Ten of the wires are internally connected and are called Guide *A* electrodes; a second group of ten internally connected wires adjacent to the first set are called Guide *B* electrodes; nine of the remaining wires are internally connected and are known as cathodes K_1 to K_9; the last electrode is called the output cathode K_0. The geometrical arrangement of the first few electrodes is illustrated in Fig. 12(a). The operation of the counting tube depends on the fact that the glow discharge always takes place between the anode and the electrode at the lowest potential. The guide *A* and *B* electrodes are biased 20 V above the potential of the cathodes so that normally the discharge rests on one of the cathodes. A simple drive circuit for a dekatron is illustrated in Fig. 13.

A large negative pulse of amplitude greater than 100 V and duration greater than 60 μsec from a univibrator is applied to the dekatron circuit. Suppose the discharge is to the cathode K_1; a large negative pulse applied

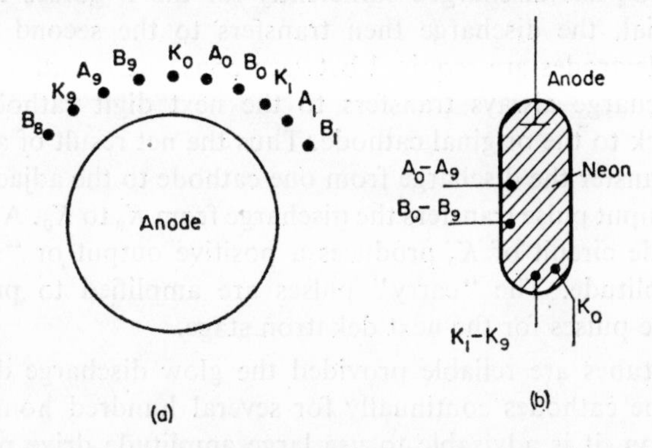

FIG. 12. (a) Geometrical arrangement of electrodes around anode disc in a dekatron counting tube; (b) circuit dekatron symbol. N.B. There are five pin connections.

† R. C. BACON and J. R. POLLARD, *Electronic Engineering* **22**, 48, 1950.

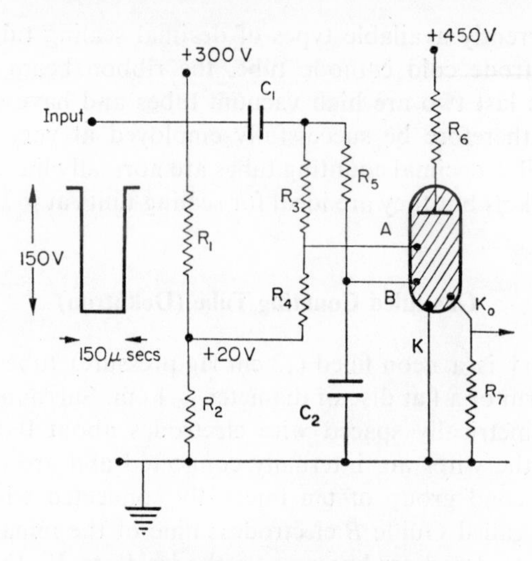

FIG. 13. Simple dekatron drive circuit.

R_1 150 kΩ	R_4 47 kΩ	R_7 47 kΩ
R_2 20 kΩ	R_5 47 kΩ	C_1 0·05 μF
R_3 47 kΩ	R_6 680 kΩ	C_2 0·002 μF

to the Guide A electrodes transfers the discharge from K_1 to guide A_1. The pulse applied to the guide B electrodes is integrated by the network $R_5 C_2$ and the potential of the B guides is still well below earth potential just after the guide A electrodes return to their normal bias potential of +20 V. The discharge transfers from A_1 to B_1 soon after the end of the input drive pulse. After C_2 has discharged sufficiently for the B guides to rise above earth potential, the discharge then transfers to the second cathode K_2. Two guide electrodes are required between consecutive cathodes to ensure that the discharge always transfers to the next digit cathode and does not jump back to the original cathode. Thus the net result of a single drive pulse is to transfer the discharge from one cathode to the adjacent cathode. Every tenth input pulse transfers the discharge from K_9 to K_0. A load resistor in the cathode circuit of K_0 produces a positive output or "carry" pulse of 15 V amplitude. The "carry" pulses are amplified to produce large negative drive pulses for the next dekatron stage.

Dekatron tubes are reliable provided the glow discharge does not rest on one of the cathodes continually for several hundred hours. For long term operation, it is advisable to use large amplitude drive pulses and to ensure that their width is considerably greater than 60 μsec. Normally, gas filled counting tubes can be relied on for counting speeds up to 5000 counts per sec. However, it is possible to design this type of tube with a resolving time as small as 10 μsec.

The ribbon-beam tube is a high vacuum device, in which a narrow electron beam from a thermionic cathode is deflected by a positive pulse of short rise time applied to a pair of deflector plates. The electron beam first passes through a slotted electrode containing ten holes, then to the anode, which itself has slots, so that part of the beam strikes a fluorescent screen. Each input pulse deflects the electron beam so that it passes through the adjacent hole of the slotted electrode and thus displaces the fluorescent spot of light on the end of the tube. There are ten stable positions of the electron beam, and each position is labelled with the appropriate digit. A detailed account of the ribbon-beam tube is given by Van Overbeek, Jonker and Rodenhuis†. This type of tube can operate satisfactorily without elaborate circuitry, with a resolving time of 30 μsec. It is possible to operate the tube with a resolving time as short as 0·25 μsec.

An ingenious high speed counting tube called the *trochotron* makes use of crossed electric and magnetic fields to focus the electron beam in one of ten stable positions. A description of the tube and a suitable driving circuit is given in the review article by Kandiah and Chaplin. Trochotrons with resolving times as short as 0·2 μsec, are obtained without resorting to elaborate circuits.

12.6. COINCIDENCE CIRCUITS

The coincidence technique has many applications in studying the time relationships of nuclear and cosmic radiations. One of the first coincidence circuits was introduced by Rossi.†† This was the first use of a "parallel" type coincidence circuit. A number of valves in parallel with a common anode load resistor, function as a number of parallel switches. A schematic diagram of the Rossi circuit with two input channels is depicted in Fig. 14.

The circuit is drawn for simplicity using triodes, but in practice pentodes are often preferred. The common anode load resistance R_1 is chosen to be a lot greater than the effective d.c. resistance R_d of each triode. The equivalent circuit is shown in Fig. 14(b). Normally V_1 and V_2 conduct small currents limited by the large value of R_1. Negative pulses from two counters are applied to inputs 1 and 2 respectively. The pulse amplitudes should be large enough to cut-off the anode current. If V_1 or V_2 is cut-off by a negative input pulse, the common rise in anode potential is only a few volts. This state of affairs corresponds to opening one of the switches K_1, K_2, in the equivalent circuit. However, if both valves are cut-off by the arrival of coincidence pulses at the input terminals, the common anode potential will rise to that of the H.T. positive line and a large positive "coincidence" output pulse is produced. This large "coincidence" pulse is easily discriminated from the small output pulses produced when one, but not both, valves are cut-off.

† Van Overbeek, Jonker, and Rodenhuis, *Philips. Tech. Rev.* **14**, 313, 1953.
†† B. Rossi, *Nature* **125**, 636, 1930.

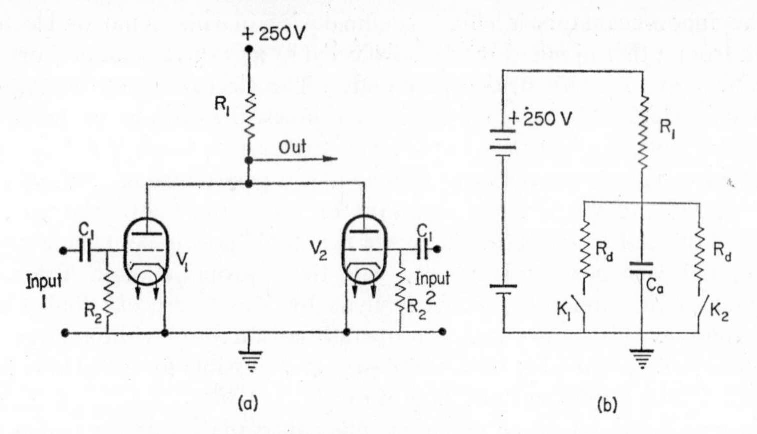

FIG. 14. (a) Two channel Rossi coincident circuit ($R_1 \sim 500\,\text{k}\Omega$); (b) equivalent circuit. $R_1 \gg R_a$.

The above description over-simplifies the action of the circuit. It is important to consider the rate of increase of the common anode potential when both valves are cut-off. The anode potential rises at a rate determined by the time constant $T(R_1 C_a)$, where C_a is the common anode-to-earth capacitance (this is increased with a three valve Rossi circuit). If the duration of the simultaneous input pulses is t_i the height of the coincident output pulse is

$$V_0 = (V_b - V_a)\left\{1 - \exp\left(-\frac{t_i}{T}\right)\right\} \tag{6}$$

where V_b is the battery voltage, and V_a is the common anode potential when K_1 and K_2 are closed. If t_i is small compared to T, the coincidence output pulse amplitude is well below the theoretical maximum of $V_b - V_a$ and it is difficult to discriminate the coincident from the non-coincident pulses. An important parameter of a coincidence circuit is the resolving time τ, defined as the minimum time interval between the beginnings of pulses at the two input channels, so that the pulses are *not* recorded as a coincidence event. If $T \ll t_i$, $\tau = t_i$; however, in the normal Rossi circuit, $T > t_i$ and τ is greater than t_i.

For higher resolution coincidence work, the "fast" Rossi circuit (Fig. 15) is preferred. The essential modification of the original circuit is the large reduction in the anode load resistor R_1 so that the time constant $R_1 C_a$ is 1 μsec. Miniature pentodes or germanium diodes are often used in place of triodes. The germanium diode D is biased by adjusting the potentiometer setting of R_3 so that it does not conduct when one or both valves is conducting. Coincident input pulses cut-off V_1 and V_2 and the common anode potential rises at a fast rate; D conducts and passes on a positive output pulse to the recording circuit.

It is always necessary to take into consideration the number of random or accidental coincidences. If the durations of the input pulses to a coinci-

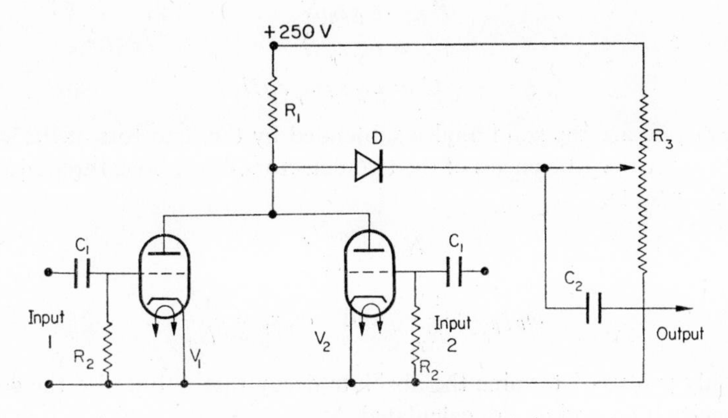

FIG. 15. "Fast" Rossi circuit.

R_1 10 kΩ C_1 50 pF
R_2 50 kΩ C_2 100 pF
R_3 20 kΩ D Germanium diode

dence circuit are different, then it is convenient to denote the resolving time by τ_{12} if the pulse in the input channel 1 precedes the input pulse in channel 2, and τ_{21} if the pulse in channel 2 precedes that in channel 1. Let N_1 and N_2 denote the number of random pulses per unit time arriving in channels 1 and 2 respectively (i.e. there is no correlation in time between the pulses in the two channels). Then the accidental number of recorded coincidences per unit time is

$$R = N_1 \tau_{12} N_2 + N_2 \tau_{21} N_1 = 2\tau N_1 N_2 \tag{7}$$

where the average resolving time is defined as

$$\tau = \tfrac{1}{2}(\tau_{12} + \tau_{21}) \tag{8}$$

For a coincident circuit with three input channels,

$$R = 3\tau N_1 N_2 N_3 + 2\tau(N_1 C_{23} + N_2 C_{13} + N_3 C_{12}) \tag{9}$$

where C_{12} is the true coincident counting rate for channels 1 and 2, etc. The random coincident rate in three channels is usually negligible in comparison with the terms in eqn. (9).

A powerful application of the coincident method is the absolute determination of the activity of a radioactive source. Consider a simple radioactive decay such as beta emission followed promptly by a single gamma ray. A small thin source with a disintegration rate N is placed close to two detectors, one for detecting the beta rays, the other for detecting the gamma ray. Let N_β and N_γ denote the single counting rates in the two detectors and C denote the true coincident rate. Then we have

$$N_\beta = \omega_\beta \varepsilon_\beta N \tag{10}$$

$$N_\gamma = \omega_\gamma \varepsilon_\gamma N \tag{11}$$

$$C = \omega_\beta \varepsilon_\beta \omega_\gamma \varepsilon_\gamma N \tag{12}$$

where ω_β, ω_γ are the solid angles subtended by the detectors at the source, and ε_β, ε_γ are the efficiencies of the two detectors. The above three equations yield the results.

$$N = \frac{N_\beta N_\gamma}{C} \tag{13}$$

$$\omega_\beta \varepsilon_\beta = \frac{C}{N_\gamma} \quad \text{and} \quad \omega_\gamma \varepsilon_\gamma = \frac{C}{N_\beta} \tag{14}$$

Not only can we determine the absolute decay rate N but also the counter efficiencies if ω_β and ω_γ are calculated.

"Fast–Slow" Coincidence Method

With the introduction of the scintillation counter in the late nineteen-forties it was realized that very fast circuits were required, if full advantage was to be taken of the very short duration scintillation pulses.

A block diagram of the "fast–slow" coincidence assembly, first introduced by Bell and Petch†, is shown in Fig. 16. The important design feature of this assembly is the placing of the fast coincidence circuit next

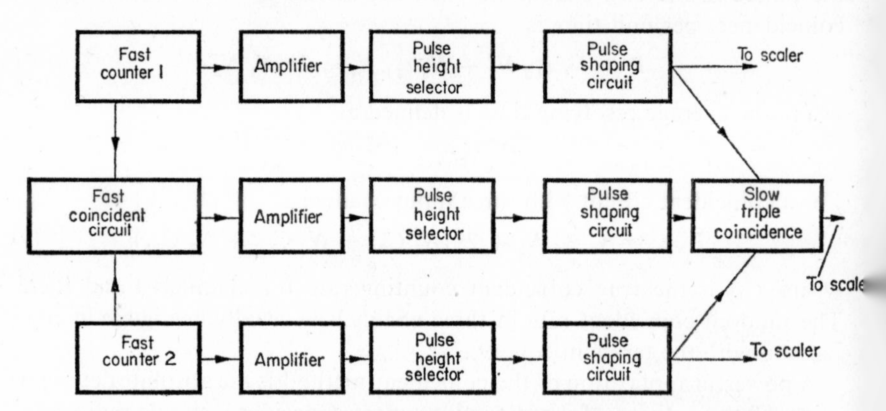

FIG. 16. Block diagram of a "Fast–Slow" coincidence unit. If the pulses from the counters are too small to operate the fast coincident circuit, fast amplifiers are inserted between the counters and the fast coincidence circuit.

† R. E. BELL and H. E. PETCH, *Phys. Rev.* **76**, 1409, 1949.

to the scintillation counters, thus avoiding any variable delays introduced in such units as the pulse height selectors. The output pulses of the fast coincidence circuit consist of genuine signal coincidences and numerous photomultiplier random coincident noise pulses. In the meantime, all output pulses of the two counters are amplified (the amplifiers need not be very fast), and fed to voltage discriminators (pulse height selectors). Signal pulses of the required amplitude are selected and generate short rectangular pulses in the pulse shaping circuits. Finally, a slow triple coincidence circuit selects, from the fast coincidences, those corresponding to the pulses of the size selected by the pulse height selectors. In this way, the random coincidence noise pulses from the fast coincidence circuit are not transmitted by the triple slow coincidence circuit. The upper and lower single channel counting rates are measured with scalers in addition to the triple coincidence counting rate.

A suitable circuit for the fast coincidence unit of Fig. 16 is that of Bell, Graham and Petch†, with a resolving time of the order of a nanosecond††.

A major factor in the success of this circuit was the discovery that it is possible to operate 1P21 photomultiplier tubes at 2500 V with gains in excess of 2×10^8. Under these conditions a single electron leaving the photocathode produces a pulse of 3 V amplitude across the anode resistor R_1. This negative pulse is large enough to cut-off the pentode V_1 (or V_2) (Fig. 17). The positive step function at the anode of V_1 (or V_2), produced when the 10 mA anode current is cut-off, has an amplitude of 1 V ($R_4 = 100\,\Omega$). The rise time of the step function is very short as R_4 is only 100 Ω. The step function signals at the anodes of V_1 and V_2 travel down coaxial cables of characteristic impedance $Z_0 = 100\,\Omega$. The far ends of the two cables are joined and connected to a 50 Ω cable shorted at its opposite end. The effective impedance at the point where the three cables meet is 25 Ω; thus the height of the pulse at this point is 0·25 V. The duration of the positive pulse reaching the germanium diode D is twice the time it takes the step function signal to travel the length of the 50 Ω cable. The signal reflected from the shorted end of the 50 Ω cable passes into the two 100 Ω cables but these are absorbed in the anode load resistors R_4. The diode D is biased by the potentiometer P so that 0·25 V pulses produced by either photomultiplier tube are not passed to the amplifier. However, coincident pulses at D are of twice the amplitude of single pulses and they are transmitted to the amplifier. The circuit is normally employed as a two channel fast coincidence circuit by using identical lengths of 100 Ω cable. The circuit can be used as a delayed coincidence circuit, by having one of the 100 Ω cables longer than the other. If organic scintillators (e.g. stilbene) are used, the circuit has a resolving time of the order of one nanosecond.

† R. E. Bell, R. L. Graham, and H. E. Petch, *Can. J. Phys.* **30**, 35, 1952.
†† One nsec $= 10^{-9}$ sec.

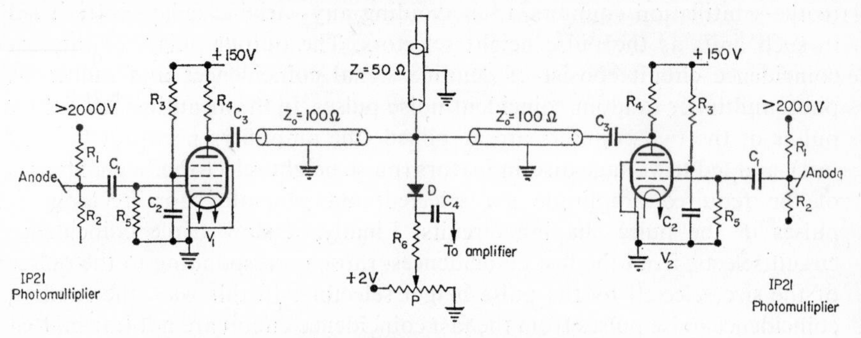

FIG. 17. Ultra-fast Coincidence Circuit of Bell, Graham and Petch. (*Can. J. Phys.*, **30**, 381, 1952)

R_1 10 kΩ	R_5 100 kΩ	C_3 0·01 μF
R_2 1 MΩ	R_6 10 kΩ	C_4 0·001 μF
R_3 20 kΩ	C_1 200 pF	D IN34
R_4 100 Ω	C_2 200 pF	V_1, V_2 6AK5

The pulses for the amplifier in the top and bottom channels of the "fast–slow" arrangement shown in Fig. 16 are taken from the last dynode of the photomultiplier tube.

Delayed Coincidence Method

There are many examples in nuclear physics where it is useful to measure the time interval between correlated events. Thus a measurement of the mean time delay between the emission of a beta ray and the subsequent gamma ray from the excited state of the daughter nucleus enables the lifetime of the state to be found. For lifetimes greater than a microsecond, a delay circuit based on sharp differentiation of the rectangular waveform produced by a triggered univibrator is convenient. The lifetime of the 22 μsec state of Ta^{181} has been measured by this delayed coincidence method.†

For excited states with lifetimes shorter than a few microseconds, delays produced by variable lengths of delay cable are more convenient. This method is based on the dependence of the propagation velocity of a pulse on the inductance and capacitance per unit length of cable.

A much favoured method of measuring time delays in the nanosecond region is to use "time-to-pulse-height-converters". The principle of operation of this type of circuit is illustrated in Fig. 18. In the quiescent state, the valve switches K_1 and K_2 are closed and the capacitor C is charged to a voltage V_0 determined by the values of R_1, R_2, and the high tension supply voltage. An input pulse at $t = 0$ opens the switch K_1 and C begins to dis-

† S. de BENEDETTI and F. K. MCGOWAN, *Phys. Rev.* **70**, 569, 1946; *Phys. Rev.* **74**, 728, 1948.

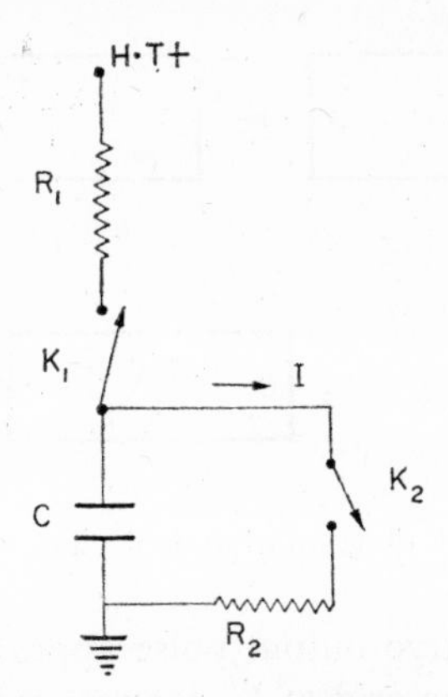

FIG. 18. Principle of "Time-to-pulse-height-converter".

charge through R_2. The discharge rate of C is arranged to be constant (not exponential), and the subsequent arrival of a pulse at time t, at a second input terminal, opens the switch K_2. The potential difference of C is then measured and this is a linear function of the time delay t. A "time-to-pulse-height-converter", which is linear for values of t as short as 10 nsec, with an accuracy of 1 nsec, is described by Weber, Johnstone and Cranberg†.

Sometimes the simple method of recording the time and amplitude of pulses by photographing their traces on high speed oscilloscopes is preferred. A number of counter telescope meson experiments have used this technique.††

Anticoincidence Circuit

An anticoincidence assembly generates an output pulse of standard height if a pulse from detector 1 appears at the input channel 1 and a simultaneous pulse from detector 2 does *not* appear at the second input channel.

In the microsecond region a convenient anticoincidence circuit (Fig. 19) is a simple modification of the Rossi circuit shown in Fig. 14(a). The lower end of the grid leak resistor R_2 is connected to a negative bias supply, so that in the quiescent state V_2 is cut-off. A negative pulse from counter 2 triggers a univibrator; the latter circuit generates a positive rectangular pulse of duration T_2, which is of sufficient amplitude to turn on the anode current in V_2. A simultaneous negative pulse from counter 1 is delayed by a short time t_d, before triggering a univibrator; the latter circuit generating a negative rectangular pulse of width T_1. $T_1 + t_d$ is chosen to be shorter than T_2, so that V_2 is still conducting at the end of the negative pulse applied to the grid of V_1. V_1 is cut-off by the negative pulse as V_2 is conducting the

† W. WEBER, C. W. JOHNSTONE and L. CRANBERG; *Rev. Sci. Instrum.* **27**, 166, 1956.
†† T. FAZZINI *et al.*, *Phys. Rev.* Letters **1**, 247, 1948.

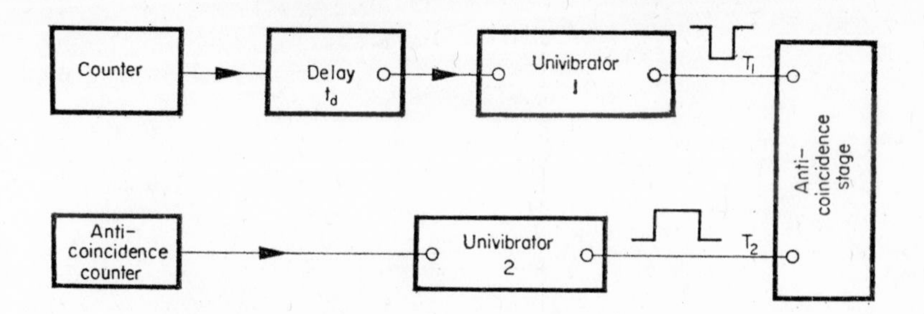

FIG. 19. Block diagram of anticoincidence assembly.

whole of this time, no large output pulse appears at the common anode. If the negative pulse at the grid of V_1 commenced before the positive pulse appeared at the grid of V_2, a large output pulse might occur. The delay unit ensures that this does not happen.

Pulses from counter 1, not in time coincidence with a pulse from counter 2, produce large output pulses because V_1 and V_2 are both cut-off for a time interval T_1.

12.7. FUTURE DEVELOPMENTS

The most important development in electronic techniques in nuclear physics, which is already under way, is the replacement of thermionic vacuum tubes by transistors. The main advantages of transistor circuits are their small physical size, modest power requirements, and great reliability. Fast semiconductor diodes and surface-barrier transistors are now available and it is possible to construct reliable transistor circuits in the nanosecond region. We have omitted descriptions of transistor circuits in this chapter. Transistor circuits applied to nuclear physics are discussed in the review articles by Kandiah and Chaplin, and Kendall.

BIBLIOGRAPHY

W. C. ELMORE and M. SANDS, *Electronics*, McGrawHill, New York 1949.
H. H. STAUB, Detection Methods in *Experimental Nuclear Physics*, Vol. 1, Ed. by E. SEGRÈ, Wiley, New York 1953.
A. B. GILLESPIE, *Signal, Noise and Resolution in Nuclear Counter Amplifiers*. Pergamon Press, London 1953.
R. L. CHASE, *Nuclear Pulse Spectrometry*, McGraw-Hill, New York 1961.
I. A. D. LEWIS and F. H. WELLS, *Millimicrosecond Pulse Techniques*, 2nd Ed., Pergamon Press, London 1959.
S. De BENEDETTI and R. W. FINDLEY, The Coincidence Method, in *Handbuch der Physik*, Vol. XLV, Springer-Verlag, Berlin 1957.

K. KANDIAH and G. B. B. CHAPLIN, New Electronic Techniques for the Nuclear Physicist in *Progress in Nuclear Physics*, Vol. 5, Ed. by O. R. FRISCH, Pergamon Press, London 1956.
H. W. KENDALL, Advances in Electronics associated with Nuclear Research in *Ann. Review of Nuclear Science*, Vol. 9, Ann. Reviews Inc., Palo Alto, California 1959.
Representative of recent delayed coincidence techniques is the determination of lifetimes as short as 10^{-11} sec: P. C. SIMMS, N. BENCZER-KOLLER, and C. S. WU, *Phys. Rev.* **121**, 1169, 1959.
DE WAARD, *Nuclear Instr.* **2**, 73, 1958.

EXAMPLES

1. A pentode amplifier stage has an unbypassed cathode resistor R_K, and a load resistor R_L which is shunted by a capacitance C. If the grid voltage is decreased suddenly by one volt, calculate the output voltage as a function of time. (Grad. I. Phys.)
2. A square wave whose peak-to-peak value is 1·0 V extends 0·5 V with respect to earth. The duration of the positive section is 0·1 sec and of the negative section is 0·2 sec. If this waveform is impressed upon a resistance–capacitance differentiating network of time constant 0·2 sec, what are the steady-state maximum and minimum values of the output waveform? (Grad. I. Phys.)
3. A linearly rising voltage pulse increases from zero to 100 μV in 2 μsec and then remains constant. This pulse is differentiated by a $C\,R$ network ($C = 40$ pF, $R = 0{\cdot}1$ MΩ) and then integrated by an $R\,C$ network ($R = 0{\cdot}1$ MΩ, $C = 20$ pF). When does the output pulse reach its peak value and what is the pulse height at this instant?
4. An Eccles–Jordan trigger circuit consists of two identical triodes with a common cathode load of 15 kΩ, equal anode loads of 47 kΩ, equal grid leaks of 150 kΩ, and anode-to-grid coupling resistances of 330 kΩ. The high tension supply is 175 V. Determine approximately the currents and voltages corresponding to the stable states. (Assume the anode current–anode voltage characteristic of each triode for zero grid voltage is: anode current in milliamperes = 0·1 × anode voltage.) (Grad. I. Phys.)
5. A current of 0·01 μamp from an ionization chamber is fed into the input of a high gain feedback d.c. amplifier. The feedback from the output is obtained from the common connection of two resistors R_1 and R_2 which are in series and connected across the output terminal and the H.T. negative line. The feedback line to the input terminal (the grid of the input valve) has a resistance R of 50 MΩ. If $R_1 = 20$ kΩ and $R_2 = 10$ kΩ, what is the voltage across the output terminals? What would be the effect of replacing R by a capacitance? (Grad. I. Phys.)

CHAPTER 13

ALPHA AND GAMMA RADIATION

13.1. SUMMARY OF PROPERTIES OF ALPHA RADIATION

In earlier chapters we have discussed some of the properties of alpha radiation. A detailed account of the early work is given in the book by Rutherford, Chadwick and Ellis. It is convenient at this point to summarize a number of the basic properties of α-particles and α-radioactivity.

(1) All nuclei of mass number A greater than about 140 are unstable against α-particle decay.

(2) α-particles are positively charged and the charge to mass ratio is in close agreement with the hypothesis that they are doubly charged He^{++} ions. Observations of the deflections of α-particles *in vacuo* produced by strong electric ($\sim$ 6000 V per cm) and magnetic fields ($\sim$ 6000 gauss) enable the velocity v, as well as the charge to mass ratio, to be determined†.

(3) The early measurements of α-particle velocities indicated that a single group of monoenergetic particles is emitted by each radioactive nuclide, the velocity v being a characteristic property of the nuclide in question. For example Rn, RaA(Po^{218}), and RaC(Bi^{214}) emit α-particles with velocities of 1·88, 1·99 and $1{\cdot}92 \times 10^9$ cm per sec, respectively.

(4) In 1930, S. Rosenblum, using a magnetic momentum spectrometer with a field strength of $\sim$25,000 gauss, showed that in many instances several groups of monoenergetic α-particles are emitted by a single nuclide. This important discovery is interpreted as evidence that following α-emission the product (daughter) nucleus may be formed in one of a number of excited states. This interpretation is supported by the observation of gamma rays in coincidence with the α-emission.

(5) The kinetic energy of the α-particles emitted in α-decay covers the range from 2 to 9 MeV. In marked contrast, the decay constant of the alpha process covers the enormous range 10^{-25} to 10^7. Geiger and Nuttall (1911) established the useful empirical law that the logarithm of the decay constant varies linearly with the logarithm of the energy of the emitted α-particles. This law is approximate and in a number of cases there are

† E. Rutherford and H. Robinson, *Phil. Mag.* **28**, 552, 1914.

large anomalies. A successful theory of α-radioactivity should account for the detailed discrepancies.

(6) The experimental methods of observing and measuring the energies of α-particles have been described in Chapter 11. α-particles have high stopping cross sections in matter and a well-defined range R. In air at 15°C, 760 mm Hg pressure, the Po^{210} α-particles of kinetic energy of 5·30 MeV, have a range of 3·84 cm. The range–energy relation of Geiger, $R = k \times E^{1.5}$ is useful for making approximate estimates of E from the observed range R. One serious drawback in detecting natural α-particles is the possibility of the particles losing, most, or all of their energy in passing through the window of the detectors. Whenever possible, the alpha source is mounted inside the sensitive volume of the detector.

Rutherford's great interest in the α-radiation was fully justified as it led to the discovery of the nuclear structure of the atom, the first artificially produced nuclear reaction $N^{14}(\alpha, p)\,O^{17}$, and the discovery of artificial positron radioactivity.

13.2. ALPHA INSTABILITY

The phenomenon of α-radioactivity is intimately connected with the exceptionally large binding energy of 28·3 MeV of the α-particle. A nucleus (Z, A) is unstable against α-emission if the mass of the nucleus $(Z - 2, A - 4)$ plus the mass of the α-particle is less than the mass of the nucleus (Z, A). Another way of looking at the criterion of instability is to consider the relevant binding energies. A nucleus is unstable against α-decay if the sum of the binding energies of the last two protons and last two neutrons is less than the α-binding energy of 28·3 MeV. By last two neutrons (or protons), we mean the two neutrons (or protons) which have the smallest binding energy. The question may be asked why heavy nuclides are not found to decay by proton or neutron emission. If a nucleus is unstable against proton decay (a proton-rich nucleus), the mean lifetime for positron emission $(p \rightarrow n + e^{+} + \nu)$ is always so short compared with the proton decay lifetime that proton emission is undetectable. A similar argument applies to the neutron-rich nuclei; negative electron emission predominates. The only exception is the phenomenon of delayed neutron emission.

Conservation of energy and the Einstein energy–mass relation allow the α-particle emission energies to be calculated if the relevant atomic masses are known. A plot of the estimated α-decay energy E against mass number A is shown in Fig. 1. Negative values of E occur for nuclides which are stable against α-decay. The energy curve crosses the line $E = 0$ just below $A = 140$. A prominent feature of the energy curve is the occurrence of two peaks near $A = 145$ and $A = 215$. These peaks are related to the shell model of nuclear structure†. According to this model, in spite

† The shell model is discussed in Chapter 20, Section 11.

of the absence of any obvious dominant central nuclear force, the nucleons are assumed to move in quasi-stationary orbits. Each nucleon moves in an orbit with a definite angular momentum comprising the vector sum of orbital and spin components. The nuclear shell model has obvious similarities to the electronic shell model of the atom. Just as certain numbers of electrons correspond to particularly stable atoms (closed shells), nuclei containing 2, 8, 20, 50, 82 or 126, neutrons or protons are exceptionally

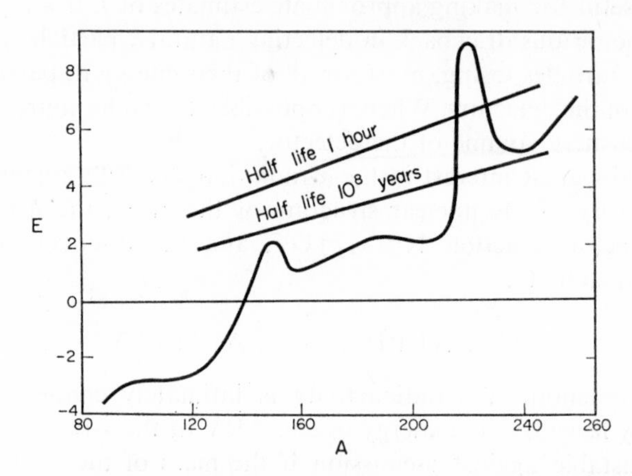

FIG. 1. Predicted α-emission energy E as a function of mass number A. (Based on T. P. KOHMAN, *Phys. Rev.* **76**, 448, 1949.)

stable. One important difference between the electron and nucleon structure is the existence of two families of shells for nucleons, one for protons and the other for neutrons. Nuclei with both types of shell completely filled are the most stable. Thus $_{82}Pb^{208}$ with 82 protons and 126 neutrons is especially stable.

The binding energy of the "last" nucleon (i.e. the least firmly bound) varies in a striking way just below and above the filling of a nucleon shell. Thus in the nucleus $_{82}Pb^{210}$ the last proton (number 82) has the high binding energy of 8·37 MeV. Adding one more proton (number 83) to form $_{83}Bi^{211}$ we find the binding energy of this proton is only 4·39 MeV, a consequence of the starting of a new proton shell. Even the next proton, the last in $_{84}Po^{212}$, has a binding energy of 5·85 MeV, well below average.

$_{84}Po^{212}$ emits exceptionally energetic α-particles (E = 8·94 MeV). This high energy is related to the double closed shell nature of the daughter nucleus $_{82}Pb^{208}$. Removing the last two protons from $_{84}Po^{212}$ involves an energy supply of (5·85 + 4·39) MeV. Removing the last two neutrons from $_{82}Pb^{210}$ involves the supply of (5·23 + 3·87) MeV. An α-particle has the high binding energy of 28·3 MeV (a double closed shell nucleus); thus the alpha energy of the decay $Po^{212} \rightarrow Pb^{208}$ should be 28·3 − (3·87 + 5·23 + 4·39 + 5·85) = 8·96 MeV, in excellent agreement with the observed energy of

8·94 MeV. The energy peaks of Fig. 1 occur near the vicinity of closed shell nuclei; the peak near $A \sim 145$ corresponds to the shell with 82 neutrons.

The most frequent mode of decay of the nuclides in the three natural radioactive series is α-emission. At certain stages in the decay chain, however, beta decay or branched alpha–beta decay occurs. The reason for this is not hard to find. For heavy nuclei the neutron number N is about 1·5 times the proton number Z. The emission of an α-particle involves the changes $\Delta N = -2$ and $\Delta Z = -2$; thus a succession of α-particle decays moves the decay chain to the neutron-rich side of the beta stability line and a beta unstable nuclide will be formed. In a few cases, the alpha and beta transition probabilites are not very different and both types of emission are observed. This is the phenomenon of radioactive branching. RaC(Bi^{214}) decays by 0·04 per cent of the total disintegrations by α-emission and by β-emission in the remaining disintegrations.

13.3. ELEMENTARY THEORY OF ALPHA DECAY

Alpha decay is a striking example of the quantum mechanical tunnel effect. In the crudest theory, the α-particle is assumed to have a semi-permanent existence inside the parent nucleus. The interaction between the bound α-particle and the rest of the parent nucleus is represented by a potential well of the shape shown in Fig. 10, Chapter 9. The potential energy curve $V(r)$ changes abruptly at the nuclear surface $r = R$; beyond R it is assumed that V is a pure Coulomb potential. Inside the nuclear surface the potential, for simplicity, is chosen as a deep rectangular well. The α-particle has an energy represented by the horizontal line E. The decay probability per unit time is written as a product

$$\lambda = n \times P$$

where n is the number of times the α-particle collides with the walls of the potential barrier in one second (at $r = R$), and P is the quantum mechanical probability of the α-particle penetrating the barrier. An approximate solution of the Schrödinger equation for the region $R < r < R_1$ has been derived in Chapter 9 (eqn. 38). The solution was based on the assumption that the emitted α-particle did not carry away *orbital* angular momentum (the α-particle spin is zero). The wave representing the escaping particle for zero angular momentum ($L = 0$) is called an S wave (waves carrying angular momentum of 1, 2, 3, . . . units are known as $P, D, F,$ . . . waves). If the emitted α-particle has finite L, the Schrödinger equation must include the potential energy of the "centrifugal barrier" (Chapter 6, Section 9). If the radial wave function of the α-particle is $\psi(r) = u(r) \exp\left(-\frac{iEt}{\hbar}\right)$, and we introduce the function

$$\varphi = r\psi \tag{1}$$

ψ satisfies the equation

$$\frac{d^2\varphi}{dr^2} + \frac{2M}{\hbar^2}\left[E - \frac{L(L+1)\hbar^2}{2M\,r^2} - V(r)\right]\varphi = 0. \tag{2}$$

In the region, $\quad R < r < R_1, \quad V(r) = \dfrac{2(Z-2)\,e^2}{r}$ (3)

and $E = M\,v^2/2$, where v is the velocity of separation of the α-particle and recoil nucleus. M is the reduced mass of the α-particle; $1/M = 1/M_\alpha + 1/M_r$, where M_α and M_r are the masses of the α-particle and *daughter* nucleus respectively. The middle term in the parentheses is the potential energy associated with the centrifugal barrier. If the parent (Z, A) is of the even–even type the nuclear spin $I = 0$, and the daughter nucleus $(Z-2, A-4)$ in its ground state must have zero spin. Hence L is always zero in the decay of even–even nuclei to the ground state of the daughter nucleus. The data for even–even nuclei do fit the Geiger–Nuttall law much better than those of the odd A type.

For S waves, $L = 0$; an approximate solution of (2)† gives for the decay probability $\lambda = n\,P$,

$$\lambda = \left[\frac{v_i}{2R}\right]\left[\frac{4(E-U)^{\frac{1}{2}}}{(B-E)^{\frac{1}{2}}}\right]\exp(-2C) \tag{4}$$

The exponential factor is the barrier penetration factor. The first two factors represent the frequency factor n. The kinetic energy of the α-particle within the well ($r < R$) is $E - U$ (Fig. 10, Chapter 9), which is proportional to v_i^2, where v_i is the velocity of the α-particle inside the nucleus (assumed to be non-relativistic). Hence††

$$v_i = v\left[\frac{E-U}{E}\right]^{\frac{1}{2}} \tag{5}$$

The term $v_i/(2R)$ in eqn. (4) is the frequency of collision of the α-particle with the potential wall at R. The second term‡ in eqn. (4) is concerned with the reflection of the alpha wave at the discontinuity in potential at R. The dominant term in the expression for λ is the exponential one which is very sensitive to the ratio E/B, where B is the Coulomb barrier height:

$$B = \frac{2(Z-2)\,e^2}{R} \tag{6}$$

The value of C in the term $\exp(-2C)$ is given by

$$C = \frac{2B\,R}{\hbar\,v}(\theta_0 - \sin\theta_0\cos\theta_0), \quad \text{where} \quad \cos^2\theta_0 = \frac{E}{B}. \tag{7}$$

† G. C. Hanna, Alpha-Radioactivity, p. 77 *et seq.*, in Vol. 3 of *Experimental Nuclear Physics*, Ed. by E. Segrè, Wiley, New York 1959.

†† v is the velocity of the α-particle when it has escaped from the nucleus.

‡ J. M. Blatt and V. F. Weisskopf, p. 358, *Theoretical Nuclear Physics*, Wiley, New York 1952.

As E/B is usually not greater than 1/3, a rough approximation is

$$2C = \left(\frac{R}{\hbar}\right)(2MB)^{\frac{1}{2}}\left[\pi\left(\frac{B}{E}\right)^{\frac{1}{2}} - 4\right] \qquad (8)$$

Substituting eqn. (6) in eqn. (8), it is easy to show that eqn. (8) is the same as eqn. (38) of Chapter 9. This solution is a rough one and it gives values of P too large by a factor of about 20 for E about 6 MeV. Nevertheless, it is useful as it indicates the strong dependence of P on E and R.

Gamow† was the first person to calculate the influence of finite L for the α-particle wave on the decay probability λ. He ignored, however, the effect of finite L on the frequency term n. According to Preston, the frequency n

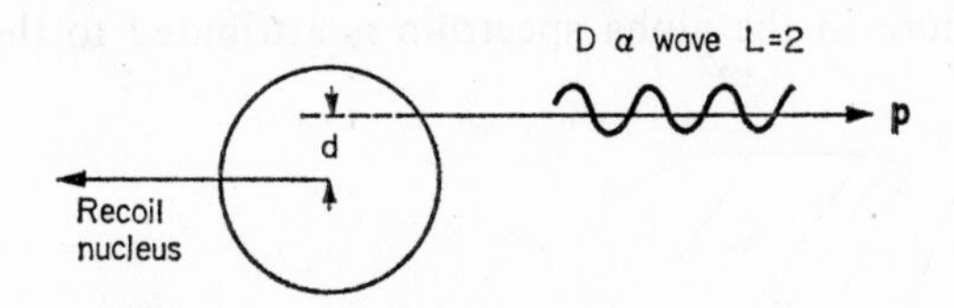

FIG. 2. Classical picture of D wave α-particle emitted by Po^{210}. The orbital angular momentum of the α-particle is $\boldsymbol{p} \times \boldsymbol{d} = 2\hbar$.

increases with L, and for $L = 4$, this increase is greater than the decrease in P associated with the centrifugal barrier. Consider, for example, the alpha decay of Po^{210} (an even–even nucleus) to the first excited state of Pb^{206}, which has a spin $I = 2$. The α-particle emitted (4·51 MeV) has orbital angular momentum $L = 2$ about the centre of the daughter nucleus. A classical estimate of the "off-centre" distance d of emission of the α-particle wave (Fig. 2) is obtained by equating $\boldsymbol{p} \times \boldsymbol{d}$, where $\boldsymbol{p}$ is the linear momentum, to $L\hbar$.

For $\quad E = 4{\cdot}51$ MeV, $\quad pc = \sqrt{(2 \times 4 \times 938 \times 4{\cdot}51)}$ MeV

For $\quad L = 2, \quad d = \dfrac{2 \times 1 \times 10^{-27} \times 3 \times 10^{10}}{\sqrt{(8 \times 938 \times 4{\cdot}51)} \times 1{\cdot}6 \times 10^{-6}}$ cm $\sim$ 3 fermi.

The distance d is less than half the nuclear radius of Pb^{206}. This means that the centrifugal barrier does not reduce the penetration probability by a large factor (for $L = 2$, the value of P is roughly halved; for $L = 4$, P decreases by nearly a factor of ten). When the increase in n associated with increasing L is taken into account, the ratio of λ_L/λ_0, where λ_L and λ_0 are the decay probabilities for L and $L = 0$ respectively, has been calculated and found to increase at first and then decrease beyond $L = 4$ (Table 1).

† G. GAMOW and C. L. CRITCHFIELD, *Theory of the Atomic Nucleus and Nuclear Energy Sources*, Oxford 1949.

TABLE 1

L	0	1	2	3	4	5
$\frac{\lambda_L}{\lambda_0}$	1	1·75	1·98	1·75	1·23	0·73

13.4. THE FINE STRUCTURE OF ALPHA RAY ENERGIES

In 1930, S. Rosenblum in Paris, using the 180 ton Bellevue electromagnet capable of producing a magnetic field of 23,000 gauss, measured the momentum of the α-particles emitted by several alpha sources†. He showed that some alpha sources emitted several groups of α-particles of different energy. This fine structure in the alpha spectrum is attributed to the energy level

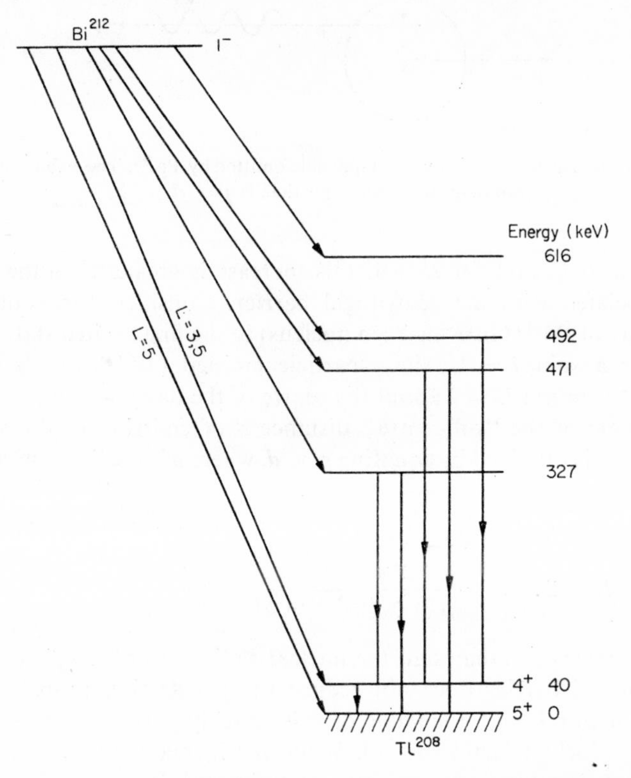

FIG. 3. Alpha-decay scheme of Bi^{212}. Six groups of monoenergetic α-particles are observed. The observed γ-ray transitions are indicated by vertical lines.

† Many α-ray magnetic spectrometers make use of the 180° focusing principle (see Chapter 14). The "BR" value for a 6 MeV α-particle is $\sim 4 \times 10^5$ gauss-cm, necessitating very strong fields acting over large areas.

scheme of the daughter nucleus. The correctness of this theory is supported by the observation that the observed γ-ray energies emitted by the daughter nucleus agree, within experimental error, with the *difference* in the disintegration energy of the alpha groups. The decay scheme for ThC (Bi^{212}) is illustrated in Fig. 3. The fine structure of the alpha spectrum is given in Table 2. The disintegration energy in the third column is the sum of the alpha kinetic energy and the recoil kinetic energy of the daughter nucleus ThC″ (Tl^{208}). The relative intensities of the alpha groups are given in the fourth column. In the last column, the partial decay constants are isted. The sum of the partial decay constants is the total decay constant λ.

TABLE 2. $Bi^{212} \rightarrow Tl^{208} + \alpha$-DECAY

Group	Alpha energy MeV	Disintegration energy MeV	Relative intensity %	Decay constant sec^{-1}
1	6·084	6·201	27·2	$1{\cdot}75 \times 10^{-5}$
2	6·044	6·161	69·9	$4{\cdot}50 \times 10^{-5}$
3	5·763	5·874	1·7	$0{\cdot}11 \times 10^{-5}$
4	5·621	5·730	0·15	$0{\cdot}01 \times 10^{-5}$
5	5·601	5·709	1·1	$0{\cdot}06 \times 10^{-5}$
6	5.000	5·585	0·016	$0{\cdot}005 \times 10^{-5}$

The relative intensities of the alpha groups reveals the inadequacies of the elementary treatment of α-decay. The most abundant group is is expected to be the highest energy group, for the decay probability is dominated by the exponential factor $\exp(-2C)$, which falls away very rapidly with decreasing energy. The highest energy transition in the decay of Bi^{212} involves a spin change of 5 units and the centrifugal barrier, associated with the emission of an alpha wave carrying away 5 units of orbital angular momentum, represents a strong hindrance factor in the decay probability. Moreover, in terms of a more realistic model of α-decay, we should consider the preformation of the α-particle from two protons and two neutrons, and in Bi^{212} the two protons do not come from the same shell. Shell effects do influence the preformation probability and should be included in more refined treatments of α-decay.

On the whole, the fit between theory and experiment is much better for the even–even nuclides. This fact is probably a result of the pairing-off of nucleon spins. The α-particle is probably formed from two protons and two neutrons with their spins already paired-off.

A simple decay scheme is that of Po^{210}, an even–even nuclide. Two groups of alphas are emitted: one of energy 5·299 MeV and the other of energy 4·510 MeV with an intensity $1{\cdot}2 \times 10^{-5}$ times that of the more energetic group. The lower energy α-particles are emitted in the transitions to the 804 keV excited state of Pb^{206}. In the decay of Po^{210} there are no complications arising from crossing filled nucleon shells. According to the elementary Gamow theory, ignoring the effect of finite L in the 4·51 MeV emission ($L = 2$, as we have a transition from a O^+ ground state to a 2^+ excited state), the relative intensity of the two groups of α-particles is given by

$$\exp\left[-\left(\frac{R}{\hbar}\right)(2MB)^{\frac{1}{2}}\pi\left\{\left(\frac{B}{E_1}\right)^{\frac{1}{2}}-\left(\frac{B}{E_2}\right)^{\frac{1}{2}}\right\}\right] \tag{9}$$

where E_1 and E_2 are the disintegration energies corresponding to the alpha kinetic energies of 5·30 and 4·51 MeV, B is the barrier height (~ 33 MeV) and R the nuclear radius (~ 7 fermis). The Gamow approximate expression agrees with the observed low intensity of the 4·51 MeV group to a factor of the order of two. In the elementary treatment, E is the only variable in this decay and one has the opportunity of comparing the barrier penetration factors for the same radius R, the same barrier height B, but different energies E.

An interesting phenomenon related to alpha decay and excited nuclear states is the existence of long-range α-particles. There are two alpha emitters, RaC′(Po^{214}) and ThC′(Po^{212}), in which groups of α-particles of very low intensity are found with energies *higher* than the main group. In the case of RaC, twelve higher energy groups have been observed. ThC′ emits three high energy groups. The kinetic energies of the α-particles and their relative abundances are given in Table 3. The main energy group is given an arbitrary abundance of 10^6.

TABLE 3. ThC′ (Po^{212}) LONG-RANGE-ALPHAS. (HALF-LIFE ThC′, 3×10^{-7} SEC.)

Group	Kinetic energy of alphas (MeV)	Energy (MeV) of excited state	Relative abundance
Main	8·776	0	10^6
1	9·488	0·726	35
2	10·418	1·674	20
3	10·539	1·797	180

The low abundance of the long range α-particles is associated with excited states of the *parent* nucleus. The parent nucleus of ThC′ is ThC. ThC is an example of a radioactive isotope which has a branched decay; in 35·4 per cent of the decays it emits α-particles (the α-decay scheme is illustrated in Fig. 3.), in the remaining 64·6 per cent decays it emits β-particles, ${}_{83}Bi^{212} \rightarrow {}_{84}Po^{212}$. Po^{212} has a very short half-life (3×10^{-7} sec) and it is studied in secular equilibrium with its parent Bi^{212}. The β-decay of Bi^{212}, may form Po^{212} in several excited states as well as in the ground state. These excited states are unstable against γ-emission with a mean lifetime of the order of 10^{-12} sec. Normally γ-emission would occur before α-emission. However, the mean life, before α-decay occurs from the ground state of Po^{212}, is as short as 10^{-7} sec, and it is evident, from the dependence of decay rate on alpha energy E, that the mean life for α-decay from an excited state of Po^{212} should be several orders of magnitude smaller than 10^{-7} sec. Hence the

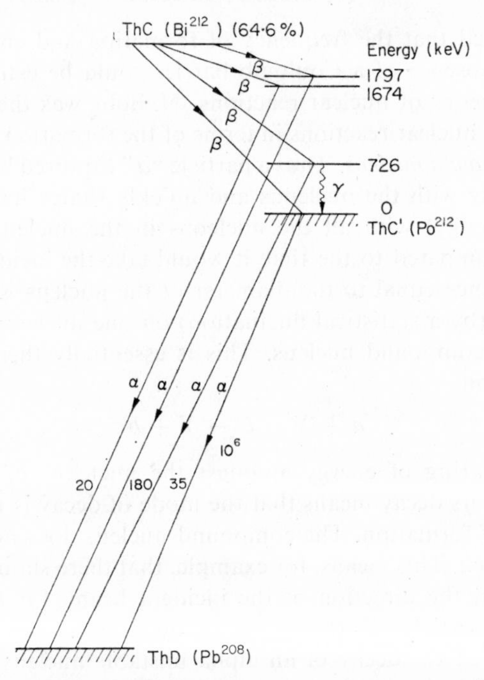

FIG. 4. The β–α decay sequence illustrating the long range α-particles emitted by Po^{212}. The numbers adjacent to the alpha-transition lines are the relative intensities of the four groups.

possibility arises that α-emission competes with γ-emission in the decay of the excited states of Po^{212}. The process is illustrated in Fig. 4. The relative intensities of the alpha groups are partly determined by the relative frequencies of the β-decay of Bi^{212} to the excited states of Po^{212}. Following α-decay, the population of the excited states of the daughter nuclei usually decreases rapidly with excitation energy. But in this example the excited states of Po^{212} are formed as a result of β-decay and the decay probability is not such a sensitive function of the beta energy. Thus the relative populations of the excited states of Po^{212} are not small compared with that of the ground state.

13.5 MULTI-BODY THEORIES OF ALPHA DECAY

The most unsatisfactory feature of the one-body theory of alpha radioactivity is the assumption that the α-particle exists within the nucleus for a large fraction of the time. Various attempts have been made to develop more realistic theories of alpha decay. Two such attempts are based on the *statistical* model and the *shell* model of the nucleus.

(1) Statistical Model

Bethe suggested that the frequency of formation and emission of an α-particle in the absence of a Coulomb barrier could be estimated by using the statistical theory of nuclear reactions. N. Bohr was the first person to treat low energy nuclear reactions in terms of the formation and subsequent decay of a *compound nucleus*. Thus a particle "a" captured by a nucleus "X" interacts strongly with the nucleons and quickly shares its energy (kinetic plus binding energy) with all the nucleons in the nucleus. After a time interval, long compared to the time it would take the incident particle "a" to travel a distance equal to the diameter of the nucleus, sufficient energy is concentrated (by a statistical fluctuation) on one nucleon "b" for it to be emitted by the compound nucleus. This is essentially the Bohr model of a nuclear reaction

$$a + X \rightarrow C \rightarrow Y + b$$

The efficient sharing of energy amongst the nucleons of the compound nucleus prior to its decay means that the mode of decay is unrelated to the specific mode of formation. The compound nucleus does not "remember" how it was formed. This means, for example, that there should be azimuthal symmetry, about the direction of the incident beam, for the direction of emission of the particle "b" (b may be a γ-quantum).

Bethe compared the decay of an alpha unstable nucleus with the decay of a compound nucleus by neutron emission (no Coulomb barrier). The measurements of neutron capture cross sections at the time (1937) were in agreement with a neutron "level width" Γ_n given by

$$\Gamma_n E_n^{-\frac{1}{2}} \sim 4 \times 10^{-4} (\text{eV})^{\frac{1}{2}} \tag{10}$$

where E_n is the neutron kinetic energy in eV. A typical α-particle kinetic energy observed in α-decay is ~ 6 MeV, so the α-particle width Γ_α, in the absence of a Coulomb barrier, is $\sim \Gamma_n$. For $E_n = 6$ MeV, Γ_α is ~ 1 eV at $E_\alpha = 6$ MeV. According to the uncertainty principle, the level width Γ and the mean lifetime τ of an excited state of a system are related by

$$\Gamma \tau \sim \hbar \sim 6 \times 10^{-16} \text{ eV-sec} \tag{11}$$

For

$$\Gamma_\alpha \sim 1 \text{ eV}, \quad \tau_\alpha \sim 6 \times 10^{-16} \text{ sec} \tag{12}$$

The time τ_α is the mean time interval before an alpha-unstable nucleus would decay in the absence of a Coulomb barrier. This lifetime is about 10^5 times longer than the one-body model estimate of $(2R)/v_i$.

The first approach to a more realistic theory of alpha decay was discouraging as it reduced the theoretical decay constants λ by a factor of 10^4 to 10^5. Alternatively if experimental values of the decay constants were used to obtain nuclear radii, the "new" radii were about 30 per cent larger than the values derived by the elementary theory. An improvement in the theory was realised when it was found experimentally, and shown theoretically, that the level width Γ is proportional to the average level spacing in the region of excitation energy concerned. Cohen† argued that the mean lifetime for alpha decay in the absence of a barrier should be calculated from an estimate of the level width Γ_α at zero excitation and not at an excitation energy of ~ 6 MeV. For heavy nuclei, the average level spacing near 6 MeV is ~ 10 eV. It is not easy to define precisely what one means by average spacing at the ground state, for the first few states are widely separated. Cohen† estimated a value of level spacing ~ 100 keV. Rasmussen asserts that a better estimate is ~ 1 MeV. Nevertheless, the mean lifetime against alpha decay should be reduced from the Bethe estimate of 6×10^{-16} sec to

$$\tau_\alpha = \frac{10}{10^5} \times 6 \times 10^{-16} \sim 10^{-20}\ \text{sec}$$

This statistical theory yields values of λ ten times smaller than the one-body model.

(2) Nucleon Overlap Model

An interesting approach to the theory of the alpha disintegration process is that of Tolhoek and Brussaard.†† These authors stress the importance of determining the mean free path, l_α, of α-particles within nuclear matter. In an earlier paper‡, Tolhoek and Brussaard discuss the motion of the α-particle in a deep nuclear well. However, they now believe that this concept has very little physical sense because the experimental evidence favours an α-particle mean free path

$$l_\alpha \ll R$$

where R is the nuclear radius.

The mean free path l_α is the average distance an α-particle travels through nuclear matter before dissociating. At the present time no successful attempts at calculating l_α have been made. One method of estimating l_α is to determine

† B. L. Cohen, *Phys. Rev.* **80**, 105, 1950.
†† P. J. Brussaard and H. A. Tolhoek, *Physica* **24**, 263, 1958.
‡ H. A. Tolhoek and P. J. Brussaard, *Physica* **21**, 449 1955.

experimentally the imaginary part of a Woods–Saxon optical model potential for the elastic scattering of α-particles of kinetic energy between 20 and 40 MeV by heavy nuclei. l_α will depend on the α-particle energy; nevertheless, the tentative assumption is made that l_α for the α-particle emitted in radioactive decay is of the same order of magnitude. The best estimate of l_α is

$$1{\cdot}0 < l_\alpha < 1{\cdot}5 \text{ fermi}$$

Thus l_α is small compared to the radius of a heavy nucleus ($R \sim 8$ fermi), and it is roughly equal to the nuclear surface skin thickness s ($s \sim 1{\cdot}3$ fermi), where s is the radial distance corresponding to the density of the nuclear matter falling from 0·80 to 0·20 of the density at the centre of a heavy nucleus. Hence it is not reasonable to treat the α-particle as a sub-unit moving through the interior of the nucleus, although it is still possible to use this concept in the low density surface region of a heavy nucleus.

These considerations naturally lead to the idea that the α-particle emitted in alpha radioactivity is formed from four nucleons (two protons and two neutrons) in the outer regions of the alpha unstable nucleus. Tolhoek and Brussaard have proposed that the α-particle is formed from four nucleons in well-defined shell model† states of high energy. This is supported by the experimental evidence that the majority of alpha transitions lead to a low lying excited state or the ground state of the daughter nucleus. If the assumption is made that the emergence of the α-particle takes place from four nucleon shell model states without disturbing the remaining $A - 4$ nucleon shell model states, then it is possible to describe the α-emission process in terms of boundary conditions at the surface of the nucleus. The wave representing the α-particle tunnelling through the Coulomb barrier is matched to an internal shell model wave function.

The calculation of shell model nucleon wave functions has made considerable progress in the last few years and it should be possible to subject the theoretical method outlined above to a number of experimental tests. The calculation of *absolute* alpha emission probabilities is, in principle, possible; but it must be remembered that absolute decay rates are very sensitive to the nuclear radius parameter r_0. A more realistic approach is to compare the relative intensities of the α-ray groups emitted by spherical nuclei. The influence of the orbital angular momentum carried away by the emerging α-particle is also susceptible to calculation. The alpha disintegration of spheroidal nuclei is discussed in the next section.

13.6. ALPHA DECAY OF SPHEROIDAL NUCLEI

Several of the rare earth nuclei have large electric quadrupole moments. This property is related to their *spheroidal* shape. A spheroidal charge distribution will set up an anisotropic Coulomb barrier and this should have an

† The nuclear shell model is discussed in Chapter 20, Section 11.

effect on the decay of an alpha unstable nuclide. One would expect the barrier penetration factor to be increased for α-emission in the direction of the long axis of the nucleus. Apart from the electrostatic effect, the electric quadrupole interactions have a significant effect on the decay rate.

Experimentally the anisotropic emission of α-particles from spheroidal nuclei has been studied by aligning the nuclear spin axes at a low temperature. At normal temperatures the random thermal energy $\sim kT$ is sufficient to destroy any alignment of the nuclear spins. Thus any angular correlation effects are smeared out by the random spatial orientation of the assembly of nuclei.

Alignment of nuclear spin vectors can be partially achieved at low temperatures through the interaction of either the nuclear magnetic or electric quadrupole moments with magnetic or electric fields. Thus an assembly of nuclei, each of spin I, magnetic dipole moment μ, populate $2I + 1$ nuclear magnetic sub-states in a magnetic field H. The sub-levels are equally spaced with an energy interval $\frac{\mu H}{I}$. Nuclear moments are of the order of $\frac{e\hbar}{2Mc}$ (5×10^{-24} erg gauss^{-1}), where M is the proton mass. For a system of nuclei in thermal equilibrium, the population n_m of the mth sub-state is determined by the Boltzmann relation $n_m = N \exp\left(-\frac{E(M)}{kT}\right)$, where $E(M)$ is the energy of the sub-state m. A significant difference in population of the sub-states is achieved if $E(M) \sim kT$. At 1°K, $kT \sim 10^{-16}$ ergs °K^{-1}, and magnetic fields of the order of 10^7 gauss would be needed to obtain a significant degree of nuclear alignment. Significant nuclear alignment has been obtained by working at lower temperatures $\sim$0·01°K.

Pound† was the first to propose that in certain crystals the *gradient* of the internal electrostatic field might be strong enough to interact with the nuclei if they had an electric quadrupole moment, and produce a level splitting $E(M)$ of the order of kT at 1°K. The potential energy of the quadrupole–electric field interaction depends on the nuclear spin I, but is of the order of

$$e\frac{\partial^2 V}{\partial x^2} \times Q \tag{13}$$

where e is the fundamental charge, ($4{\cdot}8 \times 10^{-10}$ e.s.u.),

Q is the nuclear quadrupole moment (cm^2) and $-\frac{\partial^2 V}{\partial x^2}$ is the gradient of the electrostatic field at the nucleus (e.s.u.). Field gradients as high as 10^{15} e.s.u. are needed to produce a significant degree of nuclear alignment. In certain crystals, nuclei are situated within a very asymmetrical electron cloud distribution and nuclear alignment is obtained at low temperatures.

† R. V. Pound, *Phys. Rev.* **76**, 1410, 1949.

The angular distributions of the alpha radiation† emitted by the aligned nuclei Np^{237}, U^{235} and U^{233} have been measured by physicists at Oak Ridge. The Pound method of nuclear alignment was used. A single crystal of the salt $U^{238}O_2Rb(NO_3)_3$ coated with a thin layer of U^{233} rich material was cooled to about 1°K. The U^{233} nuclei are situated in a crystalline electric field where there is a strong field gradient. The α-particles emitted by the aligned U^{233} nuclei were detected with a gold coated n-type germanium counter.

The angular distribution of the U^{233} α-particles as a function of the temperature T was found to be ††

$$W(\theta, T) = 1 + \frac{A_2}{T} P_2(\cos\theta)$$

with $A_2 = -0{\cdot}053 \pm 0{\cdot}002$.

θ is the angle between an emitted α-particle and the crystalline c-axis.

If the suggestion that only S and D waves in α-particle emission are important, then, in the alpha decay of U^{233}, the S and D waves are of approximately equal amplitude and of opposite sign.

Recently the temperature dependence of the α-particle anisotropy from aligned Np^{237} nuclei has been extended to 0·2 °K. The α-emission is found to occur along the angular momentum vector and is independent of the shape of the nucleus.

13.7. GAMMA RADIATION

In many beta and alpha transitions the daughter nucleus is formed in an excited state. The excited nucleus does not have enough energy to emit a nucleon and it usually decays by an electromagnetic transition (γ-ray). We shall not attempt to present the theory of electromagnetic transition rates by rigorous quantum mechanics, but instead treat the phenomenon from a semi-classical point of view.

Before discussing the gamma de-excitation of excited nuclei following alpha or beta decay, it is instructive to consider the more general case when there is enough excitation energy for a nucleon to be emitted. The competition between nucleon and gamma modes of de-excitation is complicated by many factors such as the existence of Coulomb or centrifugal barriers, angular momentum and parity selection rules. Nevertheless, the gamma decay probability is, in principle, reduced below the nucleon emission probability by a factor at least equal to the fine structure constant $e^2/(\hbar c)$ ($= 1/137$). This follows from the following semi-classical argument.

† See the review article: L. D. Roberts and J. W. Dabbs, *Ann. Rev. Nuclear Science* **11**, 175, 1961.

†† J. W. T. Dabbs, L. D. Roberts and G. W. Parker, *Bull. Am. Phys. Soc.* Ser. 2, **2**, 31, 1957.

Ignoring Coulomb and centrifugal barriers, a nucleon, if it has sufficient energy, would escape from a nucleus in a time of the order of R/v, where R is the nuclear radius and v is the speed of the nucleon within the nucleus. A proton describing an orbit of radius R with a speed v has a radial acceleration v^2/R and, according to classical electromagnetic theory it will radiate electromagnetic radiation with a power of the order of

$$\frac{e^2}{c^3}\left(\frac{v^2}{R}\right)^2$$

In terms of protons of energy $\hbar\,\omega$, where $\omega = v/R$, the probability per unit time of a photon transition is

$$\sim \frac{e^2}{\hbar\, c}\left(\frac{v}{c}\right)^2\left(\frac{v}{R}\right)$$

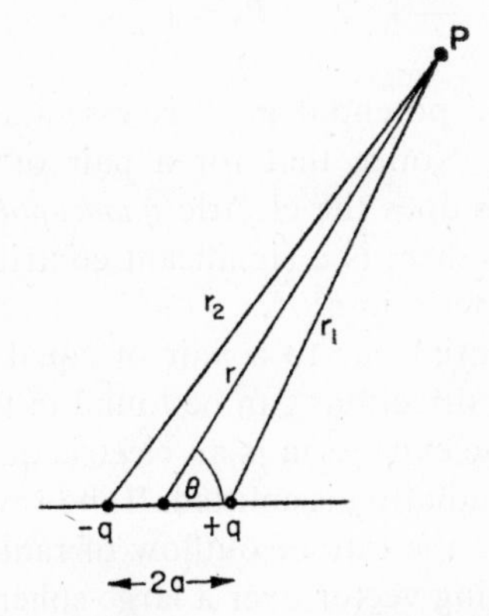

FIG. 5. Electric dipole of moment $q \times 2a$. A distant point P has polar coordinates (r, θ) with respect to the centre of the dipole.

As $(v/c)^2$ is necessarily less than unity, the transition probability for γ-emission is down by a factor at least equal to $e^2/(\hbar\, c)$ on the nucleon emission probability rate v/R.

It is traditional in classical electrostatics to develop the field due to a group of closely spaced static electric charges as a series of rapidly decreasing terms. Consider a pair of point electric charges $+q$ and $-q$ separated by a distance $2a$ (Fig. 5). The electrostatic potential at $P(r, \theta)$ is given by

$$V = \frac{q}{r_1} - \frac{q}{r_2} \tag{14}$$

Now we can write r_1 and r_2 in the form

$$r_1^{-1} = r^{-1}\left\{1 + \left(\frac{a^2}{r^2} - \frac{2a}{r}\cos\theta\right)\right\}^{-\frac{1}{2}}$$

$$r_2^{-1} = r^{-1}\left\{1 + \left(\frac{a^2}{r^2} + \frac{2a}{r}\cos\theta\right)\right\}^{-\frac{1}{2}}$$

Expanding these expressions by the binomial theorem, we obtain

$$\frac{1}{r_1} = \frac{1}{r} + \frac{a}{r^2}\cos\theta + \frac{a^2}{r^3}\left(\frac{3\cos^2\theta - 1}{2}\right) + \frac{a^3}{r^4}\left(\frac{5\cos^3\theta - 3\cos\theta}{2}\right) + \quad (15)$$

$$\frac{1}{r_2} = \frac{1}{r} - \frac{a}{r^2}\cos\theta + \frac{a^2}{r^3}\left(\frac{3\cos^2\theta - 1}{2}\right) - \frac{a^3}{r^4}\left(\frac{5\cos^3\theta - 3\cos\theta}{2}\right) + \quad (16)$$

Substituting these expansions for r_1^{-1} and r_2^{-1} in eqn. (14), we obtain

$$V = \frac{2a\,q\cos\theta}{r^2} + \frac{2q\,a^3}{r^4}\left(\frac{5\cos^3\theta - 3\cos\theta}{2}\right) + \cdots \quad (17)$$

The coefficients of $a^{n-1}r^{-n}$ in the expansion (15) for r_1^{-1} are the Legendre polynomials $P_n(\cos\theta)$. The first few are $P_0 = 1$, $P_1 = \cos\theta$,

$$P_2 = \left(\frac{3\cos^2\theta - 1}{2}\right) \qquad P_3 = \left(\frac{5\cos^3\theta - 3\cos\theta}{2}\right), \cdots$$

For distances $r \gg a$, the potential at P is essentially that of an *electric dipole* of moment $2aq$. Notice that for a pair of charges the *monopole* term in $1/r$ drops out, as does the electric *quadrupole* term in a^2/r^3. If r is not a lot greater than a, there is a significant contribution to the potential at P due to the *octupole* term in a^3/r^4.

The electrostatic potential due to a pair of equal dipoles placed end to end pointing in opposite directions can be found in the same way. The first non vanishing term in the expansion is an electric quadrupole term.

For static charges no radiation is emitted. If, however, the various electric moments vary with time, the rate of outflow of radiant energy is given by the integral of the Poynting vector over a large sphere

$$\iint \frac{c}{4\pi}(\boldsymbol{E} \times \boldsymbol{H}) \cdot d\boldsymbol{S}$$

In the case of an oscillating electric dipole moment, $\boldsymbol{p} = \boldsymbol{p}_0 \sin\omega t$, the radiated power is given by

$$P = \frac{2}{3c^3}\left|\frac{\partial^2 p}{\partial t^2}\right|^2$$

The time average of P over one period is

$$\overline{P} = \frac{1}{3}\frac{\omega^4}{c^3}|p_0|^2 \quad (18)$$

Quantum theory insists that the radiation is emitted in discrete energy quanta $\hbar\omega$; thus we can divide eqn. (18) by $\hbar\omega$ and obtain the transition probability for photon emission in unit time

$$\frac{1}{3}\frac{\omega^3}{\hbar c^3}|p_0|^2 \quad (19)$$

Alternatively the mean lifetime τ against photon emission is given by the reciprocal of eqn. (19)

$$\tau = \frac{3\hbar^4 c^3}{E^3} \frac{1}{|p_0|^2} \tag{20}$$

where E is the photon energy.

For atomic systems, electric dipole moments p_0 are of the order of $e\,r_0$, where e is the electron charge ($4{\cdot}8 \times 10^{-10}$ e.s.u.) and r_0 is ~ 1 Å. For yellow light, $E \sim 2$ eV, and thus we find that τ for an electric dipole transition is expected to be of the order of 10^{-8} sec. There is no doubt that the majority of excited atomic states have this order of lifetime. When an excited atom emits a spectral line in the visible region, the wavelength of the emitted radiation is large compared to the linear dimensions of the atom. This is also true for gamma ray spectra emitted by excited nuclei (the wavelength of a 1 MeV photon is 1259 fermi compared with the radius of 7·5 fermi for the uranium nucleus). This means that we can write the interaction energy associated with the radiative transition as

$$E\,e\,z$$

where the electric field E is, to a good approximation, uniform across the nucleus; z is the displacement of the charge e. Theoretical attempts to predict the rates of emission of gamma radiation by excited nuclei have usually been made in terms of model transitions involving a *single nucleon.* In electric transitions, for example, we picture a proton moving in a quasi-stationary nuclear orbit with a definite angular momentum and energy making a transition to a lower energy orbit. In quantum mechanics, transition rates are determined by time-dependent perturbation methods in terms of matrix elements of the type

$$\int \psi_f^* \, z \, \psi_i \, d\tau$$

ψ_f and ψ_i are the wave functions of the final and initial states of the transition. If the approximation that the interaction energy is equal to Eez is relaxed, smaller terms of the form $\left(\frac{z}{\lambda}\right)^L$ appear in conjunction with matrix elements of the type $\int \psi_f^* \, z^L \, \psi_i \, d\tau$ where $L = 2, 3$, and λ is the wavelength of the emitted photon.

In the atomic case, the lifetime against the emission of electric quadrupole radiation ($L = 2$) is up by a factor of $\sim 10^6$ on the electric dipole ($L = 1$) lifetime. It is very unlikely that an excited atom, with a lifetime as long as 10^{-2} sec against photon emission, will emit light. In all probability the excitation energy will be transferred to another atom or the wall of the containing vessel; consequently, optical radiation is normally electric dipole radiation ($E\,1$). An excited nucleus, on the other hand, is well screened by its cortêge of electrons and, if some selection rule forbids the emission of dipole radiation, the nucleus can remain in this state until a gamma photon is emitted through an electric quadrupole transition ($E\,2$).

The intensity distribution of electric quadrupole radiation is quite different from that radiated by an oscillating dipole. A simple intensity pattern for electric quadrupole radiation is shown in Fig. 6. Unfortunately it is, in general, not possible to recognize the type of radiation emitted by nuclei from the intensity distribution, as their spin axes are randomly orientated in space.

In addition to the interaction between the charged nucleons inside the nucleus and the electromagnetic field there is an interaction of the magnetic moments of the nucleons with the field. There is a contribution to the

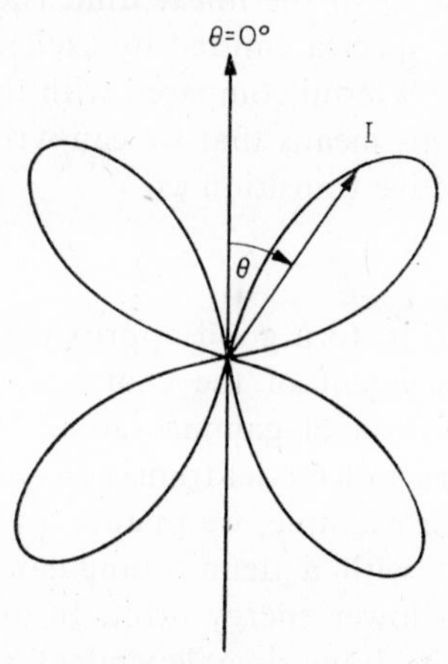

FIG. 6. Polar diagram of radiation pattern emitted by an electric quadrupole. I is proportional to $\sin^2 2\theta$.

magnetic interaction from the orbital angular momentum as well as from the intrinsic spin of a nucleon. (The neutron though is has no resultant electric charge has a magnetic moment of $-1{\cdot}9$ nuclear magnetons.) Electromagnetic transitions arising from the magnetic interaction with the radiation field can be expanded in a series of multipole terms: magnetic dipole ($M\,1$), magnetic quadrupole ($M\,2$), magnetic octupole ($M\,3$) . . . etc.

An important feature of electromagnetic transitions is the angular momentum carried away by the emitted photon. The transition is also characterized by whether or not ("yes" or "no") the parity of the atomic or nuclear states involved in the transitions are equal or opposite. In an electric dipole transition ($E\,1$), the parities of the initial and final states of the radiating system are different, and one unit of angular momentum is carried away by the photon. As the photon travels with the unique velocity c, its spin axis is parallel or anti-parallel to the direction of motion in all Lorentz frames of reference. In higher order multipole transitions, more than one unit of angular momentum is carried away by the emitted photon. This is possible, in spite of the intrinsic spin of $\hbar$ of the photon, because the photon may have orbital angular momentum about the centre of mass of the radiating system. However the orbital angular momentum vector is perpendicular to the spin axis of the photon and it is never possible for the resultant emitted angular momentum to be zero. Thus transitions between atomic or nuclear states of zero angular momentum ($0 \rightarrow 0$ transitions) can never take place by photon de-excitation. If, sufficient energy is available ($> 2m\,c^2$) a $0 \rightarrow 0$ transition may occur by the simultaneous emission of an electron–positron pair. The 6·05 MeV O^+ state of O^{16} decays to the O^+ ground state by pair emission.

The angular momentum vector $\boldsymbol{L}$ of a photon emitted in a transition between two nuclear states of angular momentum $\boldsymbol{J}_i$ and $\boldsymbol{J}_f$ is given by the vector law,

$$\boldsymbol{L} = \boldsymbol{J}_i - \boldsymbol{J}_f$$

The magnitude of the vector $\boldsymbol{L}$ is always an integral multiple of $\hbar$ and may, in general, assume one of the values between $J_i + J_f$ and $|J_i| - |J_f|$. The values of L and the parity change (if any) between the initial and final nuclear states, for electric and magnetic electromagnetic transitions of multipolarity 2^L, are summarized in Table 4. A convenient convention for electric (magnetic) transitions of multipolarity 2^L is $E\,L(M\,L)$.

TABLE 4

CHANGES IN SPIN AND PARITY OF NUCLEAR STATES IN *E–M* TRANSITIONS

L	1	2	3	4	5
Electric multipole	$E\,1$	$E\,2$	$E\,3$	$E\,4$	$E\,5$
Parity change	Yes	No	Yes	No	Yes
Magnetic multipole	$M\,1$	$M\,2$	$M\,3$	$M\,4$	$M\,5$
Parity change	No	Yes	No	Yes	No

A few simple examples of these rules may be helpful. Thus, if $J_i = 2$ and $J_f = 0$, there is no parity change, and pure electric quadrupole radiation ($E\,2$) is emitted. If $J_i = 3$, and $J_f = 1$, there is no parity change, and the magnitude of $\boldsymbol{L}$ may be equal to 2, 3 or 4, corresponding to $E\,2$, $M\,3$ (magnetic octupole) or $E\,4$ transitions. The emitted radiation may be a mixture of these types.

Useful estimates of electromagnetic transition probabilities, based on a single particle model, have been made by Weisskopf.† By a single particle model we mean that in an electric transition, a single proton moving in a quasi-stationary orbit within the nucleus with total angular momentum $L + \frac{1}{2}$ makes a transition to a state of zero orbital angular momentum

† J. M. BLATT and V. F. WEISSKOPF, p. 627, *Theoretical Nuclear Physics*, Wiley, New York 1952.

(the proton still retains its intrinsic spin of half a unit). The Weisskopf model estimates of the electric and magnetic transition probabilities per unit time are

$$\begin{aligned} \lambda_E(L) &= \frac{4{\cdot}4(L+1)}{L[(2L+1)!!]^2}\left(\frac{3}{L+3}\right)^2\left(\frac{E_\gamma}{197}\right)^{2L+1} R^{2L} \times 10^{21}\ \text{sec}^{-1} \\ \lambda_M(L) &= \frac{1{\cdot}9(L+1)}{L[(2L+1)!!]^2}\left(\frac{3}{L+3}\right)^2\left(\frac{E_\gamma}{197}\right)^{2L+1} R^{2L-2} \times 10^{21}\ \text{sec}^{-1} \end{aligned} \tag{21}$$

E_γ, the photon energy, is measured in MeV and R, is the nuclear radius in fermis. The symbol $(2L+1)!!$ denotes the product $1 \times 3 \times 5 \times \ldots (2L+1)$.

The Weisskopf model values of λ_E and λ_M or alternatively, Γ_E and Γ_M where the widths are given by $\hbar\,\lambda_E$ and $\hbar\,\lambda_M$, are very useful for comparing measured energy level widths. The transition is then of particular interest if it seriously departs from the Weisskopf estimate.†

The Weisskopf model estimates of $\lambda_E(L)$ and $\lambda_M(L)$ have the following characteristics.

(1) For a given multipole order L, λ increases as E_γ^{2L+1}. For $A \sim 100$, $\lambda_E(2) \sim 10^6\ \text{sec}^{-1}$ for $E_\gamma \sim 0{\cdot}1$ MeV and $\lambda_E(2) \sim 10^{11}\ \text{sec}^{-1}$ for $E_\gamma \sim 1$ MeV.

(2) For a given multipole order L, a magnetic transition is less probable than the electric by a factor of 10 to 100.

(3) For a given γ-ray energy, the transition probability decreases by a factor of 10^5 to 10^8 for each increase in L by one unit.

It is sometimes possible to identify the multipolarity of a gamma ray transition from a measurement of the mean lifetime of the initial nuclear state. Care must be exercised, however, for the Weisskopf one-particle model estimates may sometimes be badly out.

The lifetime of a transition between two states with a large spin difference is very long, especially if the energy difference is small. O. Hahn in 1921 observed that $UX_2(Pa^{234})$ decayed by beta emission with a half-life of 6·7 hr in addition to the predominant 1·14 min beta decay. The correct explanation of this curious phenomenon, known as *nuclear isomerism*, was put forward in 1936 by von Weizsäcker. He suggested that Pa^{234} is sometimes formed in a nuclear state of large spin following the beta decay of $UX_1(Th^{234})$. The half-life of the gamma decay of the excited state of Pa^{234} is 6·7 hr.

13.8. ANGULAR CORRELATIONS††

Consider an assembly of nuclei in the same excited state, with a definite energy, spin, and parity. Normally the spin axes of the nuclei are randomly oriented. Suppose a nucleus decays by α- or β-emission and the daughter

† D. H. Wilkinson, pp. 852–889 in *Nuclear Spectroscopy*, Part B, Ed. by F. Ajzenberg–Selove, Academic Press 1960.

†† See Chapter 20, Section 10.

nucleus is formed in one of several excited states. The nuclear spin axis of the new state is *not* unrelated to the direction of emission of the α- or β-radiation. Thus if the daughter nucleus decays *before* it is disoriented by local disturbing electromagnetic fields, there is an angular correlation of the direction of emission of the γ-ray and the direction of emission of the α- or β-particle. In addition, if the daughter nucleus decays by two or more gamma transitions in cascade, it is to be expected that there will be a correlation between the directions of the γ-rays. The directional correlation between two γ-rays emitted in cascade is usually expressed as a series in Legendre polynomials $P(\cos\theta)$

$$W(\theta) = 1 + a_2 P_2 \cos(\theta) + a_4 P_4(\cos\theta) +$$

where

$$P_2(\cos\theta) = \tfrac{1}{2}(3\cos^2\theta - 1)$$

$$P_4(\cos\theta) = \tfrac{1}{8}(35\cos^4\theta - 30\cos^2\theta + 3)$$

and a_2, a_4 are correlation coefficients.

$W(\theta)$ is the probability that the angle between the directions of two cascade γ-rays is θ. The theory of angular correlations relates the spins and parities of the nuclear states and radiations to the correlation function $W(\theta)$. References to the theory of angular correlations are given in the bibliography at the end of the chapter.

The experimental study of the directional correlation of successive radiations is based on measuring the coincidence rate of the two radiations with different detectors, the angle θ between the detectors and the source being variable. It is assumed that the time delay between the emission of the two radiations is less than the resolving time of the coincidence circuit. The function $W(\theta)$ is obtained by measuring the coincidence rate as a function of θ, after correction for accidental coincidences. For good results a number of precautions is essential. The source should be very thin and small in bulk. The detectors should subtend small solid angles at the source, otherwise θ is not accurately specified. The detectors should be shielded from scattered radiation, especially radiation scattered from the other detector. In detecting gamma radiation, pulse height selection from the detector (scintillation unit) is desirable for checking the energy of the γ-rays. A correction for deorientation of the correlation by local atomic fields in the source may be important.† The disturbing effect is greatly reduced in liquid sources. Disorientation is likely to be severe for excited nuclei with large quadrupole moments due to their interaction with local electric field gradients. Krohn *et al.*†† have studied the α–γ correlation in the decay ${}_{95}Am^{241} \rightarrow {}_{93}Np^{237}$ using liquid sources. They showed that the disorienting

† A. Abragam and R. V. Pound, *Phys. Rev.* **92**, 943, 1953.
†† V. E. Krohn, T. B. Novey and S. Raboy, *Phys. Rev.* **105**, 234, 1957.

or attenuation effect of the medium can be represented by exponential factors, $G_K(t) = \exp(-\lambda_K t)$, in the angular correlation series

$$W(\theta, t) = \Sigma\, G_K(t) A_K P_K(\cos\theta)$$

For the α–γ cascade via the 59·6 keV level of Np^{237}, the lifetime of the excited state is 7×10^{-8} sec, which is long enough for the disorienting effect in a solid source to be large. In solutions, it was found that the most important attenuation factor $G_2(t)$ corresponds to an experimental value of $\lambda_2 \sim 13 \times 10^6$ sec^{-1}.

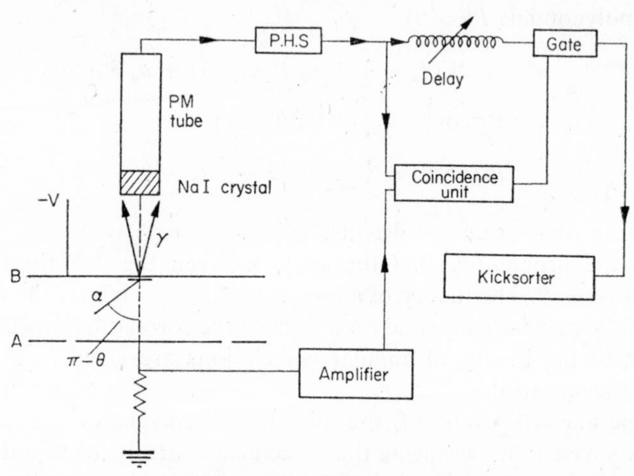

FIG. 7. α–γ correlation experiment. Method of G. VALLADAS *et al.* (*J. Phys. Radium*, **16** 125, 1955.)

In the simplest α–γ cascades, the correlation function $W(\theta)$ is found to agree with a theoretical $\sin^2 2\theta$ distribution (Fig. 6). An example of this occurs in the alpha decay of Po^{210} to the first excited level of Pb^{206}, an $0^+ \xrightarrow{\alpha} 2^+ \xrightarrow{\gamma} 0^+$ cascade with $E\,2$ radiation.

It is difficult to overestimate the importance of the introduction of scintillation detectors in place of Geiger counters in angular correlation work. The low detection efficiency of Geiger counters for γ-rays meant that very long experimental runs were necessary to obtain a large number of coincidence events. With scintillation counters, the number of coincidences observed in a day may exceed the number recorded by Geiger counters in continuous use for ten years.

One of the best methods of investigating α–γ cascades is illustrated in Fig. 7. A small thin alpha source is mounted on the high (negative) voltage electrode B of a pulse ionization chamber filled with an argon–carbon dioxide mixture. The height of the α-particle pulses (with a short "clipping" time) is proportional, for a given α-particle energy, to $\left(1 - \dfrac{\bar{r}\cos(\pi - \theta)}{d}\right)$, where $\bar{r}$ is the distance from the source to the centroid of the charge distribution of the ionization track, and d is the separation of the parallel plates of the chamber. α-particles are recorded in coincidence with gamma rays detected by the NaI scintillation counter (θ is the angle between the α and γ directions).The pulse height selector (P.H.S.) rejects pulses due to γ-rays of the "wrong" energy. The amplified α-pulses and the γ-pulses from the P.H.S. unit operate a fast coincidence circuit. The delay unit is inserted to allow for the response time of the coincidence circuit; the output pulses from the latter open the "gating" circuit and transmit the α-pulses. The α-pulses are then sorted according to height in a multi-channel pulse height analyser ("kick sorter"). This method is very time saving as it allows the simultaneous recording of α–γ correlations over a wide range of θ. There is a simple relation between θ and the height of the α-pulses sorted in the kick sorter.

So far, we have discussed the principles of directional correlation experiments. A determination of the function $W(\theta)$ in a two γ-ray cascade is sufficient to establish the angular momentum of each ray. If one can determine the *polarization* of one of the gamma cascade rays it is also possible to determine the parity sequence. A device sensitive to the polarization, that is, to the direction of the electric field $\boldsymbol{E}$ of γ-radiation was first developed by Metzger and Deutsch.† This gamma polarimeter is suitable for moderate energy γ-rays (E_γ not $\gg m\,c^2$) and it makes use of the dependence of the differential Compton scattering cross section on the state of polarization of the incident gamma ray. According to Klein and Nishina, the differential cross section $\frac{d\sigma(\varphi, \varepsilon)}{d\omega}$, depends on φ the angle of scattering of the γ-ray by an electron and ε the angle between the electric vectors of the incident and scattered γ-rays.

$$\frac{d\sigma(\varphi, \varepsilon)}{d\omega} = \frac{1}{4}\left(\frac{e^2}{m\,c^2}\right)^2 \left(\frac{E'}{E}\right)^2 \left[\frac{E}{E'} + \frac{E'}{E} - 2 + 4\cos^2\varepsilon\right] \tag{22}$$

where E and E' are the energies of the incident and scattered γ-rays. For low values of E, E' is not much less than E (a few per cent) and the cross section reduces to the approximate form

$$\frac{d\sigma(\varphi, \varepsilon)}{d\omega} = \left(\frac{e^2}{m\,c^2}\right)^2 \cos^2\varepsilon \tag{23}$$

Unpolarized γ-radiation is partially polarized by Compton scattering and incident polarized radiation is scattered preferentially in a direction normal to the plane defined by the linear momentum of the incident photon and its electric field vector $\boldsymbol{E}$. The polarimeter devised by Metzger and Deutsch

† F. Metzger and M. Deutsch, *Phys. Rev.* **78**, 551, 1950.

is shown in Figs. 8 and 9. Two γ-rays γ_1 and γ_2, emitted in cascade, are detected respectively by the scintillators B and A subtending a correlation angle θ at the small source. If the γ-ray is Compton scattered from B into the scintillator C a triple coincidence is recorded. The triple coincidence rate is sensitive to the polarization of γ_1. For example, suppose we denote

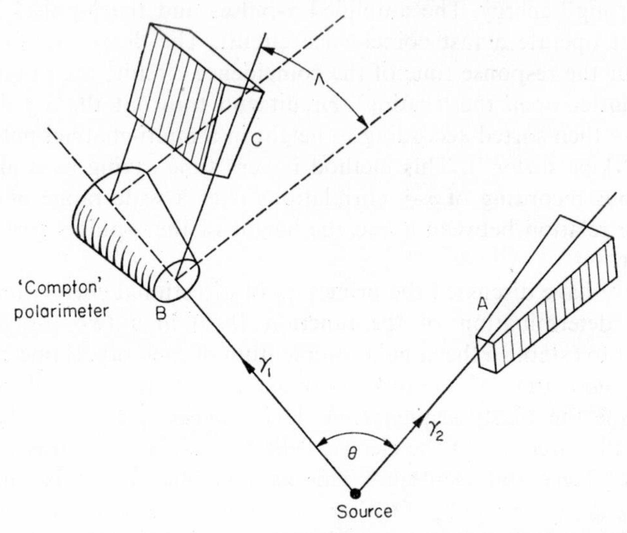

FIG. 8. Polarimeter of Metzger and Deutsch. A, B, C are scintillators operated in triple coincidence to detect the γ_1, γ_2 cascade. γ_1 is Compton scattered from B into C.

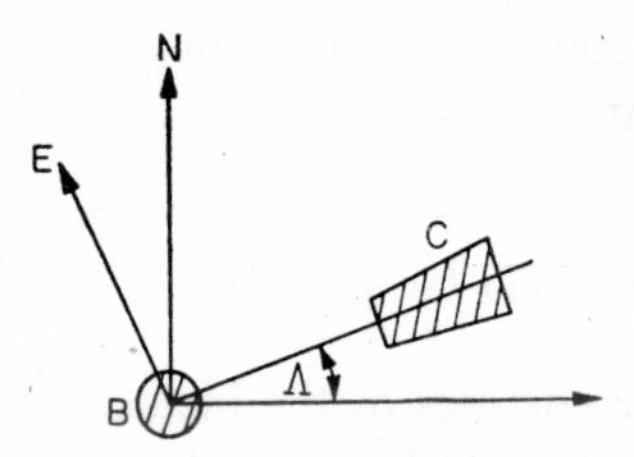

FIG. 9. Cross section through polarimeter B–C of Fig. 8. N is the normal to the plane of the γ-rays γ, and γ_2. E is the polarization vector of γ_1.

the triple coincidence count when $\theta = 90°$ and $\Lambda = 0°$ by $N_{||}$, and the count when $\theta = 90°$ and $\Lambda = 90°$ by $N_{\perp}$. Then if the electric vector $\boldsymbol{E}$ of γ_1, is normal to the plane of γ_1 and γ_2, $N_{||} > N_{\perp}$. Rotating the scintillator C around the axis of B varies the angle Λ and the triple coincidence rate alters. For full advantage to be taken of the polarimeter, its sensitivity as a function of the angle between $\boldsymbol{E}$ and the axis of C must be determined. Sometimes a determination of the sign of $N_{||} - N_{\perp}$ is sufficient to determine the parity of the γ_1 ray.

If $E_\gamma \gg m c^2$, the Compton scattered γ-rays are predominantly in the forward direction, that is, at small angles to the incident γ-ray and it is difficult from the geometry viewpoint, to construct a successful polarimeter. Other polarization-sensitive events have been employed. These include the polarization of the electron and positron produced in pair creation ($E_\gamma > 2m c^2$), and the direction-polarization correlation of photoelectrons released by low energy gamma quanta. Above 3 MeV, there is a correlation between the angle θ between the directions of the proton and neutron and the electric vector $\boldsymbol{E}$ of the γ-ray in the photo-disintegration process $d(\gamma, n)p$.

13.9. MEASUREMENT OF GAMMA RAY ENERGIES

A large number of methods of measuring γ-ray energies have been used. Some of the methods, yield results of accuracy of the order of 1 per cent. These methods are often useful, but for more precise energy determinations more elaborate techniques must be employed. The crystal diffraction spectrometer in the hands of Du Mond has enabled γ-ray energies up to 1 or 2 MeV to be determined, in the case of sources of *high specific activity*, to a precision of 1 part in 10^5, a remarkable achievement.

For low energy γ-rays (< 80 keV), the sharp discontinuity in absorption coefficient at the K photoelectric absorption edge of an absorber sometimes allows the accurate determination of γ-ray energies. For example, 79 keV gamma radiation has much greater transmission through gold (K absorption edge at 80·713 keV), compared with platinum (K absorption edge at 78·379 keV). Alvarez† used this technique to identify the soft X-rays emitted by a low Z atom decaying by orbital electron capture. The method was sensitive enough to confirm the belief that the X-rays are characteristic of the daughter atom.

Many determinations of γ-rays are based on the measurement of the linear absorption coefficient of the radiation (usually in Pb for energetic radiation), with a "good" geometry arrangement (Fig. 10). This entails fine collimation of the radiation from the source and the prevention of scattered radiation from nearby materials and Compton scattered (i.e. lower energy) radiation in the absorber from reaching a well-shielded counter. To minimize the effects of scattering, some investigators favour suspending the source, absorber, and detector high above the ground and well away from walls and any scattering material.

Monoenergetic γ-radiation is absorbed exponentially,

$$I = I_0 \exp(-\mu t)$$

† L. W. ALVAREZ, *Phys. Rev.* **54**, 486, 1938.

where μ is the linear absorption coefficient (cm^{-1}) and t the thickness (cm) of the absorber. μ can be written in the form $\mu = n(\sigma_{PE} + \sigma_C + \sigma_{PP})$, where n is the number of absorber atoms per cm^3, σ_{PE}, σ_C and σ_{PP} are the photoelectric, Compton, and pair production absorption cross sections of an atom for the γ-radiation. If these cross sections are known, one may be found to be dominant (e.g. in Pb at low energy $\sim$ 100 to 200 keV, $\sigma_{PE} \gg \sigma_C$ and σ_{PP} is zero as $E_\gamma < 2m\,c^2$). It is interesting to realise that the discovery of the neutron was held back because the process of gamma absorption

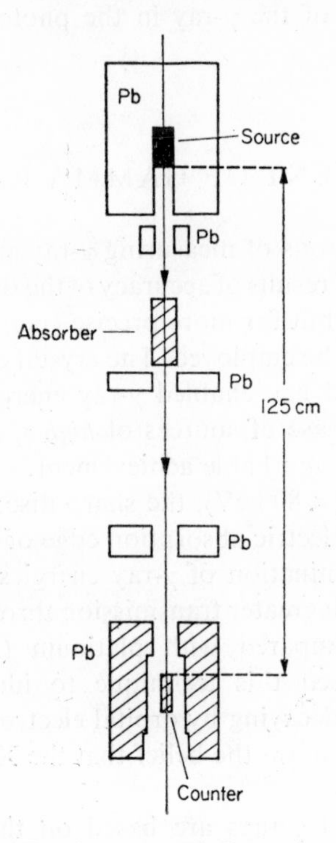

FIG. 10. "Good geometry" absorption experiment.

by pair creation was unknown at the time (1930). The supposedly very hard γ-rays, produced by irradiating some light elements (e.g. Be) with α-particles, were, in fact, neutrons. If pair creation had been known at the time it would have been realised that σ for γ-rays rises rapidly above $E_\gamma \sim 3$ MeV in Pb due to pair creation.

Soft γ-ray energies < 50 keV have been measured in gas proportional counters. The great development in scintillation spectroscopy in the last decade, especially the advent of large volume liquid scintillators and the manufacture of very large NaI(Tl) crystals has meant that the measurement of the energy of moderate and fairly high energy γ-rays with an accuracy approaching 1 per cent is commonplace. The very important gamma absorption cross sections as a function of E_γ in NaI are illustrated in Fig. 11.

The most popular of the accurate methods of determining γ-ray energies is based on the measurement of the momenta (and hence the kinetic energies) of electrons ejected from a thin absorber (called a radiator or converter) by the γ-radiation. For example, if γ-rays are incident, *in vacuo*, on a thin lead sheet, various energy groups of electrons escape from the surface of the metal, corresponding to the photoelectric ejection of bound atomic

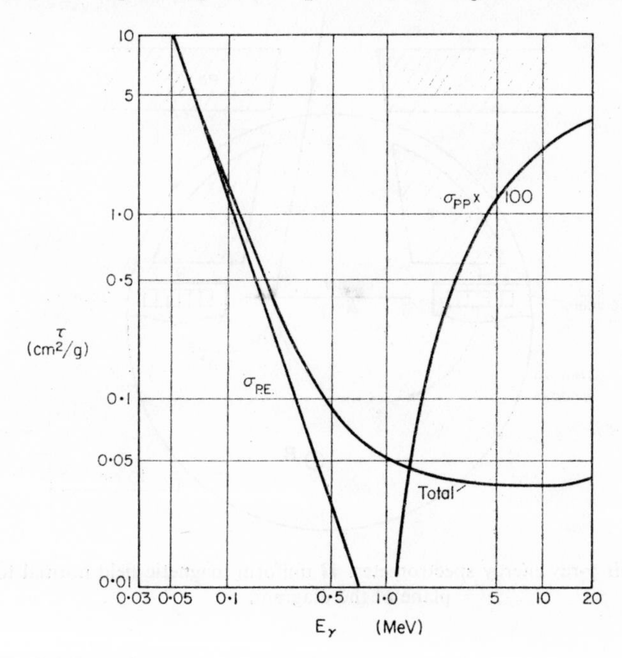

FIG. 11. Absorption of γ-rays in NaI. N.B. σ_{pp} cross section is multiplied by 100. The ordinate is $\tau = \mu/\varrho$, the mass absorption coefficient.

electrons. If the binding energy of the electrons is known, the electrons escaping from the surface of the radiator will have a kinetic energy $E_e = E_\gamma - E_K$, where E_K is the electron binding energy. The momentum of the electrons, $p = BRe$, can be determined by measuring the radius of curvature of the trajectory in a uniform magnetic field normal to the direction of emission.

For high energy gamma rays, $E_\gamma > 5$ MeV, pair spectrometers have proved to be ideal for determining E_γ, provided a fairly high gamma flux is available. A classic example is the determination of the energy of the two γ-rays (14·7 MeV and 17·6 MeV) produced when lithium is bombarded with low energy protons ($\sim 0{\cdot}5$ MeV) $Li^7(p, \gamma)\,Be^8$. The pair creation cross section increases slowly just above the threshold energy of 1·02 MeV but more rapidly at higher energies. A γ-ray spectrometer for high energy radiation invented by Walker and McDaniel† is illustrated in Fig. 12. The γ-rays produced in a nuclear reaction (e.g. (p, γ), (n, γ) etc.) are first collimated and allowed to impinge on a thin (~ 5 mg/cm^2) metal converter A mounted *in vacuo*. The electrons and positrons created in A are predominantly emitted in the forward direction and they are bent by a uniform magnetic field B in opposite directions so that after describing

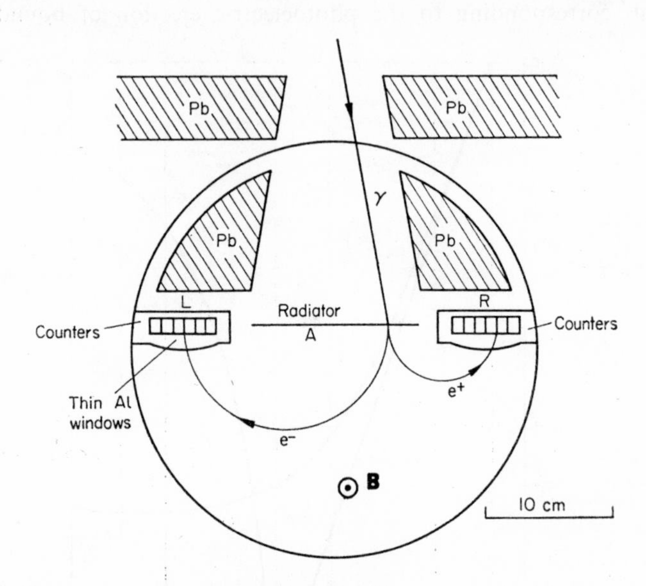

FIG. 12. Pair γ-ray energy spectrometer. $\boldsymbol{B}$ uniform magnetic field normal to the plane of the diagram.

a semi-circle they pass through slits into a detector. In the instrument shown in Fig. 12, the detectors consist of two rows of four Geiger counters, labelled L and R. Later developments of pair spectrometers make use of scintillation detectors.††

The total kinetic energy shared by the pair is equal to $E_\gamma - 1{\cdot}022$ MeV. The available energy is not usually equally shared between the electron and the positron. If, however, the two particles are created with relativistic kinetic energies, their energies E^- and E^+ are nearly given by

$$E^- = p^- c \quad \text{and} \quad E^+ = p^+ c \tag{24}$$

where p^- and p^+ are the momenta of the electron and the positron. In a uniform magnetic field B directed normal to the plane of the trajectories

† R. WALKER and B. MCDANIEL, *Phys. Rev.* **74**, 315, 1948.
†† B. B. KINSEY and G. A. BARTHOLOMEW, *Can. J. Phys.* **31**, 537, 1953.

of the particles, the radii of curvature of the paths of the pair of particles are equal to

$$r^- = \frac{p^-}{B\,e} \quad \text{and} \quad r^+ = \frac{p^+}{B\,e} \tag{25}$$

$$R = r^- + r^+ = \frac{1}{B\,e\,c}(E^- + E^+) = \frac{E_\gamma - 1{\cdot}02}{B\,e\,c} \tag{26}$$

The important conclusion is drawn that the *sum* of the radii of the trajectories is a function of E_γ and B. The left and right counters are connected so that coincidences due to the detection of an electron and a positron between a pair of counters at a fixed distance apart (equal to R) are recorded. The field B is varied until a peak coincidence rate is recorded corresponding to a group of monoenergetic gamma rays. Notice it is not essential to know where in the converter A the pairs are created. For accurate determinations of E_γ (to 0·1 or 0·2%) a number of corrections is necessary. Scattering in the converter of the electrons and positrons is important and for this reason in spite of the increase of σ as Z^2, converters of fairly low Z such as $_{13}$Al or $_{29}$Cu are used. Divergence of the incident gamma beam and the finite width of slits in front of the detectors also contributes to the error of the energy determination. It is a characteristic of magnetic semi-circular spectrometers that the line shape of the detected gamma peak is steep on the high energy side. The extrapolated edge of the high energy side of the peak is used to calculate the total momentum. The counting efficiency of pair spectrometers falls off very sharply at the low energy end, $E_\gamma < 6$ MeV. Pair spectrometers have been used with gamma energies as high as 100 MeV; unfortunately they have a low detection efficiency.

Low energy γ-ray wavelengths were first measured using crystal diffraction techniques by Rutherford and Andrade†. Later in 1929 Frilley measured the wavelengths of seventeen nuclear γ-rays in the radium series. The shortest wavelength corresponded to $E_\gamma \sim 0{\cdot}8$ MeV. The wavelength measurement technique of determining energies from $E_\gamma = (h\,c)/\lambda$ is appealing, but unfortunately two factors strongly mitigate against the success of the method. The Bragg angle θ for reinforcement in the scattering of γ-radiation from the lattice planes of a crystal is very small for short wavelengths ($\sim$ 15 min for 1 MeV rays). It is therefore very difficult to resolve the strong directly transmitted gamma beam by a crystal, and the very weak diffracted beam. The second difficulty is related to the very small reflecting power of the lattice planes, which varies as λ^2.

An important development in the crystal diffraction method was the introduction of the *bent* crystal focusing spectrometer††. The Du Mond

† E. Rutherford and E. N. da C. Andrade, *Phil. Mag.* **27**, 854, 1914 and **28**, 263, 1914.

†† J. Du Mond, *Rev. Sci. Instr.* **18**, 626, 1947.

γ-ray spectrometer is depicted in Fig. 13. The γ-rays from a small but intense source S ($\sim$ 1 curie!) are diffracted by the (310) lattice planes of a bent quartz crystal C held in a steel frame. The crystal is cut and then bent so that (310) lattice planes produced intersect on the focal circle, of 2 m diameter at F. This arrangement that if a γ-ray from the "point" source S falls on a (310) lattice plane at the correct angle to satisfy the Bragg equation $2d \sin\theta = \lambda$, then all the (310) lattice planes are correctly oriented. A lead collimator A cut with the various channels at different angles, prevents

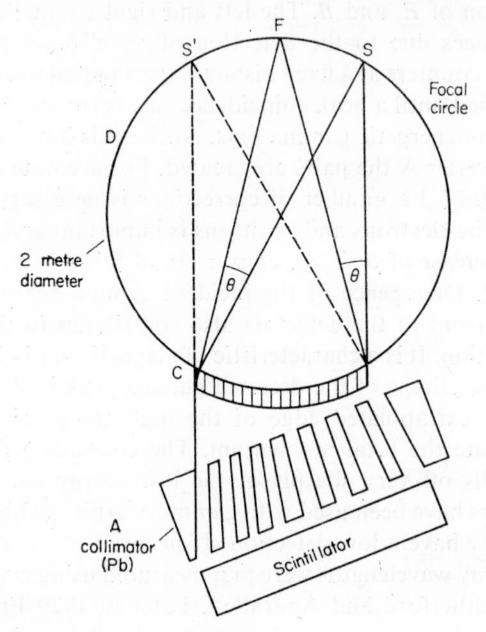

FIG. 13. Du Mond crystal spectrometer. S—source, C—bent crystal, A—lead collimator. (*Ann. Rev. Nuclear Science*, **8**, 166, 1958.)

the intense directly transmitted rays from reaching the large NaI(Tl) detector, but permits the diffracted rays at angle 2θ with respect to the direct beam to reach the scintillator. The diffracted rays appear to diverge from the virtual source S′. The angle θ is varied by moving the source S round the circumference of the focal circle. The essential advantage of the bent crystal method is that it avoids the necessity of collimating the incident γ-rays and makes full use of the whole of the aperture of the crystal. Du Mond has shown that it is possible to measure γ-wavelengths as short as 0·01 Å, corresponding to energies as high as 1·3 MeV. For energies up to $\sim$ 0·5 MeV, the crystal diffraction method is capable of yielding results with an error as small as 1 part in 10^4. At the upper limit, $\sim$ 1·3 MeV, the determinations are not as precise.

Photographic quartz crystal spectrometers of simple design have been used to record Coulomb excited γ-rays†. A high beam current (30 mA) of 3·7 MeV protons bombards a water-cooled copper target on which is deposited a thin target layer. The incident protons have too low an energy to penetrate the Coulomb barrier of the target nucleus, but in Rutherford scattering near the nucleus, the Coulomb field of a proton may excite the nucleus to a low lying state. The excited nucleus decays by γ-emission and as the majority of Coulomb excited γ-rays have an energy less than $\sim$150 keV the crystal spectrometer wavelength determinations are of high accuracy. To excite higher states heavy ion beams are needed.

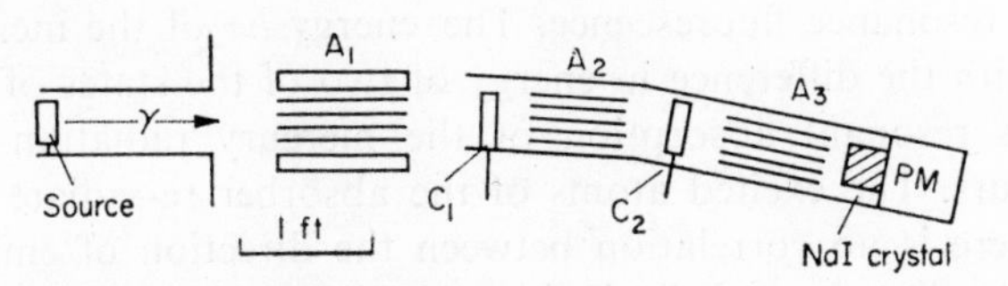

FIG. 14. Two crystal (C_1, C_2) γ-ray spectrometer. A_1, A_2, A_3, Soller slit baffles (redrawn from DU MOND, *Ann. Rev. Nuclear Science*, **8**, 176, 1958).

The intensity of the γ-rays diffracted by the lattice planes of a crystal increases with the thickness of the crystal. There is an optimum thickness ($\sim$5 cm for the (211) planes of calcite), beyond which the effect of absorption outweighs the increased reflecting power of the lattice planes. Unfortunately, it is difficult to bend large quartz crystals which are thicker than 2 or 3 mm without breaking them. An alternative approach to the measurement of γ-ray wavelengths makes use of diffraction by two *thick* ($\sim$2 cm) *flat* crystals in succession (Fig. 14).

The flat two-crystal spectrometer has been used to measure the wavelengths of neutron capture (n, γ) γ-rays at Chalk River. The source material S is placed outside the shield of a reactor in an intense flux of thermal neutrons. The material is continuously irradiated and in some cases the gamma activity is as high as 1000 curies. Three Soller-slit baffles A_1, A_2, and A_3, constructed of very accurately parallel lead partitions, are placed between the source and the first calcite crystal C_1, between C_1 and the second calcite crystal C_2, and between C_2 and the scintillation detector. The two crystals are rotated and controlled by an optical servo-mechanism so that the second crystal is in the correct position for the (211) planes (d = 3·03 Å) of C_2 to reflect the γ-radiation if the corresponding planes of C_1 are in the correct position. If high quality crystals are used, the two-crystal spectrometer has a very high resolving power. γ-rays of energy of the order of 1 MeV have been determined with a resolution of 0·4 per cent. This resolution figure

† See the review article by DU MOND, p. 163 *et seq.* of Vol. 8, *Annual Review of Nuclear Science*, Ann. Reviews Inc. 1958.

could probably be improved by a factor of ten if the (310) planes of high quality thick quartz crystals ($d = 1{\cdot}18$ Å) were used. The limit to resolution is determined by the angular spread of the mosaic blocks comprising the crystals.

13.10. RESONANCE FLUORESCENCE

The phenomenon of resonance fluorescence with visible and ultraviolet light has been known for a long time. The resonant scattering of the 2537 Å ultraviolet line of the mercury spectrum by mercury vapour is a striking example of resonance fluorescence. The energy $h\nu$ of the incident photon coincides with the difference in energy of two of the states of the mercury atom. Thus resonant absorption of the mercury radiation by mercury vapour occurs. The excited atoms of the absorber re-radiate the mercury line, but there is no correlation between the direction of emission of the light and the direction of the incident radiation. The effect is equivalent to resonant scattering.

Kuhn† in 1929 suggested that it might be possible to conduct analogous scattering experiments with γ-rays. A number of attempts to observe resonant scattering with γ-radiations was made in the following twenty years, all without success. Why is it relatively easy to observe resonance fluorescence with visible light but not with γ-radiation? The answer is connected with the fact that when an atom or nucleus radiates a photon, the atom or nucleus must recoil to conserve momentum. The recoiling atom or nucleus takes a share of the available energy E_0. E_0 is equal to the difference in energy of the two states of the radiating atom or nucleus. If E is the energy of the emitted photon ($E < E_0$), its momentum is E/c. The atom or nucleus recoils with a momentum in the opposite direction, also of magnitude E/c. The kinetic energy of the recoil particle is $E^2/2Mc^2$, where M is the mass of the atom or nucleus. The energy of the photon is given by

$$E = h\nu = E_0 - \frac{E^2}{2Mc^2} \tag{27}$$

or

$$\Delta E = E_0 - E = \frac{E^2}{2Mc^2} \tag{28}$$

Equation (28) gives the important result that the energy shift $E_0 - E$ increases as E^2 and it is much more pronounced for high energy photons. For the mercury line 2537 Å, $E \sim 5$ eV, $M \sim 180$ a.m.u., and $E_0 - E < 10^{-10}$ eV, corresponding to $\Delta E/E_0 \sim 10^{-11}$. For a γ-ray of energy $\sim 0{\cdot}5$ MeV emitted by a nucleus of mass number $A \sim 100$, $\Delta E \sim 1{\cdot}3$ eV, corresponding to

† W. Kuhn, *Phil. Mag.* **8**, 625, 1929.

$\Delta E/E_0 \sim 2 \times 10^{-6}$, which is much greater than the value for the mercury ultraviolet line.

The degree of resonance scattering depends on the value of $\Delta E/E_0$ in comparison with the natural width Γ of the excited state radiating the line. For electric dipole $E1$ transitions in the optical region, the mean lifetimes of the excited states are $\sim 10^{-8}$ sec; substituting this value in

$$\Gamma\tau \sim 6 \times 10^{-16} \text{ eV sec}$$

$$\Gamma \sim 6 \times 10^{-8} \text{ eV}$$

The shift in energy of the photon ΔE ($\sim 10^{-10}$ eV) is very small compared to the natural width of the line. This means that the photon energy strongly overlaps the energy of the excited state of a resonant absorbing atom and resonance fluorescence is observed. If electric dipole radiation was a common type of nuclear radiation (unfortunately it is not), level widths as large as 1 eV might occur for 1 MeV gamma radiation, and there would be some overlap of the gamma energy and the energy of the excited state of a resonant absorbing nucleus. Even for the fastest $M1$ decays, τ is $\sim 10^{-13}$ sec and $\Gamma < 10^{-2}$ eV. The γ-ray energy E is well off the centre of the resonant line and no observable effect is found.

For practical purposes, little error arises in calculating $\Delta E = E_0 - E$ if E_0 replaces E in the right-hand side of eqn. (28);

$$\Delta E = \frac{E_0^2}{2Mc^2} \tag{29}$$

In addition to the energy lost to the recoiling nucleus on emission, kinetic energy is transferred to the absorbing nucleus as a whole when the γ-photon is absorbed. The energy shift is therefore $2\Delta E$.

The cross section σ for resonance fluorescence†, when the only mode of de-excitation of the scattering nucleus after it absorbs a γ-photon of energy E is the emission of the γ-ray, is given for an isolated level by

$$\sigma = g\frac{\lambda^2}{8\pi}\left[\frac{\Gamma^2}{(E-E_0)^2 + \frac{1}{4}\Gamma^2}\right] \tag{30}$$

where g is a statistical weight factor which takes care of the multiplicity of the ground and excited states of the nucleus

$$g = \frac{2I_1 + 1}{2I_0 + 1}$$

I_1 and I_0 are the spins of the excited and ground states respectively. λ is the wavelength of the incident ray. E_0 is the energy and Γ the width of the

† H. A. Bethe and G. Placzek, *Phys. Rev.* **51**, 450, 1937.

excited state responsible for the absorption. The cross section formula is of the form first derived by Breit and Wigner in relation to the resonant absorption of neutrons (Chapter 15, Section 5).

In order to observe resonance absorption or scattering with γ-rays the energy shift $2\Delta E = E_0^2/M c^2$ must be restored in some way. The resonance condition might be restored if the γ-ray of interest is radiated by a nucleus

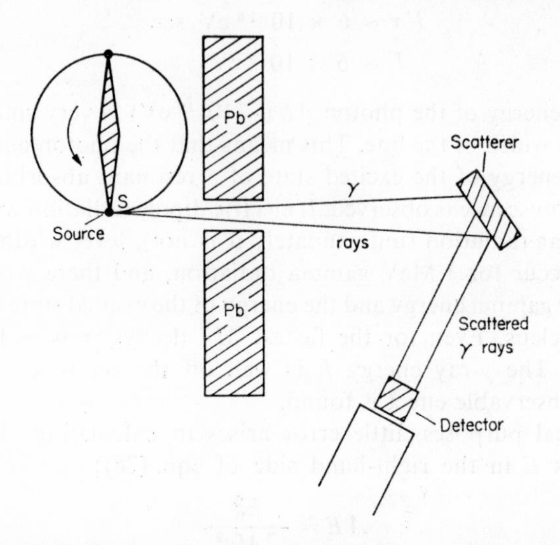

FIG. 15. Schematic diagram of rotor method of observing fluorescent scattering.

which is still recoiling from a shortly preceding beta or gamma transition. If the radiating nucleus is approaching the scatterer with a velocity $u = E/(Mc)$, following the emission of a preceding β- or γ-ray in the opposite direction, the Doppler energy shift is $\frac{uE}{c} = \frac{E^2}{Mc^2} = \frac{E_0^2}{Mc^2}$ and the resonance condition is exactly satisfied. An outstanding application of this process, in which information is obtained about the direction of emission of the preceding radiation, is the determination of the helicity of the neutrino (Chapter 14, Section 8).

Moon proposed that the resonance condition could be restored by bodily moving the gamma source towards the scatterer. A resonant scattering experiment of this type† is illustrated in Fig. 15. An activated gold source produced by the Au^{197} (n, γ) Au^{198} reaction is electroplated on to the tips of a 6 in. diameter steel rotor which can rotate up to peripheral speeds of 8×10^4 cm per sec.

Au^{198} decays by β-emission to Hg^{198} and there is a strong 0·411 MeV γ-line radiated by Hg^{198}. A series of baffles surrounding the rotor allows

† P. B. MOON, *Proc. Phys. Soc.* A **64**, 76; 1951.

γ-rays leaving the source in the forward direction to fall upon a liquid mercury scatterer. Elastically scattered γ-rays are detected by a NaI(Tl) scintillation counter. The latter is biased so that lower energy photons produced by inelastic scattering (e.g. Compton scattering) are not recorded. It is difficult to do this if there is present in the gamma beam incident on the scatterer a strong gamma component of energy above E_0 such that

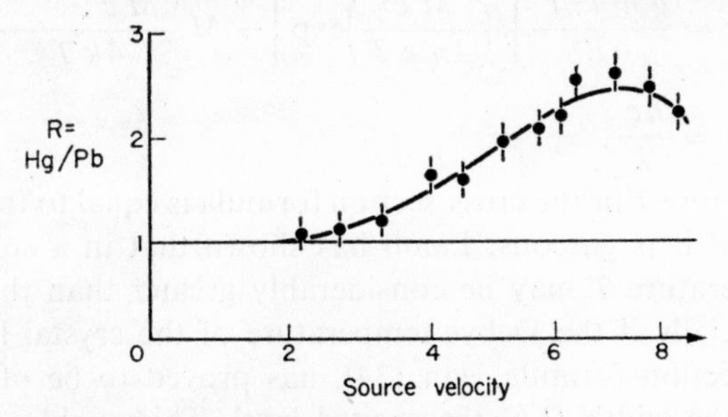

FIG. 16. Rotor experiment. Source velocity unit is 10^4 cm per sec. R is the ratio of the counting rate of γ-rays scattered by mercury and lead. (P. B. MOON and W. G. DAVEY, *Proc. Phys. Soc.*, A **66**, 956, 1953.)

Compton scattering of this group reduces the energy to $\sim E_0$. There is a significant increase in the number of elastically scattered γ-rays with a broad maximum corresponding to a source velocity $u \sim 7 \times 10^4$ cm/sec for the resonant scattering of 0·411 MeV rays by mercury. The thermal motion of the atoms in the source and the absorber are responsible for the absence of a sharp maximum in the scattering efficiency–source velocity curve (Fig. 16). The probability that the source and absorbing nuclei have a relative velocity component v in the direction of the γ-ray is given, on the assumption of a Maxwellian distribution, by

$$P(v)\,dv = \sqrt{\left(\frac{M}{4\pi kT}\right)}\exp\left(-\frac{Mv^2}{4kT}\right)dv \tag{31}$$

In addition to the velocity component v, there is the source component u, producing a total energy increase of $\frac{E}{c}(u+v)$. The energy shift $\Delta E = E_0 - E$ is now given by

$$\Delta E = \frac{E^2}{Mc^2} - \frac{E}{c}(u+v) \tag{32}$$

The resonant scattering cross section eqn. (30), combined with eqns. (31) and (32) becomes

$$\sigma = \frac{g\lambda^2}{8\pi}\int_{-\infty}^{+\infty}\sqrt{\left(\frac{M}{4\pi kT}\right)}\exp\left(-\frac{Mv^2}{4kT}\right)\frac{\Gamma^2}{\frac{E^2}{c^2}\left[\frac{E}{Mc}-u-v\right]^2+\frac{1}{4}\Gamma^2}\,dv \tag{33}$$

The integrand has a very sharp maximum near $v = \frac{E}{Mc} - u$. The width of this maximum at half height is equivalent to a velocity range $dv \sim c\frac{\Gamma}{E}$. The expression given by eqn. (33) then reduces to the approximate formula

$$\sigma = \frac{g\,h^2\,c^2\,\Gamma}{4E^3}\sqrt{\left(\frac{M\,c^2}{4\pi\,k\,T}\right)}\exp\left\{-M\frac{\left(\frac{E}{Mc}-u\right)^2}{4k\,T}\right\} \tag{34}$$

where $E = h\,\nu = \frac{hc}{\lambda}$.

The temperature T in the cross section formula is equal to the temperature of the source if it is gaseous. Lamb has shown that in a solid source the effective temperature T may be considerably greater than the source temperature, especially if the Debye temperature of the crystal lattice is high.

The cross section formula, eqn. (34), has proved to be of practical use in estimating the width Γ of the excited level. This enables the lifetime τ of the state to be determined and it has proved to be complementary to the delayed coincidence method. Lifetimes as short as 5×10^{-14} sec have been measured by the resonant scattering method. Accuracy depends partly on estimating the contribution to elastic scattering by non-resonant processes such as Rayleigh scattering (scattering by bound electrons) and Thomson scattering (scattering by the nuclear electric charge). Future improvements in discriminating against non-resonant scattering may depend on the difference in the angular distributions of the various scattering processes.

Malmfors† has successfully demonstrated the resonance scattering of γ-rays using a stationary source and scatterer. The source is heated to a high temperature (e.g. a gold source is heated to its melting point of 1063°C) and the large increase in the Doppler broadening of the gamma line energy is sufficient to restore the resonance condition for some of the emitted γ-rays.

13.11. THE MÖSSBAUER EFFECT

The recoil energy of a nucleus emitting γ-radiation destroys the exact conditions for observing resonant absorption and scattering by the same type of nucleus. Assuming *free* recoil of the radiating nucleus, the nuclear recoil energy is $E^2/2Mc^2$ where E is the energy of the γ-ray. In 1958, R. L. Mössbauer made the important discovery that the emission of the 129 keV γ-radiation of Ir^{191} is sometimes not accompanied by the recoil of the nucleus.†† The recoil momentum and energy are transferred to the crystal as a whole, and even for a tiny crystalline source the effect of this recoil

† K. G. MALMFORS, *Ark. Fys.* **6**, 49, 1953.

†† R. L. MÖSSBAUER, *Z. Physik* **151**, 124, 1958: *Naturwissenschaften* **45**, 538, 1958; *Z. Naturforsch.* **14**a, 211, 1959.

energy is negligible. About twenty or so recoilless gamma transitions are now known. The theory of recoilless emission shows that the effect is most likely to occur if,

(1) The γ-ray energy E is small. The best example, to date, is the 14·4 keV transition of Fe^{57}.

(2) The temperature of the crystal source is small.

(3) The Debye temperature Θ_D of the crystal lattice is high.

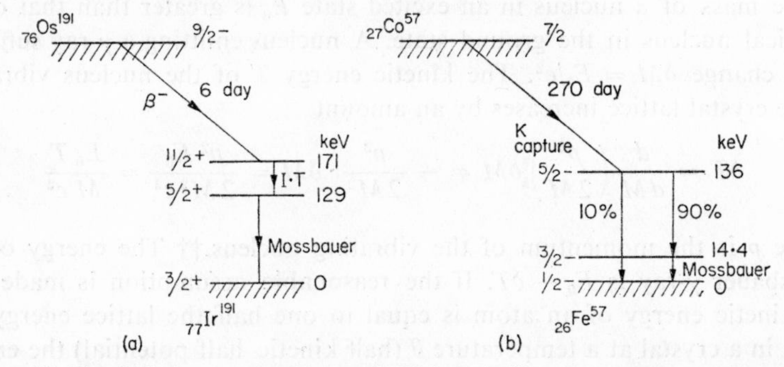

FIG. 17. The Mössbauer transitions of 129 keV (Ir^{191}) and 14·4 keV (Fe^{57}). The sources are Os^{191} and Co^{57}. The latter source is produced by cyclotron bombardment (Fe^{56} (d, n) Co^{57}). The energies, spins, and parities of the various states are given.

This characteristic temperature is related to the maximum (cut-off) frequency ν_m of the quantized lattice vibrations by $h\,\nu_m = k\,\Theta_D$. For Fe, $\Theta_D \sim 420°K$. About 1 per cent of the Ir^{191} transitions at 80°K are recoilless, in contrast to $\sim$ 70 per cent for the 14·4 keV Fe^{57} transitions at room temperature. The decay schemes leading to the Mössbauer excited states of Ir^{191} and Fe^{57} are shown in Fig. 17. The natural widths and lifetimes of the excited states are: 5×10^{-6} eV and $1{\cdot}3 \times 10^{-10}$ sec for the 129 keV level of Ir^{191}, and $4{\cdot}6 \times 10^{-9}$ eV and $1{\cdot}4 \times 10^{-7}$ sec for the 14·4 keV level of Fe^{57}.

The Mössbauer transitions are of great importance because they remove the fundamental effect responsible for the difficulty in observing resonant absorption. Mössbauer observed that at 80°K the 129 keV radiation from Ir^{191} is strongly absorbed by natural crystalline iridium foil (Ir^{191} abundance is 38·5%), provided there is no relative motion between source and absorber. A relative velocity v of 2 cm per sec reduces the absorption by half. The Doppler energy shift $\frac{vE}{c}$ is sufficient to destroy the resonance condition. A relative velocity of 0·1 mm per sec is sufficient to produce a marked reduction in the resonant absorption of the 14·4 keV Fe^{57} Mössbauer radiation by an Fe^{57} absorber. (Natural iron contains 2·17% Fe^{57}, so it is usual to use iron foil absorbers enriched in Fe^{57}).

Complications arise in interpreting the study of small energy shifts if the source and resonant absorber are at different temperatures. This is a result of the Doppler effect associated with the emission of the radiation by a nucleus vibrating around its equilibrium lattice site. The Doppler shift depends on the component of the velocity of the nucleus in the direction of emission of the γ-ray. Now it is true that the average value of this velocity component over the time interval of emission of the gamma wave train ($\sim 10^{-7}$ sec for the 14 keV iron line) is nearly zero, but there is a small second order effect depending on v^2/c^2. This can be estimated as follows.†

The mass of a nucleus in an excited state E_0 is greater than that of an identical nucleus in the ground state. A nucleus emitting a γ-ray suffers a mass change $\delta M = E_0/e^2$. The kinetic energy T of the nucleus vibrating in the crystal lattice increases by an amount

$$\delta T = \frac{d}{dM}\left(\frac{p^2}{2M}\right)\delta M = -\frac{p^2}{2M^2}\cdot\delta M = \frac{p^2 E_0}{2M^2 c^2} = \frac{E_0 T}{M c^2} \tag{35}$$

where p is the momentum of the vibrating nucleus.†† The energy of the Mössbauer γ-ray is $E_0 - \delta T$. If the reasonable assumption is made that the kinetic energy of an atom is equal to one half the lattice energy per atom in a crystal at a temperature θ (half kinetic–half potential) the energy shift ΔE for a Mössbauer line is given by

$$\frac{\Delta E}{E_0} = \frac{C_p \Delta\theta}{2c^2} \tag{36}$$

where $\Delta\theta$ is the difference in the temperature of the source and the resonant absorber (C_p is the specific heat). Notice that if there is no temperature difference the resonance condition is restored by a decrease in the kinetic energy of vibration of the absorbing nucleus. Strictly speaking,

$$\delta T = -\frac{(E_0 - \delta T)}{M c^2} T \cong -\frac{E_0 T}{M c^2}$$

For Fe^{57} at 300°K, ($C_p \sim .13$) and $\Delta E = 3{\cdot}2 \times 10^{-11}$ eV per °K. This small shift away from the resonance is not negligible in some Mössbauer applications.

Test of the Principle of Equivalence

It is recognized that there are three crucial tests of Einstein's General Theory of Relativity. These are

(1) The advance of the perihelion of the orbit of a planet. The elliptic orbits are not closed but precess at a slow rate. The effect is most marked for Mercury and the increase in the longitude of the perihelion is about 43 seconds of arc per century.

† B. D. Josephson, *Phys. Rev. Letters* 4, 341, 1960.

†† N.B. Here we assume that p is constant during a Mössbauer transition.

(2) A ray of light passing close to the sun is bent by the gravitational field of the sun. For a ray of light grazing the sun's limb the expected deflection is 1·75 seconds of arc.

(3) The period of a natural clock (e.g. the period of a sharp atomic spectral line) in a gravitational field is increased. There should therefore be an increase in the wavelength of the spectral lines radiated by atoms situated in a gravitational field. For an atom in the surface of the sun, the wavelength shift towards the red is expected to be

$$\frac{\delta\lambda}{\lambda} = 2{\cdot}1 \times 10^{-6}$$

There is a thirty-fold increase for the White Dwarf Companion of Sirius.

A number of astronomical observations have in the main supported these predictions. Nevertheless, the direct evidence in support of the general theory is very meagre and more accurate tests are highly desirable.†

The Mössbauer effect has made it possible to carry out *laboratory-scale* tests of the Einstein Principle of Equivalence (1911). This is an integral part of Einstein's theory of gravitation†† and can be briefly stated as follows: "A system in a uniform gravitational field is completely equivalent to a uniformly accelerated system". In other words, it is always possible in a uniform gravitational field to transform to a system of space–time coordinates so that gravity disappears. Consider an observer in a uniform gravitational field of intensity g with two identical atomic clocks of period τ_0 at rest relative to the observer. By the principle of equivalence, we can abolish the effect of gravity if the observer at rest relative to the clocks moves with a constant acceleration g. Suppose the clocks are at a distance h apart, with the line joining them pointing in the direction of the acceleration g. The time for a light signal to travel from one clock to the other is $t = h/c$.

During the time interval t, in the equivalent system (no gravity) the receiving clock will have increased its velocity in the direction of the acceleration by an amount $v = g\,t = g\,h/c$. Hence there is a Doppler effect with regard to the period of the wave train reaching the receiving clock. The observed period τ is, for small v, given by

$$\tau = \tau_0\left(1 + \frac{v}{c}\right) = \tau_0\left(1 + \frac{g\,h}{c^2}\right) \tag{37}$$

In terms of the frequencies, ν_0 and ν, and writing $\Delta\varphi$ for the change in gravitational potential $g\,h$ (in the gravitational system), the last equation becomes

$$\nu = \nu_0\left(1 - \frac{\Delta\varphi}{c^2}\right) \quad \text{for} \quad v \ll c. \tag{38}$$

† L. I. Schiff, *Am. J. Phys.* **28**, 340, 1960.

†† Fock, however, is very critical of the "orthodox" theory of gravitation and contends that the importance of the principle of equivalence is overestimated. (See reference at the end of Chapter 3.)

The fractional frequency change is

$$\frac{\Delta \nu}{\nu_0} = \frac{\Delta \varphi}{c^2} = \frac{g\,h}{c^2} = 1{\cdot}09\,h \times 10^{-18} \qquad (39)$$

If $h\,\nu_0 = E_0$ is the energy of the Mössbauer γ-ray (14·4 keV) from Fe^{57}, the gravitational shift in the γ-ray energy over a vertical path length h is $\Delta E_g = 14{\cdot}4 \times 1{\cdot}09\,h \times 10^{-15} = 1{\cdot}57\,h \times 10^{-14}$ eV. The natural width Γ of the 14·4 keV line is $4{\cdot}6 \times 10^{-9}$ eV, so it looks as though it requires very large values of h to obtain a gravitational shift to upset the resonant absorption condition. With h as small as 3×10^3 cm, $\Delta E_g \sim 1\%\,\Gamma$ and a measurable reduction in resonant absorption should result. The gravitational shift of 3×10^{-11} eV at 20 m will tend to be masked by the temperature

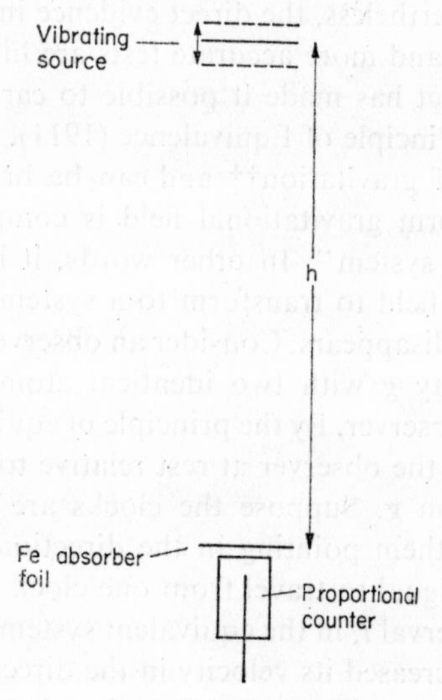

FIG. 18. Gravitational shift experiment. Mössbauer γ-rays emitted from a vibrating Fe source "fall" through a gravitational potential difference gh. Proportional counter records γ-rays transmitted by Fe^{57} absorber.

Doppler shift if the Fe^{57} source and Fe^{57} absorber differ in temperature by as much as 1°C.

Experiments to observe the predicted gravitational shift have been independently carried out at Harwell† and Harvard.†† The Harwell group electro-deposited a Co^{57} source on an iron disc which is mounted about 40 ft above a 5 in. diameter foil containing 4 mg/cm² of iron enriched in Fe^{57} (Fig. 18). A proportional counter, filled with krypton to ~ 20 cm Hg

† T. E. CRANSHAW, J. P. SCHIFFER and A. B. WHITEHEAD, *Phys. Rev. Letters* **4**, 163, 1960.

†† R. V. POUND and G. A. REBKA JR., *Phys. Rev. Letters* **4**, 33, 1960.

pressure is placed underneath the absorbing iron foil to detect the transmitted 14 keV gamma rays. The detection efficiency of the counter for 14 keV gamma rays is high as the K absorption edge of Kr is just below 14 keV.

The gravitational energy shift of the Mössbauer γ-rays "falling" from the source to the absorber increases the transmission of the foil and the counting rate rises. The source is mounted on a transducer device and vibrated to and fro at 50 c/s. Maximum resonant absorption occurs when the Doppler shift produced by moving the source exactly compensates the gravitational shift. The transmitted γ-rays are recorded by two scalers for alternate halves of the vibrating cycle. The mean counting rate in alternate half cycles is slightly different due to the asymmetry introduced by the gravitational shift. The asymmetry corresponds to a Doppler velocity of $\sim 4 \times 10^{-5}$ cm per sec. The first experiments did not recognize the importance of keeping the source and absorber temperatures the same to within a small fraction of 1°C. The results of the Harwell and Harvard experiments are compatible with the theoretical predictions of the principle of equivalence to an accuracy of about 5 per cent; systematic errors, may, however, be as large as 3 per cent. Another interesting experiment investigated the gravitational energy shift produced artificially in a rapidly rotating system.†

BIBLIOGRAPHY

Sir E. Rutherford, J. Chadwick and C. D. Ellis, *Radiations from Radioactive Substances*, Cambridge University Press, 1930.

G. C. Hanna, Alpha Radioactivity, p. 77 *et seq.*, in Vol. 3 of *Experimental Nuclear Physics*, Ed. by E. Segrè, Wiley, New York 1959.

I. Perlman and J. O. Rasmussen, Alpha Radioactivity, p. 109 *et seq.* in Vol. XLII of *Handbuch der Physik*, Ed. by S. Flugge, Springer-Verlag, Berlin 1957.

J. M. Blatt and V. F. Weisskopf, *Theoretical Nuclear Physics*, Wiley, New York 1952.

M. Deutsch and O. Kofoed-Hansen, Gamma Rays, p. 259 *et seq.* in Vol. 3 of *Experimental Nuclear Physics*, Ed. by E. Segrè, Wiley, New York 1959.

Two earlier excellent review articles on the Mössbauer effect are W. E. Burcham, *Science Progress* **48**, 630, 1960.

H. Lustig, *Am. J. Phys.* **29**, 1, 1961.

F. R. Metzger, Resonance Fluorescence in Nuclei, in *Progr. Nuclear Physics*, Vol. 7, 53, 1959.

G. A. Bartholomew, J. W. Knowles and G. E. Lee-Whiting, Precision Measurement in Gamma-Ray Spectroscopy in *Reports on Progr. Physics* **23**, 453, 1960.

† H. J. Hay, J. P. Schiffer, T. E. Cranshaw and P. A. Egelstaff, *Phys. Rev. Letters* **4**, 165, 1960.

CHAPTER 14

BETA DECAY

14.1 INTRODUCTION

There are three modes of beta radioactivity: negatron emission, orbital electron capture and positron emission. Negatron emission is much more common than the other decay processes and it was the negatrons (negative electrons) emitted by beta unstable nuclides in equilibrium with uranium which led to the discovery of radioactivity by Becquerel. β-rays are easily distinguished from α-particles by their considerably greater range in matter and the opposite sense of deflection in a magnetic field.

Measurements of the specific charge $\frac{e}{m}$ of β-particles were first made by Bucherer in 1909, which agreed with the hypothesis that β-particles are swiftly moving electrons. The Bucherer experiment was also a test of the Einstein mass–velocity law for high speed charged particles. Zahn and Spees†, using a source of radioactive Cu^{64}, determined the specific charge of the negatrons and positrons by an electric and magnetic field deflection method. Cu^{64} is one of the rare isotopes which decays by all three beta processes (β^- 39%, β^+ 19%, electron capture 42%, half-life 12·8 hr). It has also been demonstrated that the charge carried by an individual β-particle is equal to the electron charge. The most elegant proof of the identity of β-particles and electrons is provided by the experiment of M. Goldhaber and G. Scharff-Goldhaber.†† They showed that characteristic line X-rays are *not* radiated when *slow* β-rays are stopped in a solid. This supports the contention that β-particles and electrons are identical, for the Pauli exclusion principle forbids the capture of β-particles into filled L and K electron shells of the stopping atoms. Slow β-particles must be used so that K shell photo-ionization is energetically impossible. In marked contrast, X-rays are emitted when slow negative muons are stopped in a solid, the muons having their distinct M, L, and K shell states. Finally, we note that positrons emitted in beta decay are found to annihilate with atomic electrons in agreement with the Dirac picture that the positron is the antiparticle of the electron.

† C. T. Zahn and A. H. Spees, *Phys. Rev.* **58**, 861, 1940.

†† M. Goldhaber and G. Scharff-Goldhaber, *Phys. Rev.* **73**, 1472, 1948; also W. T. Davies and M. A. Grace, *Proc. Phys. Soc.* A **64**, 846, 1951.

Beta decay is a nuclear process, although electrons are not considered to be semi-permanent constituents of the nucleus. In those cases in which the product of beta decay is itself radioactive it is often possible to separate the product by chemical means and show that it is an isotope of the adjacent element in the Periodic Table. Soddy was one of the early pioneers in this field of analysis. After the invention and development of the mass spectrometer, it becames possible in certain cases to separate the *inactive* decay product by chemical means and identify the charge and mass by the mass spectrometer. The charge number Z increases by one unit in negatron decay and decreases by one unit in positron decay and orbital electron capture.

The most important discovery in the history of β-radioactivity was that the kinetic energy of the emitted electrons forms a *continuous* distribution from zero up to a maximum, T_0. The maximum kinetic energy T_0 corresponds closely to that expected from the exact rest mass energies of the parent and daughter atoms, due allowance being made for the possibility of the daughter nucleus being created in an excited state. The excited daughter nucleus subsequently decays by γ-emission or by the process known as *internal conversion*. The first decisive demonstration of the continuous momentum (or energy) spectrum from a beta source was given by Chadwick† using a magnetic spectrometer. For some time, attempts were made to account for the continuous energy distribution in terms of the loss of energy of β-rays of a single energy E_0 by scattering in the source. These attempts were motivated by the understandable desire to retain the law of conservation of energy in beta decay. If only a single particle is emitted in the beta decay of a nucleus, there is an apparent loss of energy equal to $T_0 - T$, where T is the kinetic energy of the emitted electron. The emission of two electrons would increase Z by $+2$. This is not observed. Proof that one electron is emitted per nuclear disintegration is furnished by arguments of the following type. Consider RaD (Pb^{210}) in equilibrium with the subsequent members of the series:

$$\text{RaD }(\text{Pb}^{210}) \xrightarrow[19{\cdot}4\,\text{y}]{\beta^-} \text{RaE }(\text{Bi}^{210}) \xrightarrow[5\,\text{d}]{\beta^-} \text{RaF }(\text{Po}^{210}) \xrightarrow[138\,\text{d}]{\alpha} \text{RaG }(\text{Pb}^{206})$$

The average kinetic energy of the β-rays of Ra E is much greater than those of RaD and it is easy to discriminate against the low energy RaD rays. Now, it is well established that one α-particle (5·3 MeV) is emitted per nuclear disintegration of RaF and, if RaE is in equilibrium with RaF, the rate of emission of electrons by RaE should be equal to the rate of emission of α-particles by RaF. This has been observed, supporting the view that only one electron is emitted in the decay of a nucleus of RaE.

The conservation of energy in beta decay corresponds to the maximum kinetic energy of the emitted electrons E_0. This is shown in a convincing

† J. Chadwick, *Verhandl. deut. Physik. Ges.* **16**, 383, 1914.

way by considering the branched decay of ThC (Bi^{212}) (Fig. 1). The energy release in the decay of ThC via ThC″ to the ground state of ThD is $6{\cdot}203 + 1{\cdot}793 + 3{\cdot}203 = 11{\cdot}199$ MeV. For the decay of ThC to ThD via ThC′ the energy realese is $2{\cdot}248 + 8{\cdot}948 = 11{\cdot}196$ MeV. The agreement in the energy release is very good when the maximum kinetic energy of the beta transitions are used. If the energy change is calculated on the basis

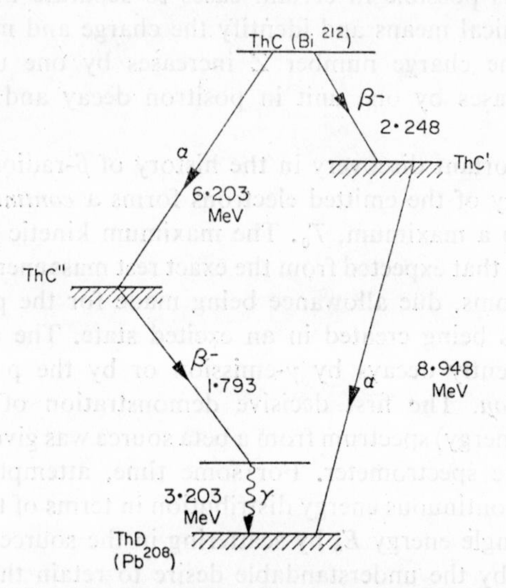

FIG. 1. Branched disintegration of ThC. (Energy cycle argument.) Decay energies include nuclear recoil energies.

of the *mean* kinetic energy of the β-rays emitted in the decay of ThC (0·750 MeV) and ThC″ (0·587 MeV) the difference in the energy release by the two routes to ThD is $\sim 0{\cdot}3$ MeV, which is much greater than the probable errors in the energy values. It is therefore not true to say that, although energy conservation is violated in a single nuclear decay, over a large number of disintegrations it is conserved.

There is also an apparent failure to conserve linear and angular momentum in beta decay. The emitted electron does not usually travel in a direction opposite to that of the recoil velocity of the product nucleus. Consider the beta decay of an even-A (integral spin) nucleus. There is no change in mass number A in beta decay so that the nuclear spin change must be integral; for example ${}_6C^{14}$ (spin zero, an even–even nucleus) decays into ${}_7N^{14}$ with spin 1. The emitted electron has an intrinsic spin of $\frac{1}{2}$ and if it carries away *orbital* angular momentum the total angular momentum associated with the emitted electron must also be half integral (orbital angular momentum is always quantized in integral units of $\hbar$). Thus angular momentum is not conserved in the decay of an even-A nucleus.

A way out of the difficulty was first suggested by Pauli (1933). Assuming that energy and momentum are rigorously conserved in every nuclear decay, a second particle in addition to the electron must be emitted in beta decay. Attempts to detect this hypothetical particle failed, so it seemed reasonable to postulate that it is neutral. The name *neutrino* ("little neutral") was coined. The rest mass of the neutrino is much less than that of the electron; today, in fact, it is believed that it is zero and therefore, like the photon, a neutrino always travels with velocity c. The neutrino (symbol ν) is a fermion with intrinistic spin $\frac{1}{2}$†. The first convincing support of the neutrino hypothesis came soon after Pauli's suggestion, with the successful theoretical prediction of the shape of the beta energy spectrum by Fermi (1934). Bethe and Peierls (1934) showed theoretically that, if the only way of capturing neutrinos is by the inverse process to beta decay, neutrinos in normal matter would have an absorption mean free path of $\sim 10^{22}$ cm, corresponding to a cross section of $\sim 10^{-44}$ cm^2! Another neutrino problem, which for a long time remained unsolved, was whether or not the neutral particles emitted in β^- and β^+ decay were the same. The weight of evidence today supports the view that the two neutrinos are different particles; one is the antiparticle of the other. By convention, we call the "neutrino" emitted in e^- decay an *antineutrino* ($\bar{\nu}$) and reserve the name *neutrino* for the particle emitted in β^+ decay and orbital electron capture.

The three types of beta decay are represented by the decay equations: (The four particles concerned all have spin $\frac{1}{2}$ and angular momentum can thus be conserved):

$$\left.\begin{array}{ll} \beta^- \text{ decay} & n \rightarrow p + e^- + \bar{\nu} \quad (1a) \\ \beta^+ \text{ decay} & p \rightarrow n + e^+ + \nu \quad (1b) \\ \text{electron capture} & p + e^- \rightarrow n + \nu \quad (1c) \end{array}\right\}$$

In β^- decay a neutron inside the nucleus transforms into a proton, the disintegration energy and momentum being shared between the electron, antineutrino and product nucleus. The latter has only a very small share of the available energy (for a nucleus of mass $A \sim 100$, and an electron kinetic energy ~ 1 MeV, the nuclear recoil energy is ~ 10 eV). In positron decay, a proton inside the nucleus changes into a neutron, a positron (e^+) and a neutrino being emitted. Electron capture decay occurs when an orbital electron, usually from the K shell, interacts with a nuclear proton, converting the latter into a neutron, a neutrino being emitted. The only observable radiations following electron capture are the characteristic X-rays of the product atom as the extra-nuclear electrons settle down and fill in the hole in the K shell. Formally it is often useful to regard the emission of a particle as being equivalent to the absorption of its antiparticle and vice versa.

† The possibility of a spin assignment of $\frac{3}{2}$ is ruled out by considerations of the shape of the beta energy spectrum.

Transferring the positron from the right-hand side to the left-hand side of the eqn. (1b) and turning it into an electron we obtain eqn. (1c). This explains why the same type of neutrino is emitted in β^+ and electron capture decay. Transferring the antineutrino on the right-hand side of eqn. (1a) to the other side, and changing it into a neutrino ν we obtain eqn. (1c).

A classification of the light particles, muons, electrons, and neutrinos into *leptons* and *antileptons* is fruitful. There is considerable evidence that these light particles obey the law of conservation of leptons. This principle states that the number of leptons minus the number of antileptons does not change in any interaction or decay process. Defining the negatron (e^-) to be a lepton, the classification scheme of light particles is given in Table 1.

TABLE 1

Leptons	Antileptons
e^- (L)	e^+ (R)
ν (L)	$\bar{\nu}$ (R)
μ^- (R)	μ^+ (L)

The attached symbol (*L*) or (*R*) refers to the left or right-handedness of the particle's *helicity*. For the moment we ignore this property. To illustrate the principle of conservation of leptons, consider the following processes:

(1) The production of annihilation gamma radiation

$$e^+ + e^- \rightarrow 2\gamma$$

Electric charge is conserved, momentum and energy are conserved, and the *difference* between the lepton and antilepton number remains zero.

The annihilation process $e^- + p^+ \rightarrow 2\gamma$ does not occur. It would involve a failure of the lepton law and also the law of conservation of *baryons*. (a baryon is an elementary particle of rest mass equal to or greater than that of a proton).

(2) β^- decay; $n \rightarrow p + e^- + \bar{\nu}$. Lepton and baryon conservation is satisfied. The same applies to β^+ decay and electron capture.

(3) There is little doubt that the muon behaves in all respects as a "heavy electron". A recent determination of its magnetic moment agrees to within 2 parts of 10^5 with the theoretical prediction. Muon decay is closely analogous to beta decay and is an example of a "weak" interaction.

$$\mu^+ \rightarrow e^+ + \bar{\nu} + \nu$$

The muon decays into an electron and a neutrino–antineutrino pair. The energies of the electrons from muons decaying at rest exhibit the beta-like energy distribution. Reference to Table 1, for example shows that in μ^+ decay we have one antilepton before decay, and two antileptons and one lepton after decay, satisfying the conservation law.

(4) The pion is not classified as a lepton, as it interacts strongly with nucleons. However its radioactive decay is a weak process. To satisfy the law of conservation of leptons the following assignments are made

$$\pi^+ \rightarrow \mu^+ + \nu$$
$$\pi^- \rightarrow \mu^- + \bar{\nu}$$

In the decay of a pion at rest, the muon and neutrino (or antineutrino) travel in opposite directions and therefore the muon has a unique kinetic energy.

14.2. MEASUREMENT OF β-RAY ENERGIES

The kinetic energies of the negatrons and positrons emitted in beta decay cover a continuous range from zero up to a maximum value, which is characteristic of the beta-active isotope. The maximum kinetic energy varies over a wide range throughout the list of beta unstable nuclei. The smallest maximum kinetic energy is ~ 18 keV for tritium (H^3) and the largest ~ 13 MeV for the 0·02 sec isotope, B^{12}.

The loss of energy of β-particles by ionization and radioactive collisions has been briefly discussed in Chapter 11. The factors determining the range

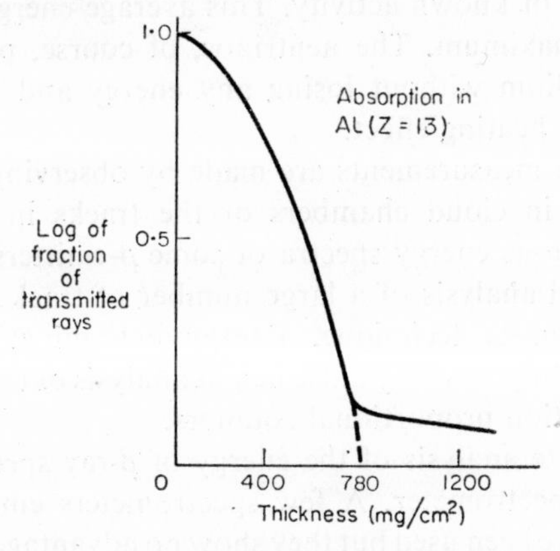

FIG. 2. Absorption of β-rays from P^{32} source in aluminium. Maximum kinetic energy is 1·7 MeV.

of β-particles in matter are complex, partly because of the large amount of scattering, and partly because of the continuous spectrum of kinetic energies. It is therefore surprising to find that, if the fraction of the β-rays transmitted by an absorber is plotted against absorber thickness, an approximately exponential attenuation is found. A semilogarithmic absorption plot for the β-rays from a P^{32} source is shown in Fig. 2. The "thickness" of the absorber is measured as an areal density $\varrho\, t$ (in mg/cm²), where ϱ

is the volume density and t the linear thickness. The absorption curve is then nearly independent of the absorber. Aluminium, however, is generally used for moderate energy beta sources. Beyond a thickness of ~ 780 mg/cm^2 of aluminium there is a marked change in the absorption graph. The thickness of 780 mg/cm^2 corresponds to the maximum distance the most energetic electrons from the decay of P^{32} can travel in aluminium. This thickness is called the *range* R of the betas from P^{32}. The more penetrating radiation is bremsstrahlung generated by the β-rays as they slow down in the aluminium absorber. The amount of bremsstrahlung increases rapidly with the atomic number. Feather has shown that there is an approximate linear relation connecting the maximum kinetic energy E of the β-rays and the range R in matter. Useful equations due to Glendenin for E values between 0·15 and 3 MeV are†

$$R = 0{\cdot}542\,E - 0{\cdot}133, \quad 0{\cdot}8 < E < 3 \text{ MeV} \tag{2a}$$

$$R = 0{\cdot}407\,E^{1{\cdot}38} \quad 0{\cdot}15 < E < 0{\cdot}8 \text{ MeV} \tag{2b}$$

where E is in MeV, and the range R is in g per cm^2. Measurement of the range R enables the maximum beta energy to be determined to ~ 1 per cent. The *average* kinetic energy of the β-rays can, in some cases, be determined by measuring the rate of production of heat by the total absorption of the rays from a source of known activity. This average energy is usually about one third of the maximum. The neutrinos, of course, pass clean through the absorbing medium without losing any energy and make a negligible contribution to the heating effect.

Sometimes range measurements are made by observing the photographs of electron tracks in cloud chambers or the tracks in nuclear emulsion plates. The continuous energy spectra of some β-emitters have been determined by statistical analysis of a large number of track lengths, a tedious and not very accurate technique. Energy determinations of moderate accuracy are frequently made by pulse height analysis of the signals produced in gas and scintillation proportional counters.

The most accurate analysis of the energy of β-ray spectra is carried out with a magnetic spectrometer. A few spectrometers employing deflection by electric fields have been used but they show no advantages over the magnetic deflection instruments. The two basic requirements of a β-ray spectrometer are high collection efficiency at the detector and high energy resolution. The first requirement is particularly important for sources of low specific activity. Spectrometers are usually classified as *flat*, with the principal component of the bending magnetic field normal to the electron trajectories, or *longitudinal* with the principal component of the focusing field nearly parallel to the electron trajectories ("lens" type). All the early work on the analysis of β-ray spectra was made with transverse *homogeneous* flat mag-

† L. E. Glendenin, *Nucleonics* **2** [1], 12, 1948.

netic spectrometers. One drawback, serious with weak sources, of this type of instrument is the inability to focus the electrons emitted from a point source at a point. Focusing occurs in one plane (compare a cylindrical optical lens) and a point object is imaged as a line. In 1946, Siegbahn and Svartholm developed a new type of spectrometer which produced *double* focusing in the sense that a point source was imaged as a point. No spectrometer is perfect; spherical and other aberrations are usually present. Before discussing the double focusing principle, we consider some of the basic equations relvant to spectrometers in general.

An electron travelling with speed v in a plane perpendicular to a uniform magnetic field B (transverse field) describes a circular path of radius R, where

$$B e v = \frac{m v^2}{R} \tag{3}$$

or

$$p = m v = B R e \tag{4}$$

where m is the relativistic mass of the electron.

The momentum p of the electron is proportional to the "$B R$" value. The $B R$ value is often quoted instead of the momentum or kinetic energy. Extensive tables of electron kinetic energies and the corresponding $B R$ values are available.† The kinetic energy E is given by

$$E = m c^2 - m_0 c^2 = \{(B R e c)^2 + (m_0 c^2)^2\}^{\frac{1}{2}} - m_0 c^2 \tag{5}$$

An electron of kinetic energy 50 keV corresponds to $B R \sim 800$ gauss-cm; 500 keV corresponds to $B R \sim 3000$ gauss-cm.

It is the momentum, rather than the kinetic energy, which is directly determined by a magnetic spectrometer. To convert a momentum distribution of electrons $n(p)dp$, where this measures the number of electrons in the narrow momentum interval p to $p + dp$, into an energy distribution $n(E)dE$, we use the formula for non-relativistic particles,

$$E = \frac{p^2}{2m} \tag{6}$$

$$dE = \frac{p\,dp}{m} \tag{7}$$

Now

$$n(p)\,dp = n(E)\,dE \tag{8}$$

Thus

$$n(E) = n(p)\frac{m}{p} \tag{9}$$

In a magnetic spectrometer the finite width of the slit in front of the detector corresponds to the acceptance of electrons with a small range in R.

† Appendix VIII, p. 926 in *Beta and Gamma Ray Spectroscopy*, Editor K. SIEGBAHN, North-Holland Publishing Co., Amsterdam 1955.

For a constant field, the momentum spread dp of the electrons entering the detector is given by

$$dp = B\,e\,dR. \quad (10)$$

For a given geometry, dp is proportional to B, so it is necessary to divide the number of recorded electrons at a given field setting by B to obtain a number proportional to the function $n(p)$.

The Double Focusing Spectrometer

The double focusing spectrometer invented by Svartholm and Siegbahn† makes use of the focusing principles involved in the design of the betatron and cyclotron. Kerst and Serber†† showed that charged particles circulating in a transverse magnetic field, which decreases gradually with radial distance, execute simple harmonic oscillations in the median plane $z = 0$ and in the vertical direction z. Using cylindrical coordinates (r, θ, z), the plane of symmetry of the magnetic field is the plane $z = 0$; here $B_z = B_0$, $B_r = 0$, $B_\theta = 0$. The median plane $z = 0$ is depicted in Fig. 3(a). 0 is the origin of coordinates and R is the radius of the central electron trajectory. In Fig. 3(b) three rays are shown all with the same radial coordinate R, but different z coordinates along their paths. The difference in the directions of emission

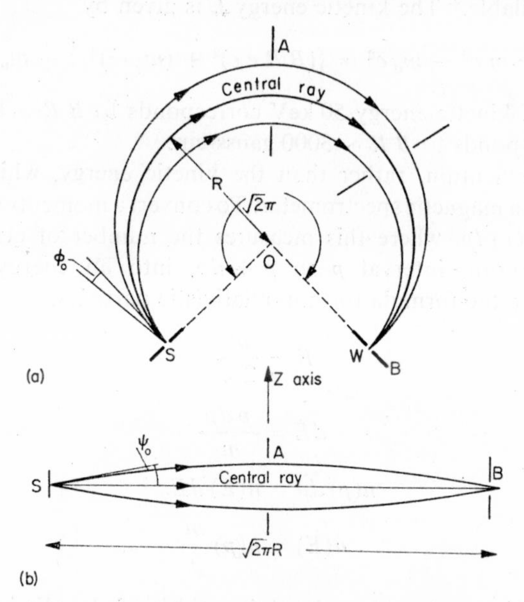

FIG. 3. Principle of double focusing spectrometer.

† N. SVARTHOLM and K. SIEGBAHN, *Ark. Mat., Astr., Fys.* A **33**, No. 21, 1946; see also p. 66–72 of the last reference.

†† D. KERST and R. SERBER, *Phys. Rev.* **60**, 53, 1941.

of the central ray and a ray just grazing the edge of the slit A in the median plane is denoted by φ_0. The corresponding angle in a vertical plane (Fig. 3(b)), is ψ_0.

The z component of the magnetic field is chosen so that it decreases with increasing r, in the vicinity of the central ray at $r = R$, according to the equation

$$B = B_0\left(\frac{R}{r}\right)^n \quad \text{where} \quad 0 < n < 1 \tag{11}$$

B is the vertical component of the field in the median plane.

The gradient of B is

$$\frac{\partial B}{\partial r} = -n\frac{B}{r} \tag{12}$$

for an electron trajectory close to the central ray (φ_0 and ψ_0 are small angles). The angular frequencies of oscillations in the radial direction and the z direction are given by

$$\omega_r = \omega\sqrt{(1-n)} \tag{13}$$

$$\omega_z = \omega\sqrt{n} \tag{14}$$

$\omega = B_0(e/m)$ is the angular velocity of rotation of an electron moving along the central trajectory, and n is the field parameter defined by the field-form eqn. (11). These oscillations are generally known as "betatron" oscillations as they first came to light in the development of the betatron accelerator. If n is chosen to be 0·50, $\omega_r = \omega_z = \omega/\sqrt{2}$. Thus electrons after sweeping through an angle $\theta = \sqrt{2}\pi$ projected on to the median plane will have returned to the median plane in their z oscillation and to the central ray trajectory $r = R$ in their radial oscillation. If the point source S and detector slit W subtend an angle at 0 of $\sqrt{2}\pi$ (254° 33′), the rays leaving S at small values of φ_0 and ψ_0 should be sharply focused at W. It also turns out that the focusing is good for quite large values of φ_0 and ψ_0.

The relative line width at the bottom of a sharp electron energy line†, for a double focusing spectrometer can be shown to be ($n = 0{\cdot}50$);

$$\mathcal{R} = \frac{s}{4R} + \frac{w}{4R} - \frac{h^2}{32R^2} - \frac{1}{3}\varphi_0^2 \tag{15}$$

s is the source width and h the source height (in the z direction), w is the width of the detector slit and φ_0 is determined by the aperture of A (Fig. 3(a)). Precision double focusing spectrometers with R as large as 50 cm have been used; this corresponds to a small relative line width. A suitable magnet designed to give the correct field-form is shown in Fig. 4. Very accurate electron spectra measurements are sometimes carried out with iron-free focusing spectrometers. The magnetic field is *accurately* proportional to the current in the spectrometer coils.

† $\mathcal{R}$ is a good measure of the resolving power.

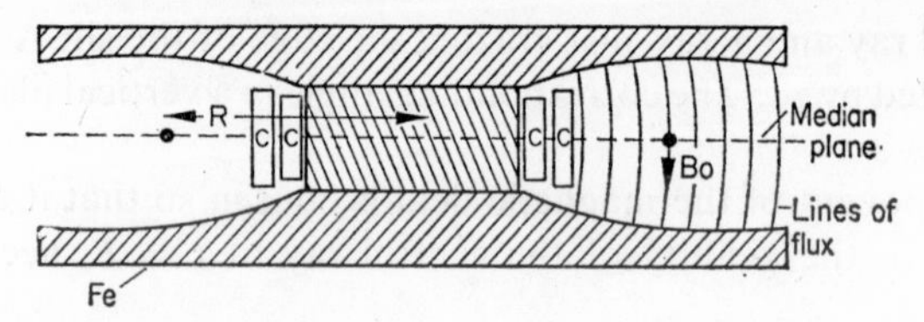

FIG. 4. Cross-section of electromagnet of double focusing spectrometer. B varies as $r^{-\frac{1}{2}}$. C—current coils.

Magnetic Lens Spectrometers

There is a close analogy between the effect of an axial magnetic field on the trajectories of electrons travelling at small angles to the field and the focusing effect of a converging lens on paraxial rays of light. It is convenient to divide magnetic spectrometers into *long* and *short* lens instruments. In

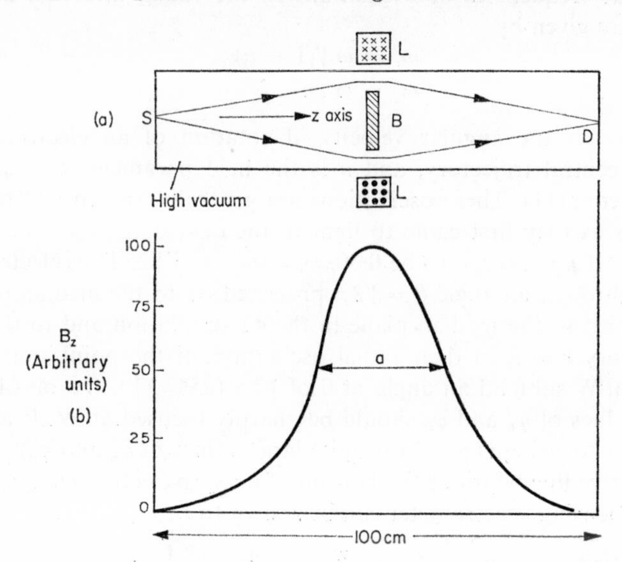

FIG. 5. (a) Short lens beta-spectrometer. S—source, B—baffle, D—detector, L—lens coils; (b) variation of axial component B_z between source and detector.

the former type, the axial magnetic field acts over the whole length of the spectrometer. The short lens spectrometer has a focusing magnetic field extending over a relatively short length of the instrument; the field is usually produced by current carrying coils wrapped round the central regions of the instrument (Fig. 5). The lens spectrometers must be very carefully oriented so that the magnetic field has cylindrical symmetry about the line joining the source and detector. Elementary electron optics yields the result that the focal length of a short axial magnetic lens, for electrons of momentum $B\,Re$, is given by

$$\frac{1}{f} = \frac{1}{4(B\,R)^2} \int_{-\infty}^{\infty} B_z^2\,dz$$

The main contribution to the integral is provided by the axial field B_z over a short length near the centre of the lens coil. The well-known thin lens formula of optics connecting object distance, image distance, and focal length is applicable. However, this does not take into account spherical and other lens aberrations. A useful approximate expression for the focal length of a short magnetic lens for electrons of momentum $B\,Re$ is

$$f = \frac{8(B\,R)^2}{a\,B_0^2\,\pi} \tag{17}$$

where B_0 is the axial field at the centre of the lens coil and a is the half-width of the axial distribution (Fig. 5b). If the centre of the lens is half way between the source and detector aperture $l = 4f$, where l is the source–aperture distance. For $l = 100$ cm, a focal length of 25 cm is obtained for electrons of $B\,R$ value 1000 gauss-cm (kinetic energy ~ 81 keV) with $B_0 \sim 120$ gauss and a 7 cm. With rays of light the real image formed by a converging lens is inverted; this can be thought of as a rotation of 360° about the axis of the lens. For a short magnetic lens, the rotation angle θ is not usually 360°. In the example just quoted θ is $\sim 80°$.

14.3. THEORY OF BETA DECAY

Beta decay is absolutely forbidden unless certain mass inequalities hold for the two isobars concerned. Consider the negatron decay of the nuclide $(Z, A) \rightarrow (Z + 1, A)$. The atomic mass of the parent atom ${}_{Z}M^{A}$ must be greater than the mass of the daughter atom ${}_{Z+1}M^{A}$. The mass difference appears as kinetic energy shared between the emitted electron, neutrino and recoil atom. The recoil energy is usually negligible compared to the electron and neutrino energy.

In positron decay $(Z, A) \rightarrow (Z - 1, A)$, the following inequality between the atomic masses and electron rest mass m must hold:

$${}_{Z}M^{A} > {}_{Z-1}M^{A} + 2m$$

The $2m$ term arises because there is one surplus atomic electron after positron decay and, of course, the newly created positron of rest mass m.

In orbital electron capture $(Z, A) \rightarrow (Z - 1, A)$

$${}_{Z}M^{A} > {}_{Z-1}M^{A}$$

The available energy is shared between the emitted neutrino, the recoiling daughter atom, and the radiated X-rays. The neutrino energy is unique, as this form of decay results in two not three particles, and it is usually much greater than the energy of the subsequent X-rays.

It is interesting to note that if the mass difference of the atoms (Z, A) and $(Z - 1, A)$ is less than $2m$, electron capture is energetically possible but positron decay is impossible. There are many examples of this; electron capture occurs without competition by positron decay. A number of positron unstable nuclides do undergo branched disintegrations, electron capture competing with positron decay. About ten nuclides (Cu^{64} is an example) are known to decay by all three beta decay processes.

Fermi Theory (1934)†

Fermi's theory of beta decay is based on two assumptions:

(1) The principle of energy conservation in the decay process, the available energy being shared between the emitted electron and the hypothetical neutrino. The rest mass of the neutrino is zero or very small compared to that of the electron.

(2) The beta transition is analogous to the emission of electromagnetic radiation by an atom. The interaction coupling the light particles, electron and neutrino (leptons) with the heavy particles (nucleons) is, of course, different from the interaction between the electric charge e and the electromagnetic field of the photon.

It turned out that the empirical constant g in beta decay, replacing the electric charge e in photon decay, was far too small to explain the strong nuclear forces responsible for binding together the nucleons in a nucleus. Beta decay is an example of what is called a *weak interaction*. Weak interactions are discussed in more detail in Chapter 21. In the Fermi treatment, the interaction between the nucleons and leptons is assumed to be *local*; the idea of exchange particles (bosons) as the agents of transmission of the weak interaction is not introduced. This contrasts sharply with the picture of virtual photons and pions as the agents of force in the electromagnetic and strong nuclear interactions. Recently, considerable interest has been revived in the question of whether or not an electrically charged boson (spin 1) is associated with weak interactions (Chapter 21).

Dirac derived an expression for the transition probability per unit time W of an atomic system to emit a photon, using time—dependent perturbation theory. In the case of beta decay, in place of W we write $I(p)\,dp$, the probability per unit time of the nucleus emitting an electron of momentum in the range p_e to $p_e + dp_e$.

$$I(p_e)\,dp_e = \frac{2\pi}{\hbar}\varrho(E)\left|\int \psi_f\, H\, \psi_i^*\, d\tau\right|^2 \qquad (18)$$

† E. Fermi, *Z. Physik* **88**, 161, 1934.

$\varrho(E)$ is the number of final energy states of the system per unit energy interval. ψ_f is the wave function of the system in its final state, ψ_i is the wave function of the system in its initial state. H is the Hamiltonian operator associated with that part of the interaction responsible for the beta transition.

It is convenient to treat negatron decay as formally equivalent to the reaction.

$$\nu + n \rightarrow p + e^-$$

The initial state of the system is represented by the product $\psi_\nu\, u_i$ where ψ_ν is the wave function of the neutrino evaluated at the position of the transforming nucleon and u_i is the initial nuclear wave function. Similarly $u_f\, \psi_e$ represents the final state of the system. If the Coulomb interaction of the emitted electron wave with the product nucleus is small (low Z and high electron energy) ψ_e is a plane wave

$$\psi_e^* = \frac{1}{V^{\frac{1}{2}}} \exp\left(- \frac{i}{\hbar} \boldsymbol{p}_e \cdot \boldsymbol{r}\right) \tag{19}$$

The neutrino wave function is

$$\psi_\nu = \frac{1}{V^{\frac{1}{2}}} \exp\left(- \frac{i}{\hbar} \boldsymbol{p}_\nu \cdot \boldsymbol{r}\right) \tag{20}$$

V is the volume of an arbitrary sized box; $\boldsymbol{p}_e$ and $\boldsymbol{p}_\nu$ are the momenta of the electron and neutrino respectively; $\boldsymbol{r}$ is the position coordinate.

The transition probability eqn. (18) becomes

$$I(p_e)\, dp_e = g^2 \frac{2\pi}{\hbar} \varrho(E) \left| \int u_f^* \frac{1}{V} \exp\left\{ - \frac{i}{\hbar} (\boldsymbol{p}_e + \boldsymbol{p}_\nu \cdot \boldsymbol{r})\right\} u_i\, d\tau \right|^2 \tag{21}$$

The perturbation has been assumed to be of the form

$$H = g\, \psi_e^*\, \psi_\nu$$

where the constant g (units erg cm^3) is analogous to the charge e in the photon decay theory.

The exponential factor in eqn. (21) can be written

$$\exp\left\{ - \frac{i}{\hbar} (\boldsymbol{p}_e + \boldsymbol{p}_\nu \cdot \boldsymbol{r})\right\} = 1 - \frac{i}{\hbar} (\boldsymbol{p}_e + \boldsymbol{p}_\nu \cdot \boldsymbol{r}) - \frac{1}{\hbar^2} (\boldsymbol{p}_e + \boldsymbol{p}_\nu \cdot \boldsymbol{r})^2 + \cdots \tag{22}$$

If the electron and the neutrino have momenta of the order of one to three units of $m\,c$ (typical), the second term in the expression is roughly equal to

$$\frac{2 m\, c\, R}{\hbar} \sim \frac{1}{50}$$

R is the nuclear radius, $\sim 4 \times 10^{-13}$ cm for a medium-sized nucleus. The wave functions are very small when $r > R$; hence the substitution $r = R$.

As a good approximation the exponential factor is equal to unity, and eqn. (21) simplifies to

$$I(p_e)\,dp_e = \frac{g^2}{V^2}\,\frac{2\pi}{\hbar}\varrho(E)\left|\int u_f^*\,u_i\,d\tau\right|^2 \tag{23}$$

The matrix element $M = \int u_f^*\,u_i\,d\tau$, depends on the degree of overlap of nuclear wave functions in the initial and final states.

The density of states factor $\varrho(E)$ is derived on the assumption that all possible divisions of the available energy E_e between the electron E_0 and the neutrino E_ν are equally likely. (E_e is the total energy, including the rest mass energy $m\,c^2$, of the electron.)

It is useful at this stage to employ the concept of *phase space* familiar in the kinetic theory of gases. The position and momentum of two leptons can be represented by a point in phase space, the space containing six spatial and six momentum dimensions. It is easy to show that each state for a pair of leptons is associated with a phase space volume of h^6. Using spherical polar coordinates in this phase space, consider the state corresponding to an electron lying within a volume element $d\,V_e$ with a momentum of magnitude between p_e and $p_e + dp_e$, whose direction lies within the elementary solid angle $d\Omega_e$ and the neutrino lying within the volume $d\,V_\nu$ . . . etc. The element of volume in the electron–neutrino phase space expressed in polar coordinates is

$$p_e^2 \sin\theta_e\,dp_e\,d\theta_e\,d\varphi_e\,d\,V_e\,p_\nu^2 \sin\theta_\nu\,dp_\nu\,d\theta_\nu\,d\varphi_\nu\,d\,V_\nu \tag{24}$$

Now

$$d\Omega_e = \sin\theta_e\,d\theta_e\,d\varphi_e \quad \text{and} \quad d\Omega_\nu = \sin\theta_\nu\,d\theta_\nu\,d\varphi_\nu \tag{25}$$

The number of states associated with the phase space volume given by eqn. (24) is, using eqn. (25), equal to

$$\frac{1}{(2\pi\,\hbar)^6}\,p_e^2\,dp_e\,d\Omega_e\,d\,V_e\,p_\nu^2\,dp_\nu\,d\Omega_\nu\,d\,V_\nu \tag{26}$$

Now

$$p_\nu = \frac{E_\nu}{c} = \frac{(E_0 - E_e)}{c} \tag{27}$$

and

$$|dp_\nu| = \frac{dE_e}{c} \tag{28}$$

From eqns. (26), (27) and (28), and writing $\varrho(E_e)\,dE_e$ for the number of final states in the energy range E_e to $E_e + dE_e$, we obtain

$$\varrho(E_e)\,dE_e = \frac{1}{(2\pi\,\hbar)^6}\,\frac{1}{c^3}\,p_e^2(E_0 - E_e)^2\,dp_e\,d\Omega_e\,d\Omega_\nu\,d\,V_e\,d\,V_\nu\,dE_e \tag{29}$$

Integrating over all angles for the directions of $\mathbf{p}_e$ and $\mathbf{p}_\nu$ and integrating over the volume V, eqns. (23) and (29) yield the result

$$I(p_e)\,dp_e = \frac{g^2|M|^2}{2\pi^3\,c^3\,\hbar^7}(E_0 - E_e)^2\,p_e^2\,dp_e\ \text{sec}^{-1} \tag{30}$$

The nuclear matrix element $M = \int u_f^* u_i \, d\tau$ is usually not known, as little is known about nuclear wave functions.

If the restriction to low Z nuclei and high electron energies E_e is relaxed, the plane wave for the emitted electron must be replaced by a distorted Coulomb wave function. The Coulomb barrier effect can be taken into account by including an extra factor in the numerator of the right-hand side of eqn. (30).

$$F(Z, E_e) = \frac{2\pi\eta}{1 - \exp(-2\pi\eta)} \tag{31}$$

where $\eta = \pm \frac{Ze^2}{\hbar v}$, and v is the velocity of the electron at a great distance from the nucleus. The positive sign for η is taken for negatrons and the negative sign for positrons. Theoretical electron energy distribution curves

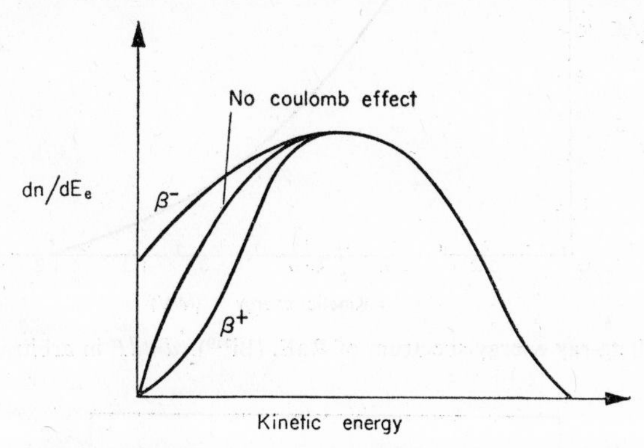

FIG. 6. Theoretical β-energy spectrum (Fermi theory).

based on eqn. (30), with and without the correction term $F(Z, E_e)$ included, are shown in Fig. 6. The effect of the Coulomb barrier is only serious at low electron energies; the barrier depresses the observed number of low energy positrons and raises the number of low energy negatrons. The energy spectrum of the negatrons in the decay of RaE (Bi^{210}) is shown in Fig. 7.

The predicted shape of the beta spectrum can be tested by writing the Coulomb corrected form of eqn. (30) as

$$\sqrt{\left[\frac{I(p_e)}{[F(Z, E_e)\, p_e^2]}\right]} = C(E_0 - E_e) = C(T_0 - T_e) \tag{32}$$

where $C = \frac{g|M|}{(2\pi^3 c^3 \hbar^7)^{\frac{1}{2}}}$, and T_0 and T_e are kinetic energies. A plot of the function on the left-hand side of eqn. (32) against T_e, the electron kinetic energy, should be a straight line intersecting the kinetic energy axis at T_0. This form of graph is known as a *Kurie* plot. The spectrum of Pm^{147} ($T_0 = 0{\cdot}223$ MeV) is plotted in this way in Fig. 8.

Many of the early Kurie plots were non-linear at low electron energies. This form of discrepancy is now known to be due to insufficient attention being paid to achieving very thin sources and eliminating back scattering from the source support. It can be shown that if the neutrino rest mass is finite the shape of the Kurie plot should be non-linear at the end point T_0. Careful analysis of a number of beta spectra has supported the view that

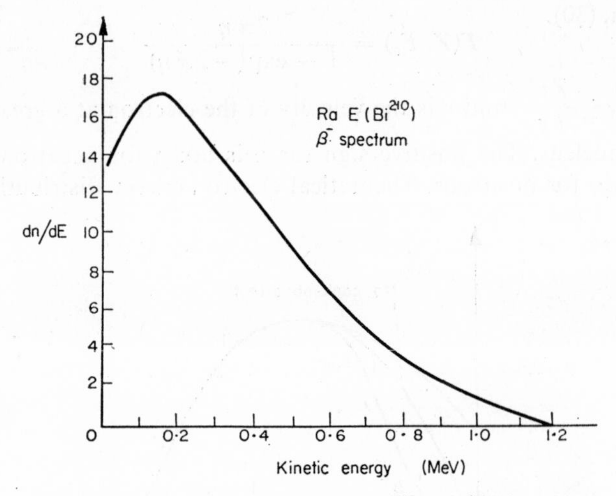

FIG. 7. Beta-ray energy spectrum of RaE. (Bi^{210}). dn/dE in arbitrary units.

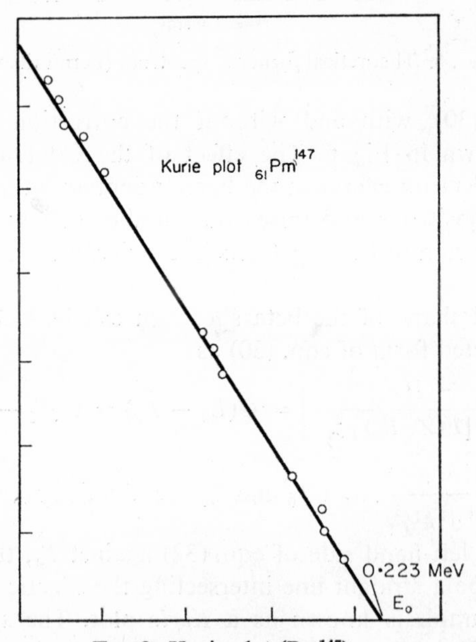

FIG. 8. Kurie plot (Pm^{147}).

$m_\nu \ll m_e$. One practical advantage of the Kurie way of representing a spectrum is that it is much easier to determine T_0 by the extrapolation of a straight line, instead of from a curve like Fig. 7.

Integrating $I(p_e)$ between $p_e = 0$ and $(p_e)_{max}$ we obtain the beta decay constant

$$\lambda = \frac{g^2 |M|^2 m^5 c^4 f}{2\pi^3 \hbar^7} \tag{33}$$

where f is a function of Z and E_0 defined by the integral

$$f = \int_0^{(p_e)\max/mc} F(Z, E_e) \frac{(T_0 - T_e)^2}{(m c^2)^2} \left(\frac{p_e}{m c}\right)^2 \frac{dp_e}{m c} \tag{34}$$

If $T_0 \gg m c^2$ and $F(Z, E_e) \sim 1$, f varies roughly as T_0^5. This T_0^5 dependence connecting λ and T_0 was first noticed by Sargent in 1933.

It is more instructive to compare *comparative-half-lives* rather than the normal half-lives. The comparative-half-life of a beta unstable nuclide is defined as $f\,t$, where t is the half-life and

$$f\,t = f \frac{\ln 2}{\lambda} = \frac{2\pi^3 \hbar^7 \ln 2}{g^2 m^5 c^4 |M|^2} \tag{35}$$

The key point about eqn. (35) is the inverse connection between $f\,t$ and $|M|^2$. Thus $f\,t$ values throw light on nuclear matrix elements or vice versa. For example, in the beta decay of mirror nuclei ($H^3 \rightarrow He^3$, etc.) one expects almost complete overlap of the nuclear wave functions responsible for the beta transition; thus, $|M|^2$ should be of the order of one. The $f\,t$ values of the fastest beta transitions (super-allowed transitions) are of the order of 2000 sec. It is usual to compare $\log_{10} f\,t$ values and these in the majority of cases cover the range 3 to 10; there are a few exceptionally high values (strongly forbidden transitions), e.g. K^{40}, $t \sim 1{\cdot}4 \times 10^9$y, $\log f\,t \sim 18$.

The beta decay of O^{14} (a positron emitter) is of special interest as it involves a $0 \rightarrow 0$ transition. The best value of the interaction constant g (at least for the so-called Fermi transitions) is obtained from a careful determination of the end point energy of the spectrum. A recent determination† of the end-point, by measuring the threshold energy of the reaction $C^{12}(He^3, n)O^{14}$, gives the value

$$g = 1{\cdot}42 \times 10^{-49} \text{ erg/-cm}^3$$

So far we have considered "allowed" transitions characterized by the absence of any *orbital* angular momentum carried away by the emitted leptons (S waves). There are many known examples where it is not permissible to simplify the integral in eqn. (21) and replace the exponential factor by unity. If the first term in the expansion of the integral in eqn. (21)

† J. W. Butler and R. O. Bondelid, *Phys. Rev.* **121**, 1770, 1961.

vanishes, the second term must be considered. The matrix element is much smaller and the $\log ft$ value is correspondingly increased by a factor of 3 or 4. This type of decay is known as a *forbidden* decay and is associated with the emission of orbital angular momentum. Forbidden transitions are classified as first, second, third, . . ., etc., corresponding to the emission of $P, D, F, \ldots$ lepton waves. For each increase in degree of forbiddingness, the $\log ft$ value increases. We discussed in the preceding chapter the effect on the alpha decay rate of increasing orbital angular momentum. The increase in the centrifugal barrier with increasing L tends to reduce alpha decay rates, but the effect is much less severe than the decrease in λ with increasing L for beta decay. It is easy to see why this should be so. If we repeat the calculation, illustrated by Fig. 2 of Chapter 13, for the emission of an electron and antineutrino with orbital angular momentum $L = 1$, and assume that

$$|(\mathbf{p}_e + \mathbf{p}_\nu) \times \mathbf{d}| \sim 3\,m\,c\,d, \quad \text{then}$$

$$d \sim \hbar/(3m\,c) > 100 \text{ fermi.}$$

Thus d, the effective distance of the "point" of generation of the electron wave from the centre of the nucleus, is much greater than the nuclear radius

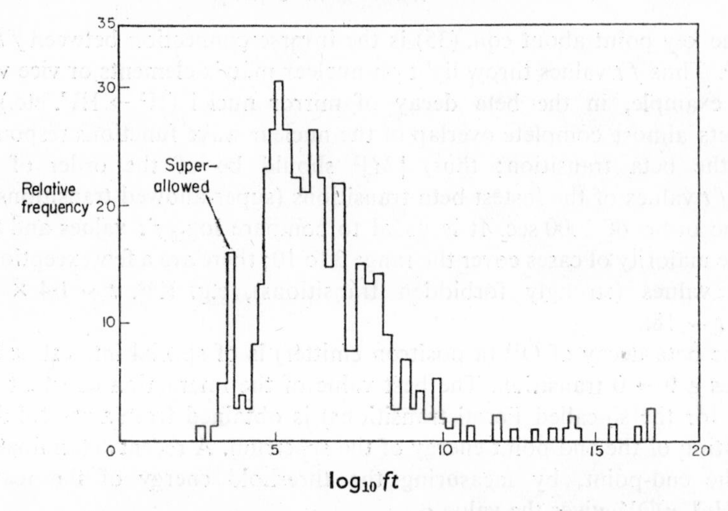

FIG. 9. Frequency distribution of comparative half-lives of beta-emitters. N.B. the sharp peak at $\log ft \sim 3{\cdot}5$ corresponds to super-allowed transitions.

and it is not surprising to find that the decay rate for P wave ($L = 1$) emission is reduced by a large factor. A frequency distribution of experimental $\log ft$ values is shown in Fig. 9. The values do not fall into narrow groups corresponding to allowed, first forbidden, and second forbidden transitions. The absence of sharply defined groups is a reflection of the variation of nuclear wave functions.

Fermi and Gamow–Teller Transitions

All leptons have an intrinsic spin angular momentum of $\frac{1}{2}$. In beta decay the two leptons emitted either have their spin axes antiparallel ($S = 0$, singlet state) or parallel ($S = 1$, triplet state). For allowed transitions the orbital angular momentum radiated is zero ($L = 0$) and as L is even there is no change in parity. The selection rules for the two types of allowed beta radiation are given in Table 2. The emission with lepton spins antiparallel is called a *Fermi* transition; that with spins parallel is called a *Gamow–Teller* transition.

TABLE 2

Fermi		Gamow–Teller	
$\Delta I = 0$ No parity change		$\Delta I = \pm 1, 0$; not $0 \rightarrow 0$ No parity change	
Scalar S	Vector V	Tensor T	Axial–Vector A
$a_s = -1$	$a_v = +1$	$a_T = +\frac{1}{3}$	$a_A = -\frac{1}{3}$

ΔI refers to the change in the magnitude of the nuclear angular momentum. The parity of the initial and final nuclear states is the same in both types of allowed transition. Notice that in beta decay connecting two nuclear states of spin zero the transition is pure Fermi. Only a few $0 \rightarrow 0$ allowed Fermi transitions are known. One example is the positron decay of ${}_8O^{14} \xrightarrow[72\text{ sec}]{} {}_7N^{14*} + e^+ + \nu$, $T = 72$ sec. O^{14} is an even–even nucleus and therefore is spinless. The ground state of N^{14} is well established as a spin 1 state; however, the positron decay of O^{14} feeds the 2·31 MeV excited state of N^{14} which has zero spin. The negatron decay of Co^{60} to the 4^+ state of Ni^{60} is a pure Gamow–Teller transition as the ground state of Co^{60} is a 5^+ state. Both the O^{14} and Co^{60} decays are allowed as the $\log ft$ values are of the correct order of magnitude (3·52 for O^{14}). Many beta decays are mixtures of Fermi and Gamow–Teller transitions. This is always possible in allowed decays in which $I_i = I_f \neq 0$, where the subscripts i and f refer to the initial and final nuclear states. Unfortunately, many spin assignments involved in beta transitions are not known and it is not always possible to be sure of the type of transition.

For first forbidden transitions ($L = 1$), we have the selection rules:

Fermi Transition	$\Delta I = \pm 1$	Parity change
Gamow–Teller Transition	$\Delta I = 0, \ \pm 1, \ \pm 2$	Parity change.

The elementary theory of beta decay outlined above is essentially a non-relativistic treatment. To extend the theory to make it as general as possible, the operators involved in the beta decay Hamiltonian should be invariant to all Lorentz transformations (proper rotations in the four-dimensional space of special relativity). This aspect of beta decay theory is too advanced to discuss in detail in this book. However, the main idea is to express that part of the nuclear Hamiltonian responsible for the beta decay interaction as the sum of five terms

$$H = H_s + H_V + H_T + H_A + H_P$$

where H_s, H_V, ... involve characteristic weak coupling constants g_s, g_V, ... and the wave functions of the two nucleons and two leptons together with certain combinations of matrices (first introduced by Dirac in the relativistic theory of the electron). The symbols *S*, *V*, *T*, *A* and *P* in this context stand for *scalar*, *vector*, *tensor*, *axial-vector* and *pseudoscalar*.

There is no experimental evidence in support of any pseudoscalar transitions and this type is not considered. It can be shown theoretically, that if the two leptons are emitted with opposite spins (Fermi transition), the two possible modes of decay go via the scalar and vector interactions. In Gamow–Teller transitions the possible interactions are tensor and axial-vector. One of the main aims of beta decay physics in the past decade has been the study of aspects of beta radiation which throw more light on the degree of *S* and/or *V* interactions, and *T* and/or *A* interactions. The weight of evidence is now strongly in favour of *V* and *A* interactions. One observational difference in the effects of the four types of interaction is the predicted angular correlation between the directions of emission of the electron (positron) and antineutrino (neutrino). This correlation $W(\theta)$, where θ is the angle between the directions of emission of the antineutrino and the electron, is

$$W(\theta) = 1 + a(v/c)\cos\theta$$

The values of the coefficient *a* for the four types of relativistically invariant interaction are given in Table 2. Unfortunately, it is difficult to study this angular correlation because we cannot directly observe the direction of travel of the antineutrino. It is possible to deduce the angle θ from observations of the directions of emission of the electron and recoil nucleus. The experiments are difficult and have sometimes been unreliable. Ruby and Rustad† investigated the angular correlation for the beta decay of He^6, a $0^+ \rightarrow 1^+$ Gamow–Teller transition.

$$He^6 \xrightarrow[0{\cdot}82\,\text{sec}]{\beta^-} Li^6$$

They obtained a correlation coefficient $a = 0{\cdot}34 \pm 0{\cdot}13$, favouring a tensor interaction (Table 2). Later developments conflicted with this result and in 1958 Ruby and Rustad withdrew their result. The recoil experiments of Herrmannsfeldt *et al.*†† with the 1·83 sec positron emitter Ar^{35}

† B. M. RUSTAD and S. L. RUBY, *Phys. Rev.* **90**, 370, 1953; **97**, 991, 1955.

†† W. B. HERRMANNSFELDT *et al.*, *Phys. Rev.* **107**, 641, 1957, *Bull. Am. Phys. Soc.*, Ser. II **3**, 52, 1958.

($T_0 \sim 3{\cdot}5$ MeV) showed that the angular correlation coefficient a in this decay lay between $+0{\cdot}7$ and $+1{\cdot}0$. This fits the vector interaction as the Ar^{35} decay is almost pure Fermi. In beta decay by the vector interaction the electrons (positrons) and antineutrinos (neutrinos) tend to be emitted in the same direction, thereby transferring a large recoil momentum to the product nucleus.

14.4. MUON DECAY

The important meson decay sequence $\pi \rightarrow \mu \rightarrow e$ was discovered with the aid of photographic plates in high flying balloons. One of the most puzzling features of this decay sequence is that the direct $\pi \rightarrow e$ decay is expected as the following argument shows. Pions are associated with strong nuclear forces. The anomalous magnetic moment of the neutron is a consequence of the neutron spending part of its life dissociated in the virtual state $n \rightarrow p + \pi^-$. Thus we anticipate that a pion may momentarily split into a virtual nucleon-antinucleon pair

$$\pi^+ \leftrightarrow p + \bar{n}$$

$\bar{n}$ is the symbol for the antineutron.

Now we may observe the decay (transfer n to the other side of (1b)).

$$p + \bar{n} \rightarrow e^+ + \nu$$

The net result is $\pi^+ \rightarrow e^+ + \nu$, which has occurred via the intermediate virtual state $p + \bar{n}$. The direct decay† of pions into electrons has been observed but is $\sim 10^{-4}$ as frequent as the decay via the "heavy electron" or muon

$$\pi^+ \rightarrow \mu^+ + \nu; \quad \pi^- \rightarrow \mu^- + \bar{\nu}$$

On the assumption that the free pion decay is an example of a "Universal Fermi Weak Interaction" it has been predicted that the $\pi \rightarrow e$ decay constant λ_e and the $\pi \rightarrow \mu$ decay constant λ_μ are related by

$$\frac{\lambda_e}{\lambda_\mu} = \left(\frac{m_e}{m_\mu}\right)^2 \left(\frac{m_\pi^2 - m_e^2}{m_\pi^2 - m_\mu^2}\right)$$

using the values $m_\mu = 206{\cdot}9\ m_e$ and $m_\pi = 273{\cdot}3\ m_e$, $\lambda_e \sim 1{\cdot}3 \times 10^{-4}\ \lambda_\mu$, in good agreement with the Geneva experiments.

The subsequent decay of the muon is also an example of the universal weak interaction.

$$\mu^\pm \rightarrow e^\pm + \nu + \bar{\nu}$$

† T. Fazzini *et al.*, *Phys. Rev. Letters* **1**, 247, 1958; G. Impeduglia *et al.*, *Phys. Rev. Letters* **1**, 249, 1958.

The electron energy spectrum is similar to the continuous beta spectrum. The muon decay electron spectrum has been determined with photographic plates and cloud chamber photographs.

The positron spectrum from the decay of a μ^+ at rest is shown in Fig. 10. It has a maximum kinetic energy of $\sim$ 53 MeV corresponding to nearly one half of the available energy $(m_\pi - m_\mu)c^2$. The positron takes its maximum share of the energy if the neutrino pair travel in the same direction but opposite to that of the positron.

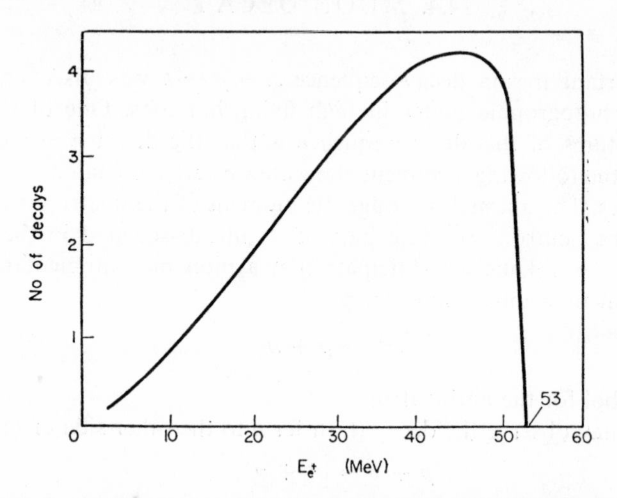

FIG. 10. Positron spectrum of kinetic energies in the decay of μ^+ at rest.

Feynman and Gell-Mann† have computed the mean lifetime of the muon on the assumption that the Fermi β-decay constant g is applicable to muon decay. They assumed that weak interactions are always of the vector or axial–vector type; this is clearly indicated by the helicity experiments (see Section 14.8). The theoretical mean lifetime of $2{\cdot}26 \pm 0{\cdot}04\,\mu$sec is in excellent agreement with the experimental value of $2{\cdot}22 \pm 0{\cdot}02\,\mu$sec. Paradoxically this agreement is rather disturbing because the value used is based on the lifetime of the decay of O^{14}. Now in beta decay one would expect that when a nucleon (neutron say) is temporarily split into a virtual proton–pion pair the nucleon has temporarily lost its "electron-emitting power" (sometimes called "Fermi charge"). In muon decay there are no strong nuclear force effects to be considered. In view of the excellent agreement between the predicted and experimental muon lifetimes, Feynman and Gell-Mann have advanced the theory†† that the "Fermi charge" is not lost whilst a neutron is dissociated into a proton–pion virtual state.

† R. P. FEYNMAN and M. GELL-MANN, *Phys. Rev.* **109**, 193, 1958.

†† This is known as the "conserved vector current" hypothesis. Se the review article of Feynman and Gell-Mann listed at the end of Chapter 21.

14.5. DIRECT EVIDENCE FOR THE ANTINEUTRINO

After the initial success of the Fermi theory of beta decay, more thought was given to the possibility of obtaining direct evidence for the existence of the neutrino. In the nineteen-forties, a number of recoil experiments was conducted to show that the neutrino in beta decay carried away the "right" momentum to conserve momentum. The first successful recoil experiment depended on the accurate measurement of the recoil energy of Li^7 following K capture by Be^7. The Be^7 source consisted of a very thin deposit on platinum. The energy E_ν of the emitted neutrino in the decay $Be^7 + e^- \rightarrow Li^7 + \nu$ was expected to be $\sim 0{\cdot}87$ MeV as this is the Q-value of the $Li^7(p, n)\,Be^7$ reaction. The recoil kinetic energy T of the Li^7 atom should be given by

$$T = \frac{P_\nu^2}{2M} = \frac{E_\nu^2}{2Mc^2} = 57{\cdot}3 \text{ eV}$$

where M is the mass of the Li^7 atom.

The recoil ions of Li^7 leaving the thin surface layer were detected by an electron multiplier and it was shown that no ions reached the multiplier, if a retarding potential of ~ 56 V was applied.

In spite of the success of the recoil type of experiment, Reines and Cowan spent about ten years in obtaining direct evidence for the emission of antineutrinos in negatron decay. The reaction they studied was the reverse of negatron decay. A large proton target was exposed to the high flux of "pile" antineutrinos associated with the highly β^- active fission products of a nuclear reactor.

$$p + \bar{\nu} \rightarrow n + e^+ - 1{\cdot}8 \text{ MeV}.$$

The method of detection depends on the identification of both the neutron and the positron. The reaction is endothermic; only pile antineutrinos with an energy greater than 1·8 MeV can make the reaction go.

The theoretical cross section has been evaluated and it is interesting to find that, as recent experiments have shown, the antineutrinos are longitudinally polarized (i.e. their spin axes point in their direction of travel, that is to say, the particles spin in a clockwise sense as they advance); the capture cross section should be double that corresponding to an equal mixture of left and right longitudinally polarized particles. On the *two component* theory, i.e., assuming right polarized antineutrinos, the cross section for the reaction $p + \bar{\nu} \rightarrow n + e^+$ is

$$\sigma = \left[\frac{2\pi^2 \ln 2}{(f\,t)_n}\right] \langle p_e\, T_e \rangle \frac{\hbar^3}{c^2 (m\,c)^5} \tag{36}$$

$(f\,t)_n$ is the $f\,t$ value for the free neutron decay, and $\langle p_e\, T_e\rangle$ is the product of the positron momentum and kinetic energy averaged over the spectrum of incident antineutrino energies. Unfortunately, it is difficult to obtain an accurate estimate of $\langle p_e T_e \rangle$ because of the uncertainty in the energy distribution of pile antineutrinos. On the two-component neutrino theory the best estimate of σ is $\sim (10) \times 10^{-44}$ cm^2. The results of the Reines Cowan experiment favour the two-component theory. The very small antineutrino capture cross section is a direct reflection of the weakness of beta interactions. If the capture process is compared to that of electron capture one can understand the very small cross section of the former process.

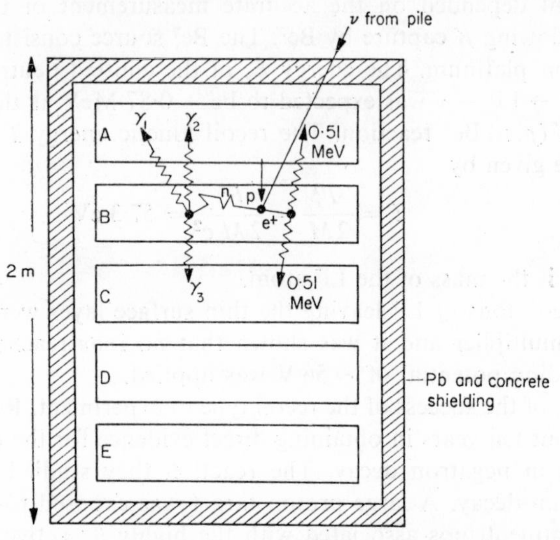

FIG. 11. Reines and Cowan "Identification" experiment.

The antineutrino must interact with the proton during the short time interval ($\sim 10^{-23}$ sec) it takes to cross the proton, whereas an orbital electron spends part of its whole time within the nucleus.

The experimental layout of the Reines–Cowan experiment is illustrated in Fig. 11. Two tanks of "proton targets" (aqueous solutions of cadmium chloride) B and D are interposed between three liquid scintillator tanks A, C and E. Each scintillator tank contains 1400 l. of triethylbenzene (T.E.B.) and 3 g per l. of *p*-terphenyl. These tanks are "viewed" with a large number of 5 in. photomultiplier tubes. The target tanks B and D each contain 200 l. of water with as much as 40 kg of dissolved $CdCl_2$. The five tanks and photomultiplier tubes are heavily screened from pile γ-rays and neutrons. The following sequence of events is looked for. If an antineutrino is captured by a proton in a target tank B or D (see tank B in Fig. 11), light flashes will be produced in coincidence in A and C provided the 0·51 MeV photons, from the annihilation of the positron in B, enter the respective scintillator tanks. A delayed group of light pulses should occur about 5 μsec after the 0·51 MeV gamma pulses when the fast neutron from the reaction $\bar{\nu} + p \rightarrow n + e^+$, has slowed down to thermal energy and been captured by a cadmium nucleus

$Cd^{113}(n, \gamma)\, Cd^{114}$. The capture γ-rays have a total energy of 9·1 MeV. The electronic circuits record delayed coincidences between the coincident 0·51 MeV photon pulses in A and C or C and E and the cadmium capture γ-ray pulses $\sim 5\,\mu$sec later. If pulses occur simultaneously in all three scintillators these are rejected. As a further check, the output pulses from the tanks A, C and E, are viewed on a three beam oscilloscope and the sizes of the pulses are measured to see if they agree with the expected values.

In view of the importance of this experiment, Reines and Cowan† carried out a number of further tests. These included

(1) Varying the concentration of Cd. The number of "true" events decreased in the expected manner.

(2) Placing different thicknesses of lead sheet between a target and a detector tank to reduce the number of 0·51 MeV γ-rays reaching the scintillator. This reduced the number of "true" events in the expected manner.

(3) Reducing the number of target protons by half, by replacing half the H_2O molecules by D_2O.

This reduced the signal by the expected amount.

The "signal" counting rate of this antineutrino "identification" experiment† was $3{\cdot}0 \pm 0{\cdot}2$ counts per hr, with a signal to background ratio of ~ 4 to 1.

A later experiment†† was carried out to obtain a much larger signal rate in order to improve the accuracy of the cross section measurement. Unfortunately, this decreased the signal to background ratio by a factor of about 20. In this experiment a much larger (1400 l) single tank of scintillator loaded with 1·8 g per l. of cadmium octoate is used. This solution functions as the proton target as well as the scintillator. A large scintillator tank placed above the main tank acted as an anticoincidence guard detector to discriminate against cosmic rays.

The antineutrino capture cross section averaged over the incident spectrum of energies is given by

$$\bar{\sigma} = \frac{R}{3600\,\varphi\, n\, \varepsilon^{+}\, \varepsilon_n}$$

where R is the signal count rate (reactor on) $\sim 36 \pm 4$ per hr.

n is the number of target protons, $8{\cdot}3 \times 10^{28}$,

ε^{+} is the efficiency of positron detection $\sim 0{\cdot}85 \pm 0{\cdot}05$,

ε_n is the efficiency of neutron detection $\sim 0{\cdot}10 \pm 0{\cdot}02$,

and φ is the antineutrino flux near the reactor

$\varphi \sim 1{\cdot}3 \times 10^{13}\,\mathrm{cm^{-2}\,sec^{-1}}$, assuming 6·1 antineutrinos are released per fission.

† F. Reines and C. L. Cowan, *Nature* **78**, 446, 1956; C. L. Cowan, F. Reines *et al.*, *Science* **124**, 103, 1956.

†† F. Reines, C. L. Cowan *et al.*, *Phys. Rev.* **113**, 273, 1959; F. Reines, *Neutrino Interactions* in Vol. 10, *Annual Review of Nuclear Science* 1960.

The main uncertainties lie in the difficult estimate for φ and the low efficiency for neutron detection. Any future repetition of the experiment should try to increase ε_n by a large factor. The cross section is

$$\bar{\sigma} = (11{\cdot}0 \pm 2{\cdot}6) \times 10^{-44}\ \text{cm}^2$$

This result is in good agreement with the prediction of the two-component neutrino theory.

The Davis Experiment

If the neutral leptons emitted in β^+ and β^- transitions are different, then solar neutrino released in the positron decay of N^{13} and O^{15} and in the thermonuclear reaction $p + p \rightarrow d + e^+ + \nu$, would not be expected to contribute any background to the Reines–Cowan experiment. On the other hand, solar neutrinos might be detected by the capture process

$$\nu + {}_{17}\text{Cl}^{37} \rightarrow {}_{18}\text{Ar}^{37} + e^-$$

Davis has shown that it is possible to sweep out the argon from a few thousand gallons of CCl_4 with helium gas, and fill a counter. Ar^{37} can be detected by the K capture process $\text{Ar}^{37} + e^- \xrightarrow[35\text{ days}]{} \text{Cl}^{37} + \nu$.

Davis irradiated a large volume of CCl_4 with an intense *antineutrino* flux from a reactor and showed that the quantity of Ar^{37} produced was far below the expected value if $\bar{\nu} \equiv \nu$; that is, the reaction

$$\bar{\nu} + \text{Cl}^{37} \rightarrow \text{Ar}^{37} + e^-$$

does not occur†.

14.6. DOUBLE BETA DECAY††

Consider a pair of isobars differing in nuclear charge by 2 units. If the atom of lower charge number Z is heavier than the other member of the pair, but lighter than neighbouring isobars at $Z - 1$ and $Z + 1$, decay by double negatron emission may occur:

$$(Z, A) \xrightarrow{2\beta^-} (Z + 2, A)$$

Energetically β^- and β^+ single decay of the isobar (Z, A) is absolutely forbidden. If single beta decay was possible, it would prevent the observation of the much slower process of double beta decay.

If the neutral leptons emitted in β^- and β^+ decay are identical particles then neutrinoless double beta decay could occur. This prediction is based on the assumption that the neutrino produced in the virtual intermediate state $n \rightarrow p + e^- + \nu$, is immediately absorbed by another neutron,

† R. Davis, *Phys. Rev.* **97**, 766, 1955.

†† H. Primakoff and S. P. Rosen, *Rep. Progr. Physics* **22**, 121, 1959, Physical Society, London.

$\nu + n \rightarrow p + e^-$; the net result is $2n \rightarrow 2p + 2e^-$ with no real neutrino emission. This argument is only valid if $\nu \equiv \bar{\nu}$. The expected half-life is ~ 1000 times less if neutrinoless double beta decay occurs. The increase in decay rate follows from the fact that the virtual neutrino in the intermediate state can have a wide range of energy, thereby increasing the volume of phase space associated with the decay process. A second feature of neutrinoless double beta decay is the unique kinetic energy for the pair of electrons. Many attempts to observe double beta decay have been made using nuclear emulsion plates, cloud chambers, and scintillation coincidence counting techniques. Theoretical estimates of the double beta decay half-life of Nd^{150} are between 2×10^{13} and 2×10^{17} y if $\nu \equiv \bar{\nu}$, and $> 10^{21}$ y if $\nu \not\equiv \bar{\nu}$. Observations support the view that the half-life of Nd^{150} is $> 4 \times 10^{18}$ y. This and other results support the contention that the neutrino and antineutrino are different particles.

14.7. VIOLATION OF PARITY CONSERVATION IN BETA DECAY

The suspicion that parity conservation might be violated in certain weak decay interactions was first entertained by T. D. Lee and C. N. Yang. This revolutionary idea arose in connection with the "τ–θ decay puzzle". An important class of mesons found in meagre quantities in cosmic rays and now copiously produced using proton synchrotons is the K mesons. The K^+meson is a positively charged particle of rest mass 967 m_e with a mean lifetime of $1{\cdot}2 \times 10^{-8}$ sec. At one time the evidence suggested that there were two distinct K^+ mesons; the θ^+ particle, which decays into a π^+ and a π^0 meson, and the τ^+ particle which decays into two π^+ and one π^- meson. These particles had the same mass, same charge, and same lifetime. The obvious suggestion that τ and θ represented different decay modes of the same K^+ particle was rejected, because it was easy to show that the τ and θ particles must have opposite parities. Many arguments were presented to explain this anomaly; for example, it was suggested that the τ and θ particles might have a small mass difference of a few MeV. Eventually, in 1956, it was seriously suggested that in K meson decay parity is not conserved. The θ and τ "particles" represent competing decay modes of the same K^+ particle (θ^+ decay occurs in 29% of all K decays, τ^+ in 6%).

Lee and Yang studied the evidence of many decays and reactions and came to the conclusion that parity is strictly conserved in *strong* nuclear and electromagnetic processes, but that there was no decisive evidence for weak interactions, including beta decay. To test the parity principle it is necessary to observe a *pseudoscalar* quantity involved in the interaction. A pseudoscalar quantity is one which, although it does not change under rotation, changes sign under reflection. The first experiment which clearly demonstrated the violation of parity conservation in beta decay was performed by Wu, Ambler, Hayward, Hoppes, and Hudson, at the National Bureau of Standards, Washington†. They measured the pseudoscalar $(\boldsymbol{I}_i \boldsymbol{p}_e)$ in the beta decay of Co^{60}. $\boldsymbol{I}_i$ is the spin of the Co^{60} nucleus before the transition and $\boldsymbol{p}_e$ is the linear momentum of the emitted electron. The polar vector $\boldsymbol{p}_e$ changes sign under the parity reflection operation $P : \boldsymbol{p}_e \rightarrow -\boldsymbol{p}_e$. The axial vector $\boldsymbol{I}_i$ does not change sign under the parity operation (angular momentum $\boldsymbol{I}$ can be written as a vector product of the type $\boldsymbol{r} \times \boldsymbol{p}$ and as $\boldsymbol{r}$ and $\boldsymbol{p}$ both change sign under reflection, $\boldsymbol{I}$ does not).

Beta Decay of Polarized Co^{60} Nuclei

In the Wu experiment (Fig. 12) the spin axes of Co^{60} nuclei are partially polarized by applying a magnetic field of $\sim 10^5$ gauss to the source at a temperature of 0·01°K. The Co source is a 0·002 in. layer grown on the surface of a single paramagnetic crystal of cerium magnesium nitrate. The crystal is mounted in a vacuum cryostat and cooled to the low temperature of 0·01°K by adiabatic demagnetization. Fortunately, external

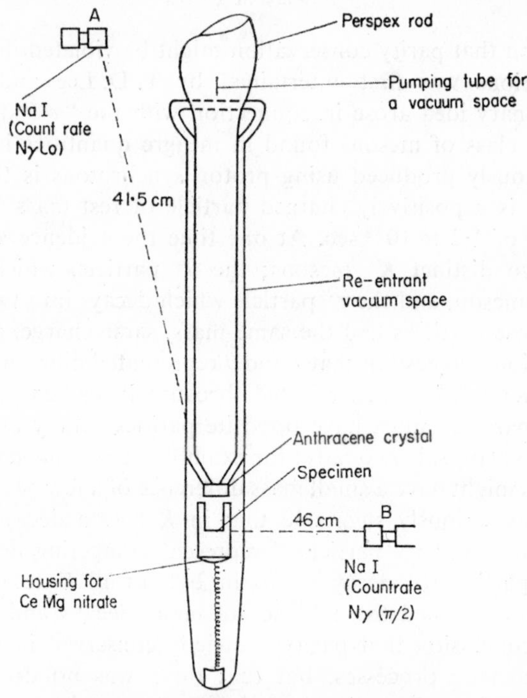

FIG. 12. Wu *et al.* experiment. Co^{60} nuclei are polarized by a vertical magnetic field produced by a solenoid (not shown).

† Wu *et al.*, *Phys. Rev.* **105**, 1413, 1957.

magnetic fields of 10^5 gauss are not required to orient the nuclear magnetic moments. A method discovered independently by Rose and Gorter is used. A field B of a few hundred gauss, produced by a solenoid with its axis vertical, is strong enough to orient the electronic magnetic moments of the paramagnetic ions in the cold crystal. The local magnetic field at the nucleus of a paramagnetic ion (Co^{60}) is $\sim 10^5$ gauss; thus polarization of the ionic moments ensures nuclear polarization. It is vital to the success of this experiment that nuclear polarization and not just alignment is achieved. Alignment means that the nuclei are oriented, but with no preference for the magnetic moments to be parallel, as distinct from antiparallel to the alignment direction.

The β-particles (negatrons) emitted by the polarized Co^{60} nuclei are detected by an anthracene crystal mounted 2 cm above the source. The light flashes in the scintillator are transmitted by a 4 ft long Perspex light pipe to a photomultiplier tube mounted outside the cryostat. In addition to beta detection, two NaI(Tl) crystals record the intensity of the cascade γ-rays from Ni^{60} close to the axis of polarization (crystal A) and at right angles to it (crystal B). The aligned nuclei produce an asymmetric pattern

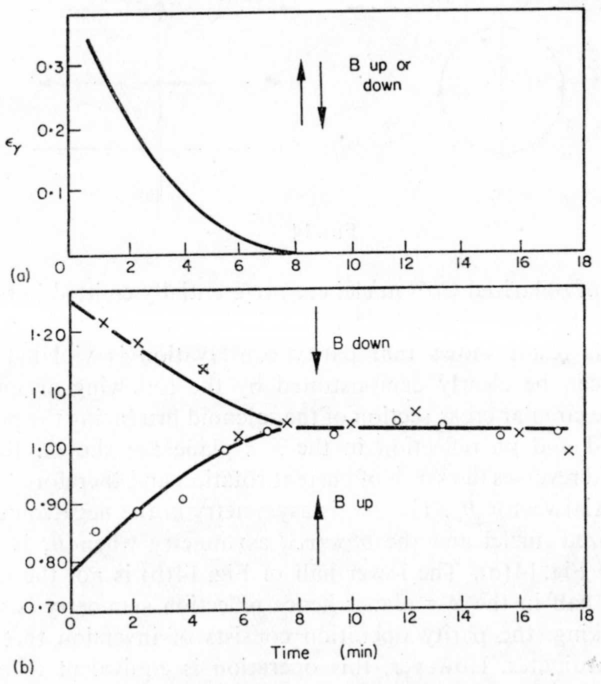

FIG. 13. (a) γ-ray anisotropy ε_γ as a function of warm-up time. $\varepsilon_\gamma = [N_\gamma(\pi/2) - N_\gamma(0)]/N_\gamma(\pi/2)$;
(b) β-asymmetry. Ordinate is counting rate (B up or down) divided by mean counting rate after polarization is destroyed ($t > 10$ min).

of γ-radiation, with the intensity in the axial direction smaller than the transverse intensity†. The $E2$ electromagnetic transitions in the decay $C^{60}(5^+) \rightarrow Ni^{60}(4^+)\gamma(2^+)\gamma(0^+)$ do not violate parity conservation and there is reflection symmetry of the radiation pattern relative to a plane transverse to the polarization axis.

The beta asymmetry up and down the polarization axis is measured by recording the β-particle counting rate just after cooling the crystal to 0·01°K, first with the polarizing field vertically upwards, and then with the field pointing downwards. The degree of polarization decreases as the crystal warms up and this is followed by measuring the decrease in the equatorial–polar gamma asymmetry (Fig. 13). The beta polar asymmetry is shown in Fig. 13(b). The results are quite definite: negatrons emitted in

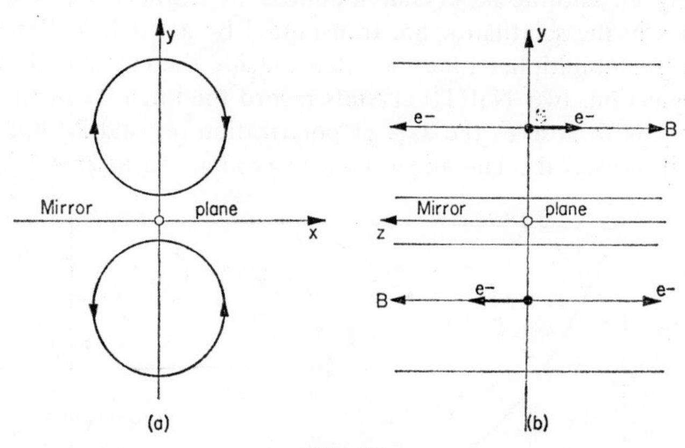

FIG. 14

the β^- decay of polarized Co^{60} nuclei are preferentially emitted in the direction opposite to that of the Co^{60} spin axis. The average value of $\boldsymbol{I}_i \boldsymbol{p}_e$ is negative. This result shows that parity conservation is violated in beta decay. This can be clearly demonstrated by the following argument. In Fig. 14(a), the circular cross section of the solenoid producing the polarizing magnetic field and its reflection in the x–z plane are shown. Reflection of the solenoid reverses the sense of current rotation and therefore the direction of the axial vector B_z. The z-axis asymmetry in the negatron emission of the polarized nuclei and the *observed* asymmetry when B_z is reversed are shown in Fig. 14(b). The lower half of Fig. 14(b) is not the reflection of the upper half in the x–z plane; hence reflection symmetry is violated. Strictly speaking, the parity operation consists of inversion through the origin of coordinates. However, this operation is equivalent to a mirror

† B. BLEANEY *et al.*, *Proc. Roy. Soc.* A **221**, 170, 1954. The Co^{60} nuclei were aligned by an internal crystalline field effect at ~1°K, first suggested by Bleaney. This method would not show the beta asymmetry as polarization does not occur.

reflection followed by a rotation through π radians about an axis through the origin perpendicular to the mirror plane. If rotation symmetry is violated so is the principle of conservation of angular momentum and there is no evidence of this in strong or weak interactions.

A similar experimental study of the angular distribution of the positrons emitted by polarized Co^{58} nuclei showed that the average value of $\boldsymbol{I}_i \boldsymbol{p}_e$ where $\boldsymbol{p}_e$ is the linear momentum of a positron, is positive. This result means that a mirror reflection of the experimental arrangement depicted in the upper half of Fig. 14(a) would agree with experiment, provided the mirror reflection of an electron is a positron! The operation of changing the sign of the electric charge of an elementary particle is called *charge conjugation*. Thus beta decay is invariant under the composite operation $C\,P$, where P is the parity operation and C the operation of charge conjugation.

Another symmetry operation of considerable interest is that of *time reversal* T. Invariance of the fundamental laws of physics under time reversal means that a positive sense of time cannot be distinguished from a negative sense of time (replacing t by $-t$ reverses all velocity and momentum vectors). An important theorem in elementary particle physics† is the "$C\,P\,T$" theorem. Briefly, this states that all interactions, strong or weak, are invariant under the combined operations of C, P and T taken in any order. Melvin†† has expressed this theorem in a vivid way; "The processes seen directly in matter look exactly like those in a film of processes in antimatter—taken through a mirror—and run off backwards". In beta decay the combined operation $C\,P$ is conserved. The $C\,P\,T$ theorem demonstrates that beta decay is invariant under time reversal.

14.8. THE HELICITY OF PARTICLES IN BETA DECAY

Lee and Yang suggested that the violation of parity in beta decay was a direct consequence of the longitudinal polarization of the emitted electrons and neutrinos. The term *helicity* has been coined to represent the state and degree of longitudinal polarization of particles and photons. The helicity, $\mathscr{H}$ of a particle is defined as

$$\mathscr{H} = \hat{\sigma}\,\hat{p}$$

where $\hat{\sigma}$ is a unit vector in the spin direction of the particle and $\hat{p}$ is the unit vector in the direction of the linear momentum of the particle. It is not difficult to prove (see the review article by L. Grodzins cited in the bibliography) that, if a system has well defined parity, the expectation value of $\mathscr{H}$ must be zero. It is now firmly established that the helicity of electrons

† G. Lüders, *Annals of Physics* **2**, 1, 1957.
†† M. A. Melvin, *Revs, Mod. Physics* **32**, 477, 1960.

emitted in beta decay is given by

$$\mathscr{H} = \pm \frac{v}{c} \qquad (\beta\text{-decay})$$

where v is the velocity of the electrons and the plus sign applies to positrons and the negative sign to negatrons. For highly relativistic electrons, $\mathscr{H} \to \pm 1$. For neutrinos ($v = c$): the helicity has been shown to be $+1$ for antineutrinos and -1 for neutrinos. Alternative symbols for complete helicity are R and L, corresponding to right circularly polarized and left circularly polarized particles. An R polarized particle is one which rotates in a clockwise sense as it recedes from the observer.

In the short period of two years from 1957 to 1959 a large number of helicity measurements on electrons, γ-rays, and neutrinos was made. We shall discuss three of these; the pioneer experiment of Frauenfelder and co-workers at Illinois on the helicity of negatrons emitted by unpolarized Co^{60} nuclei, the experiment of Deutsch *et al.* on the helicity of positrons emitted in the pure Fermi decay of Ga^{66}, and the classic measurement of the helicity of neutrinos emitted in the electron capture decay of Eu^{152} by Goldhaber, Grodzins and Sunyar.

The helicity of the negatrons emitted in the beta decay of Co^{60} nuclei was determined by Frauenfelder *et al.* in the following way†. First, it is worth emphasizing that it is not necessary to align or polarize the nuclei. Negatrons emitted from a thin β source S with a velocity $\sim 0{\cdot}49\,c$ ($\sim$ 77 keV) are selected by the cylindrical electrostatic energy filter A B and bent through an angle of $\sim 108°$ by the applied electric field $2V/d$ (Fig. 15(a).) The electrostatic field has little effect on the spin orientation of the electrons and they emerge from the filter with their spins *transverse* to their linear momentum $\boldsymbol{p}_e$. The negatrons are then observed after scattering through equal angles θ_L or θ_R by a thin gold foil placed normal to the negatron beam. As long ago as 1929, Mott showed that nuclear scattering of transversely polarized electrons is influenced by the orientation of the electron spin vector $\boldsymbol{\sigma}$ relative to the orbital angular momentum vector $\boldsymbol{L}$ of the electron in its orbit around the scattering nucleus. The two cases, with $\boldsymbol{\sigma}$ and $\boldsymbol{L}$ parallel, $\boldsymbol{\sigma}$ and $\boldsymbol{L}$ antiparallel, are illustrated in Fig. 15(b) and (c). This spin–orbit interaction is well known in atomic spectroscopy and arises through the magnetic interaction of the electron spin and the nucleus. The spin–orbit force is greatest when $\boldsymbol{\sigma}$ and $\boldsymbol{L}$ are antiparallel and more electrons are scattered to the left through angle θ_L than to the right through the same angle. This was verified by counting the scattered electrons in the θ_L and θ_R directions with Geiger or scintillation counters. The difference in left and right scattering enabled the helicity of the negatrons to be calculated. Using gold foil of thickness $0{\cdot}15$ mg/cm² (thin foil is essential to reduce

† H. Frauenfelder *et al.*, *Phys. Rev.* **106**, 386, 1957.

plural scattering in the foils, a helicity value of $\sim -0{\cdot}4$ for $0{\cdot}49\,c$ negatrons was obtained, in good agreement with $-v/c$ considering the difficulties of the experiment.

Deutsch *et al.* have measured the helicity of the positrons emitted in the positron decay of the pure Fermi emitter, 9·5 hr Ga^{66}. The principle of this determination depends on two phenomena.

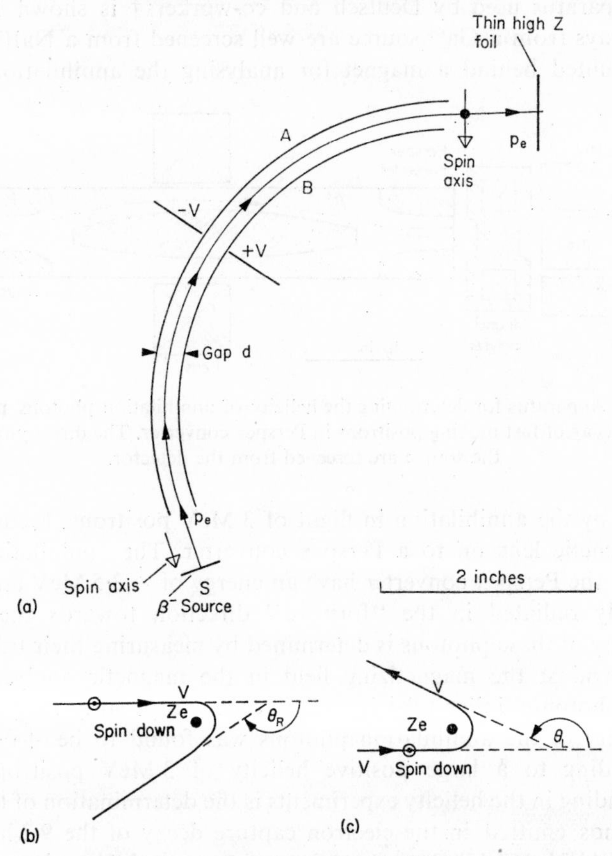

FIG. 15. (a) Frauenfelder β^- helicity experiment; (b) Electron with spin axis normal to the plane of the orbit scattered to the right by high Z nucleus through angle θ_R, $\boldsymbol{\sigma}$ and $\boldsymbol{L}$ are parallel; (c) Electron with spin axis down scattered by nucleus to the left through angle θ_L, $\boldsymbol{\sigma}$ and $\boldsymbol{L}$ are antiparallel.

(1) The helicity of a fast moving positron annihilating with an electron is transferred to the higher energy photon in two quantum decay. $\mathscr{H}_\gamma \cong \mathscr{H}_{\beta^+}$.

(2) The helicity of gamma quanta can be distinguished by measuring their transmission through a block of iron magnetized (a) in the direction of travel of the photons (b) opposite to the direction of the photons. A simple explanation of this effect is given by Konopinski. When the magnetizing

field in the iron is parallel to the direction of travel of right circularly polarized photons ($\mathscr{H}_\gamma = +1$), the polarized electrons in the iron atoms (~ 2 per atom) have their spin axes antiparallel to the photon spin axis and they can absorb energy from the photons by flipping their spins. Thus photons of helicity -1 are more readily transmitted when the magnetizing field is parallel to the linear momentum of the photons.

The apparatus used by Deutsch and co-workers† is shown in Fig. 16. Direct γ-rays from a Ga^{66} source are well screened from a NaI(Tl) scintillator, mounted behind a magnet for analysing the annihilation photons

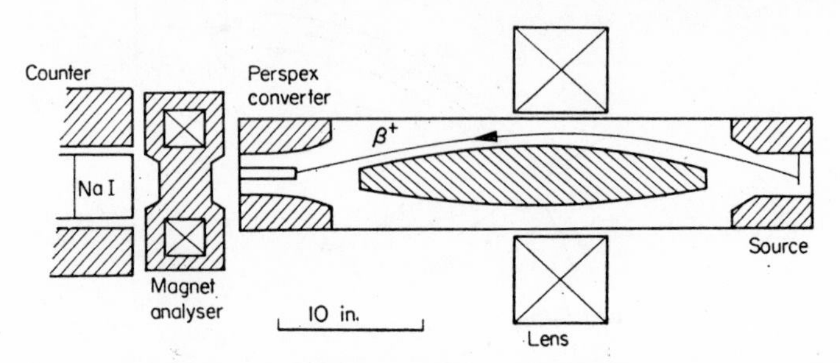

FIG. 16. Apparatus for determining the helicity of annihilation photons produced by the decay of fast moving positrons in Perspex converter. The direct γ-rays from the source are screened from the detector.

produced by the annihilation in flight of 3 MeV positrons, focused by the short magnetic lens on to a Perspex converter. The annihilation quanta created in the Perspex converter have an energy of $\sim 3{\cdot}5$ MeV and are predominantly radiated in the "forward" direction towards the detector. The helicity of these photons is determined by measuring their transmission with an against the magnetizing field in the magnetic analyser. Notice that the photomultiplier tube is well screened from stray magnetic fields. The helicity of the annihilation photons was found to be $+0{\cdot}95 \pm 0{\cdot}14$ corresponding to a large positive helicity of 3 MeV positrons.

Outstanding in the helicity experiments is the determination of the helicity of neutrinos emitted in the electron capture decay of the 9·2 hr isomeric state of $_{63}Eu^{152}$ by Goldhaber, Grodzins and Sunyar.†† The relevant portions of the decay scheme of the isomeric 0^- state of Eu^{152} are illustrated in Fig. 17(a). The nucleus decays by K capture (absorbing half a unit of spin from the K shell) to form an excited 1^- state of Sm^{152}, 961 keV above its ground level. The K capture process is a pure Gamow–Teller transition and the spin of the emitted neutrino must be antiparallel to the spin of the 961 keV Sm^{152} state (Fig. 17(b)). There are, however, two possibilities: the recoil nucleus and neutrino both have $\mathscr{H} = 1$ (tensor interaction) or they

† M. DEUTSCH *et al.*, *Phys. Rev.* **107**, 1733, 1957.
†† M. GOLDHABER, L. GRODZINS and A. W. SUNYAR, *Phys. Rev.* **109**, 1015, 1958.

both have $\mathscr{H} = -1$ (axial-vector interaction). The helicity experiment is based on the measurement of the helicity of the γ-rays emitted when the 10^{-13} sec lifetime 961 keV state of the recoil nucleus decays. The 961 keV photons inherit the helicity of the excited recoil nucleus, for the ground state of $_{62}Sm^{152}$ is, of course, spinless and there is no helicity. The apparatus used in the experiment is shown in Fig. 18. The europium source is mounted inside an analysing magnet and the NaI(Tl) detector is screened by a conical

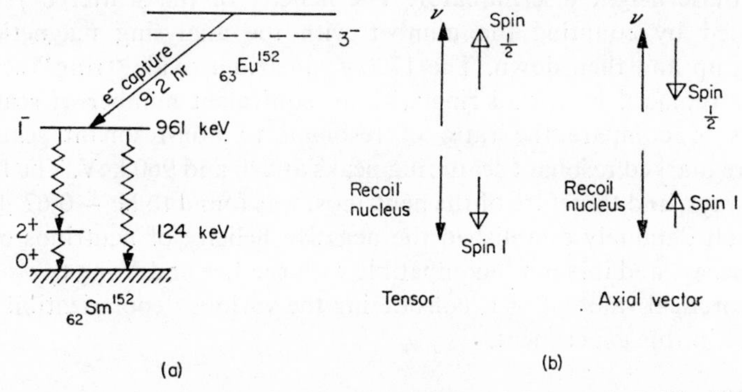

FIG. 17. (a) Portion of decay scheme of isomeric (9·2 hr) state of $_{63}Eu^{152}$; (b) linear momenta and spins of emitted neutrino and Sm nucleus for tensor and axial-vector decays (pure Gamow–Teller transition).

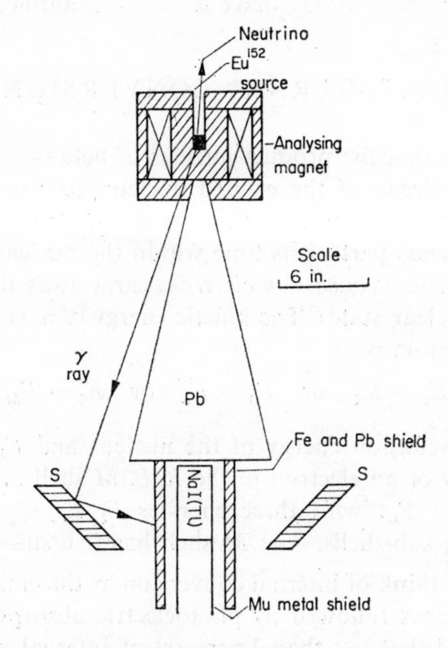

FIG. 18. Goldhaber–Grodzins–Sunyar experiment. 961 keV γ-rays resonantly scattered by Sm_2O_3 scatterer (S) are detected by 2 in. × $3\frac{1}{2}$ in. NaI(Tl) scintillator.

lead absorber from the direct γ-rays in the decay sequence. If, however, a neutrino is emitted at a small angle to the right of the axis of symmetry of the apparatus (see Fig. 18), the recoil nucleus moves in the opposite direction and decays in $\sim 10^{-13}$ sec, without changing its spin orientation or losing all its recoil momentum. Thus the energy of the radiated γ-ray may be restored and the condition for resonance scattering obtained. Resonantly scattered γ-rays are detected by the scintillator and analysed with a pulse height discriminator. The helicity of the scattered γ-rays is determined by counting the number with the analysing magnetic field pointing up and then down. The 1700 g samarium oxide "ring" scatterer could be replaced by a lead ring with an equivalent number of scattering electrons to compare the ratio of resonant to non-resonant scattering. There are marked resonant scattering peaks at 840 and 960 keV. The helicity of the γ-rays, and therefore of the neutrinos, was found to be $-0{\cdot}67 \pm 0{\cdot}15$. This result definitely established the negative helicity of neutrinos emitted in beta decay, and it is not incompatible with the Lee and Yang two-component theoretical value of -1, considering the various depolarization effects operative in this experiment.

Summary

(1) Particle and antiparticle always have opposite helicity.
(2) Negatrons in beta decay have $\mathscr{H} = -v/c$; positrons $\mathscr{H} = +v/c$.
(3) Neutrinos in beta decay have $\mathscr{H} = -1$, antineutrinos $\mathscr{H} = +1$.

14.9. INTERNAL CONVERSION

It often happens that the product nucleus of beta decay is formed in an excited state. The decay of the excited nucleus does not always proceed by γ-radiation. The excitation energy may be directly transferred to an atomic electron, which spends part of its time within the nuclear volume, ejecting it from the atom. These *conversion electrons* carry away the spin and parity changes of the nuclear states. The kinetic energy of a conversion electron escaping from an atom is

$$E_e = E_0 - E_K \quad \text{or} \quad E_0 - E_L \quad \text{or} \quad E_0 - E_M \quad \text{etc.}$$

where E_0 is the excitation energy of the nucleus and $E_K, E_L, E_M, \ldots$ is the binding energy of an electron in the K, L, M shell ... There is in fact a fine structure to E_L, with three energies $E_{L_1} E_{L_2} E_{L_3}$ corresponding to $2s_{\frac{1}{2}}$, $2p_{\frac{1}{2}}$, and $2p_{\frac{3}{2}}$ sub-shells. The M shell has five sub-shells.

It is tempting to think of internal conversion as the emission of a photon by the excited nucleus followed by photoelectric absorption in the parent atom. It is believed that less than 1 per cent of internal conversions occur in this manner.

In the preceding chapter it was emphasized that if two nuclear states have zero spin no single photon transition connects the states. If $I_i = I_f = 0$ and there is no parity change, de-excitation can occur through the emission of a single bound atomic electron. If there is a parity change, two conversion electrons or one electron and one photon may appear.

In the early history of β-radiation internal conversion electrons were an extra source of confusion for they appeared in the β-energy spectrum as superimposed monoenergetic groups. A simple example of internal conversion is shown in the momentum spectrum of the β-radiation emitted

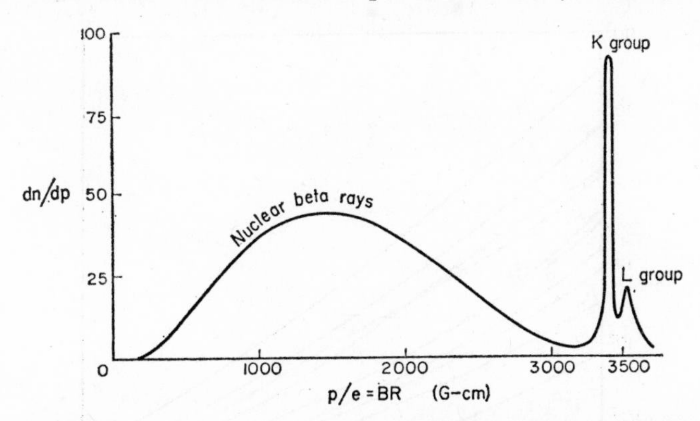

FIG. 19. Nuclear β-ray spectrum of Cs^{137}. Two groups of internal conversion electrons are superimposed. The fine structure effect of L sub-shells is not resolved.

by Cs^{137} (Fig. 19). The L shell conversion electrons have a higher energy than the K group, the difference in energy being $E_K - E_L$; the K conversion electrons easily out-number the L conversion electrons. There are some examples of very complicated internal conversion transitions; Rd Ac has 32 conversion lines.

It is convenient to define internal conversion coefficients

$$\alpha_K, \alpha_L, \alpha_M \quad \text{or} \quad \alpha_{L_1}, \alpha_{L_2}, \alpha_{L_3}, \text{ etc.}$$

$$\alpha_K = \frac{n_K}{n_\gamma}, \quad \alpha_L = \frac{n_L}{n_\gamma}, \text{ etc.}$$

n_K is the number of K shell internal conversion electrons emitted in unit time and n_γ is the number of γ-photons emitted in unit time . . . The photons of interest are those radiated in the de-excitation of the excited state responsible for the internal conversion.

The total number of nuclear transitions in unit time is

$$n_{\text{total}} = n_\gamma + n_K + n_{L_1} + n_{L_2} + n_{L_3} + n_{M_1} + \cdots, \text{ etc.}$$
$$n_{\text{total}} = n_\gamma(1 + \alpha_K + \alpha_L + \alpha_M + \cdots)$$

There is a number of ways of measuring internal conversion coefficients (see the article by D. Alburger pp. 19–26, cited in the bibliography). The simplest method is to measure n_γ and n_e with detectors of known solid angle and efficiency. To measure α_K say, it is necessary to distinguish between K and L conversion electrons and to discriminate against γ-rays not associated with the nuclear transition responsible for the internal conversion.

Experimental determinations of internal conversion coefficients are helpful in assigning multipole orders to the nuclear electromagnetic transitions. M. E. Rose and others have done extensive theoretical calculations on internal conversion coefficients. The main trends of variation of α_K are

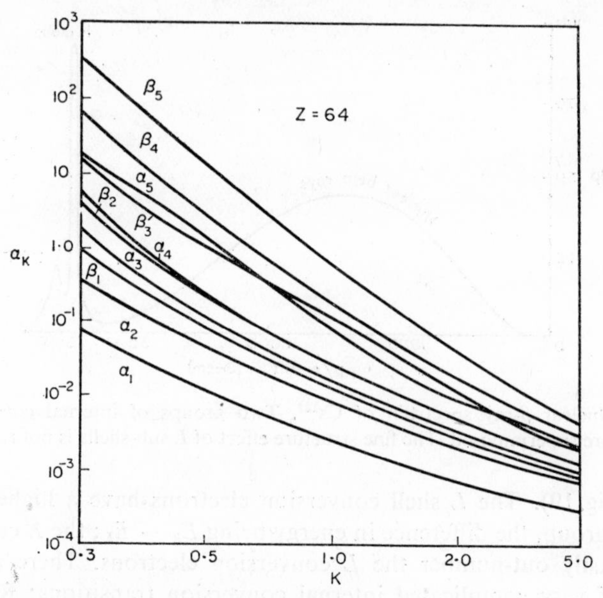

FIG. 20. Internal conversion coefficient α_K for $Z = 64, \alpha_1 \equiv E\,1$ transition, $\beta_2 \equiv M2$, etc.

(1) For a fixed energy E and atomic number Z, α_K increases with the multipole order of the transition.

(2) For a given Z and multipole order, α_K decreases nearly logarithmically with the energy E. Conversion coefficients are therefore high for isomeric transitions (long lived transitions between nuclear states with a large spin difference).

(3) For a given energy and multipole order, α_K increases with Z; e.g., α_K for a 0·5 MeV $E2$ transition is $7{\cdot}3 \times 10^{-3}$ at $Z = 54$ and $3{\cdot}1 \times 10^{-2}$ at $Z = 92$.

Unfortunately, it is not always possible to identify the multipolarity of the nuclear electromagnetic transition from the α_K value. The internal conversion coefficients curves for certain magnetic transitions are not well separated from some of the electric transition curves. Fig. (20). $\alpha_1, \alpha_2, \ldots$

$\beta_1, \beta_2, \ldots$ denote electric dipole, quadrupole, and magnetic dipole, quadrupole transitions. The transition energy is expressed as $K m c^2$, where $m c^2$ is the rest mass energy of the electron.

Sometimes it is easier to measure internal conversion ratios such as $\alpha_K/\alpha_L = n_K/n_L$. Theoretical curves for α_K/α_L for $Z = 85$, as a function of the transition energy Kmc^2 are given in Fig. 21. A combination of measurement of α_K and α_K/α_L may often lead to an unambiguous multipolarity assignment whereas a single measurement is not sufficient.

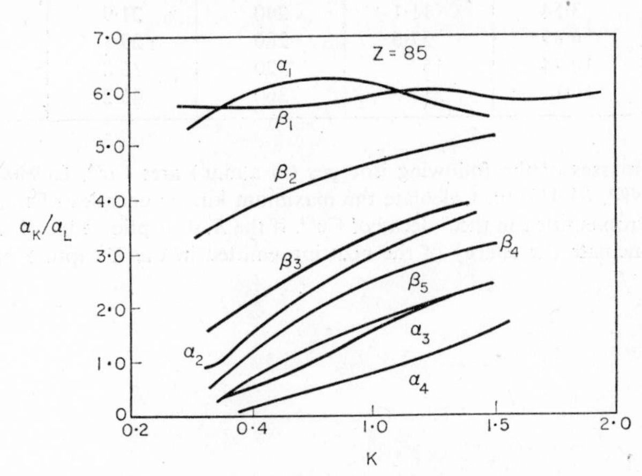

FIG. 21. Ratio of α_K, α_L coefficients, $Z = 85$.

BIBLIOGRAPHY

Beta and Gamma Ray Spectroscopy, Ed. by K. SIEGBAHN, North-Holland Publishing Co. Amsterdam 1955.

M. DEUTSCH and O. KOFOED-HANSEN, Part XI in *Experimental Nuclear Physics*, Vol. III, Ed. by E. Segrè, Wiley, New York 1959.

E. J. KONOPINSKI and L. M. LANGER, *Ann. Rev. of Nuclear Sci.* **2**, 261, 1953.

E. J. KONOPINSKI, *Ann. Rev. of Nuclear Sci.* **9**, 99, 1959.

R. BOUCHEZ and P. DEPOMMIER, Orbital Electron Capture by the Nucleus, *Reports on Progr. Physics* **23**, 395, 1960.

B. W. RIDLEY, The Neutrino in *Progr. Nucl. Phys.* **5**, 188, 1956.

L. GRODZINS, Measurement of Helicity in *Progr. Nucl. Phys.* **7**, 163, 1959.

J. J. SAKURAI, Weak Interactions in *Progr. Nucl. Phys.* **7**, 243, 1959.

A. LUNDBY, Weak Interactions in *Progr. Elementary Particles and Cosmic Ray Physics*, Vol. **5**, p. 1–p. 96, North-Holland Publishing Co. Amsterdam 1960.

D. E. ALBURGER, Nuclear Isomerism in *Handbuch der Physik*, Vol. 42, p. 1–94, Springer-Verlag, Berlin 1957.

EXAMPLES

1. The spectrum analysis of the beta rays from a very thin C_s source has a sharp large peak at a "*BR*-value" of $3{\cdot}390 \times 10^{-3}$ weber per mm². If this peak is due to *K* shell internal conversion from the 0·664 MeV level of the nucleus, calculate (in keV) the *K* shell binding energy. Is your answer compatible with a single-electron-atom estimate?

2. The 49 d isomeric state of In^{114} decays to the ground state and then by β-emission to the ground state of $_{50}Sn^{114}$ with a half-life of 72 sec. The following counting rates n of the beta spectrum were obtained for a thin source in secular equilibrium with the isomeric state. The spectrometer is the 180° focusing type with a radius of curvature of 21·3 cm. The momentum resolution $\Delta p/p$ is independent of p. The Coulomb factor for the beta transition is $F(Z, p)$. Plot a Kurie graph and estimate the end-point of the energy spectrum.

B (gauss)	$F(Z, p)$	n (min^{-1})	B (gauss)	$F(Z, p)$	n (min^{-1})
80	3·54	11·1	240	21·9	456
120	6·89	57·6	280	29·1	502
160	10·74	157	320	36·8	353
200	16·1	313	360	45·2	80·7

3. The atomic masses of the following isotopes (in a.m.u.) are: Cu^{64}, 63·949934; Zn^{64}, 63·949320; Ni^{64}, 64·948130. Calculate the maximum kinetic energies of the negatron and the positron emitted in the β-decay of Cu^{64}. If the K absorption edge of zinc occurs at 1·28 Å, calculate the energy of the neutrino emitted in the K capture process for Cu^{64}.

CHAPTER 15

THE NEUTRON

15.1. DISCOVERY

The sequence of events culminating in the discovery of the neutron was

(1) The observations by Bothe and Becker† that many elements of low atomic number emitted a penetrating radiation when exposed to α-particles. The natural assumption was made that the penetrating radiation consisted of hard γ-rays.

(2) I. Curie and F. Joliot†† carried out similar experiments and found that the penetrating radiation emitted by Be, when bombarded with Po

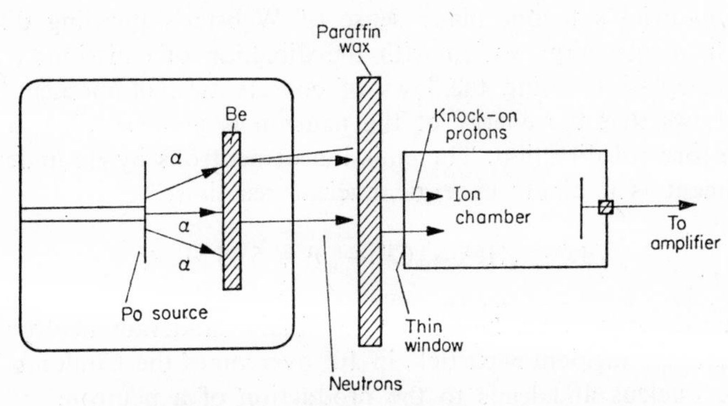

FIG. 1. Neutrons resulting from the α-bombardment of Be target knock protons out of hydrogenous target. Protons enter ionization chamber and produce intense ionization.

α-particles (5·3 MeV), had a linear absorption coefficient of 0·15 cm^{-1} in lead. At the time (1932) it was not known that the minimum absorption coefficient of γ-radiation in lead is greater than 0·15 cm^{-1} (the absorption process of pair creation had not been discovered).

The French workers also made the important discovery that if a sheet of paraffin wax is placed between the α-irradiated beryllium foil and an

† W. BOTHE and H. BECKER, *Zeit. f. Phys.* **66**, 289, 1930; *Naturwiss.* **19**, 753, 1931.
†† I. CURIE and F. JOLIOT, *Compt. Rendus* **194**, 273, 1932.

ionization chamber the ionization current increases (Fig. 1). This phenomenon is a result of the ejection of long range protons from the hydrogeneous material under the impact of the penetrating radiation emitted by the beryllium. However, they incorrectly attributed the recoil of the protons to the collisions of high energy photons.

(3) At Cambridge, Webster† observed that the energy of the "photons" emitted by the beryllium varied according to their direction of emission. "Photons" emitted in the direction opposite to that of the incident α-particles had a considerably smaller energy than those emitted in the forward direction.

(4) Chadwick†† made an extensive series of measurements of the energies of recoil of protons and other light nuclei ejected from thin targets by the penetrating "Be-radiation". The recoil energies were measured with a pulse ionization chamber and amplifier. The assumed "Compton-like" collisions between photons and nuclei were incompatible with Chadwick's measurements. However, Chadwick showed that if the penetrating radiation from alpha-irradiated beryllium (and other light elements) consisted of neutral particles, *neutrons*, of mass of the order of the proton mass, the recoil observations could be explained in terms of elastic neutron–nuclear collisions. Chadwick's theory made sense of Webster's puzzling discovery that the neutron energy varied with the direction of emission: a simple classical calculation, using the laws of conservation of momentum and energy, shows that the energy of the neutron is greatest when it comes off in the forward direction. The emission of neutrons by Be under alpha bombardment is a highly exoergic nuclear reaction:

$$_4Be^9 + {}_2He^4 \rightarrow {}_6C^{12} + {}_0n^1 + 5{\cdot}65 \text{ MeV}$$

Strong alpha sources are necessary to obtain moderate neutron fluxes as only about 1 incident α-particle in 10^5 overcomes the Coulomb barrier of the Be nucleus and leads to the production of a neutron.

The discovery of the neutron is one of the most important events in the history of Nuclear Physics. Heisenberg immediately realized the significance of Chadwick's discovery and put forward the suggestion that protons and neutrons and not protons and electrons are the constituent particles of the atomic nucleus. The comparatively late date of the discovery of the neutron is partly due to the similarity in the properties of the neutron and high energy photons, and the confusing effect that gamma rays as well as neutrons are usually associated with neutron sources.†††

† H. C. Webster, *Proc. Roy. Soc.* A **136**, 428, 1932.
†† J. Chadwick, *Nature* **129**, 321, 1932; *Proc. Roy. Soc.* A **136**, 692, 1932.
††† N. Feather, *Science Progress* **33**, 240, 1938.

15.2. NEUTRON SOURCES

Radioactive Sources

The nuclear reaction leading to the discovery of the neutron is extensively used as a convenient low intensity neutron source. The source consists of an intimate mixture of about 5 parts of fine beryllium powder to 1 part of radium (usually in the form of a suitable salt).The majority of the neutrons is produced by the (α, n) reaction

$$Be^9 (\alpha, n) C^{12} + 5{\cdot}65 \text{ MeV} \quad (1)$$

However, if the radium is in secular equilibrium with its decay products, extra neutrons are released through the (γ, n) reaction

$$Be^9 (\gamma, n) Be^8 \rightarrow 2He^4 \quad (2)$$

Only gamma rays with energies above 1·67 MeV are of use, as 1·67 MeV corresponds to the binding energy of the last neutron in Be^9. There are gamma rays of energy 1·69, 1·75, 1·82, 2·09, and 2·42 MeV present in the radium source. The product nucleus of the (γ, n) reaction, Be^8, is unstable and promptly (within 10^{-15} sec) decays into two α-particles. At first sight, it looks as if these α-particles might produce new neutrons through reaction (1); however, they are of low energy (0·1 MeV) and the cross section is vanishingly small.

The neutron source described above is isotropic; it is accompanied by a high background of γ-radiation and it produces neutrons over a wide energy range from 0 to 13 MeV. The energy spectrum is complex for several reasons:

(1) The occurrence of two reactions (α, n) and (γ, n) and the presence of several groups of α-particles and γ-rays.

(2) The loss of energy of α-particles by ionization before nuclear capture (the loss must not be very large otherwise the Coulomb barrier strongly inhibits capture).

(3) The dependence of neutron energy E_n on the direction of emission relative to the incoming α-particle.

A serious disadvantage of this type of source is the difficulty of obtaining exactly predictable and reproducible source strengths. Thus they are not suitable as standard neutron sources. A typical yield of a Ra–Be source is

$10-18 \times 10^6$ neutrons per sec per curie of Ra.

A convenient radioactive source, when the high gamma background is undesirable, is a Po–Be mixture, with a typical yield of

3×10^6 neutrons per sec per curie of Po^{210}.

The Po–α–Be source has the disadvantage that the neutron intensity decays with a half-life of 138 d (the half-life of Po^{210} (RaF.)).

Photoneutron Sources

The majority of nuclei have a neutron binding energy of 5 MeV or more. Two exceptions are Be^9 and H^2, with binding energies for the last neutron of 1·67 and 2·23 MeV respectively. Convenient reproducible sources can be obtained by placing a strong monoenergetic gamma source at the centre of a surrounding sphere or cylinder of beryllium or heavy water. A standard photoneutron source consisting of a MsTh or Na^{24} gamma source placed at the centre of a spherical vessel filled with heavy

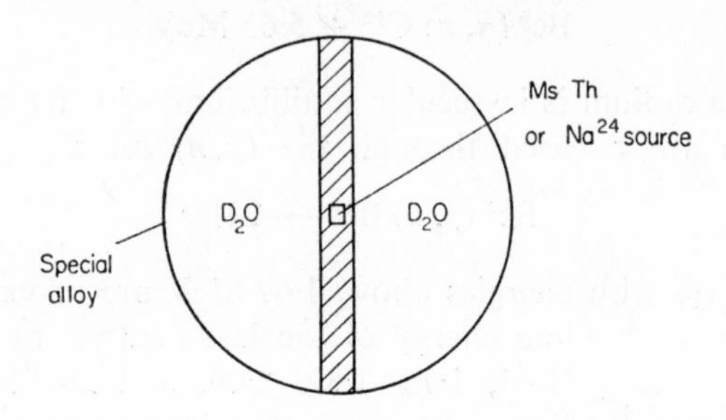

FIG. 2. One form of standard photoneutron source. MsTh or Na^{24} γ-source placed at the centre of a spherical container filled with heavy water.

water is shown in Fig. 2. The yield of neutrons due to 1 g of Be or D_2O at a distance of 1 cm from 1 curie of various gamma sources is given in Table 1. The table also lists the half-life T of the gamma (and therefore the neutron) source, the energy of the γ-rays E_γ, and the energy E_n of the photoneutrons.

The advantages of this type of source are:

(1) The reproducible neutron strength.

(2) The approximately monoenergetic nature of the neutrons.

(3) The choice of E_n by choosing a suitable value of E_γ.

(4) The wide variety of artificial gamma sources available from atomic reactors.

TABLE 1. RADIOACTIVE (γ, n) SOURCES

Gamma source	Target	T	E_γ (MeV)	E_n (MeV)	Yield
Na^{24}	Be	14·8 hr	2·76	0·83	13×10^4
Na^{24}	D_2O	14·8 hr	2·76	0·22	27×10^4
Y^{88}	Be	87 d	1·9, 2·8	0·16	10×10^4
Y^{88}	D_2O	87 d	2·8	0·31	$0·3 \times 10^4$
Sb^{124}	Be	60 d	1·7	0·025	19×10^4

The neutron yield is given in neutrons per second. The drawback of the Na^{24} source is the short half-life of 14·8 hr. The Be–Sb^{124} source is a very convenient source of intermediate energy neutrons with a relatively long half-life of 60 d.

Neutron sources based on the photo-production of neutrons using high energy X-rays are discussed in the following section.

Charged Particle Sources

The invention of the Van de Graaff machine, the cyclotron, and other charged particle accelerators led to the rapid development of new neutron sources. These sources are usually based on either the (p, n) reaction or the (d, n) reaction. Accelerator sources possess several advantages over the radioactive sources:

(1) Higher neutron intensity.

(2) Wide flexibility in control of energy of accelerated protons (or deuterons) with consequent control on neutron energy.

(3) Possibility of producing high energy neutrons using highly exoergic (d, n) reactions.

(4) The neutron beam can be switched off or pulsed in a series of short duration bursts. This is a great advantage in many neutron cross section experiments.

We now consider a few of the commonly used (p, n) and (d, n) sources.

$$\underline{H^3\,(p, n)\,He^3} \qquad \underline{Q = -0{\cdot}764\ \text{MeV}}$$

This endoergic reaction is a convenient source of neutrons of moderate energy. The target usually consists of a tritium gas-filled chamber with a very thin entrance window to allow the incoming collimated proton beam to enter the target chamber with little loss of energy. All charged particle reaction cross sections fall off rapidly at low projectile energies because of the repulsive Coulomb barrier. In this particular reaction, the cross section increases nearly linearly from about 0·17 barns at an incident proton kinetic energy E_p of 1·2 MeV to 0·56 barns for protons with $E_p = 2{\cdot}4$ MeV.

Applications of the laws of conservation of energy and momentum, using the precise atomic mass values of the nuclei concerned, enable one to calculate the kinetic energy of the neutron emitted at an angle θ with respect to the forward direction (direction of incidence of the proton). The calculation is valid, provided the product nucleus is not formed in an excited state. For low values of E_p, not only is the cross section small, but the neutron energy in each possible direction of emission is double-valued. Thus the advantage of a monoenergetic source is lost. At higher bombarding energies the ambiguity of the neutron energy vanishes. A useful nomograph for reading off the neutron kinetic energy E_n at all values of θ for a wide range of E_p values is described in the article by B. T. Feld† (the McKibben nomograph).

For $E_p = 2{\cdot}0$ MeV, in the forward direction ($\theta = 0$), $E_n = 1{\cdot}2$ MeV.

For $E_p = 3{\cdot}0$ MeV, in the forward direction ($\theta = 0$), $E_n = 2{\cdot}2$ MeV.

$\underline{Li^7 (p, n) Be^7}$ $\qquad$ $\underline{Q = -1{\cdot}646 \text{ MeV}}$

The cross section varies in a complicated way with the proton energy E_p. It has a maximum at $E_p = 2{\cdot}2$ MeV of about 0·5 barns. This reaction provides a convenient source of intermediate energy neutrons.

For $E_p = 2{\cdot}0$ MeV, in the forward direction ($\theta = 0$), $E_n = 230$ keV.

$\underline{H^2 (d, n) He^3}$ $\qquad$ $\underline{Q = +3{\cdot}265 \text{ MeV}}$

The low binding energy of the deuteron is responsible for the exoergic nature of the majority of (d, n) reactions. The $C^{12}(d, n) N^{13}$ reaction is an exception to the rule with a Q value of $-0{\cdot}28$ MeV.

The outstanding feature of (d, n) neutron sources is the possibility of producing neutrons with high energies (~ 20 MeV) without using very high energy deuteron accelerators.

One of the earliest reactions employed as a neutron source is the *d–d* reaction. The Coulomb barrier is as small as it can be for a pair of charged particles and a useful yield of 2·5 MeV neutrons ($\theta = 0$) is obtained with incident deuterons accelerated through a potential difference as low as 50 kV! A suitable target, when maximum yield is the main aim, is one of heavy ice produced by freezing heavy water on to a liquid air-cooled metal surface. For $E_d = 1{\cdot}5$ MeV, a good yield of 5 MeV neutrons in the forward direction is obtained (for $\theta = 180°$, E_n is 1·8 MeV).

$\underline{H^3 (d, n) He^4}$ $\qquad$ $\underline{Q = 17{\cdot}6 \text{ MeV}}$

The availability of tritium as a target material (gas target usually) has provided a convenient source of fast neutrons. The very high Q value of the tritium reaction is a consequence of the small nuclear mass of He^4 (high binding energy). For incident deuterons of energy E_d about 200 keV, neutrons of 14 MeV are emitted in the forward direction. Increasing E_d to 2·5 MeV increases E_n ($\theta = 0$) to about 20 MeV.

The $Li^7 (d, n) Be^8$, $Q = 15{\cdot}0$ MeV; and the $Be^9 (d, n) B^{10}$, $Q = 3{\cdot}79$ MeV, reactions are useful neutron sources using cyclotron accelerated deuterons. However, monoenergetic neutrons are not found because the product nuclei can be formed in one of several excited states.

Ultrafast Neutrons

Neut ons of energy of the order of 50 MeV or more are not conveniently produced by moderate energy particle accelerators. However, deuterons accelerated to about 200 MeV in a synchro-cyclotron can readily be

† See bibliography at the end of the chapter.

"stripped" into protons and neutrons by directing the deuteron beam to pass through a thin copper target.† The stripped neutrons have a wide spread in energy centred about a mean energy $\sim E_d/2$.

X-ray Sources

High energy X-ray machines are convenient sources of high energy neutrons through the (γ, n) reaction. Electrons accelerated to high energies (20 MeV or more) in linear accelerators, betatrons, synchrotrons, etc. produce copious fluxes of high energy photons when they impinge on target elements of high atomic number. The high flux of photons releases large number of neutrons within the target material and nearby objects. The disadvantage of this type of source is the wide spread in neutron energy. The possibility of pulsing the electron beam and thereby obtaining a pulsed source of neutrons is a decided advantage.

Reactor Sources

The outstanding source of neutrons from the point of view of intensity is the atomic reactor. Thermal neutron fluxes as high as 10^{14} per cm^2 per sec are available from large atomic reactors. There is a number of neutron physics techniques (e.g. neutron diffraction) which are essentially impractical without resource to these high neutron fluxes. The disadvantages of reactor sources are the wide spread in neutron energy and the impossibility of directly pulsing the neutron source.

15.3. NEUTRON DETECTION

The problem of detecting slow neutrons is essentially different from that of detecting fast neutrons. The basic reason for the different techniques is the marked dependence of neutron reaction cross sections on the neutron kinetic energy.

Neutrons have a very small interaction with electrons and do not therefore ionize matter to any marked extent. To detect the presence of neutrons we must rely on some nuclear interaction with a reasonably large cross section. For low energy neutrons, the most suitable neutron reaction is

$$B^{10}(n, \alpha)Li^7 \qquad Q = 2{\cdot}78 \text{ MeV}$$

For thermal neutrons (0·025 eV) of velocity $v = 2{\cdot}2 \times 10^5$ cm per sec, the cross section for this reaction is 3770 barns. However, if the target is natural boron the effective cross section is reduced to 710 barns because the abundance of the B^{10} isotope is only 18·83%. This (n, α) reaction

† Recently neutrons of energy >300 MeV have been produced by stripping 650 MeV deuterons accelerated in the Birmingham synchrotron.

cross section accurately obeys the $1/v$ law up to energies of the order of 1 keV. Thus for 1 keV neutrons, the cross section is given by

$$\sigma = \sigma_0 \sqrt{\frac{0{\cdot}025}{1000}} = 18{\cdot}8 \text{ barns}$$

where σ_0 is the cross section for neutrons of 0·025 eV energy.

The large Q value of the $B^{10}(n, \alpha) Li^7$ reaction makes it eminently suitable for the detection of slow neutrons. Ionization chambers with boron coated electrodes or proportional counters filled with boron trifluoride vapour (often enriched in the B^{10} isotope) are in common use. Neutrons are detected through the relatively large amount of ionization produced by the α-particle and the lithium nucleus. Full advantage of the proportional counter is taken to discriminate neutron induced pulses from smaller background gamma pulses.

The $1/v$ dependence of the (n, α) cross section for the boron reaction limits the BF_3 counter to low energy neutrons. Provided the flux of neutrons passing through a BF_3 counter contains no significant contribution above 1 keV, the strict $1/v$ law means that the detector counting rate is proportional to the neutron density of the beam.

Hanson and McKibben† invented a boron counter–moderator arrangement which has a nearly uniform sensitivity to neutrons in the energy range 10 keV to 3 MeV. One of their shielded "long" counters is shown in Fig. 3. Fast neutrons are moderated (i.e. they are rapidly reduced to thermal energies by elastic collisions with the nuclei of the moderator) in the paraffin wax surrounding a long thin cylindrical BF_3 proportional counter. This counter operates satisfactorily when there is a relatively high scattered neutron background. The detector efficiency for neutrons incident on the 8 in. circle on the front face is less than 1 per cent.

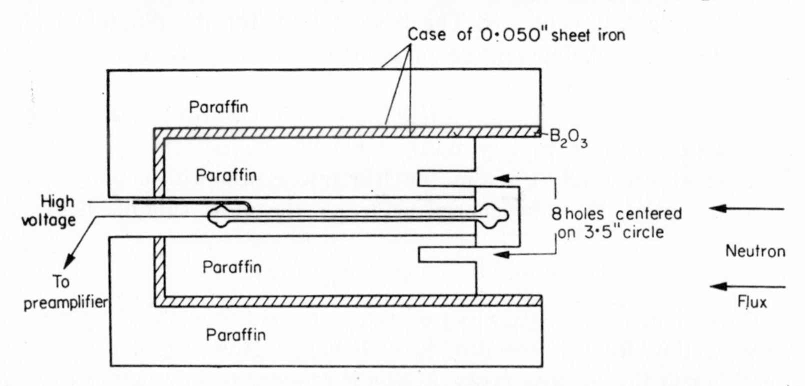

FIG. 3. A long BF_3 proportional counter embedded in paraffin. (Hanson and McKibben design.)

† A. O. HANSON and J. L. MCKIBBEN, *Phys. Rev.* **72**, 673, 1947.

An alternative to the boron type of slow neutron detector is the fission ionization chamber. The most common form of fission ionization chamber contains a thin wall coating of U^{235} or Pu^{239}. These isotopes of uranium and plutonium have fission cross sections of several hundred barns for thermal neutrons. The fission fragments have large energies (> 50 MeV) and if one of them escapes from the thin surface layer of the fissionable material into the gas of the chamber, a large, easily distinguished, ionization pulse is generated.

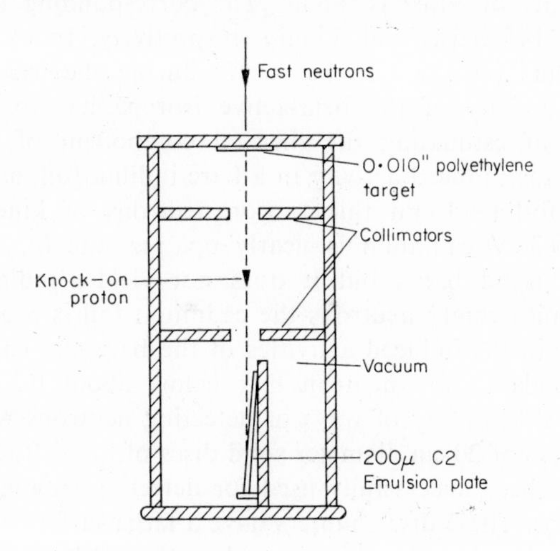

FIG. 4. Fast neutron detector system.

In Chapter 11 a brief account of the detection of neutrons by nuclear emulsion plates was given. Slow neutrons may be detected through the $N^{14}(n, p)\,C^{14}$ exothermic reaction; tracks with a range corresponding to 0·6 MeV protons are produced. However, if there is a background of fast neutrons, it may be difficult to discriminate between the protons released in the $N^{14}(n, p)$ reaction and fast recoil protons set in motion by (n, p) scattering. A useful method of detecting fast neutrons is to record recoil protons from a hydrogeneous target external to the emulsion plate as shown in Fig. 4. In this method, only protons involved in head-on collisions enter the emulsion and from their measured range it is possible to deduce the energy of the incident neutrons.

Emulsions impregnated with boron, lithium, or fissile material (U^{235}), are useful for detecting slow neutrons.

The important discovery made by Fermi, soon after the discovery of the neutron, that many elements exposed to a flux of *thermal* neutrons become radioactive, has led to a useful method of detecting slow neutrons. Thin foils of a suitable element (manganese, indium and rhodium are often used) are exposed to a neutron flux φ for a time interval greater than six or seven times the half-life of the induced activity. The induced activity is close to the saturation value

$$\varphi \bar{\sigma} N$$

where $\bar{\sigma}$ is the (n, γ) capture cross section, averaged over the incident neutron spectrum and N is the number of nuclei of the target element. The (n, γ) cross section should be large, and the half-life of the induced activity several minutes. Mn^{55} has an (n, γ) cross section of ~ 13 barns and the half-life of Mn^{56} is 2·6 hr. The corresponding figures for In^{115} and In^{116} are 145 barns and 45 min, respectively. In order to calculate the neutron flux (assumed to be steady during the irradiation period), the absolute activity of the beta-active isotope has to be determined. One method of estimating the thermal component of a neutron flux is to measure the induced activity in a bare indium foil, and one wrapped in cadmium foil (~ 1 mm thick). For neutrons of kinetic energy less than about 0·3 eV cadmium is nearly opaque (the (n, γ) cross section is several thousand barns but it does not yield a radioactive isotope), whereas for epithermal† neutrons the cadmium foil is nearly transparent. The *difference* in the induced activities of the bare and cadmium-shielded foils corresponds to the neutron flux below about 0·3 eV.

There is a wide variety of ways of detecting neutrons with scintillation counters. Arrays of 20 cm diameter solid discs of fused B_2O_3 (B^{10} enriched) and ZnS have been successfully used for detecting slow and intermediate energy neutrons. These disc counters have a large surface area and produce fast neutron-induced pulses (rise time less than 0·1 μsec). The detection efficiency is of the order of 1 per cent for 1 keV neutrons. When large volume detectors are required, liquid scintillators containing boron compounds are often used. For example, methyl borate dissolved in terphenyl (scintillator) and phenylcyclohexane (main solvent) is an efficient detector of slow neutrons. When large scintillation tanks are used it is worth while to use walls of high reflecting power (e.g. Al_2O_3, MgO, TiO_2...R $\sim$ 95 to 97%) as the scintillation light may be reflected from two or three walls before reaching the cathode of the photomultiplier. There is always the problem of distinguishing pulses due to neutrons and γ-rays; the actual shape of the scintillation pulse may help in this discrimination.

Fast neutrons are conveniently detected†† by hydrogeneous scintillators such as anthracene, stilbene and suitable plastics. An ingenious scintillation detector of fast neutrons is shown in Fig. 5. A number of small plastic scintillating spheres is immersed in a non-hydrogeneous fluid (e.g. $C_6Cl_3F_3$) of nearly the same refractive index. The liquid is a non-scintillator and optically couples the plastic spheres via a quartz rod to

† Slow neutrons just above the thermal region, e.g. $>0·3$ eV are called epithermal neutrons.

†† TAYLOR, LÖNSJÖ and BONNER, *Phys. Rev.* **100**, 174, 1955.

the 4 cm diam. cathode of a photomultiplier tube. The diameter of the spheres is chosen so that the recoil protons from fast neutron collisions just dissipate their energy inside the spheres. γ-Rays produce small pulses because the Compton or photoelectrons do not dissipate a large fraction of their energy in the small spheres (adjacent spheres are well separated so that a recoil electron does not pass from one sphere to the next). In this way, neutron pulses are easily distinguished from gamma pulses. This arrangement has been used in determinations of elastic

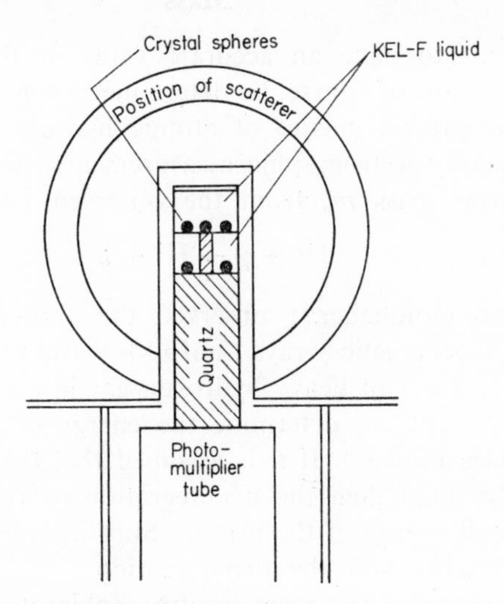

FIG. 5. Neutron Scintillation Counter (TAYLOR, LÖNSJÖ and BONNER. *Phys. Rev.*, **100**, 174, 1955.)

scattering cross sections of various media for fast neutrons. The neutron scatterer is in the form of a spherical shell surrounding the detector. The optimum diameters of the plastic spheres for detecting neutrons of kinetic energy 3·5, 4·5, 7·0, and 14 MeV are 1·5, 2·5, 6·0 and 10 mm respectively.

Fast neutrons can be observed by photographing the tracks of recoil protons in a hydrogen–water vapour filled cloud chamber. At a pressure of $\frac{1}{3}$ atm, recoil protons of 50 keV have a range of 7 mm.

15.4. BASIC PROPERTIES OF THE NEUTRON

Neutron Spin

There is a great deal of indirect evidence that the neutron has a spin of $\frac{1}{2}$ and no evidence to the contrary. Some of this evidence is based on the binding energy and spin of the deuteron. The experimental fact that the magnetic moment of the deuteron is nearly equal to the algebraic sum of the magnetic moments of the neutron and proton strongly supports the assumption that, if we assume a deuteron spin of 1 and a proton spin of $\frac{1}{2}$, the spin of the neutron is $\frac{1}{2}$.

Although the neutron has no net electric charge†, it has a large magnetic moment (see Chapter 16, Section 1). This unexpected property is related to the pionic-structure of the neutron.

Mass

It is important to have an accurate value of the mass of the free neutron. This cannot, of course, be determined from a mass spectrograph. However, if the precise masses of atomic hydrogen and deuterium are known (from mass spectrographic measurements), it is possible to determine the neutron mass m_n from the observed binding energy of the deuteron.

$$H^2 + \gamma \rightarrow H^1 + n$$

Chadwick and Goldhaber†† observed the photodisintegration of the deuteron by monoenergetic γ-rays (2·615 MeV from ThC″). The deuteron target was in the form of heavy hydrogen gas in a cloud chamber and it was therefore possible to determine the energy of the released protons from a range measurement. If it is assumed that the neutron and proton mass are nearly equal then the disintegration energy E_d is nearly equal to twice the recoil energy of the proton. Substituting the mass-equivalents for the γ-ray energy and the disintegration energy, the neutron mass can be found using the best mass-spectrographic *atomic* masses of hydrogen and deuterium.

$$M(H^2) + \frac{E_\gamma}{931 \cdot 1} = M(H^1) + M_n + \frac{E_d}{931 \cdot 1}$$

E_γ and E_d are measured in MeV and 931·1 is the energy equivalent in MeV of 1 atomic mass unit.

A more accurate method is that of Bell and Elliott††† who took advantage of the high thermal neutron flux at Chalk River. They carefully measured the energy of the γ-rays emitted by protons when they capture thermal neutrons ($p + n \rightarrow d + \gamma$). They obtained a value of 2·230 ± 0·007 MeV for the capture γ-ray energy. This result, combined with the best atomic mass values of hydrogen and deuterium, gives

$$M_n = 1 \cdot 008986 \pm 0 \cdot 0000015 \text{ a.m.u.}$$

† PURCELL, RAMSEY and SMITH, have shown that if the neutron has an electric dipole moment, it is very small, corresponding to two charges $+e$ and $-e$ closer together then 5×10^{-20} cm. N. F. RAMSEY, *Molecular Beams*, p. 202. Oxford University Press, 1956.

†† J. CHADWICK and M. GOLDHABER, *Nature* **134**, 237, 1934.

††† R. E. BELL and L. G. ELLIOTT, *Phys. Rev.* **79**, 282, 1950

Beta Decay of Free Neutron

The first accurate determination of the mass of the neutron established the important fact that the neutron mass *exceeds* the mass of the hydrogen atom. Thus the beta decay of the free neutron is an energetically possible process

$$n \rightarrow p + e^- + \bar{\nu} + 782 \text{ keV}$$

The radioactive decay releases an energy of 782 keV (calculated from the precise mass values). If the β-decay is an "allowed" transition with a $\log ft$ value of $\sim 3{\cdot}5$ (see Chapter 14) the anticipated half-life of the free neutron is about 15 min.

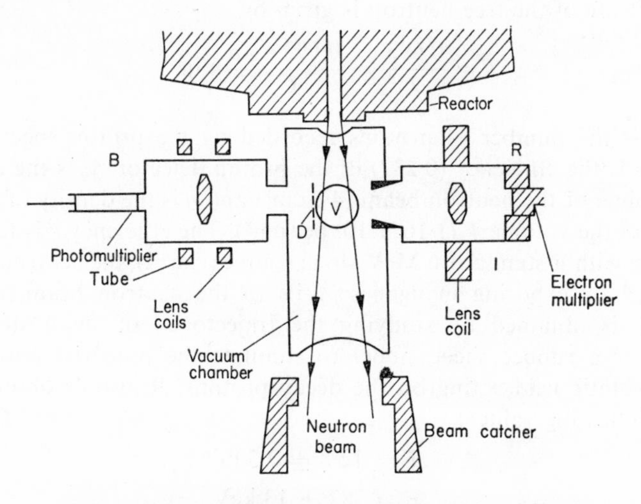

FIG. 6. Robson's determination of free neutron half-life.

A number of determinations of the half-life of the free neutron has been made. Robson†, using the large thermal neutron flux from the Chalk River reactor, not only observed the decay of the neutron, but also succeeded in measuring the energy spectrum of the decay electrons. Robson's experimental arrangement is shown in Fig. 6. A large flux ($1{\cdot}5 \times 10^{10}$ neutrons/cm^2/sec) of thermal neutrons from the Chalk River reactor passes through a long high vacuum chamber. Some of the neutrons decaying in the sensitive volume V (~ 5 cm^3) of the beam are recorded. A thermal neutron will decay into a proton and an electron and an antineutrino. If the recoil electron is emitted towards the entrance aperture of the lens-type β-ray spectrometer B it may be recorded along with its momentum. The decay proton is formed with a very small fraction of the disintegration energy and it is repelled by the deflector

† J. M. ROBSON, *Phys. Rev.* **78**, 311, 1950; *Phys. Rev.* **83**, 349, 1951.

plate D, maintained at a potential of $+13$ kV with respect to the earthed vacuum chamber. The resulting 13 keV proton enters the proton spectrometer R on the right and is focused by the lens field on to the electron multiplier detector (the proton pulses are easily distinguished from β- or γ-ray pulses). The decay of a neutron in the sensitive volume V is recorded if a beta pulse is followed within 0·8 to 1·0 μsec by a proton pulse (the time delay is inserted to compensate for the time of flight of 13 keV protons through the proton spectrometer). For each setting of the β-ray spectrometer lens current, decay electrons are recorded over a 24 hr period of the reactor operation (the proton lens spectrometer is permanently set at 10·5 A to focus the 13 keV protons).

The half-life of the free neutron is given by

$$T = \frac{0{\cdot}693}{\lambda} = \frac{0{\cdot}693\,\varepsilon\, Vn}{C}\,\text{min}$$

where C is the number of protons recorded by the proton spectrometer per min, ε is the efficiency (0·237) of the proton detector, V is the effective decay volume of the neutron beam (4·7 cm^3) and n is the density of thermal neutrons in the volume V ($1{\cdot}16 \times 10^4$ per cm^3). The efficiency ε is found by calibration with a standard 6 MeV alpha source (Cm^{242}), the neutron density is obtained by exposing manganese foils to the neutron beam, and the volume V is obtained by studying the trajectories of small steel balls rolling over a rubber sheet model to simulate the potential gradient of the electrostatic field acting on the decay protons. Robson's observations gave the following values:

$$T = 12{\cdot}8 \pm 2{\cdot}5\ \text{min}$$

$$E = 782 \pm 13\ \text{keV}$$

where E is the end point of the beta spectrum.

Recently, a more accurate determination of T by a Russian group† by a similar method gave the value

$$T = 11{\cdot}3 \pm 0{\cdot}3\ \text{min}.$$

An alternative method, of some interest, is that of D' Angelo†† at the Argonne National Laboratory, who photographed, at the rate of 2 stereo-pairs a second, the decay electrons of a thermal neutron beam traversing the continuously sensitive volume of a diffusion cloud chamber. This is a difficult experiment and it is essential that the gamma background inside the cloud chamber should be very small, otherwise electrons arising from gamma interactions with the walls and gas of the chamber may be mistaken for decay electrons. The large gamma background

† A. N. Sosnovskii *et al.*, *Soviet Physics* (JETP) **8**, 739, 1959.

†† N. D'Angelo, *Phys. Rev.* **114**, 285, 1959.

associated with a well-collimated beam of thermal neutrons from the reactor is eliminated by totally reflecting the neutrons from a 5 ft long magnetic mirror. The cloud chamber is surrounded with thick lead screening and the materials of the chamber are chosen from elements with small (n, γ) cross sections. D'Angelo's result is

$$T = 12{\cdot}7 \pm 1{\cdot}9 \text{ min.}$$

Neutron–Electron Interaction

The measurement of the magnetic moment of the neutron is described in Chapter 16. There is an interaction when a neutron approaches an electron, through the magnetic dipole fields of the two spin $\frac{1}{2}$ particles. This magnetic interaction, which understandably is strongly dependent on the relative spin orientation of the two particles, shows up to the best advantage in the scattering of slow neutrons by paramagnetic and ferromagnetic materials, where there is a considerable degree of alignment of the electron spins. If one considers the scattering of slow neutrons by inert gases of large atomic number (Xe and Kr) there is no neutron–electron magnetic interaction as the electron spins are paired off in the closed shell atoms. If there exists a neutron–electron interaction in addition to the dipole one, it may show up in the angular distribution of the scattered neutrons†. For thermal neutrons, the de Broglie wavelength $\lambda(\sim 1 \text{ Å}) \gg R$ (the nuclear radius), and the neutron–nuclear scattering is isotropic ($\sigma \sim 1{\cdot}0$ barn). The wavelength is roughly equal to the diameter of the noble gas atom and one therefore expects to see an anisotropic neutron–electron scattering cross section determined by an atomic structure factor.

A number of workers†† have carefully examined the angular distribution of slow neutrons scattered by Kr, Xe, and also by liquid metals (Pb and Bi). A small anisotropy was found in all cases, which is attributed to a very small non-magnetic neutron–electron interaction.

An elegant and more accurate study of this interaction is that of Hughes *et al.*††† They measured the critical angle of reflection of "cold" neutrons ($\lambda = 6{\cdot}7$ Å, obtained by filtering thermal neutrons by graphite—see Sect. 15.8) from the interface between liquid oxygen and bismuth. It is usual to express the non-spin dependent neutron–electron interaction by a square potential well of depth V_0 and width $e^2/(m\,c^2) = 2{\cdot}8$ fermi, the classical electron radius.

† This approach was first suggested by E. U. Condon, *Phys. Rev.* **49**, 459, 1936.

†† E. Fermi and L. Marshall, *Phys. Rev.* **72**, 1139, 1947.
M. Hamermesh, G. R. Ringo, A. Wattenberg, *Phys. Rev.* **85**, 483, 1952.
W. W. Havens, I. I. Rabi and L. J. Rainwater, *Phys. Rev.* **72**, 634, 1947; **75**, 1295, 1949; **82**, 345A, 1951.

††† D. J. Hughes, J. Harvey, M. Goldberg and M. Stafne, *Phys. Rev.* **90**, 497, 1953.

Hughes' experiment gave the result

$$V_0 = 3860 \pm 370 \text{ eV}.$$

This potential corresponds to a scattering cross section by a bound electron of 4×10^{-7} barns, which is very small compared to the nuclear scattering cross section of the order of 1 barn.

15.5. NEUTRON REACTIONS–RESONANCES

Slow neutron reactions have been extensively investigated partly because the reaction cross sections tend to be large at low energies and partly because the number of types of reaction is severely limited. For slow neutrons, apart from elastic scattering (inelastic scattering is energetically impossible), the main reactions are:

(1) radiative capture (n, γ); in many cases the product nucleus is beta unstable.

(2) (n, p) or (n, α), mainly confined to low Z nuclei as the Coulomb barrier strongly inhibits charged particle emission from heavy nuclei.

(3) nuclear fission, severely restricted to a few heavy nuclei, e.g. U^{233}, U^{235}, Pu^{239}.

The production of β-active nuclides by neutron irradiation was discovered in 1934 by Fermi and his school in Rome.† In certain cases, e.g. silver, Fermi made the important discovery that, if the neutron source (Rn–α–Be) was surrounded by hydrogeneous material such as paraffin wax or water, the induced activity of the silver foil was increased enormously. Fermi correctly attributed this phenomenon to the action of the hydrogenous material as a neutron *moderator*; that is, fast source neutrons are rapidly slowed down by elastic collisions with the light hydrogen nuclei (protons). In addition, he postulated that the (n, γ) capture cross section of the irradiated foil (silver) increases as the neutron energy decreases. Some neutrons are, of course, lost by nuclear capture in the moderator; that is why heavy water (D_2O) is a much better slowing down medium than ordinary (light) water (H_2O) because the (n, γ) cross section of deuterium is very small.

Shortly afterwards, the first evidence of the existence of neutron *resonance* was obtained.†† It was found that many nuclei possess very large capture cross sections (several thousands of barns or more) for neutrons of certain definite energies. This phenomenon suggests some form of resonance absorption familiar in many branches of physics.

An important theoretical development at this stage was the Bohr theory of the compound nucleus.‡ Briefly, Bohr conjectured that because of the close packing of nucleons within the nucleus and their strong

† E. Fermi *et al.*, *Proc. Roy. Soc.* A **146**, 483, 1934.

†† P. B. Moon and J. R. Tillman, *Proc. Roy. Soc.* A **153**, 476, 1936.

‡ N. Bohr, *Nature* **137**, 344, 1936.

mutual interaction, a captured neutron quickly shares its energy (kinetic energy of the incident neutron plus its binding energy in the compound nucleus) with all the nucleons to form a compound nuclear system in an excited state.

This compound nuclear system has a lifetime τ, long compared with the time it would take the incident particle to cross the nuclear diameter. The compound nuclear system is formed in one of several quasi-stationary states. The energy of each of these excited states is not perfectly sharp, but possesses a natural width Γ, where $\Gamma\tau \sim \hbar$. The compound nuclear system eventually decays by concentrating sufficient energy on a nucleon or a preformed α-particle, or if the Coulomb barrier is high, the system decays electromagnetically by γ-emission.

If the energy of activation of the compound nucleus (the energy of the incident neutron plus its binding energy in the compound system) exactly corresponds to the excitation energy of one of the quasi-stationary states, the probability of neutron capture is strongly enhanced and we have the phenomenon of resonance absorption. In a classic paper in nuclear physics, Breit and Wigner† developed a resonance formula analogous in many respects to the dispersion formula of resonance absorption of optical radiation. In the single-level formula, where one assumes that the resonance energies of the compound nucleus are widely spaced and do not interfere with each other, the cross section for the neutron capture process at a neutron kinetic energy E in the vicinity of the resonance energy E_0 is

$$\sigma_c = g\,\pi\,\lambda\!\!\!^{-2}\left[\frac{\Gamma_n\Gamma}{(E-E_0)^2+\Gamma^2/4}\right] \tag{3}$$

where g is the statistical weight factor, $\lambda\!\!\!^{-} = \lambda/2\pi$; λ is the wavelength of the incident neutron in the centre of mass system.

Γ is the width (eV) of the excited compound nuclear level, Γ_n is the partial neutron width, which can be defined by the relation $\Gamma_n\tau_n \sim \hbar$. ($\tau_n$ is the mean lifetime of the excited system if all modes of decay, except re-emission of a neutron of energy E, are turned off.) To obtain the (n,γ) reaction cross section $\sigma(n,\gamma)$, we must multiply σ_c by the probability that the compound nucleus decays by γ-emission. This probability is equal to $\frac{\Gamma_\gamma}{\Gamma}$, where Γ_γ is the gamma reduced width, defined by the relation $\Gamma_\gamma\tau_\gamma \sim \hbar$, and τ_γ is the mean lifetime of the excited system assuming gamma decay is the only permitted de-excitation mechanism. Thus we obtain for the (n,γ) cross section:

$$\sigma(n,\gamma) = g\,\pi\,\lambda\!\!\!^{-2}\left[\frac{\Gamma_n\Gamma_\gamma}{(E-E_0)^2+\Gamma^2/4}\right]. \tag{4}$$

† G. Breit and E. P. Wigner, *Phys. Rev.* **49**, 519, 1936.

The statistical weighting factor depends on the neutron spin $s = \frac{1}{2}$, the spin I of the target nucleus, the orbital angular momentum l of the incident neutron about the target nucleus, and the angular momentum J of the compound nuclear system (in its excited state). For randomly oriented neutrons and target nuclei (unpolarized)

$$g = \frac{(2J+1)}{(2s+1)(2I+1)} = \frac{1}{2}\frac{(2J+1)}{(2I+1)} \tag{5}$$

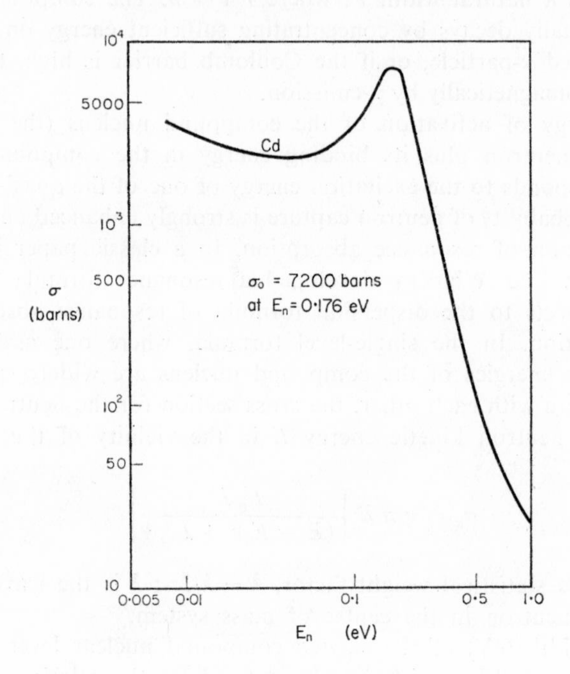

FIG. 7. Total cross section of cadmium showing resonance peak at a neutron energy of 0·176 eV (Notice logarithmic scales).

For slow neutrons, the incident neutron waves are necessarily in an s-state (l = 0) and $J = I \pm \frac{1}{2}$. For all even–even nuclei $I = 0$ and $J = \frac{1}{2}$, giving

$$g = 1. \quad \text{for} \quad l = 0, \quad I = 0$$

For $I > 0$, $\qquad J = I \pm \frac{1}{2}$ and

$$g = \frac{1}{2}\left(1 \pm \frac{1}{2I+1}\right)$$

The large (n, γ) resonance of Cd (this is due to the Cd^{113} isotope of natural abundance 12·26 per cent) at 0·176 eV is shown in Fig. 7.

The maximum (n, γ) cross section occurs when $E = E_0$ and is equal to

$$\sigma_{max}(n, \gamma) = 4\pi \lambda\!\!\!^{-2} g \frac{\Gamma_n \Gamma_\gamma}{\Gamma^2} \tag{6}$$

For $E = E_0 \pm \Gamma/2$, $\sigma = \frac{1}{2}\sigma_{max}$ and Γ is the full width at half maximum. A sharp resonance corresponds to a narrow width Γ and thus to an excited state of long life. What is the largest capture cross section we can possibly have? This will occur when $\Gamma_n = \Gamma_\gamma = \Gamma/2$; we are assuming that (n, γ) and (n, n) are the only possible processes. Putting $g = 1$, its maximum possible value, we get $\sigma = \pi \lambda\!\!\!^{-2}$.

Now $\lambda\!\!\!^{-} = \hbar/p$, where p is the momentum of the incident neutron, and at the resonance energy, $E_0 = \dfrac{p^2}{2m} = \dfrac{\hbar^2}{2m\lambda\!\!\!^{-2}}$.

Thus the largest resonance cross section is

$$\sigma = \frac{\pi \hbar^2}{2m E_0} \tag{7}$$

If the resonance energy E_0 occurs at 0·025 eV (thermal energy at room temperature), $\sigma \sim 26 \times 10^6$ barns! The isotope Xe^{135}, a 9·2 hr fission product produced in about 6 per cent of the fissions of U^{235}, has the largest known thermal resonance (n, γ) of $3{\cdot}5 \times 10^6$ barns.

Resonances are observed in the elastic scattering of neutrons by nuclei. The Breit–Wigner formula given by eqn. (4) does not apply in this case. Besides compound nucleus scattering (i.e. absorption and re-emission of a neutron of the same energy), the incident neutron wave is scattered by the nucleus as if it were an impenetrable sphere; this type of scattering is known as potential or shape-elastic scattering. Well away from resonance energies, potential scattering dominates; near resonances, the resultant scattering consists of an incoherent cross section and a coherent cross section which is the result of interference between the compound nucleus scattering amplitude and the potential scattering amplitude. For slow neutrons ($l = 0$), where the only processes are elastic scattering and radiative capture (for nuclei with $A > 30$, charged particle products are strongly inhibited), $\Gamma = \Gamma_n + \Gamma_\gamma$ and the elastic scattering cross section is given by

$$\sigma(n, n) = g \pi \lambda\!\!\!^{-2} \left| \frac{\Gamma_n}{(E - E_0) + i\Gamma/2} + 2\frac{R}{\lambda\!\!\!^{-}} \right|^2 + 4\pi R^2(1 - g) \tag{8}$$

R is the target nucleus radius and $\lambda\!\!\!^{-} \gg R$. The first term involves the square of the resultant amplitude—representing a coherent interference between the two scattering processes. The term $4\pi R^2(1 - g)$ represents the incoherent part of the potential scattering. The resonance scattering is not symmetrical about the resonance energy E_0; in fact, the cross section has a minimum on the low energy side of E_0 and falls off less rapidly on the high energy side. The minimum cross section occurs at an energy

$$E_{\min} \simeq E_0 - \frac{\lambda \Gamma_n}{2R} \tag{9}$$

The shape of the scattering resonance curve for a hypothetical spin 0 nucleus is illustrated in Fig. 8.

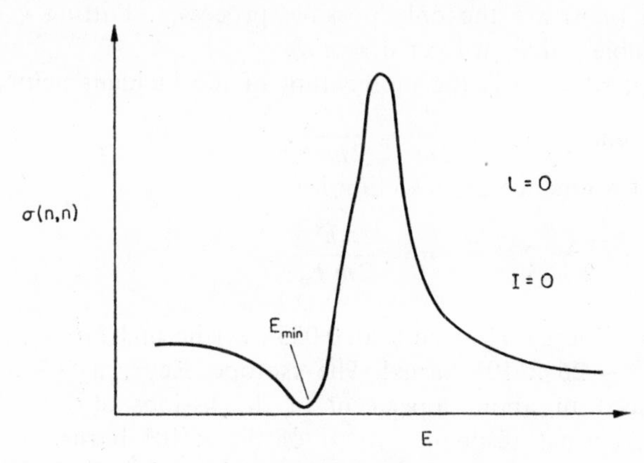

FIG. 8. Hypothetical scattering resonance for slow ($l = 0$) neutrons by spin 0 nucleus.

The 1/v Law

Let us return to eqn. (4) and consider the lowest energy resonance of the compound nucleus. For neutron energies $E \ll E_0$, $\sigma(n,\gamma)$ is proportional to $\lambda^2 \Gamma_n \Gamma_\gamma$. Now it seems reasonable to assume that the partial width Γ_γ is independent of E at low energies. This is not the case for the partial width Γ_n. The probability of the compound elastic emission of a neutron of energy E (momentum p) is proportional to the density of states in momentum space around p. Γ_n is therefore proportional to $p^2\, dp/dE$ or p, as $dE = (p/m)\,dp$. Thus

$$\sigma(n,\gamma) \sim \lambda^2 p \sim \frac{1}{p}$$

or

$$\sigma(n,\gamma) \quad \text{varies as} \quad \frac{1}{v}, \quad \text{for} \quad E \ll E_0. \tag{10}$$

The best example of this is the $B^{10}(n,\alpha)Li^7$ process; that is an (n,α) reaction at thermal energies. The gradual rise of $\sigma(n,\gamma)$ for Cd^{113} below the resonance energy of 0·176 eV is an example of the $1/v$ trend at low neutron energies.

Doppler Width

One has to be cautious in applying the Breit–Wigner resonance formulae in the thermal energy region. In place of the incident neutron energy E we must substitute, E_{rel}, the relative kinetic energy of approach of a neutron and the target nucleus.

$$E_{rel} = \frac{m}{2}(v + V)^2 = E + (2m\,E)^{\frac{1}{2}}\,V + \frac{1}{2}m\,V^2 \tag{11}$$

where $E = \frac{1}{2}m\,v^2$, the kinetic energy of the neutron in the laboratory system, and V is the velocity of the target nucleus towards the incident neutron beam. For a gaseous target at a temperature T, the fraction of molecules with a velocity component in the range V to $V + dV$ is given by the Maxwell distribution law

$$\left(\frac{M}{2\pi\,k\,T}\right)^{\frac{1}{2}} \exp\left(-\frac{M\,V^2}{2k\,T}\right) dV \tag{12}$$

where M is the mass of a molecule and k is Boltzmann's constant. Differentiating E_{rel} with respect to V in eqn. (11) and eliminating dV, we obtain for the fraction of molecules with a relative kinetic energy E_{rel} to $E_{rel} + dE_{rel}$,

$$\left(\frac{1}{\pi}\right)^{\frac{1}{2}} \exp\left[-\left(\frac{E_{rel} - E}{D}\right)^2\right]\frac{dE_{rel}}{D} \tag{13}$$

where

$$D = 2\left(\frac{m\,E\,k\,T}{M}\right)^{\frac{1}{2}} \tag{14}$$

D is called the "Doppler width". In place of the single energy E in eqn. (4) we must substitute E_{rel} and obtain the cross section from the integral

$$\bar{\sigma}(E) = \left(\frac{1}{\pi}\right)^{\frac{1}{2}} \frac{1}{D}\int_0^\infty \sigma(E_{rel}) \exp\left\{-\left(\frac{E_{rel} - E}{D}\right)^2\right\} dE_{rel} \tag{15}$$

where $\bar{\sigma}(E)$ is the cross section averaged over the distribution of molecular energies and $\sigma(E_{rel})$ is obtained by putting $E = E_{rel}$ in eqn. (4). This is a cumbersome integral to evaluate. We quote† two useful approximations: if $\Gamma \gg D$ the peak cross section σ_0, which occurs when $E = E_0$, is unaffected. On the other hand, if $\Gamma \ll D$, the peak cross section is greatly reduced to

$$\left(\frac{\pi^{\frac{1}{2}}}{2}\right)\frac{\Gamma}{D}\sigma_0$$

† p. 84 of the article by P. Morrison in *Experimental Nuclear Physics* Vol. 2, Ed. by E. Segrè, Wiley, 1953.

Although the atoms in a solid target at a temperature T do not follow Maxwell's law for this temperature, Lamb† has shown that the Maxwell distribution is a good approximation provided T is replaced by the equivalent temperature T_{eq}, where T_{eq} is related to the ratio of T and the Debye temperature of the crystalline solid.

15.6. MEASUREMENTS OF NEUTRON CROSS SECTIONS AS A FUNCTION OF ENERGY

An accurate knowledge of neutron cross sections and especially the way they vary with energy is of interest for two reasons; it reveals the detailed energy level structure of the compound nuclei involved in neutron reactions and it provides vital quantitative data necessary for the efficient design of chain-reacting piles.

The determination of total neutron cross sections, which includes scattering as well as absorption, is in principle a straight forward procedure. A sample of uniform thickness x is inserted in a beam of well collimated neutrons of energy E, the detector is placed well beyond the specimen and it is shielded from all scattered neutrons. The ratio of the neutron counting rate of the detector, with and without the sample in the beam, the so-called transmission T, yields the value of the total neutron cross section σ,

$$T = \exp(-n\,\sigma\,x)$$

where n is the number of nuclei per cm^3.

Unfortunately, many practical neutron sources (e.g. reactors) do not produce mono energetic neutrons. Even accelerator sources do not provide neutrons with a high degree of mono chromaticity for accurate cross section analysis. A great deal of effort has been put into the design of techniques for selecting monoenergetic neutrons from heterogeneous neutron sources.†† This development hes gone hand in hand with the introduction of more intense neutron sources and more efficient detectors, especially in the intermediate energy range (1 keV). We now consider in turn some of these techniques.

Crystal Spectrometer

For thermal and epithermal neutrons ($E < 10$ eV) a mono chromatic neutron beam can be selected by diffraction from a single crystal. This method is only practical with an intense source of low energy neutrons, for the efficiency of diffraction is small and it decreases as $1/E^2$. This

† W. Lamb, *Phys. Rev.* **55**, 190, 1939.

†† The magnitude of this effort can be judged by consulting Vol. 4 of the *Proceedings of the International Conference on the Peaceful Uses of Atomic Energy* (Geneva, 1955) United Nations, and Vol. 14 of the Second Conference (Geneva, 1958).

rules out all neutron sources except the high power reactor, and an important property of the epithermal neutron flux escaping through a collimator in the shield of such a reactor is the dE/E intensity distribution (equal fluxes in successive energy decades: 1 to 10, 10 to 100 eV . . .).

A schematic diagram of a crystal spectrometer, or mono chromator as it is often called, is shown in Fig. 9. The instrument is large and massive

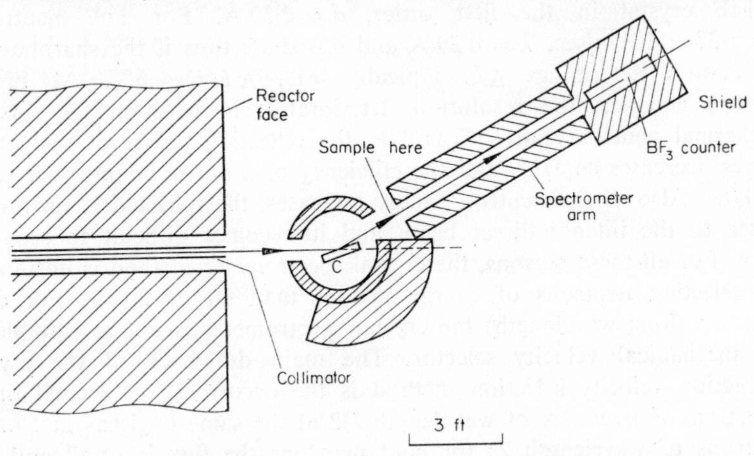

FIG. 9. Schematic diagram of crystal spectrometer.

in comparison with the well-known Bragg X-ray spectrometer; this is a characteristic of neutron diffraction apparatus. A well-collimated beam of thermal neutrons is diffracted by a prominent set of lattice planes of a large well-shielded single crystal. The neutrons, diffracted according to Bragg's law, enter a second long collimator before entering a well-shielded BF_3 counter. The heavy spectrometer arm is automatically driven so that it is always in the correct angular position to receive the diffracted beam. If θ is the glancing angle of the incident neutrons on the lattice planes of the crystal C, then the crystal "selects" neutrons of wavelength λ according to Bragg's law

$$2d \sin\theta = n\lambda \tag{16}$$

where n is the order of reflection, and d is the spacing of the lattice planes. The selected neutrons pass through the sample under investigation before entering the second collimator.

The energy resolving power dE/E and the intensity of the reflected neutrons both decrease with increasing neutron energy. To appreciate the former point, differentiate eqn. (16)

$$\Delta\lambda = \frac{2d}{n} \cos\theta \, d\theta \tag{17}$$

or

$$\frac{\Delta\lambda}{\lambda} = \left|\frac{\Delta v}{v}\right| = \cot\theta \, \Delta\theta \tag{18}$$

Now $$\frac{\Delta E}{E} = 2\frac{\Delta v}{v} = 2\cot\theta\,\Delta\theta \tag{19}$$

For small θ, $$\frac{\Delta E}{E} = 2\frac{\Delta\theta}{\theta} \tag{20}$$

To illustrate these results, consider reflection by the (111) planes of a LiF crystal in the first order, $d = 2{\cdot}32$ Å. For 1 eV neutrons, $v = 1{\cdot}38 \times 10^4$ m/sec, $\lambda = 0{\cdot}29$ Å and $\theta \sim 3{\cdot}5°$; thus if the sharpness of collimation determines $\Delta\theta$, typically $0{\cdot}1°$, $\Delta E/E \sim 6\%$. At higher neutron energies, the resolution deteriorates; in addition the flux of epithermal neutrons falls off as $1/E$, the reflecting power of the lattice planes decreases as $1/E^2$, and the efficiency of a boron counter decreases as $1/E^{\frac{1}{2}}$. Also as the neutron energy increases, the reflected beam moves closer to the intense direct beam and it becomes difficult to separate them. For all these reasons, the crystal spectrometer method is unsuitable for selecting neutrons of energy greater than 10 or 20 eV. For cold neutrons (long wavelength) the crystal spectrometer is not as suitable as the mechanical velocity selector. The main drawback of the crystal diffraction velocity selection method is the occurrence of second order reflection of neutrons of wavelength $\lambda/2$ at the same angle as first order neutrons of wavelength λ; for cold neutrons the flux is small and the second order contribution is relatively large.

In addition to LiF, crystals of NaCl, Be, or quartz are commonly used. The technique of bent-crystal-focusing, described in Chapter 13, using quartz has been successfully employed. One important point in favour of the choice of a crystal of Be is the small unit cell and if, in addition, the (421) lattice planes are used to select the required neutrons a spacing d as small as $0{\cdot}75$ Å is obtained. This small spacing helps considerably in resolving the reflected and direct beams for neutron energies about 1 eV.

Mechanical Velocity Selectors ("Choppers")

The principle of the mechanical velocity selector cross section measurement is as follows. A high flux beam of heterogeneous neutrons is interrupted by a rapidly rotating shutter which is normally opaque to the neutron beam. The neutron beam is thus broken up into a series of short bursts at a definite pulse repetition frequency. Neutrons then arrive at a detector after travelling a distance l down a flight tube (usually partially evacuated) and their time-of-flight t depends on their velocity v ($v = l/t$). In the early experiments, the detector was made sensitive for a short interval (usually approximately equal to the burst duration of the chopped neutron beam) at a time t after the passage of a group of neutrons through the rotating chopper. In the slow neutron chopper of Fermi, Marshall, and Marshall† (Fig. 10), the BF_3 neutron counter, 1·46 m beyond the rotating cylinder, was made sensitive by a signal derived from a beam of light, reflected from a mirror fixed to the axis of the rotating cylinder, on to a photoelectric cell. Thus with a fixed time delay t, the counter records neutrons of velocity in the vicinity of $1/t$. The cross section of a specimen is obtained by measuring the transmission T. This measurement yields the total cross section for approx-

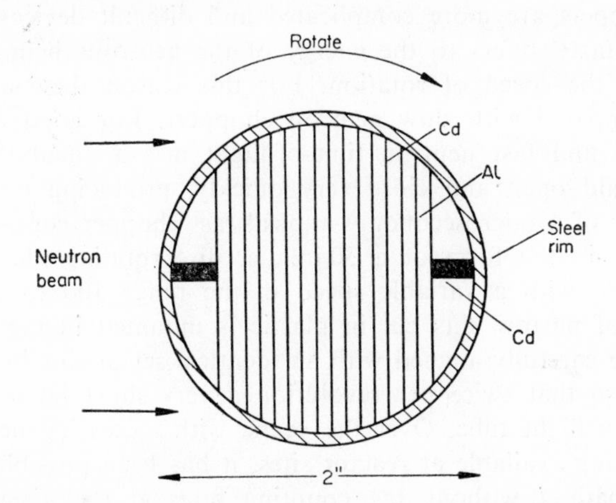

FIG. 10. Slow neutron Chopper of Fermi and Marshall.

imately monoenergetic neutrons of velocity l/t. To determine the complete cross section spectrum of the sample is, however, a tedious business, for a whole series of measurements with different time delays t is required. Nowadays, elaborate electronic equipment is used to sort out the neutrons arriving at a continuously sensitive detector according to their time of arrival. Some of the most sophisticated arrangements have more than 1000 time-sorting channels, so that neutron transmissions for more than 1000 slightly different energies are simultaneously recorded. This obviously involves a great saving in time.

No velocity selector gives perfect resolution. The time width of the detecting channels and any jitter in the response time of the counter must always be included in an estimate of the resolution. For simplicity, let us assume the neutron burst duration and the detector channel width are both equal to Δt. It is useful to specify the resolution of the complete time-of-flight apparatus by the ratio $\Delta t/l$ in μsec/m.

The problem of designing a successful chopper for slow neutrons is rather different to that for intermediate or fast neutrons. The Fermi slow chopper shown in Fig. 10 consists of a rapidly rotating cylinder

† E. FERMI, J. MARSHALL and L. MARSHALL, *Phys. Rev* **72**, 193, 1947.

(max. speed 15,000 r.p.m.) made up of alternate layers of cadmium (0·006 in. thick) and aluminium (0·03 in.). Twice per revolution, when the layers are within $\pm 3°$ of the horizontal direction of the incident neutron beam, a burst of neutrons is transmitted. Above about 0·3 eV the Cd sheets become too transparent and a more satisfactory chopper uses materials with a large scattering cross section, e.g. nickel, steel, or nickel-coated cadmium.

Fast choppers are more complicated and difficult devices to operate. The term "fast" refers to the energy of the neutrons being interrupted and not to the speed of rotation. For this reason they are large and massive compared with slow neutron choppers. For good resolution in intermediate and fast neutron time-of-flight measurements, the neutron shutter should open and close very quickly, producing neutron bursts of the order of a microsecond. A typical fast chopper consists of a high speed rotor in the form of a 30 in. dia. disc rotating about a flexible vertical shaft, with a variable speed in the range 100 to 15,000 r.p.m. A number of narrow slits cut in plastic is mounted in the heavy rotor and they are carefully aligned with an identical set of slits in a stationary collimator, so that twice per revolution a very short burst of neutrons enters a long flight tube. Over the years, with increasing neutron intensities becoming available at reactor sites, it has been possible to increase the flight path l without the counting rates at the distant detectors becoming too small. With flight paths as long as 100 m resolutions as small as 0·01 μsec/m are attainable.

Electrically Pulsed Neutron Sources

It is, of course, not possible to pulse the neutron source directly when the source is a chain-reacting pile. However, when neutrons are produced by artificially accelerated charged particles, it is practical to either pulse the ion source of the accelerator, or to pulse the accelerated beam of particles by passing it through a pair of deflector plates. It is possible for example, to pulse the ion source of a cyclotron, but much shorter duration pulses ($\sim$ 10 nsec.) are obtained by post-acceleration deflection. An example of this technique, in studying the inelastic scatteg of fast neutrons, is given later in this chapter.

One of the best methods of generating short intense neutron bursts suitable for time-of-flight experiments is the pulsed electron accelerator. The latest machine of this type installed at Harwell† accelerates short pulses of electrons ($\sim$ 0·25 μsec) to an energy of 30 MeV with a peak beam current of 300 mA. The high energy electrons strike a high atomic number target (U or Hg), which serves the dual purpose of producing

† M. J. Poole and E. R. Rae, *Nature* **185**, 280, 1960.

energetic bremsstrahlung, which in turn liberates neutrons through the (γ, n) reaction. The electron, and therefore the neutron pulses, are repeated several hundred times a second. About 5×10^{16} neutrons/sec are produced during the pulse duration. With intensities of this order, flight paths of 100 m are feasible. One important disadvantage of this type of neutron source is the intense flash of γ-rays which reaches the neutron detector before the neutrons. This is particularly serious if the capture γ-rays of a specimen at the far end of the flight tube are being investigated using a gamma detector.

A recent development of the pulsed electron–neutron source is the introduction of the "neutron booster".† The heavy target used to stop the high energy electrons is surrounded by a sub-critical assembly of U^{235}, which increases by a factor of ten the neutron output by fast neutron multiplication. The Harwell booster consists of a nearly spherical assembly of 37 kg of 90% enriched U^{235} surrounded by about 1 cm of natural uranium. The amount of fissile material must be sufficient to produce a fast neutron chain reaction but not enough to be critical! The booster itself is surrounded with tanks of water, 2 cm thick, to moderate the neutrons so that the majority of them emerge in the energy range from 1 eV to 100 keV. B^{10} metal powder is placed between the moderator and the fissile material to absorb any slow neutrons from the moderator diffusing back into the uranium. If this happens, these returning neutrons produce "late" fissions, thereby releasing further neutrons and drawing out the length of the neutron pulse in an undesirable way. The B^{10} has a very small absorption effect on the fast fission neutrons passing into the moderator ($1/v$ cross section law).

15.7. INELASTIC SCATTERING OF NEUTRONS (n, n')

If an incident neutron has sufficient energy, it may form a compound nucleus which breaks up by emitting a neutron of energy considerably below the incident energy. The original nucleus is now left in an excited state, and in most cases it promptly decays to the ground state by γ-emission. This process is called inelastic neutron scattering and it is denoted by the symbol X (n, n') X^*, where X and X^* represent the ground and excited states of the target nucleus respectively. For nuclei of mass number $A > 100$, inelastic scattering is the most likely nuclear reaction for neutrons in the energy range 0·1 to 10 MeV. At higher energies, the (n, $2n$) reaction, where two neutrons are emitted from the compound nucleus, becomes energetically possible; whereas at lower energies inelastic scattering is impossible because there is insufficient energy to leave the final nucleus in an excited state. For the lightest elements,

† M. J. Poole, *Contemporary Physics*, Vol. **2**, No. 1, p. 15, 1960.

the Coulomb barrier effect is not so severe, and charged particle products may compete with neutron emission, e.g. (n, p) (n, α).

Inelastic neutron scattering is of interest for several reasons. First, it provides a means of exciting and studying the energy levels of many nuclei, unhampered by the necessity for correcting for Coulomb barrier penetration. An accurate knowledge of the inelastic scattering cross section of materials used in the construction of reactors (including shielding) is of practical value, for the dominant process by which fast neutrons lose their energy in medium and heavy elements is inelastic scattering.

An ingenious way of measuring inelastic cross sections is the so-called "sphere transmission method".† The material under investigation is in the form of a thin spherical shell which completely surrounds an isotropic neutron source; the neutron detector is placed outside the shell at a distance large compared with the radius of the shell. Provided the only neutron interaction in the shell is elastic scattering, the neutron counting rate at the detector is the same with and without the shell in position. On the other hand, if any neutrons are removed in the shell or inelastically scattered, the detector counting rate is reduced by the presence of the shell. We are assuming that the neutron detector is energy sensitive and that its threshold is set above the energy level of inelastically scattered neutrons. For a shell thin enough for multiple neutron collisions to be negligible, the transmission T is related to the inelastic cross section σ_i by

$$T = \exp(-N\sigma_i)$$

where N is the number of nuclei per cm^2 of the shell. Here σ_i includes possible (n, p), (n, γ), (n, d), $(n, 2n)$ reactions as well as (n, n'). However, at energies just below the $(n, 2n)$ threshold, for heavy elements the (n, n') contribution easily outweighs all the other inelastic processes.

If the neutron source is anisotropic, the above argument breaks down. Bethe has shown theoretically that the method will work with an anisotropic source, provided the spherical shell surrounds the detector, with the source some distance away. The fast neutron detector shown in Fig. 5, depicts this arrangement with the scattering shell surrounding the scintillation counter.

Until recently the usual way of studying inelastic scattering has involved the energy measurement of the scattered neutrons in terms of the energy of recoil protons in hydrogeneous material. Alternatively the subsequent γ-rays following the de-excitation of the product nucleus have been measured with NaI crystal detectors.

An elegant method of studying inelastic scattering of neutrons was introduced by Cranberg at Los Alamos. This made full use of the great

† H. H. Barschall, *Rev. Mod. Phys.* **24**, 120, 1952.

improvement in fast electronic timing techniques.† The velocity and therefore the energy of neutrons scattered by a target are determined by a time-of-flight measurement. Monoenergetic neutrons of 2·5 MeV are produced by bombarding a tritium-filled gas target with protons from a Van de Graaff accelerator (Fig. 11) using the H^3 (p, n) He^3 reaction. The neutron beam is pulsed by passing the proton beam through a pair of

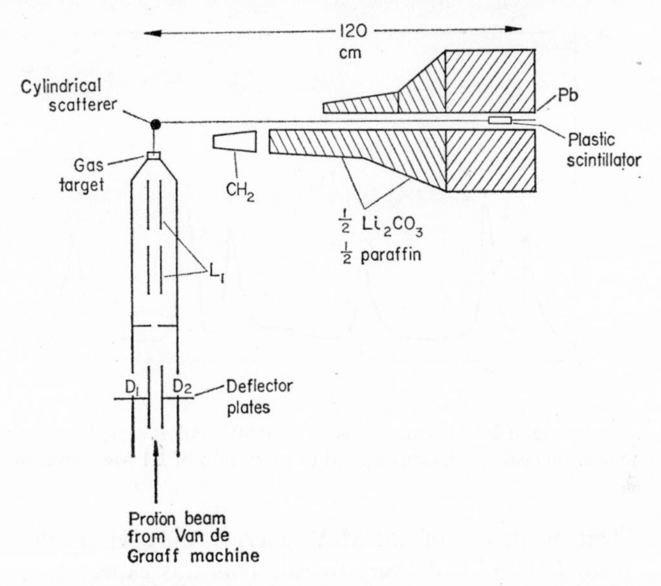

FIG. 11. Time-of-flight measurement of inelastic neutron scattering.

deflector plates D_1 and D_2 supplied with a 3·7 Mc/s radio-frequency voltage. Only protons passing through these plates when the deflecting voltage is nearly zero reach the tritium target. Two bursts of protons per radio-frequency cycle of duration 2*n*. sec reach the gas target. The pulsed 2·5 MeV neutrons travel about 10 cm before they are incident on a hollow cylindrical scatterer (typical dimensions 5 cm long, 2 cm outside diameter, 0·95 cm internal diameter). Neutrons scattered through an angle θ (90^0 is shown in Fig. 11 in the laboratory system) are detected by a plastic scintillation counter 1·2 m away. Elaborate screening arrangements are made to prevent neutrons direct from the gas target reaching the scintillator.

A 1 MeV neutron has a velocity of $1{\cdot}4 \times 10^9$ cm per sec, and it therefore travels 120 cm in about 90 nsec. With a time-to-pulse height converter, the neutrons reaching the detector are sorted according to their

† L. CRANBERG, "*Proceedings of the International Conference on the Peaceful Uses of Atomic Energy*", Vol. **4**, p. 40 (Geneva, 1955).

time-of-flight in channels ~ 2 nsec wide. A zero time signal is derived once per cycle from the radio-frequency deflector plate voltage. The spectrum of neutrons scattered by titanium at 90° is shown in Fig. 12. Pulses occur in the scintillator twice per cycle in the following time order: de-excitation γ-ray, elastic scattered neutrons, and last, inelastically scattered neutrons responsible for exciting the 1·1 MeV level of titanium.

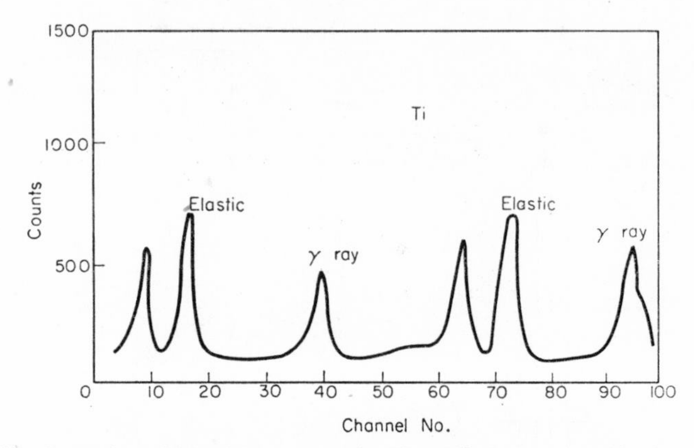

FIG. 12. Scattering of 2·5 MeV neutrons by Ti at 90°. Pulses sorted in time-of-flight channels. Inelastic peaks correspond to excitation of 1·1 MeV level of Ti.

With incident neutrons of 2·5 MeV energy, only elastically scattered neutrons from C^{12} and Ca^{40} were found. This was expected, for the first excited states in C^{12} and C^{40} are known to occur at 4.4 and 3·35 MeV respectively.

15.8. NEUTRON OPTICS

There is a number of phenomena, involving the interaction of slow neutrons with matter in bulk, which are conveniently described by the words "neutron optics". These phenomena include diffraction, refraction, total reflection, and polarization. Although some of these effects were predicted in the early days of neutron physics, they were not actively studied until intense neutron fluxes from reactors became available.

Neutrons which have been slowed down by elastic collisions with the nuclei of the moderator (graphite, D_2O, etc.) of a reactor, tend to have a Maxwellian distribution appropriate to a temperature of the order of 100°C. The root-mean-square velocity v of the thermal neutrons, appropriate to the absolute temperature T, is given by the equation.

$$\frac{1}{2} m v^2 = \frac{3}{2} k T \tag{21}$$

where m is the neutron mass and k is Boltzmann's constant. The de Broglie wavelength λ of neutrons of velocity v is $\frac{h}{mv}$, so we have for neutrons of velocity v the relation

$$\lambda = \frac{h}{\sqrt{(3mkT)}} \tag{22}$$

if $T = 100°C$, $\lambda = 1{\cdot}33$ Å, which is comparable to X-ray wavelengths used in diffraction, e.g. Cu $K\alpha$, $\lambda = 1{\cdot}54$ Å.

As the wavelengths of thermal neutrons are comparable to the spacing of adjacent lattice planes in crystals, it is no surprise to observe coherent diffraction effects similar to those produced by characteristic X-rays. However, the atomic scattering mechanisms for X-rays and neutrons are quite different. X-rays are scattered by the atomic electron cloud distribution (Thomson scattering) and nuclear scattering is negligible. Apart from magnetic scattering by the electron cloud of an atom, the scattering of neutrons is essentially nuclear in character.

At small angles, the coherent scattering amplitude of atoms for X-rays varies in a smooth way throughout the periodic table, increasing roughly as the atomic number Z. This is in sharp contrast with the nuclear scattering amplitude for thermal neutrons, which varies in an erratic way from element to element (there is often a considerable variation amongst the isotopes of a single element). The total variation in nuclear scattering amplitude covers a range of two or three. Another important distinction between the coherent scattering of X-rays and thermal neutrons lies in the angular variation of the scattering amplitude. For X-rays, the atomic scattering factor falls away at large angles due to destructive interference of X-rays scattered by different regions of the electron cloud (Chapter 4). This is not the case for thermal neutrons; their wavelength λ is very long compared with the *nuclear* radius and consequently the nuclear scattering amplitude does not vary with the angle of scattering.

The neutron scattering length b of a single nucleus for slow neutrons of wavelength λ is defined in the following way. Consider an incident train of plane monochromatic neutrons travelling along the z-axis. The neutron wave-function (chosen to have unit amplitude) is

$$\psi = \exp(ikz) \tag{23}$$

where $k = \frac{2\pi}{\lambda}$ is the incident wave number.

For slow neutrons the nucleus scatters the incident wave isotropically, so that the resultant wave—the sum of the incident and the spherically symmetrical scattered wave—is of the form

$$\psi = \exp(ikz) - \left(\frac{b}{r}\right)\exp(ikr) \tag{24}$$

where r is the distance from the scattering nucleus to the point of observation. The quantity b is the nuclear scattering length. It can easily be expressed in terms of the coherent scattering cross section σ of the nucleus, for the latter is defined by

$$\sigma = \frac{\text{Number of neutrons scattered per unit time by a nucleus}}{\text{Incident flux of neutrons}}$$

$$\sigma = \frac{4\pi r^2 v(b/r)^2}{v} = 4\pi b^2 \tag{25}$$

where we have considered the number of neutrons of velocity v crossing a large sphere of radius r in unit time.

We have already discussed the coherent scattering of slow neutrons by nuclei and have seen that, in general, there is interference between the potential (shape–elastic) and resonance scattering (compound–elastic). If the resonance contribution for neutrons of wavelength λ is negligible, the scattering is pure potential scattering and

$$\left.\begin{aligned} \sigma &= 4\pi b^2 = 4\pi R^2 \\ \text{and} \quad b &= R \end{aligned}\right\} \tag{26}$$

where R is the nuclear radius (the nucleus behaves as an impenetrable sphere to the incident neutron wave). In many instances, the resonance contribution to the scattering is not negligible, and if, for example, the neutron energy E is small compared to the nearest resonance energy E_0 a useful approximation for the scattering length is

$$b = R - \frac{\Gamma_n}{2kE_0} \tag{27}$$

It may happen that the negative resonance term outweighs the potential term and hence b is a negative length. This is known to occur in a few cases (H^1, Li^7, Ti, V, Mn, Ni^{62}), but the majority of nuclei have positive scattering lengths. From the form of eqn. (24), we see that if b is positive, the neutron wave is scattered by the nucleus with a phase change of π (this normally occurs in X-ray scattering by electrons); whereas if b is negative there is no phase change on scattering.

In the scattering of thermal neutrons by nuclei of finite spin (I not zero), the scattering length is spin-dependent. Complications arise if more than one isotope is present, so for the moment we restrict the discussion to scattering by a single nuclear species. Compound nucleus scattering of slow neutrons takes place through the formation of states of spin $I + \frac{1}{2}$ and $I - \frac{1}{2}$. The scattering lengths for these two states will be different, so we denote them by b_+ and b_- respectively. The relative probability of formation of the states $I + \frac{1}{2}$ and $I - \frac{1}{2}$ is $(I + 1)/I$. The coherent scattering cross section is obtained by squaring the resultant scattering length

$$\sigma_{\text{coh}} = 4\pi\left\{\frac{I+1}{2I+1}b_{+} + \frac{I}{2I+1}b_{-}\right\}^{2} \tag{28}$$

The total scattering cross section σ is obtained by adding the separate intensities, weighted according to the probability of formation of the compound nuclear state,

$$\sigma = 4\pi\left\{\frac{I+1}{2I+1}b_{+}^{2} + \frac{I}{2I+1}b_{-}^{2}\right\} \tag{29}$$

Subtracting eqn. (28) from eqn. (29) we obtain the incoherent scattering cross section. This type of scattering cannot give rise to constructive interference effects, and in diffraction by a regular assembly of nuclei (crystal lattice) incoherent scattering is a nuisance as it adds to the general background of scattered radiation. The situation may arise where the incoherent scattering is so large it tends to mask the diffracted neutron beams. One of the worst examples occurs with normal hydrogen H^1 with scattering lengths of opposite sign; $b_+ = +10{\cdot}4$ and $b_- = -47$ fermi. Substituting these values and $I = \frac{1}{2}$ in eqn. (28) we find that σ_{coh} is only 1·8 barns, whereas the incoherent cross section is as large as 79 barns. For H^2 ($I = 1$), the cross sections are quite different with only a relatively small incoherent cross section: $\sigma_{\text{coh}} = 5{\cdot}4$ barns, $\sigma_{\text{incoh}} = 2{\cdot}0$ barns. The determination of the position of hydrogen atoms in crystals of ice, LiH, etc., is much easier by neutron diffraction if deuterium is substituted for hydrogen. In X-ray analysis it is not possible to determine the positions of hydrogen atoms in molecules as the X-ray scattering by the single electron is very weak. This state of affairs does not apply to neutron scattering provided the intense incoherent scattering is avoided by using deuterated compounds. The close similarity in the X-ray atomic scattering factors of neighbouring atoms in the periodic table prevents the precise determination of the lattice positions of atoms such as Fe and Co in Fe–Co alloys. The neutron scattering from Fe and Co differs considerably so that it is easy to discriminate between the two atoms.

Incoherent scattering also occurs when one of the elements in a crystal has two or more isotopes. To avoid the added complication of spin incoherence consider two isotopes with zero nuclear spin (e.g. Fe^{54} and Fe^{56}). The two isotopes will be randomly distributed throughout the lattice points in the crystal. If c_1 and c_2 are the fractional abundances of the two isotopes and b_1 and b_2 are their respective scattering lengths, then the coherent scattering cross section is

$$\sigma_{\text{coh}} = 4\pi(c_1 b_1 + c_2 b_2)^2 \tag{30}$$

The total scattering cross section is

$$\sigma = 4\pi(c_1 b_1^2 + c_2 b_2^2) \tag{31}$$

For Fe^{54}, $c_1 = 0{\cdot}085$, $b_1 = 4{\cdot}2$ fermi; for Fe^{46}, $c_2 = 0{\cdot}915$, $b_2 = 10{\cdot}1$ fermi, and $\sigma_{coh} = 11{\cdot}4$ barns with $\sigma = 11{\cdot}7$ barns. The situation is more complicated when both spin and isotope incoherence effects are present.

Neutron Refraction and Reflection

In Chapter 4, we derived an expression for the refractive index of a medium for X-rays (eqn. (24)). By analogy, we can write down a similar expression for the refractive index of a medium for thermal neutrons. The nuclear scattering length b replaces the electron scattering length e^2/mc^2 and n denotes the number of nuclei per cm³ instead of the number of electrons per cm³. The refractive index for neutrons of wavelength λ is given by

$$q = 1 - \frac{n\lambda^2 b}{2\pi} \tag{32}$$

If b is positive, q is slightly less than unity and it may be possible to observe the phenomenon of total *external* reflection. For a medium with b negative in sign no strong reflection is possible. The critical glancing angle at the plane interface of the medium and a vacuum is

$$\theta_c = \lambda\left(\frac{nb}{\pi}\right)^{\frac{1}{2}} \tag{33}$$

Fermi and Marshall† made an extensive study of the reflection of monochromatic neutrons from mirrors made of many elements. Their experimental arrangement is shown in Fig. 13. A collimated beam of neutrons from a high flux reactor is incident on a CaF_2 crystal (monochromator). Neutrons of wavelength 1·873 Å are selected by Bragg reflection and the diffracted beam is very finely collimated by cadmium slits before falling

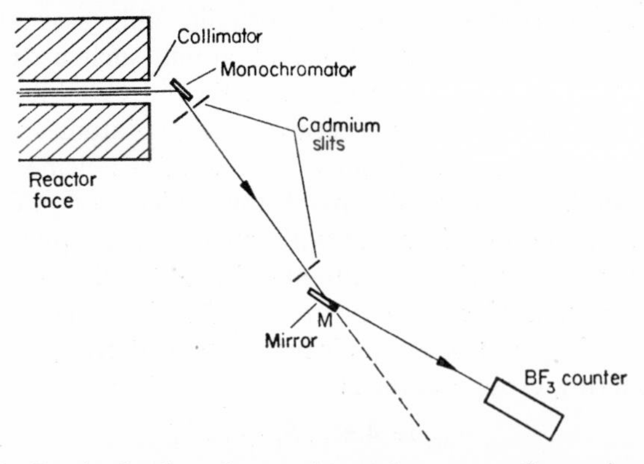

FIG. 13. Total reflection of monochromatic neutrons from mirror M.

† E. FERMI and L. MARSHALL, *Phys. Rev.* **71**, 666, 1947.

on the mirror M at a very small glancing angle θ. If $\theta < \theta_c$ an intense neutron beam is reflected into the neutron detector. The observation of a strong reflected beam leads to the inference that the sign of b is positive.

Once the signs of b of several elements have been established by mirror reflection, a method of comparing them for a pair of elements is based on measuring the intensities of diffracted beams from a suitable binary compound. Consider, for example, the even and odd order reflections from the (111) planes of a face centred cubic crystal. In the X-ray diffraction, the odd order reflections from the (111) planes of a NaCl

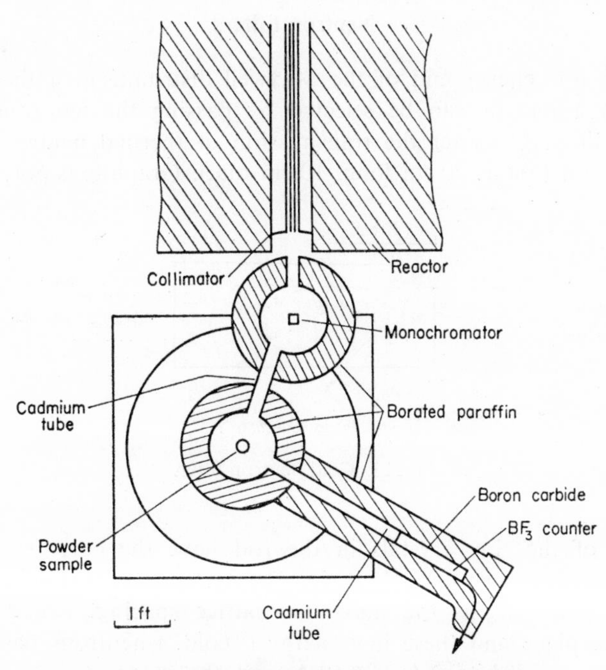

FIG. 14. Powder diffraction neutron spectrometer.

crystal are weak and the even orders are strong. This is also found to be true for the neutron diffraction from NaCl. However, with LiF the reverse is true; the odd neutron reflections are strong. This means that the scattering lengths of Li and F are opposite in sign (it is now known that b is negative for Li). The neutrons reflected from a plane of Li atoms experience no phase change on reflection, whereas the planes of F atoms reflect with a phase change of π (similar to the X-ray reflections). Reflections from MnO crystals show that Mn and O have opposite scattering lengths (Mn has the negative scattering length).

The quantitative determination of the sign and magnitude of scattering lengths is discussed in full in the book by Bacon. The magnitude of b

can, of course, be found if the critical angle θ_c can be measured. However, the majority of determinations are based on the careful measurement and interpretation of the neutron diffraction from powder specimens of elements and suitable compounds.

The experimental layout of a typical neutron diffraction apparatus is shown in Fig. 14. A single crystal (lead is often used) acts as a monochromator and reflects a monochromatic beam of thermal neutrons on to a single crystal or powder specimen. A typical powder specimen fills an aluminium can 3 cm high, 1·5 cm dia. and wall thickness 0·25 mm.

Neutron Filters

The very low energy end of the Maxwell distribution of thermal neutrons from a reactor can be selected by passing the neutrons through a suitable filter. Consider the transmission of thermal neutrons through a graphite rod (about 20 cm long, 10 cm dia.). Graphite is polycrystalline

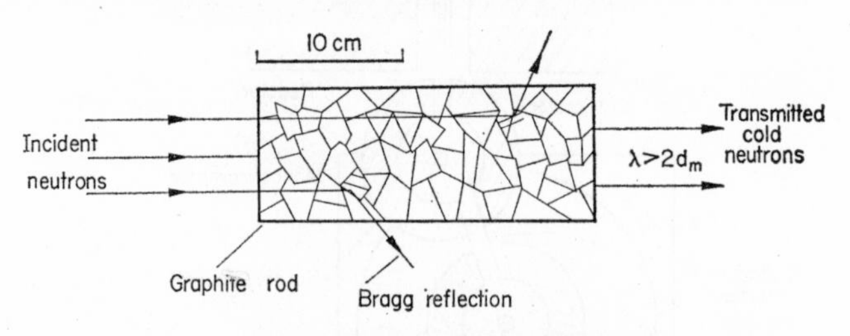

FIG. 15. Cold neutron filter.

and some of the tiny crystals in the rod have the correct orientation to reflect the neutron waves (Fig. 15). For neutrons of wavelength greater than $2d_m$, where d_m is the maximum lattice spacing, Bragg reflection cannot take place and these low energy ("cold") neutrons pass through the filter. For graphite $2d_m = 6{\cdot}69$ Å and the mean wavelength of the transmitted neutrons is about 7·1 Å, corresponding to neutrons in thermal equilibrium with matter at 18°K. It is important, of course, that the nuclear absorption of neutrons in the filter is small (boron is quite unsuitable).

Neutron Polarization

So far we have considered the nuclear scattering of slow neutrons by nuclei. In addition to the nuclear scattering there may be a significant contribution from electron scattering if the atom is paramagnetic. The scattering length of a paramagnetic atom is equal to

$$b \pm b_m$$

where b is the nuclear scattering length and b_m is the magnetic scattering length due to the magnetic dipole neutron–electron interaction. The positive sign applies when the neutron spin is parallel to the magnetic moment of the atom, the negative sign when it is antiparallel. The magnetic scattering length includes an atomic form factor which depends on $\sin\theta/\lambda$, and an angular factor depending on the relative directions of the magnetic moment of the atom, the neutron spin, and the direction of the *change* of the neutron momentum on scattering.

The transmission of a beam of thermal neutrons through a thick sheet of iron magnetized to saturation is governed by absorption and scattering cross sections; the latter includes a coherent component due to the alignment of the atomic magnetic moments. The scattering cross section σ is given by

$$\sigma = \sigma_0 \pm p$$

where the signs correspond to neutron spins parallel and anti parallel to the direction of magnetization. σ_0 is the cross section for an unmagnetized sample, and p the polarization cross section is a complicated average of the interference between nuclear and magnetic scattering. The existence of two scattering cross sections is responsible for the production of a partially polarized beam of neutrons on transmission through magnetized iron. More of the incident neutrons are scattered when the neutron spin is parallel to the magnetic field; thus the transmitted beam contains more neutrons with spins antiparallel to the field. The degree of polarization P is defined by the ratio

$$P = \frac{n_+ - n_-}{n_+ + n_-}$$

where n_+ and n_- are the numbers of neutrons with spins parallel and antiparallel to the field.

This method of obtaining a beam of polarized neutrons was first suggested by Bloch†, who later used this method in the determination of the neutron magnetic moment.

In addition to a two-valued scattering cross section in a magnetized medium, there are two different refractive indices q depending on whether the neutron spin is parallel or antiparallel to the magnetic field.

$$q = 1 - \frac{n\lambda^2 b}{2\pi} \pm \frac{\mu_n B}{E} \tag{34}$$

In this expression, μ_n is the magnetic moment of the neutron, B the magnetic flux density in the medium, and E the kinetic energy of the incident neutrons. The critical glancing angle of a neutron beam incident

† F. Bloch, *Phys. Rev.* **50**, 259, 1936.

on a magnetized mirror is given by

$$\theta_c = \left[\frac{n\,\lambda^2}{\pi}(b \pm b_m)\right]^{\frac{1}{2}} \tag{35}$$

where
$$b_m = \frac{\pi\,\mu_n\,B}{n\,\lambda^2\,E}$$

or, as $\lambda^2 = \dfrac{h^2}{p^2}$ and $E = \dfrac{p^2}{2m}$, where p is the neutron momentum and m the neutron mass,

$$b_m = \frac{2m\,\pi\,\mu_n\,B}{n\,h^2} \tag{36}$$

b_m is the effective scattering length.

From eqn. (35), we have the interesting possibility that if $b_m > b$, only one neutron spin component is totally reflected. This situation arises with magnetic mirrors of Co or Co–Fe alloys and a high degree of polarization is obtained by reflecting a collimated beam of unpolarized thermal neutrons from such a mirror at a small glancing angle. An example of the application of this method of polarizing a neutron beam is given in the next chapter.

15.9. THE SLOWING-DOWN OF FAST NEUTRONS

In this section, we consider the slowing down of fast neutrons to thermal energies through successive elastic collisions with the nuclei of the medium. This is the process of neutron *moderation.*

Consider the collision of a neutron (unit mass) of velocity v_1 with a stationary nucleus of mass A, the neutron being scattered with a velocity v_2 through an angle φ (Fig. 16a). If we use the centre-of-mass system (Fig. 16b), the neutron has a velocity $(A/A+1)\,v_1$, and the nucleus

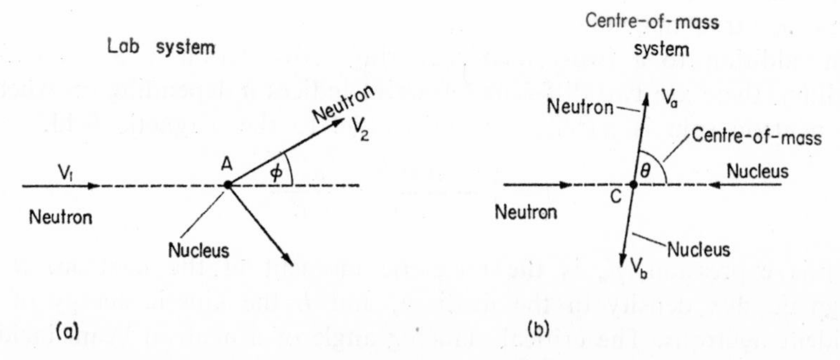

FIG. 16. Elastic collision of a neutron with a nucleus at rest in the laboratory system.

a velocity $v_1/(A+1)$ towards the centre of mass. The scattered neutron and recoiling nucleus move in opposite directions in the centre-of-mass system with velocities v_a and v_b, where $v_a = A\,v_b$. Writing down the conservation of kinetic energy equation

$$\frac{1}{2}\frac{A^2 v_1^2}{(A+1)^2} + \frac{1}{2}A\frac{v_1^2}{(A+1)^2} = \frac{1}{2}v_a^2 + \frac{1}{2}A\,v_b^2$$

From this equation, and $v_a = A\,v_b$, we find that

$$v_a = \frac{A\,v_1}{A+1}, \quad v_b = \frac{v_1}{A+1}$$

This shows that the speeds of the neutron and the nucleus are the same before and after an elastic collision in this system. The relation between

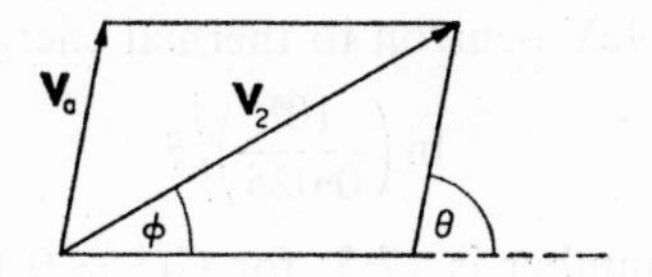

FIG. 17.

the scattering angles θ and φ are shown in Fig. 17. Two important relations immediately follow

$$v_2^2 = v_1^2\frac{(A^2+2A\cos\theta+1)}{(A+1)^2} \tag{37}$$

$$\cos\varphi = \frac{A\cos\theta+1}{(A^2+2A\cos\theta+1)^{\frac{1}{2}}} \tag{38}$$

If E_1 and E_2 denote the kinetic energies of the neutron before and after the collision in the laboratory system, then eqn. (37) becomes

$$\frac{E_2}{E_1} = \frac{1}{2}\{(1+\alpha)+(1-\alpha)\cos\theta\} \tag{39}$$

where
$$\alpha = \left(\frac{A-1}{A+1}\right)^2 \tag{40}$$

The scattered neutron has a kinetic energy between the limits of $\alpha\,E_1$ (when $\theta=\pi$) and E_1 (when $\theta = 0$). To determine the average energy of the scattered neutrons, we assume that the angular distribution of scattered neutrons is isotropic in the centre-of-mass system. Thus the fraction of neutrons scattered between angles θ and $\theta + d\theta$ is the fractional solid angle $\frac{1}{2}\sin\theta\,d\theta$.It is convenient to measure the energy loss on scattering on a logarithmic scale. ξ, the average logarithmic energy decrement per collision, is given by

$$\xi = \overline{\ln\left(\frac{E_1}{E_2}\right)} = -\int_0^{\pi} \ln\left[\frac{1}{2}\{(1+\alpha)+(1-\alpha)\cos\theta\}\right]\frac{1}{2}\sin\theta\, d\theta$$

This can be integrated by parts to give

$$\xi = 1 + \frac{\alpha}{1-\alpha}\ln\alpha \tag{41}$$

This equation shows that the fractional energy loss on scattering is independent of the initial neutron energy. The importance of the parameter A is shown by eqn. (41): for hydrogen $A = 1$ ($\alpha = 0$) and $\xi = 1$, hence the average energy of the scattered neutron is $1/e$ times the initial energy; for a heavy nucleus such as U^{238}, α is slightly less than unity and very little energy is lost in a collision. The average number of collisions to reduce a 1 MeV neutron to thermal energy (0·025 eV) is equal to

$$\ln\left(\frac{10^6}{0{\cdot}025}\right)\Big/\xi$$

For H, this average number is 17·5; for C($\xi = 0{\cdot}158$) the number is 111; for Pb ($\xi = 0{\cdot}0096$) the number of collisions is 1800.

A medium suitable for acting as a good moderator should have a large ξ, a small scattering mean free path λ_s and a large absorption mean free path λ_a. The *moderating ratio* of four media are given in Table 2, where the moderating ratio is defined as $\xi\dfrac{\lambda_a}{\lambda_s}$

TABLE 2

Moderator	Moderating ratio
Water	72
Heavy water	12,000
Be	159
Graphite	170

The slowing down of fast neutrons in a moderator of not too small A can be treated approximately as follows. Consider neutrons of kinetic energy E, velocity v (laboratory system) moving in a medium where the scattering mean free path λ_s is independent of E. If the value of ξ is fairly small, the slowing-down process can be treated as a continuous process. In a short time interval dt, neutrons of velocity v travel a distance $v\,dt$ and the mean number of nuclear collisions is $\dfrac{v\,dt}{\lambda_s}$. The average logarithmic energy decrement is independent of v; thus the average decrease in $\ln E$ in the interval dt is $\xi \dfrac{v\,dt}{\lambda_s}$

$$-d(\ln E) = \xi \frac{v\,dt}{\lambda_s}$$

$$-\frac{dE}{E} = \frac{\xi}{\lambda_s}\sqrt{\frac{2}{m}}\,E^{\frac{1}{2}}\,dt$$

where $E = \frac{1}{2} m v^2$ (m is the neutron mass).

Thus the slowing-down time t from an energy E_0 to thermal energy E_{th} is given by

$$t = -\frac{\lambda_s}{\xi}\sqrt{\frac{m}{2}}\int_{E_0}^{E_{th}} \frac{dE}{E^{3/2}}$$

$$t = \frac{\lambda_s}{\xi}\sqrt{(2m)}\left(\frac{1}{E_{th}^{\frac{1}{2}}} - \frac{1}{E_0^{\frac{1}{2}}}\right)$$

Provided $E_0 \gg E_{th}$, t is independent of E_0 (the initial rate of loss of energy is large; inelastic scattering may also occur). In pure graphite, $\xi = 0{\cdot}158$ and $\lambda_s \sim 2{\cdot}6$ cm, and this gives for the slowing-down time to thermal energy ($E_{th} = 0{\cdot}025$ eV), $t = 150\,\mu$sec. The continuous slowing down theory cannot be applied to heavy water (ξ is too large) and a more elaborate calculation shows that $t \sim 40\,\mu$sec.

Once the neutrons reach thermal energy they *diffuse* through the medium, neither losing nor gaining energy on average, until they are absorbed or escape from the moderator. The average diffusion time t_d is equal to λ_a/v, where λ_a is the absorption mean free path and v is the thermal neutron velocity for an infinite medium (no leakage). In pure graphite, $\lambda_a \sim 28$ m, $v_{th} \sim 2200$ m/sec and thus $t_d \sim 12$ msec.

An important aspect of the slowing-down and diffusion processes is the average distance the neutrons travel from their position of birth. A convenient parameter for the slowing-down process is the Fermi age τ, defined by

$$\tau \equiv \frac{1}{6}\overline{r^2}$$

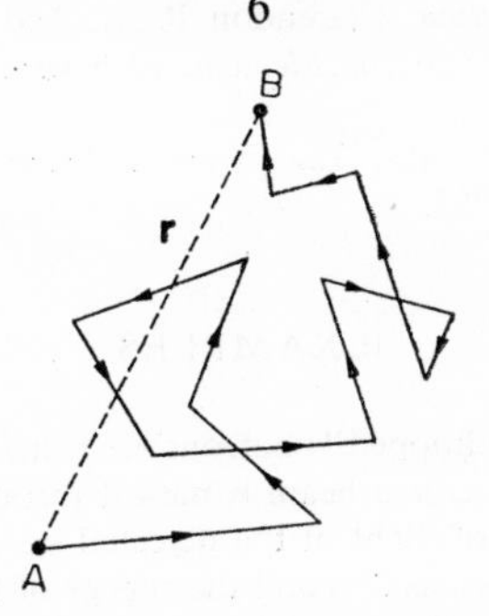

FIG. 18. Neutron born at *A* loses energy in successive nuclear collisions and becomes thermal at *B*. ***AB*** is the crow-flight path ***r***.

where $\overline{r^2}$ is the mean square crow-flight distance a neutron travels from birth (energy E_0) to where it becomes thermal (energy E_{th}). A slowing-down path is illustrated in Fig. 18. Table 3 lists theoretical and experimental values of τ for three moderators.

TABLE 3

Moderator	τ (cm^2) (theory)	τ (cm^2) (expt)	L (cm)
Water	33	31	2·9
Heavy water	120	110	110
Graphite	350	310	50

The diffusion length L of thermal neutrons is defined by

$$L^2 \equiv \frac{1}{6}\overline{r^2}$$

where $\overline{r^2}$ is the mean square crow-flight distance a neutron travels from where it becomes thermal to where it is absorbed. The diffusion lengths of the three moderators discussed above are given in the last column of Table 3. The theory of slowing-down and diffusion of neutrons in a medium is an important branch of reactor physics and is discussed in a number of specialized treatises (see bibliography).

BIBLIOGRAPHY

B. T. FELD, The Neutron in *Experimental Nuclear Physics* Vol. 2, Ed. by E. SEGRÈ, Wiley, New York 1953.

Fast Neutron Physics, Vol. 1, Ed. by J. L. FOWLER and J. B. MARION, Interscience Publishers, New York 1960.

D. J. HUGHES, *Pile Neutron Research*, Addison-Wesley Cambridge, Massachusetts 1953.

G. E. BACON, *Neutron Diffraction*, Clarendon Press, 2nd Edition, 1962.

S. GLASSTONE and M. C. EDLUND, *The Elements of Nuclear Reactor Theory*, MacMillan, London 1953.

A. M. WEINBERG and E. P. WIGNER, *The Physical Theory of Neutron Chain Reactors*, Chicago University Press, 1958.

EXAMPLES

1. 72 per cent of a beam of "chopped" neutrons are transmitted by a tungsten sample of thickness 8·0 g cm^{-2}. The incident beam is passed through a "fast chopper" of burst length 6 μsec and the time-of-flight of the detected beam over 10 m is 325 μsec. Calculate the total neutron cross section and the energy of the neutrons. If the "detector-on" time is 6 μsec estimate the energy resolution in electron-volts. (Atomic weight of tungsten is 184.)

2. Calculate the "slowing down time" of 2 MeV neutrons to thermal energy (0·025 eV) in graphite and the subsequent "diffusion time". (Density of graphite is 1·60 g cm^{-3}, atomic weight of carbon is 12; epithermal neutron scattering cross section in graphite is 4·8 barns, the thermal neutron absorption cross section is 4·5 millibarns.)
3. Monochromatic neutrons of wavelength 1·873 Å are obtained by Bragg reflection from a fluorite crystal and they experience total external reflection from a beryllium surface up to a critical glancing angle of 11·2 minutes of arc. Estimate the sign and magnitude of the scattering length of beryllium. (Density and atomic weight of Be: 1·83 g cm^{-3}, 9·02, respectively.)
4. A 5·0 μA beam of 2·5 MeV protons from a Van de Graaff accelerator is incident on a gas target of tritium (2 cm thick, gas pressure 120 cm of Hg, at 20°C). If the cross section of the neutron-producing reaction is 0·55 barns at E_p = 2·5 MeV, calculate the total number of neutrons produced per second.
5. The following data was obtained in Robson's determination of the free neutron half-life:
   Number of protons detected per minute = 705,
   Protons "captured" by spectrometer from a neutron beam volume of 4·7 cm^3,
   Efficiency of electron multiplier for 13 keV protons = 23·7%,
   Difference in saturated induced activity of 0·05 g manganese foil (with and without cadmium cover) when exposed to neutron beam = 0·404 mc.
   Neutron capture cross section of Mn^{55} (100% abundance) for 2200 m per sec neutrons = 10·7 barns.

   Calculate the free neutron half-life.
6. The following method of determining the free neutron half-life has been suggested. A highly evacuated vessel of very low neutron capture cross section is exposed continuously for one month to a thermal neutron beam ($2{\cdot}2 \times 10^5$ cm/sec) flux of 1×10^{15} neutrons per cm^2 per sec. The pressure of the hydrogen inside the vessel is related to the neutron half-life. What are the difficulties and likely sources of error of this method?

CHAPTER 16

NUCLEAR MAGNETISM

16.1. MOLECULAR BEAM RESONANCE METHODS

In Chapter 8 we described some of the basic properties of angular momentum and nuclear moments. Here we shall be primarily concerned with the experimental methods of determining nuclear magnetic moments.

The magnetic dipole moment $\boldsymbol{\mu}$ and the angular momentum (spin) $\boldsymbol{I}$ of a nucleus are collinear vectors related by the equation.

$$\boldsymbol{\mu} = g_n \mu_N \boldsymbol{I} \tag{1}$$

where g_n is the nuclear g-factor (unfortunately unpredictable at this stage of the theory of elementary particles) and μ_n is the *nuclear magneton*:

$$\mu_N = \frac{e\hbar}{2Mc} = 5{\cdot}0504 \times 10^{-24} \text{ erg gauss}^{-1}$$

where M is the proton rest mass.

One of the most important properties of the angular momentum operator in quantum mechanics† is that the maximum *observable* component of the vector $\boldsymbol{I}$ (of length $[I(I+1)]^{\frac{1}{2}}$) is equal to I. Consequently, the maximum component of $\boldsymbol{\mu}$ in any specified direction (e.g. that of a magnetic field) is given by

$$\mu = g_n \mu_N I \tag{2}$$

It is standard practice to refer to the scalar quantity μ as the magnetic moment of the nucleus.

The first *accurate* measurements of molecular, atomic and nuclear magnetic moments were carried out by I. I. Rabi and his school at Columbia University††. A schematic diagram of a typical molecular beam magnetic resonance apparatus is shown in Fig. 1. The design of the source depends on the vapour pressure and boiling point of the substance under investigation. If the boiling point is well above room temperature, the source consists of a small oven O containing a small quantity of

† E. Feenberg and G. E. Pake, *Notes of the Quantum Theory of Angular Momentum*, Addison–Wesley, Cambridge, U.S.A. 1953.

†† Consult the treatise by N. F. Ramsey, *Molecular Beams*, Oxford University Press, 1956.

the substance. Molecules of the vapour emerge from a very fine slit (typical dimensions 0·015 mm by 0·8 cm) with a wide distribution of velocities. Fast pumps maintain a high degree of vacuum (10^{-7} mm Hg) in the main part of the apparatus to reduce scattering of the molecular beam to a negligible value.

Let us consider a beam of LiCl molecules. In the ground state of the molecule, the total electronic magnetic moment is zero so we are only

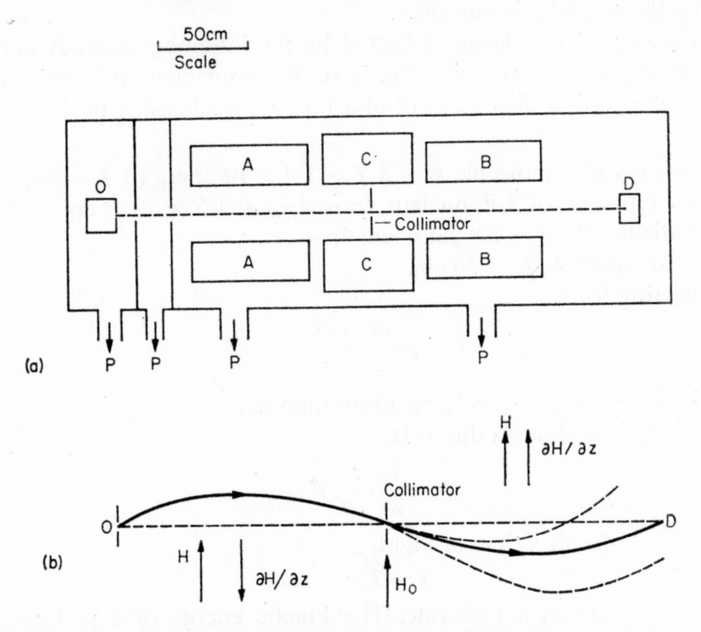

FIG. 1. (a) Rabi Molecular-beam magnetic resonance method. O—oven; D—detector, P—fast pumps; (b) paths of molecules through the collimator.

concerned with the nuclear moments of the Li and Cl nuclei. The LiCl molecules will impinge on the beam detector D, provided they pass through the fine central slit and do not experience any resultant deflection by the three magnetic fields A, B and C (Fig. 1). The magnetic fields A and B are strong vertical fields ($\sim$ 12,000 gauss) and they are also highly inhomogeneous with vertical gradients of the order of 10^5 gauss/cm. The A and B fields point in the same direction but their gradients $\partial H/\partial z$ are antiparallel. The C field, placed between the A and B regions, is a *homogeneous* vertical field H_0 parallel to the A and B fields.

Consider a LiCl molecule emerging from the oven O in a direction inclined at a small angle above the axis of symmetry of the apparatus. In the absence of any deflecting force, such a molecule would not pass through the central slit (at the centre of the C field) and therefore would not reach the detector. However, the molecule may be deflected downwards by the field gradient $\partial H/\partial z$ in the A region so that it passes through the central slit. In the B field it experiences an equal and opposite deflection and reaches D (Fig. 1 (b)).

A convenient detector for LiCl is a hot tungsten wire. A neutral Li atom striking the hot wire gives up its valency electron to the surface of the wire and the residual Li^+ ion escapes. The molecular beam is detected by the small ionic current.

The trajectory of a molecule deflected by the inhomogeneous A and B fields is greatly exaggerated in Fig. 1 (b). To appreciate this point, let us estimate the vertical displacement of a LiCl molecule using the following data:

Kinetic energy of a molecule $E \sim kT \sim 1{\cdot}4 \times 10^{-13}$ erg (if $T = 1000°K$).
Magnetic moment of Li^7 nucleus, $\mu \sim 3\mu_N \sim 1{\cdot}5 \times 10^{-23}$ erg gauss^{-1}.
Field gradient $\partial H/\partial z \sim 10^5$ gauss cm^{-1}.
Length of magnet A, $L \sim 50$ cm.
The deflecting force

$$F = \mu \frac{m}{I} \frac{\partial H}{\partial z} \tag{3}$$

where m is the nuclear magnetic quantum number.

The vertical deflection produced is

$$z = \frac{1}{2} \frac{F}{\mathscr{M}} t^2 \tag{4}$$

where t is the molecule's time of flight,

$$t \sim L/v \tag{5}$$

and $\mathscr{M}$ is the mass of a molecule. The kinetic energy of a molecule is

$$E = \tfrac{1}{2}\mathscr{M} v^2 \tag{6}$$

Combining eqns. (3), (4), (5) and (6) we obtain

$$z = \frac{\mu}{4} \frac{m}{I} \frac{1}{E} \frac{\partial H}{\partial z} L^2 \tag{7}$$

The maximum deflection occurs if $m = I$, and, in this case, we obtain $z \sim 0{\cdot}07$ mm! This small deflection emphasizes one of the major experimental difficulties in molecular beam experiments.

Returning to the LiCl experiment, we now consider the passage of the LiCl molecules through the uniform vertical H_0 (C Magnet). In this field, the nuclear magnetic moment vector of the Li^7 nucleus precesses around the field H_0 with the Larmor angular frequency (Eqn. (42), Chapt. 2).

$$\omega_L = \gamma H_0 = \frac{\mu}{I\hbar} H_0 \tag{8}$$

where $\gamma = \mu/I\hbar$ is the gyromagnetic ratio of the nucleus. Notice that the Larmor frequency is independent of the magnetic sub-state of the nucleus; that is, ω_L does not depend on the angle the vector $\boldsymbol{\mu}$ makes with the magnetic field $\boldsymbol{H}_0$.

In the centre of the C field a small loop of wire supplied with radio frequency current produces a small alternating magnetic field of amplitude $2H_1$ at an angular frequency ω. This field is generated in a direction perpendicular to $\boldsymbol{H}_0$ and it can be regarded as equivalent to the superposition of two circularly polarized fields of amplitude H_1 and frequency ω, but rotating in opposite senses (Fig. 2).

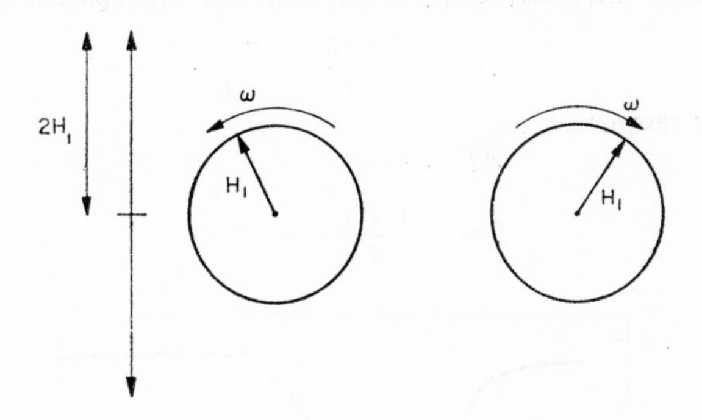

FIG. 2. Linear oscillating magnetic field of amplitude $2H_1$ and its two circular rotating components.

The basic principle of the resonance method is to obtain an accurate match of the Larmor frequency of nuclear precession ω_L and the frequency ω of one of the rotating field components. At resonance there is a strong possibility that the nuclear spin axis will be flipped to an adjacent magnetic sub-state. Selection rules restrict the transitions to $\Delta m = \pm 1$. Another way of regarding the resonance transition is in terms of the Zeeman energy level diagram (Fig. 3). The radio-frequency loop supplies photons of energy $\hbar\,\omega$ to the surrounding field. At resonance

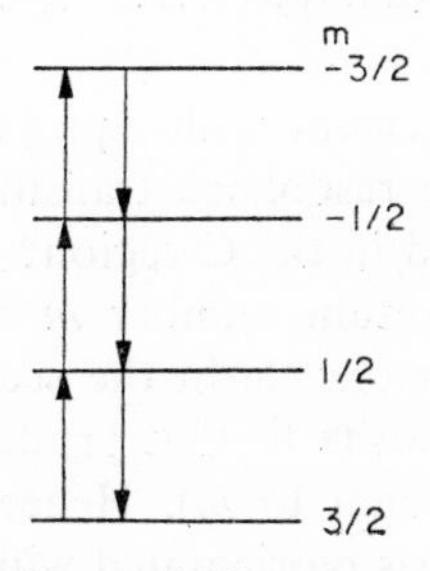

FIG. 3. Nuclear magnetic energy levels of Li^7 nucleus ($I = 3/2$). Upward transitions ($\Delta m = -1$) correspond to resonant absorption. Downward transitions ($\Delta m = +1$) correspond to stimulated emission.

these photons are strongly absorbed by the nuclear spins ($\Delta m = -1$). Such photons also induce the nuclear spins to emit radiant energy ($\Delta m = +1$). In the radio-frequency part of the electromagnetic spectrum spontaneous emission is negligible.

The difference in magnetic energy of nuclei in the lowest and highest magnetic sub-levels is $2\mu H_0$. This result is analogous to the classical expression for the work done in rotating a dipole through half a turn from the field to the anti-field direction. There are $2I + 1$ magnetic sub-levels and $2I$ energy intervals; thus, adjacent levels are spaced in energy by

$$\Delta E = \frac{2\mu H_0}{2I} = \frac{\mu H_0}{I} \tag{9}$$

At magnetic resonance,

$$\Delta E = \hbar \omega \tag{10}$$

$$\hbar \omega = \frac{\mu H_0}{I} \tag{11}$$

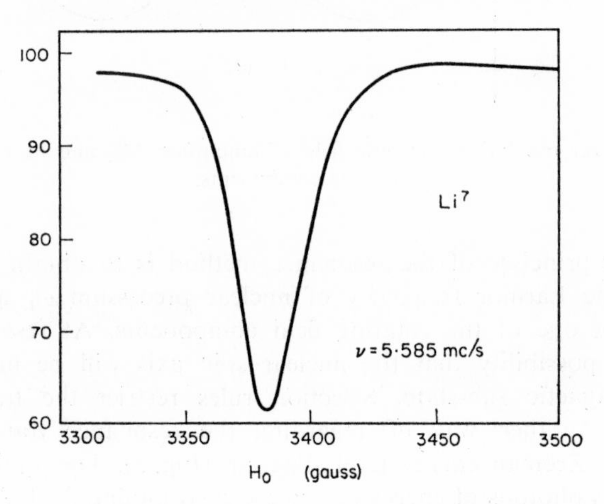

FIG. 4. Resonance curve for Li^7 nucleus observed in LiCl. The ordinate is the detector reading (I. I. RABI *et. al.*, *Phys. Rev.* **55**, 526, 1939).

This expression is in agreement with eqn. (8) if we put $\omega = \omega_L$. How is it possible to observe the resonance transitions of the nuclear moments in the radio-frequency field in the C region? Resonance transitions change the nuclear magnetic quantum number m by ± 1. This means that the vertical deflection of the molecule in the second inhomogeneous field (B) will not be equal and opposite to that produced by field A (from eqn. (7) we see that z is proportional to m). Hence a LiCl molecule which has had the Li^7 nuclear spin axis reorientated will miss the detector D. Hypothetical trajectories of such molecules are shown in Fig. 1 (b). Resonance is detected by a decrease in the detector current. It is usual to represent the resonance by plotting the detector current as a function of the field strength H_0, keeping the radio-frequency constant. The resonance curve shown in Fig. 4, is not as sharp as one would expect from a consideration of the resonance flipping of the nuclear spin in the uniform field H_0. However, it must be realised that the Li^7 nucleus is situated in a small local magnetic field produced by the Cl^{35} (or Cl^{37}) nucleus in the same molecule. In addition, there may be a perturbation due to existence of a nuclear quadrupole moment.

If the resolution of the equipment is increased, the single broad resonance curve is split into a number of closely spaced resonances. The resulting resonance pattern is called the radio-frequency spectrum of the molecule.

The Quadrupole Moment of the Deuteron

A theoretical analysis of the radio-frequency spectrum of molecular deuterium led to the important conclusion† that the deuteron has an intrinsic electric quadrupole moment.

A molecular beam investigation of D_2 requires a different type of source and detector. The source consists of a controlled deuterium gas leak, maintained at 80°K (the low temperature prevents the excitation of high molecular rotation states). The hot wire detector of the LiCl experiment is replaced by a Stern–Pirani gauge. This type of gauge consists of a small chamber (7·5 cm × 0·5 cm × 0·06 cm) containing one or more thin parallel strips of platinum mounted parallel to the long dimension of the chamber. The strips are heated electrically and they reach thermal equilibrium about 100°C above the chamber wall temperature. Molecules which enter the chamber through the long narrow slit in the wall do not easily escape. Thus if a molecular beam falls on the entrance slit the gas pressure inside the chamber rises. Heat is lost from the platinum strips by gaseous conduction and the molecular beam is detected by the fall in the electrical resistance of the strips (this is the well-known principle of the Pirani low pressure gauge).

The radio-frequency spectrum of molecular deuterium at 1·300 Mc/s is illustrated in Fig. 5. This complex spectrum is the result of a number of interactions within the molecule. The radio-frequency spectrum of molecular hydrogen is complex; nevertheless, the fine structure could be understood in terms of magnetic interactions alone. With D_2 and HD all such attempts failed. If, however, one assumes that there is an additional term in the interaction energy, associated with a finite electrical quadrupole moment of the deuteron, the observed resonance curve can be explained. The detailed theory of this interaction is given in the book

† J. M. B. Kellogg, I. I. Rabi, N. F. Ramsey, and J. R. Zacharias, *Phys. Rev.* **57**, 677, 1940.

by Ramsey. The interaction is related to the energy of orientation of the nuclear quadrupole moment in the inhomogeneous electric field at the site of the deuteron within the molecule. This interaction energy is proportional to $Q\,q$

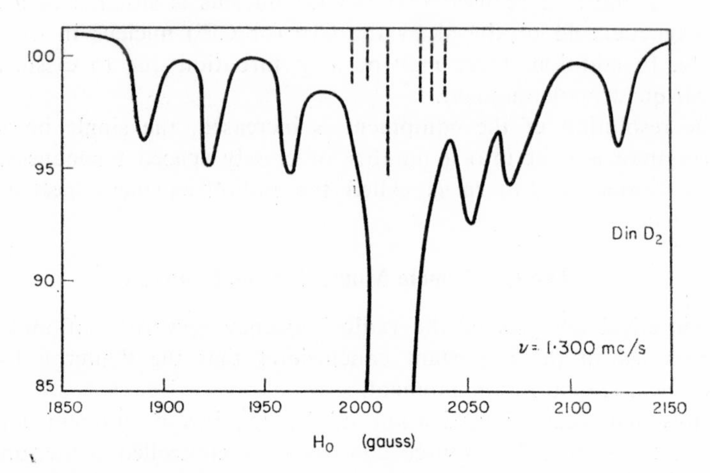

FIG. 5. Radio-frequency spectrum of molecular deuterium at 80°K. Dotted lines indicate predicted spectrum on the assumption $Q = 0$ for the deuteron.

where Q is the nuclear quadrupole moment and q is the electric field gradient at the position of the deuteron. The difficulty of obtaining high accuracy for Q is connected with the uncertainty in calculating the electric field gradient q. A recent re-evaluation of the field gradient† in the deuterium molecule gives for the deuteron quadrupole moment

$$Q = 2{\cdot}82 \times 10^{-27}\ \text{cm}^2$$

The Magnetic Moment of the Neutron

It is firmly established that the neutron is a spin $\frac{1}{2}$ particle. A naive argument would, however, predict zero magnetic moment as the net charge of the neutron is zero. The strong interaction of neutrons with neutrons and protons is believed to be a consequence of meson exchange forces. Thus even an isolated (free) neutron is surrounded for part of its time by a cloud of virtual negative pions

$$n \rightarrow p + \pi^-$$

It is therefore not surprising that the neutron has a finite (negative) magnetic dipole moment.

† J. P. AUFFRAY, *Phys. Rev. Letters* **6**, 120, 1961.

As it is not possible to keep a sample of free neutrons in a small container, the neutron magnetic moment has been determined by resonance beam methods. Neutron beams from cyclotron-induced reactions (d, n) or high flux reactors are convenient sources. The neutrons are reduced to thermal velocities (~ 2200 m/sec) by a hydrogeneous moderator before they are collimated by cadmium sheets.

It is necessary in this type of experiment to produce and detect a beam of *polarized* neutrons. A number of methods of producing polarized neutrons has been described in Chapter 15. Bloch† polarized a neutron beam by passing it through a thick sheet of iron magnetized to within

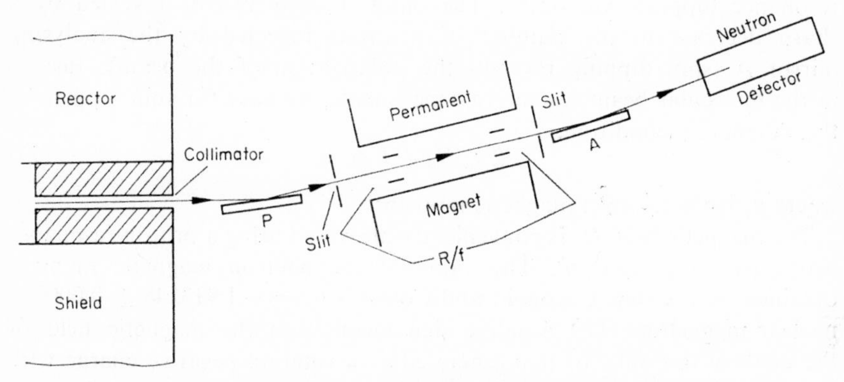

FIG. 6. Experimental arrangement of Corngold, Cohen and Ramsey's determination of the neutron's magnetic moment (P—polarizing magnetic mirror, A—analysing magnetic mirror).

0·1 per cent of saturation. A better method, achieving a much higher degree of polarization, is to reflect the beam at a very small glancing angle from a magnetized mirror. The most accurate determination of the neutron magnetic moment has been made using this polarization technique.††

Ramsey's method is shown in Fig. 6. A collimated beam of thermal neutrons (intensity 700,000 counts/min) is incident at a glancing angle of 17′ on a magnetic mirror P. An alloy of 93% Co and 7% Fe is a suitable material for the mirror. The reflected neutron beam has a polarization as high as 90%. The polarization P is defined by

$$P = \frac{n_+ - n_-}{n_+ + n_-} \tag{12}$$

where n_+ is the number of neutrons with their spins parallel to the magnetic field in the mirror, and n_- is the corresponding number with their spins antiparallel.

† F. BLOCH, D. NICODEMUS and H. H. STAUB, *Phys. Rev.* **74**, 1025, 1948.
†† V. W. COHEN, N. CORNGOLD and N. F. RAMSEY, *Phys. Rev.* **104**, 283, 1956.

The beam of polarized neutrons passes through a 5 ft long uniform magnetic field H_0 ($\sim$ 8500 gauss). The beam is then reflected at a small angle from a second magnetic mirror A (magnetized in the same direction as P). The intensity of the doubly reflected beam ($\sim$ 7500 counts/min) is recorded by a well-screened BF_3 proportional counter.

The neutron spins in the long magnetic field are flipped by two radio-frequency current loops mounted 42 in. apart. (Ramsey† had previously shown that the method of using two separated current loops produces narrower resonance lines.) If the angular frequency of the radio-frequency supply coincides with the Larmor angular frequency of the neutron spins, resonance flipping will occur. The onset of resonance is revealed by a sharp decrease in the number of neutrons reflected by the analysing mirror A (spin flipping reverses the polarization of the beam). Just as in the molecular beam resonance experiments, we have for spin $\frac{1}{2}$ particles the resonance condition.

$$2\mu_n H_0 = \hbar\,\omega \tag{13}$$

where μ_n is the neutron magnetic moment.

The magnetic field H_0 is conveniently measured using a proton resonance probe (see next section). The value of the neutron magnetic moment obtained by Ramsey, Corngold and Cohen is $\mu_n = -1{\cdot}913148 \pm 0{\cdot}000066$ nuclear magnetons. The negative sign means that the magnetic field of the neutron is similar to that generated by a rotating negative charge with its spin axis parallel to that of the neutron.

16.2. NUCLEAR MAGNETIC RESONANCE IN BULK MATTER

In 1945, E. M. Purcell†† at Harvard and independently F. Bloch††† at Stanford showed that it is possible to measure nuclear moments with high precision using bulk samples of matter. The magnetic moment of the proton, for example, can be determined using a 0·5 cm³ sample of water. The new methods are known collectively by the title of "Nuclear Magnetic Resonance". Today the main emphasis of nuclear magnetic resonance is as a tool for elucidating many aspects of the solid and liquid state. It is now a well established analytical technique in organic chemistry. Naturally our primary interest in this chapter lies in the determination of nuclear magnetism, but it is necessary to touch briefly on the relaxation mechanisms whereby the nuclear moments interact with the surrounding medium.

† N. F. Ramsey, *Phys. Rev.* **78**, 695, 1950.

†† E. M. Purcell, H. C. Torrey. and R. V. Pound, *Phys. Rev.* **69**, 37, 1946; N. Bloembergen, E. M. Purcell and R. V. Pound, *Phys. Rev.* **73**, 679, 1948.

††† F. Bloch, W. W. Hansen, M. Packard, *Phys. Rev.* **70**, 474, 1946.

Let us consider the determination of the magnetic moment of the proton using a small water sample by the Purcell method. A small tube filled with water is inserted inside a small coil (typical dimensions, 12 turns of 18 s.w.g. copper wire, 1·5 cm long, 0·7 cm internal diameter). This sample coil forms the inductive branch of a tuned parallel *L–C* circuit and it is supplied with radio-frequency current at an angular frequency ω. The sample coil is rigidly mounted in the gap of a high quality magnet with its axis perpendicular to the homogeneous magnet field H_0 (a typical value of H_0 is 10,000 gauss). The amplitude $2H_1$ of the oscillating magnetic field produced by the radio-frequency current is usually less than 0·1 gauss; that is, $H_1 \ll H_0$. Nuclear magnetic resonance occurs if the angular frequency ω of the radio-frequency field coincides with the proton spin precession frequency ω_L in the field H_0.

Purcell and Bloch use different methods for detecting the occurrence of resonance. Bloch employs a second, pick-up coil, mounted orthogonally to the "driving coil", to detect resonance through an induced e.m.f. We shall not discuss the details of the Bloch method. In the method of Purcell, resonance is detected by the slight reduction in the Q factor of the *L–C* circuit, associated with the absorption of radio-frequency energy from the sample coil. The resonance phenomenon can be thought of as either a matching of the Larmor precession frequency with one of the circularly polarized components of the oscillating magnetic field, or as a match between the photon energy $\hbar\omega$ and the energy difference ΔE between the two magnetic sub-states ($m = +\frac{1}{2}$ and $m = -\frac{1}{2}$).

$$\hbar\omega = \frac{\mu}{I} H_0 \tag{14}$$

Apart from the obvious differences in the size and design of the Rabi and Purcell type of experiment, it is important to realize that the mutual nuclear interactions between nuclei in different molecules are negligible in a molecular beam (molecular density is as small as 10^9 per cm^3). This is not the case for nuclei in normal matter (1 cm^3 of water at room temperature contains 7×10^{22} protons). It is vital for the success of the Purcell or Bloch type of experiment that there should be an interaction between the assembly of nuclear spins and the surrounding "lattice" (the term "lattice" is still retained for liquid or gaseous samples). To appreciate this important point, let us consider what happens when the field H_0 is switched on in the absence of the radio-frequency field. Initially there will be equal numbers of protons in the magnetic sub-states $m = +\frac{1}{2}$ and $m = -\frac{1}{2}$. Through the transfer of energy from the proton spins to the heat reservoir comprising various internal degrees of freedom of the lattice, the spin system will eventually reach a state of thermodynamic equilibrium when the population of each magnetic substate is proportional to the Boltzmann factor

$$\exp\left(-\frac{\mu H_0}{kT}\right) \tag{15}$$

where k is Boltzmann's constant and T is the lattice temperature. For protons in the state $m = +\frac{1}{2}$, μH_0, the magnetic energy of orientation is $+\frac{1}{2}\gamma \hbar H_0$; for the $m = -\frac{1}{2}$ state, μH_0 is $-\frac{1}{2}\gamma \hbar H_0$. Hence the ratio of the populations of the $m = +\frac{1}{2}$ and the $m = -\frac{1}{2}$ states is given by

$$\frac{n(+\frac{1}{2})}{n(-\frac{1}{2})} = \exp\left(\frac{\gamma \hbar H_0}{kT}\right) = \exp\left(\frac{2\mu H_0}{kT}\right) \tag{16}$$

$2\mu H_0$ is the energy separation of the magnetic sub-levels. At room temperature

$$\frac{2\mu H_0}{kT} \ll 1$$

and eqn. (16) reduces to

$$\frac{n(+\frac{1}{2}) - n(-\frac{1}{2})}{n(-\frac{1}{2})} = \frac{n(+\frac{1}{2}) - n(-\frac{1}{2})}{n(+\frac{1}{2})} = \frac{2\mu H_0}{kT} \sim 7 \times 10^{-10} H_0$$

For $H_0 = 10{,}000$ gauss, the excess population $n_0 = n(+\frac{1}{2}) - n(-\frac{1}{2})$ is only 7×10^{-6} times the population of each sub-level!

The mechanisms whereby the nuclear spin system transfers energy to the surrounding lattice are known collectively by the name "spin–lattice relaxation" and the rate of approach of the spin system to thermal equilibrium is determined by a spin–lattice relaxation time T_1. If two chemically inert gases, at normal pressure initially at different temperatures are allowed to mix, a common equilibrium temperature is very rapidly attained because of the high collision frequency of the molecules ($\sim 10^9$/sec). The relaxation time for this process is therefore very short (10^{-6} sec or less). In marked contrast, the establishment of thermal equilibrium between the nuclear spins and the lattice may take several seconds or minutes! This is a direct consequence of the relative isolation and protection of the nuclei by the surrounding atomic electrons. For liquids however, the spin–lattice relaxation time T_1 may be as short as 10^{-2} or 10^{-3} sec.

Let us assume that at $t = 0$ (when H_0 is switched on), the excess population of the proton spin states $n = n(+\frac{1}{2}) - n(-\frac{1}{2})$ is zero. The proton system is characterized by an infinite spin temperature $T_s = \infty$. The spin systems cools until it reaches the lattice temperature T. However, the heat capacity of the lattice is enormously greater than that of the spin system. So the rise in temperature of the lattice is very small. The approach to equilibrium, in the absence of a radio-frequency field, is described by the equation

$$\frac{dn}{dt} = \frac{(n_0 - n)}{T_1} \tag{17}$$

where n is the excess population, and n_0 is the excess population when equilibrium is attained. Integrating eqn. (17) we obtain

$$n = n_0 \left\{1 - \exp\left(-\frac{t}{T_1}\right)\right\} \tag{18}$$

The presence of a radiation field at resonance, modifies the last two equations. Let W denote the probability per unit time of inducing a transition from one magnetic sub-state to the other. The probability for resonance absorption and resonance emission is the same; that is,

$$W_{\frac{1}{2}\to-\frac{1}{2}} = W_{-\frac{1}{2}\to\frac{1}{2}} \tag{19}$$

The approach to equilibrium is determined by the equation

$$\frac{dn}{dt} = \frac{(n_0 - n)}{T_1} - 2nW \tag{20}$$

The factor of 2 in the last term of eqn. (20) appears because each transition between the two magnetic levels changes the excess population by two. The steady state excess population is the result of two competing processes—spin–lattice relaxation mechanisms tending to equalize the spin and lattice temperatures, and the radio-frequency field tending to increase the spin system temperature by equalizing the level populations. Integrating eqn. (20), we obtain

$$n = \frac{n_0}{1 + 2WT_1}\left[1 - \exp\left(-\frac{(1 + 2WT_1)}{T_1}t\right)\right] \tag{21}$$

The modified time constant $T_1\ (1 + 2WT_1)^{-1}$ is less than the spin–lattice value T_1 and the new steady state excess population n_s is less than n_0

$$n_s = \frac{n_0}{1 + 2WT_1} \tag{22}$$

Equation (22) has very important consequences. If the radio-frequency driving field is too large, $2WT_1$ may be considerably greater than unity and n_s is much smaller than n_0 (if $n_s \ll n_0$ the system is said to be *saturated*). The nuclear magnetic resonance phenomenon is detectable through the *difference* between the absorption and emission of photons by the nuclear spins and it is obviously desirable that n_s should be as large as possible.

We must now consider the mutual interactions of the spins (spin–spin interaction) as distinct from the spin–lattice interaction. The magnetic field at a distance r from a dipole moment μ is $\sim \mu/r^3$. Thus, the magnetic field 1 Å distant from a dipole moment of one nuclear magneton is

~ 5 gauss. Each nuclear moment is situated in a small local magnetic field H_{loc} generated by adjacent nuclei in the lattice. In a homogeneous applied field H_0, the nuclei are situated in a field ranging from $H_0 + H_{loc}$ to $H_0 - H_{loc}$. Since the resultant field differs from nucleus to nucleus, there is a distribution in the Larmor precession frequencies $\delta\,\omega_L$ given by

$$\delta\omega_L \sim \gamma\, H_{loc} \sim \frac{\mu}{I\,\hbar} \cdot \frac{\mu}{r^3} \sim \frac{\mu^2}{\hbar\, r^3} \sim 10^4\ \text{sec}^{-1} \tag{23}$$

The relative phases of the precessing nuclear moments change at such a rate that a pair of them will drift out of phase in a time of the order of $1/\delta\omega_L$. Mutual exchange of energy between neighbouring nuclear spins may occur through the interaction of the local precessing magnetic fields. It is convenient to introduce the concept of a spin–spin relaxation time $T_2 \sim 1/\delta\omega_L$ as a rough measure of the lifetime of a nuclear spin state.

The transition probability W between two nuclear magnetic sub-states, designated by magnetic quantum numbers m and m', is given by quantum mechanics as

$$W = \tfrac{1}{2}\gamma^2\, H_1^2 |\langle m\,|I|\, m'\rangle|^2\, g(\nu) \tag{24}$$

where $2H_1$ is the amplitude of the linear oscillating radio-frequency magnetic field, $\langle m\,|I|m'\rangle$ is a matrix element, and $g(\nu)$ is a normalized function describing the shape of the nuclear magnetic absorption line as a function of the frequency in a fixed magnetic field H_0:

$$\int_0^\infty g(\nu)\, d\nu = 1$$

For a very sharp resonance line, $g(\nu)$ has a very large value at the centre of the resonance line. The matrix elements of the nuclear spin operator are zero unless $|m - m'| = 1$ and then†

$$|\langle m\,|I|\, m'\rangle|^2 = \tfrac{1}{2}(I + m)\,(I - m + 1)$$

For spin $\frac{1}{2}$ nuclei, eqn. (24) reduces to

$$W = \tfrac{1}{2}\gamma^2\, H_1^2\, g(\nu) \tag{25}$$

The value of $g(\nu)$ at the centre of the resonance line is related to the spin–spin relaxation time T_2 and it is standard practice to define T_2 by the relation

$$T_2 = \tfrac{1}{2} g(\nu)_{\max}. \tag{26}$$

Combining eqns. (22), (25) and (26), we obtain

$$n_s = \frac{n_0}{1 + \gamma^2\, H_1^2\, T_1\, T_2} \tag{27}$$

† See E. U. Condon and G. H. Shortley, *The Theory of Atomic Spectra*, Cambridge University Press 1935.

In liquids the resonance lines are very narrow, whereas in crystalline solids and powders the line width may be several gauss wide at a fixed driving frequency. The observed width of the nuclear resonance signal in a liquid sample may, in fact, be determined by the inhomogeneity of the applied field H_0 over the volume of the sample. The explanation of the narrowing of the resonance line lies in the rapid tumbling and rotation of the molecules of the liquid; the effective local field H_{loc} at each nucleus has a time average value nearly zero. (The time for a water molecule to turn over at room temperature is $\sim 10^{-11}$ sec, which is a very short interval when compared with the radio-frequency period of 10^{-7} sec.)

If excessive saturation of the nuclear spin system is to be avoided ($n_s \sim n_0$), H_1, T_1 and T_2 must be small. Short relaxation times and a small oscillating field amplitude H_1 are desirable. For distilled water at room temperature $T_1 \sim 3$ secs; this value of T_1 can be reduced by a factor of a thousand or more by dissolving a small amount of a paramagnetic salt (e.g. manganese sulphate) in the water. There is a strong relaxation mechanism associated with the magnetic dipole interaction of the proton spins and the paramagnetic ions.

There have been many variations in the methods of observing the nuclear magnetic resonance signal since the original experiments of Purcell and Bloch†. A schematic diagram of the apparatus used by Bloembergen, Purcell and Pound is shown in Fig. 7. A radio-frequency voltage is applied to two adjacent arms of a tuned bridge circuit. The resistive loads R of 50 Ω match the characteristic impedance of the supply cable. The parallel L–C circuits are tuned to the signal frequency (typical value 30 mc/s). The sample coil has the same inductance as the dummy coil; the former, however is wound round the sample tube and it is placed inside the strong homogeneous field H_0. A half-wavelength line A B connects the output terminals of the two tuned circuits so that the input signal to the high quality communications receiver is normally very small. The bridge can be adjusted so that the voltages across the two coils are equal in phase and in amplitude by varying the capacitances C_1 and C_3 (C_1 and C_2 are ganged so that $C_1 + C_2$ remains constant; for tuning purposes C_1, C_2 and C_3 are effectively in parallel).

When the applied signal frequency is equal to the Larmor precession frequency of the nuclear spins in the field H_0, radio-frequency energy is absorbed by the sample. The decrease in the Q factor of the sample coil reduces the amplitude of the voltage across the coil and consequently there is an increase in the amplitude of the signal applied to the receiver. To view the resonance phenomenon on the screen of a cathode ray oscilloscope the field H_0 is modulated at a very low audio-frequency

† See p. 47 E. R. Andrew, *Nuclear Magnetic Resonance*, Cambridge 1955.

by a sweeping field of about 5 gauss amplitude. Every time the sample field sweeps through resonance an output voltage from the receiver produces a vertical deflection on the oscilloscope screen. The X plates are driven with a voltage derived from the low frequency generator. Thus a resonance absorption line is traced on the screen of the oscilloscope. It is not difficult to obtain a signal from protons in water but

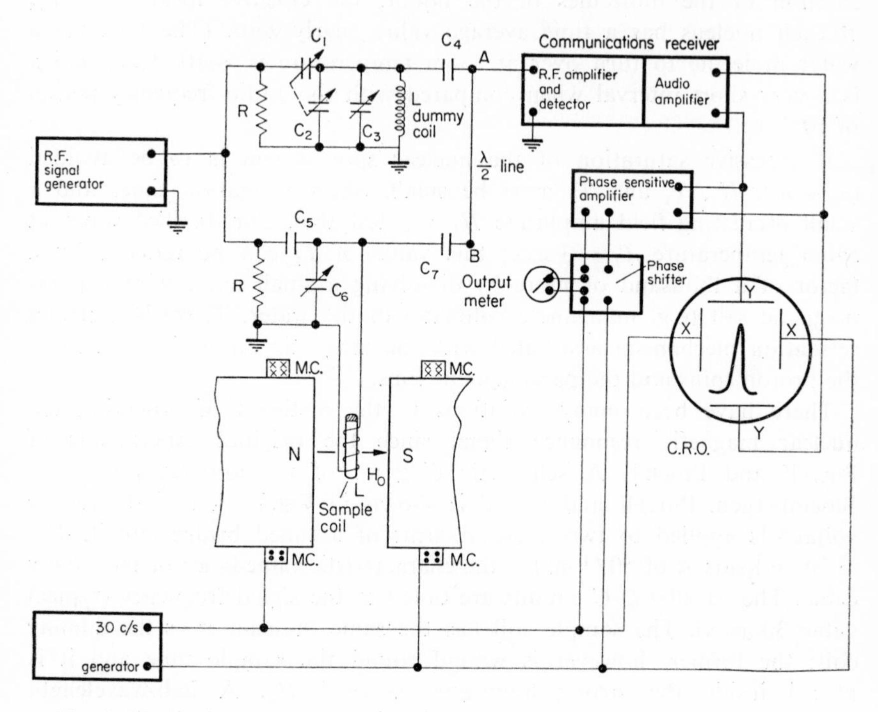

FIG. 7. Nuclear magnetic resonance apparatus of Bloembergen, Purcell and Pound.

there are many cases where the signal is too weak to display on an oscilloscope. To increase the signal-to-noise ratio a phase-sensitive amplifier is often used. In the phase-sensitive amplifier the low frequency modulation component of the output signal of the receiver is mixed with a sinusoidal signal of the same frequency derived from the low frequency generator. The output signal of the phase-sensitive amplifier contains a mean voltage component which is proportional to the amplitude of the nuclear signal. If a d.c. meter with a time constant of 1 sec or more is used to detect the output signal only noise components within a bandwidth of 1 c/s or less of the low frequency are recorded; in this way a marked improvement in signal-to-noise ratio is achieved.

In order to determine an accurate value of the proton magnetic moment from the magnetic resonance condition $2\mu H_0 = \hbar\omega$, it is necessary to measure the field H_0 with high precision (the accurate measurement of the radio-frequency ω is a standard part of radio engineering). At the National Bureau of Standards in Washington, Thomas, Driscoll and Hipple† used an electromagnet with very large pole pieces (22 cm × 32 cm) to provide the homogeneous field H_0. The value of H_0 was accurately determined by measuring the vertical force exerted on 10 cm long copper wires carrying an accurately measured direct current. The error in H_0 was not greater than about 2 parts in 10^5. Once the proton magnetic moment is found in absolute units, other nuclear moments can be compared with the proton moment by finding the ratio of the nuclear resonance frequencies in the same field (common-field method).

16.3. OPTICAL DETECTION OF NUCLEAR MAGNETIC RESONANCE

The normal methods of observing nuclear magnetic resonance in gases require pressures above one atmosphere otherwise the resonance signal is lost against the noise background. A novel method of observing nuclear magnetic resonance in mercury vapour at a pressure as low as 10^{-5} mm Hg has recently been developed.†† This is an optical method employing the technique invented by A. Kastler††† and known by the name "*optical pumping*".

Let us consider the resonance absorption (fluorescence) of the strong ultraviolet spectral line (2537 Å) of mercury by mercury vapour. For simplicity suppose the absorbing gas consists of the Hg^{199} isotope only (nuclear spin $I = \frac{1}{2}$), and the mercury light source contains the separated Hg^{204} isotope. The atomic energy levels of the Hg^{199} atom relevant to the resonance fluorescence of the 2537 Å line are shown in Fig. 8(a). In the ground state, an S_0 state, there is no electronic angular momentum; thus the quantum number $F = \frac{1}{2}$, $(\boldsymbol{F} = \boldsymbol{L} + \boldsymbol{S} + \boldsymbol{I})$, is the same as the nuclear spin. The excited $^3P_1$ state has a large splitting of 727 cm^{-1} between the $F = \frac{1}{2}$ and $F = {}^3/_2$ sub-states. If the mercury atoms are situated in a homogeneous magnetic field H_0 there is an additional Zeeman splitting (Fig. 8(b)). The energy gap ΔE between the two magnetic sub-states of the $^1S_0$ level is proportional to H_0, and for moderate fields, ΔE corresponds to a very small wave number ($\sim 10^{-6}$ cm^{-1}). The ultraviolet radiation emitted by the Hg^{204} light source will excite Hg^{199}

† H. A. Thomas, R. L. Driscoll and J. A. Hipple, *Phys. Rev.* **75**, 902, 1949; *ibid.* **78**, 787, 1950.

†† J. Brossel, 15th Holweck Lecture, p. 1. *Year Book of the Physical Society*, 1960, The Physical Society, London; B. Cagnac and J. Brossel, *Comptes Rendus, Acad. Sci.*, Paris **249**, 77 and 253, 1959.

††† A. Kastler, *J. Phys. Radium* **11**, 255, 1950; *J. Opt. Soc. Amer.* **47**, 460, 1957.

atoms to the $F = \frac{1}{2}$ sub-state of the $^3P_1$ level; the $F = {}^3/_2$ sub-state is too far off resonance to be excited. Optical pumping of Hg^{199} is obtained in the following way. Circularly polarized resonance radiation from the Hg^{204} light source is incident on Hg^{199} vapour in a direction parallel to a homogeneous magnetic field H_0. Suppose the sense of the polarized photons (σ^+ photons) is such that they add one unit of angular momentum to an absorbing Hg^{199} atom, i.e. $\Delta m = +1$; then the only transition that takes place is between the $m = -\frac{1}{2}$ sub-state of the ground level

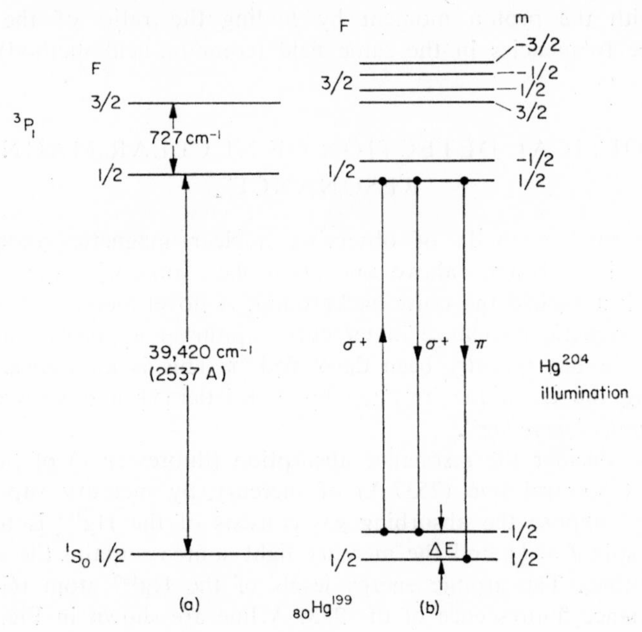

FIG. 8. (a) "Optical Pumping" of Hg^{199} atoms by circularly polarized resonance radiation (2537 Å) from Hg^{204}; (b) Zeeman level splitting in magnetic field H_0.

and the $m = +\frac{1}{2}$ sub-state of the $^3P_1$, $F = \frac{1}{2}$ level (Fig. 8(b)). The $m = \frac{1}{2} \rightarrow m = {}^3/_2$ transition between the $^1S_0$ and the $^3P_1$, $F = {}^3/_2$ states is still too far off resonance as the Zeeman energy splittings are very small. The excited Hg^{199} atoms decay to the ground state by spontaneous photon emission, either by emitting σ^+ radiation or π (linearly polarized $\Delta m = 0$) radiation. The net result of the resonance fluorescence process is an increase in the population of the $m = +\frac{1}{2}$ level of the $^1S_0$ state at the expense of the $m = -\frac{1}{2}$ ground state level. Through the absorption and re-emission of the 2537 radiation, atoms have been "pumped" from the $m = -\frac{1}{2}$ to the $m = +\frac{1}{2}$ level. Thus a considerable degree of *nuclear* alignment has occurred, as the angular momentum in the ground state of the atom is purely nuclear in origin. We have seen in the previous section that the population difference of the $m = +\frac{1}{2}$ and $m = -\frac{1}{2}$ levels in thermodynamic equilibrium is exceedingly small. By optical pumping we effectively cool the nuclear spin system of the atoms in the $^1S_0$ state to a temperature of the order of 10^{-6} to 10^{-7}°K!

The schematic arrangement of the apparatus to detect nuclear magnetic resonance by optical pumping is shown in Fig. 9. A very important feature is the light source, which must provide a very intense 2537 Å line. Brossel and Cagnac employed a small disc-shaped vessel (2·5 cm diameter, 2 mm thick) filled with argon to a pressure of 8 mm and containing 10^{-3} g

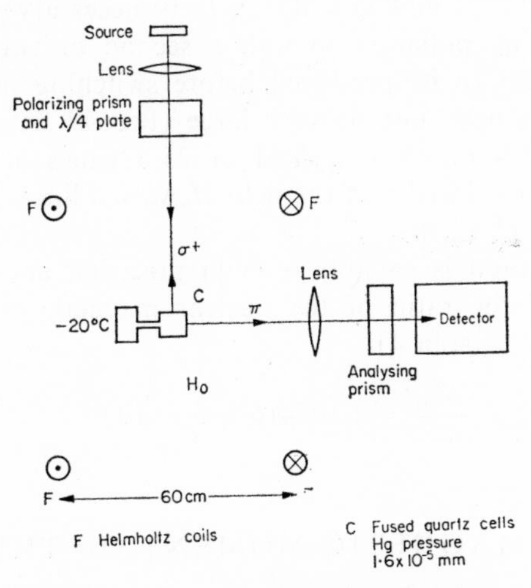

FIG. 9. Schematic arrangement for optical detection of nuclear magnetic resonance.

of the separated Hg^{204} isotope. The electrode-less light source is excited by an ultra-high-frequency magnetron source delivering 100 watts of power at 2400 Mc/s. The resonance radiation is collimated and the σ^+ circularly polarized component is produced using a polarizing prism and a quarter-wave plate. A small cube of fused quartz C contains Hg^{199} vapour in equilibrium with mercury in a connecting vessel at -20°C (vapour pressure $\sim 1{\cdot}6 \times 10^{-5}$ mm). The incident σ^+ 2537 Å radiation enters the quartz cell parallel to a homogeneous magnetic field H_0 produced by a pair of Helmholtz coils (60 cm in diameter) supplied by a well-stabilized d.c. power pack. The fluorescent radiation emitted in a direction at right angles to H_0 is linearly polarized and is detected using an analysing prism and a photomultiplier tube.

A radio-frequency magnetic field H_1 is applied to the vapour sample and means are provided for varying this frequency over a small range. If the resonance condition

$$\Delta E = h\nu = 2\mu H_0$$

is satisfied, where μ is the magnetic moment of the Hg^{199} nucleus, transitions between the $m = \frac{1}{2}$ and $m = -\frac{1}{2}$ levels of the ground state of the Hg^{199} atoms occur, thereby tending to equalize the populations of the two levels. This process can be regarded as a form of radio-frequency pumping reducing the high degree of nuclear alignment produced by optical pumping. An increase in the population of the $m = -\frac{1}{2}$ level is revealed by an increase in the intensity of the resonance π radiation. This is the signal used to detect nuclear magnetic resonance. In an experiment with Hg^{199}, the intensity of the π radiation changed by a factor of 3, corresponding to an initial degree of alignment characterized by populations $n(-\frac{1}{2}) = 17\%$, $n(+\frac{1}{2}) = 83\%$. It is necessary after turning on the optical pumping radiation to wait a second or two for a sufficient degree of alignment to be produced before switching on the alternating magnetic field. H_0 need not be very large (Brossel detected the nuclear resonance of Hg^{201} nuclei in a field of 35·6 gauss at a frequency of ~ 10 kc/s and also showed that the field H_0 varied linearly with frequency in the range 5 to 15 kc/s).

The optical method is capable of high precision and Brossel and his group determined the ratio of the nuclear magnetic moments of Hg^{201} (spin $^3/_2$) amd Hg^{199} (spin $\frac{1}{2}$)

$$\frac{\mu_{201}}{\mu_{199}} = 1{\cdot}107416 \pm 5 \times 10^{-6}$$

16.4. THE MAGNETIC MOMENT OF THE MUON†

The experimental measurement of the magnetic moment of the muon is intimately connected with the discovery of the non-conservation of parity in the decay of the pion and the muon.

$$\pi^{\pm} \rightarrow \mu^{\pm} + \nu(\bar{\nu})$$
$$\mu^{\pm} \rightarrow e^{\pm} + \bar{\nu} + \nu$$

The pioneer experiment of Garwin, Lederman and Weinrich†† which clearly established the failure of the parity law is described in Chapter 21. The important discovery, in the context of this chapter is that the muons formed in pion decay are longitudinally polarized with their spin axes preferentially orientated parallel to their linear momentum vectors. If the muons are brought to rest in a target medium, which does not seriously depolarize the muons, the decay electrons are preferentially emitted in a *backwards* direction.††† If the stopped muons precess in a

† We shall assume throughout this section that we are dealing with positive muons.
†† R. L. Garwin, L. M. Lederman and M. Weinrich, *Phys. Rev.* **105**, 1415, 1957.
††† J. I. Friedman and V. L. Telegdi, *Phys. Rev.* **105**, 1681, 1957.

magnetic field the angular distribution of the decay electrons varies at the Larmor precession frequency of the muon magnetic moment.

Accurate determinations of the muon magnetic moment have been made by investigating the spatial distribution of the decay electrons emitted by stopped muons precessing around a known uniform magnetic field. The muon g-factor can be calculated from the expression,

$$\mu = g \frac{e}{2m_\mu c} \frac{\hbar}{2} \tag{28}$$

where μ is the magnetic moment of the muon, m_μ is the muon rest mass (the muon spin is $\frac{1}{2}$). It is necessarry to know the muon mass m_μ with a high degree of precision. The best value of the muon mass has an accuracy of the order of 1 part in 10^4

$$m_\mu = (206{\cdot}76 \pm 0{\cdot}03)\, m_e\dagger$$

where m_e is the electron rest mass. Thus it is not possible to determine the g-factor of the muon by this method to an accuracy higher than 1 part in 10^4.

There is a number of reasons why a precise determination of the muon g-factor would be of great interest. If the muon behaves in all respects as a heavy electron it should exhibit an anomalous g-factor, predicted by quantum electrodynamics to be

$$g = 2(1 + a) \tag{29}$$

where the anomalous part

$$a = \frac{g-2}{2} = \frac{\alpha}{2\pi} + 0{\cdot}75\frac{\alpha^2}{\pi^2} + \;= 0{\cdot}001165 \tag{30}$$

where $1/\alpha = 137{\cdot}04$ (the fine structure constant).

The first term is associated with the emission and re-absorption of virtual photons by the "bare" muon.

If there is a breakdown in the laws of quantum electrodynamics at distances as small as l, the anomalous part of the muon g-factor is modified

$$a = \frac{\alpha}{2\pi}\left[1 - \frac{2}{3}\left(\frac{l}{\lambda_\mu}\right)^2\right] \tag{31}$$

where $\lambda_\mu = \dfrac{\hbar}{m_\mu c}$ is the reduced muon Compton wavelength (1·9 fermi). Notice that as the muon Compton wavelength is 207 times smaller than that of the electron, a measurement of the anomalous part of the muon g-factor is a more sensitive test of the laws of quantum electrodynamics than the analogous electron experiment.

† J. LANTHROP *et al.*, *Nuovo Cimento* **17**, 114, 1960.

Recently a direct determination of the anomalous part of the muon g-factor has been made at CERN Geneva.† This very difficult experiment is based on the method used to measure the anomalous g-factor of the electron.††

The muon experiment is illustrated in Fig. 10. High energy pions from a cyclotron decay in flight, and positive muons of momentum 150 MeV/c are selected by a bending magnet and focused by the lenses Q_1 and Q_2 on to a beryllium moderator. The muons lose energy in the

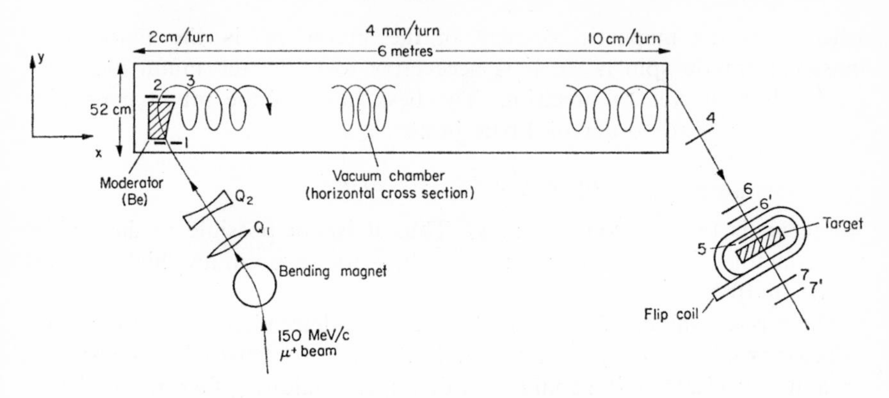

FIG. 10. Schematic arrangement of CERN apparatus to determine the muon g-factor.

moderator and emerge with a momentum of about 87 MeV/$c \pm 10\%$. The moderator is mounted at one end of a 6 m long vacuum chamber which is placed in the rectangular-shaped gap of an 85 ton electromagnet. The strong vertical magnetic field ($\sim$ 16 kilogauss) is not uniform, but is designed so that in the horizontal median plane (see Fig. 10) it is independent of the x coordinate, but depends on the y coordinate such that

$$B_z = B(1 + a\,y + b\,y^2 + c\,y^3) \tag{32}$$

The field gradient $\partial B_z/\partial y = a\,B$ produces a drift to the right with a "step–size" per turn given by

$$S = \pi\, R^2\, a\dagger\dagger\dagger \tag{33}$$

where R is the cyclotron orbit radius ($R = 19$ cm in the field B of 15·8 kilogauss). The term by^2, with b negative, provides vertical focusing

† G. CHARPAK, F. J. M. FARLEY, R. L. GARWIN, T. MULLER, J. C. SEN, V. L. TELEGDI and A. ZICHICHI, *Phys. Rev. Letters* **6**, 128, 1961.

†† D. F. NELSON, A. A. SCHUPP, R. W. PIDD and H. R. CRANE, *Phys. Rev. Letters* **2**, 492, 1959.

††† See eqn. 15 (a) p. 12, in J. G. LINHART, *Plasma Physics*, North Holland Publishing Co., Amsterdam 1960.

and the term cy^3 modifies the step size to

$$S = \pi R^2(a + 0{\cdot}75\, c\, R^2) \tag{34}$$

c is chosen to give constant S for all R values in the neighbourhood of the mean radius. The step–size is large ($\sim$ 2 cm/turn) near the moderator to get the muons quickly away. A slow transition in the field gradient reduces S to 4 mm/turn over the major portion of the muon walk. At the right-hand end of the vacuum chamber the step–size is increased to 10 cm/turn so that the muons pass easily out of the vacuum chamber. A change in the field of 0·1 per cent from one end of the storage region to the other would produce a 2·5 cm sideways displacement of the orbit. To prevent loss of muons by sideways drifting the local irregularities in the field are corrected by magnetic shims.

The polarized muons enter the vacuum chamber with their spin axes parallel to their momentum vector. If muons behaved like Dirac particles with a g-factor of exactly 2, the angular velocity of rotation ω_s of the spin axis around the vertical field would be exactly equal to the cyclotron angular frequency ω_c. Thus the muons would retain their longitudinal polarization in the magnetic field. If, as theoretically anticipated, the muon g-factor is not exactly 2, the muon spin rotates $(1 + \gamma\, a)$ times as fast† as the linear momentum vector, where γ is the ratio of the total energy of the muon to its rest mass energy and $a = (g - 2)/2$. After drifting for a time t in the magnetic field the angle between the spin axis and the momentum will increase from zero to

$$\theta = (\omega_s - \omega_c)\, t = \omega_c\, \gamma\, a\, t = B\, \omega_0\, a\, t \tag{35}$$

where ω_0 is the cyclotron angular frequency for very low energy muons ($\gamma = 1$) in unit magnetic field.

The muon storage time t is in the range from 2·0 to 6·5 μsec. Increasing the storage time beyond 7 or 8 μsec is not worthwhile because the mean life of a muon at rest is 2·2 μsec. A complicated electronic system measures the storage time to 1 per cent and makes sure that less than 0·1 per cent of the injected muons are counted as the wrong parent for an emerging muon.

It is necessary to measure the polarization angle θ as well as the storage time t, in order to calculate the factor a from eqn. (35). The polarization angle is measured in the following way. The muons emerging from the storage field are stopped in a non-depolarizing target of methylene iodide, where the magnetic field is less than 0·1 gauss. Half the muons stopped in the target have their spin axes flipped clockwise 90° by a pulsed vertical magnetic field produced by an aluminium tape coil wrapped round the target. The other half are flipped anticlockwise through 90°.

† H. Mendlowitz and K. M. Case, *Phys. Rev.* **97**, 33, 1955.

Electrons emitted "backwards" from the stopped muons are registered as a 6–6′ coincidence in coincidence with pulses from counters 4 and 5 gated by counters 1, 2 and 3 (no pulse from counter 7). These events are stored in channels 1–50 of a pulse height analyser as a function of the storage time of the parent muon in the magnet field. Similar events associated with "forward" decaying electrons (detected by counters 7 and 7′) are stored according to storage time in channels 51–100. The asymmetry A is defined by

$$A = \frac{C_n^+ - C_n^-}{C_n^+ + C_n^-}$$

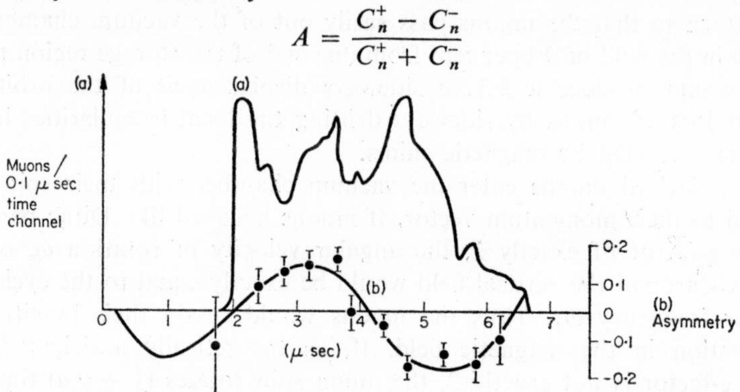

FIG. 11. (a) Muon storage time distribution; (b) asymmetry curve.

where C_n^+ and C_n^- are the counts recorded in the nth channel for $\pm 90°$ flipping. In Fig. 11(b) the asymmetry A is plotted as a function of storage time. The time distribution of the muon storage time is also shown. The asymmetry is zero for storage times which correspond to $\theta = n\pi$ (n an integer). The maximum asymmetry of $+0{\cdot}17$ occurs for a storage time of about 3·2 μsec and corresponds to approximately 525 cyclotron revolutions; the polarization angle θ is 270°. The orientation of the spin axis of such a muon stopped in the target is shown in Fig. 12(a) together with a pictorial representation of the inherent angular distribution of the decay electron (the length of each vector is proportional to the probability of the electron being emitted in this direction). In Fig. 12(b) and (c) the situation when the spin axis has been flipped $+90°$ and $-90°$ is depicted. The ratio of the number of decay electrons recorded by the counters 6–6′ and 7–7′ is $^{35}/_{25}$ when the spin is flipped by $+90°$ and $^{25}/_{35}$ for a spin flip of $-90°$. The asymmetry is

$$A = \frac{35 - 25}{35 + 25} = 0{\cdot}17$$

This experiment gave the result†

$$a_{\text{expt}} = 0{\cdot}001145 \pm 0{\cdot}000022$$

† A revised value of $(1 \cdot 162 \pm 0 \cdot 005) \times 10^{-3}$ is given in a later paper: G. CHARPAK *et al*, *Phys. Letters* **1**, 16, 1962.

This result is within 2 per cent of the theoretical value calculated by quantum electrodynamics. The following important conclusions can be drawn.

(1) The muon appears to be a heavy electron. The large muon–electron mass difference is not explained.

(2) There is no breakdown in the laws of quantum electrodynamics down to distances as short as 7×10^{-14} cm.

(3) The muon radius is less than $2{\cdot}5 \times 10^{-14}$ cm.

(4) If there is some fundamental unit of length in Nature it is less than 2×10^{-14} cm.

(5) The experimental value of the muon *g*-factor combined with an accurate measurement of the muon spin precession frequency gives for the rest mass of the muon.

$$m_\mu = (206{\cdot}77 \pm 0{\cdot}01)\, m_e$$

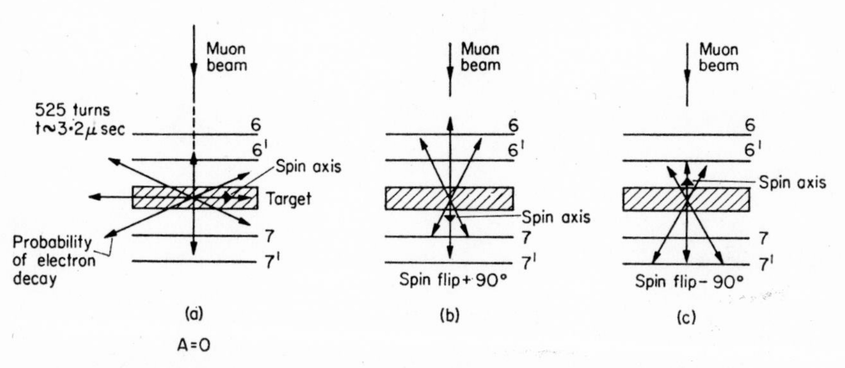

FIG. 12. (a) Muon of storage time $t = 3{\cdot}2\,\mu$sec stopped in target with spin axis pointing to the right ($\theta = 270°$). Vectors indicate decay probability distribution; (b) muon spin flipped through $+90°$ (Counts recorded by 6–6′ are considerably greater than counts recorded by 7–7′); (c) muon spin flipped through $-90°$.

BIBLIOGRAPHY

N. F. RAMSEY, *Nuclear Moments* in *Experimental Nuclear Physics*, Vol. 1. Ed. by E. Segrè, Wiley, New York 1953.

N. F. RAMSEY, *Molecular Beams*, Oxford University Press, 1956.

E. R. ANDREW, *Nuclear Magnetic Resonance*, Cambridge University Press, 1955.

The most comprehensive treatise on N.M.R. is A. ABRAGAM, *The Principles of Nuclear Magnetism*, Oxford University Press, 1961.

EXAMPLES

1. At what radio-frequency does nuclear magnetic resonance occur for a water sample in a uniform magnetic field of 10,000 gauss? (The proton magnetic moment is 2·793 nuclear magnetons, 1 nuclear magneton is $0{\cdot}5050 \times 10^{-23}$ erg gauss^{-1}.) What is the corresponding frequency in the earth's field, where the horizontal component is 0·18 gauss and the angle of dip is 69°?

2. Nuclear magnetic resonance occurs at frequencies of 34·06 Mc/s and 9·009 Mc/s for an aqueous solution of sodium hydroxide in a uniform magnetic field of 8000 gauss. Calculate the magnetic moment (in nuclear magnetons) of the Na^{23} nucleus (abundance 100 per cent). Na^{23} has a nuclear spin of 3/2.
3. A 0·10 cm³ water sample at 17°C is placed in a very homogeneous magnetic field H_0 of 10,000 gauss. What is the difference in population of the two magnetic sub-states of the protons in the water sample? A linear oscillating magnetic field of amplitude 0·10 gauss is applied at the exact proton resonance frequency. The spin–spin relaxation time is 10^{-4} sec and the spin–lattice relaxation time T_1 is varied by altering the small amount of paramagnetic salt added to the sample. If T_1 is 10^{-3} sec, how long does it take for the excess proton population in the lower magnetic sub-state to reach 0·85 of its new saturation value (assume H_0 is applied first)? What is the rate of rise of temperature of the sample if $T_1 = 10^{-3}$, 10^{-2} sec?

CHAPTER 17

NUCLEAR FISSION

17.1. INTRODUCTION

In 1934, Fermi and his colleagues began their extensive search for radioactive isotopes induced by neutron irradiation of the elements. A large number of induced activities was found, and it was speculated that the neutron irradiation of the elements at the top of the periodic table (Th, Pa, U) might lead to the formation of new transuranic elements. No suspicion was entertained, however, that certain heavy nuclei might break into two roughly equal nuclear fragments when they capture a neutron.

The irradiation of natural uranium is complicated by the existence of three isotopes: U^{234}, 0·005%; U^{235}, 0·71%; U^{238}, 99·28%. The production of transuranic elements by neutron irradiation does occur, but it requires stronger neutron sources than the Ra–Be type. McMillan and Abelson† first identified the 23·5 min and the 2·33 d activities produced by the irradiation of uranium with neutrons generated by the $Be^{9}(d, n)\,B^{10}$ reaction as isotopes of uranium and neptunium (element 93):

$$_{92}U^{238}\,(n, \gamma)\,_{92}U^{239}$$

$$_{92}U^{239} \xrightarrow[\text{min}]{23\cdot5} {}_{93}Np^{239} + e^- + \bar{\nu}$$

$$_{93}Np^{239} \xrightarrow[2\cdot33\text{d}]{} {}_{94}Pu^{239} + e^- + \bar{\nu}$$

The isotope of element 94, plutonium, is an α-emitter (decaying to U^{235}) with a half-life of about 20,000 y.

The discovery of nuclear fission, in 1939, preceded the identification of neptunium and plutonium. Hahn and his colleagues in Berlin found several short lived activities in neutron-irradiated uranium salts.†† In studying the chemical properties of one of these activities, of half-life 3·5 hr, they concluded that it probably was an isotope of element 88 (Ra), for they had ruled out on chemical grounds the possibilities of actinium (89), thorium (90), protactinium (91), uranium(92) and elements 93 and 94. Nevertheless, the hypothetical $_{92}U\,(n, 2\alpha)\,_{88}Ra$ reaction with

† E. M. McMillan and P. H. Abelson, *Phys. Rev.* **57**, 1185, 1940.

†† The discovery of fission isotopes is described in the book, O. Hahn, *New Atoms*, Elsevier Press, 1950.

thermal neutrons was considered a very unlikely process. To settle the identity of the 3·5 hr activity, Hahn and Strassmann tried to separate the "Ra" isotope from barium by the technique known as fractional crystallization (used 50 years before by Madame Curie in the isolation of radium). The 3·5 hr activity, however, could not be separated from Ba; and its daughter activity had all the chemical and physical properties of lanthanum. After a further series of chemical tests, Hahn came to the conclusion that neutron irradiation of uranium led to the production of a radioactive isotope of barium (element 56). This conclusion was viewed with scepticism by the majority of nuclear physicists at the time, for they could not see how a nucleus of an element near the middle of the periodic table could be produced by the bombardment of uranium with slow neutrons.

A tentative physical explanation was put forward by Lise Meitner and O. R. Frisch†. They suggested that the uranium nucleus on capturing a neutron is set into oscillation, thereby resembling a vibrating drop of liquid. If the vibrating nucleus develops a thin waist in the middle, the Coulomb repulsion of the two halves may overcome the nuclear surface tension forces and result in the splitting or *fission* of the nucleus into two roughly equal mass fragments. The fission process is expected to release a large amount of energy, for nuclei near the middle of the periodic table have a mean binding energy of the order of 8·5 MeV per nucleon in contrast to uranium with a value of about 7·6 MeV per nucleon. Assuming fission of a nucleus of mass $A \sim 240$ into two similar fragments with $A \sim 120$, the anticipated energy released in fission is $\sim 2 \times 120 \times 8{\cdot}5 - 240 \times 7{\cdot}6 \simeq 200$ MeV! Another simple way of roughly estimating the fission energy is to write down the Coulomb energy E_c of the two nuclear fission fragments at the moment of fission, assuming their separation is equal to the sum of their nuclear radii. Suppose uranium fissions into xenon ($Z_1 = 54$) and strontium ($Z_2 = 38$); notice that the sum of the atomic numbers is 92, the atomic number of uranium. The separation d of the centres of these nuclei when they are just touching is about $1{\cdot}5 \times 10^{-12}$ cm. Thus the Coulomb energy

$$E_c = \frac{Z_1 Z_2 e^2}{d} = \frac{54 \times 38 \times (4{\cdot}8 \times 10^{-10})^2}{1{\cdot}5 \times 10^{-12} \times 1{\cdot}6 \times 10^{-6}} \text{ MeV}$$

$$E_c \sim 200 \text{ MeV}.$$

Frisch†† confirmed the fission hypothesis by exposing an ionization chamber, with thin layers of uranium deposited on the electrodes, to thermal neutrons. The ionization chamber was connected to a linear amplifier and clear evidence was obtained for the high energy of the

† L. Meitner and O. R. Frisch, *Nature* **143**, 239, 1939.
†† O. R. Frisch, *Nature* **143**, 852, 1939.

fission fragments from the large size of the pulses. The fission pulses have a wide distribution in size, which is compatible with the radiochemical evidence that the fission process can take place in many different ways. The distribution in the energy of the fission fragments from uranium irradiated with slow neutrons is shown in Fig. 1. Fission energies are obtained from the total ionization produced in argon; the fragments have a very short range as they ionize matter intensely. Unlike α-particles, however, the specific ionization of fission fragments is greatest at the beginning of their range (when the net charge of the fragment is greatest); along their track they continually pick up electrons thereby reducing the ionizing power of the fragment.

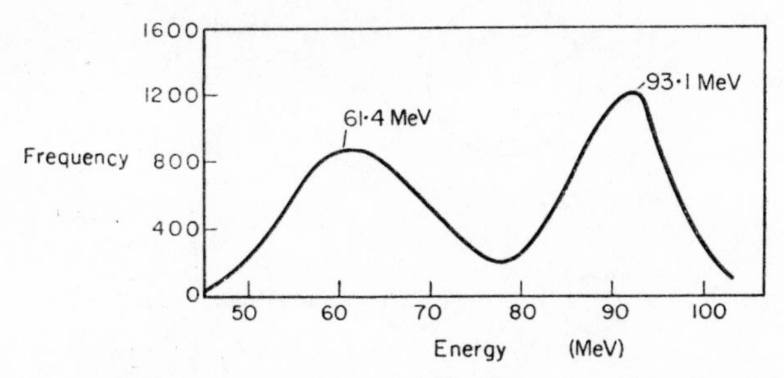

FIG. 1. Relative frequency of fission fragment energies (U^{235} irradiated with slow neutrons).

It is useful to picture the fission of a nucleus as happening in three distinct stages (Fig. 2). The fission of uranium with slow neutrons is confined to the U^{235} isotope (first suspected by N. Bohr) and it is the compound nucleus U^{236} which undergoes fission. The fission of the compound nucleus of charge Z_0 and mass A_0 produces two excited nuclei of charge Z_1 and Z_2 and mass A_1 and A_2. Within about 10^{-15} sec, these excited nuclei emit a few neutrons and occasionally α-particles. The emission of neutrons is likened to the evaporation of molecules from a heated liquid drop. Near the end of this short de-excitation period, γ-rays are emitted and we obtain a pair of nuclei (Z_3, A_3) and (Z_4, A_4). These nuclei are still neutron-rich, in spite of the neutron evaporation process, and are unstable against negative beta decay. Provided these nuclei have half-lives which are not too short, they are detectable by radiochemical methods. Following a series of beta transformations, the fission fragments change into stable end-products characterized by (Z_5, A_5) and (Z_6, A_6). A typical beta decay chain is

$$_{54}Xe^{140} \xrightarrow{16\text{ sec}} {}_{55}Cs^{140} \xrightarrow{66\text{ sec}} {}_{56}Ba^{140} \xrightarrow{2\cdot8\text{ d}} {}_{57}La^{140} \xrightarrow{40\text{ hr}} {}_{58}Ce^{140} \text{ (stable)}$$

The prompt emission of neutrons and the subsequent beta decay is a consequence of the greater neutron–proton number ratio in heavy nuclei compared with stable nuclei near the middle of the periodic table.

17.2. MASS DISTRIBUTION OF FISSION FRAGMENTS

In a very small fraction of nuclear fissions (less than 1 in 10^4), the nucleus splits into three fragments of roughly the same size. Sometimes fission into two heavy fragments and a high energy α-particle occurs. We shall ignore these rare modes of fission and concentrate on the two fragment mode.

The fission of U^{235} on neutron capture into two fragments can occur in a large number of different ways. The statistical distribution of mass between the fission fragments has been studied by standard radiochemical

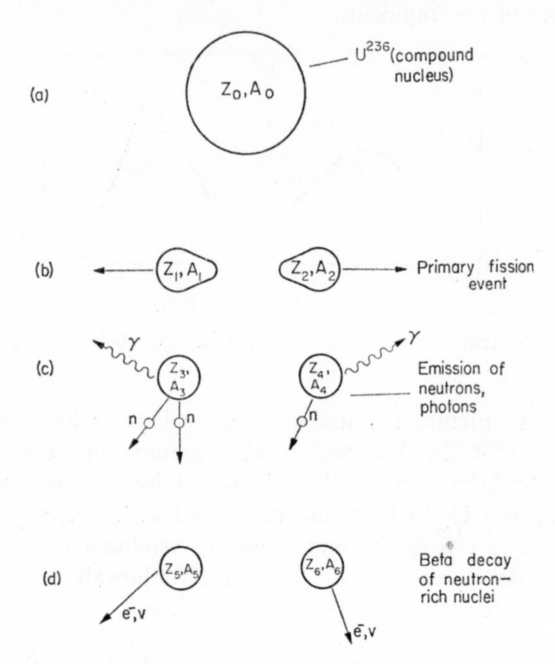

FIG. 2. Various stages of fission process and subsequent de-excitation of nuclei.

techniques. In all probability the radiochemical analysis identifies nuclei somewhere between the stages of the evaporation of neutrons and the final stable nuclei at the end of the beta decay chains. Radiochemical mass-yield measurements are accurate to about 10 per cent. Mass spectroscopic determinations are now used, and they yield results accurate to about 3 per cent. The mass yields for the thermal neutron fission of U^{235} are shown graphically in Fig. 3, based on data collected by Katcoff†. The yield for the heavy and light fission fragments is plotted as a per cent number normalized to 100 per cent for each type of fragment separately. The

† S. KATCOFF, *Nucleonics* **16**, 78, April 1958.

two curves are adjusted so that the sum of the masses of the heavy and the corresponding light mass fragments is 233·5. The mass difference, 236 − 233·5 = 2·5, is the average number of prompt neutrons emitted in the fission of the compound nucleus of U^{236}. The most probable division of mass between the fragments is close to $A = 139$ and $A = 95$. The occurrence of symmetric fission—that is, fission into fragments of equal mass is a very rare event and occurs in about 0·01 per cent of all cases.

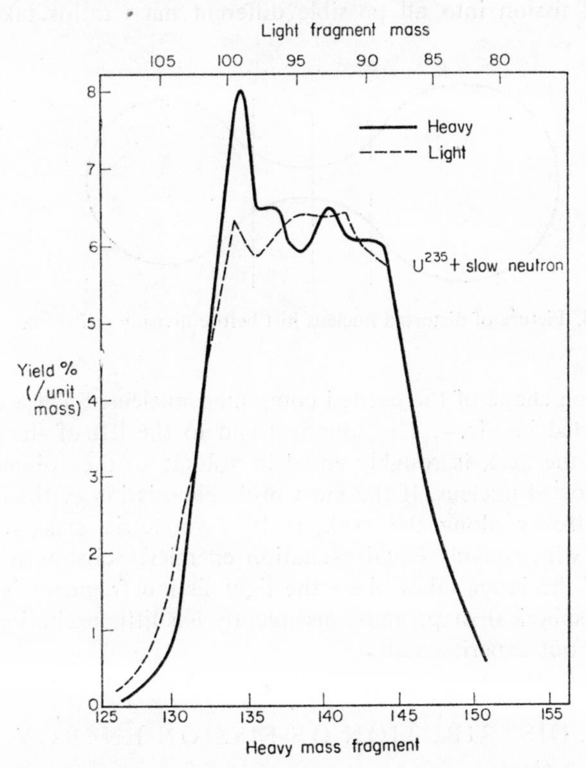

FIG. 3. Mass distribution of nuclei formed in fission of U^{235} by thermal neutrons.

The shapes of the mass distribution depend on the type and energy of the projectile inducing fission. Two general features are found at high projectile bombarding energies: the tendency towards symmetric fission increases, and the distribution in mass becomes much wider. These features are clearly shown in the fission of uranium with 150 MeV protons and in the fission of bismuth with 60 MeV protons and 190 MeV deuterons. There is good evidence that the tendency to symmetric fission is associated with fissions which require high excitation energies.

The highly asymmetric distribution of mass in low energy excitation fission is one of the more striking features of the fission phenomenon.

A completely satisfactory theory of fission should be able to explain the origin of this asymmetry and the general shape of the mass distribution curves. A number of tentative explanations of the asymmetry has been suggested, but it has not been possible to decide which of these (if any), or which combination of ideas, is correct. A discussion of the origin of the asymmetric mass distribution is given in the review article by Halpern (see bibliography). One possible explanation of asymmetric fission is that fission into all possible different mass ratios takes place

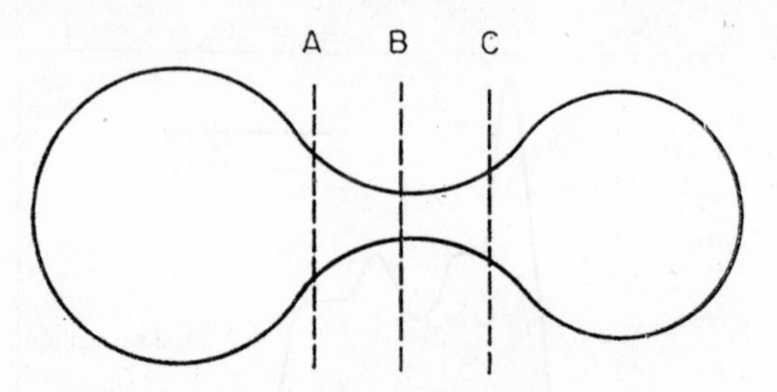

FIG. 4. Picture of distorted nucleus just before division (scission).

from a common shape of the excited compound nucleus. Such a common shape is depicted in Fig. 4. The spherical end to the left of the plane A at the end of the neck is roughly equal in volume to the volume of the rest of the distorted nucleus. If the most probable scission of the distorted nucleus is half-way along the neck at B, asymmetric mass fragments are produced with roughly equal excitation energies. Scission at A or C is unlikely; if the latter takes place the light fission fragment is formed with nearly a spherical shape and consequently has little excitation energy (this is borne out experimentally).

17.3. DISTRIBUTION OF FISSION ENERGY

The total energy released in the fission of a nucleus is divided between the kinetic energy of the fission fragments, prompt neutrons and γ-rays, β-particles and antineutrinos (γ-rays may be emitted following beta decay). In a few cases (see later) delayed neutrons are emitted. The distribution of the energy between these particles in the slow neutron fission of U^{235} is given in Table 1. The major fraction of the energy is associated with the kinetic energy of the fragments.

A small fraction of the neutrons associated with nuclear fission are not emitted immediately after scission (within 10^{-15} sec). In the slow neutron fission of U^{235}, less than 1 per cent of the emitted neutrons are *delayed* with respect to the scission events. There are five or six groups of delayed neutrons; each group is characterized by a definite half-life. One group of delayed neutrons is observed with a half-life of 55·6 sec, which is the same as the half-life of Br^{87}. Now Br^{87} is a possible fission product and it seems very probable that the delayed neutrons are neutrons emitted immediately after the beta decay of Br^{87}. Thus if the Kr^{87} nucleus, formed as the result of the beta decay of a nucleus of Br^{87}, is created in an excited state it promptly emits a neutron (the "last" neutron, the 51st in Kr^{87} has an abnormally low binding energy). In a similar way the 22 sec group of delayed neutrons is associated with prompt neutron emission from an excited state of Xe^{137}, following the beta decay of 22 sec I^{137}. The existence of delayed neutrons is of vital importance in the practical control of the chain reaction in a nuclear reactor.

TABLE 1. FISSION OF U^{235} BY SLOW NEUTRONS

Form	Energy (MeV)
Kinetic energy of fission fragments	167 ± 5
Prompt neutrons	5
Prompt gamma rays	6 ± 1
Beta decay energy	8 ± 1·5
Antineutrino energy in beta decay	12 ± 2·5
Gamma radiation	6 ± 1
Total energy	204 ± 7

17.4. SPONTANEOUS FISSION

The important discovery was made in 1940, by Flerov and Petrzhak†, that uranium spontaneously undergoes fission (the half-life is much longer than the well-known alpha decay value). This process of spontaneous fission occurs without any excitation energy and it seems very probable that it occurs as the result of a quantum mechanical penetration of an electrostatic potential barrier inhibiting the immediate break-up of the heavy nucleus. In one gram of natural uranium about one spontaneous fission occurs every 100 sec. The spontaneous fission half-life is lower by a factor of a hundred or so for the even mass nuclides of a given isotope ($U^{235} \cdots 2 \times 10^{17}$ y, $U^{238} \cdots 8 \times 10^{15}$ y). Measurements of spontaneous fission half-lives of many of the new transuranic isotopes have been of value as they have revealed some systematic trends. One important general observation is that the logarithm of the fission half-life falls off as Z/A increases. This is an over-simplification but, nevertheless, one does find that the heavier even-A isotopes of high Z (~ 100) nuclei have short half-lives.

† G. N. FLEROV and K. A. PETRZHAK, *Phys. Rev.* **58**, 89, 1940.

17.5. AVERAGE NUMBER OF NEUTRONS RELEASED IN FISSION

The number of neutrons evaporated from the highly excited nuclei formed on scission is a statistical factor. The probabilities of the emission of n neutrons in the fission of U^{235} with 80 keV neutrons are set out in Table 2. The most probable number is 2 and the average number $\bar{\nu}$ per fission is 2·45.

TABLE 2. $\bar{\nu} = 2{\cdot}45$

n	0	1	2	3	4	5
Prob.	0·02	0·17	0.36	0·31	0·12	0·03

Increasing the incident neutron energy to 1·25 MeV increases $\bar{\nu}$ to 2·65. This is a consequence of the increased excitation of the compound nucleus. An interesting discovery, using a coincidence method, is that about 30 per cent more of the prompt neutrons are evaporated from the light fragment than from the heavy one in the thermal neutron fission of the nuclides U^{233}, U^{235} and Pu^{239}.

A high value of $\bar{\nu}$ is desirable for the maintenance of a fission chain reaction, and one advantage of the Pu^{239} isotope over U^{235} as a reactor fuel is that $\bar{\nu}$ is as high as 3·0 for Pu^{239}. A few experimental values of $\bar{\nu}$ for spontaneous fission isotopes are given in Table 3.

TABLE 3

Nuclide	$\bar{\nu}$
Th^{230}	1·24 ± 0·15
U^{238}	2·30 ± 0·20
Pu^{240}	2·23 ± 0·05
Cm^{242}	2·59 ± 0·11
Cf^{254}	3·90 ± 0·14
Fm^{254}	4·05 ± 0·19

17.6. FISSION CROSS SECTIONS

There have been many measurements of the thermal neutron fission cross sections of various nuclides†. Some of these are given in Table 4 and it is seen that there is considerable doubt the absolute values of these cross sections.

† See Vol. 15 of *Proc. Intern. Conference. Peaceful Uses Atomic Energy*, 2nd Conf., Geneva 1958.

The slow neutron cross sections of fissionable nuclides have been examined as a function of neutron energy E using time-of-flight methods ("choppers") and the crystal spectrometer. Nuclear fission with low energy neutrons exhibits many marked resonances at definite energies,

TABLE 4. THERMAL NEUTRON FISSION CROSS SECTIONS

Nuclide	σ_f (barns)	σ_f/σ_{abs}
U^{233}	518 ± 4 530 ± 8	0·90
U^{235}	556 ± 6 576 ± 15 542 ± 4 590 ± 6 623 ± 14	0·84
Pu^{239}	779 ± 5	0·7
Pu^{241}	1055 ± 8	0·8
Am^{242}	6390 ± 500	0·75

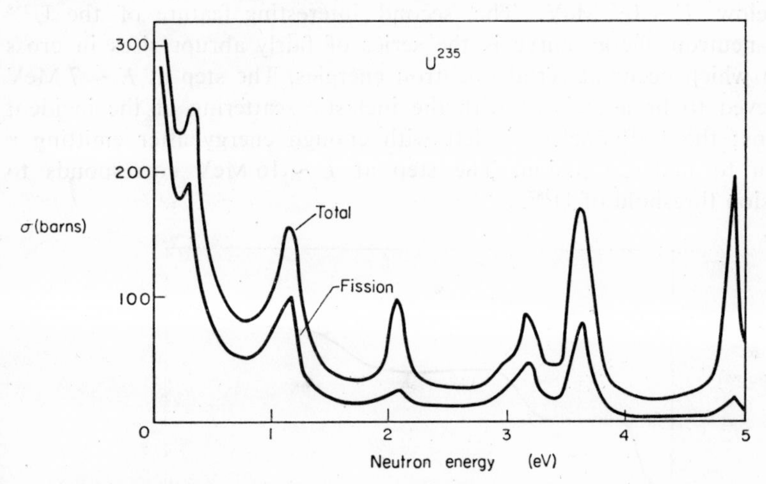

FIG. 5. The total and fission cross sections in U^{235} in the range 0·1 to 5 eV. (Based on crystal spectrometer measurements of Shore and Sailor.)

typical of compound nucleus formation. The total σ_t and fission σ_f cross sections of U^{235} with neutrons of energy in the range 0·1 to 5 eV are shown graphically in Fig. 5†. The partial widths Γ_γ, Γ_f of several of the resonances of neutron induced fission of U^{235} are given in Table 5.

† F. J. SHORE and V. L. SAILOR, Vol. 15, p. 118, *Proc. Intern. Conference Peaceful Uses Atomic Energy*, 2nd Conf. Geneva 1958.

From the data in Table 5 we see that the average fission width is about 0·06 eV and the radiative–capture widths are approximately constant with a value of about 0·03 eV. The fission widths in contrast show fairly large fluctuations from level to level.

TABLE 5. RESONANCES IN NEUTRON FISSION OF U^{235} Γ(meV)

E_0 (eV)	Γ_γ	Γ_f
0·29 ± 0·005	34 ± 7	105 ± 5
1·13 ± 0·01	30 ± 10	120 ± 15
2·04 ± 0·03	30 ± 6	14 ± 3
2·82 ± 0·05	—	70 ± 45
3·14 ± 0·02	—	135 ± 25
3·61 ± 0·02	—	65 ± 10
4·84 ± 0·02	—	20 ± 10

The fission cross section of U^{238} as a function of neutron energy E is shown in Fig. 6. The following features are noteworthy. The cross section falls off steeply below $E \sim 1{\cdot}5$ MeV and is very difficult to measure below $E \sim 0{\cdot}5$ MeV. The second interesting feature of the U^{238} fission–neutron energy curve is the series of fairly abrupt rises in cross section which occur at certain neutron energies. The step at $E \sim 7$ MeV is believed to be associated with the inelastic scattering of the incident neutrons; the U^{239} nucleus is left with enough energy after emitting a neutron to undergo fission. The step at $E \sim 16$ MeV corresponds to the fission threshold of U^{237}.

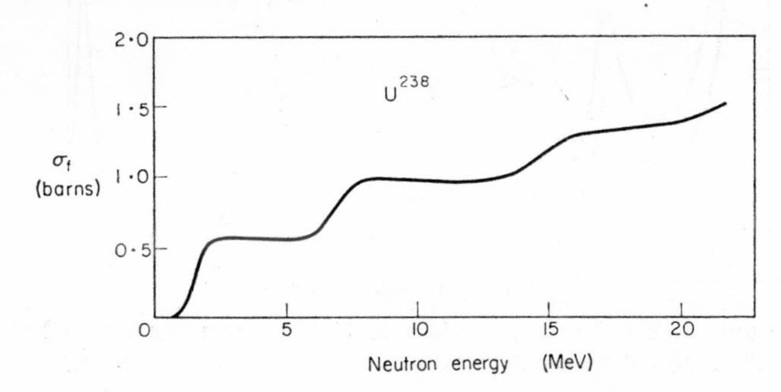

FIG. 6. Fast-neutron fission cross section of U^{238}.

17.7. THEORY OF NUCLEAR FISSION

Any nucleus, if it receives sufficient excitation energy, may undergo fission. However, let us confine our considerations to the fission of the heaviest nuclei, those, in fact, with the smallest mean binding energy per nucleon. The immediate splitting of a heavy nucleus into two medium weight nuclear fragments is prevented by a fission potential barrier; that is, the heavy nucleus is in a metastable state, awaiting the supply of an amount of energy E_t (the threshold energy) to lift it over the fission barrier. This is a classical argument and the existence of spontaneous fission shows that if the nucleus is in an energy state just below the top of the fission barrier, fission may occur through barrier penetration. A hypothetical diagram of the fission barrier for a heavy nucleus is shown in Fig. 7. Here r is the separation of the two fission fragments and for $r > r_1 + r_2$, where r_1 and r_2 are the radii of the fragments, the energy is the familiar Coulomb potential. The heavy nucleus will undergo fission if it receives an amount of energy equal to or greater than E_t.

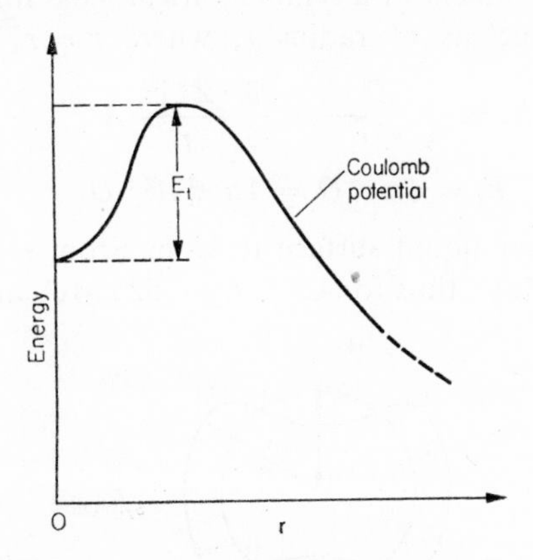

FIG. 7. Hypothetical fission barrier for heavy nucleus. E_t is the fission threshold energy.

Heavy nuclei can be fissioned by photons, protons, deuterons, etc. . . . as well as by neutrons. The minimum photon energy required to induce fission is a convenient measure of the fission threshold energy E_t. A few fission threshold energies measured in this way are Th^{232} – 5·8, U^{233} – 5·4, U^{235} – 5·7, U^{238} – 5·8, Pu^{239} – 5·4 (all energies given in MeV). Fission thresholds have also been determined from (n, f) and (d, pf) reactions. There is some ambiguity in the definition of threshold energy in these cases (see the review article by Halpern p. 259). The (d, pf) reaction† is compared to the (d, p) reaction in the same target nucleus. The nucleus is excited by a neutron captured from the incident deuteron, and the proton flies away without entering the nucleus (this is an example of a "stripping" reaction); the excited compound nucleus may then undergo fission.

† A proton is emitted and then fission occurs.

The outstanding contribution to the theory of fission was made soon after the discoveries of Hahn, Meitner and Frisch. N. Bohr and J. Wheeler†, and independently J. Frenkel in Russia, developed a model of nuclear fission in terms of a vibrating drop of incompressible electrically charged "nuclear liquid". They made use of the concept of nuclear surface tension associated with the tendency of a deformed nucleus to return to its original spherical shape. In the context of the liquid drop model of fission, there are only two energy terms which contribute to the change in binding energy of the vibrating excited nucleus: the Coulomb energy E_c and the surface energy E_s. The latter is associated with the property that surface nucleons contribute less to the nuclear binding energy than other (internal) nucleons. These energy terms have been discussed in relation to the establishment of a semi-empirical mass formula (Chapter 8). For an unexcited nucleus of radius r, where $r = r_0 A^{1/3}$,

$$E_c = \frac{3}{5}\frac{Z^2 e^2}{r} = \frac{3}{5}\frac{Z^2 e^2}{r_0} A^{-1/3} \tag{1}$$

$$E_s = 4\pi r^2 O = 4\pi r_0^2 A^{2/3} O \tag{2}$$

where O is the nuclear liquid surface tension. From semi-empirical mass data, $4\pi r_0^2 O \sim 13$ MeV; thus for U^{238}, $E_s \sim 520$ MeV and $E_c \sim 830$ MeV.

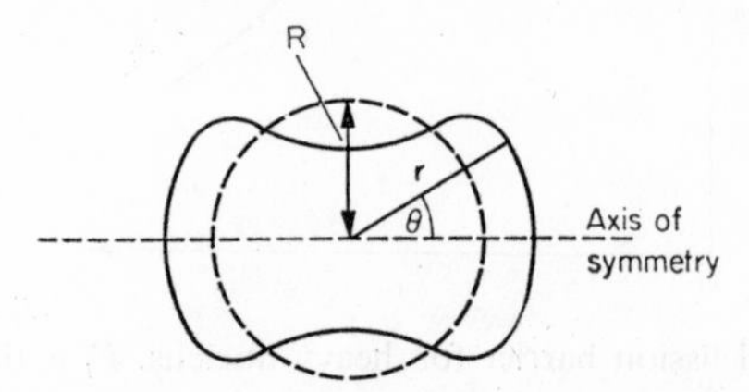

FIG. 8. Hypothetical axial symmetric deformation of nucleus.

When the nucleus is deformed its surface area increases thereby increasing E_s; this assumes no change in the volume of the nucleus and the constancy of the surface tension O. On the other hand, the Coulomb energy E_c decreases as the mean distance between the protons inside the nucleus increases with increasing amplitude of vibration. As the amplitude of vibration increases the net energy change increases at first but then passes through a maximum and decreases. The maximum corresponds to a critical energy and configuration: the nucleus is on the point of fission.

For the sake of simplicity it is useful to assume that the deformed nucleus has axial symmetry and its surface is defined by the polar coordinates (r, θ) measured from the centre of the nucleus. The deformed nuclear surface (Fig. 8) is represented (for small distortions) by

$$r = R[1 + \alpha_2 P_2(\cos\theta)] \tag{3}$$

† N. BOHR and J. A. WHEELER, *Phys. Rev.* **56**, 426, 1939. See also D. L. HILL and J. A. WHEELER, *Phys. Rev.* **89**, 1102, 1953.

where R is the radius of the spherical nucleus and α_2 is a distortion parameter. P_2 is the second Legendre polynomial, $P_2(\cos\theta) = \frac{1}{2}(3\cos^2\theta - 1)$.

Bohr and Wheeler obtained for the surface and Coulomb energies for small axial distortions

$$E_s' = 4\pi\, r_0^2\, A^{2/3}\, O[1 + \tfrac{2}{5}\alpha_2^2 \cdots] \tag{4}$$

$$E_c' = \frac{3}{5}\,\frac{Z^2 e^2}{r_0}\,A^{-1/3}\,[1 - \tfrac{1}{5}\alpha_2^2 \cdots] \tag{5}$$

Thus the energy changes accompanying the small distortion are given by

$$\Delta E_s = E_s' - E_s = +\tfrac{2}{5}\alpha_2^2\, E_s. \tag{6}$$

$$\Delta E_c = E_c' - E_c = -\tfrac{1}{5}\alpha_2^2\, E_c. \tag{7}$$

For the nucleus to be stable against small distortions the ratio x must be less than one, where

$$x = \left|\frac{\Delta E_c}{\Delta E_s}\right| = \frac{1}{2}\,\frac{E_c}{E_s} \tag{8}$$

Using the values, $E_s = 520$ MeV and $E_c = 830$ MeV for U^{238}, we obtain the value $x \sim 0{\cdot}8$ for U^{238}; hence it is stable against prompt spontaneous fission. Nuclides with $x = 1$ have a Z^2/A value $1/1{\cdot}08$ times that of U^{238}, that is about 45. Thus nuclei with $Z^2/A \geqq 45$ are unstable against fission.

The energy changes in the fission of a nucleus (Z, A) of radius R into two identical nuclei each of charge $Z/2$ and radius r are easily found: $(R^3 = 2r^3)$

$$\Delta E_s = 2 \times 4\pi\,\frac{R^2\,O}{2^{2/3}} - 4\pi\,R^2\,O = (2^{1/3} - 1)\,E_s = +0{\cdot}26\,E_s$$

$$\Delta E_c = 2 \times \frac{3}{5}\left(\frac{Z}{2}\right)^2 \frac{e^2}{R}\cdot 2^{1/3} - \frac{3}{5}\,\frac{Z^2}{R}\,e^2 = (2^{-2/3} - 1)E_c = -\,0{\cdot}74\,x\,E_s$$

The net energy released in symmetrical fission is $(0{\cdot}74x - 0{\cdot}26)E_s$ and provided $0{\cdot}35 < x < 1$, this is an exothermic process. Although the nucleus (Z, A) is stable against small α_2-type distortions, we see that if sufficient excitation energy is supplied to the nucleus it will pass through a critical shape and undergo fission with a net energy release.

It is possible to estimate the degree of distortion of a nucleus in the critical state by equating the measured threshold energy E_t to the sum of the changes in E_s and E_c

$$E_t = \Delta E_s + \Delta E_c = \tfrac{1}{5}\alpha_2^2(2E_s - E_c) \tag{9}$$

For U^{238} the photofission threshold energy is 5·8 MeV, $E_s = 520$ MeV and $E_c = 830$ MeV; thus

$$\alpha_2^2 = \frac{5 \times 5{\cdot}8}{1040 - 830} \sim \frac{1}{7}$$

In the critical state,

$$\Delta E_s = \frac{1040}{35} \sim 29 \text{ MeV}$$

and

$$\Delta E_c = -\frac{830}{35} \sim -23 \text{ MeV}$$

The threshold energy is the relatively small difference of two fairly large energies. It is obvious that the reverse procedure of calculating E_t from a number of assumed distortion parameter values is not very accurate.

It is not difficult to explain why the nuclides U^{233}, U^{235}, Pu^{239} are fissionable with slow neutrons whereas U^{238} and Th^{232} are not. In the former instances, neutron capture leads to the formation of an even–even nucleus with the additional excitation energy provided by the paired nucleon spin binding energy.

The liquid drop model of fission has a number of shortcomings which should not be overlooked. The assumption that only the energy terms E_s and E_c are involved in the shape distortions of the nucleus is questionable. Also it is doubtful whether it is satisfactory to insert a surface tension value O based on a semi-empirical value for a non-vibrating nucleus. A criticism of a different kind is the impossibility of calculating fission threshold energies for all possible modes of distortion. In practice, a number of plausible models of the distorted nucleus is considered in turn and the threshold energy is calculated in each case; the minimum value is assumed to correspond to the observable threshold.

Theory of Spontaneous Fission

It is natural to try and develop a theory of spontaneous fission along the lines of the quantum mechanical theory of alpha decay. The fission problem is more difficult as it is very difficult to have a clear picture of the exact shape of the fission potential barrier $V(r)$. In view of this uncertainty, it is assumed, for simplicity, that the barrier is the inversion of the parabolic function

$$V = \tfrac{1}{2} K(r - r_0)^2$$

where r is the separation of the two fission fragments and r_0 is the separation at the top of the barrier (Fig. 9).

The fission barrier penetration factor is proportional to

$$P = \exp\left(-\frac{2}{\hbar}\int_a^b \sqrt{[2M(V - E)]}\, dr\right) \qquad (10)$$

M is the reduced mass of the two fragment system and $(V - E)$ is the negative kinetic energy in the barrier region. b, the width of the barrier, is $2r_0$ and is easily shown to be given by

$$\frac{b}{2} = \sqrt{\frac{2E}{K}} \tag{11}$$

where E, in this context, is the threshold energy.

Using the parabolic form of V, the barrier integral is easily evaluated and yields

$$P = \exp\left(-\frac{2\pi}{\hbar}\sqrt{\frac{M}{K}}\cdot E\right)$$

or,

$$P = \exp\left(-\frac{b}{2}\frac{\pi}{\hbar}\sqrt{(2ME)}\right) \tag{12}$$

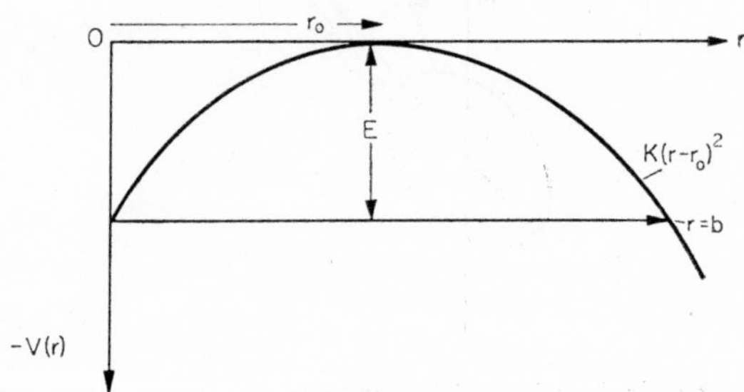

FIG. 9. Parabolic fission potential barrier.

For U^{238}, $E \sim 6$ MeV and a reasonable value for b is $1{\cdot}5 \times 10^{-12}$ cm, then as $M \sim 240/4 \sim 60$ a.m.u.

$$P \sim \exp\left(-\frac{1{\cdot}5 \times 10^{-12} \times 3{\cdot}14}{2 \times 1{\cdot}05 \times 10^{-27}}\sqrt{\frac{2 \times 60 \times 9{\cdot}6 \times 10^{-6}}{6{\cdot}02 \times 10^{23}}}\right) \tag{13}$$

$$P \sim \exp(-100) \tag{14}$$

If we assume, as in the theory of alpha decay, that the heavy nucleus approaches the fission barrier about 10^{20} times per sec, the estimated fission half-life turns out to be of the right order of magnitude.

17.8. THE ANGULAR DISTRIBUTION OF FISSION FRAGMENTS

A satisfactory theory of fission must be able to explain the observed angular anisotropy of the fission fragments with respect to the direction of the incident beam of particles inducing fission in the target nuclei.

It is found, for example, that for incident photons just above the threshold energy, the fission fragments of even–even nuclei are strongly peaked at right angles to the incident beam, whereas the angular distributions of the fragments from the fission of odd mass nuclei are nearly isotropic.

To understand this curious phenomenon it is necessary to make use of the important contributions of A. Bohr and his school on the theory of "collective motion of the nucleons" in certain types of nuclei†. Nuclei with several nucleons outside closed nucleon shells are non-spherical in shape, and they can be excited to states which are essentially vibrations or rotations of the deformed nucleus.

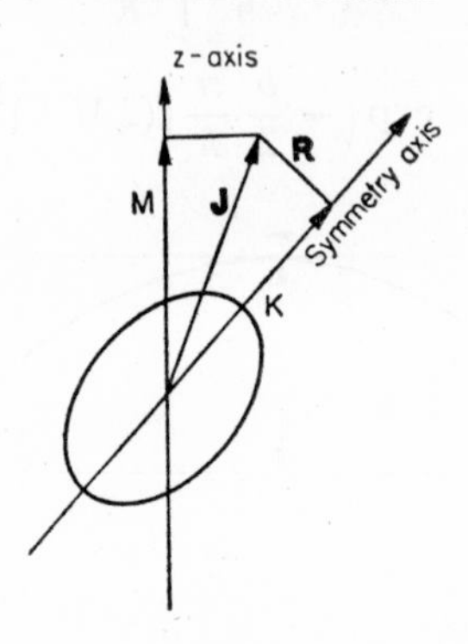

FIG. 10. Spheroidal nucleus. Angular momentum and components.

Consider, for example, a heavy deformed nucleus (with axial symmetry) which can possess rotational energy associated with the changing orientation of the nucleus in a fixed external coordinate system. There is a close analogy here between the rotational states of a deformed nucleus and the familiar rotational energy levels of a diatomic molecule. The relevant angular momenta of the nucleus are (Fig. 10):

$\boldsymbol{J}\hbar$, of magnitude $(J(J+1))^{\frac{1}{2}}\hbar$, the total angular momentum of the system,

$M\hbar$, the component of $\boldsymbol{J}\hbar$ in the z-direction (chosen to correspond to the direction of the incident particle beam when we are considering fission of the nucleus), and

$K\hbar$, the component of $\boldsymbol{J}\hbar$ along the symmetry axis of the nucleus.

The component of $\boldsymbol{J}\hbar$ perpendicular to the symmetry axis, $R\hbar$, represents the angular momentum associated with the collective rotation of the nucleus. On the other hand, the component $K\hbar$, along the symmetry axis, represents the resultant intrinsic angular momentum of the nucleons within the nucleus. If the intrinsic angular momentum K

† See Chapter 20, Section 12.

vanishes, the collective rotational energy of the nucleus is given by the well-known formula

$$E_{\text{rot}} = \frac{\hbar^2}{2\mathcal{J}} J(J+1) \tag{15}$$

where $\mathcal{J}$ is the effective moment of inertia associated with the collective rotation. Thus non-spherical nuclei should have a rotational band structure characterized by different values of J. This remarkable prediction is found to be a close representation of the spectra of several nuclei.

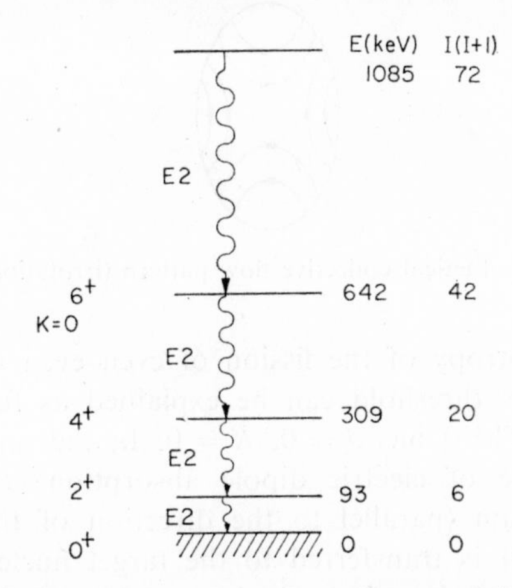

FIG. 11. Simple rotational energy level diagram of Hf^{180} ($K = 0$). $E\,2$ γ-rays are observed.

The rotational spectrum of the even–even nucleus Hf^{180} (strongly non-spherical) is depicted in Fig. 11. As $K = 0$, it is impossible, because of reflection symmetry, to distinguish orientations of the nucleus produced by a rotation of 180° about an axis perpendicular to the symmetry axis. The rotational states all have even parity and hence J is restricted to even values: 0, 2, 4, . . ., etc. The observed energies of the electric quadrupole ($E2$) transition γ-rays are in good (not perfect) agreement with the simple rotational formula. The effective moment of inertia $\mathcal{J}$ ($\sim 2{\cdot}3 \times 10^{-47}$ g cm^2) is less than half the value calculated on the assumption the nucleus rotates as a rigid sphere ($^2/_5\, m\, r^2 \sim 5{\cdot}8 \times 10^{-47}$ g cm^2). This result suggests the rotational moment of inertia is concerned only with the nucleons outside closed shells. One hypothetical flow pattern, which would rotate the spheroidal shape in space, is illustrated in Fig. 12.

The collective modes of excitation are believed to play an important role in the fission of heavy nuclei†. As the deformed nucleus passes

† A. BOHR, Vol. 2, p. 151, *Proc. Intern. Conference Peaceful Uses Atomic Energy*. 1st Conference, Geneva 1955.

through the critical shape for fission (the saddle-point) nearly all the excitation energy is located in the potential energy of deformation. The nucleus near the saddle point is essentially "cold" and the different quantum states are widely spaced in energy. These states, each one corresponding to a different mode of fission ("fission channels"), have a spectrum of energies similar to the observed low lying rotational states of nuclei.

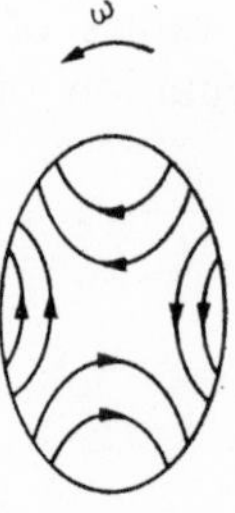

FIG. 12. Hypothetical collective flow pattern (irrotational flow).

The angular anisotropy of the fission of even–even nuclei by photons of energy just above threshold can be explained as follows. The target nucleus (e.g. U^{238}, Th^{232}) has $J = 0$, $K = 0$. In the photofission process one has an example of electric dipole absorption ($E1$) and one unit of angular momentum (parallel to the direction of the incident beam, the z-axis of Fig. 10) is transferred to the target nucleus. It is assumed that the compound nucleus is excited to a 1^- rotational state of the $K = 0$ rotational band. Just above the threshold this is the only state responsible for fission at the saddle-point. Thus the angular momentum brought in by the incoming photon is associated with collective rotation of the compound nucleus and not with a spin change of one of the nucleons. This collective rotational motion is reflected in the preferred direction of emission of the fission fragments; the line of separation of the two fragments tends to occur perpendicular to the angular momentum vector. This is the explanation of the transverse emission of fission fragments observed in the photofission of even–even nuclei. At photon energies several MeV above threshold, the observed anisotropy decreases. This is not unexpected as several 1^- rotational states may be excited and associated with possible fission channels.

The anisotropies observed in fission induced by neutrons and charged particles at low and medium excitation energies are more difficult to understand. An account of the theory of these effects is given in the review article by Halpern (see bibliography) and in the paper by Halpern and Strutinski†.

† I. HALPERN and V. M. STRUTINSKI, Vol. 15, p. 408, *Proc. Intern. Conference Peaceful Uses Atomic Energy*, 2nd Conference, Geneva 1958.

BIBLIOGRAPHY

L. A. TURNER, *Revs. Mod. Phys.* **12**, 1, 1940.
W. J. WHITEHOUSE, *Progress in Nuclear Physics* **2**, 120, 1952.
I. HALPERN, *Ann. Rev. Nuclear Science* **9**, 245, 1959.
There is a large collection of papers on Nuclear Fission in Vol.15 of *Proc. International Conference Peaceful Uses Atomic Energy*, 2nd Conference, Geneva 1958.

CHAPTER 18

PARTICLE ACCELERATORS

18.1. INTRODUCTION

The possibility of building machines capable of accelerating charged particles to energies in the MeV region was first seriously considered in the late nineteen-twenties. By this time the study of nuclear reactions with natural alpha sources was nearly exhausted. Rutherford, in 1919, was the first to observe a nuclear disintegration, namely the (α, p) reaction when nitrogen nuclei are bombarded with RaC α-particles. The use of naturally occurring alpha sources suffers from a number of serious disadvantages: the current of α-particles is diverging and is of low intensity ($\sim 10^{-9}$ A or less); the energy of the particles is limited to the range 4 to 8 MeV; this restricts the study of nuclear reactions to elements of low atomic number. It is useful to remember that the cross section for nuclear reactions with charged particles is always very small, unless the projectile particle energy is comparable with the height of the nuclear Coulomb barrier; for protons, the Coulomb barrier varies between about 1 MeV for very light nuclei and 15 MeV for the heaviest nuclei.

For technical reasons, it is usually impractical to attempt to accelerate electrons in a machine designed for the acceleration of light ions such as protons, deuterons, helium ions . . ., etc. It is therefore more convenient to consider electron accelerators separately. Moreover, the use of high energy electrons in nuclear physics is mainly confined to the study of photo-nuclear reactions initiated by bremsstrahlung photons produced by the impact of electrons on high atomic number targets. One application of high energy electrons (in the range 200 MeV to 1 GeV†) deserves special mention; this is the detailed study of the electric charge distribution of atomic nuclei by measuring the angular distribution of elastically scattered electrons (Chapter 9).

It might be helpful at this stage to list the main types of particle accelerator in use today, together with their typical range of energy. The trend to higher and higher energies has, however, only been achieved at the expense of beam intensity. A typical cyclotron, for example, has a circulating beam current of several milliampères, whereas the output

† 1 GeV = 10^9 eV (in the U.S.A. this is known as 1 BeV).

of a high energy proton synchrotron is pulsed with a mean beam current less than 10^{-9} amp. In the last few years more attention has been devoted to the problem of increasing beam intensity in high energy accelerators. The "fixed field alternating-gradient" cyclotron (F.F.A.G. cyclotron), which is being studied at a number of research centres at the present time, holds out good promise of a hundred fold increase in beam intensity.

TABLE 1. CHARGED PARTICLE ACCELERATORS

Type of accelerator	Energy	Date
Voltage-multiplier rectifier unit	0·2–1 MeV	1930
Van de Graaff generator	0·5–8 MeV	1930
Tandem Van de Graaff	10–15 MeV	1958
Cyclotron	2–25 MeV	1931
Linear proton accelerator	10–50 MeV	1954
Synchrocyclotron	20–700 MeV	1945
Proton synchroton:		
Weak focusing	1–10 GeV	1952
Strong focusing (A-G)		
CERN machine	25 GeV	1960
Brookhaven machine	30 GeV	1961

TABLE 2. ELECTRON ACCELERATORS

Type of accelerator	Energy	Date
High voltage X-ray tube	1 MeV	1930
Betatron	20–300 MeV	1940
Electron synchrotron	30–1500 MeV	1945
Linear electron accelerator	4–1000 MeV	1946

The dates given in the third column of Tables 1 and 2 are the approx imate dates of the first machine of the type concerned. A number of special types of accelerator such as the electron "microtron" and the "Hilac" heavy ion (e.g. Ne^{6+}) accelerator are not listed above.

With reference to Table 1, it is worthwhile noting that the higher energy accelerators are not only invaluable for producing high excitation energy nuclear reactions, but are ideal for producing pions, *K* mesons, nucleons and hyperons. The first laboratory-produced pions† were obtained using a synchrocyclotron. Pion production becomes significant in the bombardment of nuclei with protons of energy greater than 200 MeV. Proton synchrotrons, such as the 3 GeV Cosmotron at Brookhaven, have proved ideal for producing the heavier *K* mesons. The discovery of the antiproton was made with the 6·3 GeV Berkeley proton accelerator.

† E. GARDNER and C. M. LATTES, *Science* **107**, 270, 1948.

18.2. "POTENTIAL DROP" ACCELERATORS

The obvious way of accelerating particles of charge e is to let them move in a vacuum tube through a potential difference V, thereby gaining a kinetic energy eV. One of the difficulties of this method is the design and manufacture of vacuum accelerating tubes which will withstand high potential gradients. It is important that such tubes should be designed so that there is a uniform potential gradient along their complete length. For this reason, the modern accelerating tube is built in sections and has a large number of external corona shields (circular metal hoops) fitted along its length to ensure the establishment of a uniform potential gradient.

Voltage-multiplier Unit

A "potential drop" accelerator depending on the rectification of alternating current and incorporating a voltage multiplication system is illustrated in Fig. 1. This type of circuit is associated with the pioneer

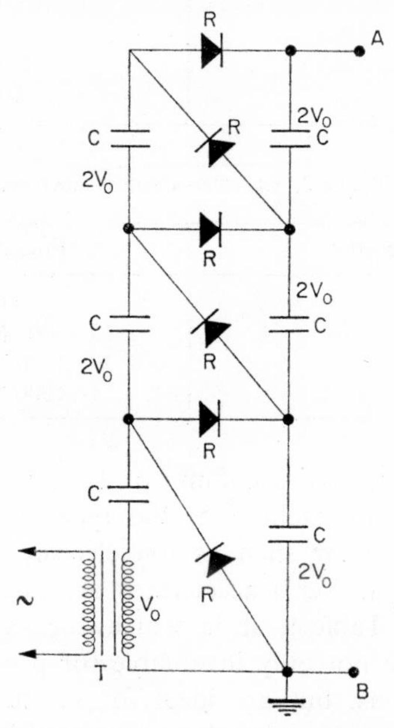

FIG. 1. Voltage-multiplier unit (Cockcroft–Walton type).

experiments of Cockcroft and Walton at the Cavendish Laboratory in the early nineteen-thirties. In Fig. 1, T is a high voltage transformer delivering a secondary peak voltage V_0. The capacitors C are charged via the high voltage rectifiers R. The maximum d.c. potential from a voltage-multiplier of the type shown in Fig. 1 is 6 V_0; on load, the output voltage will drop below this value.

Van de Graaff Accelerator

The basic physical principles of the electrostatic machine invented by R. Van de Graaff† in 1931 are illustrated in Fig. 2. Electric charge is sprayed from the sharp points of a metal comb held at a positive potential of several tens of kilovolts on to a moving insulated belt. The charge on the moving belt is removed by a second metal comb mounted inside

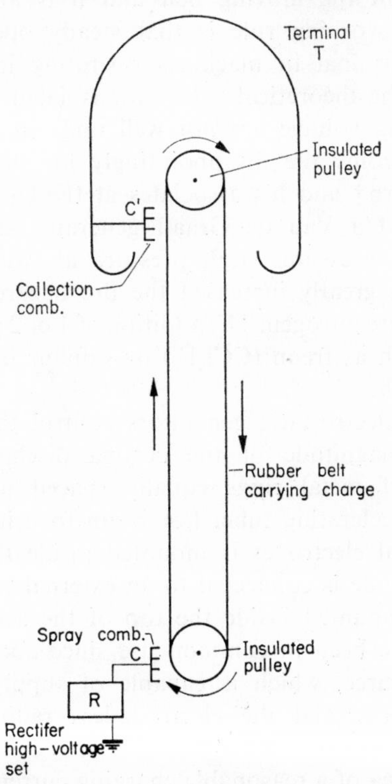

FIG. 2. Diagram illustrating basic principles of electrostatic generator.

a large metal electrode (the terminal) at the top of the generator. The high voltage terminal must, of course, be supported by an insulating column.

The potential of the terminal will gradually increase as it acquires charge from the moving belt. The terminal voltage, at any moment, is equal to Q/C, where Q is the charge on the terminal and C the effective capacitance to earth. The maximum potential of the terminal is limited by electrical breakdown of the surrounding atmosphere, insulation failure of the terminal supports or the accelerating vacuum tube. The successful operation of the modern version of the early Van de Graaff machine is the outcome of improvements in all forms of insulation.

† R. J. VAN DE GRAAFF, *Phys. Rev.* **38**, 1919, 1931.

The electric field at the surface of a spherical terminal electrode of radius R is V/R, where V is the potential of the electrode. In dry air at atmospheric pressure the dielectric strength is about 30 kV/cm. Thus, in theory, a spherical electrode of 1 m radius should hold a potential of 3 million volts before breakdown of the surrounding air. In practice, it is impossible to have an isolated spherical terminal; it must contain an opening to admit the moving belt and it is attached to insulating supports. A rough working rule is that steady operating potentials of the high voltage terminal in machines operating in atmospheric air is about *one-third* of the theoretical values for isolated spheres. The reasons for this low working voltage are not well understood.

In order to overcome the disappointingly low breakdown voltage in atmospheric air, Herb† and his associates at the University of Wisconsin successfully operated a Van de Graaff generator surrounded by air at several atmospheres pressure. High pressure air was soon found to be unsatisfactory for it greatly increased the fire hazard. Modern machines often use high pressure nitrogen. The addition of 1 or 2 per cent of an electro-negative vapour such as freon (CCl_2F_2) or sulphur hexafluoride improves the dielectric strength.

The majority of electrostatic generators control the terminal potential by adjusting the magnitude of the corona discharge current passing between a series of metal rings equally spaced along the outside of the high vacuum accelerating tube. For beam focusing purposes, a series of coaxial cylindrical electrodes is mounted inside the accelerating tube. Each focusing electrode is connected to an external corona ring electrode. The ion source is mounted inside the top of the accelerating tube. Two types of source have been in common use since about 1950: the Philips ionization gauge source, which is capable of supplying pulsed currents of several milliampères; and the electrode-less radio-frequency gas discharge.

To obtain some idea of a reasonable charging current of a Van de Graaff machine, let us assume that a maximum electric field of 20 kV/cm perpendicular to the surface of the belt can be tolerated. If the surface density of charge σ on the insulating belt is uniform the field normal to the surface is $2\pi\sigma$.

$$20 \text{ kV/cm} = \frac{2 \times 10^4}{300} \text{ e.s.u.}$$

$$\sigma = \frac{2 \times 10^4}{300 \times 2\pi} \simeq 10 \text{ e.s.u.} = 3{\cdot}3 \times 10^{-9} \text{ coulomb/cm}^2.$$

For a typical belt speed of 20 m/sec and a belt 50 cm wide, the maximum charging current is equal to $3{\cdot}3\ 10^{-9} \times 2 \times 10^3 \times 50 = 330\mu$A.

† R. G. Herb, D. B. Parkinson and D. W. Kerst, *Rev. Sci. Instr.* **6**, 261, 1935.

It is standard practice to use a second set of sharp points inside the high voltage terminal to induce negative charge on the downward moving belt. The ideal system is one in which the belt carries equal and opposite charges up and down. With the numerical data given above, the total terminal charging current is about two-thirds of one milliampère.

The potential of the high voltage terminal is conveniently measured with a generating voltmeter. In this instrument, a set of rotating vanes alternately covers and exposes an insulated electrode mounted close to the inside wall surface of the high pressure vessel. The interrupted electrostatic field between the terminal and the insulated electrode induces an alternating potential on the latter, which is rectified and recorded by a d.c. meter; this type of voltage measurement is not very precise and more elaborate means must be adopted for absolute measurements. A few absolute voltage calibration points are obtained from the known threshold voltages of certain nuclear reactions such as the $Li^7\,(p, n)\,Be^7$. A more general method of precision measurement is to measure the energy of the accelerated ions with a high quality electrostatic or magnetic analyser.

The upper energy limit of the modern Van de Graaff machine is about 6 MeV, although a few very large machines have been operated at potentials as high as 8 million volts. The outstanding advantage of the Van de Graaff machine over all other types of accelerator is the sensitivity and control of the voltage. Modern machines include servo-control systems which automatically hold the terminal voltage constant to a small fraction of one per cent. One common method of control regulates the corona discharge current.

In spite of the high beam current of the cyclotron, the Van de Graaff machine is nearly always preferred in the study of nuclear reactions in the low energy region (1 to 6 MeV). The sharpness of the energy of the accelerated particles (protons, deuterons, alphas) is often of paramount importance.

Van de Graaff machines can be designed to operate satisfactorily in the horizontal position. One of this design is used as the first stage of acceleration in the Brookhaven 3 GeV proton synchrotron.

The Tandem Van de Graaff

An ingenious method of doubling the particle energy acquired in a Van de Graaff accelerator was conceived as long ago as 1937 by W. H. Bennett and H. Kallmann. The principle of the method is as follows. The ion source is at earth potential and *negative* ions (e.g. hydrogen nuclei surrounded by *two* orbital electrons) are extracted from the source and fall through a potential difference V in reaching a high voltage electrode, which is electrically connected to the terminal of a Van de Graaff machine. When the negative ions are travelling with their maximum energy they are passed through an electron "stripper" which removes the orbital electrons. The positively charged particles emerging from the "stripper" (bare nuclei) are repelled by the positive high voltage electrode and finally reach a target at earth potential with effectively twice the energy they acquire in the normal type of Van de Graaff machine. Apart from the advantage of doubling the projectile energy, the tandem Van de Graaff machine has the practical advantages of having both the ion source and target at earth potential.

For nearly twenty years no serious attempt was made to build a voltage doubling machine of this type. The fundamental difficulty was the inability to produce a practical negative hydrogen ion source. However, in 1955, Herb and his associates succeeded in designing an ion source which yielded about 30 μA of negative hydrogen ions. The first double-ended (tandem) electrostatic machine to be built and brought into successful operation was at Chalk River, Canada, in 1958, and it yielded a 0·3 μA beam of protons at an energy of 10 MeV.

Two tandem machines have been in operation in the United Kingdom since 1959; one at A.E.R.E., Harwell, the other at A.W.R.E. Aldermaston. The electrostatic generators are housed in vertical pressure vessels about 50 ft high with a radio-frequency ion source at the top of the machine. At A.W.R.E. the accelerated negative ions are stripped by passing them through a thin layer of gas, whereas a thin carbon foil (4 mg/cm^2 thick) is used as a stripper in the A.E.R.E. machine. Target currents of a few microampères at effective energies up to 12 MeV have been obtained. The obvious drawback of the tandem machine is the low beam current compared to the conventional Van de Graaff accelerator.

There is a very important field of study of nuclear reactions (especially with heavy nuclei) in the 10–20 MeV region and the tandem machine is a very promising tool for this (see Chapter 20). Plans have been made to build combinations of tandem and single-ended machines which effectively triple the final particle energy.

Another interesting possibility is to extract negative ions of, for example, oxygen, O^-, from an ion source, accelerate them to about 5 MeV, then strip off several electrons (six) forming a multi-charged positive ion O^{+++++} (written O^{5+}) and accelerate them to a final energy of $5 + 25 = 30$ MeV by allowing them to return to earth potential. Such energetic oxygen ions would be very useful in exciting target nuclei by the process known as Coulomb excitation (i.e. the nucleus is excited by the Coulomb field of a charged particle as it passes close to the nucleus).

18.3. THE CYCLOTRON

The most important event in the history of charged particle accelerators was the invention, in 1931, of the *cyclotron* by E. O. Lawrence. The outstanding feature of this type of accelerator is the attainment of high particle energy without the aid of excessively high potential sources. A second major advantage is the absence of the necessity of installing an accelerating tube capable of withstanding high potential gradients.

The cyclotron derives its name from the fact that the ions (protons, deuterons, etc.) travel in quasi-circular orbits inside the machine under the influence of a strong magneto-static field. The machine depends for its successful operation on the use of a resonance accelerating principle, first used by Wideröe† in a linear accelerator. The ions gain energy from a radio-frequency electric field when they cross the gap between two hollow metal electrodes connected to an alternating voltage supply. The time of transit of the ions between the electrodes must always be such that the alternating voltage has the correct phase to accelerate rather than decelerate the ions. The ions gain energy in a series of increments each time they cross an inter-electrode gap; in this way it is possible to attain energies much higher than the equivalent peak accelerating voltage. The kinetic energy of the accelerated particles has, of course, been derived from the radio-frequency voltage supply.

The main physical principles of the operation of a cyclotron can be understood from Fig. 3. An ion source is located at the centre of a high vacuum chamber, the latter being placed between the flat pole-pieces of a large electromagnet. Two accelerating electrodes known as the "dees" are mounted inside the vacuum chamber and are electrically connected to a radio-frequency voltage source. The dees are hollow metal electrodes semi-cylindrical in shape, whose length is short compared with their radius. The time-constant magnetic field is nearly uniform across the vacuum chamber and is in the vertical direction (for the moment we shall disregard the exact shape of the field required for beam focusing). This field is essentially a guide field restraining the ions to move in quasi-circular orbits in a horizontal plane (normal to the guide field B). Suppose, for example, we consider a positive ion of charge e moving in the horizontal median plane through the point A, well away from the dee gap (Fig. 3a). Although a potential difference is applied to the dees, the electric field is confined to the region of the dee gap, and a charged particle at A experiences *no* electric force, only a magnetic force of magnitude $B e v$ acting radially inwards (v is the linear speed of the particle and B the flux density of the vertical magnetic field.) Suppose the charged particle reaches the edge of the dee gap at B when the phase of the applied dee voltage is such that the electric field across the gap from B to C will accelerate a positive electric charge (the left-hand dee is positive and the right-hand dee is negative at this moment). In moving from B

† R. Wideröe, *Arch. Elektrotech.* **21**, 387, 1928. A linear resonance accelerator capable of accelerating mercury ions to 1·26 MeV with a 10 Mc/s power supply of peak voltage 42 kV is described by D. H. Sloan and E. O. Lawrence, *Phys. Rev.* **38**, 2021, 1931.

to C the particle gains energy from the electric field and it consequently moves on a circular orbit of increased radius when it is well inside the right-hand dee (in the electric field free region).

The magnetic resonance principle of the cyclotron is essentially to match the angular velocity ω of the circulating charged particles and the angular frequency of the radio-frequency voltage applied to the dees.

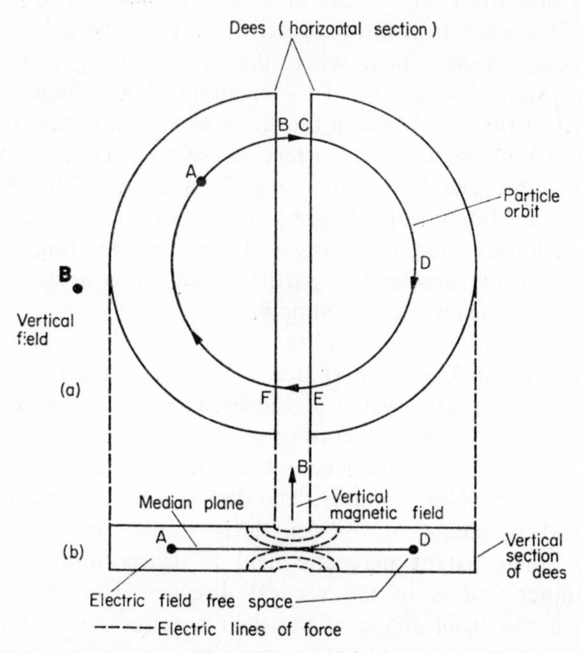

FIG. 3. (a) Horizontal section of dees. A · · · B · · · C · · · D · · · E · · · F · · · charged particle orbit; (b) vertical section of dees. Electric field (dotted lines) is confined to region of dee gap. Horizontal plane of symmetry is known as the median plane.

Thus, if a charged particle moves from B to C and experiences an accelerating field it will arrive at point E exactly half a radiofrequency cycle later and again experience an accelerating field as it moves from E to F (at this moment the right-hand dee is at a positive potential with respect to the left-hand dee). The accelerated particle spirals outwards in a sequence of quasi-semicircular orbits of increasing energy. Near the dee gap where the particle gains energy from the electric field the trajectory is non-circular. The angular frequency of rotation of ions about the vertical field B is given by the familiar expression

$$\omega = B\frac{e}{m} \tag{1}$$

(if we use m.k.s. units, B is measured in webers/m^2, e in coulombs and m, the particle mass, in kg: 1 weber/m^2 is equal to 10^4 gauss). In a uniform magnetic field, ω at first sight seems to be independent of the speed of the particle, a most desirable result, as the particle will always take the same time to travel half a circular turn and will remain in strict resonance with the electric field throughout the acceleration period. However, this pre-supposes the constancy of the mass of the particle, a valid assumption provided the speed of the particle remains non-relativistic during its acceleration. We shall return to this important aspect of the cyclotron later.

An estimate of the kinetic energy gained by an ion in orbiting outwards to the edge of the dees can easily be made. The final speed of an ion is equal to $R\omega$, where R is the dee radius. Assuming the relativistic increase in mass is small, the final kinetic energy is given by

$$T = \tfrac{1}{2} m(R\omega)^2 \qquad (2)$$

Substituting eqn. (1) in eqn. (2) we obtain

$$T = \frac{1}{2}\frac{B^2 R^2 e^2}{m} \qquad (3)$$

For singly charged ions (protons, deuterons), the kinetic energy can be given directly in electron volts by dividing the right-hand side of eqn. (3) by e, as 1 eV is equal to e joules

$$T = \frac{1}{2}\frac{B^2 R^2 e}{m} \quad \text{eV} \qquad (4)$$

Two important results follow from eqn. (4): the final particle energy is proportional to the square of B and to the square of the dee radius R. The upper practical limit of B, with an iron-cored magnetic circuit, is determined by the height of the vacuum chamber and the saturation properties of the magnetic material. A value around 18 kilogauss (1·8 weber/m^2) is an upper limit to B. The radio-frequency f to resonate with protons at this field value is approximately 27 Mc/s. Increasing the dee radius R requires a corresponding increase in the radius of the pole-pieces of the electromagnet, which greatly increases the size, weight and cost of the most expensive part of the accelerator. It is customary to quote the pole-face diameter of the electromagnet to give some idea of the dee radius (R must be less than one half the pole-face diameter of the cyclotron).

The accelerated particles must emerge from the dee system if they are to strike an external target. One method of beam extraction is illustrated in Fig. 4. The positive ions are pulled out of the dee, when the dee potential is instantaneously zero, by a negatively charged deflector plate P (typical potential -50 kV).

A cyclotron electromagnet is shown in cross-section in Fig. 5. The vacuum chamber is mounted between the flat horizontal pole-faces. The ratio of the diameter to the pole-face gap is usually in the range 5 to 10. The magnetic field in the gap should be independent of the azimuthal angle θ but it should decrease with increasing radius to provide magnetic focusing. The direct current supplied to the exciting coils is automatically

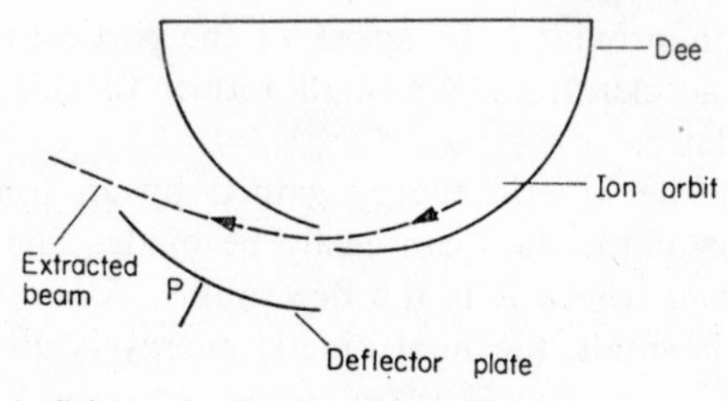

FIG. 4. Schematic diagram illustrating beam extraction.

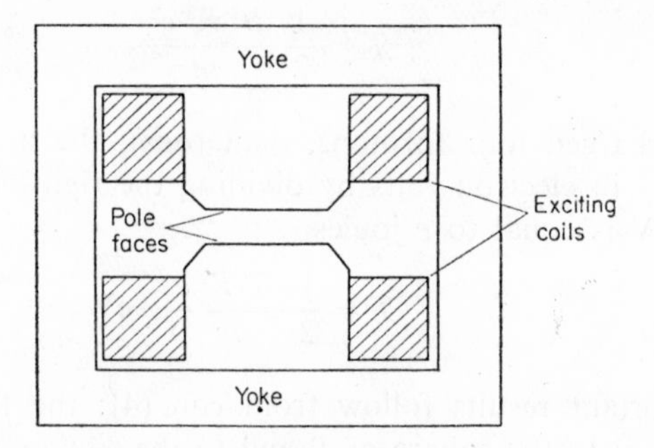

FIG. 5. Cross-section of typical cyclotron electromagnet.

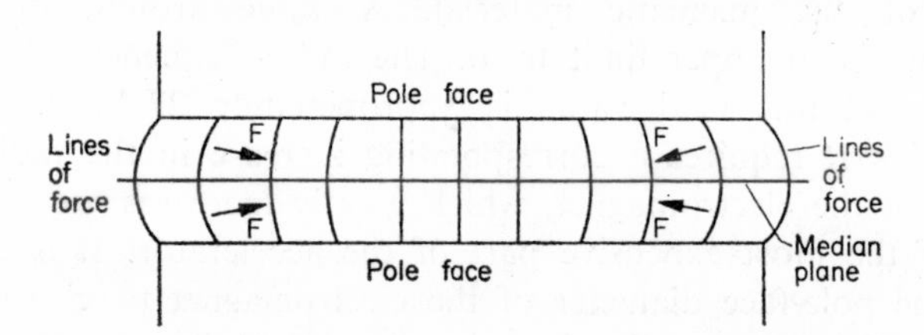

FIG. 6. Restoring force F produced by magnetic field shaping.

regulated so that the cyclotron resonance frequency does not drift. The magnet of a large cyclotron may weigh as much as 400 tons and require a hundred or more kilowatts of power to excite the magnetizing coils.

It is vital that restoring forces return the ions to the median plane of the dees if they drift away from this plane. This is achieved by shaping the magnetic field so that the vertical component B_z decreases with increasing distance from the centre of the dees. The flux lines bulge outwards as we move outwards (Fig. 6) and it is easy to see that if an ion drifts above or below the median plane (on the median plane the lines of force are vertical and B_r is zero) there will be a magnetic restoring force directing the displaced ions back towards the median plane. The returning ions overshoot the median plane and consequently execute small amplitude oscillations in the z direction. We shall presently see that the ions oscillate radially about the equilibrium orbit because of the field shape. These radial and vertical oscillations are known as *betatron* oscillations, as they were first investigated† in relation to the operation of the electron accelerator known as the betatron.

The problem of applying the radio-frequency voltage to the dees of a cyclotron is one of power radio-engineering. Various methods of exciting the dees have been used. It is useful to remember that the dees of a cyclotron provide a capacitance loading of the order of 200 pF on the radio-frequency circuit. At a typical operating frequency the dees have a reactance of the order of 50 Ω and thus they need a current supply of 6000 A if the inter-dee voltage is as high as 300 kV. The dee current is confined to a surface layer of about 10^{-3} cm thick (skin effect) and the effective resistance is of the order of 0·03 Ω. The power dissipated, I^2R, is thus of the order of 100 kW. If the ions are accelerated to 15 MeV and the beam current is 1 mA, 15 kW of power are absorbed by the beam. The radio-frequency system not only must supply a large amount of power, but it must have very good frequency stability. Various systems have been used, including a self-excited grounded-grid oscillator, a self-excited push-pull oscillator with the dees part of the anode circuit, and a master (crystal controlled) oscillator supplying a power push-pull amplifier.

The question may be asked ... "Why use a dee voltage as high as 300 kV in order to accelerate the ions, as the final particle energy is independent of the inter-dee voltage?" The answer lies in the fact that the cyclotron frequency $B\,e/m$ decreases as the ions spiral outwards: m increases (a relativistic effect) and B decreases (a necessity for focusing). If the inter-dee voltage is small the ions move outwards in a tightly coiled spiral and require a large number of increments of energy from the electric field. The gradual drift of the cyclotron frequency away from the dee supply voltage frequency means that the ions may cross the dee gap so much out of phase with the electric field that they are decelerated. This is more likely to happen if the ions receive small increments of energy each time they cross the gap between the dees.

The chief characteristics of some of the cyclotrons in operation today are given in Table 3.

† D. W. Kerst and R. Serber, *Phys. Rev.* **60**, 53, 1941.

TABLE 3.† CYCLOTRONS

Pole–face dia. (in.)	Institution	Location	Date	Magnet weight (tons)	Field (kG)	R.F. power kW	Freq. Mc/s	Particles accelerated	Energy (MeV)
90	Univ. of California	Livermore, California	1955	350	9	380	4–9·5	Protons Deuterons	14
86	Oak Ridge Nat. Lab.	Oak Ridge, Tennessee	1950	400	8·8	250	13·4	Protons	22
83	Nobel Institute	Stockholm, Sweden	1951	400	10·7	180	8·1	Deuterons	22
61·5	Univ. of Birmingham	Birmingham, England	1948	300	13·5	140	10·2	Deuterons	20
42·5	Univ. of Kyoto	Kyoto, Japan	1955	82	17·5	100	13·1	Deuterons	15·3

† Based on data tabulated in *Handbuch der Physik*, Vol. 44, 1959.

18.4. THE SYNCHROCYCLOTRON

The increase of particle mass with energy imposes a practical upper limit of about 25 MeV on the conventional cyclotron designed for proton or deuteron acceleration. The mass of a 25 MeV proton is about 2·5 per cent greater than its rest mass and the cyclotron resonance frequency is reduced by about 2·5 per cent. The departure from strict resonance at higher energies would require the application of excessively high voltages to the dees.

In 1945, it was suggested independently by McMillan and Veksler† that a method of accelerating particles to very high energies, maintaining strict cyclotron resonance, should be successful if the dee voltage is frequency modulated. The operation of a frequency modulated or synchro-cyclotron, as it is usually called, makes use of the existence of "*phase stable orbits*". Consider a charged particle of kinetic energy T rotating on a circular orbit in exact resonance with the dee voltage. The cyclotron resonance frequency is given by

$$\omega = \frac{Be}{m} = \frac{B e c^2}{m c^2} = \frac{B e c^2}{T + m_0 c^2} \tag{5}$$

where m_0 is the rest mass of the particle.

Suppose the particle crosses the dee gap at the moment the dee voltage is zero and about to become decelerating (such as the moment labelled 0 in Fig. 7). If the particle is in strict resonance with the electric field it will always cross the dee gap when the electric field is zero and it will therefore neither gain nor lose energy. To show that this is a phase

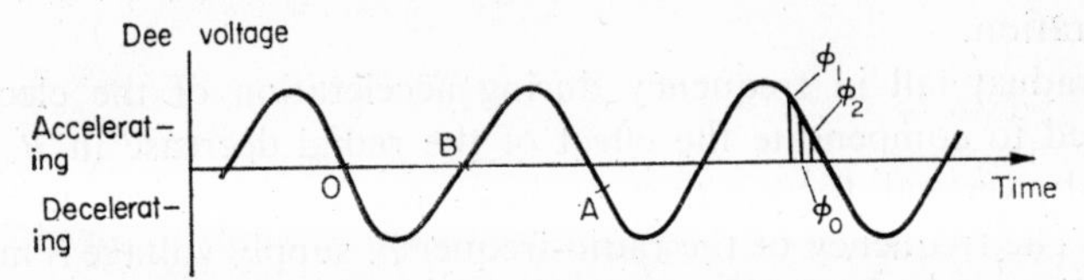

FIG. 7. Diagram illustrating principle of phase stable orbits.

stable orbit (i.e. it always crosses the dee gap at the same phase angle of the electric field), consider a small increase in energy of the particle to $T + dT$. Increasing the kinetic energy increases the linear speed of the particle, but according to eqn. (5), the angular velocity ω *decreases*. Thus particles of energy $T + dT$ arrive *late* at the dee gap and will experience a small decelerating field (see point A in Fig. 7), thereby reducing their kinetic energy and tending to return them to their original phase. A similar argument shows that particles losing a small amount of energy

† E. M. McMillan, *Phys. Rev.* **68**, 143, 1945; V. Veksler, *J. Phys.. U.S.S.R.* **9**, 153, 1945.

reach the dee gap early and gain energy, tending to return to their original phase. On the other hand, it is not difficult to see that particles crossing the dee gap when the voltage is zero and about to become accelerating will be unstable and move away from the zero phase angle (point B).

The operation of the synchrocyclotron is based on the slow rate of variation of the frequency of the accelerating voltage. The maximum frequency of the dee voltage is designed to be

$$\omega_0 = \frac{B\,e\,c^2}{m_0\,c^2} \tag{6}$$

corresponding to ions near the ion source with a very small kinetic energy. The frequency of the dee voltage falls slowly (compared with ω_0) and a bunch of ions crossing the dee gap at a phase angle φ_0 just gain sufficient energy to arrive back at the dee gap at the same phase angle. In other words, the decrease in rotation frequency due to a single energy increment matches the decrease in frequency of the electric field. The ions oscillate in phase between φ_1 and φ_2 when they cross the gap but the oscillations are stable if φ_0 is on the falling part of the sine curve. Thus, in a synchrocyclotron the ions are not continuously accelerated but one bunch per modulation cycle is caught on a phase stable orbit and accelerated to the edge of the dee. The ions which are accelerated are in strict resonance with the electric field and they traverse a great distance as the orbit radius expands very slowly. In contrast with the fixed frequency cyclotron the required amplitude of the accelerating voltage is small (15 kV is typical) as there is no drift in phase during the period of acceleration.

The gradual fall in frequency during acceleration of the electric field is designed to compensate the effect of the radial decrease in B, required to provide vertical focusing, as well as the larger effect due to mass increase. The frequency of the radio-frequency supply voltage is modulated by including a mechanically rotating capacitor, whose capacitance varies cyclically at a low audio-frequency. It is usual in the synchrocyclotron to use only one dee electrode; an earthed open flat electrode is placed opposite the straight edge of the dee. The dee may be mounted at the end of a resonance transmission line. The oscillator voltage and power is much smaller than that required in the conventional cyclotron.

The mean circulating beam current in a synchrocyclotron is about one microampère. The target for the high energy beam often consists of an internal probe placed at the required radial distance to intercept particles of a selected energy. The deflection of the circulating particles to produce an external beam is difficult, mainly because of the small increase in orbit radius per turn. An important development in the art of beam extraction was the successful application of the "*regenerative peeler*" method† by Crewe and Le Couteur in increasing the extracted proton beam current of the Liverpool 156-inch synchrocyclotron.†† This method depends for its success on inducing radial oscillations of the particles near the end of their acceleration in order to ease the problem of final extraction. The oscillations are produced by designing the magnetic field so that there is a narrow angular sector of about 5° where the field is weakened, followed by a small sector further on where the field is increased above average. Particles passing through the weak-field region

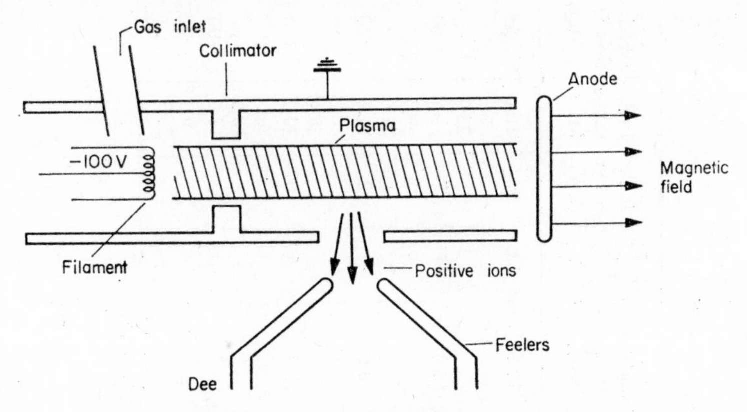

FIG. 8. Ion source of Livingston and Jones.

(the "peeler") are deflected outwards reaching their maximum displacement 90° beyond the peeler. The strong-field region (the "regenerator") has the opposite effect deflecting the particles inwards. On successive passages through the peeler and regenerator the amplitude of the oscillations increases, the emerging beam passing through an iron channel which shields the particles from the deflecting magnetic field.

It is surprising to learn that the ion source is probably the least completely understood component of a cyclotron. One modern form, designed by Livingston and Jones‡ is shown schematically in Fig. 8. The tungsten filament (0·15 in. thick) is heated with a large current (a hundred or more ampères) and it is held at a negative potential of − 100 V. Electrons emitted from the filament travel towards the anode but follow a trajectory which spirals rapidly around the lines of force of the strong magnetic field (the radius of the electron orbits may be as small as 0·001 in.). The anode gradually acquires a negative charge and potential, repelling newly arriving electrons so that they oscillate to and fro between the filament and the anode. Gas is admitted to the ionization chamber through an

† J. L. TUCK and L. C. TENG, *Phys. Rev.* **81**, 305, 1951.
†† A. V. CREWE and K. J. LE COUTEUR, *Rev. Sci. Instr.* **26**, 625, 1955.
‡ M. S. LIVINGSTON and R. J. JONES, *Rev. Sci. Instr.* **25**, 522, 1954.

TABLE 4.† SYNCHROCYCLOTRONS

Pole-face dia. (in.)	Institution	Location	Date	Magnet weight (tons)	Magnet power (kW)	Magnetic field (kG)	R.F. voltage (kV)	R.F. power (kW)	Freq. range Mc/s	Modulation freq. Mc/s	Particle	Energy (MeV)
197	CERN.	Geneva, Switz.	—	2500	750	18·8	12	25	16·6 to 28·7	55	Protons	600
184	Univ. of California	Berkeley, California	1946	4300	750	15·0	17	17	9·8 to 22·9	60	Protons Deuterons Alphas	350 195 390
170	Univ. of Chicago	Chicago, Illinois	1950	2073	650	18·6	—	12	11·8 to 28·6	60	Protons Deuterons Alphas	450 256 512
158	Univ. of Liverpool	Liverpool, England		1650	860	18·9	6·5	10	29·2 to 18.9	110	Protons	410
110	A.E.R.E.	Harwell, England	1949	720	300	16·2	10	12	18·9 to 26·3	100	Protons	175

† Based on data tabulated in *Handbuch der Physik*, Vol. 44, 1959.

inlet valve and molecules are ionized by electron impact in the region shown shaded in Fig. 8. This shaded region constitutes what is known as an "arc plasma"—a region of nearly equal concentrations of positive ions and electrons, and, therefore of very weak electric field. The positive ions slowly escape out of the side of the ionization chamber, pulled out by the "feelers" shown in Fig. 8, which are essentially projections from the dee electrode.

The upper energy limit of synchrocyclotrons ($\sim$ 700 MeV for protons) is determined by the size and cost of the magnet. The largest magnets in use have a pole-face diameter of the order of 17 ft. The characteristics of a few of the synchrocyclotrons in use today are listed in Table 4.

18.5. THE PROTON SYNCHROTRON

The proton synchrotron is the only machine, to date, which is capable of accelerating protons to energies greater than 1 GeV. In this section we will concentrate on the weak-focusing type of accelerator, leaving the discussion of the principle of the strong-focusing (alternating-gradient) machine to the next section.

One of the essential differences between the synchrocyclotron and the synchrotron is that in the latter the protons are confined to a *constant* orbit radius r_0 by a *time-varying* magnetic field. The orbit radius r_0 is much greater than the dee radius of the largest cyclotron, but the cost of the magnet is reduced by omitting the central region and using a large ring magnet.

The basic components of a proton synchrotron are shown schematically in Fig. 9. Before entry into the circular vacuum chamber (the "race-track"), protons are pre-accelerated by a linear accelerator to an energy of several MeV (see data in Table 5). The synchrotron is a pulsed machine; a short burst of protons enters the race-track when the vertical magnetic field of the ring magnet has risen to a few hundred gauss (see data in Table 5). The flux density B of the field, at the instant of injection of the protons into the race-track, must match the linear momentum p of the protons

$$p = B r_0 e \quad (7)$$

The injection values of B given in Table 5 satisfy eqn. (7), where r_0 is the equilibrium radius and p is the momentum corresponding to the injection energy.

Once per revolution† the protons pass through a radio-frequency cavity and receive an energy increment of the order of 1 keV (see Table 5). The total time-of-flight of the protons is 1 or 2 sec and during this time the protons travel a distance of the order of 10^5 km! During the whole

† The Dubna synchrotron has two accelerating cavities (see Table 5).

of this journey the protons must not deviate more than a few inches from the equilibrium orbit in the centre of the race-track. The gas pressure must be as low 10^{-6} mm Hg in order to reduce loss of the proton beam by gas scattering. Gas scattering is most marked at low particle energies; that is why an injection energy of at least 1 MeV is desirable. The approximate gas pressures in the race-track at which 10 per cent of the protons are lost by gas scattering are given in Table 5.

As the protons circulate, gaining energy at each revolution, they would strike the outer wall of the race-track vacuum chamber unless

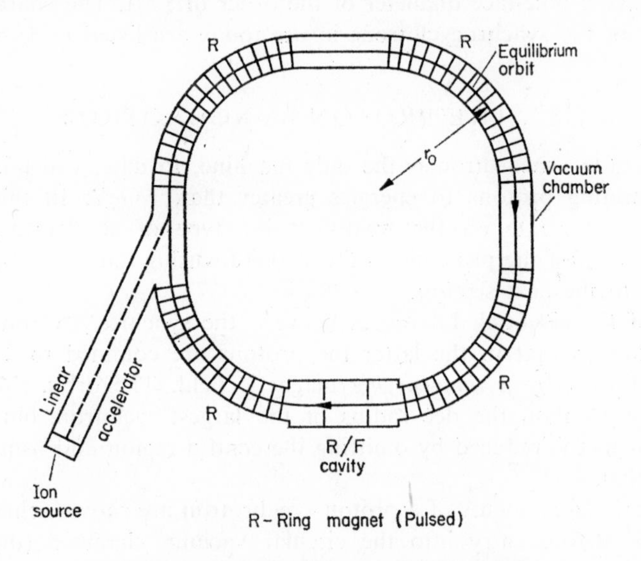

FIG. 9. Schematic layout of proton synchrotron.

the guiding magnetic field increases at the correct rate to keep them on a fixed radius r_0. In addition, the frequency of the accelerating electric field must slowly increase to keep in strict resonance with the slowly increasing frequency of revolution of the protons. The flux densities of the field at injection and at the end of the acceleration, and the initial and final radio-frequencies are given in Table 5.

The time-varying magnetic field is produced by suddenly applying a large voltage (see Table 5) to the copper windings of the ring magnet. The rate of growth of B is primarily determined by the resistance and inductance of the winding (the inductance varies as the current increases due to changes in the permeability of the iron core). After acceleration, the magnet current is reduced to zero; there is then a pause of a few seconds before the next cycle is started. A typical cycle is shown in Fig. 10, together with the variation of the radio-frequency f during the acceleration period. The power supplies for a synchrotron magnet are formidable. For example, the Bevatron magnet is supplied by two 46,000 kVA generators, each on its own shaft with a 67 ton flywheel and 3600 h.p. induction motor. Details of the complicated switching mechanisms involved are given in some of the references given at the end of this chapter.

The cross section of the Cosmotron C–shaped magnet is shown in Fig. 11. The cross-hatched areas indicate the positions of the copper

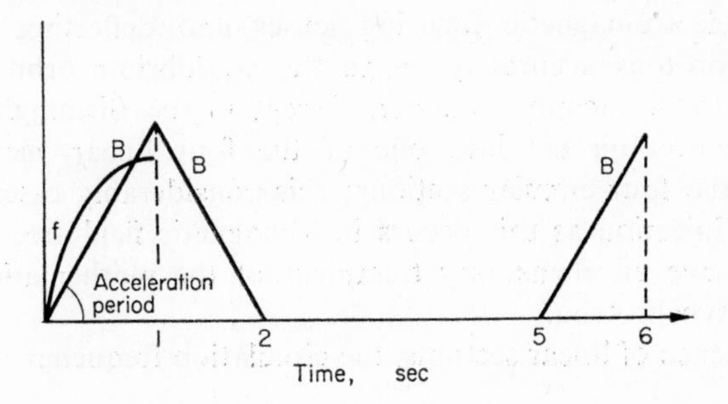

FIG. 10. Rise and fall of *B*.

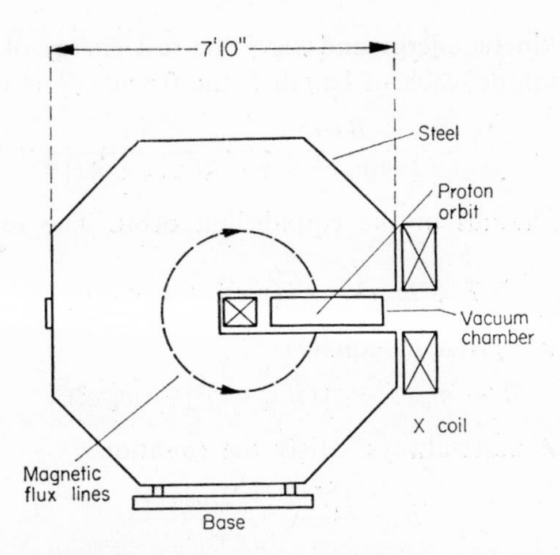

FIG. 11. Cross section of $\frac{1}{2}$ in. thick soft iron lamination of C-magnet (Cosmotron).

windings. The magnet gap widens towards the outside of the ring magnet to provide the necessary field gradient for focusing. The vacuum chamber, rectangular in cross section, fits in the magnet gap. It is necessary to construct the ring magnet in laminations to reduce losses due to eddy currents; the laminations in the Cosmotron are of $\frac{1}{2}$ in. hot-rolled soft iron plate, arranged in bundles of twelve. Adjacent bundles are mounted so that they are slightly diverging outwards in order to form a complete ring magnet of the required radius of curvature.

There is considerable variation in the design of the pre-accelerator in the four synchrotrons listed in Table 5. In the Cosmotron, a horizontal Van de Graaff machine is used; in the Bevatron, the protons from the ion source are accelerated by a 460 kV voltage multiplier and then by a linear accelerator to 9·9 MeV before injection into the race-track. An important part of the complete machine is the injection system—the system of electromagnetic focusing lenses and deflecting plates which guides the protons accurately on to the equilibrium orbit at the centre of the race-track vacuum chamber. Except in the Birmingham machine, the protons are injected into one of the four linear vacuum sections connecting the four circular sections; this considerably eases the difficult problem of injection as this occurs in a magnetic field–free region.

We now give an elementary treatment of the mathematical theory of the proton synchrotron.

In the absence of linear sections, the circulation frequency of the protons is given by

$$f = \frac{\omega}{2\pi} = \frac{B\,e\,c^2}{2\pi(m_0\,c^2 + T)}$$

where T is the kinetic energy and $m_0\,c^2$ the rest energy of a proton. With four straight sections, each of length l, the frequency is reduced to

$$f = \frac{B\,e\,c^2}{2\pi(m_0\,c^2 + T)} \cdot \frac{2\pi\,r_0}{(2\pi\,r_0 + 4l)} \tag{8}$$

where r_0 is the radius of the equilibrium orbit. The total energy of a proton is

$$T + m_0\,c^2 = \sqrt{[(p\,c)^2 + (m_0\,c^2)^2]}$$

Using the relation given by eqn. (7),

$$T + m_0\,c^2 = \sqrt{[(B\,r_0\,e\,c)^2 + (m_0\,c^2)^2]} \tag{9}$$

Solving for B, B must always satisfy the equation

$$B = \frac{\sqrt{[T(T + 2m_0\,c^2)]}}{r_0\,e\,c} \tag{10}$$

Substituting eqn. (10) in eqn. (8), f must always satisfy the equation

$$f = \frac{c\sqrt{T(T + 2m_0\,c^2)}}{(m_0\,c^2 + T)} \, \frac{1}{(2\pi\,r_0 + 4l)} \tag{11}$$

During the early stages of acceleration when $T \ll m_0\,c^2$, eqn. (11) simplifies to

$$f = \frac{c}{(2\pi\,r_0 + 4l)} \sqrt{\frac{2T}{m_0\,c^2}} \tag{12}$$

The values given in Table 5 at injection will be found to satisfy eqn. (12). At the final energy (> 1 GeV), the relativistic eqn. (11) must be used.

In practice, the frequency of the radio-frequency oscillator is controlled by a signal derived from the rising magnetic field in the magnet gap, so that eqn. (8) is satisfied to an accuracy of 0·1 per cent during the whole of the acceleration period.

The circulating protons execute radial and vertical (betatron) oscillations about the equilibrium orbit. The magnetic field is shaped so its vertical component decreases with increasing radius

$$B_z = B_0 \left(\frac{r_0}{r}\right)^n, \quad \text{where} \quad 0 < n < 1 \tag{13}$$

B_0 is the vertical component of B on the equilibrium orbit. The field is designed so that there is no azimuthal component of B; $B_\theta = 0$ for all r and z.

Differentiating eqn. (13) we can write

$$n = -\frac{r}{B_z}\frac{\partial B_z}{\partial r} \tag{14}$$

The magnetic field is irrotational, so curl $B = 0$ and

$$\frac{\partial B_z}{\partial r} = \frac{\partial B_r}{\partial z} \tag{15}$$

The equation of motion of a proton in the vertical (z) direction is

$$m\ddot{z} = B_r e v \tag{16}$$

Integrating eqn. (15), we get

$$B_r = \frac{\partial B_z}{\partial r} \cdot z \quad \text{as} \quad B_r = 0 \quad \text{when} \quad z = 0 \tag{17}$$

Combining eqns. (14), (16) and (17), we obtain

$$m\ddot{z} = -n\frac{B_z}{r} e v z$$

For small amplitude oscillations at constant radius r_0,

$$\ddot{z} = -n\left(\frac{B_0 e}{m}\right)\left(\frac{v}{r_0}\right) z \tag{18}$$

The cyclotron angular frequency is equal to

$$\omega = \left(\frac{B_0 e}{m}\right) = \left(\frac{v}{r_0}\right) \tag{19}$$

Combining eqns. (18) and (19) we obtain the equation of simple harmonic motion

$$\ddot{z} = -n\,\omega^2 z$$

Hence, the angular frequency of vertical oscillations is given by

$$\omega_z = \omega \sqrt{n} \tag{20}$$

To obtain the frequency of small amplitude radial oscillations we write down the equation of motion

$$m\ddot{x} = m\frac{v^2}{r} - B_z e v \tag{21}$$

where $x = r - r_0$ and $x \ll r_0$.

In terms of x, eqn. (13) becomes

$$B_z = B_0\left(1 - \frac{x}{r}\right)^n = B_0\left(1 - n\frac{x}{r}\cdots\right) \tag{22}$$

Expanding $\frac{1}{r}$ in terms of x, we obtain

$$\ddot{x} = \frac{v^2}{r_0}\left(1 - \frac{x}{r_0}\cdots\right) - B_0\frac{ev}{m}\left\{1 - n\frac{x}{r_0}\left(1 - \frac{x}{r_0}\right)\cdots\right\} \tag{23}$$

$$\ddot{x} = v\left\{\omega\left(1 - \frac{x}{r_0}\right) - \omega\left(1 - n\frac{x}{r_0}\right)\right\} \tag{24}$$

as $v = r_0\omega$, we obtain the equation

$$\ddot{x} = -\omega^2(1 - n)x, \quad \text{for} \quad x \ll r_0 \tag{25}$$

and the angular frequency of radial oscillations is

$$\omega_r = \omega\sqrt{(1 - n)} \tag{26}$$

It is interesting to find that both ω_z and ω_r are smaller than ω. If ω_r and ω_z have an integral ratio, the radial and vertical oscillations will be strongly coupled and energy may be transferred from one of the oscillations to the other, resulting in the disastrous growth of the amplitude of one of the oscillations. Resonances must be avoided, so certain values of n, such as 0·2, 0·5, . . ., etc., are not used. A detailed treatment of the theory of betatron oscillations brings out the important result that the amplitude of the oscillations decreases as the magnetic field rises (it varies inversely as the square root of B).

In addition to the betatron oscillations, which are a result of the field shape, the protons oscillate in phase as they cross the accelerating gap. These phase oscillations are associated with oscillations in energy superimposed on the predicted rise of energy with time. There is a radial oscillation accompanying the energy oscillation but the frequency is 100 to 10,000 times less than the cyclotron frequency. A calculation of the minimum dimensions of the vacuum chamber involves a detailed treatment of the expected phase and betatron oscillations.

The design of the radio-frequency accelerating system is complicated by the wide sweep in frequency required. The actual acceleration process

TABLE 5.† FOUR WEAK-FOCUSING PROTON SYNCHROTRONS

Parameter	Birmingham, England	Cosmotron, Brookhaven, U.S.A.	Bevatron, Berkeley, U.S.A.	Synchro-phasotron, Dubna, U.S.S.R.	Units
Final proton energy	1	3	6·2	10	GeV
Orbit radius, r_0	4·50	9·14	15·24	28	m
No. of straight sections	0	4	4	4	m
Length of each section, l	—	3·05	6·10	8	m
Field index, n	0·67	0·6	0·6	0·65	
Magnet cross-section	2·44 × 2·44	2·38 × 2·38	6·25 × 2·9	7·5 × 5·3	m
Weight of magnet steel	800	1650	9700	36,000	tons
No. of exciting turns (magnet)	24	48	88	44	
Weight of copper (magnet)	10	70	350	460	tons
Initial voltage (magnet)	1100	5400	14,000	11,000	V
Peak magnet current	12,500	7000	8300	12,800	A
Peak magnetic energy	7	12	80	14·8	MJ
Rise time of field	1	1	2	3·3	sec
Repetition rate	6	12	10	5	per min
Injection field	210	295	300	150	G
Peak field	12,600	13,800	15,400	13,000	G
Magnet gap	0·21 × 0·5	0·24 × 0·92	0·33 × 1·68	0·4 × 2·0	m
Proton injection energy	0·46	3·6	9·9	9·0	MeV
Initial cyclotron frequency	300	360	355	182	kc/s
Final cyclotron frequency	9·7	4·18	2·47	1·45	Mc/s
Energy gain per turn	0·2	1	1·5	2·5	keV
No. of accelerating gaps	1	1	1	2	
Approx. pressure/10% loss	1	4	10	7	10^{-6} mm Hg

† Based on data tabulated in *Handbuch der Physik*, Vol. 44, 1959.

can be thought of in several ways: as a transformer in which the circulating protons constitute a single turn secondary; as a loaded cavity resonator, . . ., etc. The cavity resonator of the Cosmotron, for example, is loaded with a material of high magnetic permeability and dielectric constant (a ferrite). In this machine the frequency of the oscillator is varied by controlling the inductance of a ferrite-cored coil with an auxiliary d.c. winding.

To convey some idea of the values of the parameters of a proton synchrotron, a list of them is given in Table 5 for four operating machines; the Birmingham 1 GeV machine; the Cosmotron at Brookhaven, New York; the Bevatron at Berkeley, California; and the Synchrophasotron at Dubna, U.S.S.R. The table is nearly self-explanatory. A general comment is worth making: the repetition rate of these machines is rather low, with about 10^{11} protons accelerated per pulse. Future machines will aim at considerably higher repetition rates and higher beam intensities.

18.6. THE A–G SYNCHROTRON

The field index n of the magnetic field of a synchrotron is defined by eqn. (13)

$$B_z = B_0\left(\frac{r_0}{r}\right)^n$$

So far we have considered synchrotrons with n lying between the limits of 0 and 1. If $n > 1$, the field falls away more rapidly than $1/r$ and there is no radial magnetic restoring force. However, large positive values of n would produce intense vertical focusing; that is, the frequency $\omega_z \gg \omega$, and the amplitude of the vertical betatron oscillations of the circulating particles would be reduced by a large factor. Large negative values of n (the field increasing rapidly with radius), on the other hand, would result in $\omega_r \gg \omega$ and a large reduction in the amplitude of the radial betatron oscillations. Large field gradients produce either strong vertical or strong radial focusing at the expense of strong defocusing in the radial or vertical directions respectively.

In 1952 Courant, Livingston and Snyder† published an important paper explaining a new principle of strong focusing using an alternating–gradient (A–G) magnetic field. This principle had been discovered independently (but not published) by N. Christofilos in Greece in 1950. The new principle essentially involves a guiding magnetic field, which has strong field gradients ($|n|$ is several hundred), but has alternate short segments of the ring magnet with n positive, then n negative, n positive . . ., etc. Such a system of alternating magnetic sections is equivalent to a

† E. Courant, M. S. Livingston and H. Snyder, *Phys. Rev.* **88**, 1190, 1952.

series of magnetic lenses, which converge the particles in one coordinate and diverge them in the other. It is a well-known property of a lens system in optics that a series of equally spaced converging and diverging lenses of focal lengths f and $-f$ respectively, behaves like a converging lens system. For a pair of thin lenses, of focal lengths f_1 and f_2, the equivalent focal length F is given by

$$\frac{1}{F} = \frac{1}{f_1} + \frac{1}{f_2} - \frac{t}{f_1 f_2}$$

with $f_1 = -f_2$, $F = f_1^2/t$, where t is the separation of the lenses.

In spite of the sharp divergence in the radial or the vertical directions in a given magnet section, the resultant effect of many alternate sections

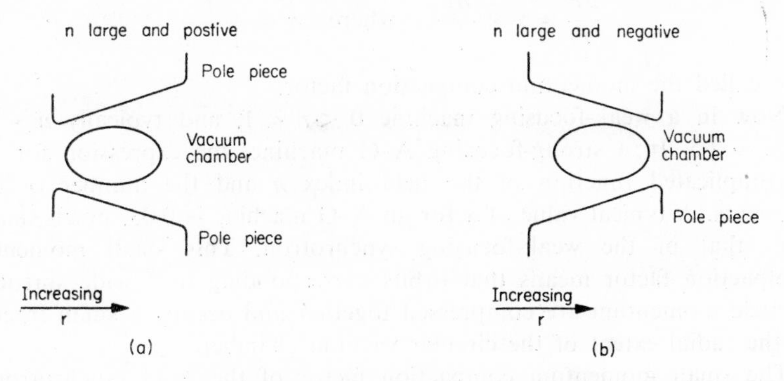

FIG. 12. Magnet cross-section in A–G machine.

is to produce strong focusing in both directions. Strong positive and negative field gradients can be produced with a magnet gap of the shape shown in Fig. 12(a) and (b). In the 25 GeV CERN A–G proton synchroton, the orbit radius is 100 m and there are 100 magnetic units comprising the complete ring magnet (there are 100 reversals of the field gradient). The field index n has a magnitude of 282 in this machine.

A detailed treatment of the theory of A–G focusing is out of place here (see bibliography), but it is worthwhile emphasizing the necessity of avoiding resonances which would lead to a catastrophic increase in the radial or vertical amplitude of oscillation. Thus, if Q_r or Q_v, (the number of free radial or vertical oscillations per revolution) is an integer there is a resonance between this oscillation and the corresponding Fourier component of the inevitable azimuthal variation of B_0 round the circumference of the magnet. Other resonances, for example those corresponding to half integral values of Q_r and Q_v must be avoided. In the CERN machine, $Q_r = 6{\cdot}2$ and $Q_v = 6{\cdot}3$.

Another important feature of the A–G synchrotron is the phenomenon known as *momentum compaction.* The concept can also be applied to the weak-focusing type of synchrotron (n independent of azimuth). The equilibrium orbit has a radius r, where $p = B\,r\,e$. Taking logarithms and differentiating, we obtain

$$\frac{dp}{p} = \frac{dB}{B} + \frac{dr}{r} \tag{27}$$

Now
$$n = -\frac{r}{B}\frac{dB}{dr}$$

Hence we can write

$$\frac{dp}{p} = (1 - n)\frac{dr}{r}$$

or
$$\frac{dr}{r} = \alpha \times \frac{dp}{p}, \quad \text{where} \quad \alpha = \frac{1}{1 - n} \tag{28}$$

α is called the momentum compaction factor.

Now in a weak-focusing machine $0 < n < 1$, and typically $n \sim 0{\cdot}6$, so $\alpha \sim 2{\cdot}5$. In a strong-focusing A–G machine, the expression for α is a complicated function of the field index n and the number of field segments. A typical value of α for an A–G machine is 0·03, much smaller than that of the weak-focusing synchrotron. This small momentum compaction factor means that orbits corresponding to a wide spread in particle momentum are compressed together and occupy a small fraction of the radial extent of the circular vacuum chamber.

The small momentum compaction factor of the A–G synchrotron is responsible for the occurrence of a phase transition energy. Consider a particle of momentum p moving round the equilibrium orbit of radius r. If it has its momentum increased to $p + dp$, then the fractional change in its period of revolution

$$\frac{dt}{t} = \frac{dr}{r} - \frac{dv}{v} \tag{29}$$

where dr is the increase in orbit radius and dv is the increase in the linear speed of the particle (N.B. the changes in r and v oppose one another). It is easy to show that

$$\frac{dt}{t} = \left(\alpha - \frac{E_0^2}{E^2}\right)\frac{dp}{p} \tag{30}$$

where, E_0 is the rest energy of the particle and E is the total energy of the particle.

In a weak-focusing machine, as $0 < n < 1$, $\alpha > 1$, and dt/t has always the same sign as dp/p. This is not the case in an A–G machine with small positive values for α. At the initial stages of acceleration, the velocity term in eqn. (29) exceeds the radius term, due to the strong momentum compaction, and dt/t is negative for a positive value of dp/p. Above a critical or transition energy

$$E = \frac{E_0}{\alpha^{\frac{1}{2}}} \tag{31}$$

dt/t is positive for a positive increase in dp/p.

This changeover can be understood, for at relativistic velocities the velocity term does not increase rapidly and the radius term in eqn. (29) exceeds the velocity term. The existence of the transition energy is important for the following reason. At low particle energies, the protons must cross the radio-frequency gap when the accelerating voltage is *increasing* (dt/t is opposite in sign to dp/p). Above the transition energy, the protons must cross the accelerating gap when the voltage is falling for phase stability to be ensured. At the transition energy itself, t is independent of r and p and phase stability vanishes. Thus a serious loss of particles may occur at the transition energy, and if they are to be accelerated to higher energies, the phase of the accelerating voltage must be abruptly shifted at the transition energy so that the particles cross the accelerating gap when the voltage is falling.

At one time it was thought that the transition energy would represent a formidable obstacle to the acceleration of protons to higher energies. Provided the accelerating voltage frequency is automatically tracked at the correct theoretical value, it has been found that the transition energy can be passed with no loss of particles so long as the timing error of switching the phase of the accelerating voltage is not greater than a few milliseconds (± 3 msec for the CERN machine).

In the CERN A–G synchrotron†, two automatic systems are used in controlling the frequency of the accelerating voltage. In the early stages of acceleration (the protons are injected into the race-track from a 50 MeV linear accelerator), the frequency is controlled via an analogue computer which derives its input signal from the rising magnetic field. At higher energies the frequency tracking must be tightly controlled and the circulating bunch of protons is used directly to induce a signal on pick-up electrodes placed inside the vacuum chamber. This is the input signal for a servo-system automatically controlling the frequency of the accelerating voltage.

So successful is the strong focusing of the CERN synchrotron that the vacuum chamber can fit inside a magnet gap with dimensions as small as 14 cm × 7 cm. The orbit radius of 100 m is more than three times that of the 10 GeV Dubna conventional synchrotron, yet the weight of the magnet steel is only 3400 tons, about one-tenth that of the Dubna magnet.

† J. B. ADAMS, *Nature* **135**, 568., 1960.

The CERN synchrotron has amply confirmed the principle of A–G focusing and a number of other machines of this type is under construction. About 10^{10} protons are accelerated per pulse in the CERN synchrotron and the repetition frequency is 20 pulses per minute. The severe radiation shielding problem has been solved by building the ring magnet inside an annular subterranean tunnel. The temperature inside the tunnel is controlled to 1°C as a precaution against misalignment of the magnet sectors due to thermal expansion.

18.7. THE BETATRON

The betatron is an electron accelerator which uses the principle of electromagnetic induction as the accelerating force. Electrons moving in a circular annular vacuum chamber (the "doughnut") under a guiding magnetic field are accelerated by a time-varying magnetic flux linking the electrons' orbit. The first successful machine was built by D. W. Kerst in 1940.† In the betatron, the rate of increase of the flux linking the electrons' orbit is very slow compared to the circulation frequency. The electrons are accelerated continuously during the epoch of the rising magnetic field. In order that the electrons are held on a fixed orbit of radius r_0, a certain relation between the flux density at the orbit B_0 and the total flux linking the whole orbit must be satisfied. This relation is easily derived. For an electron of linear momentum p, moving on a circular orbit of radius r_0, we have

$$p = B_0 r_0 e$$

and

$$\frac{dp}{dt} = r_0 e \frac{dB_0}{dt} \tag{32}$$

The electromotive force accelerating the electrons is equal to $d\varphi/dt$, where φ is the total magnetic flux linking each orbit.

The effective electric field E, accelerating an electron is given by

$$E\, 2\pi r_0 = \frac{d\varphi}{dt} \tag{33}$$

The effective electric force acting on an electron is $e\,E$, and

$$e\,E = \frac{dp}{dt} \tag{34}$$

Combining eqns. (32), (33) and (34) we obtain

$$\frac{d\varphi}{dt} = 2\pi r_0^2 \frac{dB_0}{dt} \tag{35}$$

† D. W. Kerst, *Phys. Rev.* **58**, 841, 1940; **60**, 47, 1941.

Integrating, we obtain the required "flux condition"

$$\Delta\varphi = 2\pi r_0^2 \Delta B_0 \tag{36}$$

This condition must be satisfied during the whole of the acceleration period if the electrons are to be kept on a constant radius r_0.

A useful estimate of the final energy of the accelerated electrons can be made as follows. Suppose the electrons are accelerated during one quarter cycle (time interval $\pi/2\omega$) of the flux $\varphi = \varphi_0 \sin\omega t$, linking the orbit. The average energy gained per orbit by an electron during this quarter period is

$$e\overline{\frac{d\varphi}{dt}} = e\,\omega\,\varphi_0 \frac{\int\limits_0^{\pi/2\omega} \cos\omega\, t\, dt}{\dfrac{\pi}{2\omega}} = e\,\omega\,\varphi_0 \cdot \frac{2}{\pi} \tag{37}$$

During most of their journey the accelerated electrons have a speed close to that of light (a 1 MeV electron has a speed of 0·94 c); thus the total distance travelled during the time $\pi/2\omega$ is nearly $c\,\pi/2\omega$ and each electron makes

$$\frac{c\,\pi}{2\omega}\bigg/ 2\pi\, r_0 = \frac{c}{4\omega\, r_0} \quad \text{revolutions} \tag{38}$$

The final kinetic energy T of an electron is the average energy gained per revolution multiplied by the number of revolutions; hence

$$T = \frac{e\,c\,\varphi_0}{2\pi\, r_0} \tag{39}$$

For an orbit radius of 80 cm and a peak flux φ_0 of 1·5 webers, T is approximately 100 MeV. An interesting feature of eqn. (39) is the independence of the final energy T on the angular frequency ω of the changing flux. The value of ω should not be too small (typically 300) otherwise the time of acceleration is increased and the loss of energy by radiation (ignored in the derivation of eqn. (39)) increases.

A schematic drawing of the vertical cross section of a typical betatron magnet and vacuum chamber is shown in Fig. 13. The field is shaped so that the flux condition, eqn. (36), is always satisfied and the field at the orbit has an index n in the range 0 to 1. This is to provide vertical and radial focusing as discussed earlier in this chapter (the radial and vertical oscillations about the equilibrium orbit were first discussed, with reference to the betatron, by Kerst and Serber). The annular vacuum chamber ("doughnut") is made of glass, coated on the inside with a thin layer of silver to prevent the accumulation of surface charges. However, the silver film has a low conductivity so that induced eddy currents, which set up disturbing magnetic fields, are kept at low values. Electrons are injected into the equilibrium orbit at an energy of 20 to 50 kV from a pulsed electron gun, when the changing field has the correct value to guide them on to an orbit of radius r_0. The electrons, however, must move inwards by a sufficient amount to avoid hitting the back of the electron gun after the first (and subsequent) revolutions.

Beam extraction is possible but it is difficult to achieve a high extraction efficiency. The high energy electrons are often used to produce high

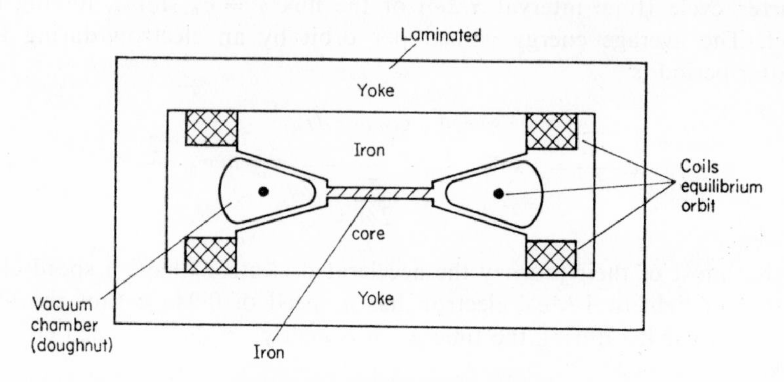

FIG. 13. Cross section of betatron.

energy photons by allowing the circulating beam to strike an internal target. At the desired instant, the electrons are deflected on to the X-ray target by passing a current pulse through a set of coils close to the vacuum chamber.

18.8. THE ELECTRON SYNCHROTRON

The fundamental principles of the electron synchrotron are similar to those of the proton synchrotron. A short pulse of electrons from an electron gun is accelerated to 50 keV or so and then accelerated to an energy of several MeV, before receiving their major increment of energy by the synchrotron mechanism. During the last stage of acceleration the electrons are guided on a fixed circular orbit by a rising magnetic field. The electrons receive energy when they cross the gap in a cavity resonator excited by a radio-frequency voltage. One important difference between the synchrotron acceleration of electrons and protons is that in the former case an electron with an energy of a few MeV has a speed very close to that of light and consequently the frequency of the accelerating voltage does not need to be varied. The radius of the equilibrium orbit in the electron synchrotron is smaller than that of the proton synchrotron for a comparable final particle energy. For high energy electrons, $T \gg E_0$, where E_0 is the rest energy and T is the kinetic energy, and $T = cp = Brec$.

Thus if the peak flux density is 1 weber/m² (10,000 gauss), and the equilibrium radius is 1 m, $T = 300$ MeV. If the final energy is to be 1·5 GeV, $r = 5$ m for a peak flux density of 10,000 gauss.

The electrons are injected into the doughnut-shaped vacuum chamber of the synchrotron at a lower momentum than in the proton machine. The magnetic field is only 10 or 20 gauss at injection and the effect of stray fields due to eddy currents must be carefully compensated. The ring magnet current is either pulsed or of low audio-frequency (mains power frequency), and the magnet is constructed of laminated sheets of transformer steel to minimize the eddy currents. There is a good reason for keeping the number of revolutions of the electrons in the synchrotron as low as possible. This is to reduce the total loss of energy by the circulating electrons through the emission of electromagnetic radiation (this loss is insignificant in the proton accelerator).

The circulating electrons are expected to emit radiation bacause they have a centripetal acceleration. Schwinger† has shown that the process can be predicted using classical arguments, and that the total energy radiated by an electron of total energy E in one revolution is

$$\varDelta E = \frac{4\pi}{3}\left(\frac{e^2}{r}\right)\left(\frac{E}{E_0}\right)^4 \qquad (40)$$

A useful practical formula is

$$\varDelta E = 88{\cdot}5\frac{E^4}{r} \qquad (41)$$

where $\varDelta E$ is in keV, E in GeV, and r in metres. The spectrum of the radiation covers a wide range of frequencies from the circulation frequency of the electrons to the region of soft X-rays. The radiation appears as a brilliant blue light to the eye and it is confined to a narrow cone in the tangential direction. Because of the fourth power dependence on E, the loss of energy by radiation becomes very serious at very high energies. It is essential that the electrons gain at least as much energy from the accelerating field as they lose by radiation. The problem of radiation loss does not arise in the electron linear accelerator and this is one of the reasons for favouring this type of accelerator at ultra-high energies.

Several methods of pre-acceleration have been used in the electron synchrotron. In the earlier machines, a pulsed electron beam from an electron gun is accelerated to an energy of 2 to 4 MeV using the betatron mechanism. In order to satisfy the betatron flux condition, flux bars are required inside the electron orbit. These bars saturate at the end of the betatron acceleration and the radio-frequency voltage is switched on to take over the synchrotron acceleration process.

† J. Schwinger, *Phys. Rev.* **75**, 1912, 1949.

Many of the recently constructed electron synchrotrons use a Van de Graaff generator or a linear accelerator as an injector. The 1·3 GeV synchrotron at Cornell employs a 2 MeV Van de Graaff machine as a pre-accelerator. This type of injector has the advantage of providing a well-collimated highly monoenergetic beam of electrons. However, the injection energy is rather low and the electron velocity is only 0·98 c.

In practice several types of radio-frequency cavity have been used. One of the simplest is a quarter-wavelength resonant cavity, formed by coating the inner and outer surfaces of an angular sector of the doughnut-shaped ceramic vacuum chamber with conducting material. The accelerating voltage is developed across a narrow insulating gap near one end of the cavity. The conducting walls of the cavity are cut longitudinally to reduce the eddy currents set up by the synchrotron magnetic field. If the synchrotron is designed to be of the race-track type, it is usual to make the cavity of solid copper sheet and mount it inside a straight magnetic field-free section. As the ultimate energy of the electron synchrotron is increased the radio-frequency problem becomes more severe because of the serious loss of energy by radiation. Thus in the design plans of a 6 GeV machine†, sixteen resonant cavities are included, requiring a total power supply of 800 kW, which is greater than the anticipated magnet power supply of 580 kW.

For electron synchrotrons of final energy above 1 GeV, the advantages of A–G focusing are considerable and the majority of high energy machines in operation are of this type.

18.9. THE LINEAR ACCELERATOR

The concept of a linear accelerator is one of the oldest in accelerator history. After the invention of the cyclotron in 1931, the idea was abandoned and was not seriously re-considered until 1945. During the Second World War the invention of radar led to the successful development of vacuum tubes capable of delivering megawatts of pulsed radio-frequency power at centimetre wavelengths. These technological developments are responsible for the success of the modern proton and electron linear accelerators. At one time it was believed that the expense of the magnet in a large cyclic accelerator would favour the use of linear accelerators in the very high energy region. However, the advent of the ring magnet A–G focusing type of machine has modified these economic arguments. One of the most attractive features of the linear accelerator is the relative ease of injection and extraction of comparatively large beam currents.

The design considerations of proton and electron linear accelerators are basically different for the fundamental reason that the less massive

† The Harvard–M.I.T. A-G electron synchrotron project.

electron travels most of the time with a velocity very close to that of light. Protons, on the other hand, have a low initial velocity (0·05 c for a 1 MeV proton) and they gain speed along the total flight path.

The Travelling-wave Electron Accelerator

Electromagnetic waves of suitable wavelength can be propagated through hollow metal pipes. These pipes, usually circular or rectangular in cross section, are called "wave guides". In a smooth cylindrical guide of radius a, the phase velocity of a wave of wavelength λ (λ is the free space wavelength) is given by

$$\frac{c}{v_p} = \left[1 - \left(\frac{\lambda}{\lambda_c}\right)^2\right]^{\frac{1}{2}} \tag{42}$$

λ_c is the "cut-off" wavelength. The phase velocity v_p is greater than c for all wavelengths and when $\lambda = \lambda_c$ the phase velocity becomes infinite. No waves can be propagated through the guide if $\lambda > \lambda_c$. In free space

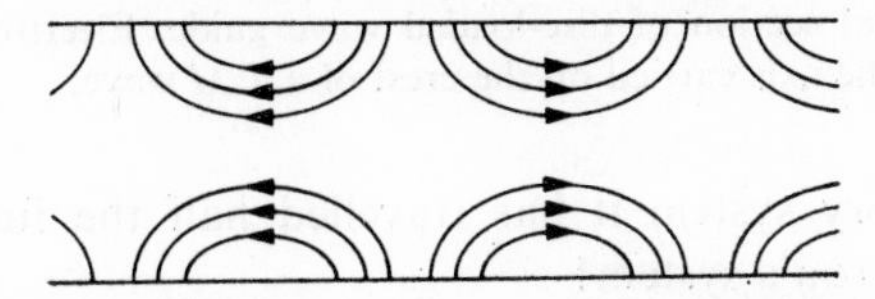

FIG. 14. Electric field pattern of E_{01} wave in cylindrical wave guide. Magnetic field lines are closed loops in transverse cross section.

the electric and magnetic fields of a travelling wave are perpendicular to the direction of propagation. This is not the case for a travelling electromagnetic wave in a wave guide. The so-called TM modes (or E modes) have a transverse magnetic field and an axial component for the electric field. The E_{01} mode of propagation in a cylindrical guide is sketched in Fig. 14.

If a bunch of electrons is injected along the axis of a guide carrying an E_{01} travelling wave it may be possible for the electrons to be accelerated by the axial electric field of the wave and thereby reach high energies. However, for this mechanism to operate the bunch of electrons must always feel an accelerating field and hence they must travel with the same velocity as the phase velocity of the wave. The smooth cylindrical wave guide is useless for this purpose as $v_p > c$. The phase velocity can be reduced to a value less than c by loading the guide with a series of coaxial perforated discs (Fig. 15). Near the injection end of the loaded guide the electron velocity may be of the order of $c/2$ ($v = c/2$ for 79 keV electrons) and the phase velocity of the wave must be adjusted to this value. After travelling a short distance the electron velocity is very close to c and the phase velocity is made equal to c and remains at this value over the remaining length of the accelerator.

The tendency for the electron bunch to diverge under the influence of the transverse field components can be compensated in the initial stages of acceleration by an externally applied d.c. axial magnetic field. Once the electrons reach an energy of a few MeV defocusing effects become ineffective. This is a consequence of the great fore-shortening of the longitudinal dimension of the accelerator from the moving electron's frame of reference. Thus a 1 GeV accelerator of total length 220 ft seems to be only 26 cm long to an electron, and when it has travelled

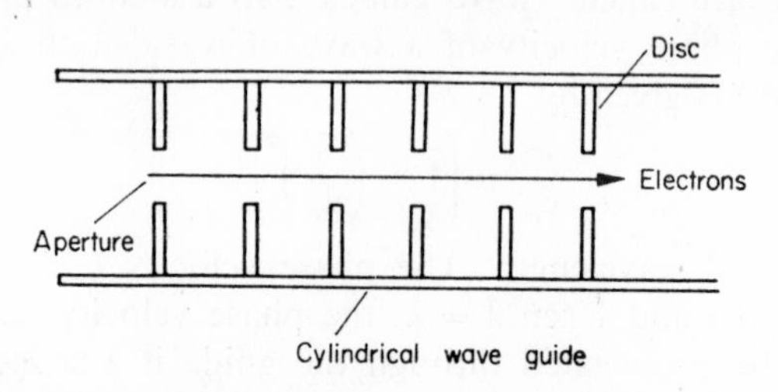

FIG. 15. Longitudinal section of disc-loaded wave guide. Electrons travel along the axis carried on the crest of a TM wave.

5 ft in the laboratory system it has travelled half the full length of the machine in the electron's system!

The travelling wave accelerator was pioneered in England by Fry and his associates†. In the original design the travelling E_{01} wave (3000 Mc/s) was absorbed in a load at the high energy end equal to the characteristic impedance of the wave guide. A 4 MeV machine was then built in which the output power was successfully fed back into the input end. This machine was used as a pulsed photo-neutron source at A.E.R.E. Harwell.

In the U.S.A. the travelling wave accelerator owed its development mainly to Hansen and his group at Stanford University. Using high power klystron amplifiers, a 220 ft long 1 GeV accelerator has been in operation for the last few years. A 2 mile long 40 GeV accelerator is now being built at Stanford.

A few technical details of the Stanford 1 GeV accelerator may be of interest.†† The wave guide is 220 ft long and 3 in. in diameter; it is divided into 10 sections, each of which is fed with high frequency power from a separate klystron amplifier. The 22 klystron amplifiers each have a maximum power output of 17 MW and they are driven by a common master oscillator. The use of a master oscillator (3000 Mc/s) simplifies the correct phasing of the microwaves fed into the ten accelerating sections. Design considerations of electrical efficiency (such as the

† D. W. FRY *et al.*, *Nature* **160**, 351, 1947; *Nature* **162**, 859, 1948.

†† A comprehensive review of this machine is given in *Rev. Sci. Instr.* **26**, pp. 134–204, 1955.

optimum shunt inpedance of the accelerator, etc.) led to a choice of disc spacing d of a quarter of a guide wavelength ($d \sim 1$ in.). Electron pulses of 0·5 μsec duration are injected 60 times every second at an injection energy of 80 kV. The duration of the output pulse from the klystrons is about 2 μsec and these are pulsed at the correct moment to accelerate the injected bunch of electrons.

The Stanford accelerator produces about 10^{11} electrons per pulse at a maximum energy of 1 GeV. Another useful feature of this type of machine is the ease of extracting a beam at intermediate energies along the length of the accelerator.

The Proton Linear Accelerator

The technique of accelerating protons in a linear machine differs in several ways from that of the electron accelerator. The main difference arises because of the much lower injection speed of protons; a 4 MeV proton has a velocity of about 0·1 c. The method of reducing the phase velocity of an electromagnetic wave in a cylindrical wave guide by spacing a number of perforated discs along its axis becomes impractical for phase velocities below about 0·4 c. This rules out the possibility of accelerating a low energy beam of protons by matching the phase velocity of the wave to the particle velocity.

To accelerate protons a long cylindrical resonant cavity is excited in a TM_{010} mode with an *infinite* phase velocity; that is the electric field of the wave has the same phase at all points along the axis of the cylinder. However, in alternate half cycles the electric field has the wrong polarity for accelerating the protons and it is necessary to arrange that the protons are shielded from the field during these half cycles. This shielding is obtained by mounting a series of coaxial hollow metal electrodes, known as "drift tubes", along the axis of the large cylindrical cavity. The drift tubes increase in length, but decrease in diameter, from the low to the high proton energy end of the accelerator. The increase in length is to allow for the increase in particle velocity; the protons must cross the gap between two drift tubes when the electric field is accelerating and increasing with time. The decrease in drift tube diameter is necessary in order to keep the resonance frequency uniform along the length of the accelerator. The electric field pattern of a TM_{010} mode of the accelerator cavity containing several drift tubes is shown in Fig. 16.

Unfortunately a bunch of protons crossing the gap between two drift tubes diverges. Unlike the cyclic accelerators, the linear accelerator requires the protons to cross the accelerating gap when the electric field is increasing with time, for an increase in particle energy increases the linear velocity and the protons arrive early at the next gap and feel a weaker field. This phase stability condition, however, means that the protons crossing a gap (Fig. 17) will experience a resultant outwards force as they have a greater axial velocity in the right-hand half of the gap. One method of solving this difficulty is to distort the electric field

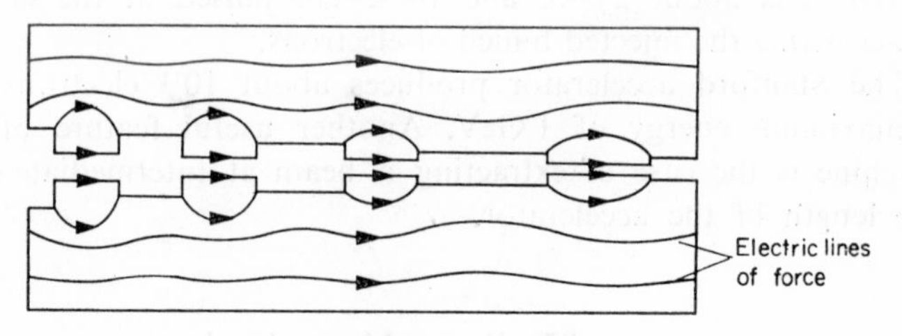

FIG. 16. Longitudinal section of resonant cavity with drift tubes excited in TM_{010} mode (standing wave).

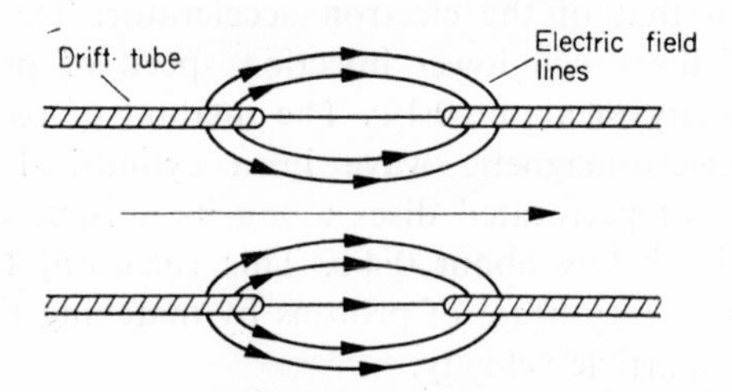

FIG. 17. Electric field lines across accelerating gap.

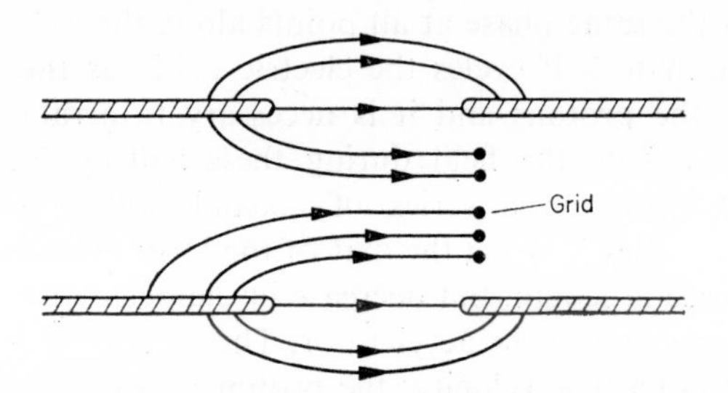

FIG. 18. Electric field distorted by presence of grid in front of right-hand drift tube (focusing field).

so that the lines of force converge inwards towards the right-hand drift tube. A grid placed just in front of the right-hand drift tube distorts the field in the desired way (Fig. 18). However, a focusing grid or foil in front of each drift tube intercepts or scatters some of the protons and results in a considerable loss in beam intensity. An alternative approach to the focusing problem is to install electric quadrupole lenses along the axis of the accelerator or use strong magnetic focusing.

PLATE II.

50 MeV proton linear accelerator (Rutherford High Energy Laboratory, Harwell). Photograph shows the machine with the vacuum and liner lid off the third tank revealing the drift tubes.

The first proton accelerator embodying these principles was built by Alvarez† at Berkeley in 1946–47. Protons of 4 MeV energy are injected from a Van de Graaff generator along the axis of a cylindrical resonant cavity of total length 40 ft and diameter 39 in. There are 47 drift tubes varying in dimensions from 4·4 in. in length (4·7 in. in diameter) to 10·9 in. in length (2·7 in. in diameter). The machine accelerates 400 μsec bursts of protons to a final energy of 32 MeV. The output current has the high time averaged value of 0·2 μA. The proton beam has a diameter as small as 2 mm with an angular spread of only 0·001 radian. The normal repetition frequency is 15 pulses per sec. One interesting difference from the electron accelerator is the use of a considerably lower radio-frequency. In the Alvarez proton accelerator the cavity is excited at 200 Mc/s from a group of phase locked triode oscillators (total power required is about 2 MW).

The highest energy to date for this type of proton accelerator is about 70 MeV. Apart from its use as a basic proton accelerator, linear accelerators have proved to be ideal as injectors for proton synchrotrons. In addition to proton acceleration, linear accelerators have been designed and built for accelerating heavy ions.

18.10. CONCLUSION

The art of accelerating charged particles is still being actively pursued and a number of lines of research looks very promising. The full potentialities of the alternating-gradient focusing principle, for example, have not yet been put into practice. One type of accelerator which is being studied is the "Fixed Field Alternating Gradient" machine (FFAG machine). One of the consequences of A–G focusing is the large momentum compaction: particles with a wide spread in momentum are compressed into a narrow range of radii. Theoretically it should be possible to accelerate particles from a low to a high energy in a *fixed* (d.c.) magnetic field with a small change in particle radius. Synchrotrons and cyclotrons of this type are definite possibilities. An FFAG cyclotron, however, requires a magnetic field which varies with azimuth in order to provide the necessary A–G focusing.

Perhaps the most interesting idea in accelerator physics at the moment is the possibility of a "colliding beam" machine. The requirements of conservation of momentum in the collision of a moving and a stationary particle means that a large fraction of the kinetic energy of the incident particle is associated with the motion of the centre of mass of the system. At high energies, the available energy in the centre of mass system increases only as the square root of the energy of the incident particle

† L. Alvarez *et al.*, *Rev. Sci. Instr.* **26**, 111, 1955.

in the laboratory system (Eqn. (65), Chapter 3). If, however, it could be arranged for beams of protons, each of the same energy, to meet head-on all the energy would be available for the creation of new particles etc. Thus two colliding 15 GeV proton beams provide 30 GeV of energy in the centre-of-mass system, equivalent to the energy in bombarding a stationary proton target with a beam of 540 GeV protons! The great practical difficulty in a colliding beam experiment is the low particle density of each beam with consequently a very small number of collisions. One possible method of achieving success may be to store two high intensity circulating beams of protons in two adjacent ring magnets, with a common tangential linear section linking the two circular vacuum chambers. When the beam currents have grown to the necessary current density the beams leave the storage magnets and travel down the linear section to collide in the central region.

BIBLIOGRAPHY

M. S. LIVINGSTON and J. P. BLEWETT, *Particle Accelerators*, McGraw-Hill, New York 1962.

M. S. LIVINGSTON, *High Energy Accelerators*, Interscience, New York 1954.

Handbuch der Physik, Vol. 44, Springer-Verlag, Berlin 1959.

E. M. MCMILLAN in *Experimental Nuclear Physics* Vol. 3, by Ed. E. Segrè, Wiley, New York 1959.

Proceedings of the CERN Symposium on High Energy Accelerators and Pion Physics, Vol. 1, Geneva 1956.

W. B. MANN, *The Cyclotron*, 4th Ed., Methuen, London 1953.

J. P. BLEWETT, The Proton Synchrotron in *Rep. Progr. Phys.* **19**, 37, 1956.

The Cosmotron Issue, *Rev. Sci. Instr.* **24**, 723–870, 1953.

Linear Accelerator Issue, *Rev. Sci. Instr.* **26**, 111–228, 1955.

Two important early reviews of linear accelerators are

D. W. FRY and W. WALKINSHAW, *Rep. Progr. Phys.* **12**, 102, 1949.

J. C. SLATER, *Rev. Mod. Phys.* **20**, 473, 1948.

An excellent non-mathematical article on focusing is

T. G. PICKAVANCE, *Progress in Nuclear Physics*, Vol. 4, 142–170, Pergamon Press, London 1955.

For future developments see the article by

D. L. JUDD, Conceptual advances in Accelerators in *Ann. Rev. Nucl. Sci.*, Vol. 8, 181–216, Annual Reviews Inc., Palo Alto, California 1958.

EXAMPLES

1. Deuterons are accelerated in a fixed frequency cyclotron to a maximum dee orbit radius of 88 cm. The magnetic flux density across the dees has a mean value of 14,000 gauss. Calculate the energy of the emerging deuteron beam, and the frequency of the dee voltage.

   What change in magnetic flux density is necessary if the cyclotron is required to accelerate doubly charged helium ions? (Frequency of dee voltage is unchanged.) (Atomic masses: $H^2 = 2{\cdot}014735$ a.m.u., $He^4 = 4{\cdot}00387$ a.m.u.)

2. A synchrocyclotron is designed to accelerate deuterons. It has the following parameters:

   Flux density at the centre = 15,000 gauss.

   Flux density at the periphery of the dee = 14,310 gauss.

   Calculate the maximum frequency of the dee voltage.

   If the dee voltage frequency is modulated between this maximum and a minimum of 10·0 Mc/s, calculate the gain in energy of a deuteron. If the modulation frequency is 60 c/s, calculate (approx.) the total flight path of a deuteron from the ion source to the edge of the dee.
3. In the "Cosmotron" proton synchrotron there are four quadrants of radius 9·144 m, and four connecting straight sections each of length 3·048 m. Protons are injected at 3·6 MeV. Calculate the magnetic flux density at the moment of injection, the speed of the protons, and the frequency of the accelerating voltage. The protons are accelerated to a final kinetic energy of 3 GeV; calculate the maximum magnetic flux density and the maximum frequency of the accelerating voltage.
4. A Betatron has the following parameters:

   Magnet current supply frequency = 60 c/s.

   Peak flux density at electron orbit = 4000 gauss.

   Orbit diameter = 66 in. (1 in. = 2·540 cm).

   Electron injection energy = 50 kV.

   Calculate the maximum kinetic energy of an electron and the approximate total time-of-flight.
5. The field-index n for the Cosmotron magnet is 0·60. Using the data given in question 3, calculate the expected radial displacement of the protons from their correct orbit if the frequency error is $+0{\cdot}1$ per cent (a) soon after injection (B is small), (b) when B reaches 14,000 gauss.

CHAPTER 19

NUCLEAR FORCES

19.1. THE DEUTERON

The obvious approach to the fundamental problem of nuclear forces is to begin with the study of the interaction of two nucleons. There are two general methods of investigation: the study of *n–p* and *p–p* scattering events over a wide range of energy, and the study of the deuteron. The deuteron is the only two nucleon bound system; no bound states exist for the di-proton or di-neutron.

In contrast to all other nuclei, the binding energy W of the deuteron is very small. It is known with high accuracy from observations of the photodisintegration of the deuteron using monochromatic γ-rays. We shall adopt an experimental value: $W = 2{\cdot}225 \pm 0{\cdot}002$ MeV. The angular momentum of the deuteron is one unit (in terms of $\hbar$). This is established, for instance, by observations of the relative intensities of alternate spectral lines of the band spectrum of molecular deuterium. The simplest assumption to make is that the ground state of the deuteron is an S state (no orbital angular momentum of the nucleons relative to the centre of mass) with the nucleon spins parallel. This state is a triplet state, ${}^3S_1$. However, the important discovery that the deuteron has a small but finite electric quadrupole moment implies that the deuteron must spend part of its time in a state of finite orbital angular momentum. This conclusion is also supported by the observation that the sum of the magnetic dipole moments of the proton and neutron do not exactly equal the magnetic moment of the deuteron:

$$\mu_p + \mu_n - \mu_d = 0{\cdot}0223 \pm 0{\cdot}0001 \quad \text{nuclear magnetons}$$

The electric quadrupole moment and the magnetic moment discrepancy can be explained if the ground state is a mixture of the triplet states ${}^3S_1$ and ${}^3D_1$. The states each have even parity ($L = 0$ and $L = 2$ respectively) and the percentage probability of finding the deuteron in the D state is $4 \pm 2\%$. There is some conflicting evidence from the electromagnetic interactions of the deuteron that the D state probability is as high as 8 per cent.

In view of the fact that the deuteron spends most of the time in the spherically symmetrical S state we will, for the moment, ignore the D state contribution to the deuteron wave function. What do we know about the nuclear force between the neutron and proton? In an S state the force must be central, and is it simplest at this stage to assume it depends only on the separation r of the nucleons and not on their relative velocity or orientation of the nucleon spins with respect to the line joining the nucleons. Such a force is a conservative force and therefore can be written as the gradient of a potential energy function $V(r)$. In spite of formidable mathematical difficulties in the meson theory of nuclear forces, there is now little doubt that the basic nucleon interaction is through the exchange of virtual pions. Two important aspects of the nuclear force are explained by the pion exchange theory: the force is very strong at separations of the order of one fermi (10^{-13} cm); and it has a short range, that is, it practically vanishes beyond a nucleon separation of two fermis.

The Schrödinger wave equation for an S state of the deuteron is

$$\frac{1}{r^2}\frac{d}{dr}\left(r^2\frac{d}{dr}\right)\psi(r) + \frac{2\mu}{\hbar^2}[E - V(r)]\,\psi(r) = 0 \qquad (1)$$

μ is the reduced mass of the system, nearly equal to $\frac{1}{2}M$, where M is the proton or neutron mass. The solution of eqn. (1) is greatly simplified by introducing a new wave function $u(r)$ where

$$\psi(r) = \frac{u(r)}{r} \qquad (2)$$

Substituting eqn. (2) in eqn. (1) we get

$$\frac{d^2u}{dr^2} + \frac{M}{\hbar^2}[E - V(r)]\,u = 0 \qquad (3)$$

Next comes the important question of the equation for $V(r)$, the internucleon potential energy. Fortunately it turns out that calculations of the deuteron wave function $u(r)$ are not very sensitive to the exact shape of $V(r)$. For simplicity, we represent $V(r)$ by a square well of depth V_0 and radius b_s where b is the range of the nuclear force (Fig. 1).

$$V = 0, \qquad \text{for} \quad r > b$$

$$V = -V_0, \quad \text{for} \quad r < b$$

The deuteron binding energy is the negative of $E(W = -E)$, so we can now write eqn. (3) as

$$\frac{d^2u}{dr^2} + \frac{M}{\hbar^2}(V_0 - W)\,u = 0, \quad r < b \qquad (4)$$

$$\frac{d^2u}{dr^2} - \frac{M}{\hbar^2}W\,u = 0, \quad r > b \qquad (5)$$

Acceptable solutions of $\psi(r)$ must be well-behaved; thus $u(r) \to 0$ as $r \to 0$, otherwise $\psi(0)$ becomes infinite. The solution of eqn. (4), therefore, does not contain a term in $\cos kr$. Acceptable solutions of eqns. (4) and (5) are

$$u = A \sin kr, \quad r < b \tag{6}$$

and

$$u = B e^{-\gamma r}, \quad r > b \tag{7}$$

where,

$$k = \frac{\sqrt{[M(V_0 - W)]}}{\hbar} \tag{8}$$

and

$$\gamma = \frac{\sqrt{(MW)}}{\hbar} \tag{9}$$

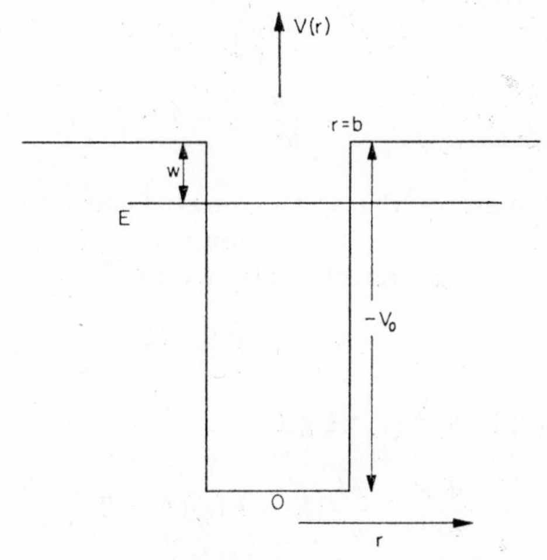

FIG. 1. Nuclear square potential well of depth V_0 E represents the total energy of the system: W is the nuclear binding energy.

The function $u(r)$ and its spatial derivatives are continuous; the same properties must be true for the logarithm of $u(r)$:

$$d(\ln u) = k \cot kr, \quad r < b$$
$$d(\ln u) = -\gamma, \quad r > b$$

Hence at $r = b$

$$k \cot kb = -\gamma \tag{10}$$

The binding energy of the deuteron is small; this suggests that $W \ll V_0$ may be a reasonable assumption. Then

$$\cot kb = -\frac{\gamma}{k} = -\sqrt{\frac{W}{V_0}} \tag{11}$$

Thus $\cot kb$ is negative and small in magnitude. For the ground state solution of $u(r)$, $kb = \pi/2 + \varepsilon$, where ε is a small positive angle. The error is not very large if we put

$$k\,b = \frac{\pi}{2}$$

and then eqn. (8) becomes

$$V_0\,b^2 \simeq \frac{\pi^2\,\hbar^2}{4M} \tag{12}$$

From eqn. (12) we can determine the product $V_0\,b^2$ of the potential well, but not V_0 and b separately. The same observed binding energy W would result from a weak force and a long range as from a strong force and a short range. Various considerations (such as pion theory) show that b is not greater than about 2 fermis. With a range value

$$b = 1{\cdot}7 \text{ fermi} \tag{13}$$

eqn. (12) yields for the depth of the well a value

$$V_0 = 35 \text{ MeV} \tag{14}$$

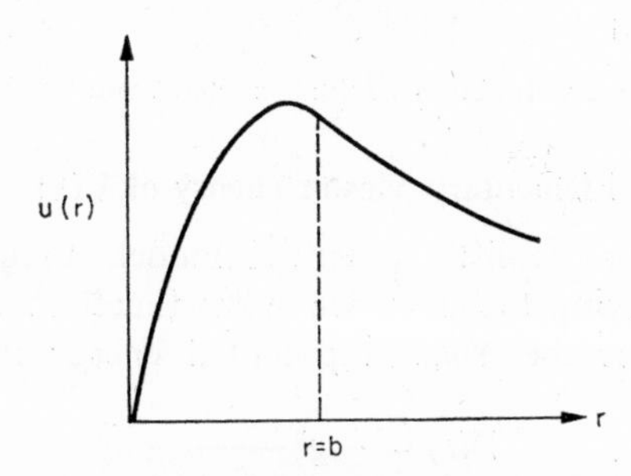

FIG. 2. Deuteron wave function (ground state) on the assumption of a square potential well.

This value for V_0 justifies the assumption that $V_0 \gg W$. In Fig. 2 the deuteron ground state wave function $u(r)$ is sketched. An important feature of the wave function is the appreciable amplitude well beyond the range b of the nuclear force. In fact, the exponential decrease of $u(r)$ beyond $r = b$ allows us to regard the constant $1/\gamma$ as a measure of the deuteron radius R

$$R = \frac{1}{\gamma} = \frac{\hbar}{\sqrt{(M\,W)}} = 4{\cdot}31 \text{ fermi} \tag{15}$$

The deuteron radius R is more than twice the size of the nuclear range b. For about half the time, the proton and neutron are outside the range of the nuclear force in the deuteron (hence the low binding energy W). This diffuseness of the deuteron structure is a consequence of the quantum mechanical tunnel effect; the wave function $u(r)$ leaks into the classically forbidden region $r > b$. It is a very near thing that there is even one bound state for the deuteron as both the potential and relative kinetic energies of the nucleons are large compared to W.

No bound excited states of the deuteron have been observed. This result is an agreement with the theory. For instance, for all S states, $k\,b < \pi$ for all bound states. But the wave function $u(r)$ of the first excited S state would have one radial node between $r = 0$ and $r = b$ (Fig. 3) and $k\,b > \frac{3\pi}{2}$, which contradicts the previous statement. It is not difficult to prove† that there are no bound states for finite values of L.

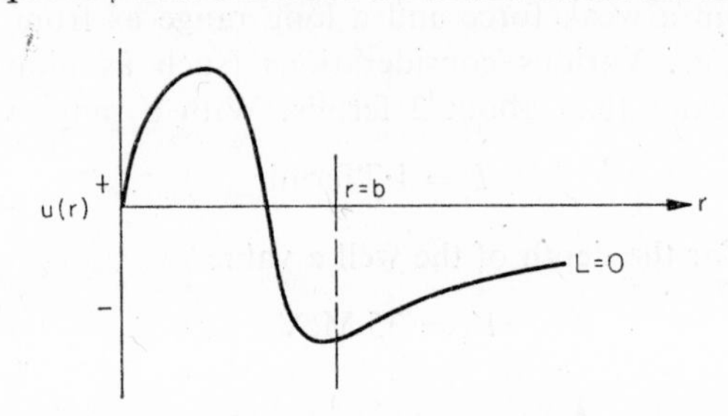

FIG. 3. Hypothetical wave function of first excited state of deuteron (S state).

Elementary Meson Theory of V(r)

A number of more realistic potential models than the square well has been used in solving the deuteron wave function. Perhaps the most interesting of these is the *Yukawa* potential energy function (Fig. 4)

$$V(r) = -g^2 \frac{e^{-r/\lambda}}{r} \tag{16}$$

g is a constant, and λ is the range of the pion-exchange force, namely, the pion Compton wavelength;

$$\lambda = \frac{h}{m\,c} = 1{\cdot}4 \text{ fermi} \tag{17}$$

where m is the rest mass of the pion (273 times the rest mass of the electron). There are good reasons for believing that this potential is not valid for inter-nucleon separations much less than λ.

The Yukawa function is obtained as follows. The nuclear force is a consequence of the interaction between some basic property of a nucleon, the nucleon "charge" g, and the surrounding pion field. This is analogous to our picture of electric charges interacting with an electromagnetic field. One of the important differences between the pion and the electromagnetic field is that the quanta of the former have a finite rest mass,

† See for example p. 47 of H. A. BETHE and P. MORRISON, *Elementary Nuclear Theory*, 2nd Ed. (Wiley, New York 1956).

whereas the quanta of the latter (photons) have zero rest mass. To obtain a pion wave equation we express the total energy E of a pion in terms of the pion rest mass energy $m c^2$ and its momentum p

$$E^2 = c^2 p^2 + m^2 c^4 \tag{18}$$

The energy E and momentum component p_x are represented by the operators (see Chapter 6)

$$E = i\hbar \frac{\partial}{\partial t} \quad \text{and} \quad p_x = -i\hbar \frac{\partial}{\partial x} \tag{19}$$

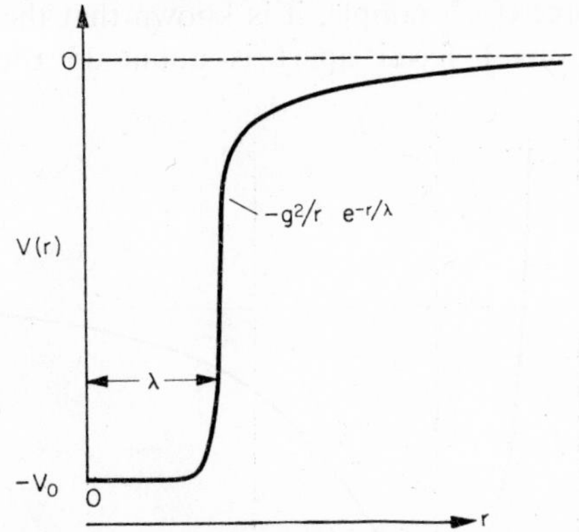

FIG. 4. Yukawa potential well for the deuteron.

Introducing a pion wave function φ (a scalar), we obtain the Klein–Gordon wave equation

$$\nabla^2 \varphi - \frac{1}{c^2}\frac{\partial^2 \varphi}{\partial t^2} - \frac{m^2 c^2}{\hbar^2}\varphi = 0 \tag{20}$$

If we put $m = 0$, we return to the well-known wave equation

$$\nabla^2 \varphi - \frac{1}{c^2}\frac{\partial^2 \varphi}{\partial t^2} = 0.$$

Now the simplest type of electromagnetic field is the electrostatic field, where $\partial\varphi/\partial t = 0$. What is the corresponding static pion field? It is the analogue of Laplace's equation in the absence of electric charges, but in the presence of charges we require the analogue of Poisson's equation

$$\nabla^2 \varphi = 4\pi e \varrho \tag{21}$$

where e is the magnitude of the electronic charge and ϱ is the electron particle density. In place of electric charges we have nucleon charges interacting with the pion field. If we consider the static pion potential due to a single point nucleon "charge" g at the origin $r = 0$, we obtain the equation

$$\nabla^2 \varphi - \frac{1}{\lambda^2}\varphi = 4\pi g \delta(r) \tag{22}$$

λ is the pion Compton wavelength and $\delta(r)$ is the Dirac delta function ($\delta(r) = 1$ at $r = 0$ and $\delta(r) = 0$ at finite r). It is not difficult to show that the Yukawa potential energy function $V(r) = g\,\varphi(r)$ corresponds to a solution of eqn. (22). A rough estimate of the constant g^2 from the estimated depth of 30 or 40 MeV for the Yukawa well at $r \sim \lambda$ can be made. A more significant result is obtained by comparing the magnitude of the dimensionless ratios $g^2/\hbar c \sim 1$ and the fine structure constant $e^2/(\hbar c) \sim 1/137$. The greater magnitude of $g^2/\hbar c$ is a consequence of the considerably greater strength of the nuclear force compared to the electromagnetic force (for example, it is known that the nuclear attraction between two protons 1 fermi apart is about 35 times as big as the

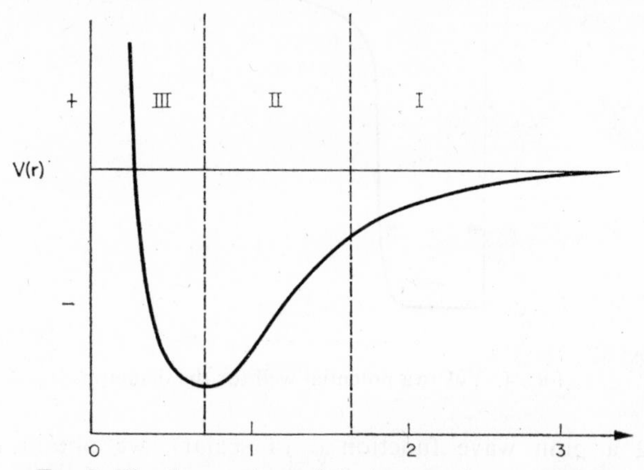

FIG. 5. The three regions of the inter-nucleon potential.

Coulomb repulsion). The fact that the electromagnetic constant $e^2/\hbar c \ll 1$ is of great *practical* mathematical importance, because it means that second and higher order perturbations in calculations of electronic binding energies can be relatively easily carried out (e.g. the Lamb shift); the corrections appear as small terms depending on $e^2/\hbar c$, $(e^2/\hbar c)^2$, etc. ... In pion theory these perturbation calculations do not converge as the corresponding constant $g^2/\hbar c$ is not small compared to unity. This is the main reason for the slow progress of pion theory.

It is convenient to classify pion interactions in three inter-nucleon ranges of r. This view was first emphasized by the Japanese physicist Taketani in 1949. The three regions are

(1) The outer (classical) region: $r > 1{\cdot}5\,\lambda$. This is known as the classical region because the pion exchange potential can be calculated without introducing the quantization of the pion field. It is the region in which the nuclear force acts through the exchange of single virtual pions (one-pion exchange) and it is the only region where the theory is in good agreement with experimental observations.

(2) The intermediate region: $0{\cdot}7\,\lambda < r < 1{\cdot}5\,\lambda$. The theory is not very satisfactory in this range: it is complicated by the onset of two-pion exchange forces, nucleon recoil effects etc.

(3) The inner region: $r < 0{\cdot}7\,\lambda$. There is practically nothing known at all about this region. It seems probable, however, that in many states the force between two nucleons at very short separations becomes strongly repulsive. The existence of this "hard" repulsive core to the nuclear potential was first suggested by Jastrow.† It is possible that in this inner region contributions to the potential arise from the exchange of virtual K mesons as well as from pions.

A sketch of the nuclear potential energy $V(r)$ covering these three ranges is given in Fig. 5. The shape in the inner region is very hypothetical.

The Tensor Force

A satisfactory theory of the deuteron must account for the small positive electric quadrupole moment of the deuteron

$$Q = 2{\cdot}82 \times 10^{-27}\ \text{cm}^2$$

corresponding to a prolate spheroidal distribution of electric charge. The fact that the magnetic moments of the neutron and the proton do not add up to that of the deuteron must also be explained. To remove the spherical symmetry of a ground state, corresponding to a pure S state, we must mix in a small amount of some state of finite *orbital* angular momentum. The most likely combination of states is a mixture of $^3S_1$ and $^3D_1$. Both these component states have even parity and they have a greater binding energy than the *odd* parity $^3P_1$ state (states of odd orbital angular momentum in a two nucleon system have odd parity). Thus we exclude the possibility of the $^3P_1$ state. The small quadrupole moment of the deuteron can be explained in terms of a small percentage of the $^3D_1$ state mixed with a large percentage of the spherically symmetrical $^3S_1$ state.

In order to explain the distortion in the shape of the deuteron wave function it is necessary to postulate that in the triplet D state the nuclear force is not purely central. There is a new type of force present—a tensor force—which depends on r and also on the orientation of the nucleon spins, with respect to the line joining the spins. This tensor force is analogous to the classical force between two magnetic dipoles. The tensor potential energy is written in the form

$$V_T(r)\,S_{12} \tag{23}$$

† R. Jastrow, *Phys. Rev.* **81**, 165, 1951.

where S_{12} is a tensor operator. The most convenient way of writing this operator is†

$$S_{12} = \frac{3(\boldsymbol{\sigma}_1 \boldsymbol{r})(\boldsymbol{\sigma}_2 \boldsymbol{r})}{r^2} - \boldsymbol{\sigma}_1 \boldsymbol{\sigma}_2 \tag{24}$$

$\boldsymbol{r}$ is the inter-nucleon separation vector. $\boldsymbol{\sigma}_1$ and $\boldsymbol{\sigma}_2$ are the Pauli spin operators for the proton and neutron respectively.†† The second term is included so that the scalar function S_{12} averaged over all directions of $\boldsymbol{r}$ vanishes.

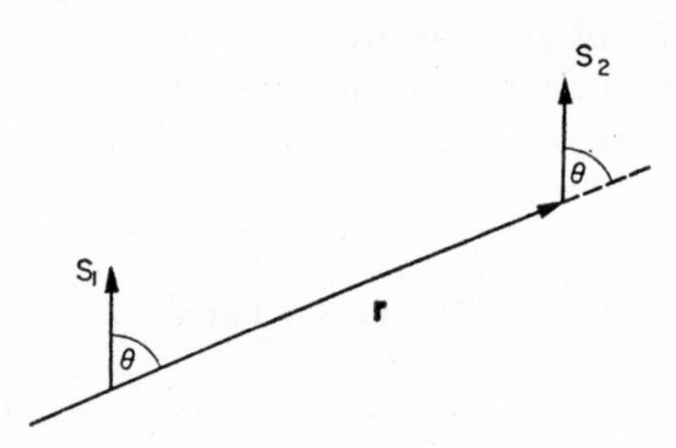

FIG. 6. Triplet state of two nucleons (parallel spins). θ is the angle between spin vector and radial vector.

The form of S_{12} is obtained by general considerations of symmetry: that, for example, the function should be invariant with respect to the displacement, rotation and inversion of the observer's coordinate axes. Polar vectors like $\boldsymbol{r}$ change sign on inversion of axes; but axial vectors like $\boldsymbol{\sigma}$ transform like the vector angular momentum $\boldsymbol{r} \times \boldsymbol{p}$ and if $\boldsymbol{r} \to -\boldsymbol{r}$ and $\boldsymbol{p} \to -\boldsymbol{p}$, $\boldsymbol{\sigma}$ does not change sign on inversion. The terms $\boldsymbol{\sigma}_1 \boldsymbol{r}$ and $\boldsymbol{\sigma}_2 \boldsymbol{r}$ change sign on inversion (pseudo-scalars) but the product $(\boldsymbol{\sigma}_1 \boldsymbol{r})(\boldsymbol{\sigma}_2 \boldsymbol{r})$ does not; neither does $\boldsymbol{\sigma}_1 \boldsymbol{\sigma}_2$.

From the properties of the nucleon spin operators it is not difficult to show that $S_{12} = 0$ when the nucleon spins are antiparallel (singlet state). The vanishing of the tensor force is to be expected as there is no resultant spin vector to act as a preferred direction. Thus in singlet states the potential energy function is always purely central.

The triplet states of the $n - p$ two nucleon system are illustrated in Fig. 6. In classical language, the tensor operator can be written

$$S_{12} = 3\cos^2\theta - 1 \tag{25}$$

where θ is the angle between the nucleon spins and the nucleon separation vector $\boldsymbol{r}$. If $V_T(r)$ is negative, then the potential energy $V_T(r)\, S_{12}$ is a minimum when $\theta = 0$ ($S_{12} = +2$). Thus we anticipate that in the ground state of the deuteron, the line joining the nucleons should be parallel to the resultant spin vector. This agrees with the observed sign of the

† W. RARITA and J. SCHWINGER, *Phys. Rev.* **59**, 436, 1941.
†† See Appendix B.

quadrupole moment which corresponds to a prolate spheroidal charge distribution.

There are three possible values of the orbital angular momentum for a system with total angular momentum of one unit, namely, $L = 0$, $L = 1$, and $L = 2$. The $L = 1$ triplet state, however, has odd parity (L odd) and in a two-nucleon system states of odd parity have more energy than states of even parity. For this reason, we expect the ground state of the deuteron to be a mixture of the even parity states $^3S_1$ and $^3D_1$, but not to contain any contribution from the $^3P_1$ state.

The wave function of the ground state of the deuteron when the tensor force contribution is included can be written as

$$\psi = \psi_S + \psi_D$$

where ψ_S and ψ_D are contributions from the S and D states respectively. The solution of the wave equation in the presence of the tensor force is much more difficult than the solution for a purely central potential.† It is necessary to introduce "spin angle" wave functions as ψ is now a function or r, θ and φ. For this reason we summarize some of the theoretical results.

The wave function of the deuteron is of the form

$$\psi = \frac{u(r)}{r}\chi_S + \frac{w(r)}{r}\chi_D \tag{26}$$

where χ_S and χ_D are the angular parts of the wave function. $u(r)$ and $w(r)$ are the radial parts of the wave function. Two important properties of the radial functions are

(1) $u^2(r)\,dr$ is the probability of finding the two nucleons in the S state with a separation between r and $r + dr$.

(2) $w^2(r)\,dr$ is the probability of finding the two nucleons in the D state with a separation between r and $r + dr$.

The probability of finding the deuteron in the $^3S_1$ state is given by the integral

$$P_S = \int_0^\infty u^2(r)\,dr \tag{27}$$

and the probability of finding the deuteron in the ^3D state is given by the integral

$$P_D = \int_0^\infty w^2(r)\,dr \tag{28}$$

The wave functions $u(r)$ and $w(r)$ are normalized so that $P_S + P_D = 1$.

† The solution of the wave equation is described in a number of books: p. 99, J. M. Blatt and V. F. Weisskopf, *Theoretical Nuclear Physics*. Wiley, New York 1952. p. 98, H. A. Bethe and P. Morrison, *Elementary Nuclear Theory*, 2nd. Ed., Wiley, New York 1956.

Exact solutions of the wave equation are not possible. However, it is found that there is an important connection between the D state probability P_D and the range of the tensor force b_T. A schematic drawing of the D state radial wave function $w(r)$ for an assumed value of b_T is shown in Fig. 7. Near $r = 0$, $w(r)$ increases rapidly with increasing r (roughly as r^3), and outside $r = b_T$, $w(r)$ falls away inversely as the square of r. $w(r)$ passes through a sharp maximum near $r = b_T$. If a smaller value of b_T is selected, the height of the maximum increases

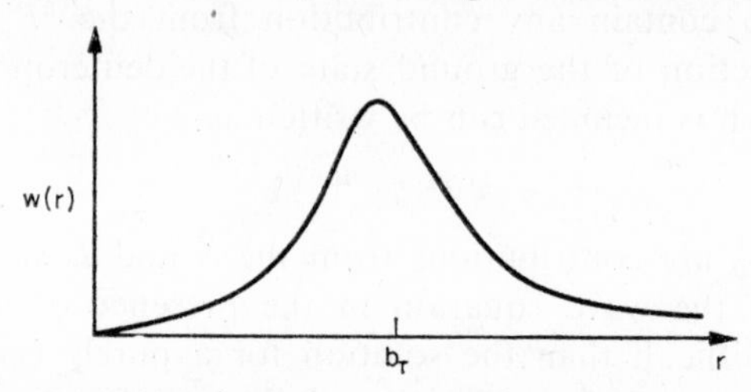

FIG. 7. Radial wave function $w(r)$. Notice maximum near $r = b_T$.

and the total area under the curve of $w(r)$ increases, corresponding to an increase in the D state probability. Thus an experimental determination of the D state probability determines the range of the tensor force. An estimate of P_D can be made by plausible arguments concerning the difference of the sum of the magnetic moments of the neutron and proton and the magnetic moment of the deuteron. There is, however, considerable uncertainty in the exact value of P_D; it probably lies between 2 and 8 per cent. This fixes the range of the tensor force b_T at between 2 and 3 fermis.

Thus the tensor force has a longer range than the central force.

19.2. THE SCATTERING OF NEUTRONS BY PROTONS

Information about the inter-nucleon force can be obtained by studying the scattering of neutrons by protons. There is no complication in this case due to Coulomb forces. We shall first of all consider the protons to be at rest in the laboratory system, and provided the incident neutrons have an energy greater than about 1 eV the protons can be regarded as free particles. For neutrons with kinetic energy less than 1 eV the binding energy of the protons in molecules or the crystal lattice is not negligible, and the protons no longer scatter as free particles.

In Chapter 15, Section 9, we discussed the transformation from the laboratory frame of reference (L-frame) to the centre-of-mass frame (C-frame). In describing the elastic scattering of neutrons by free protons it is more convenient to use the centre-of-mass system. Two simple results obtained from the equations in Chapter 15 are (for non-relativistic incident velocities).

(1) The total kinetic energy E of the two nucleons in the C-system is one half the incident kinetic energy of the neutron in the L-system: $E = \frac{1}{2} E_{lab}$.

(2) The angle of scattering θ of the neutron in the C-system is twice the angle of scattering in the L-system: $\theta = 2\theta_{lab}$.

Both these relations follow from the equality of the neutron and proton masses.

In the centre of mass system the wave equation for the n–p system is

$$\nabla^2\psi + \frac{M}{\hbar^2}[E - V(r)]\,\psi = 0 \tag{29}$$

At large distances from the centre of scattering the solution of eqn. (29) is expected to be of the form

$$\psi = \exp(i\,k\,z) + \frac{\exp(i\,k\,r)}{r}\cdot f(\theta) \tag{30}$$

The term $\exp(i\,k\,z)$ represents a plane wave of wavelength $\lambda = 2\pi\,\lambda\!\!\!^{-}$, where $\lambda\!\!\!^{-} = 1/k$, travelling along the z-axis towards the origin (scattering centre). This plane wave describes an incident parallel beam of mono-energetic particles of intensity v particles per unit cross-sectional area per unit time. The number of particles elastically scattered through an angle θ, per unit time, so that they cross an element of area dS normal to the radius vector $\boldsymbol{r}$, is

$$\frac{v}{r^2}|f(\theta)|^2\,dS = v\,|f(\theta)|^2\,d\Omega$$

where $d\Omega$ is the element of solid angle equal to $2\pi\sin\theta\,d\theta$. Now the differential cross section for elastic scattering into the element of solid angle $d\Omega$ at angle θ is given by

$$\sigma(\theta)\,d\Omega = \frac{\text{Number of particles scattered into } d\Omega \text{ per sec}}{\text{Number of incident particles per cm}^2 \text{ per sec}}$$

Thus

$$\sigma(\theta)\,d\Omega = \frac{v\,|f(\theta)|^2\,d\Omega}{v} = |f(\theta)|^2\,d\Omega$$

or

$$\sigma(\theta) = |f(\theta)|^2 \tag{31}$$

The second term in eqn. (30) represents an outgoing scattered spherical wave. The angular factor $f(\theta)$ in general varies with θ, but there is axial symmetry about the z-axis.

Before considering solutions of the wave equation, eqn. (29), let us consider the wave equation *in the absence of a scattering centre* ($V(r) = 0$ at all r).

$$\nabla^2\,\psi + \frac{M\,E}{\hbar^2}\,\psi = 0 \tag{32}$$

This has the solution

$$\psi = \exp(i\,k\,z) \tag{33}$$

where

$$k = \frac{1}{\lambda} = \frac{\sqrt{(M\,E)}}{\hbar}$$

It was first shown by Lord Rayleigh that it is possible to represent a plane wave as the sum of a series of spherical waves about the origin of spherical coordinates. Thus we can write eqn. (33), the solution of $\nabla^2 \psi + k^2 \psi = 0$, as an infinite series

$$\psi = \exp(i\,k\,z) = \exp(i\,k\,r\cos\theta) = \sum_{l=0}^{\infty} F_l(r)\,P_l(\cos\theta) \tag{34}$$

l is an integer representing the number of the *partial wave*. We shall see presently that l is the orbital angular momentum quantum number of the partial wave. $P_l(\cos\theta)$ is the Legendre polynomial of order l. The functions $F_l(r)$ are solutions of the radial part of eqn. (32).

$$\frac{1}{r^2}\,\frac{d}{dr}\left(r^2\frac{dF}{dr}\right) + \left[k^2 - \frac{l(l+1)}{r^2}\right]F(r) = 0 \tag{35}$$

This equation is very similar to Bessel's equation and $F_l(r)$ is related to the Bessel function of half-integral order $l + \frac{1}{2}$ by

$$F_l(r) = \sqrt{\left(\frac{\pi}{2k\,r}\right)}\,J_{l+\frac{1}{2}}(k\,r) \tag{36}$$

For incident neutrons of kinetic energy less than 10 MeV (in the L-system) we shall see that the only partial wave involved in scattering is the $l = 0$ or S wave. The scattering is then spherically symmetric in the C-system. In the absence of a scattering potential it is convenient to write,

$$\psi = \exp(i\,k\,z) = \frac{\sin kr}{kr} + \left[\exp(i\,k\,z) - \frac{\sin kr}{kr}\right] \tag{37}$$

The terms in the brackets correspond to terms in the expansion series eqn. (34) with $l > 0$. The averaged value of this quantity over all directions in space is easily shown to be zero.† The first term in eqn. (37) corresponds to the spherically symmetric partial wave (S wave).

Let us now consider the modification to ψ when the nuclear scattering force is "switched on". For S wave scattering, only the first ($l = 0$) partial wave is affected and we can therefore write the wave function in the presence of the scattering potential $V(r)$ as

$$\psi = \psi_s + \left[\exp(i\,k\,z) - \frac{\sin kr}{kr}\right] \tag{38}$$

† See N. F. Ramsey, p. 491 in *Experimental Nuclear Physics*. Vol. 1, Ed. by E. Segrè, Wiley, New York 1953.

The wave function ψ_s is spherically symmetrical and thus we can write

$$\psi_s = \frac{u(r)}{r} \tag{39}$$

where $u(r)$ is a solution of the radial wave equation

$$\frac{d^2u}{dr^2} + \frac{M}{\hbar^2}\left[E - V(r)\right]u(r) = 0 \tag{40}$$

Now the range b of the nuclear potential is small, and for $r > b$, $V(r) = 0$ and eqn. (40) has the solution

$$u = C\sin(kr + \delta_0) \tag{41}$$

where δ_0 is some phase angle. Thus the complete wave function is

$$\psi = \frac{C\sin(kr + \delta_0)}{r} + \left[\exp(ikz) - \frac{\sin kr}{kr}\right] \tag{42}$$

Comparing eqns. (42) and (37) we see that the effect of "switching on" the nuclear force is merely to introduce a phase shift δ_0 in the sinusoidal S wave component.

Writing $\sin kr$ as $\dfrac{\exp(ikr) - \exp(-ikr)}{2i}$ and

$\sin(kr + \delta_0)$ as $\dfrac{\exp(ikr)\exp(i\delta_0) - \exp(-ikr)\exp(-i\delta_0)}{2i}$

we can express eqn. (42) in the form

$$\psi = \exp(ikz) + \frac{\exp(ikr)}{r}\left(\frac{C\exp(i\delta_0) - 1/k}{2i}\right) - \frac{\exp(-ikr)}{r}\left(\frac{C\exp(-i\delta_0) - 1/k}{2i}\right) \tag{43}$$

The last term in eqn. (43) involves the factors $\dfrac{\exp(-ikr)}{r}$ and therefore corresponds to an ingoing spherical wave. This is clearly impossible and therefore the coefficient

$$C\exp(-i\delta_0) - \frac{1}{k} = 0$$

$$C = \frac{\exp(i\delta_0)}{k} \tag{44}$$

Hence

$$\psi = \exp(ikz) + \frac{\exp(ikr)}{r}\left(\frac{\exp(2i\delta_0) - 1}{2ik}\right) \tag{45}$$

Comparing this with the standard solution (30), we obtain

$$f(\theta) = \frac{\exp(2i\,\delta_0) - 1}{2i\,k} = \frac{\exp(i\delta_0)}{k}\;\frac{(\exp(i\,\delta_0) - \exp(-\,i\,\delta_0))}{2i}$$

$$f(\theta) = \frac{\exp(i\,\delta_0)\sin\delta_0}{k} \tag{46}$$

From eqns. (31) and (46) we find that as $|\exp i\,\delta_0| = 1$

$$\sigma(\theta) = \frac{\sin^2\delta_0}{k^2} = \lambda\!\!\!^{-2}\sin^2\delta_0 \tag{47}$$

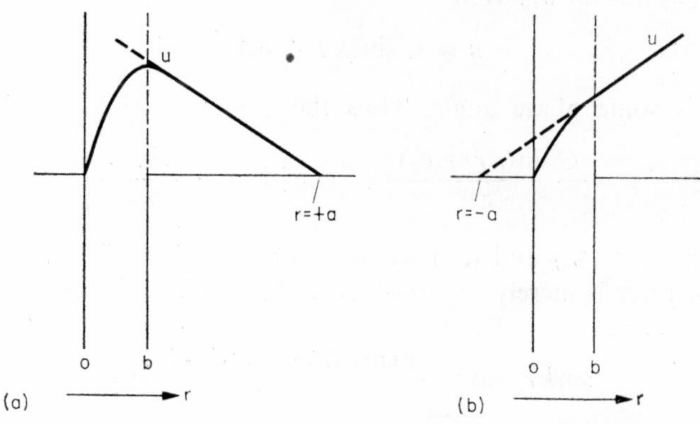

FIG. 8. Illustration of geometrical interpretation of "scattering length" a. (a) a is positive for scattering from a bound state; (b) a is negative for scattering from an unbound state.

Thus the scattering cross section is determined by the phase shift δ_0. Obviously if the nuclear force is "switched off" $\delta_0 = 0$ and there is no scattering at all.

For neutrons of very low energy scattered by "free" protons, $\lambda\!\!\!^{-}$ is very long and k is very small. Now $\delta_0 \to 0$ as $k \to 0$ otherwise $\sigma(\theta) \to \infty$. Thus for low energy neutrons, δ_0 is small and $f(\theta)$ can be written

$$f_0 = \frac{\delta_0}{k} = -\,a \tag{48}$$

where the quantity a is called the "scattering length" (after Fermi and Marshall). For long wavelength neutrons, eqn. (41) becomes

$$u(r) = C(kr + \delta_0) = Ck(r - a) \tag{49}$$

Thus the scattering length a is the intercept on the r-axis, for very low energy neutrons, when a linear extrapolation of $u(r)$ is made from a point just beyond the range of the nuclear force. Two cases are illustrated in Fig. 8; (a), the scattering length is positive for scattering from a bound state and (b), negative for scattering from an unbound state.

For very slow neutrons we can write

$$\psi = \exp(i\,k\,z) + \frac{a}{r}\exp[i(k\,r + \pi)] \tag{50}$$

Thus if the scattering length is positive there is a phase change of π on scattering.

For S wave scattering $\sigma(\theta)$ is independent of θ and therefore the total scattering cross section is given by (using eqn. (47)),

$$\sigma = 4\pi\,\lambda\!\!\!^{-2} \sin^2\delta_0 \tag{51}$$

and for very low energy neutrons eqn. (51) becomes

$$\sigma = 4\pi\,a^2 \tag{52}$$

which is analogous to the scattering by an impenetrable sphere of radius a.

Let us now assume that the scattering potential well can be represented by a simple square well of the type we used in discussing the deuteron ground state

$$V(r) = 0, \quad \text{for } r > b$$

$$V(r) = -V_0, \text{ for } r < b$$

Inside the well, $r < b$, and the wave equation is

$$\frac{d^2u}{dr^2} + \frac{M}{\hbar^2}(E + V_0)\,u(r) = 0 \tag{53}$$

and

$$\psi(r) = \frac{u(r)}{r}$$

The total energy E is positive (unbound system). This equation has the simple solution

$$u(r) = A \sin K\,r \tag{54}$$

where

$$K = \frac{\sqrt{[M(E + V_0)]}}{\hbar} \tag{55}$$

(the cosine solution is excluded, because $\psi(r)$ must remain finite at the origin).

Outside the well where $r > b$, the solution of the wave equation can be written in the form

$$u(r) = B \sin(k\,r + \delta_0) \tag{56}$$

At $r = b$, the two solutions and their derivatives with respect to r must match

$$\therefore A \sin K\,b = B \sin(k\,b + \delta_0)$$

and $$K\,A \cos K\,b = k\,B \cos(k\,b + \delta_0)$$

Dividing, we obtain the boundary condition

$$K \cot K b = k \cot(k b + \delta_0) \tag{57}$$

In the analogous problem of the deuteron ground state we obtained the boundary condition at $r = b$ (eqn. (10)) as

$$k \cot k b = -\gamma \tag{58}$$

where

$$k = \frac{\sqrt{[M(V_0 - W)]}}{\hbar} \tag{59}$$

W is the deuteron binding energy

$$\gamma = \frac{\sqrt{(M W)}}{\hbar} \tag{60}$$

Now $V_0 \gg W$ and if $V_0 \gg E$ for an unbound system, the wave function $u(r)$ inside the well is nearly the same for the deuteron and the n–p scattering system. The boundary conditions eqns. (57) and (58) are also nearly identical, and to a first approximation

$$\frac{\sqrt{(M E)}}{\hbar} \cot\left[\left(\frac{\sqrt{[M E]}}{\hbar}\right) b + \delta_0\right] \simeq -\frac{\sqrt{(M W)}}{\hbar} \tag{61}$$

Also as b is small, $\frac{\sqrt{(M E)}}{\hbar} b$ is small compared with δ_0, so that

$$\cot \delta_0 \simeq -\sqrt{\left(\frac{W}{E}\right)} \tag{62}$$

Now

$$\sin^2 \delta_0 = \frac{1}{1 + \cot^2 \delta_0} \simeq \frac{E}{E + |W|} \tag{63}$$

where $|W|$ is the magnitude of the binding energy. Substituting eqn. (63) in eqn. (51) we obtain the approximate result

$$\sigma = \frac{4\pi}{k^2} \frac{E}{E + |W|} = \frac{4\pi \hbar^2}{M} \frac{1}{E + |W|} \tag{64}$$

For incident neutrons of kinetic energy $E_{\text{lab}} < 10$ MeV, only S wave scattering is involved. To justify this statement it is useful to give a semi-classical interpretation of the analysis of the incident wave into partial waves of different l values. A parallel beam of monoenergetic particles travelling parallel to the z-axis with linear momentum p can be divided into a series of cylindrical zones (Fig. 9). If d is the impact parameter of a particle, the angular momentum of the particle about the scattering centre is $p\,d$ and this must be quantized. The quantization of angular momentum, however, does not mean that there are only certain discrete allowed values of d. The uncertainty principle does not allow us to define exactly the impact parameter d. Nevertheless, we can say that the majority of particles with an angular momentum quantum number l will have an impact parameter lying between the limits

$$\frac{\hbar l}{p} \quad \text{and} \quad \frac{\hbar}{p}(l+1)$$

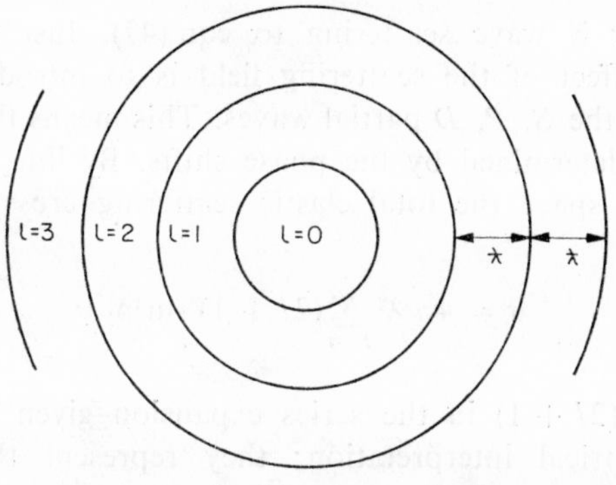

l=3 l=2 l=1 l=0 ƛ ƛ

FIG. 9. Division of incident beam of particles into zones of orbital angular momentum. Each zone has a radial width $\lambda\!\!\!^-$.

Now $p = \frac{\hbar}{\lambda\!\!\!^-}$, where $\lambda\!\!\!^- = \frac{\lambda}{2\pi}$ and λ is the de Broglie wavelength of the incident particles. Thus particles with an angular momentum l are confined to the cylindrical zone defined by the radii

$$\lambda\!\!\!^- l \quad \text{and} \quad \lambda\!\!\!^-(l+1) \tag{65}$$

Incident particles of zero angular momentum ($l = 0$) are confined to the central zone of radius $\lambda\!\!\!^-$. The energy of a particle corresponding to $\lambda\!\!\!^-$ is

$$E_{\text{lab}} = 2E = \frac{2p^2}{2\dfrac{M}{2}} = \frac{2\hbar^2}{M\lambda\!\!\!^{-2}} \tag{66}$$

where M is the nucleon mass and $\lambda\!\!\!^-$ is measured in the C-system. If the finite range b of the neutron–proton force is less than $\lambda\!\!\!^-$, only neutrons in the central zone (S neutrons) will be scattered; neutrons of finite angular momentum do not pass close enough to the scattering centre to feel the nuclear force. Putting $b = \lambda\!\!\!^- = 2{\cdot}8$ fermi, the corresponding neutron energy is

$$E_{\text{lab}} = \frac{2 \times 10^{-54}}{(1{\cdot}6 \times 10^{-24})(2{\cdot}8 \times 10^{-13})^2(1{\cdot}6 \times 10^{-6})} \text{ MeV}$$

$$E_{\text{lab}} \sim 10 \text{ MeV}$$

If the neutron energy is greater than 10 MeV but less than ~ 40 MeV, neutrons with $l = 1$ as well as $l = 0$ are involved in the scattering; that is, we have a mixture of S and P wave scattering.

A general expression† for the differential elastic scattering cross section is

$$\sigma(\theta) = \left| \frac{1}{2ik} \sum_l (2l+1)(1-\eta_e)\, P_2(\cos\theta) \right|^2 \tag{67}$$

where

$$\eta_l = \exp(2i\,\delta_l)$$

This reduces for S wave scattering to eqn (47). Just as with S wave scattering, the effect of the scattering field is to introduce phase shifts $\delta_0, \delta_1, \delta_2, \ldots$ in the S, P, D partial waves. This means that the scattering cross section is determined by the phase shifts. By integrating $\sigma(\theta)$ over all directions of space the total elastic scattering cross section is found to be

$$\sigma = 4\pi\,\lambda\!\!\!^{-2} \sum_{l=0}^{\infty} (2l+1)\sin^2\delta_l \tag{68}$$

The factors $\pi\,\lambda\!\!\!^{-2}(2l+1)$ in the series expansion given by eq. (68) have a simple geometrical interpretation; they represent the areas of the angular momentum zones shown in Fig. 9. For pure S wave scattering, eqn. (68) reduces to eqn. (51)

$$\sigma = 4\pi\,\lambda\!\!\!^{-2}\sin^2\delta_0$$

The Spin Dependence of the n–p Force

The n–p scattering cross section for very low energy neutrons (zero-energy) by free protons is, according to the approximate formula eqn. (64),

$$\sigma_0 = \frac{4\pi\,\hbar^2}{M\,W} \sim 4 \text{ barns} \tag{69}$$

This theoretical estimate is based on the deuteron binding energy W in the ground state, which is a pure triplet state. In the scattering of neutrons by protons, however, we expect that in $\frac{3}{4}$ of the scattering events the neutron and proton spins will be parallel (triplet scattering) and in the remaining scattering events the neutron and proton spins will be anti-parallel (singlet scattering). Wigner, in 1935, suggested that the n–p interaction in the singlet and triplet states might differ significantly; thus the cross section given by eqn. (69) would not agree with experiment. This is found to be the case; an accurate measurement†† of σ_0, using a mechanical velocity selector, is

$$\sigma_0 = 20{\cdot}36 \pm 0{\cdot}10 \text{ barns} \tag{70}$$

† See for example, p. 105, L. I. Schiff, *Quantum Mechanics*, McGraw-Hill, New York 1955.

†† E. Melkonian, *Phys. Rev.* **76**, 1744, 1949

This experimental zero-energy scattering cross section can be written as

$$\sigma_0 = \frac{3}{4}\sigma_t + \frac{1}{4}\sigma_s \tag{71}$$

where σ_t and σ_s are the cross sections at zero-energy in the triplet and singlet states respectively. Equation (69) is a rough estimate of σ_t; nevertheless, it enables us to estimate σ_s, using the experimental value of σ_0 inserted into eqn. (71)

$$\sigma_s \sim 70 \text{ barns} \tag{72}$$

Introducing the singlet and triplet "scattering lengths" a_s and a_t, where $\sigma_s = 4\pi a_s^2$ and $\sigma_t = 4\pi a_t^2$, we obtain the rough estimates

$$a_t \sim 5 \text{ fermi} \quad \text{and} \quad a_s \sim 24 \text{ fermi} \tag{73}$$

At this stage, the sign of a_s is still ambiguous.

The most striking confirmation of the strong influence of the *n–p* spin orientation on the *n–p* force is obtained from a comparison of the coherent scattering cross section of very slow neutrons by ortho- and para- hydrogen. The theoretical possibilities of this method were first investigated by Schwinger and Teller.† Molecular hydrogen exists in two forms: in ortho-hydrogen the two proton spins are parallel, whereas in para-hydrogen the proton spins are antiparallel. Para-hydrogen has a lower energy than ortho-hydrogen; however, the rate of conversion of ortho- to para-hydrogen at room temperature is very small and the normal concentrations are given by the statistical weight factors: 3 parts of ortho- to 1 part of para-hydrogen. At low temperatures, e.g. 20°K, in the presence of a suitable catalyst (charcoal), hydrogen is nearly 100 per cent para-hydrogen. In diatomic homonuclear molecules the resultant nuclear angular momentum determines the possible values of the electronic orbital angular momentum L: in ortho-hydrogen, $L = 1, 3, 5, \ldots$; in para-hydrogen, $L = 0, 2, 4, \ldots$ Thus at low temperatures, para-hydrogen will be in the $L = 0$ and ortho-hydrogen in the $L = 1$ electronic states. The energy levels of the lowest ortho- and para-molecular states differ by 0·023 eV and a low energy neutron ($E_n < 0{\cdot}023$ eV) cannot be scattered by a para-hydrogen molecule and invert one of the proton spins (an inelastic collision, in which an ortho–para transition occurs, with the neutron gaining energy in a collision with an ortho-molecule, is possible).

Before discussing the coherent scattering of neutrons by hydrogen molecules, we must consider the effect on the scattering cross section of the binding of the protons within the hydrogen molecule. If the scattering of neutrons can be treated†† by the perturbation method known as the

† J. Schwinger and E. Teller, *Phys. Rev.* **52**, 286, 1937.

†† H. A. Bethe and P. Morrison, *Elementary Nuclear Theory*, 2nd. Ed., p. 62.

Born approximation, the differential scattering cross section

$$\sigma(\theta) \text{ is proportional to } \mu^2 \tag{74}$$

where μ is the reduced mass of the neutron and scattering molecule. Thus the scattering cross sections of neutrons by molecular hydrogen compared to those by free protons must be multiplied by the square of $^2/_3$ divided by the square of $^1/_2$, that is by $^{16}/_9$.

Let us consider the scattering of neutrons in equilibrium with ortho- and para-hydrogen at 20°K. The mean neutron wavelength is about 7 Å, which is nine times the inter-proton separation of 0·74 Å in the hydrogen molecule. Thus to a good approximation we can consider the two protons in a given molecule as virtually at the *same place* from the point of view of the incident and scattered neutron waves. The scattering of a neutron by a para-hydrogen molecule will be a coherent mixture of singlet and triplet scattering, as one of the proton spins will be parallel to and the other one antiparallel to the spin of the incoming neutron. An ortho-molecule will, on the other hand, scatter with both its protons parallel or both antiparallel to the neutron spin.

Introducing the Pauli spin operators $\boldsymbol{\sigma}_n$ and $\boldsymbol{\sigma}_p$ for the neutron and proton, where $\boldsymbol{s}_n = \frac{1}{2}\boldsymbol{\sigma}_n$ and $\boldsymbol{s}_p = \frac{1}{2}\boldsymbol{\sigma}_p$ respectively, they have the following important properties

$$\boldsymbol{\sigma}_n \boldsymbol{\sigma}_p = 1 \text{ in the triplet interaction} \tag{75a}$$

and

$$\boldsymbol{\sigma}_n \boldsymbol{\sigma}_p = -3 \text{ in the singlet interaction} \tag{75b}$$

These results can be proved as follows. Let the total nuclear spin of the neutron and proton be written as

$$\boldsymbol{s} = \boldsymbol{s}_n + \boldsymbol{s}_p \tag{76}$$

squaring, we obtain, as $\boldsymbol{s}_n$ and $\boldsymbol{s}_p$ commute

$$\boldsymbol{s}^2 = \boldsymbol{s}_n^2 + \boldsymbol{s}_p^2 + 2\boldsymbol{s}_n \boldsymbol{s}_p \tag{77}$$

The operators $\boldsymbol{s}^2$, $\mathbf{s}_n^2$, $\mathbf{s}_p^2$ have the eigenvalues: $s(s+1)$, $s_n(s_n+1)$, and $s_p(s_p+1)$, respectively. From eqn. (77) we obtain

$$\boldsymbol{s}_n \boldsymbol{s}_p = \tfrac{1}{2}[s(s+1) - s_n(s_n+1) - s_p(s_p+1)]$$

now the neutron and proton are spin $\frac{1}{2}$ particles: $s_n = s_p = \frac{1}{2}$; hence

$$\boldsymbol{s}_n \boldsymbol{s}_p = \frac{1}{2} s(s+1) - \frac{3}{4}$$

From the definition of the Pauli spin operators,

$$\boldsymbol{\sigma}_n \cdot \boldsymbol{\sigma}_p = 4\boldsymbol{s}_n \cdot \boldsymbol{s}_p = 2s(s+1) - 3. \tag{78}$$

In the triplet state $s = \frac{1}{2} + \frac{1}{2} = 1$, in the singlet state $s = \frac{1}{2} - \frac{1}{2} = 0$, and thus we obtain the results given by eqn. (75).

A single expression can represent the scattering lengths for both triplet and singlet states: this is

$$a_{t,s} = \frac{1}{4}(3a_t + a_s) + \frac{1}{4}(a_t - a_s)\,\sigma_n\,\sigma_p \tag{79}$$

This is easily verified using the relations for $\sigma_n \sigma_p$ in the triplet and singlet states.

The scattering length for a zero-energy neutron by a hydrogen molecule is

$$a_{\text{mol}} = \frac{1}{2}(3a_t + a_s) + \frac{1}{2}(a_t - a_s)\,\sigma_n\,s_{\text{H}} \tag{80}$$

In coherent scattering we add the amplitudes *before* squaring. The operator $s_{\text{H}} = \frac{1}{2}(\sigma_{p1} + \sigma_{p2})$ is the total nuclear spin operator for the molecule. (p_1 and p_2 refer to the two protons). The scattering cross section is proportional to a^2_{mol}.

After squaring eqn. (80), we must average the terms over all spin orientations of the incident neutrons. The cross product terms involving $\sigma_n\, s_{\text{H}}$ average out to zero, but the average of the square of $\sigma_n\, s_{\text{H}}$ is obtained by writing

$$\begin{aligned}\langle(\sigma_n\, s_{\text{H}})^2\rangle_{av} &= \langle\sigma^2_{nx}\, s^2_{\text{H}x} + \sigma^2_{ny}\, s^2_{\text{H}y} + \sigma^2_{nz}\, s^2_{\text{H}z} + 2\sigma_{nx}\,\sigma_{ny}\, s_{\text{H}x}\, s_{\text{H}y} + \cdots\rangle_{av}\\ &= s^2_{\text{H}x} + s^2_{\text{H}y} + s^2_{\text{H}z} = s^2_{\text{H}} = s_{\text{H}}(s_{\text{H}} + 1)\end{aligned}$$

N.B. $\sigma^2_{nx} = 1 \cdots$ and the terms in $\sigma_{nx}\,\sigma_{ny}\, s_{\text{H}x}\, s_{\text{H}y}$ vanish.

Thus

$$a^2_{\text{mol}} = \frac{1}{4}(3a_t + a_s)^2 + \frac{1}{4}(a_t - a_s)^2\, s_{\text{H}}(s_{\text{H}} + 1). \tag{81}$$

Coherent scattering from para-hydrogen is represented by

$$a^2_{\text{para}} = \frac{1}{4}(3a_t + a_s)^2 \tag{82}$$

and for ortho-hydrogen,

$$a^2_{\text{ortho}} = \frac{1}{4}(3a_t + a_s)^2 + \frac{1}{2}(a_t - a_s)^2 \tag{83}$$

as $s_{\text{H}} = 0$ in para-hydrogen, and $s_{\text{H}} = 1$ in ortho-hydrogen. If the neutron-proton force is spin-independent, $a_t = a_s$ and σ_{ortho} and σ_{para} will be equal. The best experimental measurements of σ_{ortho} and σ_{para} are those of Sutton†

$$\sigma_{\text{para}} = 4{\cdot}0 \text{ barns} \quad \text{and} \quad \sigma_{\text{ortho}} = 125 \text{ barns} \tag{84}$$

The vast difference between these cross sections clearly demonstrates that the n–p force is strongly spin-dependent, and it also enables us to

† R. Sutton *et al.*, *Phys. Rev.* 72, 1147, 1947.

infer that the scattering length a_s is negative. To demonstrate that a_s is negative, we note that, using the estimates $a_t \sim 5$ fermi, $|a_s| \sim 24$ fermi, $\sigma_{\text{ortho}} \sim 1{\cdot}4\, \sigma_{\text{para}}$ if a_s is positive; if a_s is negative, however, $\sigma_{\text{ortho}} \gg \sigma_{\text{para}}$. The large difference between the cross sections, if the scattering lengths are opposite in sign is a consequence of the fortunate fact that the magnitudes of $3a_t$ and a_s are nearly equal. The negative scattering length of the singlet *n–p* interaction means that there is no bound singlet state of the deuteron.

There is a number of important corrections to be made before the theory of scattering of neutrons by molecular hydrogen is compared with the best experimental results. These include

(1) The effect of inelastic collisions between cold neutrons and ortho-hydrogen molecules in which the neutrons gain energy.

(2) The loss of neutrons due to the radiative capture by protons; this cross section increases at low energies.

(3) The Maxwellian distribution of the velocities of the molecules must be considered; this increases in importance as the neutron velocity decreases.

The coherent scattering of low energy neutrons by protons has been observed by studying the diffraction of neutrons by crystalline sodium hydride. A better method of determining the hydrogen scattering length is to measure the critical angle for the total reflection of collimated neutrons from a liquid mirror containing hydrogen.† The refractive index for neutrons of wavelength λ is (see Chapter 15)

$$n = 1 - \frac{a\lambda^2 N}{2\pi}$$

where N is the number of scattering nuclei per cm^3 and a is the average bound coherent scattering length. Total external reflection is possible, provided a is positive. In order to obtain total reflection from a mirror containing hydrogen (the scattering length is negative), the hydrogen must be mixed with atoms of positive scattering length. The bound coherent scattering length of C^{12} is accurately known to be $+6{\cdot}63 \pm 0{\cdot}03$ fermi. The bound coherent scattering length of hydrogen is determined from observations on the total reflection of neutrons by liquid mirrors of $C_{12}H_{18}$, C_6H_{10} and C_6H_{12}. The experimental value of a_{para} from these mirror experiments is

$$a_{\text{para}} = -(3{\cdot}78 \pm 0{\cdot}02)\ \text{fermi}. \tag{85}$$

19.3. PROTON–PROTON SCATTERING

At low energies (< 100 keV) the scattering of protons by protons is predominantly due to the Coulomb force. At higher energies, the scattering of protons by protons cannot be accounted for in terms of a pure

† M. T. Burgy *et al.*, *Phys. Rev.* **84**, 1160, 1951.

Coulomb interaction; the protons get close enough for the *p–p* nuclear force to be effective. Experimentally the study of *p–p* scattering is capable of much higher accurary than *n–p* scattering. This improvement in accuracy arises because it is possible to work with highly collimated beams of monoenergetic protons. It is also easier to detect protons through their ionizing properties.

A special feature of *p–p* scattering arises from the identical nature of the two particles involved. The protons obey the exclusion principle and therefore the wave function describing the pair of protons must change sign on the interchange of the two particles. If the spatial part of the wave function is symmetric, as it is in an *S* or *D* state, the spin wave function must be antisymmetric. For incident protons of energy below 10 MeV only *S* wave nuclear scattering is involved. Thus in low energy *p–p* scattering the nuclear interaction always occurs with the proton spins antiparallel (singlet state).

We are interested in obtaining a theoretical expression for the differential elastic scattering cross section of protons by protons. First we write down the Rutherford cross section for Coulomb scattering of particles of charge $Z_1 e$ by a particle of charge $Z_2 e$ in the centre of mass system

$$d\sigma(\theta) = \left[\frac{e^4 Z_1^2 Z_2^2}{4m^2 v^4} \operatorname{cosec}^4\left(\frac{\theta}{2}\right)\right] 2\pi \sin\theta \, d\theta \tag{86}$$

θ is the angle of scattering in the centre of mass system, m is the reduced mass of the system and v the relative speed of approach of the particles. For *p–p* Coulomb scattering, $Z_1 = Z_2 = 1$, $m = M/2$ $\theta = 2\theta_1$ (where θ_1 is the scattering angle in the lab. system). If E_0 is the kinetic energy of the incident particle in the lab. system, $E_0^2 = m^2 v^4$ and $\sin\theta \, d\theta = 4 \sin\theta_1 \cos\theta_1 \, d\theta_1$, thus in the lab. system, the Rutherford cross section becomes

$$d\sigma = \left(\frac{e^4}{E_0^2}\right)\left[\frac{1}{\sin^4\theta_1} + \frac{1}{\cos^4\theta_1}\right] \cos\theta_1 \, 2\pi \sin\theta_1 \, d\theta_1 \tag{87}$$

The additional term in $\cos^4\theta_1$, is necessary, because for every proton scattered through an angle θ_1, the other proton recoils at angle $(\pi/2 - \theta_1)$ and it is not possible to distinguish between the two protons. This Rutherford cross section, however, does not agree with experiment even at low energies where nuclear scattering is negligible. Mott showed that an extra term is necessary because of the indentity of the two particles involved in the scattering. The Mott term is

$$-\frac{e^4}{E_0^2} \frac{\cos[(e^2/\hbar v) \ln(\tan^2\theta_1)]}{\sin^2\theta_1 \cos^2\theta_1} \cos\theta_1 \, 2\pi \sin\theta_1 \, d\theta_1 \tag{88}$$

For proton energies abovə 1 MeV, $e^2/\hbar v < \frac{1}{7}$ and the cosine term involving $e^2/\hbar v$ is nearly unity, unless θ_1, is close to zero or $\pi/2$. Thus away from $\theta_1 = 0$ or $\pi/2$, for $E_0 > 1$ MeV, the Mott term is simplified, so that we can write for the p–p Coulomb scattering cross section

$$\frac{d\sigma}{d\Omega} = \frac{e^4}{E_0^2}\left[\frac{1}{\sin^4\theta_1} + \frac{1}{\cos^4\theta_1} - \frac{1}{\sin^2\theta_1\cos^2\theta_1}\right]\cos\theta_1 \qquad (89)$$

When the effects of S wave nuclear scattering are included, we obtain two extra terms; the first represents an interference effect between the Coulomb and nuclear potentials, and the second is a pure nuclear scattering term. The complete differential scattering cross section in the laboratory system for S wave nuclear scattering has been given by Breit as †

$$\frac{d\sigma}{d\Omega} = \frac{e^4}{E_0^2}\left[\frac{1}{\sin^4\theta_1} + \frac{1}{\cos^4\theta_1} - \frac{1}{\sin^2\theta_1\cos^2\theta_1} - \frac{2\hbar\, v\sin\delta_0\cos\delta_0}{e^2\sin^2\theta_1\cos^2\theta_1} + \left(\frac{2\hbar\, v}{e^2}\right)^2\sin^2\delta_0\right]\cos\theta_1 \qquad (90)$$

The quantity δ_0 is known as the "nuclear phase shift". It is not, however, the phase shift which would occur if the Coulomb field could be switched off. The nuclear phase shift δ_0 is a function of the energy E_0, smoothly increasing from a small angle at low energies to a value of about 55° at $E_0 \sim 4$ MeV. The fact that the theoretical scattering cross section at a given energy E_0 is determined by one parameter δ_0 is an important result.

The existence of the nuclear–Coulomb interference term in eqn. (90) is useful in determining δ_0 when δ_0 is small, because this term is linear in $\sin\delta_0$ and it is large compared to the last term which involves $\sin^2\delta_0$.

The theoretical cross section given by eqn. (90) has been found to be in excellent agreement with experimental measurements at all angles and energies (up to 10 MeV). If the nuclear interaction is represented by a square well of depth V_0 and radius b, a good fit with the experimental data is obtained if the following values are adopted

$$V_0 = 13{\cdot}3 \text{ MeV}, \quad \text{and} \quad b = 2{\cdot}58 \text{ fermi} \qquad (91)$$

A comparison of the nuclear p–p and n–p interactions, at energies in which S wave scattering alone is involved, shows that in the singlet S state the n–p and p–p nuclear forces differ at most by a few per cent. This near or complete equality of the n–p and the p–p nuclear force in the same spin and orbital angular momentum state is known as the hypothesis of the "charge independence of nuclear forces".

19.4. HIGH ENERGY NUCLEON–NUCLEON SCATTERING

A satisfactory theory of nuclear forces must be able to explain the approximately constant density of nuclear matter and the approximately constant binding energy per nucleon of medium and heavy nuclei. The

† G. Breit, H. M. Thaxton and L. Eisenbud, *Phys. Rev.* **55**, 1018, 1939.

saturation of nuclear forces can be explained if we assume that these forces are "exchange" forces similar to the forces in certain types of chemical molecule.

The original suggestion that nuclear forces are exchange forces is due to Heisenberg. Since the discovery of the pion and its basic properties the exchange force can be pictured in terms of the passage of pions between the two nucleons.

In addition to the saturation properties of nuclear forces, the evidence from high energy *n–p* and *p–p* scattering strongly favours the existence of exchange forces.

Historically, three types of exchange force have been investigated in great detail. These exchange forces are:

(1) *Heisenberg forces.* In this type of interaction there is an exchange of both the position and the spin coordinates of the two nucleons. It can be shown on symmetry grounds† that the force is attractive for even l triplet states and odd l singlet states, but it is repulsive in odd l triplet and even l singlet states.

(2) *Majorana forces.* This is an exchange involving the two position coordinates only. The force is always attractive for states of even l ($S, D, G, \ldots$) and always repulsive for states of odd l.

(3) *Bartlett forces.* This involves the exchange of the spin but not the position coordinates of the two interacting nucleons. The force is always attractive in the triplet state and always repulsive in the singlet state.

In addition to these types of exchange force, the complete group of short-range *non-exchange* forces is known as "Wigner" forces. The two-nucleon force seems to be predominantly a mixture of Wigner and Majorana forces. The Majorana force corresponds to the exchange of a pion between the two nucleons without changing the spins of the particles.

The scattering of high energy neutrons by protons should involve partial waves of higher angular momentum than zero. If scattering of partial waves with $l > 2$ can be neglected, the differential elastic scattering cross section is given, using eqn. (67), by

$$\sigma(\theta) = \lambda\!\!\!^{-2}\left|\sin\delta_0\, e^{i\delta_0} + 3\sin\delta_1\, e^{i\delta_1}\cos\theta + \frac{5}{2}\sin\delta_2\, e^{i\delta_2}(3\cos^2\theta - 1)\right|^2 \quad (92)$$

if δ_1 and δ_2 are both small compared to δ_0, eqn. (92) simplifies to

$$\sigma(\theta) = \lambda\!\!\!^{-2}\left[\sin^2\delta_0 + \sin 2\delta_0\left\{3\delta_1\cos\theta + \frac{5}{2}\delta_2(3\cos^2\theta - 1)\right\}\right] \quad (93)$$

For non-exchange inter-nucleon forces, all the phase shifts δ_0, δ_1, δ_2 are positive. If the Majorana exchange type of force is involved, the nuclear force is repulsive in the P state so that the phase shift δ_1 is negative.

† See p. 91 of L. R. B. Elton, *Introductory Nuclear Theory*.

Examination of eqn. (93) clearly shows that

$$\sigma(180°) < \sigma(0°) \quad \text{for} \quad \delta_0, \delta_1, \quad \delta_2 \text{ positive}$$

and
$$\sigma(180°) > \sigma(0°) \quad \text{for} \quad \delta_0, \delta_2 \text{ positive}, \quad \delta_1 \text{ negative}.$$

These results mean that if the Majorana exchange type of force predominates, back scattering is stronger than forward scattering at low angles. The experimental *n–p* scattering cross sections as a function of θ for incident neutrons of 27, 40, 90, and 300 MeV are shown in Fig. 10 (the differential cross section is measured in millibarns per steradian and θ is

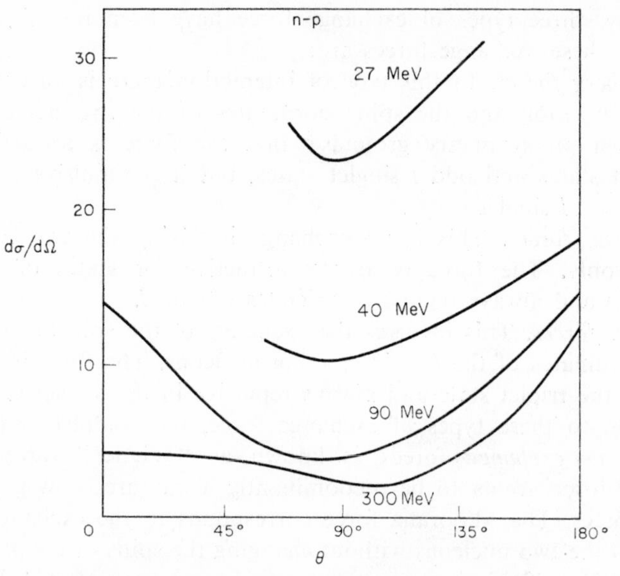

FIG. 10. The differential *n–p* scattering cross sections (in millibarns per steradian). θ measured in centre of mass system. Energies quoted on curves are neutron energies in the laboratory system.

he scattering angle in the centre of mass system). At 300 MeV, $\sigma(180°) > \sigma(0°)$, suggesting that the incident neutron exchanges a charged pion when it passes close to a target proton and then continues as a proton with a small angular deflection from its original direction. In this exchange process, in the *C*-system, the target proton which has become a neutron moves off in the opposite direction to the incident neutron. Another interesting feature of these curves is that they all exhibit a minimum in the vicinity of θ equal 90°.

The experimental differential cross sections for high energy *p–p* scattering are shown in Fig. 11. In the centre of mass system, for each proton scattered through an angle θ the other proton involved in the collision is scattered through an angle $\pi - \theta$. The differential cross section curves are therefore always symmetrical about $\theta = 90°$. At small angles, the cross section is large because it is dominated by Coulomb scattering. However, away from this small angle region the cross section is nearly independent of angle, a most unexpected result. Isotropic scattering in the *C*-system is the essential feature of pure *S* wave scattering and this is highly unlikely at incident proton energies of 100 MeV or more. At one particular energy, it might happen that interference between *P* and *D*

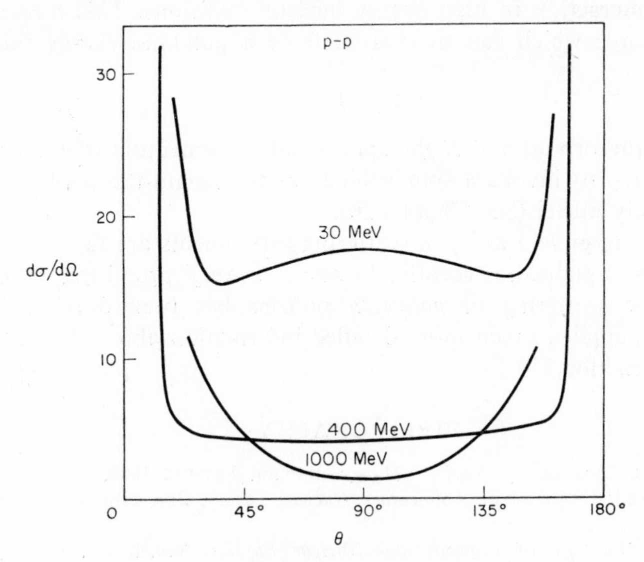

FIG. 11. The differential *p–p* scattering cross sections.

wave scattering results in a nearly isotropic scattering intensity, but this would not occur for such a wide range of proton energies. Another puzzling aspect of high energy *p–p* scattering is that above about 150 MeV, the *total* cross section is nearly independent of energy, at least up to 400 MeV. Thus in the energy range 150 to 400 MeV,

$$\frac{d\sigma}{d\Omega} = 3{\cdot}4 \pm 0{\cdot}4 \text{ millibarns per steradian} \tag{94}$$

Above 400 MeV, the observed total *p–p* cross section begins to rise significantly as the creation of pions becomes important.

One possible solution to the paradox of isotropic *p–p* scattering is based on the hypothesis of a strong repulsive force between protons when they have a separation less than about 0·5 fermi (the "repulsive core"). At high energies, the *S* wave protons pass very close to one another and it the potential is repulsive, the *S* wave phase shift becomes *negative*. If may then be possible to account for the isotropic scattering if δ_0 is allowed to become negative. The total cross section depends on the magnitude, not the sign of the phase shifts; thus if δ_0 becomes more and more negative as the energy increases, this may be the main contribution to keeping the total cross section nearly constant above 150 MeV. Another useful feature of the repulsive core hypothesis is that it obviously helps to explain the saturation of nuclear forces.

At high energies in *n–p* and *p–p* interactions, tensor forces are important. In addition, Marshak† has suggested that there may be a considerable spin–orbit interaction in high energy nucleon collisions. This means that there is a force which can be derived from a potential energy function of the form

$$V(r)\,\boldsymbol{L}\,\boldsymbol{S} \tag{95}$$

where $\boldsymbol{L}$ is the orbital and $\boldsymbol{S}$ the spin angular momentum of the system. It is necessary to invoke a spin–orbit force to explain the shell structure of many–body nuclei (See Chapter 20).

The high energy *p–p* and *p–n* scattering experiments are far from being satisfactorily explained. Recently, however, a very promising technique involving the scattering of *polarized* protons has been developed and has already supplied much more detailed information about the nucleon–nucleon interaction.††

BIBLIOGRAPHY

L. R. B. Elton, *Introductory Nuclear Theory*, Pitman, London 1959.

H. A. Bethe and P. Morrison, *Elementary Nuclear Theory*, 2nd Edition, Wiley, New York 1956.

N. F. Ramsey, Part IV of *Experimental Nuclear Physics*, Vol. 1, Ed. by E. Segrè, Wiley, New York 1953.

J. M. Blatt and V. F. Weisskopf, *Theoretical Nuclear Physics*, Wiley, New York 1952 (especially Chapters 2, 3, 4).

G. L. Squires, The Neutron-Proton Intercations in Vol. 2, *Progress in Nuclear Physics*, Ed. by O. R. Frisch, Pergamon, London 1952.

† R. E. Marshak and P. S. Signell, *Phys. Rev.* **109**, 1229, 1958.
†† O. Chamberlain *et al.*, *Phys. Rev.* **102**, 1659, 1956; **105**, 288, 1957.

CHAPTER 20

NUCLEAR REACTIONS AND NUCLEAR MODELS

20.1. INTRODUCTION

A major part of experimental nuclear physics in the last thirty years has been concerned with the investigation of nuclear reactions. A nuclear reaction is usually initiated by exposing a suitable target material to a collimated beam of monoenergetic light nuclear particles. Apart from all energy neutron reactions, the incident charged particles must have sufficient kinetic energy to have a reasonable chance of penetrating the Coulomb barrier surrounding a target nucleus†. For this reason, the majority of nuclear reactions studied in the laboratory depend on the use of a suitable charged particle accelerator. In a typical experiment, the following quantities may be measured: the intensity and energy of the incident particle beam, the number of particles ejected from the thin target in unit time, the angular distribution of the emitted particles, the energy and identity of the emitted particles, the induced activity (if any) of the product nucleus, and the recoil energy and direction of the residual nuclei. The majority of experiments involve the particle bombardment of a thin target, that is, one in which the fractional loss of energy of an incident particle is very small. Sometimes, however, a thick target is employed so that the incident particles lose a significant fraction of their energy by ionization.

At low excitation energies (< 10 MeV), the majority of nuclear reactions involve the formation of two nuclei, one nearly equal in charge and mass number to the target nucleus. Such reactions are represented by an equation of the type

$$a + A \rightarrow B + b \tag{1}$$

where a is the light projectile nucleus (proton, neutron, deuteron, H^3, He^3 or He^4) and A is the target nucleus at rest in the laboratory system. B is the product nucleus and b is a light nuclear particle which carries away the major share of the available kinetic energy. If the product

† An exception to this rule is the excitation of a target nucleus by the Coulomb field of a passing particle.

nucleus B is left in an excited state after the emission of the light particle b, it usually subsequently decays by radiating one or more gamma rays. Alternatively if B is beta unstable it decays at some later date by electron or positron emission, possibly followed by γ-emission. Nuclear reactions at low excitation energies include the following types: (n, γ), (n, p), (n, α), (α, n), (p, γ), (p, n), (d, n), (d, p), . . ., etc. Here the first symbol in the bracket denotes the bombarding particle a, the second symbol denotes the light nuclear fragment b emitted from the target. An exception to the above rule that the particles B and b are of different orders of mass, apart from the examples where the target nucleus A is very light, is the rather special case of nuclear fission which can be induced by neutrons, photons, energetic charged particles, etc. The phenomenon of fission has been discussed in Chapter 17 and will not be dealt with in this chapter.

A type of nuclear reaction which was not expected to throw a great deal of light on the problem of nuclear forces and nuclear structure is the photon–nuclear reaction. The incident gamma or bremsstrahlung photons interact relatively weakly with nuclei as this is primarily an electromagnetic interaction. Photo-nuclear experiments in the past have been handicapped by the lack of high intensity *monoenergetic* photon beams.† Photo-nuclear reactions have, however, proved to be of more interest than was originally suspected.

As the energy of the particles bombarding a target increase so does the type and variety of possible nuclear reactions. For example, with proton or neutron beams of energy 20 or 30 MeV, two light nuclear fragments may be emitted from the target nucleus. Examples of this type of process are the $(p, p\,n)$ and $(n, 2n)$ reactions.

At high projectile energies, say > 200 MeV, the nuclear reactions may involve the creation of pions, and at higher energies K mesons. One important feature at high energies is related to the fact that the wavelength of the incident particle (proton or neutron) is now small compared to the radius of the nucleus. Included in the list of high energy nuclear reactions are those produced in nuclear emulsion plates at very high altitudes by the ultra-high energy component of the primary cosmic radiation (the highest particle energy observed in cosmic radiation is $\sim 10^{19}$ eV!).

In the last few years the field of nuclear reactions has been extended to include reactions induced by accelerated ions heavier than He^4. Reactions have been observed using accelerated beams of ions as heavy as neon. A number of unusual reactions has been found, some of which are described in Section 9 of this chapter.

† This situation is improving. See S. Devons, p. 626, *Proc. Intern. Rutherford Jubilee Conf.*, Manchester 1961, Heywood, London.

There is a number of features common to all nuclear reactions, which are of great practical use in analysing the experimental data. Thus in all reactions, the following entities are conserved:

(1) The total electric charge.

(2) The total number of nucleons (this is still true at energies above 6 GeV when antinucleons may be produced, provided each antinucleon is counted as minus one nucleon).

(3) The total linear and angular momentum of the whole system are separately conserved.

(4) The total energy of the system is conserved, provided any change in mass Δm is counted as an energy change $c^2 \Delta m$.

(5) Provided we exclude beta and meson decay and other weak interactions (but not electromagnetic processes), the total parity of the system is unchanged.

Although the reaction product energies and angular distribution of emitted particles are observed in the laboratory system it is more convenient to translate the results into the frame where the centre of mass of the nuclear system is at rest. It is easy to show, for example, that the kinetic energy $(T_a)_{\text{lab}}$ of the incident particle in the laboratory system is related to the total kinetic energy of the particle a and target nucleus A in the centre of mass system, T, by

$$(T_a)_{\text{lab}} = \frac{m_a + M_A}{M_A} T \tag{2}$$

where m_a and M_A are the masses of the particles a and A, respectively. Another important parameter in a nuclear reaction is the Q of the reaction. This is the difference between the sum of the kinetic energies of the product particles (B and b) and the reacting particles (A and a). If this difference is positive, we have an exothermic reaction, which could (apart from the difficulty of penetrating the Coulomb barrier surrounding the target nucleus A) be induced by a zero energy incident particle a. Exothermic reactions can, of course, take place with zero kinetic energy neutrons as there is no repulsive Coulomb field. If, on the other hand, the sum of the kinetic energies of the reaction products is less than that of the reactants we have an endothermic reaction with a definite threshold energy below which the reaction can never take place.

The volume of data collected with regard to nuclear reactions is now so vast that it is well beyond the scope of this book to deal with the subject in any great detail. For reasons of clarity, no historical approach to the subject is attempted, but a number of reactions is discussed in terms of a theoretical framework or nuclear model. For example, the resonance reactions involving low energy neutrons and medium and heavy nuclei are usually discussed in terms of N. Bohr's theory of the formation of the compound nucleus. On the other hand, many reactions produced by protons and deuterons are best described as "direct interactions", in the sense that the incident particle interacts with one or two nucleons inside the target nucleus without forming a compound nucleus in the Bohr sense. The scattering of moderate and high energy neutrons, provided the resolving power of the detection equipment is not very high, is successfully interpreted in terms of the "optical model" (complex potential well model). A large number of nuclear properties is successfully correlated by the nuclear "shell model" and it has been shown that it is fruitful in discussing certain types of nuclear reaction.

There is a danger in using nuclear models that we overlook the fact that they grossly oversimplify the fine details of nuclear structure and overstress one or two features which are likely to be important in a given context. As long as a theoretical model is successful in interpreting a particular group of nuclear phenomena, it is in a certain sense dealing with a trivial effect, as the model is not based on the fine details of nuclear forces or nuclear structure†. Nuclear properties and reactions are interpreted in terms of the following theoretical frameworks:

(1) The Liquid Drop Model (little used apart from the classical theory of nuclear fission).

(2) The α-Particle Model (elementary theory of alpha decay; some evidence of α-particle clusters in certain nuclear reactions).

(3) The Compound Nuclear Model of N. Bohr (famous for it's interpretation of neutron resonances; Breit–Wigner dispersion formula).

(4) The statistical model.

(5) Independent Particle Models (I.P.M.), especially the nuclear shell model.

(6) The Optical Model (used for the interpretation of scattering of protons and neutrons above 1 MeV energy).

(7) Direct Nuclear Reactions (e.g. Stripping and pick-up reactions).

(8) Collective Model (theory of A. Bohr and B. Mottelson, successful in explaining certain excited levels of nuclei in terms of collective rotations or oscillations of the nucleons).

These different theoretical approaches to the subject of nuclear dynamics do not necessarily contradict each other. Thus the shell model (an I.P.M. model) does not contradict the successful use of the optical model.

† This point is emphasized by V. F. WEISSKOPF in Chapter 10, *Proc. of the Intern. Conf. on Nuclear Structure*, Edited by D. A. BROMLEY and E. W. VOGT, Kingston, Canada 1960.

20.2. GENERAL LIMITATIONS ON NEUTRON CROSS SECTIONS

The concept of cross section is basic in discussing nuclear reactions so it is worthwhile reminding the reader of its definition.
The cross section of a given type of a reaction is defined by

$$\sigma = \frac{\text{Number of events of the given type per unit time per nucleus}}{\text{Number of incident particles per unit area per unit time}} \tag{3}$$

The total cross section σ_t for neutrons is conveniently expressed as the sum

$$\sigma_t = \sigma_s + \sigma_r \tag{4}$$

where σ_s is the elastic scattering cross section (the scattered neutrons have the same kinetic energy as the incident neutrons in the centre of mass system), and σ_r is the reaction cross section which includes all other processes apart from elastic scattering. Thus inelastic neutron scattering in which the nucleus B is an excited state of nucleus A is regarded as a nuclear reaction.

Consider an incident plane wave of neutrons of unit amplitude, travelling parallel to the z-axis. This plane wave has a spatial part $\exp(i\,k\,z)$ or $\exp(i\,k\,r\cos\theta)$, where $k = 2\pi/\lambda$, and can be expanded as a series of spherical harmonics about the origin of coordinates. For $k\,r \gg 1$, the expansion is

$$\exp(i\,k\,z) = \frac{\sqrt{\pi}}{k\,r}\sum_{l=0}^{\infty}\sqrt{(2l+1)}\,i^{l+1}\left[\exp\left\{-i\left(k\,r - \frac{l\pi}{2}\right)\right\} - \exp\left\{+i\left(k\,r - \frac{l\pi}{2}\right)\right\}\right]Y_{l,0} \tag{5}$$

The terms in $\exp(-i\,k\,r)$ represent a series of ingoing spherical waves, in contrast to the terms in $\exp(+i\,k\,r)$, which represent outgoing spherical waves. As there is cylindrical symmetry about the z-axis the order m of the spherical harmonics $Y_{l,m}$ is zero, the $Y_{l,0}$ being functions of one variable, the polar angle θ. Equation (5) represents an *undisturbed* wave in the absence of any absorbing or scattering centre. If, however, a nucleus is located at the origin, the amplitudes and phases of the *outgoing* spherical waves from the origin are, in general, changed. The new wave function, for $k\,r \gg 1$ is†

$$\psi(r) = \frac{\sqrt{\pi}}{k\,r}\sum_{l=0}^{\infty}\sqrt{(2l+1)}\,i^{l+1}\left[\exp\left\{-i\left(k\,r - \frac{l\pi}{2}\right)\right\} - \eta_l\exp\left\{+i\left(k\,r - \frac{l\pi}{2}\right)\right\}\right]Y_{l,0} \tag{6}$$

† J. M. Blatt and V. F. Weisskopf, *Theoretical Nuclear Physics*, p. 320.

The complex numbers η_l represent the amplitudes and phases of the outgoing partial waves of angular momentum l. The wave function of the scattered wave is the difference between eqn. (6) and eqn. (5)

$$\psi_s = \psi(r) - \exp(i k z)$$

$$\psi_s = \frac{\sqrt{\pi}}{k r} \sum_{l=0}^{\infty} \sqrt{[(2l + 1)]}\, 1^{l+1} (l - \eta_l \exp) \left[i \left(k r - \frac{l \pi}{2} \right) \right] Y_{l,0} \qquad (7)$$

To obtain an expression for the elastic scattering cross section the flux of ψ_s through a large sphere surrounding the scattering nucleus is calculated. This integration gives the result†

$$\sigma_s^l = \pi \lambda\!\!\!^-{}^2 (2l + 1) \, |1 - \eta_l|^2 \qquad (8)$$

where σ_s^l is the elastic scattering cross section for the lth partial wave. If $\eta_l = 1$, there is no scattering. The term $|1 - \eta_l|^2$ is typical of an interference between waves of unit amplitude and complex amplitude η_l, the resultant complex amplitude being squared to give the intensity.

The reaction cross section is determined by evaluating the number of particles which enter a large sphere surrounding the nucleus without leaving it again. The wave function $\psi(r)$, eq. (6), is used in calculating the reaction cross section for the lth partial wave; the result is†

$$\sigma_r^l = \pi \lambda\!\!\!^-{}^2 (2l + 1) (1 - |\eta_l|^2). \qquad (9)$$

The total cross section for the lth partial wave is

$$\sigma_t^l = \sigma_s^l + \sigma_r^l = 2\pi \lambda\!\!\!^-{}^2 (2l + 1) (1 - Re(\eta_l)) \qquad (10)$$

where $Re(\eta_l)$ is the real part of η_l.

A number of important conclusions follows. If $|\eta_l| = 1$, $\sigma_r^l = 0$, but σ_s^l may be finite, for η_l may be complex. Thus we can have scattering without any accompanying absorption. In contrast, however, absorption is *always* accompanied by some scattering. The maximum value of the lth partial wave elastic scattering cross section is obtained when $\eta_l = 1$; it is $4\pi \lambda\!\!\!^-{}^2 (2l + 1)$. When $\eta_l = 0$, σ_s^l and σ_r^l are both equal to $\pi \lambda\!\!\!^-{}^7 (2l + 1)$; this occurs when the reaction cross section is a maximum. We see that the cross sections lie in the ranges

$$0 \leq \sigma_s^l \leq 4\pi \lambda\!\!\!^-{}^2 (2l + 1) \qquad (11)$$

$$0 \leq \sigma_r^l \leq \pi \lambda\!\!\!^-{}^2 (2l + 1) \qquad (12)$$

If the incident neutron has a high enough energy, the reduced wavelength $\lambda\!\!\!^-$ is small compared to the radius R of the nucleus. Suppose the nucleus is completely "black" to the incident neutrons, that is, all neutrons which hit the nucleus are absorbed. Then for all the partial

† J. M. Blatt and V. F. Weisskopf, *Theoretical Nuclear Physics*, p. 320.

waves involved, $\eta_l = 0$, and for higher partial waves $\eta_l = 1$. The partial waves which are absorbed correspond to

$$l \leqq \frac{R}{\lambda}$$

Then

$$\sigma_r = \sum_{l}^{R/\lambda} \pi \lambda^2 (2l + 1)$$

This arithmetical progression is easily summed, and for $\frac{R}{\lambda} \gg 1$,

$$\sigma_r = \pi R^2 \tag{13}$$

When σ_r has its maximum value, $\sigma_s = \sigma_r$; hence

$$\sigma_t = 2\pi R^2 \tag{14}$$

This is the important formula which has been used in determining nuclear radii by measuring the transmission $T = \exp(-N\sigma_t)$, where N is the number of nuclei per cm², of an absorber for high energy neutrons. The elastic scattering of short wavelength neutrons is a form of "shadow" scattering or diffraction round the edges of the nucleus (see Chapter 9, Section 2).

20.3. THE COMPOUND NUCLEUS

Prior to the classic paper of N. Bohr† on the compound nucleus theory of nuclear reactions, attempts to explain the variation of neutron cross sections were based on the assumption that the incident particle interacts with a simple square potential well.†† The simple potential well model calculations predict that elastic scattering should be the dominant process and that scattering resonances should occur at wide energy intervals of 10 or 20 MeV. The discovery by Fermi and his school, and other that slow neutron resonances in medium and heavy elements occur as close together as 1 eV and that the resonances are due to the radiative capture of neutrons showed that the potential well model is inadequate.

Bohr's theory was based on the assumption that when a nucleon reaches the surface of a nucleus it interacts strongly with the nucleons in the nucleus and coalesces, forming a compound nucleus of mass number $A + 1$. The excitation energy of the compound nucleus (incident particle kinetic energy plus binding energy in the compound nucleus) is associated with the *collective* excitation of many of the nucleons. Bohr's reasoning was based on the strong nucleon–nucleon interaction and the known dense packing of nucleons inside the nucleus. The neutron resonances

† N. Bohr, *Nature* **137**, 344, 1936.
†† H. A. Bethe, *Phys. Rev.* **47**, 747, 1935.

are associated with a series of discrete quasi-stationary quantum states of the compound nuclear system. The large number of resonance levels observed in heavy nuclei is a natural consequence of the rapid increase in the number of possible modes of excitation as the number of nucleons in the compound system increases.

The lifetime of the compound nucleus is long compared to the time it takes the incident particle to cross the nuclear diameter. The decay of the compound system occurs when sufficient energy is concentrated on a particular nucleon or group of nucleons (alpha group, for example) for it to penetrate the Coulomb and potential barriers and escape from the nucleus. As the lifetime of the compound system is long on a nuclear time scale, the intrinsically slower process of electromagnetic decay (γ-emission) competes strongly with charged particle emission. This is the explanation on the Bohr theory of the frequent occurrence of resonances in the (n, γ) cross section. The mean lifetime τ of a compound nuclear state is related to the width Γ of the resonance line by the expression $\Gamma\tau \sim \hbar$.

If the excitation energy of the compound nucleus is thoroughly shared amongst all the nucleons, it seems highly probable that its mode of decay will be independent of the mode of formation (the system has "forgotten" how it was formed). The decay of the compound system is then determined by its energy, angular momentum and parity. It often happens that there are several possible modes of decay of the compound nucleus. Each of these modes of decay is represented by a partial width Γ_i, the total width Γ being equal to the sum of all the partial widths. In certain reactions it is possible to calculate the relative probabilites of emission of different particles by a statistical treatment.

The Breit–Wigner dispersion theory of resonance reactions is based on the Bohr concept of the compound nucleus. This theory of neutron resonances has been discussed in Chapter 15. At high (> 1 MeV) incident neutron energies well defined resonances of the compound system are not observed. There are two reasons for this: the greater excitation energy reduces the lifetime of the compound nucleus, and the number of possible modes of decay (reaction "channels") increases. Both effects broaden the total width Γ of the resonance state and if this exceeds the average level spacing the concept of separate resonance levels becomes meaningless.

Ghoshal's Experiment

An interesting series of experiments to test the Bohr theory of nuclear reactions was made by Ghoshal†. The experiments were designed to study the decay of the compound nucleus $_{30}Zn^{64}$, which could be produced

† S. N. Ghoshal, *Phys. Rev.* **80**, 939, 1950.

by bombarding ${}_{29}Cu^{63}$ with protons or ${}_{28}Ni^{60}$ with α-particles. In order to produce the same state of excitation of the Zn^{64} nucleus, the α-particle kinetic energy must exceed that of the proton by about 7 MeV (this is mainly determined by the difference in the binding energy of the proton and the α-particle in Zn^{64}). The following reactions were studied

(a) $Ni^{60}(\alpha, n)\,Zn^{63}$ (d) $Cu^{63}(p, n)\,Zn^{63}$

(b) $Ni^{60}(\alpha, p\,n)\,Cu^{62}$ (e) $Cu^{63}(p, p\,n)\,Cu^{62}$

(c) $Ni^{60}(\alpha, 2n)\,Zn^{62}$ (f) $Cu^{63}(p, 2n)\,Zn^{62}$

The cross sections for these reactions, according to the Bohr theory, can be written

$$\sigma(a, b) = \sigma_c \frac{\Gamma_b}{\Gamma}$$

where σ_c is the cross section for the formation of the compound nucleus and Γ_b is the partial width for decay by the emission of particle b. If the

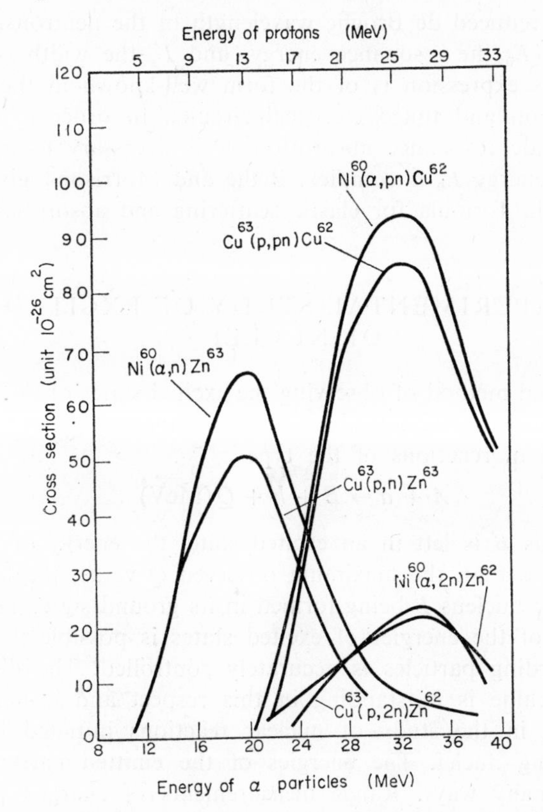

FIG. 1. Yields of the decay products of the compound nucleus Zn^{64} (Ghoshal's experiment) N.B. The proton energy scale has been shifted 7 MeV to the right.

decay of the excited Zn^{64} nucleus is independent of its mode of formation, the ratio of the reaction yields of (a), (b) and (c) should be equal to the ratio of the yields of (d), (e) and (f). Not only is this condition satisfied, but the cross sections themselves are almost equal for incident protons and α-particles. The experimental results obtained by Ghoshal, with the proton cross section curves shifted 7 MeV to the right, are shown in Fig. 1. Another interesting feature of these curves is the much greater probability of the decay of the compound system by p and n rather than $2n$ emission.

Breit–Wigner Dispersion Theory

The single-level dispersion formula for resonance of s wave neutrons is

$$\sigma_s = \frac{\pi \lambda\!\!\!^{-2} \Gamma_s^2}{(E - E_0)^2 + \frac{\Gamma_s^2}{4}} \tag{15}$$

where $\lambda\!\!\!^{-}$ is the reduced de Broglie wavelength of the neutrons, E is their kinetic energy, E_0 the resonance energy, and Γ_s the width of the level concerned. This expression is of the form well-known in the theory of optical dispersion and tuned electrical circuits. In order to extend the theory to include resonance absorption, it is necessary to assume that the resonance energy E_0 is complex. Bethe and Morrison† give a simple derivation of the formula for elastic scattering and absorption when E_0 is complex.

20.4. THE EXPERIMENTAL STUDY OF EXCITED STATES OF NUCLEI

The traditional method of observing the excited states of nuclei through the study of nuclear reactions is to measure the energy of the particle groups emitted in reactions of the type

$$A + a \rightarrow B + b + Q\,(\text{MeV})$$

If the nucleus B is left in an excited state, the energy of the emitted particle b is less than the maximum observed Q value, the latter corresponding to the nucleus B being formed in its ground state. The accurate determination of the energies of excited states is possible if the energy of the bombarding particles is accurately controlled. The modern Van de Graaff machine is outstanding in this respect and it has played a dominant part in the study of nuclear reactions initiated by charged particles striking nuclei. The energies of the emitted particles can be measured in many ways. Range measurements of charged particles in

† H. A. Bethe and P. Morrison, *Elementary Nuclear Theory*, p. 181 (2nd Ed.).

nuclear emulsion plates are capable of a precision of ± 1 per cent, the limit of accuracy being set by the straggling in the range–energy relation. Proportional and scintillation counters are frequently used, often in conjunction with multi-channel pulse height analysers. The most precise measurements, however, determine the momentum of the charged particles by bending them through 180° in a magnetic spectrometer†. An alternative method, which is limited to rather low energy particles, is to use an electrostatic analyser in which the charged particles pass between two concentric spherical electrodes††. The deflected particles are recorded by counters or photographic emulsions. The magnetic field of the momentum analyser can be measured to 1 part in 10^5 with the

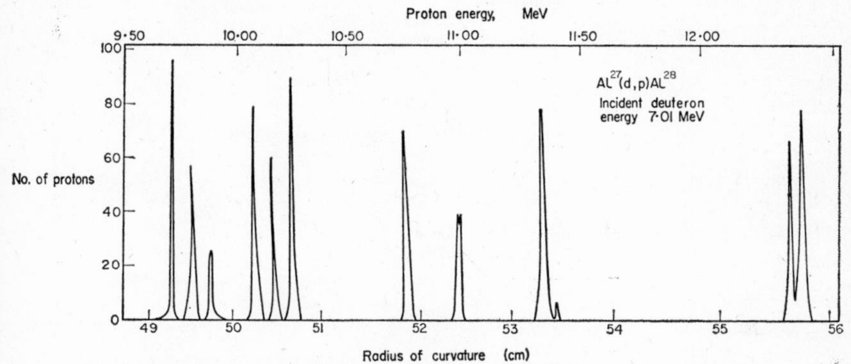

FIG. 2. Magnetic analysis of proton spectrum in Al^{27} (d, p) Al^{58} reaction (W. Buechner).

aid of a proton magnetic resonance probe unit. The energies of the different particle groups can be determined to a precision of 1 part in 2000. The precision of the magnetic analyser method is illustrated by the measurement of the proton energy groups emitted in the $Al^{27}(d, p)\,Al^{28}$ reaction. The results of the magnetic analysis of the emitted protons is illustrated in Fig. 2†††. The incident deuterons had an energy of 7·01 MeV, and the protons entering the spectrometer (field set at 9156 gauss) were emitted at 30°. The proton groups correspond to the excited states of the nucleus Al^{28}.

When the emitted particle b is a neutron, the energy determination is less precise‡; it may be found, for example, by measuring the range of knock-on protons in a nuclear emulsion plate. With the introduction of fast timing-circuits, neutron energies can now be determined by time-of-flight measurements. This method has been discussed in Chapter 15 in relation to inelastic scattering of neutrons.

† W. W. BUECHNER, review article in Vol. 5, *Progress in Nuclear Physics*, 1956.
†† C. P. BROWNE *et al.*, *Rev. Sci. Instruments* **22**, 952, 1951.
††† W. W. BUECHNER *et al.*, *Phys. Rev.* **101**, 188, 1956.
‡ Threshold measurements with neutrons can, however, be very accurate.

The electronic energy levels of an atom are dominated by a Coulomb potential and it is a well-known feature of atomic spectra that the level spacing decreases to zero as the ionization energy of the system is approached. Nuclear energy levels, on the other hand, are based on the short range inter-nucleon forces and the level spacing does not tend to zero as the dissociation energy of the nucleus is approached. By dissociation energy, we mean the mininum energy required to detach a nucleon or group of nucleons (e.g. α-particle) from the nucleus. (This is analogous to the

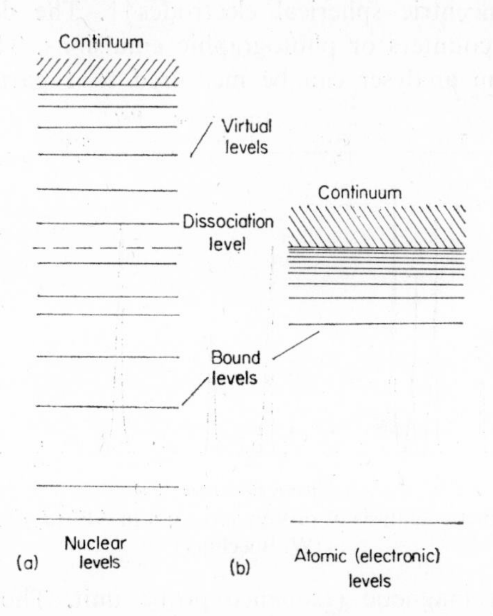

FIG. 3. Contrast between nuclear and electronic levels. (The large difference in the scale of energy in the two systems is ignored.) (Redrawn from S. DEVONS†.)

ionization potential of an atom.) Above the dissociation energy, the states of the nuclear system may still have a long lifetime measured on a nuclear time scale; in this event, there is no essential difference (apart from the finite level width of levels above the dissociation energy) between the levels above the dissociation energy and the levels below this energy. The bound energy levels, however, can only decay by γ-emis sion. The levels above the dissociation energy are known as "virtual" levels. A hypothetical pattern of nuclear energy levels for a light nucleus is contrasted with the electronic energy levels of an atom in Fig. 3†.

The measurement of γ-ray energies has been discussed in Chapter 13. For moderate accuracy, the scintillation spectrometer is often used. However, for high accuracy, some type of magnetic spectrometer is gen-

† Fig. 1, S. DEVONS, *Excited States of Nuclei*, Cambridge University Press, 1949.

erally used, in which the energies of photoelectrons, Compton recoil electrons, or electron–positron pairs are measured.

As an illustration of a nuclear reaction involving the detection of gamma radiation, let us consider the radiative capture of protons by a low atomic number nucleus. If the incident proton energy is below the threshold for the endothermic (p, n) process, the radiative capture of protons, the (p, γ) reaction, is likely to be the only process in addition

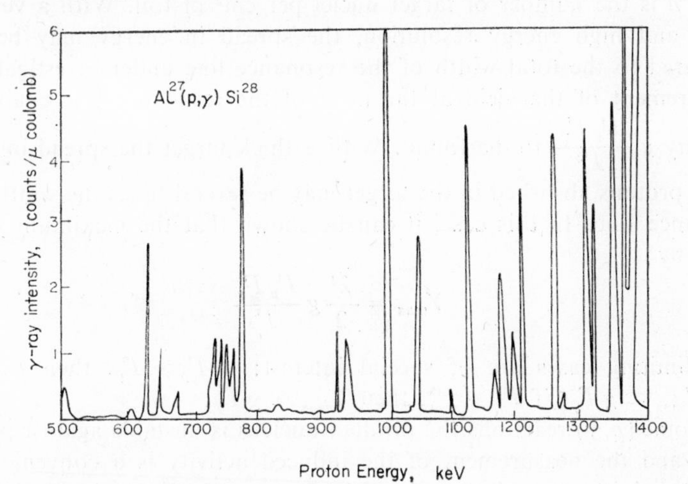

FIG. 4. Radiative capture of protons by Al^{27}. γ-ray intensity measured in counts per microcoulomb of incident protons (Brostrom *et. al.*).

to elastic scattering. In a few special cases (e.g. B^{11}, N^{15}. F^{19}, ...) α-particle emission is a competing process. The yield of capture γ-rays from the $Al^{27}(p, \gamma)\,Si^{28}$ reaction as a function of the proton bombarding energy is shown in Fig. 4†. The observations clearly show the resonance nature of the capture process. For well-separated resonances in the (p, γ) process, the reaction cross section near the resonance energy E_0 is given by

$$\sigma_r = \pi \lambda\!\!\!^{-2} g \frac{\Gamma_p \Gamma_\gamma}{(E - E_0)^2 + \frac{1}{4}\Gamma^2} \tag{16}$$

The maximum reaction cross section is therefore

$$\sigma_{\max} = 4\pi \lambda\!\!\!^{-2} g \frac{\Gamma_p \Gamma_\gamma}{\Gamma^2} \tag{17}$$

where g is a statistical factor depending on the spins involved, Γ_p is the partial width for proton re-emission (elastic scattering) and Γ_γ is

† K. J. BROSTROM *et al.*, *Phys. Rev.* **71**, 661, 1947.

the partial width for gamma decay. If elastic scattering and radiative capture are the only two processes involved, the total width

$$\Gamma = \Gamma_p + \Gamma_\gamma \tag{18}$$

The fractional yield Y of the (p, γ) capture reaction is given by (for a very thin target)

$$Y = n\,\sigma_r \tag{19}$$

where n is the number of target nuclei per cm² of foil. With a very thin target and high energy resolution, the spread in energy may be small compared to the total width of the resonance line under investigation. A measurement of the yield at the peak of the resonance line enables the quantity $g\,\dfrac{\Gamma_p \Gamma_\gamma}{\Gamma^2}$ to be found. With a thick target the spread in energy of the protons absorbed in the target may be several times the width of the resonance line. In this case, it can be shown that the maximum yield is given by

$$Y_{\text{max}} = \frac{\lambda^2}{2}\,g\,\frac{\Gamma_p \Gamma_\gamma}{\Gamma} \tag{20}$$

Two limiting cases are of special interest: if $\Gamma_p \gg \Gamma_\gamma$, then $\Gamma_p/\Gamma \sim 1$ and $Y_{\text{max}} \propto g\,\Gamma_\gamma$; if $\Gamma_\gamma \gg \Gamma_p$, then $Y_{\text{max}} \propto g\,\Gamma_p$.

In some (p, γ) reactions the product nucleus is unstable against positron decay and the neasurement of the induced activity is a convenient way of determining the yields of weak resonances. Examples include the $C^{12}(p, \gamma)\,N^{13}$ and $Mg^{24}(p, \gamma)\,Al^{25}$ reactions. Detailed information concerning many (p, γ) reactions with light nuclei, such as the $C^{12}(p, \gamma)\,N^{13}$ capture process, is of considerable astrophysical interest (Chapter 22).

20.5. ENERGY LEVELS OF MIRROR NUCLEI

The density of nuclear states increases rapidly with the mass number of the nucleus, for the same excitation energy. Partly for this reason, the level schemes of light nuclei are more accurately known than those of heavy nuclei. Also with heavy nuclei, the Coulomb barrier is a much more formidable obstacle in studying level schemes with charged particles. Amongst the light nuclei, the odd mass isobars, in which the numbers of neutrons and protons differ by ± 1, are of special interest. These "mirror" nuclei should have closely similar ground and excited states. The determination of the nuclear radii of mirror nuclei has been discussed in Chapter 9. The energy difference of the ground states of a mirror pair of nuclei is given by the relative decay energy (the proton rich member of the pair is positron unstable) corrected for the difference in Coulomb energy and the neutron–hydrogen atom mass difference.

As an example of a mirror pair, the levels of the nuclei N^{15} and O^{15} are shown in Fig. 5. In its ground state, O^{15} is positron unstable (maximum energy 2·85 MeV) with a half-life of 2 min. Notice the fairly close correspondence between the positions of the excited levels of the two nuclei. This agreement supports the contention that the *p–p* and the *n–n* nuclear forces are equal. The dissociation energies of the two nuclei are also shown; in both cases, the lowest dissociation energy corresponds to the removal of a proton. An interesting feature of the N^{15} level scheme is the large value (5·28 MeV) of the first excited state and the existence

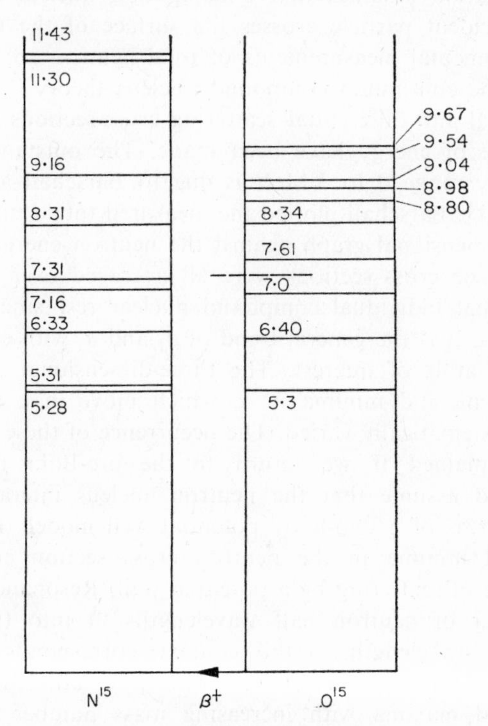

FIG. 5. Energy levels of mirror nuclei N^{15}–O^{15} (energies in MeV). Dotted lines indicate dissociation energies.

of another level is revealed by magnetic analysis of the protons emitted in the bombardment of an N^{14} target by deuterons. A useful check on the levels, deduced from measurements of the energies of the proton groups in the (d, p) reaction, is provided by measuring the capture γ-rays in the $N^{14}(n, \gamma)\, N^{15}$ reaction.

Some of the O^{15} levels have been studied by observing the energies of the γ-rays in the $N^{14}(p, \gamma)\, O^{15}$ process. Above the dissociation energy, the energy levels of O^{15} and N^{15} are more closely spaced. Some of the virtual levels of N^{15} have been deduced from the observation of resonances in the $N^{14}(n, p)\, C^{14}$ reaction.

20.6. THE OPTICAL MODEL

One of the important predictions of the statistical theory of the decay of the excited compound nucleus, in the region where the levels overlap, is that the total neutron cross section is a monotonically decreasing function of the incident energy, approaching a limiting value of $2\pi R^2$ at high neutron energies†. (R is the nuclear radius.) This "continuum" model calculation assumes that a compound nucleus is always created when the incident particle crosses the surface of the target nucleus.

The experimental measurements of total neutron cross sections do not agree with the continuum compound nucleus theory. Extensive measurements of total and differential scattering cross sections for neutrons over a wide range of energy have been made. The outstanding contribution in the energy range 0 to 3 MeV is due to Barschall and his co-workers at Wisconsin††. Barschall plotted the measured total neutron cross sections in a three-dimensional graph against the neutron energy E and the mass number A. The cross sections were all averaged over a suitable energy interval so that individual compound–nuclear resonances are not shown in the graphs. It is the general trend of σ_t and σ_s with energy E and mass number A that is of interest. The three-dimensional plots of Barschall exhibit maxima and minima in σ_t which move in a regular way as E and A are systematically varied. The occurrence of these "size" resonances is easily explained if we return to the pre-Bohr theory of nuclear reactions and assume that the neutron–nucleus interaction can be described in terms of a two-body potential well model. The widely spaced maxima and minima in the neutron cross section curves (Fig. 6) are characteristic of scattering by a potential well. Resonances occur when an exact number of neutron half wavelengths fit into the potential well. The neutron wavelength, in this context, corresponds to the energy of the neutron within the nuclear well. The systematic shift of the positions of the broad maxima with increasing mass number is a reflection of the monotonic increase of the nuclear radius R with mass number A (Barschall's results were plotted in terms of the old value of the nuclear radius constant r_0 of 1·45 fermi in the formula $R = r_0 A^{1/3}$).

The partial return to the potential well descriptions of nuclear reactions was first introduced by Fernbach, Serber and Taylor†††. They explained the scattering of high energy neutrons (90 MeV) by nuclei in terms of an "optical" model of the nucleus. At high neutron energies the nucleus appears partially transparent and the nucleus can be regarded as a homogeneous medium of complex refractive index. The index of re-

† H. Feshbach and V. F. Weisskopf, *Phys. Rev.* **76**, 1550, 1949.

†† H. H. Barschall, *Phys. Rev.* **86**, 431, 1952. M. Walt and H. H. Barschall, *Phys. Rev.* **93**, 1062, 1954.

††† S. Fernbach, R. Serber and T. B. Taylor, *Phys. Rev.* **75**, 1352, 1949.

fraction of the nuclear medium is determined by the potential energy V of the neutron in the nucleus. In contrast to the earlier potential well model of Bethe, the new model includes an imaginary term in the potential. This term represents the possibility of the incident nucleon experiencing some non-elastic interaction in the nuclear medium. The complex potential can be written

$$-(V + i\,W) \tag{21}$$

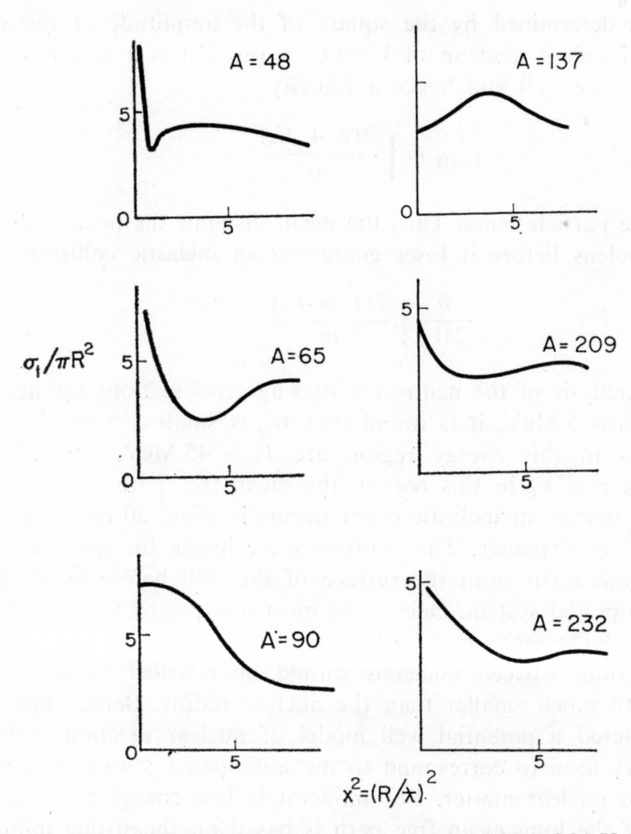

FIG. 6. Total cross sections for neutrons from about 0·05 to 3 MeV. The ordinate is $\sigma_t/\pi R^2$, where R is calculated from 1·45 $A^{1/3}$ fermi. The incident neutron energy is represented in terms of the parameter $x^2 = (R/\lambda)^2$. For $A = 140$, $E = 1$ MeV, $x^2 = 2{\cdot}7$.

and as a first approximation we treat the potential as a square well with

$$V = 0, \qquad W = 0, \qquad \text{for} \quad r > R$$

$$V = -V_0, \quad W = -W_0, \quad \text{for} \quad r < R.$$

The time-dependent part of the wave function describing the neutron within the potential well is proportional to

$$\exp\left(\frac{iEt}{\hbar}\right)\exp\left(-\frac{W_0 t}{\hbar}\right) \tag{22}$$

The mean time before the incident part coalesces to form a compound system is $\frac{\hbar}{2W_0}$; the factor of two occurs because the probability of coalescence is determined by the square of the amplitude of the wave function. An incident neutron of kinetic energy E has a kinetic energy $E + V_0$ within the well and hence a velocity

$$v_{\text{well}} = \sqrt{\frac{2(E+V_0)}{m}} \tag{23}$$

where m is the particle mass. Thus the mean distance the neutron travels within the nucleus before it loses energy in an inelastic collision is

$$\frac{\hbar}{2W_0}\sqrt{\frac{2(E+V_0)}{m}} \tag{24}$$

From the analysis of the neutron scattering cross sections for neutron energies E below 5 MeV, it is found that W_0 is small compared to V_0. Typical values in this energy region are $V_0 \sim 45$ MeV, and $W_0 \sim 1$ or 2 MeV. As $E \ll V_0$ in this region, the mean free path of a neutron in the nucleus before an inelastic event occurs is about 20 fermis, several times the nuclear diameter. The neutron wave inside the nucleus is reflected back and forth from the surface of the well before escaping or forming a compound system. One of the most unexpected features of this analysis is the large mean free path of neutrons in nuclear matter. The strong interaction between nucleons should be revealed by a neutron mean free path much smaller than the nuclear radius. Bethe† had previously considered a potential well model of nuclear reactions using a large imaginary term to correspond to the anticipated strong absorption of nucleons in nuclear matter. For moderately low energy neutrons the explanation of the long mean free path is based on the strong influence of the Pauli exclusion principle, which prevents nucleons being scattered into energy levels which are already filled. Thus if the nucleus is regarded as a collection of nucleons behaving as a Fermi gas, it is only the nucleons near the top of the Fermi energy distribution which can interact with an incoming low energy neutron. As the energy of the incoming neutron is increased, more and more of the nucleons may be scattered, as there is sufficient energy to lift them to empty states above the top of the

† H. A. Bethe, *Phys. Rev.* **57**, 1125, 1940.

Fermi sea. Thus we expect and do find that the imaginary part of the potential increases with increase in energy; for 30 MeV incident neutrons W_0 has risen to ~ 15 MeV, corresponding to a mean free path of ~ 3 fermi.

The application of the optical model to the scattering of low energy neutrons ($E < 5$ MeV) using a square complex potential well is discussed in some detail in an important paper by Feshbach, Porter and Weisskopf†. In the context of this model it is convenient to split the elastic scattering cross section into two parts

$$\sigma_S = \sigma_{CE} + \sigma_{SE} \tag{25}$$

where σ_{CE} is the compound–elastic scattering cross section and σ_{SE} is the shape–elastic scattering cross section. The two types of scattering are indistinguishable experimentally. By compound–elastic scattering we imply that the incident neutron is absorbed by the nucleus to form a compound system, subsequently (10^{-19} to 10^{-16} sec later) emitting a neutron with the same kinetic energy as that absorbed. Although the outgoing neutron has the same wavelength as the incident neutrons it is not coherent with the incident beam. In shape–elastic scattering the neutron is scattered by the potential representing the nucleus and is coherent with the incident neutron wave. Feshbach, Porter and Weisskopf obtained expressions for the "gross-structure" total cross section, the cross section for the formation of the compound nucleus (this includes compound–elastic scattering), and the shape–elastic cross section. The predictions of this model are in fair agreement with the low energy neutron measurements. The cross sections given by eqns. (8) and (9), in terms of optical model concepts, are now written

$$\sigma^l_{SE} = \pi \lambda\!\!\!^{-2}(2l + 1)\,|1 - \bar{\eta}_l|^2 \tag{26}$$

$$\sigma^l_r = \pi \lambda\!\!\!^{-2}(2l + 1)\,(1 - |\eta_l|^2) \tag{27}$$

where σ^l_{SE} is the shape–elastic cross section for the lth partial wave, and σ^l_r is the cross section for the formation of a compound nucleus for the lth partial wave. Notice that σ^l_r includes the compound–elastic scattering cross section. The complex amplitudes η_l are *averaged* over an energy interval large compared with the level spacings of the compound system.††

One important aspect of the optical model is that it can never represent a black nucleus, even if $W \to \infty$, because one cannot invent a potential well with boundary conditions such that all the incoming partial waves are completely absorbed.

† H. Feshbach, C. E. Porter and V. F. Weisskopf, *Phys. Rev.* **96**, 448, 1954.

†† These ideas are discussed by F. L. Friedman and V. F. Weisskopf in *Niels Bohr and the development of Physics*, Pergamon, London 1955.

A much better fit to the experimental cross sections is obtained if a more realistic shape is given to the complex potential well model. Analysis of elastic scattering of protons, for example, using a square complex well gave too much scattering. Woods and Saxon† introduced a potential well in which V and W vary smoothly with r, the distance from the centre of the nucleus:

$$V(r) = \frac{-(V_0 + i\,W_0)}{\left[1 + \exp\left(\dfrac{r-R}{a}\right)\right]} \tag{28}$$

A plot of the real part of this potential function is shown in Fig. 7. R is the potential radius, and is very nearly equal to the radius at which the depth of the potential well is one half its central value. The parameter a is a measure of the degree of the tapering of the potential near

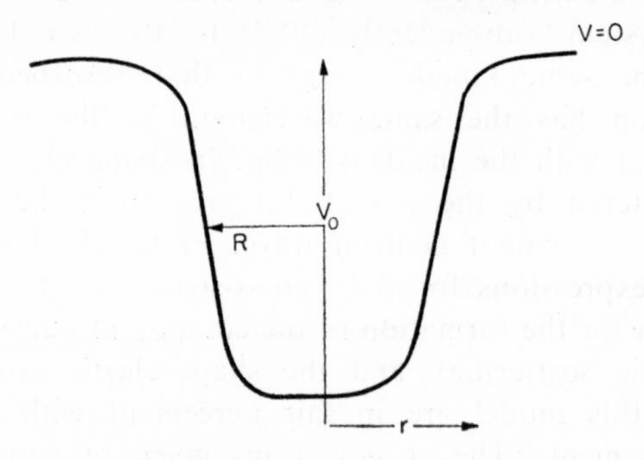

FIG. 7. Real part of Woods–Saxon Potential. When $r = R$, $V \sim -\frac{1}{2}V_0$.

the surface of the nucleus. A large a would correspond to a diffuse nuclear surface. Values of the potential radius are usually based on the formula $R = r_0\,A^{1/3}$, with r_0 in the region of 1·3 fermi. Typical values of a are between 0·50 and 0·65 fermi. The parameters V_0 and W_0 are dependent on the type and energy of the incident particle. As the incident energy E increases from zero, V_0 decreases smoothly from about 50 MeV at very low energies to about $-$ 10 MeV at 300 MeV. In contrast, the absorption part of the potential W_0 starts at a low value of $\sim$2 MeV for low energy particles and increases steadily to about 20 MeV at 100 MeV, where it remains nearly constant and eventually begins to fall at energies greater than 300 MeV.

One of the most serious difficulties of the optical model is that very little is known about the nuclear surface. The theory of the origin of the imaginary part of the potential would expect W to be a maximum

† R. D. WOODS and D. S. SAXON, *Phys. Rev.* **95**, 577, 1954.

near the nuclear surface for it is in this region that there are more empty states available for the scattered nucleons. A better fit to the experimental results is obtained if a surface absorption potential, of Gaussian shape, centred around $r = R$ is included. More refined treatments of scattering also include a potential representing a spin–orbit interaction†.

In addition to the theory of the neutron–nuclear interaction, the optical model has been successfully applied to the scattering of protons, deuterons, alpha particles and heavier ions.

The success of the optical model, in which the nucleus behaves as a "cloudy crystal ball", partially transparent to the incoming particle and partially absorptive, demonstrates that the original Bohr theory

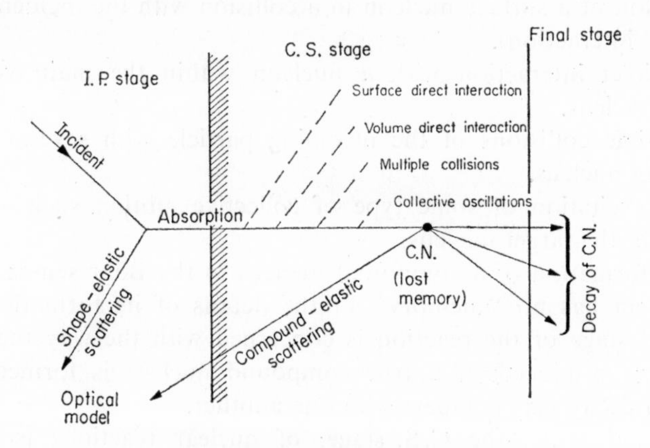

FIG. 8. Nuclear reaction scheme
(from V. F. WEISSKOPF††)

of compound–nuclear reactions is in need of modification. Thus the theory that a nuclear reaction always proceeds through the formation of a compound nuclear system and the subsequent independent decay is not valid. A more general scheme of nuclear reactions has been described by Weisskopf††, which considers other possibilites than the independent decay modes of the compound nucleus. This more general reaction scheme is illustrated in Fig. 8.

The nuclear reaction is conveniently analysed into three stages: the independent-particle (optical model) stage, the compound-system (C.S. stage) and the final stage. In the first stage of the interaction the incoming particle interacts with the nucleus as a whole and the effect can be described by a two-body potential. The incident particle retains its individuality as it is refracted and partially reflected at the surface of the well. The scattering associated

† F. E. BJORKLUND and S. FERNBACH, *Phys. Rev.* **109**, 1295, 1958; D. S. SAXON p. 197, *Proc. of the Intern. Conf. on Nuclear Structure*, Kingston, Canada 1960.

†† V. F. WEISSKOPF, *Revs. Mod. Phys.* **29**, 174, 1957.

with the partial reflection of the incident wave by the potential well is the shape–elastic part of the scattering†. The imaginary part of the potential is responsible for the absorption of the wave which penetrates into the nucleus. Absorption includes all processes which remove the incident particle from the "entrance channel". The particle can no longer be considered as an entity separate from the rest of the target nucleus.

The absorption process leads to the second stage of the nuclear reaction, the compound-system stage. The incident particle has now exchanged some energy with the target nucleus, although a compound nucleus in the Bohr meaning of the term may not be formed. Some of the possible absorption processes are

(1) ejection of a surface nucleon in a collision with the incident particle (a "direct" interaction).

(2) A direct interaction with a nucleon within the main volume of the target nucleus.

(3) Multiple collisions of the incoming particle with several nucleons of the target nucleus.

(4) The excitation of some type of collective motion such as surface vibrations of the target nucleus.

(5) The formation of a compound nucleus in the Bohr sense; the compound-system has no "memory" of the details of its formation.

The final stage of the reaction is concerned with the way the reaction products are produced. If a true compound nucleus is formed, several methods of decay may compete with one another.

The second stage, the C.S. stage, of nuclear reactions is the least well understood. There are many reactions in which the decay of the compound-system *does* depend on its mode of formation. Thus in many reactions, the particles are emitted preferentially in the forward direction. There is no doubt that many reactions lie between the extremes of a direct interaction between the incident particle and a single target nucleus nucleon, and the formation of a compound nucleus. Unless a compound nucleus is formed, the lifetime of the compound-system corresponds at most to a few crossings of the nuclear well.

20.7. STRIPPING AND PICK-UP REACTIONS

Nuclear reactions initiated by deuteron bombardment do not always take place through the formation of the compound nucleus intermediate state. Two of the most common nuclear reactions involving deuterons are the (d, p) and the (d, n) processes. These reactions are influenced by

(1) The very low binding energy of the deuteron ($W \sim 2{\cdot}2$ MeV).

† Strictly speaking, the process whereby the particle goes right through the nucleus without interacting is part of the shape–elastic scattering.

(2) The relatively large separation of the neutron and the proton in the deuteron, the average separation d being given by one half the relaxation length of the deuteron wave function (eqn. (7), Chapter 19)

$$d = \frac{1}{2}\gamma^{-1} = \frac{1}{2}\frac{\hbar}{\sqrt{(m\,W)}} = 2{\cdot}18 \text{ fermi} \tag{29}$$

where m is the proton mass.

The (d, p) or (d, n) reactions may occur through the complete fusion of the incident deuteron with the target nucleus and the subsequent decay of the compound state by a proton or neutron emission. There are, however, other possible reaction mechanisms. If the incident deuteron grazes the surface of the nucleus, one of the nucleons of the deuteron may be captured by the nucleus, the other nucleon flying away without having crossed the nuclear surface. This "stripping" process is partly a consequence of the low binding energy of the deuteron. The break-up of the deuteron may occur, without the deuteron coming into contact with the surface of the nucleus, through the Coulomb interaction. The "electric" disintegration of the deuteron† may be pictured in the following way. In the frame of reference in which the deuteron is at rest the deuteron experiences a rapidly varying electric field for a time interval $t \sim R/v$, where R is the nuclear radius and v is the velocity of approach of the nucleus. A Fourier analysis of this electric pulse shows that the deuteron is effectively bathed in electromagnetic radiation with a frequency distribution up to a maximum $\nu_m \sim 1/t \sim v/R$. If $h\,\nu_m > W$, photodisintegration of the deuteron is energetically possible. For heavy nuclei and deuterons of moderately high energy (> 10 MeV) the calculated cross section is comparable with that of the compound nuclear disintegration process.

The first experimental studies of the (d, p) reaction at very low deuteron energies showed that the reaction cross section was much higher than anticipated. The corresponding (d, n) cross section is much smaller. The theory of low energy deuteron stripping was first considered by Oppenheimer and Phillips††. They argued that at low incident energies the proton inside the deuteron will have a very small chance of penetrating the Coulomb barrier of the target nucleus. However, if the neutron in the deuteron brushes against the nuclear surface with the proton at the other end of the deuteron (the neutron–proton separation may also be enhanced by the polarizing action of the Coulomb field of nucleus) the neutron may be captured by the nucleus. At low deuteron energies the angular distribution of the stripped protons in the (d, p) reaction is isotropic in the centre-of-mass system, as only the $l = 0$ (s wave)

† J. R. Oppenheimer, *Phys. Rev.* **47**, 845, 1935.
†† J. R. Oppenheimer and M. Phillips, *Phys. Rev.* **48**, 500, 1935.

interaction is involved. At higher deuteron energies two general features appear: the (d, n) and (d, p) cross sections are roughly equal, and the angular distribution of the stripped nucleons is markedly anisotropic. The differential reaction cross section is usually strongly peaked in the forward direction. The angular distribution of the protons emitted in the $Al^{27}(d, p)\,Al^{28}$ reaction with 8 MeV deuterons (lab. system) is shown in Fig. 9 (the Al^{28} nucleus is formed in the ground state).

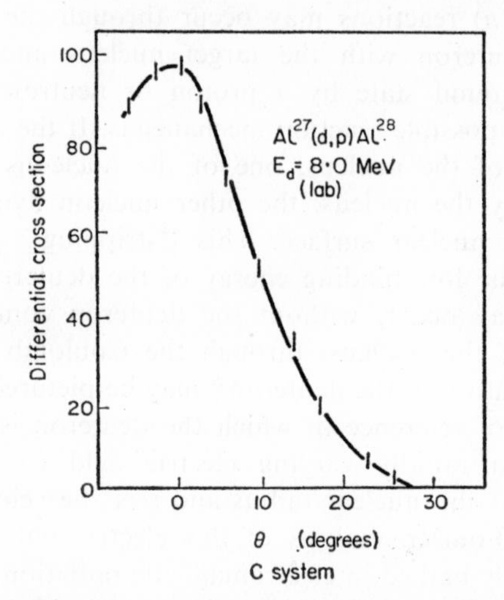

FIG. 9. Angular distribution of protons in a (d, p) reaction (cross section in arbitrary units). (HOLT and MARSHAM, *Proc. Phys. Soc., A* **66**, 249, 1953.)

At very high deuteron energies (> 100 MeV), the stripping process has proved to be of considerable practical use in producing beams of fast neutrons. Thus the stripping of 190 MeV deuterons from the Berkeley synchrocyclotron produced a roughly monoenergetic beam of 90 MeV neutrons confined to a narrow cone in the forward direction†. The theory of this high energy stripping process has been given by Serber††.

The general theory of stripping reactions has been developed by many authors, notably S. T. Butler,††† with particular emphasis on the angular distributions of the stripped nucleons. Some insight into the angular variation of the reaction cross section can be gained by relatively simple arguments. In Fig. 10 we depict the momenta involved in a (d, p) stripping reaction. If $\hbar\,\boldsymbol{k}_p$ is the momentum of the proton just after stripping, then

$$\hbar\,\boldsymbol{k}_p = \hbar\,\boldsymbol{K}_p + \tfrac{1}{2}\hbar\,\boldsymbol{k}_d \qquad (30)$$

† A. C. HELMHOLZ, E. M. MCMILLAN and D. C. SEWELL, *Phys. Rev.* **72**, 1003, 1947.
†† R. SERBER, *Phys. Rev.* **72**, 1008, 1947.
††† S. T. BUTLER, *Nuclear Stripping Reactions*, Wiley, New York 1957.

where $\frac{1}{2}\hbar \boldsymbol{k}_d$ is one half the initial momentum of the deuteron and $\hbar \boldsymbol{K}_p$ is the contribution to the momentum of the stripped proton from the internal momentum of the deuteron at the instant of stripping. The neutron from the deuteron approaches the nuclear surface with a momentum $\hbar \boldsymbol{k}_n$ given by

$$\hbar \boldsymbol{k}_n = \hbar \boldsymbol{k}_d - \hbar \boldsymbol{k}_p \tag{31}$$

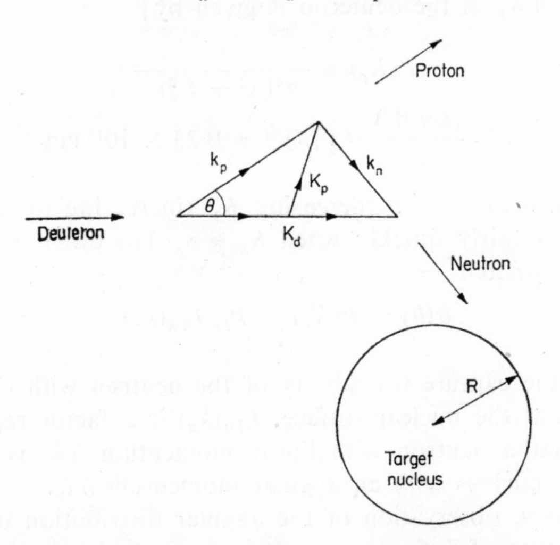

FIG. 10. Momentum relations in (d, p) stripping reaction.

Denoting the angle between the direction of travel of the stripped proton and the incident deuteron by θ, we obtain the relations

$$K_p = [(k_p - \tfrac{1}{2}k_d)^2 + 2k_p k_d \sin^2\tfrac{1}{2}\theta]^{\frac{1}{2}} \tag{32}$$

$$k_n = [(k_d - k_p)^2 + 4k_p k_d \sin^2\tfrac{1}{2}\theta]^{\frac{1}{2}} \tag{33}$$

If the neutron has an impact parameter on the target nucleus equal to R, then the orbital angular momentum of the captured neutron is (classically)

$$\hbar k_n R = \hbar l$$

or

$$k_n R = l \tag{34}$$

Thus in order to satisfy eqn. (34), k_n must have one of certain discrete values. For fixed values of k_p and k_d, this means that the possible θ values are restricted by eqns. (33) and (34). This is a semi-classical argument, and the uncertainty principle relaxes this stringent condition. Nevertheless, the emitted protons are expected to be peaked around the direction θ_l which satisfies the eqns. (33) and (34). For $l = 0$, (s wave neutrons), the nearest we can go to satisfying the two equations is to let θ have its minimum value of zero; thus we expect the protons to be peaked in the forward direction. Also from eqn. (32) we see that for fixed k_p and k_d, K_p increases with θ. Thus the probability of the proton flying away in the θ direction will include a factor representing the probability of the internal momentum of the proton in the deuteron having a value satisfying eqn. (34). Using a suitable expression for the internal wave function of the deuteron, the probability of finding the proton with a momentum $\hbar K_p$ in the deuteron is given by†

$$P(K_p) = \frac{\alpha}{\pi^2(\alpha^2 + K_p^2)^{\frac{1}{2}}} \tag{35}$$

where $$\alpha = \frac{\sqrt{(m W)}}{\hbar} = (2d)^{-1} = 0{\cdot}23 \times 10^{13}\ \text{cm}^{-1}$$

Thus $P(K_p)$ decreases with increasing K_p (increasing θ) and the probability falls off fairly quickly when $K_p \gg \alpha$. The differential (d, p) cross section can be written

$$\sigma(\theta) = P(K_p) \sum_{l_n} P_{l_n} L_{l_n}(k_n) \tag{36}$$

where P_{l_n} is the capture probability of the neutron with orbital angular momentum l_n at the nuclear surface. $L_{l_n}(k_n)$ is a factor representing the probability that a neutron with linear momentum $\hbar k_n$ is found at the surface of the nucleus with an angular momentum $\hbar l_n$.

In many cases, observation of the angular distribution of the protons enables the value of l_n in a given stripping reaction to be determined. Then if the spin and parity of the target nucleus are known, angular momentum and parity selection rules are of value in predicting or restricting the spin and parity of the residual nuclear state.

The angular distributions of the reaction end products of several other reactions such as the (p, d), (n, d), (α, p) and (p, α) are very similar in character to the (d, p) and (d, n) stripping distributions. The (p, d), (n, d) and (p, α) reactions are known as "pick-up" reactions. The (p, d) pick-up process occurs in the following way. As the incoming proton approaches the surface of the target nucleus, one of the surface neutrons is plucked out of the surface by the p–n nuclear force and the two particles travel on as a bound deuteron. The (n, d) reaction involves the pick-up of a surface proton instead of a neutron. The (α, p) reaction takes place through the stripping of the alpha particle into a proton and a triton, the latter being captured by the target nucleus; whereas the (p, α) pick-up reaction occurs through the incoming proton pulling a triton out of the target nucleus. The differential cross section of a (He^3, α) pick-up reaction is shown in Fig. 11 for the C^{13} (He^3, α) C^{12} reaction (this process involves the capture of an outer neutron from the C^{13} nucleus).

† Equation (22) in the article by R. Huby, Stripping Reactions, in Vol. 3 *Progress in Nuclear Physics*, Ed. by O. R. Frisch, Pergamon, London 1953.

An unexpected feature of several stripping angular distributions is the rise of the differential cross section in the backward direction ($\theta \rightarrow 180°$ in the C-system). This behaviour has been explained in terms of an

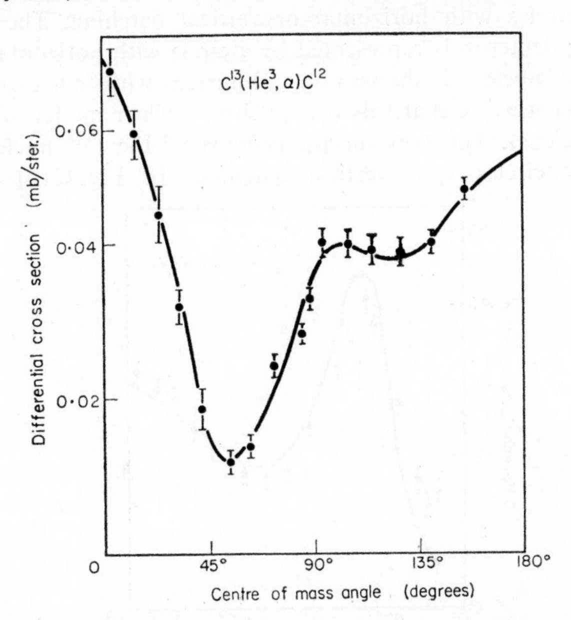

FIG. 11. Angular distribution in a (He^3, α) pick-up reaction. (H. D. HOLMGREN, *Phys. Rev.*, **106**, 100, 1957.)

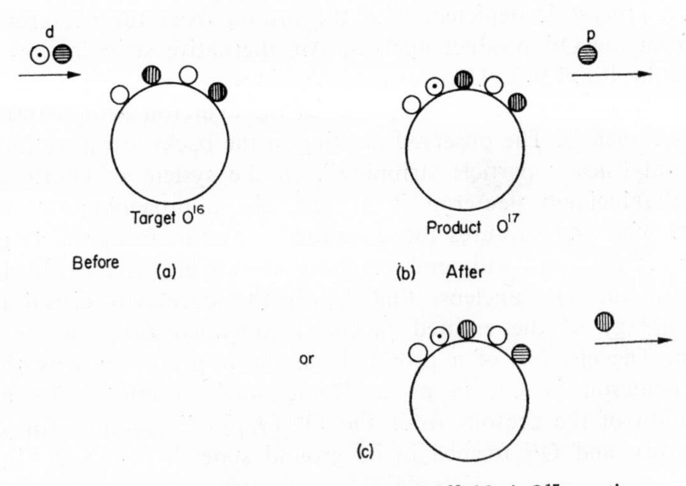

FIG. 12. Diagrammatic representation of O^{16} (*d, p*) O^{17} reaction. (After BANERJEE in *Nuclear Spectroscopy*, Part B, Edited by F. AJZENBERG-SELOVE, Academic Press, New York, 1960.)

"exchange" effect in the stripping process.† Consider as an example the reaction O^{16} (d, p) O^{17}. Two possible stripping processes are depicted in Fig. 12. In this picture, neutrons are represented by open circles and protons by circles with horizontal or vertical hatching. The proton of the incoming deuteron is represented by a circle with horizontal hatching. The O^{16} target nucleus is shown as a C^{12} nucleus with four extra nucleons (we are not suggesting that this is a realistic nuclear model of the closed shell O^{16} nucleus). The two surface protons of the O^{16} nucleus are represented by circles with vertical hatching. In Fig. 12(b) the direct

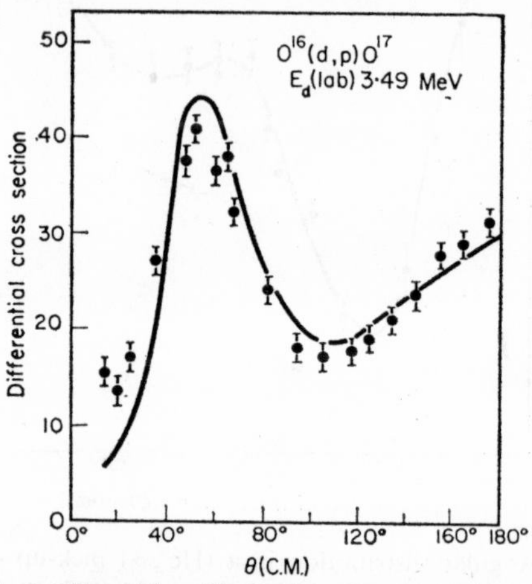

FIG. 13. O^{16} (d, p) O^{17} angular distribution (cross section in arbitrary units) (after Nagarajan and Banerjee).

stripping process is depicted, with the proton from the deuteron flying away from the O^{17} product nucleus. An alternative stripping process is depicted in Fig. 12(c). Here one of the protons of the O^{16} nucleus is emitted, the proton (and the neutron) of the deuteron being captured by the target nucleus. The observed peaking in the backward direction could arise from "heavy particle stripping". In the system of coordinates in which the incident deuteron is at rest, the approaching O^{16} nucleus interacts with and captures the deuteron, a proton from the target nucleus is stripped and will tend to continue moving in the direction of motion of the O^{16} nucleus, that is, in the backward direction. The kinetic energy of the emitted proton is obtained from the Q of the reaction. The ejection of a proton from the target nucleus by the projectile deuteron is known as a "knock-out" reaction. The angular distribution of the protons from the O^{16} (d, p) O^{17} reaction, for E_d(lab) $= 3{\cdot}49$ MeV and O^{17} formed in its ground state, is shown in Fig. 13.††

† G. E. OWEN and L. MADANSKY, *Phys. Rev.* **105**, 1766, 1957.

†† M. K. BANERJEE, *Nuclear Spectroscopy*, Part B, p. 729, Ed. by F. AJZENBERG-SELOVE, Academic Press.

The curve shows the theoretical calculation including direct and heavy particle stripping contributions.

The heavy particle stripping explanation of backward peaking must be treated with caution. The Butler stripping theory represents the incoming and outgoing particles as plane waves. Recently† a more realistic approach, known as the "Distorted Wave Born Approximation" (D.W.B.A.), takes into account the distortion of the incoming wave and the outgoing wave by the Coulomb and optical model potentials. These calculations give different results to the plane wave calculations especially at large backward angles, where the D.W.B.A. predicts considerably more scattering. Thus the backward peaking observed in the angular distributions of some stripping reactions may be due to distortion effects and not the heavy particle stripping mechanism.

20.8. PHOTONUCLEAR REACTIONS

The first photonuclear reaction to be discovered was the $H^2 + \gamma \rightarrow H^1 + n$ disintegration, using the 2·62 MeV photons from ThC″. Chadwick and Goldhaber (1934) observed this process in a cloud chamber and measured the kinetic energy of the proton. In Chapt. 15, Sect. 4, we described how this measurement, in conjunction with precise atomic mass values for hydrogen and deuterium, enabled an accurate estimate of the neutron mass to be made.

The majority of nuclei (H^2 and Be^9 are notable exceptions) have binding energies for the last proton or neutron greater than 5 MeV. This means that the γ-rays emitted by natural radioactive isotopes have insufficient energy to induce (γ, n) or (γ, p) reactions. In the nineteen-thirties extensive studies of photo-reactions†† were carried out using the 17·6 and 14·8 MeV γ-rays emitted in the 460 keV proton resonance reaction Li^7 (p, γ) Be^8.

Electromagnetic interactions with nuclei are fairly weak compared with nuclear interactions (this weakness is a consequence of the small value of the fine structure constant, (1/137). Photonuclear absorption cross sections are therefore small, at most several hundred millibarns. This fact coupled with the low intensity of the gamma radiations emitted in (p, γ) reactions means that accurate measurements of photonuclear reaction cross sections are very difficult to make. With the advent of high intensity bremsstrahlung beams from betatrons and synchrotrons the situation was much improved. One drawback of the new sources of

† W. TOBOCMAN, *Phys. Rev.* **115**, 99, 1959; D. H. WILKINSON, *Proc. Intern. Conference*, Kingston 1960.

†† W. BOTHE and W. GENTNER, *Z. Physik.* **106**, 236, 1937; **112**, 45, 1939.

photons is the continuous range of energy up to some maximum energy E_0. Thus, if, for example, a (γ, n) reaction produces a radioactive nucleus, the total induced activity by a bremsstrahlung beam is proportional to

$$\int_0^{E_0} N(E, E_0)\,\sigma(E)\,dE \tag{37}$$

where $N(E, E_0)\,dE$ is the number of photons irradiating the target in the energy interval E to $E + dE$ and E_0 is the maximum photon energy. In order to obtain the photonuclear cross section at a definite energy E_0 the difference in the integral for two nearly equal values of E_0 must be obtained. This is a notoriously inaccurate method, especially if the betatron energy is not well-stabilized. Recently, improvements in energy stabilization and methods of obtaining monochromatic photon beams from bremsstrahlung sources have been developed.†

The most striking feature of photoreactions is the existence of a "giant" resonance in the (γ, n) (γ, p) excitation curves. The energy E_m, corresponding to the peak of the (γ, p) (γ, n) cross section versus photon energy curve, decreases as the mass number A of the target nucleus increases from about 23 MeV for very light nuclei to about 12 MeV for $A \sim 240$. An approximate relation connecting E_m and A is

$$E_m = \frac{80}{A^{1/3}}\ \text{MeV}$$

The observed widths of the giant resonances fall in the range 5 to 7 MeV. The (γ, n) and the total γ-ray cross sections for ${}_{73}\text{Ta}^{181}$ are shown in Fig. 14.†† It is interesting to notice that the $(\gamma, 2n)$ threshold occurs at an energy close to the peak of the (γ, n) excitation curve (~ 14 MeV). The $(\gamma, 3n)$ process is not shown in Fig. 14 as it has a threshold energy of 21 MeV. The (γ, p) cross section is very low in the energy region considered, a consequence of the inhibiting effect of the high Coulomb barrier ($Z = 73$).

An interesting analogy exists between the quantum mechanical treatment of the resonance absorption of light by the electrons in an atom and the nuclear photo-effect. The nuclear photo-effect is more difficult to understand than the absorption of light by a single bound electric charge e but it is instructive to consider the simple case first.

In Section 16 of Chapter 6, we derived an expression for b_{mn}, where $|b_{mn}|^2$ measures the probability of an electromagnetic wave inducing a transition from the state m to the state n in a time t (eqn. (170)). If we assume the system is originally in the ground state ($m = 0$) at $t = 0$, the integral

$$\int |b_{0n}(t)|^2\,d\omega \tag{38}$$

† C. Tzara, *Compt. Rendus* **245**, 56, 1957.

†† E. A. Whalin and A. O. Hanson, *Phys. Rev.* **89**, 324, 1953.

evaluated over a small range of angular frequencies around ω_{0n}, (covering the width of the line)

where
$$\omega_{0n} = \frac{E_n - E_0}{\hbar},$$

will represent the transition probability from the ground to the nth state in a time interval t. It is not difficult to show that this probability is

$$e^2 E^2 (x_{0n})^2 \frac{\pi t}{\hbar^2} \qquad (39)$$

where E^2 is the mean squared value of the perturbing electric field of the incident light wave, assumed to be polarized with the electric field

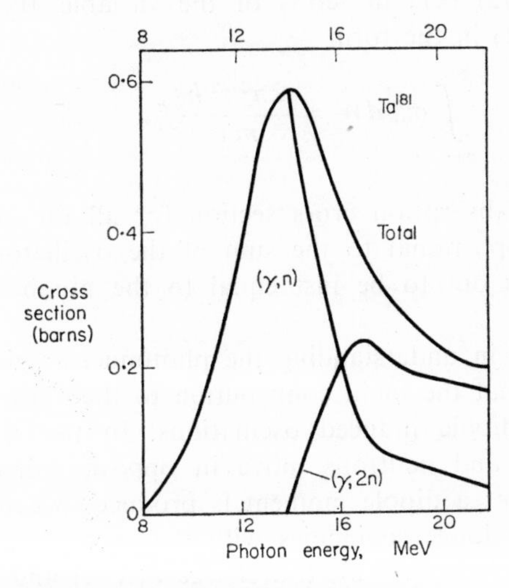

FIG. 14. Giant photonuclear resonance in Ta^{181} (after Whalin and Hanson).

parallel to the x-axis. x_{0n} is a matrix element of the x-displacement due to the field. The photon absorption cross section for this transition is obtained by dividing the probability of inducing a transition in one second (put $t = 1$ in eqn. (39)) by the incident flux of photons. The energy density of an oscillating electric field (*in vacuo*) is

$$\frac{E^2}{8\pi}$$

hence the flux of photons of energy $W = \hbar\omega$ is

$$\frac{c E^2}{8\pi W} \qquad (40)$$

The cross section integrated over the absorption line $(0 \to n)$ is

$$\int_{\text{line}} \sigma \, d\omega = \frac{4\pi^2 e^2 W (x_{0n})^2}{\hbar^2 c} \tag{41}$$

It is customary to introduce the concept of "oscillator strength", in relation to this electric dipole (E 1) transition, defined by

$$f_{0n} = \frac{2mW}{\hbar^2}(x_{0n})^2 = \left(\frac{x_{0n}}{\lambda\!\!\!^{-}_{0n}}\right)^2 \tag{42}$$

In this definition, m is the mass of the electric charged particle and $\lambda\!\!\!^{-}_{0n}$ is therefore the reduced de Broglie wavelength of the particle when it acquires a kinetic energy W. Notice that f_{0n} is a dimensionless quantity. Expressing the integral (41) in terms of the variable W, $dW = \hbar \, d\omega$, we can write eqn. (41) in the form

$$\int_{\text{line}} \sigma_{0n} \, dW = \frac{2\pi^2 e^2 \hbar}{m c} f_{0n} \tag{43}$$

The total photon absorption cross section for all the Z electrons in an atom will be proportional to the sum of the oscillator strengths, a quantity which turns out to be just equal to the number of electrons in the atom.

An important step in understanding the photonuclear giant resonance was the realization that the main contribution to the absorption process is through electric dipole induced oscillations. In the E 1 absorption process the protons and neutrons move in opposite directions in the centre of mass system; a dipole moment is produced when the centroid of electric charge no longer coincides with the centroid of mass. Each proton vibrates as if it has an electric charge $e(N/A)$ and each neutron as if it has a charge $-e(Z/A)$. The sum of the nucleon oscillator strengths, according to this simple model, is then equal to Z times (N/A), so that the integrated absorption cross section is given by†

$$\int_0^\infty \sigma_\gamma \, dE = \left(\frac{2\pi^2 e^2 \hbar}{M c}\right)\left(\frac{Z N}{A}\right) = 0{\cdot}060 \frac{Z N}{A} \text{ MeV-barn} \tag{44}$$

where E is the γ-ray energy and M is the mass of a nucleon. For a $Z = N = A/2$ nucleus, the integrated cross section becomes

$$\int_0^\infty \sigma_\gamma \, dE = 0{\cdot}015\, A \text{ MeV-barn} \tag{45}$$

† J. S. Levinger and H. A. Bethe, *Phys. Rev.* **78**, 115, 1950.

This result agrees with the Goldhaber–Teller† model of γ-ray absorption. Unlike the approach of Levinger and Bethe, which makes no appeal to any specific nuclear model for the absorption process, Goldhaber and Teller considered several possible "collective vibration" models.

The model-independent result of Levinger and Bethe quoted above, represents a minimum cross section, as the effect of exchange forces (especially the Majorana type) has not been taken into account. The exchange force is expected to increase the oscillator strength. One possible explanation†† of this increase is that following $E\,1$ gamma absorption excited nucleons will occur more frequently in p-states ($l = 1$) than in the ground state, and Majorana exchange forces are repulsive in odd-l states (see Chapter 19, Section 4) and this will increase the energy of the collective motion.

Assuming a nuclear radius constant $r_0 = 1{\cdot}5$ fermi and that the nucleons move within a square potential well, Levinger and Bethe included the effect of exchange forces in the integrated cross section

$$\int_0^\infty \sigma_\gamma \, dE = 0{\cdot}060 \frac{ZN}{A} (1 + 0{\cdot}8x) \quad \text{MeV-barn} \tag{46}$$

Here x is the fraction of exchange force in the n–p interaction. There is some evidence from high energy n–p scattering studies that x is about 0·5.

Although calculations on photonuclear absorption cross sections can be carried out using so called "sum-rules", without involving any nuclear model, more interest is aroused by model calculations, as they give more physical insight and often suggest new ways of testing the various theoretical models.†††

The first important model interpretation of photo-absorption was that of Goldhaber and Teller†. This model is essentially a collective vibration model which emphasized the $E\,1$ nature of the photon absorption process in the energy range 10 to 30 MeV. Two possible models considered were

(1) Protons and neutrons vibrate and move through each other as separately compressible fluids.

(2) Protons and neutrons vibrate relative to each other as incompressible fluids. When the two fluids have their maximum separation they no longer overlap at the nuclear surface and it is assumed that, for small displacements, the restoring force is proportional to the displacement.

Models (1) and (2) made different predictions; namely, E_m proportional to $A^{-1/3}$ for model (1) and E_m proportional to $A^{-1/6}$ for model (2). At

† M. Goldhaber and E. Teller, *Phys. Rev.* **74**, 1046, 1948.

†† J. Fujita, *Prog. Theoretical Phys.* (Kyoto) **16**, 112, 1956.

††† This point is stressed by Levinger in his book *Nuclear Photo-Disintegration*, p. 92 (see bibliography).

the time (1948) the experimental evidence favoured an inverse sixth–root power law, so model (2) was treated in more detail. Today the evidence favours the $A^{-1/3}$ power law. The high frequency of the giant resonance ($\hbar\omega \sim 20$ MeV) is a direct consequence of the tight binding between the neutron and proton fluids of the collective model. What explanation can be found for the large width of the excitation curve? Goldhaber and Teller suggest that the width of the resonance is due to coupling of the dipole vibration with other degrees of freedom of the nucleus. A great number of nuclear levels contribute to the absorption process but they all cluster around the resonance energy. The width of the resonance is the result of a damping effect associated with the coupling between the dipole vibrations and other modes of motion (one can regard this as an effect due to nuclear viscosity).

An important contribution to the theory of the photo-absorption process in terms of the nuclear shell model is due to Wilkinson.† He suggests that photonuclear reactions are initiated by a process in which there is a direct interaction between the incident photon and a particular nucleon of the target nucleus. The excited nucleon finds itself in a virtual state in which it may either escape from the nucleus or interact and amalgamate with the rest of the nucleus to form an excited compound state. It has been emphasized (Sect. 11 of this chapter) that a realistic shell model potential does *not* predict equal spacing of energy levels. How can we explain why the $E1$ transitions cluster together round the resonance energy? The explanation is based on two considerations††: the energy levels of interest are those just below the Fermi energy and these are nearly equally spaced in energy; the matrix elements for those transitions permitted for the harmonic oscillator well (one-quantum jumps) are still much greater than those forbidden for the oscillator in the shell model well.

Shell model calculations of E_m and the resonance width Γ have been made in several cases with good agreement between theory and experiment.

An interesting prediction of the collective model of gamma absorption has been verified. This concerns the dipole absorption of radiation by a strongly deformed nucleus (e.g. one of the rare earth nuclei). Two characteristic frequencies should show up, one corresponding to a "slow" vibration along the major axis of the spheroidal nucleus, and the other corresponding to a "fast" vibration along the direction of one of the minor axes. The giant resonance for such a nucleus should exhibit two peaks. The energy difference ΔE between the two peaks has been calculated for the two assumptions of the collective model: for model (1)

$$\Delta E = \varepsilon(1 - \varepsilon)\, E_m \tag{47}$$

† D. H. Wilkinson, *Physica* **22**, 1039, 1956.

†† D. H. Wilkinson, Nuclear Photodisintegration, *Ann. Rev. Nuclear Science*, Vol. 9, p. 7, 1959.

where the eccentricity is

$$\varepsilon = \frac{R_1 - R_2}{R_0} \tag{48}$$

R_1 and R_2 are the major and minor semi-axes and R_0 is the radius of the sphere with the same volume as the spheroidal nucleus. E_m is the "unperturbed" resonance energy. The anticipated splitting has been found† in the rare earth nuclei Tb^{159} and Ta^{181}. The agreement between the theoretical prediction and experiment is very satisfactory: for Tb^{159} ΔE (theoretical) is 4·0 MeV and the measured value is 3·8 MeV.

So far we have considered the primary process of absorption in photonuclear reactions. A great deal of experimental work has been done on the products of photoreactions. In many cases, the energies, angular distributions, and relative cross sections (at the same energy) for different decays, are in accord with the statistical model of the de-excitation of the compound nucleus. This is not always so and there is often strong evidence of the occurrence of direct interactions.

Above the energy of the peak of the giant resonance curve the gamma absorption cross section falls away fairly rapidly and from about 30 to about 120 MeV remains nearly constant (a typical (γ, n) cross section in this region is 100 millibarns). In the energy region above about 140 MeV the cross section gradually rises; this increase is associated with the photoproduction of pions in the target nucleus. An appreciable fraction of these pions, however, never escapes from the nucleus but are re-absorbed within the nucleus.

At high photon energies (150 to 300 MeV) an important feature of the photodisintegration process is the appearance, especially with light target nuclei, of high energy neutron–proton pairs emerging from the target nucleus with some degree of angular correlation.†† This phenomenon is explained by the "quasi-deuteron" model of Levinger.††† The key point of this model is related to the property that a high energy photon carries little momentum compared to a nucleon moving with the same energy. Thus the absorption of a photon can only take place if it interacts with a small cluster of nucleons in very close contact, which already have high momentum components. At high photon energies, the most effective cluster is simply a neutron and a proton in close contact (a "quasi-deuteron"). Neither an n–n or p–p pair is very effective as neither has a dipole moment. The absorbed photon breaks the n–p bond and the two nucleons fly apart, and in a light nucleus they both have a good chance of escaping from the nucleus.

† E. G. Fuller and M. S. Weiss, *Phys. Rev.* **112**, 560, 1958.
†† M. Q. Barton and J. S. Smith, *Phys. Rev.* **110**, 1143, 1958.
††† J. S. Levinger, *Phys. Rev.* **84**, 43, 1951.

20.9. HEAVY ION NUCLEAR REACTIONS

For the last few years linear particle accelerators, cyclotrons, and tandem Van de Graaff machines have been used to accelerate heavy ions to initiate nuclear reactions. The term heavy ion refers to a multiply-charged ion containing a nucleus of charge $Z_1 > 2$. Nuclear interactions including elastic scattering, nucleon transfer reactions, compound nuclear reactions, fission, . . ., etc. have been studied, using as projectiles ions of Li, C, N, O and Ne in the energy range 2 MeV (for Li ions) to about 200 MeV (for Ne ions), the last figure corresponding to a kinetic energy of about 10 MeV per nucleon.

The special features characterizing heavy ion interactions were first anticipated by Breit.† These features include the high excitation energy of the compound system formed when a heavy target nucleus (say O^{16}) coalesces with a heavy target nucleus, the potentialities of heavy ions for probing the region of the diffuse nuclear surface, the relatively high cross section for Coulomb excitation of the target nucleus, and the study of nuclear systems in states of very high orbital angular momentum ($l \sim 80$ or 90 in some cases).

The detection of the products of a heavy ion induced reaction is not always easy. Intensity requirements usually necessitate the use of "thick" targets and a typical spread in energy of the heavy ions produced by slowing down within the target is 1 MeV. Barrier layer semiconductor counters are especially useful for detecting heavy ions. In so-called neutron transfer reactions such as

$$S^{32} + N^{14} \rightarrow S^{33} + N^{13}$$

the product nuclei N^{13} may be identified by catching them on a thin strip and measuring the activity of the 10 min positron-unstable N^{13}. A special property of N^{13} is that all its excited states are unstable against proton emission; hence the detection of the radioactivity of N^{13} tells us that it must have been formed in its ground state.

The large masses of heavy ion projectiles compared with the usual projectiles, protons, neutrons, and deuterons, mean that a semi-classical description of nuclear scattering is often possible. An important parameter in assessing the feasibility of a semi-classical approach is η the ratio of the distance of closest approach of the projectile (charge $Z_1 e$) and the target nucleus (charge $Z_2 e$), and the reduced wavelength of the projectile in the centre-of-mass system.

$$\eta = \frac{Z_1 Z_2 e^2}{\hbar v} \tag{49}$$

† G. Breit *et al.*, *Phys. Rev.* **87**, 74 1952.

where v is the relative velocity of the projectile and target nucleus. A semi-classical treatment is possible provided $\eta \gg 1$.†

Equation (67) of Chapter 19 is a general expression for the elastic scattering cross section in terms of the phase shifts δ_l produced on the incident partial waves. Blair†† in treating elastic scattering of heavy ions assumes that

$$\eta_l = 0 \quad \text{for} \quad l \leqq l'$$

and

$$\eta_l = e^{2i\delta_l} \quad \text{for} \quad l > l'$$

These assumptions are equivalent to the statement that the elastic scattering amplitude is the amplitude for Coulomb scattering, minus the contribution to Coulomb scattering of all outgoing partial waves up to a critical value of $l = l'$, that is, the nucleus is "black" to all incoming waves up to $l = l'$. A comparison of the experimental differential elastic scattering cross section with the Blair formula enables the unknown parameter l' to be calculated. It is interesting to find that this yields a value for the nuclear radius constant r_0 in the range 1·45 to 1·68 fermis. The critical value of l, l' is related to the interaction separation R, by equating the "centrifugal energy" to the difference in the energy of approach of two nuclei E and the Coulomb barrier B

$$\frac{l'(l'+1)\hbar^2}{2\mu R^2} = E - B \tag{50}$$

μ is the reduced mass of the system and R is related to r_0 by the usual formula

$$R = r_0(A_1^{1/3} + A_2^{1/3})$$

where A_1 and A_2 are the mass numbers of the two nuclei. The experimental results for differential elastic scattering are normally expressed by plotting the ratio of the elastic and Coulomb scattering cross sections as a function of the scattering angle θ in the centre-of-mass frame. As θ increases, the ratio decreases from around unity to low values ($< 0{\cdot}1$) at $\theta > 45°$. The Blair model formula reproduces the experimental curves very well at small angles, but at large angles ($\theta > 40°$) it predicts oscillations in the elastic scattering cross section which are not found. The onset of oscillations in the theoretical curve marks the breakdown of the sharp cut-off model.

The relatively large masses of heavy ion nuclei as projectiles often result in the formation of a nuclear system of high orbital angular momentum. This feature of heavy ion induced reactions reveals itself in a number of ways. Thus if $_{50}Sn$ is bombarded with C^{12} ions, a compound

† A rigorous justification of this leads to the condition that $\eta^{\frac{1}{2}} \gg 1$ for a semi-classical description. See L. I. Schiff, *Quantum Mechanics*, p. 120, McGraw-Hill.

†† J. S. Blair, *Phys. Rev.* **95**, 1218, 1954.

nucleus of $_{56}$Ba may be formed in a high angular momentum state. The excited barium nucleus emits several neutrons one after another (this process is analogous to evaporation from the surface of a hot liquid drop), until it reaches a neutron–metastable state, the remaining excess angular momentum being carried away by a series of photons emitted in a γ-ray cascade.†

Another example of the influence of the high angular momentum states involved in heavy ion reactions is found from a study of the angular distribution of the α-particles emitted when Ni is bombarded with 160 MeV oxygen ions. The angular distribution in the centre-of-mass system is symmetrical about $\theta = 90°$ but varies as the reciprocal of $\sin\theta$, a result easily understood if we picture the α-particles being sprayed off a rotating compound nucleus.††

The bombardment of heavy target elements (above bismuth) with heavy ions, has been used to study the fission process, as this is the most likely reaction for heavy target nuclei. This type of fission has proved to be of value in yielding information about the fission of compound systems of high angular momentum. At the present time a number of laboratories is concerned with measurements of the angular distribution of the fission fragments.

One of the most interesting phenomena found in heavy ion interactions is the discovery of the transient existence of a "quasi-molecule" consisting of two C^{12} nuclei (an example of an "inverse fission" process). Evidence for the quasi-molecule $C^{12} + C^{12}$ is the appearance of a number of resonance peaks (each a few hundred keV wide) in the elastic scattering cross section of C^{12} on C^{12} when plotted against the centre-of-mass energy. The resonance peaks begin to appear about 1 MeV above the height of the Coulomb barrier in a $C^{12}-C^{12}$ collision. In marked contrast, there is no sign of any resonant structure in the corresponding curve for $O^{16}-O^{16}$ scattering, at least up to 16 MeV. Some structure is, however, seen in the elastic scattering of O^{16} on C^{12} at about a centre-of-mass energy of 13·5 MeV, which is 4 MeV above the Coulomb barrier. These important results were first reported by Bromley, Kuehner and Almqvist at Chalk River using heavy ion beams from a tandem accelerator and gold–silicon surface barrier detectors.††† The resonance structure in the elastic scattering of C^{12} on C^{12} and O^{16} on C^{12} and the absence of any structure in the O^{16}–O^{16} scattering is shown in Fig. 15, where the differential elastic scattering cross section is plotted against the centre-of-mass energy, for a single angle of scattering, namely, 90° in the centre-of-mass system.

† *Proc. Intern. Conf. Peaceful Uses Atomic Energy*, 2nd, Geneva, 1958 **14**, 151, 1958.

†† W. J. Knox *et al.*, *Phys. Rev. Letters* **2**, 402, 1959.

††† D. A. Bromley, J. A. Kuehner and E. Almqvist, *Phys. Rev. Letters* **4**, 365, 515, 1960.

A corresponding structure is found when the total-proton, gamma, neutron, or α-particle yields are plotted against the centre of mass energy for the $C^{12} + C^{12}$ reaction. Peaks of width ~ 130 keV in the yield–energy curve appear at 5·65, 5·98, 6·32 and 6·50 MeV in the centre-of-mass system. No structure is found in the yield–energy curves of the $C^{12} + N^{14}$, $C^{12} + O^{16}$, $C^{12} + Ne^{20}$ or $O^{16} + Ne^{20}$ reactions. It has been possible to associate the resonances observed at 5·65 and 5·98 MeV in

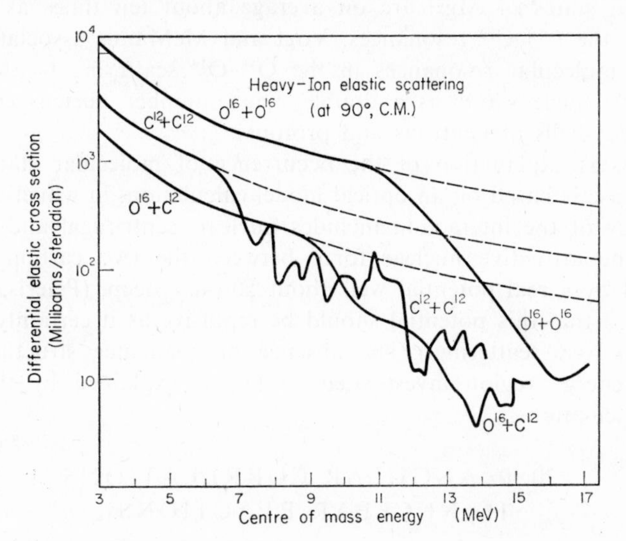

FIG. 15. Differential elastic scattering cross sections at 90° (centre-of-mass system) for $O^{16} + O^{16}$, $C^{12} + C^{12}$, and $O^{16} + C^{12}$. (The dashed curves are the Coulomb scattering formula predictions.)

the $C^{12} + C^{12}$ reaction with quasi-molecular states of angular momentum $l = 8$ and $l = 4$ respectively.

Two different explanations of the C^{12} resonances have been put forward† (these explanations may not be fundamentally different).†† The theoretical model of the $C^{12} + C^{12}$ quasi-molecular state of Vogt and McManus is based on the assumption that the carbon nuclei are deformable and thus, when their surfaces begin to overlap there is a nuclear interaction. If a quasi-molecular state of definite angular momentum is formed in a $C^{12} - C^{12}$ collision there must be a minimum in the potential energy–separation distance curve of the two nuclei at a fairly large equilibrium radius. The "sticking factor" for the two nuclei at the energies concerned is likely to be nearly unity (see remarks by Austern, p. 269,

† E. VOGT and H. MCMANUS, *Phys. Rev. Letters*, **4**, 518, 1960; R. H. DAVIS, *Phys. Rev. Letters* **4**, 521, 1960.

†† See *Proc. Intern. Conf. Nuclear Structure, Kingston, Canada* 1960, pp. 247–271, Univ. of Toronto Press.

Kingston Conference). The two deformed carbon nuclei forming a transient quasi-molecular state are prevented from approaching too close to each other by the Coulomb and the centrifugal barriers, whilst the nuclei are prevented from moving too far apart by a force related to the change in deformation of the nuclei. The carbon–carbon quasi-molecule is rotating, and the two nuclei are also vibrating relative to one another. Although this state is an excited state of the nucleus Mg^{24} the normal compound states of Mg^{24} are on average about ten times as close together as the C^{12}–C^{12} resonances. Vogt and McManus associate the absence of molecular resonances in the O^{16}–O^{16} scattering to the rigidity of the O^{16} nucleus (O^{16} is a double magic number nucleus comprising two closed shells of neutrons and protons).

The Davis explanation of the occurrence of molecular states in the C^{12}–C^{12} case is based on an optical model calculation, in which the potential energy of the interaction includes nuclear, centrifugal and Coulomb terms. The attractive nuclear force between the two carbon nuclei is described by a real potential well about 50 MeV deep. (Peierls, however, has argued that this potential should be repulsive as it certainly is in the analogous α–α scattering.) The absence of resonance structure in the O^{16}–O^{16} energy region investigated so far, is explained by the optical model calculations.

20.10. ANGULAR CORRELATIONS IN NUCLEAR REACTIONS†

In this section we give an elementary account of the theory of angular correlations in nuclear reactions. This subject is important because it proves to be a powerful method of extracting information concerning the spins and parities of excited states of nuclei. These experimental results can then be checked against the theoretical predictions of some nuclear model.

Consider a typical experimental procedure in which a stationary (thin) target is exposed to a homogeneous beam of particles travelling parallel to the z-axis. The experiment consists of measuring the angular distribution $W(\theta_1, \varphi_1)$ of the intensity of the outgoing radiation measured with respect to the z-axis, using a suitable detector. θ_1 is the angle the radius vector $\boldsymbol{r}$ from the target to the detector makes with the z-axis, and φ_1 is the angle the plane defined by $\boldsymbol{r}$ and the z-axis makes with some fixed reference plane containing the z-axis. The quantity $W(\theta_1, \varphi_1)$ is, of course, proportional to the differential cross section of the reaction being studied. If the residual nucleus is left in an excited state it will emit a second radiation and the complete process—nuclear reaction followed subse-

† L. C. BIEDENHARN, Part V. c, of *Nuclear Spectroscopy*, Part B, p. 732, Ed. by F. AJZENBERG-SELOVE, Academic Press.

quently by nuclear decay—is characterized by an angular correlation factor

$$W(\theta_1, \varphi_1, \theta_2, \varphi_2) \tag{51}$$

This factor is proportional to the probability that the particular radiation from the reaction is detected at angles θ_1, φ_1 in coincidence with the decay radiation of the excited residual nucleus at angles θ_2, φ_2 (this assumes that the time delay between the two radiations is less than the resolving time of the coincidence unit). The angular distribution given by eqn. (51) is typical of the angular momenta involved in the reaction and we have every reason to suppose that the total angular momentum and parity are conserved in nuclear reactions. Thus, in principle, it is possible to design such experiments to give spins and parities without making any assumptions about the detailed nature of the reaction.

The eigenfunctions of the angular momentum of a system may be written φ_{jm}. These are simultaneous eigenfunctions of the operators $|\mathbf{j}|^2$ and j_z, where $\mathbf{j}$ is the total angular momentum and j_z is its projection on the z-axis. If the system is definitely in the state φ_{jm}, the total angular momentum has a magnitude $\sqrt{j(j+1)}\,\hbar$ and its z-component is $m\,\hbar$. One of the important properties of eigenfunctions allows us to express any arbitrary angular momentum state as a wave function which is an expansion in terms of the angular momentum eigenfunctions.

The energy eigenfunctions of a system are usually represented as continuous functions in "real" space (x, y, z-space). In many ways, however, it is more fundamental to regard them as discontinuous "functions" in energy–space; the eigenfunctions for a closed system have unit value at the points E_n in energy–space, where E_n are the eigenvalues. The physical interpretation of a *continuous* wave function is that the probability of observing the system in an element of "configuration–space" is equal to the square of its absolute value times the volume element. Then integrating over the whole configuration space must give unity. It is desirable that the same interpretation is possible in the space of discontinuous variables. Consider a system for which $j = \frac{1}{2}$, $m = \pm\frac{1}{2}$. The most general angular momentum wave function is

$$\xi = a\,\varphi_{\frac{1}{2},\frac{1}{2}} + b\,\varphi_{\frac{1}{2},-\frac{1}{2}} \tag{52}$$

This function is zero everywhere in angular momentum space except at the point $j = \frac{1}{2}$, $m = +\frac{1}{2}$, where it has the value a, and the point $j = \frac{1}{2}$, $m = -\frac{1}{2}$, where it is equal to b. The integral over angular momentum space now appears as a summation and the process is easily visualized if ξ is regarded first as a continuous function of m having two peaks centred at $m = +\frac{1}{2}$, $-\frac{1}{2}$ but overlapping slightly. Then, as the overlap tends to zero, the sum becomes the integral

$$\int\limits_{m\text{-space}} |\xi|^2\,dm = \int \{|a|^2\,|\varphi_{\frac{1}{2},\frac{1}{2}}|^2 + |b|^2\,|\varphi_{\frac{1}{2},-\frac{1}{2}}|^2 + (a^*\,b + b^*\,a)\,\varphi_{\frac{1}{2},\frac{1}{2}}\cdot\varphi_{\frac{1}{2}:-\frac{1}{2}}\}\,dm \tag{53}$$

The probability that $m = +\frac{1}{2}$ is $|a|^2$, and similarly for $m = -\frac{1}{2}$ the probability is $|b|^2$. If two independent beams of spin $\frac{1}{2}$ particles are combined, then the wave function can be written

$$\xi = a_1 \varphi'_{\frac{1}{2}, \frac{1}{2}} + a_2 \varphi''_{\frac{1}{2}, \frac{1}{2}} \tag{54}$$

Because of the independence of the two beams, the functions $\varphi'_{\frac{1}{2}, \frac{1}{2}}$ and $\varphi''_{\frac{1}{2}, \frac{1}{2}}$ belong to different sub-spaces. However, it is convenient sometimes to regard the states of the two particles as being in the same sub-space, and this can be done if we uppose that the phase relationship between the two is completely random. The average value of a random phase difference is zero, so that the probability integral is $|a_1|^2 + |a_2|^2$. Equation (54) is an example of a "mixed" or "impure" state in contrast to eqn. (52) which is a "pure" state for which the phase relationship is perfectly definite.

Two particles each possessing angular momentum can be treated as a system with a total angular momentum equal to the vector sum of its components. Let the wave functions of the two particles considered separately be

$$\varphi'_{j_1 m_1} \quad \text{and} \quad \varphi''_{j_2 m_2}$$

eigenfunctions of different sub-spaces, each with a definite phase in its own space. The total wave function is written as a product, in keeping with the interpretation of a wave function as a probability function, because the probability of two independent events occurring together is the product of the separate probabilities. It is now convenient to transform our description of this compound state to one in which the variables are the total angular momentum, $\boldsymbol{J}$, and its z-component M. We are changing our dynamical variables and hence our configuration space in the following way

$$(j_1, m_1; j_2, m_2) \to (j_1, j_2; J, M)$$

where $\quad \boldsymbol{J} = \boldsymbol{j}_1 + \boldsymbol{j}_2 \quad \text{and} \quad M = m_1 + m_2.$ (55)

We retain the $\boldsymbol{j}_1$, $\boldsymbol{j}_2$, because we need the same number of independent variables in both systems. The eigenfunctions of this compound system are written as

$$\varphi_{JM}$$

but we must remember that they exist in a rather special space and should be written as

$$\varphi_{JM}(j_1, j_2)$$

The φ_{JM} form a complete set in the total angular momentum space just as the $\varphi'_{j_1 m_1}$ formed a complete set in the space of the angular momentum of the first particle. It follows that the product wave function can be expanded in terms of the φ_{JM}, subject to the conservation of angular momentum. Thus

$$\varphi'_{j_1 m_1} \varphi''_{j_2 m_2} = \sum_{JM} a(j_1, m_1, j_2, m_2; J, M) \varphi_{JM} \tag{56}$$

The restrictions imply that the $(J\,M\,j_1\,j_2)$ are zero unless $M = m_1 + m_2$ and the vectors $\boldsymbol{J}$, $\boldsymbol{j}_1$, $\boldsymbol{j}_2$ form a closed triangle; that is,

$$|j_1 - j_2| \leqq J \leqq j_1 + j_2 \tag{57}$$

The transformation coefficients in eqn. (56) are called vector-coupling or *Clebsch–Gordon* coefficients and are often written in the following way

$$\varphi'_{j_1 m_1}\,\varphi''_{j_2 m_2} = \sum_{JM} (j_1\,j_2\,J\,M\,|\,j_1\,m_1\,j_2\,m_2|\,\varphi_{JM}) \tag{58}$$

showing that they are used when transforming from the $(j_1\,m_1\,j_2\,m_2)$ space to the $(j_1\,j_2\,J\,M)$ space) They have been calculated for most of the cases that occur in practice†. The results are tabulated in a convenient form. The vector-coupling coefficients are real numbers.

If three angular moments are to be combined then the third component with wave functions $\varphi'''_{j_3 m_3}$ can be coupled to the φ_{JM} using eqn. (58).

In a nuclear reaction in which the incoming particle has spin $\boldsymbol{s}$ and the target nucleus spin $\boldsymbol{I}$, the total angular momentum $\boldsymbol{J}$ of the system is the vector sum of $\boldsymbol{l}$, $\boldsymbol{s}$ and $\boldsymbol{I}$, where $\boldsymbol{l}$ is the orbital angular momentum. The amplitudes of the states described by φ_{JM} will be functions of vector-coupling coefficients and the amplitudes with which the component states of s, I and l were introduced. In the absence of a nuclear interaction the method of analysis described above is just an academic exercise and the initial states could be re-obtained by uncoupling the compound states φ_{JM} to form the original wave functions of s, l and I. The incoming plane wave would pass on undisturbed leaving the target nucleus as it was. But if a nuclear reaction occurs strongly when the total angular momentum is J_1, the component of φ_{J1} in the original beam will be reduced. Because of this decrease in φ_{J1} the plane wave character of the initial beam will not be regained, and each of the amplitudes $(1 - \eta_l)$ of eqn. (7) will not be zero, implying that elastic scattering has also taken place.

Let us now consider a simple example to show how the conservation laws and coupling of angular momenta can be applied. The tandem generator at Chalk River is frequently used to accelerate heavy ions to energies up to 30 MeV. The two ions most in use are those containing the nuclei C^{12} and O^{16} (both spinless nuclei in their ground states). One of the reactions in which the angular distributions of the product α-particles have been measured is the $C^{12}(C^{12}, \alpha)\,Ne^{20}$ reaction. The Ne^{20} nucleus will be left in one of its characteristic energy states, each of which has a definite spin and parity. Corresponding to each of these states is a group of monoenergetic α-particles, each group possessing a definite

† E. U. Condon and H. G. Shortley, *Theory of Atomic Spectra*, Cambridge University Press, 1935. Chalk River Publication, Atomic Energy of Canada Ltd., A.E.C.L.-97.

angular distribution. Both target and projectile have zero spin and even (intrinsic) parity, as has the emitted α-particle.

In forming the total angular momentum we need only consider l_1, the relative orbital angular momentum of the two C^{12} nuclei, and if we take the beam direction as the z-axis the angular momentum eigenfunctions are $\varphi_{l_{10}}$. The compound states then are simply the $\varphi_{l,0}$, and we consider the one for which $l = l_1$. This state is then decomposed to some extent into a product state of the residual nucleus described by φ_{jm} and a particular relative orbital angular momentum state of the residual nucleus α-particle system $\varphi_{l_2,-m}$. Now just as the energy eigenfunctions can be represented in $x\,y\,z$-space, so can the orbital angular momentum eigenfunctions be represented in (θ, φ) space. These representatives are the spherical harmonics $Y_{lm}(\theta, \varphi)$, where θ and φ are the spherical polar angles of the line joining the α-particle to the residual nucleus, and the direction of the incident beam is the $\theta = 0$ direction. The parity of the spherical harmonics is that of l. The overall parity, which must be conserved, is that of l_1, so that the parity of the residual nucleus must be that of $(l_1 - l_2)$.

The outgoing α-particle wave contains magnetic quantum numbers different from zero, but if the detector is very small and is placed at $\theta = 0°$ or $180°$ the observed states are restricted to the φ_{l_20}, $(m = 0)$. This fact is easily understood because the α-particle is travelling along the z-axis.

The inverse of eqn. (58) applied to this situation is

$$\varphi_{l_10} = \sum_{l_2 j} (l_2\,0\,j\,0\,|\,l_2\,j\,l_1\,0|\;\varphi_{l_20}\,\varphi_{j0} \tag{59}$$

and it is a property of these particular vector-coupling coefficients that they vanish unless $(l_1 + l_2 + j)$ is even. The following scheme shows the various combinations for which the selection rule for the $(l_2 0 j 0\,|\,l_{10})$ allows α-particles to be observed at 0°.

Even j	l_1 even	l_2 even	$(l_1 - l_2)$ even
	l_1 odd	l_2 odd	$(l_1 - l_2)$ even
Odd j	l_1 even	l_2 odd	$(l_1 - l_2)$ odd
	l_1 odd	l_2 even	$(l_1 - l_2)$ odd

The additional rule that the parity of the residual nucleus is that of $(l_1 - l_2)$ means that only states of so-called "normal" parity are observed at 0° or 180°. Thus if the state of the residual nucleus (observed by means of the corresponding α-particles at 0° or 180°) has spin j where j is even, its parity is also even. If j is odd then the parity is also odd. No firm conclusions can be made in the absence of measurable intensity at 0° or 180° because the absence may be due to destructive interference among the different l-waves. Notice that conclusions may be drawn from this type of nuclear reaction experiment, without making any assumptions about the detailed mechanism of the reaction; only conservation of angular momentum and parity have been assumed.

We now turn our attention to a simple angular correlation situation in which the incoming and outgoing particles of a nuclear reaction have zero spin. Moreover, the reaction is one which takes place through the formation and decay of a single level of the compound nucleus. The angular momenta concerned in the reaction are represented in Fig. 16.

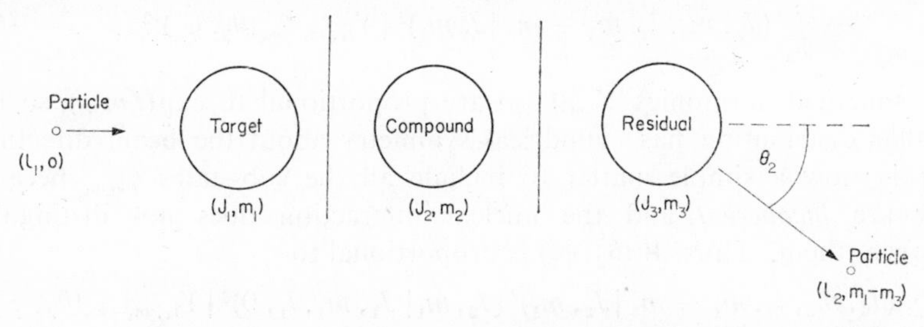

FIG. 16. Angular momenta and components in a nuclear reaction in which the incoming and outgoing light particles have zero spin.

An incident particle approaches the target nucleus with an orbital angular momentum l_1. The target nucleus has a total angular momentum J_1 and a z-component m_1 described by a wave function $\varphi_{J_1 m_1}$. There are $(2J_1 + 1)$ magnetic sub-states of the target nucleus ground state and they have random relative phases because the target has not been aligned in any way. As usual we take the direction of travel of the incident particle as the z-axis, so only $\varphi_{l_1 0}$ is present.

The two states representing the incident particle and the target nucleus combine to form a single level of the compound nucleus of spin J_2. The only possible sub-state of the compound nucleus is $\varphi_{J_2 m_1}$ because angular momentum and its z-component are conserved. The compound nucleus breaks up, emitting a spinless particle in the direction (θ_2, φ_2), leaving a single level of the residual nucleus in the state $\varphi_{J_3 m_3}$. The relative orbital angular momentum state of the emitted spinless particle is $\varphi_{l_2, m_1 - m_3}$. A restriction on m_3 is $-J_3 \leqq m_3 \leqq J_3$, but the $(2J_3 + 1)$ sub-states are *coherent* because they were all formed from the decay of a single level of the compound nucleus. For the same reason the sub-states of l_2 are coherent. Using eqn. (59) we can say that the wave function of the state of this final system is proportional to

$$\sum_{m_3 = -J_3}^{m_3 = +J_3} (J_3, m_3, l_2, m_1 - m_3 \,|\, J_2\, m_1|)\, \varphi_{J_3 m_3}\, \varphi_{l_2, m_1 - m_3} \tag{60}$$

Writing the $\varphi_{l_2, m_1 - m_3}$ as spherical harmonics, and expressing the angular distribution of the outgoing particles as the absolute square of the wave function ψ, we obtain $W(\theta_2, \varphi_2)$ proportional to

$$\sum_{m_3} \sum_{m_3'} (J_3, m_3, l_2, m_1 - m_3 \,|\, J_2\, m_1)\,(J_3, m_3', l_2, m_1 - m_3' |\, J_2\, m_1) \times \varphi_{J_3 m_3}\, \varphi^*_{J_3 m_3'}\, Y_{l_2, m_1 - m_3}(\theta_2, \varphi_2)\, Y^*_{l_2, m_1 - m_3'}(\theta_2, \varphi_2) \qquad (61)$$

The terms for which $m_3 \neq m_3'$ vanish, because as we showed above $\sum_{m_3} \varphi_{J_3 m_3} \varphi^*_{J_3 m_3'} = \delta_{m_3 m_3'}$, and the angular distribution simplifies to

$$\sum_{m_3} (J_3, m_3, l_2, m_1 - m_3 \,|\, J_2\, m_1)^2 \,|\, Y_{l_2, m_1 - m_3}(\theta_2, \varphi_2)|^2 \qquad (62)$$

The spherical harmonics $Y_{lm}(\theta, \varphi)$ are proportional to $\exp(i\, m\, \varphi)$, so the angular distribution has cylindrical symmetry about the beam direction.

It is now a simple matter to include all the sub-states $\varphi_{J_1 m_1}$ because they are *incoherent* and the nuclear interaction does not distinguish between them. Thus $W(\theta_2, \varphi_2)$ is proportional to

$$\sum_{m_1} \sum_{m_3} (J_3, m_3, l_2, m_1 - m_3 \,|\, J_2, m_1)^2\, (J_2, m_1 |\, J_1, m_1, l_1, 0)^2 \,|\, Y_{l_2, m_1 - m_3}(\theta_2, \varphi_2)|^2 \qquad (63)$$

Now suppose that the residual nucleus emits a further spinless radiation in the direction (θ_3, φ_3), which is detected in coincidence with the first particle emitted in the direction (θ_2, φ_2). Equation (61) shows that if the first particle was emitted in the state $\varphi_{l_2, m_1 - m_3}$ the residual nucleus was formed in the state φ_{J_3, m_3}. Now if this particle is detected at a particular angle (θ_2, φ_2), then, because of the angular dependence of the spherical harmonics some pairs of quantum numbers $(l_2, {}_{m_1 - m_3})$ will be more likely than others. Hence the residual nucleus has a certain degree of alignment, and when it breaks up it is not reasonable to anticipate cylindrical symmetry for the angular distribution if we are observing in coincidence with the first particle.

Returning to eqn. (60) we split $\varphi_{J_3 m_3}$ into two components representing a final nucleus in the state $\varphi_{J_4 m_4}$ and a second outgoing particle in the state $\varphi_{l_3, m_3 - m_4}$. Thus ψ is proportional to

$$\sum_{m_3} \sum_{m_4} (J_3, m_3, l_2, m_1 - m_3 \,|\, J_2, m_1)\,(J_4, m_4, l_3, m_3 - m_4 |\, J_3, m_3) \times \varphi_{J_4, m_4}\, \varphi_{l_3, m_3 - m_4}\, \varphi_{l_2, m_1 - m_3} \qquad (64)$$

If we take $|\psi|^2$, use the orthogonal properties of the φ_{J_4, m_4} and write the orbital angular momentum functions as spherical harmonics, the angular correlation function $W(\theta_2, \varphi_2; \theta_3, \varphi_3)$ is found to be proportional to

$$\sum_{m_4} \Big| \sum_{m_3} (J_3, m_3, l_2, m_1 - m_3 |\, J_2\, m_1)\,(J_4, m_4, l_3, m_3 - m_4 \,|\, J_3\, m_3) \times Y_{l_3, m_3 - m_4}(\theta_3, \varphi_3)\, Y_{m_1 - m_3}(\theta_2, \varphi_2) \Big|^2 \qquad (65)$$

The sum over the quantum numbers m_1 can be done incoherently as before. As we had foreseen there is no longer cylindrical symmetry. Also in eqn. (63) the angular distribution for the first particle behaved as though the sub-states φ_{J_3, m_3} were incoherent (the "cross-terms" disappeared from the final result). But this was because we made no observation on the states φ_{J_3, m_3}. In eqn. (65) we effectively observe these states through the way in which they decay, and we can no longer regard them as incoherent.

The full expression should contain all possible values of l_1, l_2 and l_3, and then we need to include terms expressing the matrix elements of the interactions. In addition, attention must be paid to questions of incoherence. It will be appreciated that when the effects of particles with spin are included, the final expressions are very complicated. New mathematical techniques† have been developed to deal with these complications and to take care of incoherence effects.

20.11. NUCLEAR SHELL MODEL

The nuclear shell model is based on the overwhelming experimental evidence that nuclei containing 2, 8, 20, 28, 50, 82, or 126 neutrons or protons have above average stability (the effect is not very pronounced for the number 28). These even numbers are commonly known as "magic numbers" for their existence was, for a long time, not well understood. Nuclei such as $O^{16}(Z = 8, N = 8)$ and $Pb^{208}(Z = 82, N = 126)$ are exceptionally stable and are called "doubly magic" nuclei as both Z and N are magic numbers.

It is tempting to compare the stability of the magic nuclei with the well known chemical stability of the inert gas atoms, He, Ne, Ar, ... The great stability of atoms containing 2, 10, 18 electrons is associated with the closure of an electron shell. The explanation of the electron magic numbers is based on the fact that each electron is characterized by a set of four quantum numbers, and because of the dominant influence of the Coulomb field of the nucleus on the motion of each electron, the binding energy of an electron is primarily determined by its principal quantum number n. The different electron shells correspond to successive values of n; K shell, $n = 1$; L shell, $n = 2$, ...

By analogy, we associate the nucleon magic numbers with proton or neutron shell closure. Notice that as the neutron and proton are distinguishable particles there will be two sets of shells, one for protons and one for neutrons. The existence of closed nucleon shells is, however, much more difficult to explain. First, there is no obvious dominant

† See for example the article by S. DEVONS and L. J. B. GOLDFARB, Angular Correlations in *Handbuch der Physik*, Vol. 42, Springer-Verlag, Berlin 1957.

central force analogous to the Coulomb attraction of the nucleus for the electrons. Second, the nuclear density is very large compared to the electron cloud density and therefore it is difficult to understand how a nucleon can have a fairly well defined nuclear orbit. One would expect the mean free path of a nucleon between successive nucleon–nucleon collisions inside the nucleus to be small in comparison with the nuclear diameter. An important suggestion to overcome this fundamental difficulty is due to Weisskopf. He argued that, in spite of the high density and strong nucleon interaction, a nucleon in a close encounter may not be scattered as there is no empty quantum state to receive the scattered particle. This argument is familiar in the electron theory of metals, where the exclusion principle also plays a dominant role. Thus it is possible to picture each nucleon moving inside the nucleus under the influence of some static average field of force. In other words, each nucleon occupies one of the energy levels of a suitable potential well. The positions and spacings of the energy levels will be determined by the depth, radial extent, and shape of the potential energy well.

The shell model potential energy well probably lies somewhere between the two extremes of

(1) A rectangular well of radius R, where R is the radius of the nucleus.
(2) A harmonic oscillator well, $V(r) = \frac{1}{2} M \omega^2 r^2$, where M is the nucleon mass, and ω is 2π times the "classical" oscillation frequency. One model potential that is often used is the real part of the Woods–Saxon potential (eqn. (28) and Fig. 7).

The eigenvalues of the harmonic oscillator are

$$E_\Lambda = \left(\Lambda + \frac{3}{2}\right)\hbar\,\omega, \quad \Lambda = 0, 1, 2, 3, \ldots \tag{66}$$

For each energy value E_Λ, there is a number of degenerate eigenfunctions, labelled by the orbital angular momentum quantum numbers

for Λ even, $l = 0, 2, 4, 6, \ldots$ states of even parity
for Λ odd, $l = 1, 3, 5, 7, \ldots$ states of odd parity

The eigenstates are labelled by the quantum numbers n and l, where n is the number of times the quantum number l has appeared in the sequence. The relation between Λ, n and l is

$$\Lambda = 2n + l - 2. \tag{67}$$

The pattern of energy levels for the harmonic oscillator and the infinitely deep rectangular wells are illustrated in Fig. 17. It is assumed that the energy levels of some intermediate well (Woods–Saxon) would occur somewhere between the two extremes (Fig. 17c). Notice that the degeneracies of the oscillator states $1d$ and $2s$, $1f$ and $2p$, etc. are removed in the rectangular well.

According to the positions of the energy levels in the Woods–Saxon type of well, the first proton (or neutron) shell can accommodate a maximum of two $1s$ protons (or neutrons). The second nucleon shell can accommodate up to six protons (or neutrons) in the $1p$ state, that is $2(2l+1)$ particles of the same kind. The third shell is closed when the $1d$ levels (10)

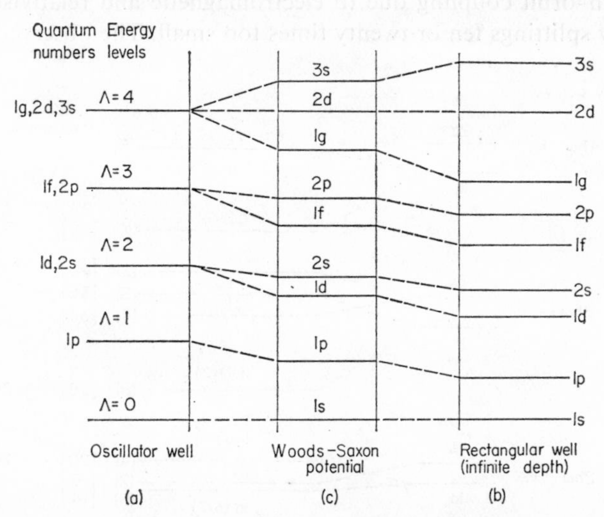

FIG. 17. Energy levels for (a) harmonic oscillator well (notice degeneracies), (b) rectangular well of infinite depth, (c) Woods–Saxon real potential well.

and the $2s$ levels (2) are fully occupied. Thus the first three magic numbers 2, 8 and 20 correspond to this level assignment. At this stage the level scheme shown in Fig. 17(c) becomes inadequate and does not predict the higher magic numbers 28, 50, 82 and 126.

In 1949, M. G. Mayer† and independently Haxel, Jensen, and Suess†† showed how the higher magic numbers can be obtained if an extra important assumption about the nucleon states is introduced. This assumption is that each nucleon experiences, in addition to the pure radial potential $V(r)$, a *strong spin–orbit interaction* of the form†††

$$f(r)\,(\boldsymbol{l}\,\boldsymbol{s}) = f(r)\,[(\boldsymbol{r}\times\boldsymbol{p})\,\boldsymbol{s}]$$

where $\boldsymbol{s}$ is the intrinsic spin of the nucleon and $\boldsymbol{r}\times\boldsymbol{p}$ is the orbital angular momentum. This spin–orbit interaction implies that each nucleon can be described by a total angular momentum quantum number.

$$j = l + \tfrac{1}{2}, \quad \text{except for} \quad l = 0 \quad \text{when} \quad j = +\tfrac{1}{2}.$$

† M. G. MAYER, *Phys. Rev.* **75**, 1969, 1949 and **78**, 16, 1950.

†† O. HAXEL, J. H. D. JENSEN, and H. E. SUESS, *Phys. Rev.* **75**, 1766, 1949.

††† The existence of this spin orbit force may be connected with the omega vector meson (see Chapter 21).

This spin–orbit force has a marked effect on the binding energy of the nucleons and it is assumed that for a given l the state $l+\frac{1}{2}$ is more tightly bound than the $l-\frac{1}{2}$ state. Moreover this spin–orbit energy splitting ΔE_l increases with l.

What justification is there for this spin–orbit level splitting? Calculations of spin–orbit coupling due to electromagnetic and relativistic effects yield energy splittings ten or twenty times too small. The observed splitting

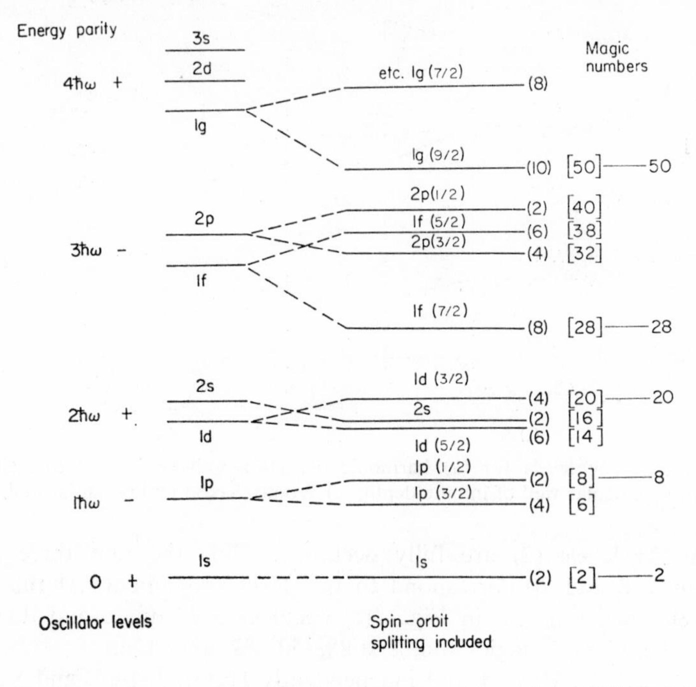

FIG. 18. Effect of spin–orbit interaction on level positions. A level labelled $1f(^7/_2)$ means $n=1, l=3, j=3+\frac{1}{2}={}^7/_2$. Each level can contain a maximum of $2(2j+1)$ protons (or neutrons). The nucleon accumulating numbers are given in square brackets.

is probably associated with the pion exchange nature of nuclear forces. There is good evidence for a strong spin–orbit interaction in, for example, the elastic scattering of protons by the spherically symmetrical nucleus He^4. The phase shifts associated with scattering in the $p_{1/2}$ and $p_{3/2}$ states of Li^5 behave quite differently; there is a resonance in the scattering near a proton energy of 2·5 MeV (lab.) where the $p_{3/2}$ phase shift goes through 90°†. Also the spin–orbit interaction is responsible for the polarization†† of the scattered protons, which is revealed by the presence of azimuthal

† D. C. DODDER and J. L. GAMMEL, *Phys. Rev.* **88**, 520, 1952.
†† M. HEUSINKVELD and G. FREIER, *Phys. Rev.* **85**, 80, 1952.

asymmetry when the scattered protons are scattered by a second nuclear target.

The effect of the spin–orbit coupling on the nucleon energy levels is depicted in Fig. 18. Thus, for example, the $1p$ level is split into two sub-levels with $j = \frac{1}{2}$ and $j = {}^3/_2$ respectively. Due to the spin–orbit force the $j = {}^3/_2$ sub-level has a lower energy (more tightly bound nucleon state). A state of given j can accommodate $2(2j + 1)$ nucleons of the same kind. These occupation numbers are written adjacent to the horizontal lines representing the energy levels in the shell model potential. The numbers in square brackets denote the total number of nucleons (of the same kind) up to and including the level in question. The shell enclosure at Z or $N = 50$ is a consequence of the large energy difference of the $1g(j = {}^9/_2)$ and $1g(j = {}^7/_2)$ levels. The large energy gap at magic number 82 (not shown in Fig. 18) is due to the large difference in energy of a proton or neutron in a $1h(j = {}^{11}/_2)$ and $1h(j = {}^9/_2)$ level.

Empirical Evidence for the Shell Model

In this section we shall discuss some of the empirical evidence in support of the shell model.

There is a marked decrease in the "last" nucleon binding energy (often called "separation" energy) when we increase Z or N from M to $M + 1$, where M is a magic number. This effect is a consequence of the $(M + 1)$th nucleon occupying a single level outside a closed shell. Compare this with the sharp drop in ionization potential between He and Li or Ne and Na. The separation energies of the "last" (least firmly bound) nucleon in the nuclei in the region of the doubly magic

TABLE 1.† LAST NUCLEON ENERGIES NEAR DOUBLY MAGIC ${}_{82}Pb^{208}_{126}$
(Energies in millimass units: lmmU = 0.931 MeV$_0$.)

Z \ N	124	125	126	127	128	
81	8.03 Tl^{205}	6.69 Tl^{206}	7.30 Tl^{207}	4.11 Tl^{208}	5.30 Tl^{209}	4.05
	7.47	8.01	9.63	7.67	9.00	
82	8.70 Pb^{206}	7.23 Pb^{207}	7.92 Pb^{208}	4.15 Pb^{209}	5.63 Pb^{210}	4.06
	3.88	3.97	4.04	4.86	4.72	
83	Bi^{207}	7.32 Bi^{208}	7.99 Bi^{209}	4.97 Bi^{210}	5.48 Bi^{211}	4.70
	5.41	5.15	5.38	5.31	6.27	
84	Po^{208}	7.06 Po^{209}	8.22 Po^{210}	4.90 Po^{211}	6.45 Po^{212}	4.63

† Reproduced from the article by ELLIOTT and LANE, *Handbuch der Physik*, Vol. XXXIX, Springer-Verlag, Berlin 1957.

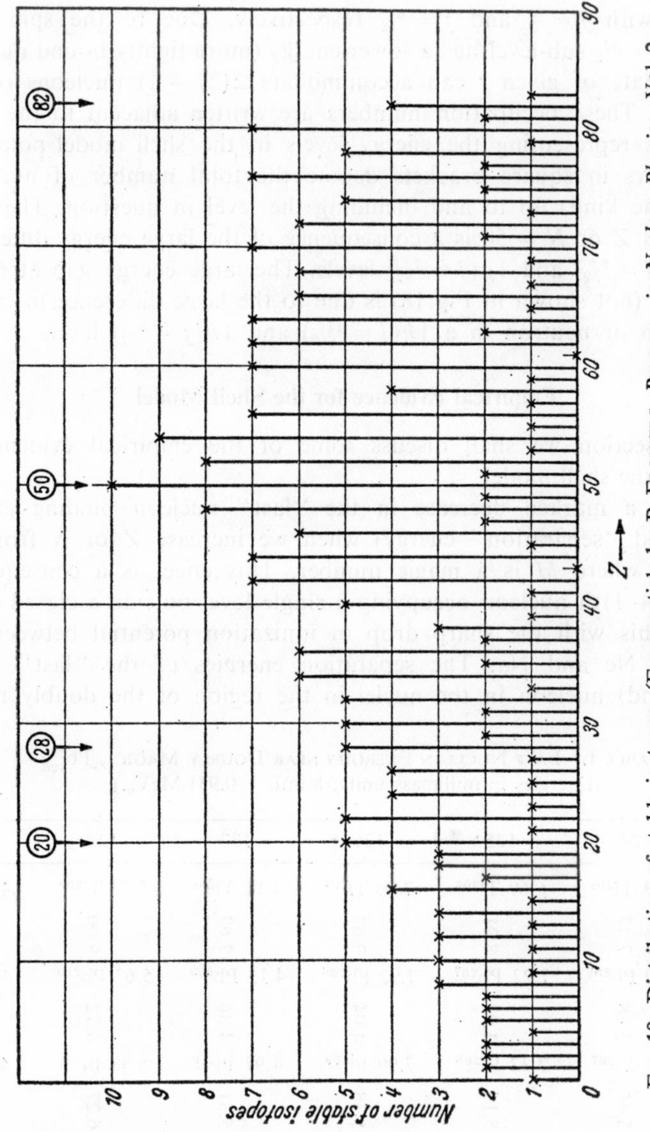

FIG. 19. Distribution of stable isotopes (From article by B. FLOWERS, *Progress in Nuclear Physics*, Vol. 2, Pergamon Press, London, 1952.)

nucleus Pb^{208} are given in Table 1. In this table the binding energies are quoted in millimass units: 1 m.m.u. = 0·931 MeV. The last neutron separation energies form horizontal rows; thus the number 4·15 between the symbols Pb^{208} and Pb^{209} refers to the fact that the separation of the 127th neutron from a Pb^{209} nucleus requires a minimum of 4·15 × 0·931 MeV. The vertical columns of numbers are the last proton separation energies.

The separation energy of the last nucleon for a nucleus with two protons or two neutrons outside a filled shell is also abnormally small but it is greater than the value for a nucleus with just one nucleon beyond a closed shell.

One of the distinctive properties of closed shell nuclei is the relatively high number of stable and long lived isotopes—a reflection of their extra stability (Fig. 19). Thus calcium ($Z = 20$) has six stable isotopes at mass numbers 40, 42, 43, 44, 46 and 48. Tin ($Z = 50$) has ten stable isotopes spread out over mass numbers 112 to 124.

The number of stable isotones (nuclei containing the same number of neutrons) for magic number nuclei is often above average. There are, for example, six isotones for $N = 50$.

The cosmic abundances of nuclei near the magic numbers are abnormally high. Abundance peaks appear near N or $Z = 56$, 90, 135 and 200. However, the top of a peak does not necessarily occur at a magic number nucleus. The peak at Fe^{56} is probably associated with the double magic nucleus Ni^{56}. The latter nucleus transforms by two successive beta transformations (electron capture) into stable Fe^{56} in a few months.

The end product of the three naturally occurring radioactive series is Pb($Z = 82$), and the neptunium series terminates at Bi^{209}($N = 126$).

The absorption cross sections for neutrons of a few MeV are abnormally small for nuclei containing 50, 82 or 126 neutrons. This is a reflection of the reluctance of such nuclei to accept an extra neutron.

The thermal neutron absorption cross sections are down by a factor of about fifty for many closed shell nuclei (Fig. 20).

The first excited states of closed shell nuclei tend to be abnormally high. This is expected as the excitation must involve the elevation of a nucleon to the next shell. The excitation energy of the first excited states of nuclei between mass numbers 140 and 190 is about 0·1 MeV; the value for Ce^{140}($N = 82$) is 1·5 MeV. The doubly magic nucleus Pb^{208} has the very high value of 2·5 MeV for the first excitation energy.

An interesting correlation is seen in the mass number distribution of isomeric transitions. Nuclear isomers are long lived excited nuclear states for which gamma decay is inhibited by the low energy and large spin change involved. Thus a plot of odd mass nuclei, with isomeric transitions of mean life greater than one second, against the odd proton or odd neutron number reveals "*Islands of Isomerism*" just below nucleon numbers 50, 82 and 126. This phenomenon is associated with the occurrence of nuclear states in the same shell with a large difference in the quantum number j. Notice, for example, the position of the $1g(j = {}^9/_2)$ level just above the $2p(j = \frac{1}{2})$ level (Fig.18) These two levels occur just before shell closure at N or $Z = 50$.

In extending the simple shell model to make predictions concerning nuclei with one or more nucleons outside a number of filled shells some account must be taken of the interaction between the "valence" nucleons,

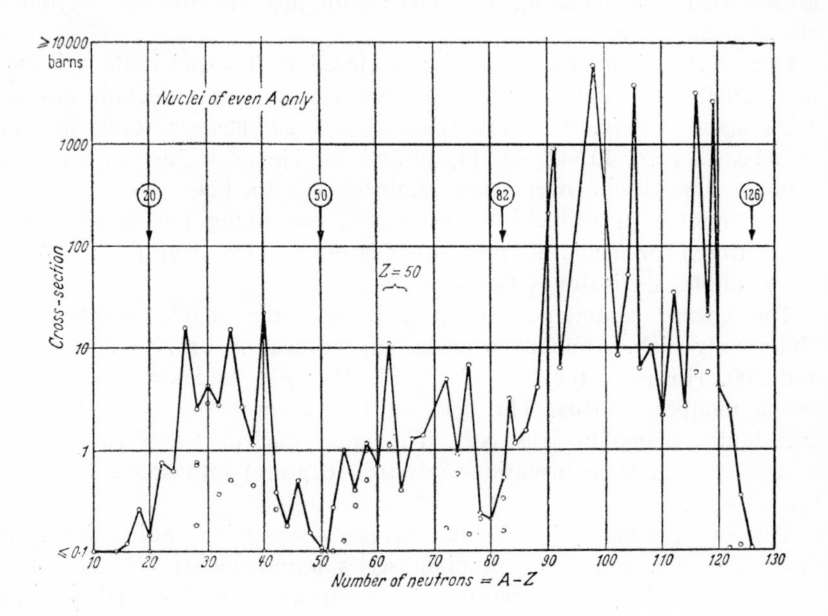

FIG. 20. Thermal neutron cross sections.

which is not included in the simple model potential. One anticipates that like nucleons in the different levels will pair off with one another so that their total angular momentum is zero (a closed shell of nucleons, like a closed electron shell, has zero resultant angular momentum). With a few exceptions, the spin of odd mass nuclei corresponds to the j value of the last odd nucleon. Thus in Co^{59} the last odd nucleon is the 27th proton, and a glance at the level scheme shown in Fig. 18 predicts that this proton occupies a $1f(j = {}^7/_2)$ level. The observed nuclear spin of Co^{59} is ${}^7/_2$.

It sometimes happens that when the shell model predicts a high nuclear spin such as ${}^{11}/_2$ the observed spin is smaller. This failure of the elementary shell model can be understood if the pairing forces between like nucleons become more effective in states of high angular momentum. In these circumstances the vacant energy levels may not fill up in order of decreasing binding energy, an unpaired nucleon being left in a level below the high spin level. An example illustrating this effect is the nucleus $_{50}Sn^{117}_{67}$: there are 17 neutrons in the outer neutron shell, with the unpaired neutron in a $3s_{1/2}$ level; the $1h_{11/2}$ level just above the $3s$ level contains two paired off neutrons, so the observed spin is $\frac{1}{2}$ and not $^{11}/_{2}$, which it would be if the order of level filling was always determined by the position of the levels.

A more severe test of the elementary shell model is to compare the measured magnetic moments of odd mass nuclei with the expected value for a single unpaired nucleon. The magnetic dipole moment μ of a single nucleon has an intrinsic spin component $\boldsymbol{\mu}_s$ and an orbital motion component $\boldsymbol{\mu}_0$

$$\boldsymbol{\mu} = \boldsymbol{\mu}_0 + \boldsymbol{\mu}_s \tag{68}$$

where

$$\boldsymbol{\mu}_0 = g_l\, \boldsymbol{l}$$

$$\boldsymbol{\mu}_s = g_s\, \boldsymbol{s}$$

The magnetic moments are measured in nuclear magnetons; g_l and g_s are the orbital and spin g-factors respectively. The magnetic dipole moment μ is normally defined as the maximum observable value of $\boldsymbol{\mu}$ in any direction; that is, μ is the expectation value of the z-component of $\boldsymbol{\mu}$, in the magnetic sub-state $m = j$. The expectation value of the vector $\boldsymbol{\mu}$ can be written

$$(j, m = j, |\boldsymbol{\mu}|\, j, m = j) = (j, m = j, |\boldsymbol{j}|\, j, m = j)\frac{(j, m = j, |\boldsymbol{\mu}\cdot\boldsymbol{j}|\, j, m = j)}{(j, m = j, |\boldsymbol{j}^2|\, j, m = j)} \tag{69}$$

Taking the z-component of this equation in the case $m = j$

$$\mu = \frac{j}{(j+1)}[g_l\, \boldsymbol{l}\cdot\boldsymbol{j} + g_s\, \boldsymbol{s}\cdot\boldsymbol{j}] \tag{70}$$

Using the relation $\boldsymbol{j} = \boldsymbol{l} + \boldsymbol{s}$, we obtain

$$2\,\boldsymbol{l}\cdot\boldsymbol{j} = \boldsymbol{j}^2 + \boldsymbol{l}^2 - \boldsymbol{s}^2 \quad \text{and} \quad 2\boldsymbol{s}\cdot\boldsymbol{j} = \boldsymbol{j}^2 - \boldsymbol{l}^2 + \boldsymbol{s}^2 \tag{71}$$

With the aid of the identities

$$\boldsymbol{j}^2 = j(j+1), \quad \boldsymbol{l}^2 = l(l+1), \quad \boldsymbol{s}^2 = s(s+1) = \tfrac{1}{2}\cdot\tfrac{3}{2} = \tfrac{3}{4}$$

eqns. (70) and (71) combine to give

$$\mu = (j - \tfrac{1}{2})\, g_l + \tfrac{1}{2} g_s, \quad \text{for} \quad j = l + \tfrac{1}{2} \tag{72a}$$

$$\mu = \frac{j}{j+1}[(j + \tfrac{3}{2})\, g_l - \tfrac{1}{2} g_s], \quad \text{for} \quad j = l - \tfrac{1}{2} \tag{72b}$$

For a proton $g_l = 1$ and $g_s = 5{\cdot}58$.
For a neutron $g_l = 0$ and $g_s = -3{\cdot}82$.

The g_s-values are based on the observed magnetic moments of the free proton and free neutron, 2·79 and $-$1·91 nuclear magnetons,† though this may not be correct for nucleons within the nucleus.

To compare the theoretical values given by 72(a) and (b) it is usual to plot the experimental μ values against the j value of the odd nucleon. If there exists perfect agreement between this theory and experiment

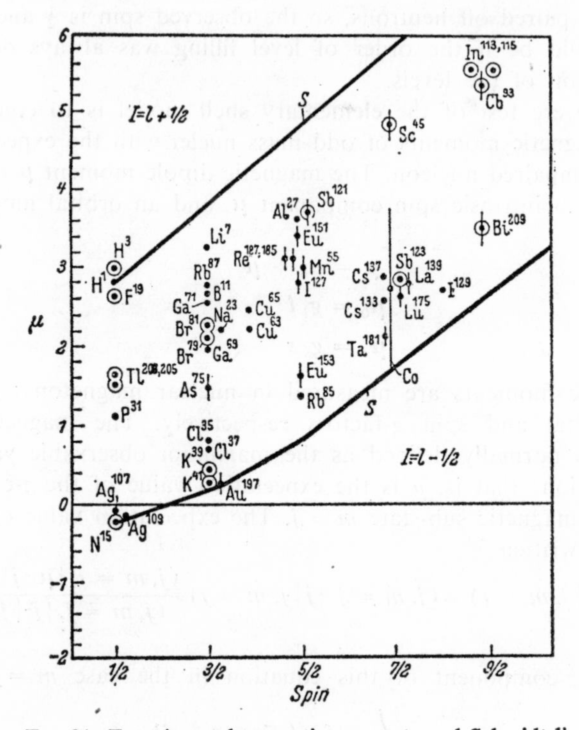

FIG. 21. Experimental magnetic moments and Schmidt lines.

the points should lie on one of two lines (*the Schmidt lines*). Although the experimental points do not fall on the Schmidt lines they are nearly all confined to the space between the lines (Fig. 21): (the point representing the triton, H^3($j = \frac{1}{2}, \mu = 2{\cdot}979$ nuclear magnetons) lies above the $j = l + \frac{1}{2}$ Schmidt line). The observed deviations are not unexpected as the odd unpaired nucleon in an odd-A nucleus would tend magnetically to polarise the nuclear core. It is usually possible, from the known nuclear spin j and the position of the representative point in the μ–j plot, to allocate the orbital angular momentum and therefore the parity of

† It has sometimes been suggested that smaller values should be employed for the odd proton or neutron in an odd mass nucleus. See, for example, p. 277 of the article by ELLIOTT and LANE.

the ground state of the nucleus. The exceptions occur when the points lie about half way between the Schmidt lines.

It is interesting to compare the predictions of the shell model with observed values of electric quadrupole moments. Closed shell nuclei, as expected, have very small moments. Nuclei with one loose nucleon outside a filled sub-shell have negative quadrupole moments.† In contrast, nuclei which require one nucleon to fill a sub-shell (nuclei with one hole) have positive moments. A good example of this occurs with the sulphur isotopes

$$ {}_{16}S^{33}_{17} \qquad Q = -0{\cdot}064 \text{ barn} $$

$$ {}_{16}S^{35}_{19} \qquad Q = +0{\cdot}045 \text{ barn} $$

For the nucleus S^{33} the $1d(j = {}^3/_2)$ sub-shell is partly occupied by the odd neutron, and Q is negative. For S^{35}, however, there are three neutrons in the $1d(j = {}^3/_2)$ sub-shell; thus the shell has one neutron hole as $2j + 1 = 4$ neutrons are needed to fill the sub-shell. At first sight it is surprising that electric quadrupole moments are associated with a single neutron. However, the interaction of the single loose neutron (or hole) with the core of the nucleus, which has an electric charge $Z e$, is responsible for the observed quadrupole moment.

The simple shell model fails completely to account for the large electric quadrupole moments found in nuclei with many loose nucleons outside a closed shell (e.g. many of the rare earth nuclei). The observed Q values are thirty or more times greater than the single-particle shell model predictions. This serious discrepancy is discussed in the section on the "Collective Model".

In the early period (1935–1945), the shell model was notorious for its inability to predict the right order of magnitude for nuclear binding energies. The shell model is essentially an "Independent Particle Model" (I.P.M.) so that the wave function of the nucleus is a product of *single* particle wave functions. The potential energy function, which determines these single particle wave functions, can be written

$$ V = V(r) - f(r)\,(\boldsymbol{l} \cdot \boldsymbol{s}) \tag{73} $$

where the second term is the spin–orbit energy, which depends on the coupling of the spin vector $\boldsymbol{s}$ of a nucleon with the orbital angular momentum vector $\boldsymbol{l}$. The total energy of the nucleus is

$$ E = \sum_{i=1}^{A} T_i + \tfrac{1}{2} \sum_{i,k}^{A} V_{ik}(\boldsymbol{r}_i - \boldsymbol{r}_k) \tag{74} $$

Here, three or more body forces have been neglected. The factor of one half in the second term of eqn. (74) is necessary because the inter-

† Electric quadrupole moments are discussed in Chapter 8, Sections 5.

action potential between each pair of nucleons i and k is counted twice in the summation. If the potential well depth V_0 is assumed to be the same for all the nucleons and the separation energy of the last nucleon is about 8 MeV, the value of V_0 is expected to be about 33 MeV†. The value of T_i for the last nucleon is about 25 MeV, hence the contribution to E of this nucleon is $25 + \frac{1}{2}(-33) = 8 \cdot 5$ MeV. The more tightly bound nucleons will contribute negative values to E; nevertheless, the total energy E may be positive, a nonsensical result. A way out of this dilemna is found if it is assumed that the well depth V_0 for a nucleon depends on its momentum p_i. It is necessary for V_0 to be as large as 70 MeV for the most tightly bound nucleon in a medium-sized nucleus. Another way of interpreting this effect is to introduce the concept of the effective mass m^* of a nucleon *in nuclear matter*.†† If m^* is chosen so that the observed nuclear binding energy and separation energy for the last nucleon agrees with the theory, values of m^* are of the order of one half the free nucleon mass m.

One of the most impressive pieces of evidence in support of the shell model occurs in a most unexpected region, namely, in high energy $(p, 2p)$ nuclear reactions.††† H. Tyren and co-workers have studied the energies, cross sections, and angular distributions of the emerging protons from light nuclei when bombarded with protons of 185 and 440 MeV energy. The $(p, 2p)$ reactions studied can be understood if the incoming proton makes a direct collision with an outer shell proton, knocking the latter out of the target nucleus, without any appreciable interaction with the rest of the nucleus. Consider the reaction in which the residual nucleus is at rest. The incident and emerging protons are coplanar, and the momenta $\boldsymbol{p}_1$ and $\boldsymbol{p}_2$ are approximately orthogonal, with $\boldsymbol{p}_1$ and $\boldsymbol{p}_2$

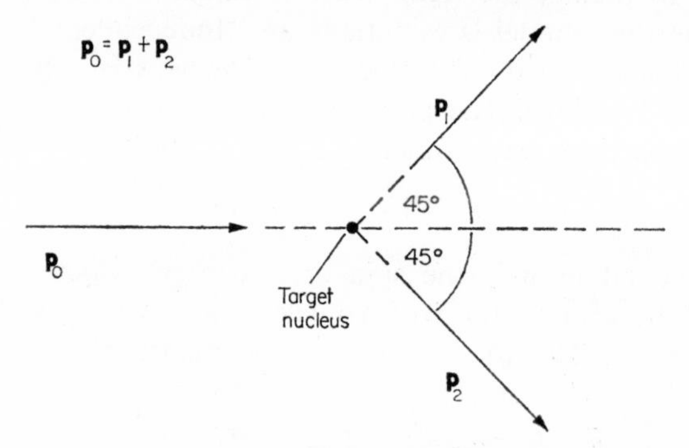

FIG. 22. Momenta of incoming and outgoing protons in $(p, 2p)$ direct interaction when residual nucleus is at rest.

† V. F. WEISSKOPF, *Revs. Mod. Phys.* **29**, 175, 1957.
†† K. A. BRUECKNER, R. J. EDEN, and N. C. FRANCIS, *Phys. Rev.* **98**, 1445, 1955.
††† P. 429–437 of *Proc. Intern. Conf. Nuclear Structure*, Kingston, Canada 1960.

making equal angles (45°) with the incident proton momentum p_0 (Fig. 22). The emerging protons are selected so that $p_1 + p_2 = p_0$. The differential cross section of the $Na^{23}(p, 2p)Ne^{22}$ reaction at an incident proton energy of 180 MeV is shown, in Fig. 23, plotted against the binding energy of the ejected proton. The peak at zero binding energy corresponds to *free* proton scattering. The peak in the cross section curve near 15 MeV binding energy is associated with the ejection of protons from the $2s$ and $1d(j = {}^5/_2)$ levels of Na^{23}. The small peak

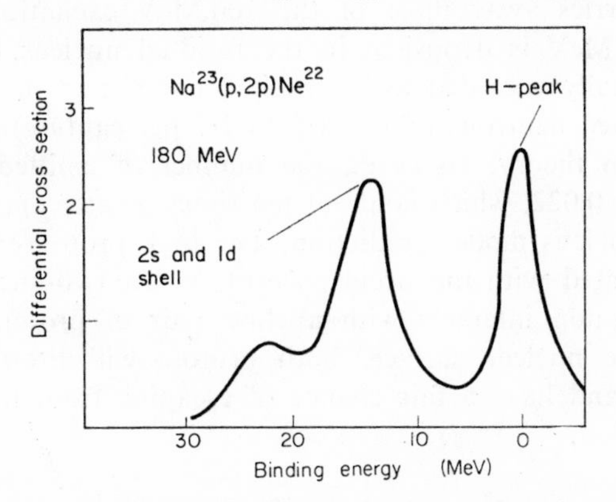

FIG. 23. Differential cross section for Na^{23} $(p, 2p)$ Ne^{22} reaction for incident protons of 180 MeV (lab.) under conditions depicted in Fig. 22. Abscissa is binding energy of ejected proton in Na^{23} nucleus.

near a binding energy of 22 MeV is probably associated with the ejection of protons from the deeper lying shells $1s$ and $1p$. The cross section is small, however, because protons knocked out of an inner shell are more likely to be absorbed within the nucleus than the ones from the outer shells. This point is illustrated by the $C^{12}(p, 2p)B^{11}$ reaction at 185 and 440 MeV. Both reactions reveal a cross section peak around 35 MeV corresponding to the $1s$ shell, but the peak is much more pronounced for the 440 MeV incident protons (the nucleus is more transparent to 440 MeV protons than 185 MeV ones).

To observe the clean knock-out of an outer shell proton, the path length of the struck proton must be smaller than the mean free path of a proton of that energy in nuclear matter. Hence the effective interaction volume is confined to the two *pole cap zones* of the target nucleus where the incoming and ejected protons only have to travel a short distance within the nucleus.

Nucleon Clusters

The simple shell model is unable to account for the evidence in favour of local clusters of nucleon pairs in the outer regions of the nucleus. The evidence for clustering is:

(1) New estimates of alpha decay constants in some heavy nuclei, using shell model wave functions, are about a thousand times less than the experimental values. Hodgson† claims, from (p, α) studies in nuclear emulsions, that the surface nucleons in Ag and Br are found in clusters 40 per cent of the time.

(2) In the orbital negative muon capture process in heavy nuclei††

$$\mu^- + p \to n + \nu$$

the neutrino carries away most of the 100 MeV excitation energy but about 10 to 15 MeV is deposited in the residual nucleus. This residual nucleus is normally regarded as an excited compound nucleus and the number of emitted neutrons (about 1·5 to 1·7 per capture) is compatible with evaporation theory. However, the number of emitted protons per capture is about 0·022, which is about ten times greater than any reasonable complex nucleus model prediction. The high proton emission probability is associated with the occurrence of surface two-nucleon clusters. If a captured muon interacts with a close pair of protons (a pseudo-deuteron) in the nuclear surface, both protons will directly receive excitation energy and have a fair chance of escaping from the nucleus by a direct interaction.

20.12. COLLECTIVE MODEL AND NUCLEAR SPECTRA

Nuclei which have a large number of loose nucleons outside filled shells are found to have electric quadrupole moments much greater than the single particle shell model estimates. In addition, these nuclei often exhibit excited states for which the gamma $E2$ decay rates are between 10^2 and 10^4 times the simple shell model values.

It was first emphasized by Rainwater††† that a single nucleon moving in an independent orbit, especially if it has a high angular momentum, will exert a centrifugal force against the inner surface of the nucleus thus tending to distort the nuclear shape from the spherical to the ellipsoidal. For a closed shell nucleus, the various nucleon orbits are oriented at random so that the overall nuclear shape is spherical. A single loose nucleon beyond a closed shell will tend to have its orbit in the equatorial plane (i.e. the plane perpendicular to the nuclear spin axis), thus setting up a slight oblate spheroidal deformation.

Nillson‡ has calculated the independent particle energy eigenvalues and wave functions for a nuclear potential well which is spheroidal in

† P. E. Hodgson, *Nuclear Physics* **8**, 1, 1958.
†† P. Singer, *Phys. Rev.* **124**, 1602, 1961.
††† J. Rainwater, *Phys. Rev.* **79**, 432, 1950.
‡ S. G. Nillson, *Dan. Mat-Fys. Medd.* **29**, No. 16, 1955; see also K. Gottfried, *Phys. Rev.* **103**, 1017, 1956.

shape and the predictions of this more realistic model work surprisingly well for deformed nuclei.†

As the number of loose particles outside the filled nucleon shells increases there is competition between the shape-deforming tendencies of the loose nucleons and the pairing force interaction. The latter effect represents the tendency of two nucleons of the same kind to couple to form states of zero angular momentum which are, of course, spherically symmetric. Thus the equilibrium shape of the nucleus depends on the relative strengths of the two effects. For nuclei with only a few loose particles, the pairing force dominates and the nuclear shape is very nearly spherical. On the other hand, nuclei with many loose particles ($150 < A < 190$ or $A > 220$) are strongly deformed as the deforming effect of the loose nucleons is a coherent one.

It was suggested by A. Bohr and B. R. Mottelson†† that with the markedly spheroidal nuclei it may be possible to excite them to relatively low lying energy states which are essentially quantum mechanical vibrations or rotations of the nuclear shape. Many examples of nuclear spectra illustrating these "collective" modes of vibration and rotation have been discovered. The collective model has, in fact, been successfully applied to the spectra of several light nuclei, where one would not at first sight expect it to work (a good example is the nucleus F^{19}).

About 1955, one or two years after the first introduction of the collective model, a powerful method of exciting low energy vibrational and rotational states was discovered. This was the method of Coulomb excitation††† in which the target nucleus is excited by the electromagnetic field of an incident charged particle passing close to but not penetrating the nuclear surface. In terms of a simple classical picture it is not difficult to imagine a spheroidal nucleus set into rotation by the perturbation of a passing charged particle.

The components of angular momentum of a strongly deformed nucleus are depicted in Fig. 10 of Chapt. 17 (Sect. 8). Notice that the collective rotational angular momentum $\boldsymbol{R}$ is normal to the symmetry axis of the nucleus. The rotational energy of the nucleus is

$$E_{\text{rot}} = \frac{1}{2\mathcal{J}} \boldsymbol{R}^2 \tag{75}$$

where $\mathcal{J}$ is the effective moment of inertia of the collective rotation.

† I. Perlman, p. 547 of *Proc. Intern. Conf. Nuclear Structure*, Kingston, Canada 1960,

†† A. Bohr and B. R. Mottelson, *Dan. Mat-Fys. Medd.* **27**, No. 16, 1953; **26**, No. 14. 1954; **30**, No. 1, 1955. A. Bohr and B. R. Mottelson, p. 1009–1032 of *Nuclear Spectroscopy*, Part B, Ed. F. Ajzenberg-Selove, Academic Press, 1960.

††† T. Huus, *Physica* **22**, 1027, 1956.

For states with zero intrinsic angular momentum, $K = 0$ and therefore $\boldsymbol{R} = \boldsymbol{J}$ and as $\boldsymbol{J}$ is quantized

$$\boldsymbol{R}^2 = J(J+1)\,\hbar^2$$

and

$$E_{\text{rot}} = \frac{\hbar^2}{2\mathcal{J}} J(J+1) \tag{76}$$

The collective rotational states for the spheroidal even–even nucleus $_{72}\text{Hf}^{180}$ are shown in Fig. 11 of Chapter 17. For nuclear states with $\boldsymbol{R} = \boldsymbol{J}$ there is no distinguishable change in orientation if the nucleus is rotated through 180° about an axis perpendicular to the symmetry axis and consequently only rotational states of even parity are allowed ($J = 0, 2, 4, 6, \ldots$). The $E2$ gamma spectra of Hf^{180} has been very accurately measured† and the agreement with the simple level scheme eqn. (76) is remarkably good, provided the moment of inertia is determined from the experimental data. The small deviations from the pure rotational spectrum is attributed to a "rotation–vibration" interaction analogous to the effect found with molecular spectra. The effective moment of inertia $\mathcal{J}$ is too small to be associated with the rotation of a *rigid* nucleus. This point is discussed in Section 17.8. A possible irrotational flow pattern of the outer nucleons of a spheroidal nucleus is shown in Fig. 12 of Chapter 17.

The magnitudes of the moments of inertia found in rotational states have been calculated†† and there is a reasonably good fit with the empirical results.

20.13. NUCLEAR REACTIONS AT HIGH ENERGIES

We conclude this chapter with a very brief summary of nuclear reactions at very high energies (an excellent survey of the field is given by Wattenberg in *Handbuch der Physik*, Vol. 40).

One crucial point in understanding high energy interactions is to appreciate the large mean free path Λ of an incident nucleon of energy > 100 MeV in nuclear matter ($\Lambda \sim 4$ fermi). The long mean free path is partly a consequence of the small reduced de Broglie wavelength of a high energy nucleon.

High energy nuclear reactions can often be considered to take place in two different stages. The first stage is a nucleon cascade. The incoming proton or neutron collides with a nucleon in the target nucleus and the two recoil particles either escape from the nucleus or make further

† G. Scharff-Goldhaber *et al.*, *Bull. Amer. Phys. Soc.* II **1**, 206, 1956.

†† B. R. Mottelson, p. 528 in *Proc. Intern. Conf. Nuclear Structure*, Kingston, Canada 1960.

collisions with nucleons of the target nucleons. Thus a number of nucleons may escape from the nuclear surface in rapid succession. Many nucleon–nucleon collisions within the nucleus are forbidden by the Pauli exclusion principle (only states above the Fermi energy are empty and can receive the scattered particles). The development of a nucleon cascade for a nucleus bombarded by a 400 MeV proton is depicted in Fig. 24. The path of each scattered nucleon is indicated until it escapes from the nucleus, and the open circles indicate the positions where scattering collisions would

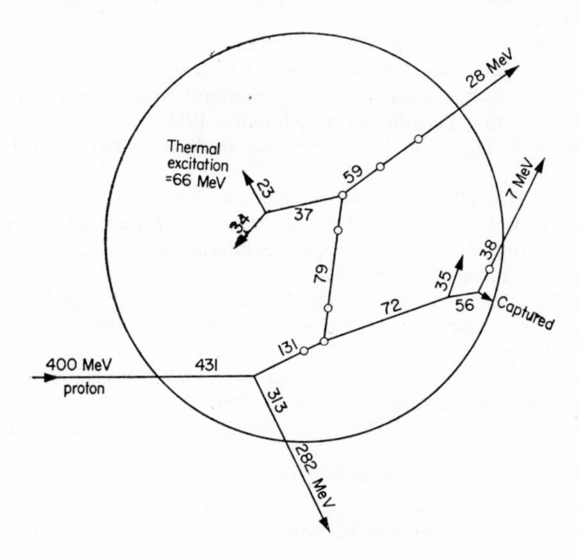

FIG. 24. Nucleon cascade.

occur but are forbidden by the Pauli principle. The complete cascade is developed within an epoch as short as 10^{-22} sec. Scattered nucleons with a kinetic energy less than 30 or 40 MeV do not escape from the nucleus but excite the entire residual nucleus. The second phase of the reaction is associated with the evaporation of much lower energy nucleons, γ-rays, by the "heated" nuclear system. The Weisskopf statistical theory is ideal for discussing and interpreting this stage of the reaction.

Another type of high energy process is the "spallation" reaction. This term refers to high energy reactions in which several rather heavy nuclear fragments are emitted from the target reaction. Radiochemical methods of identification of the products of spallation are often employed.

Probably the most important applications of high energy nucleon bombardment, is the generation of elementary particles, pions, K mesons, hyperons, etc. and the study of their decays and nuclear interactions. Some of these phenomena are discussed in Chapter 21.

BIBLIOGRAPHY

J. M. BLATT and V. F. WEISSKOPF, *Theoretical Nuclear Physics*, Wiley, New York 1952.

P. MORRISON, Part 6 in Vol. 2, *Experimental Nuclear Physics*, Ed. by E. Segrè, Wiley, New York 1953.

H. A. BETHE and P. MORRISON, *Elementary Nuclear Theory*, 2nd Ed., Wiley, New York 1956.

S. DEVONS, *Excited States of Nuclei*, Cambridge University Press, 1949.

S. T. BUTLER, *Nuclear Stripping Reactions*, Wiley, New York 1957.

W. TOBOCMAN, *Theory of Direct Nuclear Reactions*, Oxford University Press, 1961.

M. G. MAYER and J. H. D. JENSEN, *Elementary Theory of Nuclear Shell Structure*, Wiley, New York 1955.

E. FEENBERG, *Shell Theory of the Nucleus*, Princeton University Press, 1955.

J. S. LEVINGER, *Nuclear Photo-Disintegration*, Oxford University Press, 1960.

F. L. FRIEDMAN and V. F. WEISSKOPF, The Compound Nucleus in *Niels Bohr and the Development of Physics*, Pergamon Press, London 1955.

R. HUBY, Stripping Reactions in Vol. 3 *Progress in Nuclear Physics*, Pergamon Press, London 1953.

W. W. BUECHNER, The Determination of Nuclear Reaction Energies by Deflection Measurements in Vol. **5**, *Progress in Nuclear Physics*, Pergamon Press, London 1956.

A. E. GLASSGOLD, Optical Model for Nuclear Scattering in Vol. **7**, *Progress in Nuclear Physics*, Pergamon Press, London 1959.

G. E. BROWN, Foundations of the Optical Model, *Revs. Mod. Physics* **31**, 893, 1959.

A. ZUCHER, Nuclear Interactions of Heavy Ions in Vol. **10**, *Annual Review of Nuclear Science, Ann. Reviews Inc. Palo Alto*, U.S.A. 1960.

D. H. WILKINSON, Nuclear Photodisintegration in Vol. **9**, *Annual Review of Nuclear Science*. Ann. Reviews Inc. Palo Alto, U.S.A. 1959.

B. G. HARVEY, Spallation in Vol. 7 *Progress in Nuclear Physics*, Pergamon Press, London 1959.

Nuclear Spectroscopy, Part A and B, Ed. by F. AJZENBERG-SELOVE, Academic Press, New York and London 1960.

R. J. EDEN, Nuclear Models in Vol. **6**, *Progress in Nuclear Physics*, Pergamon Press, London 1957.

The following articles in Vol. 40, *Handbuch der Physik*, Springer-Verlag, Berlin 1957:

W. W. BURCHAM, Nuclear Reactions, Levels, and Spectra of Light Nuclei.

B. B. KINSEY, Nuclear Reactions, Levels, and Spectra of Heavy Nuclei.

J. RAINWATER, Resonant Processes by Neutrons.

A. WATTENBERG, Nuclear Reactions at High Energies.

The following articles in Vol. 39, *Handbuch der Physik*, Springer-Verlag, Berlin 1957:

J. P. ELLIOTT and A. M. LANE, The Nuclear Shell-Model.

S. A. MOSZKOWSKI, Models of Nuclear Structure.

EXAMPLES

1. A very thin aluminium target is bombarded with a monoenergetic beam of 2·10 MeV deuterons obtained from a Van de Graaff accelerator. Protons emitted at 90° to the incident deuteron beam are analysed with a magnetic spectrometer. The first five levels of the Al^{28} nucleus occur at excitation energies, 0 (ground level), 0·031, 0·974, 1·015, and 1·367 MeV. Compute the BR values of the first five proton groups observed in the magnetic spectrometer. Atomic masses are: Al^{27}, 26·990081; Al^{28}, 27·990771; H^2, 2·014740; n, 1·008986. Si^{28} has an atomic mass of 27·985775. A gamma transition of 1·79 MeV is observed as well as a 2·86 MeV β-ray; is this compatible with the data?

2. A tritium gas target is bombarded with a beam of monoenergetic protons of kinetic energy 3 MeV. What is the kinetic energy of the neutrons emitted at 30° to the incident beam? Atomic mass values: H^1, 1·008145; n, 1·008986; H^3, 3·017005; He^3, 3·016986.
3. The Q-value of the $Fe^{56}(d, p)Fe^{57}$ reaction is 5·42 MeV. If the binding energy of the deuteron is 2·226 MeV, calculate the binding energy of the last neutron in Fe^{57}. What is the Q-value of the $Fe^{57}(d, t)Fe^{58}$ reaction if the binding energy of the last neutron in the triton is 6·26 MeV?
4. Calculate the kinetic energies and momenta of the product nuclei in the $O^{16}(d, p)O^{17}$ reaction when the proton is emitted at 30° to the direction of the incoming beam of 8 MeV deuterons. Construct a momentum diagram and find the internal momentum of the proton in the deuteron at the moment of stripping. What is the probability of finding the proton in the deuteron with this momentum? (Atomic masses are: H^1, 1·008145; H^2, 2·014740; O^{17}, 17·004534).
5. Calculate the probability of a 20 keV proton penetrating the Coulomb barrier of C^{12} nucleus. Determine the ratio of the $C^{12}(p, \gamma)N^{13}$ reaction cross sections for protons of 20 and 30 keV kinetic energy.
6. The potential energy V of the proton–proton nuclear interaction (in a state with their spins antiparallel) varies as the inter proton distance r as follows

V (MeV)	+50	+7	−50	−74	−78	−76	−70	−56	−40	−24	−14	−9.5	−2.0	−1.0
r (fermi)	0.28	0.30	0.35	0.40	0.44	0.50	0.60	0.70	0.80	0.90	1.0	1.1	1.5	2.0

Plot a V–r curve and determine the ratio of the nuclear and Coulomb force between two protons for $r =$ 0·50, 0·60, 0·70, 0·80, 0·90, 1·0 and 1·4 fermis.

CHAPTER 21

ELEMENTARY PARTICLES

21.1. INTRODUCTION

The subject of "elementary particles" is one of the most perplexing branches of modern physics. At the present time (1962) about thirty particles (including their antiparticles) are classified as "elementary". Ultimately, it is hoped that the list will be reduced as the "structures" of some of these elementary particles are determined. We shall not attempt to give a rigorous definition of the term elementary.† A few general comments, however, may be helpful at this stage. All elementary particles are either stable or have mean lifetimes which are long on a nuclear time scale. A suitable time unit, the "flash", is given by the pion Compton wavelength $\hbar/m_\pi c$ (m_π is the pion rest mass) divided by the velocity of light.

$$\frac{\hbar}{m_\pi c^2} \sim 0{\cdot}5 \times 10^{-23} \text{ sec}$$

Unstable elementary particles always decay into two or more lighter elementary particles. A particle such as the deuteron, although stable, is regarded as a composite particle. All the elementary particles are either electrically neutral or have charges of $\pm e$. The absence of multi-charged elementary particles is one of the most puzzling features of the subject.

We now give a very brief historical survey of the discovery of the elementary particles. Fifty years ago three elementary particles were known: the electron, the proton, and the quantum of the electromagnetic field, the photon. The role of the photon is fundamentally different to that of the electron and proton; it is responsible for conveying the electromagnetic interaction between the elementary charged particles. The photon is a "cement particle" in the sense that it is responsible for the stable existence of atoms.

About 1930, three more particles were added to the list: the neutron, the positron (the first antiparticle to be found) and the neutrino. Chadwick (1932) discovered the neutron through a careful study of the kinematics of α-particle induced reactions with light nuclei. Anderson (1932)

† See, for example, the review by D. H. Wilkinson of *Theory of Elementary Particles* by P. Roman in *Contemporary Physics* **1**, 332, 1959–60, London.

observed the diverging curved tracks of an electron and a positron in a cloud chamber immersed in a strong magnetic field (the electron–positron pair was produced by the absorption of a high energy photon). The neutrino was postulated by Pauli (1933) to explain the "missing" energy and momentum (linear and angular) in beta decay. Shortly afterwards Fermi (1934) successfully predicted the correct shape of the beta momentum spectrum using the concept of Pauli's neutrino. It is interesting to note that all the phenomena in the realm of atomic physics (including beta decay) can be described in terms of seven elementary particles; the photon, the electron, the positron, the proton, the neutron, the neutrino, and the antineutrino.

In 1935, Yukawa predicted the existence of a new fundamental particle with rest mass two or three hundred times that of the electron. This new particle was invented to play an analogous role to that of the photon in electromagnetic interactions; that is, it is responsible for the strong nucleon–nucleon interaction. Soon after Yukawa's prediction, Anderson and Neddermeyer (1936) observed the track of a charged cosmic ray with the anticipated rest mass. This new particle, the mesotron (later shortened to meson) did not behave as expected; it did not, for instance, interact strongly with nuclei. This led to a period of considerable confusion, which was resolved by the discovery of Lattes, Occhialini, and Powell (1947) of a heavier particle (about 300 electron mass units) which did interact strongly with nuclei. The new particle, the pi meson or pion, did seem to behave like the Yukawa particle. It was not unexpected to find that the pion is unstable and decays with a mean lifetime of about 10^{-8} sec. What was completely unexpected was the fact that the pion did not decay into an electron (or positron) but into a charged particle, of mass around 200 electron mass units. This particle, the mu-meson or muon, decays into an electron (or positron) with a mean lifetime of two microseconds. The muon is the particle first observed in cosmic radiation by Anderson and Neddermeyer in 1936. The muon appears to behave in all known respects as a heavy electron, apart from the fact that it decays into an electron, and consequently it is logical to classify the muon with the electron as a lepton (see below) and not as a meson.

Between the years 1947 and 1955 elementary particle physics entered a period of great confusion through the observation, in cosmic radiation and in high energy accelerator experiments, of a number of transient particles with masses greater than that of the pion (during this period the 3 GeV proton synchroton at Brookhaven and the 6 GeV machine at Berkeley came into operation). The new transient particles can be divided into two main groups: the *K mesons* or kaons, with masses close to 1000 electron mass units; and the *hyperons* with masses greater than the neutron but less than the deuteron. In the past decade an intensive experimental programme has been concerned with the determination of the masses, spins, parities, lifetimes and decay modes of these "strange" particles. The results of this programme are given in Table 1.

Apart from the fundamental problem of the gravitational interaction, which plays a negligible part in elementary particle interactions, there are three kinds of force in Nature. The three kinds of interaction are

(1) The "strong" nuclear force associated with the pion–nucleon and nucleon–nucleon interaction.

(2) The medium–strong electromagnetic forces; the Coulomb interaction is the most familiar example.

(3) The "weak" forces, the most mysterious of the three classes, responsible for such slow processes as the beta decay of the neutron and the decay of the muon.

The relative strengths of the three types of interaction can be estimated as follows. Let us first consider the best understood force, the electromagnetic interaction. A typical electromagnetic process is the scattering of a photon by an electron. In Chapt. 1, Sect. 3, we derived an expression for the Thomson scattering cross section of an electron for a photon. This process can be visualized as the absorption and re-emission of the photon by the electron. The Thomson scattering cross section is (Eqn. (18) Chapter 1)

$$\sigma_T = \frac{8\pi}{3}\left(\frac{e^2}{m\,c^2}\right)^2$$

This expression can be re-written in terms of the dimensionless fine structure constant, $\alpha = e^2/(\hbar\,c)$, and the electron Compton wavelength, $(\hbar/m\,c)$.

$$\sigma_T = \frac{8\pi}{3}\left(\frac{e^2}{\hbar\,c}\right)^2\left(\frac{\hbar}{m\,c}\right)^2$$

Thus we see that σ_T and also σ_c† (the Compton scattering cross section) for low energy photons $E \ll m\,c^2$, is dependent on α; the square appears because we are dealing with a two photon process. Thus it appears reasonable to measure the strength of the electromagnetic interaction by the dimensionless constant

$$\alpha = \frac{e^2}{\hbar\,c} = \frac{1}{137}$$

In Chapter 19, we outlined an elementary theory of the pion–nucleon interaction and introduced the concept of a "nucleon charge" g, analogous to the electric charge e. The strength of the nuclear interaction is represented by the magnitude of the dimensionless coupling constant

$$\frac{g^2}{\hbar\,c}$$

† The Klein–Nishina formula for the Compton scattering cross section reduces to the Thomson formula for low energy γ-rays (see p. 234 of J. M. Jauch and F. Rohrlich, *The Theory of Photons and Electrons*, Addison–Wesley, 1955).

From the observed strength of the pion–nucleon interaction the best estimate of this coupling constant is about 15, a thousand times the electromagnetic coupling constant α. (If the so called pseudo-vector theory of pion–nucleon forces is used a dimensionless constant of the order of 0·1 is obtained, but this is still much larger than the fine structure constant.)

To obtain an estimate of the intrinsic strength of the weak interaction characteristic of beta decay we start from an experimental estimate of the Fermi β-coupling parameter G (written as g in Eqn. (21), Chapt. 14)

$$G = 1{\cdot}4 \times 10^{-49} \text{ erg cm}^3$$

To convert this to a dimensionless form we introduce the pion Compton wavelength ($\hbar/m_\pi c$) and obtain a dimensionless constant

$$\mathscr{G}^2 = \frac{G^2}{(\hbar c)^2}\left(\frac{m_\pi c}{\hbar}\right)^4 \sim 3 \times 10^{-14}$$

The interaction radius of the four fermions involved in the beta decay interaction (neutron, proton, electron and neutrino) is assumed to be of the order of the pion Compton wavelength, 1·4 fermi. Changing this interaction distance to the Compton wavelength of some other elementary particle such as a K meson would not greatly increase the value of $\mathscr{G}^2$.

Comparing the three basic forces of Nature we see that their relative strengths are

$$10 \text{ (Nuclear)} : 10^{-2} \text{ (Electromagnetic)} : 10^{-14} \text{ (Weak)}$$

The gravitational coupling constant is vastly smaller than any of these, being of the order of 10^{-39}.

One of the most puzzling problems of elementary particle physics is the origin of these different strengths and the curious feature that certain conservation laws (symmetry principles) are relaxed for the weak interactions and decay processes.

The elementary particles are separated into two general groups: the *bosons* and the *fermions*. Bosons are particles with intrinsic angular momentum (spin) equal to an integral multiple of $\hbar$; the photon has spin 1, whereas the pion and K mesons have zero spin. Fermions have half integral spin, and it is very probable that all the elementary particles, other than the bosons, have a spin of one half unit.† Originally, the division of particles into bosons and fermions was based on the statistical behaviour of a collection of identical particles. One of the most important differences between the two classes of particles is that there is no conservation law controlling the total number of bosons in the Universe, whereas the total number of fermions is strictly conserved. Thus we have a remarkable correlation between the intrinsic angular momentum of a particle and a fundamental conservation law. Eventually the theory of elementary particles may be able to explain this.

† See, however, the "resonances" (Sections 21.11 and 21.12).

As far as the present day scheme of elementary particles is concerned, the bosons are quanta of the electromagnetic or meson fields (it is probable that at very close separations of nucleons K mesons as well as pions act as agents of transmission of the nuclear force; the kaon Compton wavelength is $\sim 0{\cdot}4$ fermi). The interesting question remains to be answered: does the weak interaction between four fermions in beta decay and other weak processes take place through a boson field? The answer may be provided in the near future by high energy neutrino experiments.

The elementary fermions fall in two main classes: the *leptons* and the *baryons*. Before describing this classification it is necessary to mention the concept of antiparticle, first suggested by Dirac. From the fundamental symmetry in the relativistic wave equation of the electron, solutions occur for a particle which has all the reversible attributes of the electron. Such a particle, the positron, is known as the antiparticle of the electron. The only reversible properties of the electron are its electric charge and magnetic moment; the electron and positron are both stable, and they have identical masses. The possibility that the particle and antiparticle have identical properties is not excluded: two of the elementary bosons fall into this category, namely the photon and the neutral pion (we shall see that the fact that the neutral K meson, K^0, is not identical with its antiparticle $\overline{K^0}$ has some interesting consequences).

There are three leptons, the neutrino† ν (this is identified with the neutral particle emitted in positron decay and orbital electron capture), the electron e^- and the negative muon μ^-. The antiparticles of the leptons, the antileptons, are the antineutrino $\bar{\nu}$ (this is identified with the neutral particle emitted in the beta decay of the neutron), the positron e^+, and the positive muon μ^+. There is now a considerable weight of evidence that in all reactions and decay processes involving leptons and antileptons, the total number of leptons minus the total number of antileptons remains unchanged. In other words, if each antilepton is counted as minus one lepton, the number of leptons in the Universe is constant. The principle of lepton conservation was introduced in Chapter 14.

The other group of fermions all have masses in excess of the K mesons; these particles are known collectively as *baryons*. The baryons consist of the two nucleons, the proton and the neutron, and the hyperons. The hyperons divide into three main sub-groups, the Λ^0 particle (a neutral particle of mass about 2180 electron mass units), the Σ particles, (Σ^-, Σ^0 and Σ^+ with masses in the range 2320 to 2340 electron units) and the Ξ particles (Ξ^- and Ξ^0 with masses near 2580 electron units). There is no reason to doubt the existence of the antiparticles of these fermions.††

† See, however, Appendix C2, p 791.

†† The antihyperons $\overline{\Lambda^0}$, $\overline{\Sigma^+}$, $\overline{\Sigma^-}$ and $\overline{\Sigma^0}$ have been observed: G. Morpurgo, *Ann. Rev. Nuclear Science* **11**, 42, 1961.

The total number of baryons minus the total number of antibaryons is absolutely conserved in all interactions.

It might prove helpful at this stage to make a list of the fundamental laws which are valid in *all* (strong, electromagnetic, and weak) interactions.

(1) Conservation of energy (mass is, of course, regarded as a form of energy). The precision of this law is limited by the uncertainty principle and allows the creation of virtual particles for a fleeting period of time; $\Delta E \Delta t \sim \hbar$

(2) Conservation of linear momentum.

(3) Conservation of angular momentum.

(4) Conservation of electric charge. In addition we note that all elementary charges are 0, 1, or -1; multiple charges are not found.

(5) Conservation of baryons (total number of baryons minus total number of antibaryons is constant).

(6) Conservation of leptons (total number of leptons minus total number of antileptons is constant).

(7) Invariance under the combined operations of charge conjugation C (turning every particle of charge $+e$ into the antiparticle of charge $-e$, and vice-versa), parity P (reflection in a mirror) and time reversal T (reversing the direction of flow of time reverses all linear and angular velocity vectors). This is the CPT theorem of Luders, based on Lorentz invariance.

(8) Invariance under time inversion (T) (this has recently been checked for the weak interaction process the beta decay of the neutron†). It follows that if T is conserved separately, then the invariance principle CP holds for all interactions.

The first two conservation laws in the list can be shown to be equivalent to the statement that "the results of an experiment are independent of where and when it is performed". This is the principle of translational symmetry of space–time.

The principle of angular momentum conservation implies that "the result of an experiment is independent of the orientation of the apparatus". This is the principle of rotation symmetry of space–time.

In elementary particle physics electric charge is conserved in all interactions and in addition it is found that the charge of an elementary particle is always $\pm e$. Why the charge is always single for elementary charged particles is a complete mystery.

The present list of elementary particles and many of their basic properties is given in Table 1. The newly discovered omega, rho, and eta mesons are not included in this list.

† M. T. Burgy *et al.*, *Phys. Rev. Letters* **1**, 424, 1958; M. A. Clark and J. M. Robson, *Can. J. Phys.* **38**, 693, 1960.

TABLE 1. PROPERTIES OF ELEMENTARY PARTICLES

	Particle	Antiparticle	Spin	Isospin T	Strangeness S	Mass (electron units)	Mass (MeV)	Mean lifetime (sec)	Decay
Bosons	Photon γ	Self, γ	1	—	—	0	0	∞	—
	Pion π^0	Self, π^0	0	1	0	264·3	135·0	$\sim 2 \times 10^{-16}$	$\pi^0 \rightarrow \gamma + \gamma$
	Pion π^+	π^-	0	1	0	273·3	139·6	$2{\cdot}55 \pm 0{\cdot}03 \times 10^{-8}$	$\pi^+ \rightarrow \mu^+ + \nu$
	Kaon K^+	K^-	0	$\frac{1}{2}$	+1	967	494	$1{\cdot}22 \pm 0{\cdot}01 \times 10^{-8}$	
	Kaon K^0	$\overline{K^0}$	0	$\frac{1}{2}$	+1	973	498		—
Leptons	Neutrino ν	$\overline{\nu}$	$\frac{1}{2}$	—	—	0	0		—
	Electron e^-	Positron e^+	$\frac{1}{2}$	—	—	1	0·5109		—
	Muon μ^-	μ^+	$\frac{1}{2}$	—	—	206·8	105·6	$2{\cdot}21 \times 10^{-6}$	$\mu^- \rightarrow e^- + \overline{\nu} + \nu$
Baryons	Proton p	$\overline{p}$	$\frac{1}{2}$	$\frac{1}{2}$	0	1836	938·21	∞	—
	Neutron n	$\overline{n}$	$\frac{1}{2}$	$\frac{1}{2}$	0	1839	939·51	1010 ± 30	$n \rightarrow p + e^- + \overline{\nu}$
	Lambda Λ^0	$\overline{\Lambda^0}$	$\frac{1}{2}$	0	−1	2182	1115·4	$2{\cdot}51 \pm 0{\cdot}09 \times 10^{-10}$	$\Lambda^0 \rightarrow p + \pi^-$; $\Lambda^0 \rightarrow n + \pi^0$
	Sigma Σ^+	$\overline{\Sigma^+}$	$\frac{1}{2}$	1	−1	2328	1189·5	$0{\cdot}8 \times 10^{-10}$	$\Sigma^+ \rightarrow p + \pi^0$; $\Sigma^+ \rightarrow n + \pi^+$
	Sigma Σ^-	$\overline{\Sigma^-}$	$\frac{1}{2}$	1	−1	2342	1196	$1{\cdot}7 \times 10^{-10}$	$\Sigma^- \rightarrow n + \pi^-$
	Sigma Σ^0	$\overline{\Sigma^0}$	$\frac{1}{2}$	1	−1	2330	1191·5	$< 0{\cdot}1 \times 10^{-10}$†	$\Sigma^0 \rightarrow \Lambda^0 + \gamma$
	Xi Ξ^-	$\overline{\Xi^-}$	$\frac{1}{2}$	$\frac{1}{2}$	−2	2583	1320 ± 2	$\sim 10^{-10}$	$\Xi^- \rightarrow \Lambda^0 + \pi^-$
	Xi Ξ^0	$\overline{\Xi^0}$	$\frac{1}{2}$	$\frac{1}{2}$	−2	2579	1310 ± 10	$\sim 10^{-10}$	$\Xi^0 \rightarrow \Lambda^0 + \pi^0$

In all cases, T and S refer to the particle given in the first column.

† Probably less than 10^{-16} sec.

In Table 1, the masses of the particles are given in electron mass units in column 6 and in MeV in column 7. All spins are expressed in terms of $\hbar$ as unit. The total isospin T of each elementary particle is given in column 4. This concept is discussed in the next Section. The strangeness quantum number S is given in column 5. This concept is discussed in Section 8. Notice that the concept of strangeness does not apply to the photon and the leptons. The pions and nucleons have zero strangeness and the kaons and hyperons have finite strangeness (hence the term strange particles for the last two groups). Particle and antiparticle always have opposite strangeness. The only two particles which are their own antiparticles are the bosons, the photon and the neutral pion. The decay modes of the K mesons are so numerous that they have been omitted from this Table. This subject is discussed in Section 8. The particles in Table 1 are grouped in rows according to the fundamental classification: bosons, leptons (fermions), and baryons (fermions).

21.2. CONSERVATION OF ISOSPIN†

The concept of isospin or isotopic spin has proved to be very useful in comparing the energy levels of isobaric nuclei (nuclei of the same nucleon number A) and in correlating many of the observed meson–nucleon interactions.††

Soon after the discovery of the neutron, Heisenberg suggested that the proton and neutron should be regarded as different charge states of the same fundamental particle, the nucleon. The small mass difference of the two charge states is assumed to arise through the electromagnetic interaction. Looking at the mass data in Table 1, we can see that there is a close clustering in mass for the three pions π^+, π^-, π^0 and for the various kaons and hyperon groups (Λ, Σ and Ξ). The small mass difference between the charged and neutral species of pion probably would vanish if the electromagnetic interaction was "switched off".

The ideas outlined in the previous paragraph can be built into nuclear theory in several different ways. One method is to introduce an abstract space, known as isospin or charge space, and associate an isospin vector $\boldsymbol{T}$ of magnitude $\sqrt{T(T+1)}$ with each type of fundamental particle. The T values of the pion, kaon, nucleon, lambda, sigma and xi particles are given in column 4 of Table 1. The concept of isospin is not applied to the photon and the leptons.

The isospin vector formally resembles the spin angular momentum vector $\boldsymbol{s}\hbar$ of a particle. If we have a set of three axes in the abstract

† Some of the properties of Pauli spin operators and isospin operators are given in Appendix B.

†† W. E. Burcham, *Prog. Nuclear Physics* **4**, 171, 1955.

isospin space, the maximum observed component of $\boldsymbol{T}$ is denoted by T_3, corresponding to the observed component of $\boldsymbol{s}$, s_z (in ordinary space). It is helpful to label the isospin spatial axes as 1, 2, and 3, to emphasize that the vector $\boldsymbol{T}$ exists in isospin and not in ordinary space.

The total isospin of the nucleon is chosen to be

$$T = \tfrac{1}{2} \tag{1}$$

The two charge states of the nucleon correspond to

$$T_3 = +\tfrac{1}{2}, \quad \text{for the proton state} \tag{2a}$$

$$T_3 = -\tfrac{1}{2}, \quad \text{for the neutron state} \tag{2b}$$

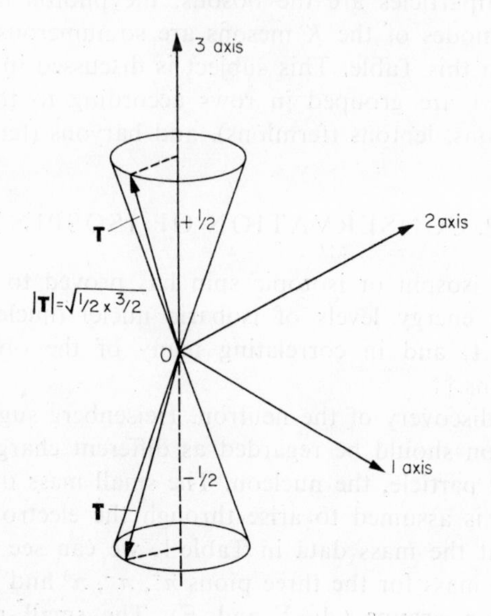

FIG. 1. Two possible orientations of nucleon isospin vector $T = \frac{1}{2}$ in charge space. The T_3 component $+\frac{1}{2}$ represents the proton state and the T_3 component $-\frac{1}{2}$ represents the neutron state.

These two states correspond to the two possible orientations of the isospin vector $\boldsymbol{T}$ in isospin space (Fig. 1). Changing a proton into a neutron is pictured as a reorientation of the vector $\boldsymbol{T}$ in isospin space.

The total isospin of the pion is chosen to be

$$T = 1 \tag{3}$$

The three charge states of the pion correspond to

$$T_3 = +1, \quad \text{for the } \pi^+ \text{ state} \tag{4a}$$

$$T_3 = 0, \quad \text{for the } \pi^0 \text{ state} \tag{4b}$$

$$T_3 = -1, \quad \text{for the } \pi^- \text{ state} \tag{4c}$$

Notice that the number of possible T_3 values for a given particle is $(2T + 1)$, analogous to the $(2J + 1)$ rule for magnetic sub-states of the angular momentum vector $\boldsymbol{J}$.

The pion and the nucleon are the only two elementary particles heavier than the muon with zero strangeness S (see column five of Table 1). For $S = 0$, the charge Q (in terms of e, the proton charge) of an elementary particle is related to T_3 by

$$Q = T_3 + \frac{B}{2} \tag{5}$$

where B is the *baryon* number; $B = +1$ for the proton, neutron, and hyperons and $B = 0$ for the pion (for the antiparticles, $\bar{p}$, $\bar{n}$, $\overline{\Lambda^0}$, etc.. . . $B = -1$). Equation (5) reduces to

$$Q = T_3 + \tfrac{1}{2}, \quad \text{for the proton and neutron} \tag{6}$$

and

$$Q = T_3, \quad \text{for the } \pi^+, \pi^\circ, \pi^- \text{ particles} \tag{7}$$

Equation (5) does not apply to particles of finite strangeness (see eqn. (75)).

The third component of $\boldsymbol{T}$, T_3, behaves as an additive quantum number. Thus a nucleus composed of Z protons and N neutrons has a total T_3 component

$$T_{3\,\text{nucleus}} = \frac{Z}{2} - \frac{N}{2} \tag{8}$$

The deuteron has $T_3 = 0$, but there are two possible values for T; 1 and 0. The two isospin states are labelled (T, T_3); that is (1, 0) and (0, 0). The (1, 0) state means that the vector $\boldsymbol{T}$ of the deuteron is oriented at right angles to the third axis in isospin space. The isospin wave functions of the two nucleon systems are given in Appendix B.

The close connection between Q and T_3 means that the principle of conservation of electric charge implies the conservation of T_3 in all interactions (strong, electromagnetic and weak). If this was all, there would be no point in introducing the concept of isospin. However, the considerable weight of experimental evidence that strong interactions are *charge independent* can be neatly expressed in terms of isospin. Charge independence means that the n–n, p–p and n–p nuclear interactions in states of the same total angular momentum and parity are indentical.

The principle of charge independence, which is invalid for electromagnetic† and weak interactions†, can be expressed as a symmetry principle: in strong (nuclear) interactions there is rotational symmetry in isospin space; that is, the result of an experiment is independent of the

† Although T is not a good quantum number in electromagnetic and weak processes the concept of isospin is still useful in discussing γ-emission and β-transitions (see the review article by BURCHAM, *loc. cit.*).

orientation of the total isospin vector $\boldsymbol{T}$ in isospin space. Thus in strong interactions, $\boldsymbol{T}$ behaves like the total angular momentum quantum number $\boldsymbol{J}$ of a system; it is a "good" quantum number.

In strong interactions, the total isospin T is conserved.

21.3. THE ELECTROMAGNETIC INTERACTION (ELECTRON, POSITRON AND PHOTON)

The electron is a spin $\frac{1}{2}$ fermion with a rest mass of 0·51098 MeV/c^2 and an electric charge e equal to $-4{\cdot}8029 \times 10^{-10}$ e.s.u. According to the Dirac quantum mechanical theory of the electron the magnetic dipole moment associated with the electron spin should be exactly one Bohr magneton. Another prediction of the Dirac theory is that the $2^2S_{\frac{1}{2}}$ and $2^2P_{\frac{1}{2}}$ atomic levels of a one electron atom should be degenerate. Both these predictions are wrong: the magnetic moment is about 0·1 per cent greater than the Dirac value and the $2^2S_{\frac{1}{2}}$ and $2^2P_{\frac{1}{2}}$ levels of atomic hydrogen have a small energy difference (Lamb shift) $h\nu$, where $\nu = 1057{\cdot}77 \pm 0{\cdot}10$ mc/s.

The antiparticle of the electron, the positron, has identical properties apart from the reversed sign of the electric charge and magnetic moment. In the absence of electrons, it is assumed that the positron like the electron is a stable particle.

The failures of the Dirac theory of the electron stems from the neglect of so called self-energy interactions. Even the classical electron theory recognized the existence of awkward mathematical infinities such as the infinite electromagnetic field energy associated with a *point* electron. New difficulties are introduced by assigning a finite spatial distribution to the electron. In the quantum theory of the electron these infinities do not vanish from the scene. There is, in addition to the infinite electrostatic self-energy, an electromagnetic self-energy arising from the interaction of the electron with the photon field.

The self-energy difficulties can be avoided by an aesthetically displeasing, but quantitatively successful procedure known as mass and charge *renormalization*. Consider the simplest type of self-energy process for an electron. An electron emits a virtual photon of energy E_γ at time t_1 and re-absorbs the photon at a later instant t_2. For a virtual process, the product $E_\gamma(t_2 - t_1)$ cannot exceed $\hbar$. It is convenient to represent this process by a simple graph known as a *Feynman* diagram (Fig. 2). A standard convention is adopted: the ordinate is chosen as the time axis, fermions are represented by full straight lines, photons by wavy lines and the other bosons (pion, kaon, . . . , etc.) by dashed lines. Thus in Fig. 2, the electron creates a virtual photon at the vertex A and re-absorbs it at the vertex B.

There is no upper limit to the maximum energy of the virtual photon emitted by the electron, and it turns out that the self-energy of the process is infinite. This is equivalent to an infinite mass term. Thus the *observed* mass of the electron m_0 consists of two parts

$$m_0 = m + \delta m$$

where m is the mass of the "bare" electron (this is essentially the mass which appears in the Dirac equation) and δm is the mass associated with the electromagnetic self-interaction. The bare electron mass is unobservable because we cannot interfere with Nature and switch off the

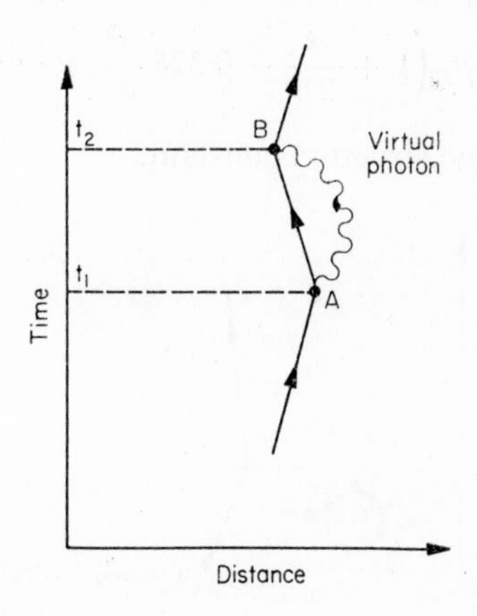

FIG. 2. Feynman diagram depicting emission and re-absorption of a virtual photon by an electron (an electromagnetic self-energy process).

electromagnetic interaction and the self-energy mass δm is infinite! This highly unsatisfactory state of affairs can be resolved as it is found that m and δm never appear on their own but always in the combination $(m + \delta m)$. Thus at the end of a quantum field calculation the known observed mass m_0 can always be substituted for $(m + \delta m)$; this curious theoretical technique is known as mass renormalization.

One of several possible virtual interaction processes for an electron in an external field of force (magnetic or electric field) is illustrated in Fig. 3. Here the external field, depicted by a cross, creates a photon which transforms into a virtual electron–positron pair at the vertex A. The pair annihilates at the vertex B producing a photon which is absorbed by the electron at the vertex C. The virtual creation and annihilation of an electron–positron pair is described as *vacuum polarization.* The effect of vacuum polarization is to slightly screen the electron from the applied field and is equivalent to a small reduction in the effective electron charge. The theoretical predictions of vacuum polarization are in excellent agreement with experiment.

The infinities arising in the theoretical treatment of an electron in an external field are different from those associated with an isolated electron. In the former case infinite energies can be removed by mass and charge renormalization but a finite energy term remains. Thus the second approximation to the magnetic moment of the electron is (the first is, of course, the Dirac prediction of one Bohr magneton μ_B),

$$\mu_e = \mu_B\left(1 + \frac{\alpha}{2\pi}\right) \tag{9}$$

If weaker interactions are included, the next approximation is

$$\mu_e = \mu_B\left(1 + \frac{\alpha}{2\pi} - 0{\cdot}328\frac{\alpha^2}{\pi^2} + \cdots\right) \tag{10}$$

$\alpha = e^2/\hbar c = {}^1/_{137}$ is the fine structure constant.

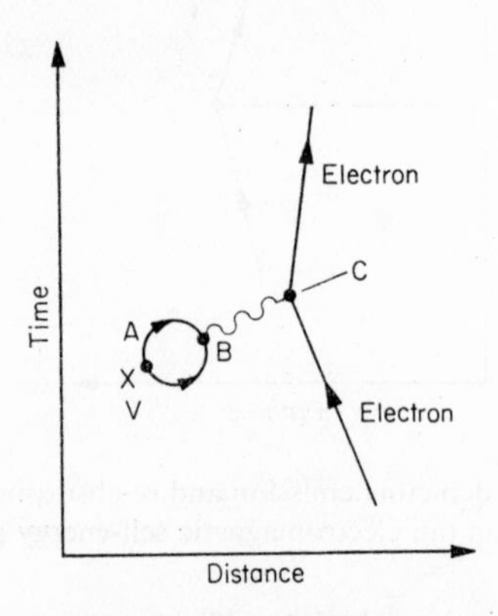

FIG. 3. Interaction of an electron with an external field (magnetic, say) represented by X (vacuum polarization interaction).

Notice that the series expansion for μ_e, rapidly converges because $\alpha \ll 1$. The theoretical prediction is in excellent agreement with the best experimental value.

Positronium†

As long ago as 1934, Mohorovičić suggested that under certain circumstances an electron and a positron might temporarily form a bound system analogous to the hydrogen atom. Such a system has been observed and it is referred to as *positronium*. Positronium can be formed, for example, by placing a small positron source inside a vessel filled with nitrogen; the positrons slow down and may then combine with the electrons of the nitrogen molecules to form positronium. There are two

† M. DEUTSCH, *Prog. Nucl. Phys.* 3, 131, 1953.

possible types of positronium: the para-form and the ortho-form. Para-positronium in its ground state has a spherically symmetric wave function corresponding to the $^1S_0$ state ($L = 0$, $J = 0$, antiparallel spins). The mean lifetime of this singlet state has been measured and it is about 10^{-10} sec, the electron–positron pair decaying into two 0·51 MeV photons travelling away in opposite directions. The other form of positronium is more interesting. In ortho-positronium the ground state is the triplet $^3S_1$ ($L = 0$, $J = 1$, parallel spins). Conservation of momentum completely forbids the decay of the ortho-form into two photons (the two photons must travel in opposite directions to conserve linear momentum and it is therefore impossible to couple their spin vectors, which are either parallel or antiparallel to their linear momentum, to give an angular momentum of one unit). Decay into three coplanar photons is not forbidden and is observed. If three photons of the same energy ($^2/_3\, m\, c^2 =$ 0·34 MeV) are created they travel away from their origin at mutual angles of 120°. It is not surprising that the mean lifetime of ortho-positronium is considerably longer than the para-form, which decays by two photon emission. The observed mean lifetime for the decay of the triplet state is about 10^{-7} sec.

Helicity of Electron and Positron

The failure of parity conservation in beta decay is associated with the non-vanishing helicity $\mathscr{H}$ of the decay leptons. Positrons and electrons emitted in beta decay tend to be longitudinally polarized; that is, their spin axes are predominantly oriented parallel (or antiparallel) to the direction of travel. In Chapt. 14, Sect. 8 we described experiments which established that

$$\mathscr{H} = -\frac{v}{c} \text{ for electrons,} \tag{11a}$$

$$\mathscr{H} = +\frac{v}{c} \text{ for positrons,} \tag{11b}$$

where v is the linear speed of the particle. For positrons emitted at nearly the speed of light $\mathscr{H}$ is nearly $+1$; that is, the positrons spin in a clockwise sense when viewed from the source.

The Photon

The photon is the quantum of the electromagnetic field. It is a boson of unit spin and is the agency of transmission of the electromagnetic interaction. The infinite range of the Coulomb potential is a consequence of the zero rest mass of the photon. Notice that if the pion rest mass was zero, the Yukawa potential (eqn. (16), Chapt. 19) would reduce to

$$V(r) = \frac{-g^2}{r} \tag{12}$$

as λ_π, the pion Compton wavelength, would become infinite. The potential energy given by eqn. (12) is analogous to the Coulomb energy $-e^2/r$.

The neutrino and the photon have a number of identical properties. The main difference in their behaviour springs from the different spin values of $\frac{1}{2}$ for the neutrino and 1 for the photon.

The spin of the photon is associated with its polarization. In a remarkably delicate torsion balance experiment, Beth† measured the torque communicated to a suspended quartz disc illuminated with polarized

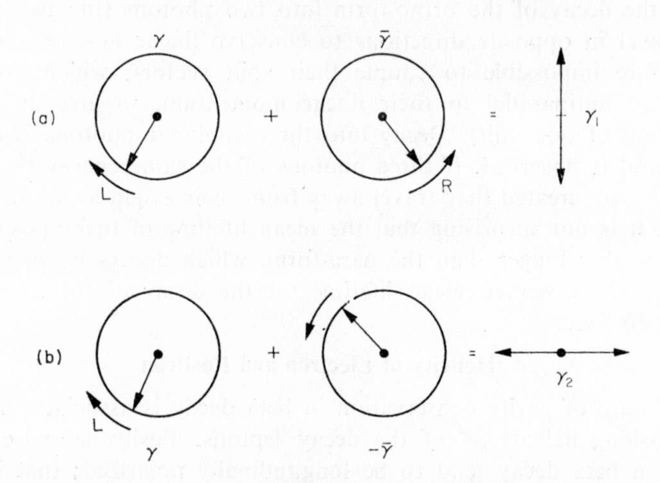

FIG. 4. Superposition of two circularly polarized components to produce plane polarized light. Direction of propagation of light is normal and into the plane of the diagram.

light. The torque $\boldsymbol{\tau}$ arises because in a birefringent medium the dielectric constant is a tensor and the electric vector $\boldsymbol{E}$ of the light wave is not parallel to the induced electric polarization $\boldsymbol{P}$ of the medium. The torque per unit volume is given by

$$\boldsymbol{\tau} = \boldsymbol{P} \times \boldsymbol{E} \tag{13}$$

Beth succeeded in detecting a "light" torque of the order of 10^{-9} dyne-cm and from his measurements he was able to show that each photon of circularly polarized light carried an angular momentum of magnitude $\hbar$ (left and right circularly polarized light corresponds to opposite senses of rotation of the photon).

A left circularly polarized light beam is here defined as a beam in which the electric vector at a given point rotates anticlockwise when viewed from the light source. A right circularly polarized photon is the mirror image of a left circularly polarized photon. In other words, a left

† R. A. BETH, *Phys. Rev.* **50**, 115, 1936.

circularly polarized photon, denoted by the symbol γ, is the antiparticle of a right circularly polarized photon $\bar{\gamma}$. In Table 1, however, the photon is given as its own antiparticle. This classification refers to plane polarized light which is conveniently regarded as a mixture of left and right circularly polarized components. Two examples are shown diagrammatically in Fig. 4. If γ is added to $\bar{\gamma}$ we obtain linearly polarized light γ_1;

$$\gamma_1 = \frac{1}{\sqrt{2}}(\gamma + \bar{\gamma}) \qquad \text{(14a), Fig. (4a)}$$

if γ is added to $-\bar{\gamma}$, we obtain linearly polarized light γ_2, polarized perpendicular to γ_1

$$\gamma_2 = \frac{1}{\sqrt{2}}(\gamma - \bar{\gamma}) \qquad \text{(14b), Fig. (4b)}$$

The factors $1/\sqrt{2}$ are normalization factors.

It is easy to appreciate that the antiparticle of γ_1 is γ_1 and the antiparticle of γ_2 is γ_2.†

21.4. THE NEUTRINO AND ANTINEUTRINO††

There now exists a considerable amount of evidence that the neutrino ν and its antiparticle, the antineutrino $\bar{\nu}$, have exactly zero rest mass. In all probability these particles also have zero electric charge and magnetic moment. The two types of neutrino differ with respect to the property known as helicity. In Chapter 14, we described an ingenious experiment which demonstrated that neutrinos emitted in beta decay (positron decay and K capture) have a negative helicity; that is, they are longitudinally polarized with their spin axes antiparallel to their direction of travel. As neutrinos and their antiparticles have zero rest mass they travel with the unique speed of light c and consequently they are probably 100 per cent polarized, i.e.

$$\mathscr{H} = +1, \text{ for antineutrinos} \qquad (15a)$$

$$\mathscr{H} = -1, \text{ for neutrinos} \qquad (15b)$$

The only direct neutrino reaction detected to date†† (1960) is the inverse of the beta decay of the neutron

$$n \rightarrow p + e^- + \bar{\nu}$$

that is,

$$\bar{\nu} + p \rightarrow n + e^+ - 1{\cdot}80 \text{ MeV} \qquad (16)$$

The neutron and the positron have a total rest mass energy 1·80 MeV greater than that of the proton; thus reaction (16) is only possible for

† These ideas are discussed by R. H. Good, *Am. J. Phys.* **28**, 659, 1960. See also the analogy between polarized light and the Pais–Piccioni neutral K experiment (Section 9).

†† See Appendix C for further evidence on neutrinos.

antineutrinos of energy greater than 1·80 MeV. The detection of this reaction is described in Chapter 14. Reines and Cowan estimated the average cross section of eqn. (16), for the antineutrino spectrum from a fission reactor as

$$\overline{\sigma}_{\bar{\nu}} = (11\cdot 0 \pm 2\cdot 5)\ 10^{-44}\ \mathrm{cm}^2 \qquad (17)$$

This is in excellent agreement with the theoretical prediction of the "two component" neutrino theory of Lee and Yang, which is based on 100 per cent longitudinal polarization of the neutrinos.

An unsuccessful attempt† was made in 1957 to detect the reaction

$$\bar{\nu} + d \rightarrow n + n + e^+ - 4\cdot 1\ \mathrm{MeV} \qquad (18)$$

This failure is not surprising as the predicted cross section for eqn. (18) is thirty times smaller than $\overline{\sigma}_{\bar{\nu}}$ for reaction (16) using pile antineutrinos.

The cross section for the absorption of monoenergetic antineutrinos by protons is expected, according to the two-component neutrino theory, to increase as E^2 above the threshold of 1·80 MeV. However at high energies, the rate of increase of the cross section is expected†† to decrease and finally level off at about $0\cdot 8 \times 10^{-38}$ cm² around an antineutrino lab. energy of 7 GeV.

At the present time, a great deal of attention is being devoted to the study of the feasibility of high energy neutrino experiments.††† A flux of high energy neutrinos and antineutrinos, free of other types of radiation, could be obtained at a neutrino detector in the following way (Fig. 5). A high energy beam of protons (30 GeV) from a synchrotron is incident on a target producing, along with other particles, an intense beam of high energy charged pions in the forward direction. These pions decay in the first few metres of their flight, emitting muons and neutrinos, mainly in the forward direction

$$\pi^+ \rightarrow \mu^+ + \nu$$

$$\pi^- \rightarrow \mu^- + \bar{\nu}$$

The muons and other particles are absorbed in a huge concrete absorber, and the neutrinos and antineutrinos from the pion and subsequent muon decays ($\mu^\pm \rightarrow e^\pm + \nu + \bar{\nu}$) then enter the neutrino detector. The latter is surrounded with an anticoincidence shield to reject cosmic ray events. The 12 GeV proton synchrotron, now under construction at the Argonne National Laboratory, Illinois, is designed to produce an external beam of 10^{13} protons per pulse, once every four seconds. This proton beam current is about one hundred times that of the CERN 25 GeV machine, and it is anticipated that a few neutrino events every hour should take place in a detector weighing a few tons.

† C. L. Cowan and F. Reines, *Phys. Rev.* **107**, 1609, 1957.

†† T. D. Lee and C. N. Yang, *Phys. Rev. Letters* **4**, 307, 1960.

††† F. Reines, *Ann. Rev. Nucl. Sci.* **10**, 1, 1960.

There is great interest in high energy neutrino interactions because the following problems, amongst many others, may be solved:

(1) Are the neutrinos emitted in the pion and muon decays identical with those emitted in beta decay?†

(2) Is the law of conservation of leptons valid for very high energy lepton interactions and decays? The study of the elastic scattering of high energy neutrinos and antineutrinos by electrons would be of value as only leptons are involved (see next question, however).

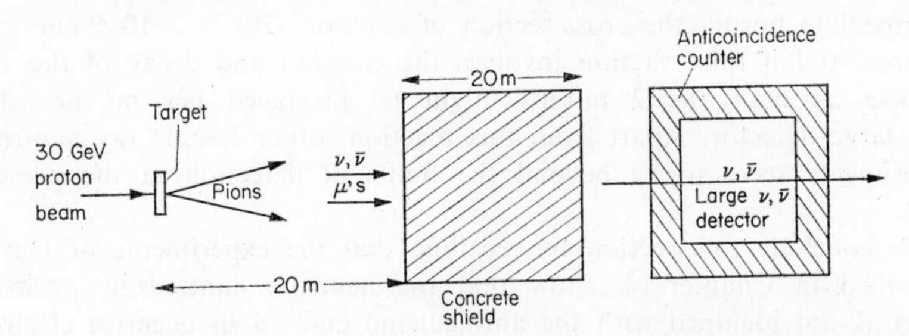

FIG. 5. Schematic arrangement for high energy neutrino and antineutrino experiments (F. REINES, *Ann. Review, Nuclear Science*, **10**, 1, 1960).

(3) Do weak interactions involving neutrinos take place through an intermediate boson stage analogous to the meson exchange theory of strong nuclear interactions?

The concept of an intermediate boson, usually denoted by Z or W, as a transmitter of the weak interaction has been considered by many authors††. If the W boson (sometimes known as a *schizon*) exists, its spin is probably one unit and its mass must exceed that of the K meson (967 electron mass units) in order to prevent the fast decay

$$K^{\pm} \rightarrow W^{\pm} + \gamma \tag{19}$$

Lee and Yang conclude that four types of schizon may exist: W^+, W^-, W^0 and $\overline{W^0}$.

One of the most exciting possibilities of the intermediate boson hypothesis is the appearance of a resonance in neutrino cross sections. Thus if $m_W \sim m_N$, where m_N is the nucleon mass, the resonance energy is estimated to be about 10^{12} eV; and if $m_W \sim m_K$, where K is the kaon mass, the resonance should occur near $2{\cdot}3 \times 10^{11}$ eV.

To illustrate the importance of these speculations, consider the possible antineutrino reaction

$$\bar{\nu} + e^- \rightarrow \bar{\nu} + \mu^- \tag{20}$$

† See Appendix C 2, p 789.

†† S. GLASHOW, *Phys. Rev.* **118**, 316, 1960; T. D. LEE and C. N. YANG, *Phys. Rev.* **119**, 1410, 1960; T. KINOSHITA, *Phys. Rev. Letters* **4**, 378, 1960.

The cross section for this process rises to the "enormous" value of 10^{-32} cm² at resonance, if the reaction occurs through the intermediate boson state W^-

$$\bar{\nu} + e^- \rightarrow W^- \rightarrow \bar{\nu} + \mu^- \quad (21)$$

The flux of antineutrinos at the surface of the earth from the decay of pions and muons produced in the atmosphere by the primary cosmic radiation, is estimated as 400 per cm² per hour. The average energy of these antineutrinos is a few hundred MeV. Even in the absence of the intermediate boson, the cross section of reaction (20) is $> 10^{-38}$ cm² per electron and if this reaction involves the creation and decay of the W^- particle as many as 2 muons might be produced per m² per day in a large detector. Apart from this reaction, other cosmic ray neutrino experiments seem to be beyond the limits of detection at the present time.

We conclude this section by recalling that the experiments of Davis, described in Chapter 14, show that the neutrino emitted in positron decay is not identical with the antineutrino emitted in negative electron decay.

$$\nu \neq \bar{\nu}$$

Davis showed that the reaction cross section for

$$\bar{\nu} + Cl^{37} \rightarrow Ar^{37} + e^- \quad (22)$$

is less than one tenth of the theoretical value on the assumption $\bar{\nu} = \nu$. Presumably if large neutrino fluxes were available on the earth, the reaction $\nu + Cl^{37} \rightarrow Ar^{37} + e^-$ could be detected.

21.5. THE MUON

The muon is without doubt the most mysterious of the elementary particles. There is good reason to believe that, apart from its decay process into an electron, the muon has all the characteristics of a heavy electron.

The rest mass of the muon has been accurately determined in the following way. Negative muons slowing down in matter are eventually captured into Bohr-like orbits. These muon orbits are much closer to the nucleus than the electron orbits because the orbit radius varies inversely as the mass of the particle. In the last few quantum jumps from one orbit to another, muonic X-rays are radiated†. For high Z absorbers, the $1s$ muon orbits penetrate the nucleus and the finite size of the nucleus strongly affects the energies of the radiated X-rays (Chapter 9,

† A good review article on mesonic X-rays is; M. B. Stearns, *Prog. Nucl. Phys.* **6**, 108, 1957.

Section 2). For elements of low atomic number, the M and L muonic X-rays have energies in good agreement with the Bohr theory (large muon orbits). Devons and co-workers† have determined the muon mass m_μ by measuring the mass absorption coefficient of the $3D_{5/2} \rightarrow 2P_{3/2}$ muon transition of phosphorus ($Z = 15$) in lead. A negative muon brought to rest in the phosphorus is recorded by a coincidence between pulses from counters 1, 2, 3, 4 and an anti-coincidence in counter 5 (Fig. 6). A muonic X-ray photon is recorded (in coincidence) by a sodium iodide detector D placed behind a lead absorber. According to the Bohr theory (corrected for reduced mass and Dirac fine structure, etc.), the wave number of the $3D_{5/2} \rightarrow 2P_{3/2}$ transition is

$$\bar{\nu} = R_\infty \left(\frac{1}{2^2} - \frac{1}{3^2}\right) Z^2 (1{\cdot}001163) \frac{m_\mu}{m_e} \tag{23}$$

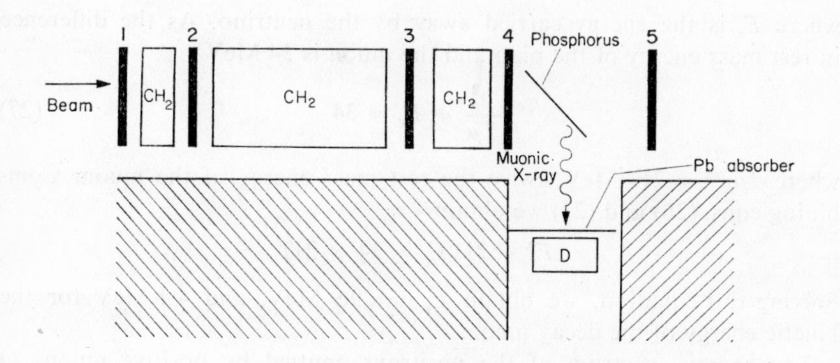

FIG. 6. Determination of negative muon rest mass (S. DEVONS *et. al.*†).

For $Z = 15$, the photon energy $E = hc\bar{\nu} \sim 88$ keV, and this energy falls on the steep part of the Pb K absorption edge, the mass absorption coefficient of the muonic X-ray in Pb enables the photon energy and wave number to be determined with high precision. The ratio of the muon and electron mass m_μ/m_e is calculated using eq. (23). Devons obtained

$$E(3D_{5/2} - 2P_{3/2}) = 88{,}017^{+15}_{-10}\,\text{eV} \tag{24}$$

yielding the result

$$m_\mu = (206{\cdot}78^{+0{\cdot}03}_{-0{\cdot}02})\, m_e \tag{25}$$

This mass ratio is in excellent agreement with the value obtained by Lanthrop *et al.*, quoted in Chapter 16, Section 4.

† S. DEVONS *et al.*, *Phys. Rev. Letters* **5**, 330, 1960.

$\pi \rightarrow \mu \rightarrow e$ decay

Muons emitted by charged pions at rest in a photographic emulsion all have the same range (apart from straggling) of 610 microns, corresponding to the emission of a muon of kinetic energy 4·1 MeV. This observation is understandable from the proposed decay scheme

$$\pi^+ \rightarrow \mu^+ + \nu$$

$$\text{Spins}\quad 0 \qquad \tfrac{1}{2} \qquad \tfrac{1}{2}$$

Both angular and linear momentum are conserved for the decay of a pion at rest, provided the muon and neutrino spins are antiparallel and they move away in opposite directions. Thus the linear momentum of the muon is

$$p_\mu = \frac{E_\nu}{c} \tag{26}$$

where E_ν is the energy carried away by the neutrino. As the difference in rest mass energy of the pion and the muon is 34 MeV

$$\frac{p_\mu^2}{2\mu} + E_\nu = 34 \tag{27}$$

where $2\mu c^2 = 211$ MeV, twice the rest mass energy of the muon. Combining eqns. (26) and (27) we obtain

$$E_\nu^2 + 211 E_\nu = 34 \times 211$$

Solving this equation, we obtain $E_\nu = 29{\cdot}9$ MeV, and 4·1 MeV for the kinetic energy of the decay muon.

The energy spectrum of the positrons emitted by positive muons at rest is shown in Fig. 10, Chapter 14. The shape of the spectrum is compatible with the three-particle decay

$$\mu^+ \rightarrow e^+ + \nu + \bar{\nu}$$

The end point energy of the positron spectrum, ~ 54 MeV, corresponds to the neutrino and the antineutrino travelling in the same direction, which is opposite to the direction of the decay positron. If the neutrino and antineutrino have opposite helicities, the sum of their spins is zero when the particles travel in the same direction; the positron spin is therefore parallel to that of the muon at the instant of decay.

Mean-life of Muon

The mean-life of the muon has been determined by several methods. These determinations normally make use of a delayed coincidence circuit. In the determination of Rossi and Nereson†, cosmic ray muons stopped in an absorbing block are recorded by an anticoincidence circuit. The

† B. Rossi and N. Nereson, *Phys. Rev.* **64**, 199, 1943.

decay electron emitted t microseconds later is detected by a battery of counters surrounding the absorbing block. The delayed coincidence rate as a function of t for a large number of observed decays enables the mean life for muons at rest to be determined. With the advent of fast efficient detectors (scintillation counters) and much higher flux muon beams, produced by the decay of artificially generated pions, more accurate delayed coincidence measurements became possible.The accepted value of the muon mean lifetime (in the rest frame of the muon) is

$$2{\cdot}21 \times 10^{-6} \text{ sec}$$

Muon Spin and Magnetic Moment

The expected magnetic moment of the muon, if it behaves purely as a heavy electron, is close to

$$2 \cdot \frac{e}{2m_{\mu} c} \cdot \frac{\hbar}{2}$$

where m_{μ} is the muon rest mass. The observed gyromagnetic ratio of the muon supports this hypothesis, provided we assume that the muon is a spin $\frac{1}{2}$ particle. There is no reason to doubt this spin assignment.

A very accurate direct determination of the anomalous part of the muon g-factor has recently been conducted at CERN (see Chapt. 16, Sect. 4). This determination demonstrated that the muon behaves in all respects as a heavy electron. An upper limit of the muon radius was obtained from this experiment

$$r_{\mu} \leqq 0{\cdot}25 \text{ fermi}$$

Non-conservation of Parity in $\pi \to \mu \to e$ Sequence

The discovery that the muons emitted in the decay of charged pions are longitudinally polarized is definite proof that parity is not conserved in this weak interaction. At the end of its life, when the muon decays into an electron, the electrons are found to be strongly polarized, proving that parity is also violated in this weak interaction.

It is interesting to realize that the violation of the parity law in the decay of the pion and the muon could have been discovered as soon as a few hundred $\pi \to \mu \to e$ tracks in emulsion plates had been recorded. Thus it is found that the majority of muons brought to rest emit their decay electrons *backwards*, that is, opposite to the direction from which the muons have come. The "memory" of the direction of motion of the stopped muon is the longitudinal polarization of the spin axis of the muon. In addition, the direction of emission of the electron must be correlated with the spin orientation of the muon at the instant of decay.

The longitudinal polarization (helicity) of positrons emitted in the decay of positive muons has been investigated by many workers. The classic experiment in this field is that of Garwin, Lederman and Weinrich† at Columbia University (Fig. 7). In this experiment, the positive muons, produced by the decay of 85 MeV positive pions from a cyclotron target, are brought to rest in a block of graphite G. Very few pions enter this block, they have nearly all been stopped in the tee-shaped absorber T.

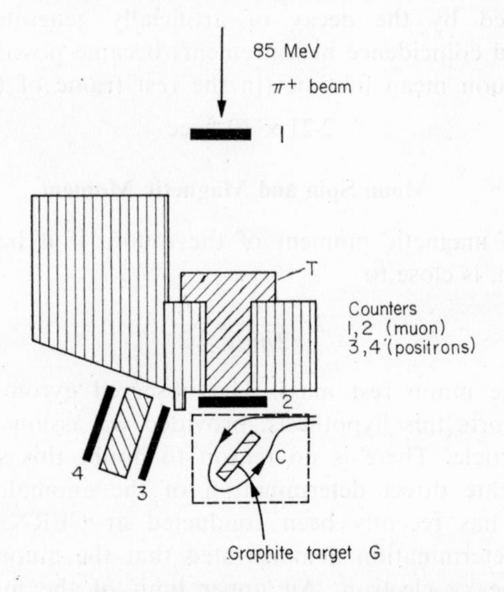

FIG. 7. Experiment of Garwin, Lederman and Weinrich (*Phys. Rev.*, **105**, 1415, 1957). Stopping of positive muon in target G is signalled by a fast 1–2 coincidence. Counters 3 and 4 constitute a positron telescope.

The muons stopped in the graphite block G precess around a steady vertical magnetic field H, which could be varied from about -500 to $+500$ oersted. In a field of 60 oersted, the Larmor precession frequency ν_L of a muon is about 1 Mc/s. Positrons of energy > 25 MeV emitted between 0·75 and 2·0 μsec after the entry and stoppage of a positive muon in the target G, are recorded by a positron counter telescope 3 and 4 (Fig. 7) fixed in space at an angle of about 100°. The positron counting rate as a function of the magnetizing current I in the coil C is measured, and is found to exhibit a cyclic behaviour (Fig. 8). The magnitude of I is directly proportional to the angle through which the muon spin axis has turned by the time the muon decays.

The angular distribution of positrons from polarized muons is

$$I_{e^+} \propto 1 + A \langle \boldsymbol{\sigma}_{\mu+} \rangle \cdot \boldsymbol{p}_{e+}$$

$\boldsymbol{\sigma}_{\mu+}$ is a unit vector parallel to the muon spin, and $\boldsymbol{p}_{e+}$ is a unit vector parallel to the linear momentum of the positron. In the arrangement

† R. L. GARWIN, L. M. LEDERMAN and M. WEINRICH, *Phys. Rev.* **105**, 1415, 1957.

of Fig. 7, the positron counting rate satisfies the equation

$$R(H, t) = \left[1 + r\,\alpha \cos\left(\frac{e\,H\,t}{m\,c} + \varphi_0\right)\right] \exp(-\lambda\, t)$$

where the gyromagnetic ratio of the muon is taken as $e/(m\,c)$ (m is the muon mass) and φ_0 is an angle depending on the geometry of the counter telescopes. Unfortunately some depolarization of the muons from their time of stoppage at $t = 0$ to their decay at time t occurs; $r(\leqq 1)$ represents this depolarization. λ is the reciprocal of the mean lifetime of a muon ($\sim 5 \times 10^5\ \text{sec}^{-1}$). The solid curve of Fig. 8 is computed from a $\left(1 - \frac{\cos\theta}{3}\right)$ positron distribution. The experimental results clearly demonstrate the failure of parity conservation in muon decay, as the distribution of emission directions of the positrons is peaked backwards with respect to the muon motion.

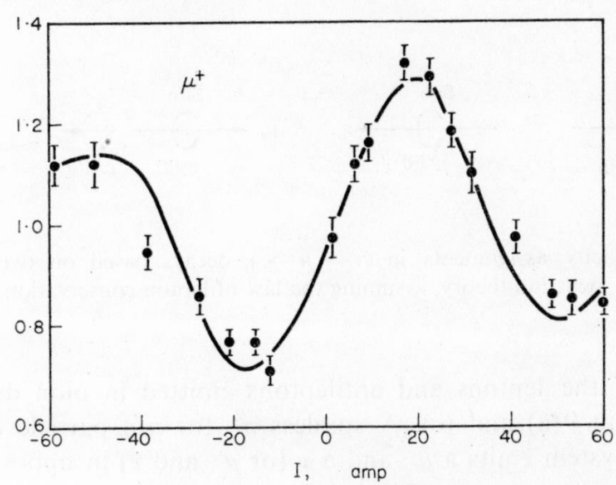

FIG. 8. Results of Garwin, Lederman and Weinrich experiment. The ordinate is the ratio of the positron counting rate with and without an applied magnetic field H. ($H = 79$ oersted per ampere.)

Helicities of Leptons and Antileptons in $\pi \to \mu \to e$ Sequence

According to the two-component neutrino theory, which assumes that neutrinos and antineutrinos are 100 per cent longitudinally polarized, the helicities of the muons, electrons, and neutrinos emitted in the $\pi \to \mu \to e$ decay sequence are

$$\mathscr{H} = -1 \quad \text{for } \nu \tag{28a}$$

$$\mathscr{H} = 1 \quad \text{for } \bar{\nu} \tag{28b}$$

$$\mathscr{H} > 0 \quad \text{for } e^+ \text{ in } \mu^+ \text{ decay} \tag{28c}$$

$$\mathscr{H} < 0 \quad \text{for } e^- \text{ in } \mu^- \text{ decay} \tag{28d}$$

$$\mathscr{H} > 0 \quad \text{for } \mu^- \text{ in } \pi^- \text{ decay} \tag{28e}$$

$$\mathscr{H} < 0 \quad \text{for } \mu^+ \text{ in } \pi^+ \text{ decay} \tag{28f}$$

The positive helicity of positrons in muon decay has been established at Liverpool by Culligan *et al.*† This helicity assignment is based on the observation that the bremsstrahlung photons generated by positrons from muon decays have a right sense of circular polarization, which shows up in the Compton scattering in magnetized iron. As a bremsstrahlung photon *inherits* the positron polarization this experiment determines the left- or right-handedness of the positron polarization. The degree of polarization is greater than 50 per cent and may be 100 per cent. The

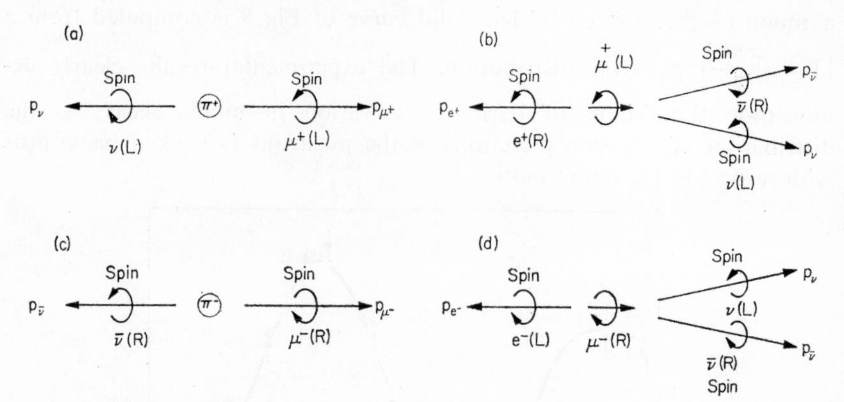

FIG. 9. Helicity assignments in $\pi \rightarrow \mu \rightarrow e$ decays based on two-component neutrino theory, assuming the law of lepton conservation.

helicities of the leptons and antileptons emitted in pion decay are illustrated in Fig. 9(a) and (c). A spinless π^+ (or π^-) particle at rest in the laboratory system emits a μ^+ and a ν (or μ^- and $\bar{\nu}$) in opposite directions with opposite momentum. Viewed from the position of the decay of the pion, the μ^+ spins anticlockwise as it recedes, the ν anticlockwise (the opposite sense of spin applies to π^- decay). In Fig. 9(b) and (d) the decays of slowly moving muons are depicted. The illustrations apply to the case when the decay electron (positron) nearly has its maximum share of the decay energy (the ν and $\bar{\nu}$ travel in nearly the same direction). The helicity assignments agree with the law of conservation of angular momentum and satisfy the rule that particle and antiparticle always have opposite helicities.

Recently a group†† in Russia has investigated the helicities of cosmic ray muons. They confirmed that the muons in the decay $\pi^+ \rightarrow \mu^+ + \nu$ have a negative helicity (28*f*), and those from the decay $\pi^- \rightarrow \mu^- + \bar{\nu}$ have a positive helicity (28c).

† G. CULLIGAN *et al.*, *Nature* **180**, 751, 1957.

†† V. A. LYUBIMOV, p. 539, *Proc. Intern. Conf. High Energy Physics*, Rochester 1960.

Negative Muon Orbital Capture

Negative muons captured into Bohr orbits surrounding nuclei may undergo nuclear capture instead of radioactive decay

$$\mu^- + p \rightarrow n + \nu + 100 \text{ MeV} \tag{29}$$

This capture process is analogous to orbital electron capture, and the probability of its occurrence depends on the atomic number Z of the nucleus. For medium and low Z, the capture cross section varies as Z^4, and for $Z \sim 11$, the nuclear capture rate is equal to the spontaneous $\mu \rightarrow e$ decay rate. The neutrino emitted in reaction (29) carries away most of the excitation energy, which is quite large because of the large rest mass energy of the muon (106 MeV).

21.6. THE PION

The pion is a spinless boson which has three different charge states: π^+, π^0 and π^-. The π^+ is the antiparticle of the π^-, and π^0 is its own antiparticle. It is convenient to assign to the pion a total isospin $T = 1$, with the three possible third component values $T_3 = 1,\ 0,\ -1$ corresponding to the π^+, π^0 and π^- states respectively.

The rest mass of the negative pion can be found by comparing the observed pionic X-ray energies for the $4f$–$3d$ orbit transitions in media of low atomic number ($Z < 20$) with the theoretical expression which contains m_π as an unknown parameter. The only important correction to the Bohr formula, apart from the reduced mass, is the effect of vacuum polarization (0·2 to 0·3 per cent). From critical absorption edge observations the rest mass of the negative pion is

$$m_{\pi^-} = (273{\cdot}2 \pm 0{\cdot}1)\, m_e \tag{30}$$

Determinations of the positive pion mass do not contradict† the assumption that

$$m_{\pi^-} = m_{\pi^+}$$

The mass of the neutral pion is found by a quite different method.†† Negative pions are slowed down and then absorbed in high pressure hydrogen gas (200 atm) in a steel vessel. Two reactions are observed

$$\pi^- + p \rightarrow n + \gamma \tag{31}$$

$$\left.\begin{aligned} \pi^- + p &\rightarrow n + \pi^0 \quad (32\text{a}) \\ \pi^0 &\rightarrow 2\gamma \quad (32\text{b}) \end{aligned}\right\}$$

† p. 34, E. R. COHEN, K. M. CROWE and J. W. M. DUMOND, *Fundamental Constants of Physics*, Interscience, New York 1957.

†† W. K. H. PANOFSKY *et al.*, *Phys. Rev.* **81**, 565, 1951; K. M. CROWE and R. H. PHILLIPS, *Phys. Rev.* **96**, 470, 1954.

Process (31) leads to the production of photons whose lab. energy is peaked around 130 MeV. The competing process described by eqns. (32) is the one we are interested in. Monoenergetic neutral pions are produced which take a fraction $m_n/m_n + m_{\pi^0}$ of the available energy (the neutron and the neutral pion move away with equal but opposite momenta). The fact that reaction (32) occurs with zero energy negative pions shows that the charged pion–neutral pion mass difference is greater than the neutron–proton mass difference. The neutral pion produced when the proton captures a zero energy negative pion has a kinetic energy of the order of 3 MeV. It decays about 10^{-16} sec later into two photons (each of energy about 70 MeV) which are emitted in opposite directions with equal momentum in the centre of mass system of the π^0 meson. Presumably the decay photons are isotropically distributed in the centre of mass system. The energies of the decay photons are measured (in the lab. system) by observing the energies of the electron–positron pairs created in a thin tantalum converter (pair spectrometers are described in Chapter 13). The observed photon energies in the lab. system range from

$$E_{\gamma\,\mathrm{min}} = \tfrac{1}{2}\, m_{\pi^0}\, c^2(1-\beta)(1-\beta^2)^{-\frac{1}{2}} \tag{33}$$

to

$$E_{\gamma\,\mathrm{max}} = \tfrac{1}{2}\, m_{\pi^0}\, c^2(1+\beta)(1-\beta^2)^{-\frac{1}{2}} \tag{34}$$

These limits are obtained from the relativistic Doppler formula (eqn. (28) Chapt. 3) for a π^0 decaying at the instant its speed is $\beta\, c$. It is easy to see that

$$p_{\pi^0}\, c = E_{\gamma\,\mathrm{max}} - E_{\gamma\,\mathrm{min}} = \Delta E_\gamma \tag{35}$$

where p_{π^0} is the momentum of the neutral pion corresponding to the speed $\beta\, c$. The observed spread ΔE_γ is ~ 30 MeV, centred around 70 MeV. The rest mass energy difference $(m_{\pi^-} - m_{\pi^0})\, c^2$ can be expanded

$$(m_{\pi^-} - m_{\pi^0})\, c^2 = (m_n - m_p)\, c^2 + \frac{\alpha^2\, c^2\, m_{\pi^-}}{2} + \frac{\frac{1}{2}(m_p + m_{\pi^-})\,\Delta E_\gamma^2}{[m_{\pi^-} - (m_n - m_p)]\, m_n\, c^2} + \cdots \tag{36}$$

The second term on the right (α is the fine structure constant) is the pion binding energy in a $1s$ Bohr orbit. The third term is the kinetic energy of the π^0. Substitution of ΔE_γ and the known masses, m_n, m_p, m_{π^-} in eqn. (36) yields a value for $m_{\pi^-} - m_{\pi^0}$

The value of $(m_{\pi^-} - m_{\pi^0})\, c^2$ is 4·6 MeV corresponding to

$$m_{\pi^-}\, c^2 = (139{\cdot}59 \pm 0{\cdot}05)\ \mathrm{MeV}$$
$$m_{\pi^0}\, c^2 = (135{\cdot}00 \pm 0{\cdot}05)\ \mathrm{MeV}$$

Mean-life of the Charged and Neutral Pion

The mean lifetimes of the charged varieties of pion have been determined by several methods. These include: measuring the ratio of the number of charged pions that survive in describing a definite arc of a spiral path in a magnetic field†, delayed coincidence measurements,†† and observations of the attenuation by decay over a definite flight length.††† In the delayed coincidence method charged pions are brought to rest in a scintillator, and the time interval between the pulse heralding the arrival of the π^+ in the crystal and the characteristic 4·2 MeV μ^+ pulse is measured, either by photographing the pulses on an oscilloscope, or inserting known time delays using calibrated lengths of delay cable. The $\pi^+ \rightarrow \mu^+ + \nu$ decay is identified by the positron pulse associated with the subsequent $\mu^+ \rightarrow e^+ + \bar{\nu} + \nu$ decay. The third method††† involves counting a total of about 50,000 charged pions (π^+ or π^-) and measuring the attenuation over a path length of about 6 ft. The best value of the mean lifetime of the charged pion is obtained from combining several measurements and is

$$(2{\cdot}55 \pm 0{\cdot}03)\ 10^{-8}\ \text{sec}$$

The decay of the neutral pion is much faster and therefore more difficult to measure than that of the charged type of pion. It is assumed that the decay of the π^0 goes through a virtual intermediate nucleon–antinucleon state $\pi^0 \rightarrow N + \bar{N} \rightarrow 2\gamma$ (N denotes a nucleon, $\bar{N}$ an antinucleon). This two stage decay involves both the strong and electromagnetic interactions but not the weak interaction; thus the mean life of the π^0 is short ($\sim 10^{-16}$ sec) and the parity law is satisfied (see later). According to a prediction of Dalitz the decay

$$\pi^0 \rightarrow \gamma + e^+ + e^- \tag{37}$$

should occur in 1·24 per cent of the total π^0 decays. This prediction has been verified; and a measurement of the mean length (unfortunately, this is a small fraction of a micron) of the gap between the origin of the $e^+ e^-$ tracks‡ in a photographic emulsion and a cosmic ray "star", where the π^0 was created, enables an upper limit to the π^0 mean lifetime to be determined.

A more accurate method of measuring the π^0 mean lifetime, is to measure the mean distance between the end of a track of a K^+ meson brought to rest in a photographic emulsion, and the origin of a Dalitz electron positron pair (Fig. 10). The sequence of events is

$$K^+ \rightarrow \pi^+ + \pi^0 + 219\ \text{MeV} \tag{38}$$

$$\pi^0 \rightarrow \gamma + e^+ + e^-\ \text{(in 1·24 per cent decays)} \tag{39}$$

The mean decay distance in an Ilford L-4 emulsion for the flight path of the π^0 is 0·122 ± 0·045 microns.‡‡ This leads to an estimate for the neutral pion mean lifetime of

$$(2{\cdot}3 \pm 0{\cdot}8) \times 10^{-16}\ \text{sec}$$

† E. A. Martinelli and W. K. Panofsky, *Phys. Rev.* **77**, 465, 1950.

†† C. E. Wiegand, *Phys. Rev.* **83**, 1085, 1951; M. Jakobson *et al.*, *Phys. Rev.* **81**, 894, 1951.

††† R. P. Durbin *et al.*, *Phys. Rev.* **88**, 179, 1952.

‡ The $e^+ e^-$ is called a Dalitz pair in the decay of the π^0.

‡‡ R. G. Glasser *et al.*, p. 30, *Proc. Intern. Conf. High Energy Physics*, Rochester 1960.

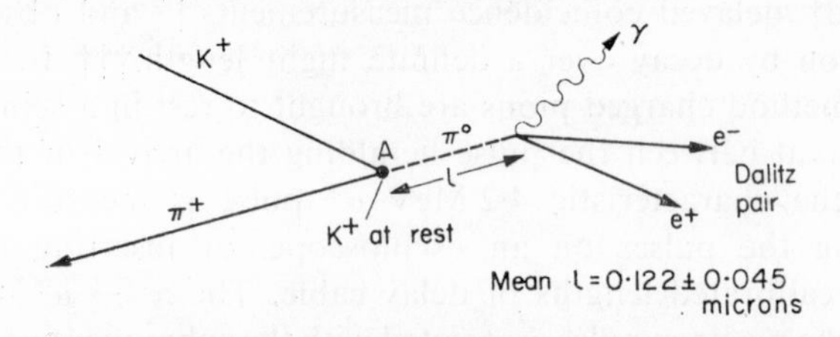

FIG. 10. K^+ comes to rest at A in nuclear emulsion and subsequently decays into π^+ and π^0. These pions move apart with opposite momenta, and after traversing a short path l in the laboratory system the π^0 decays into a γ-ray and a Dalitz pair. (N.B. the distance l' in the rest frame of the π^0 is foreshortened to l by the Lorentz contraction.)

Intrinsic Spin of the π^+, π^-, and π^0 Particles

The intrinsic spin of the π^+ particle (and therefore presumably of the π^-) is deduced by the following observations and argument. The cross section for the reaction

$$p + p \rightarrow d + \pi^+ \tag{40}$$

has been measured† for incident protons of 340 MeV energy (L-system). This produces π^+ particles of 21 MeV in the centre-of-mass system. The cross section for reaction (40) is

$$\sigma_1 = \frac{2\pi}{\hbar\, v_p} |M(E)|^2 \varrho(\pi, d) \tag{41}$$

where v_p is the velocity of the proton, and $\varrho(\pi, d)$ is the density of energy states per unit energy range of the π, d system. $M(E)$ is the appropriate matrix element for the transition at energy E. Now consider the reverse reaction

$$\pi^+ + d \rightarrow p + p \tag{42}$$

The reaction cross section is

$$\sigma_2 = \frac{2\pi}{\hbar\, v_\pi} |M(E)|^2 \varrho(p, p) \tag{43}$$

By the well-known statistical theorem of detailed balance,†† the matrix elements $M(E)$ in eqns. (41) and (43) are the same provided the cross sections are measured at the same energy. The reaction cross section σ_2 has been measured for the $\pi^+ + d \rightarrow p + p$ process†††. At the same energy E, dividing eqn. (41) by eqn. (43) we get

$$\frac{\sigma_1}{\sigma_2} = \frac{v_\pi}{v_p} \frac{\varrho(\pi, d)}{\varrho(p, p)} \tag{44}$$

† W. F. CARTWRIGHT *et al.*, *Phys. Rev.* **81**, 652, 1951.

†† See pp. 142–146, E. FERMI, *Nuclear Physics*, University of Chicago 1950.

††† D. L. CLARK *et al.*, *Phys. Rev.*, **83**, 649, 1951; R. DURBIN *et al.*, *Phys. Rev.* **83**, 646, 1951.

The density of states $\varrho(\pi, d)$ contains the statistical spin factor $2s + 1$, where s is the intrinsic spin of the pion (in units of $\hbar$). All the other factors involved in eqn. (44) can be calculated, and it is found that $2s + 1$ is equal to 1; hence $s = 0$. If the π^+ particle had spin 1, the factor $2s + 1$ would be 3, which would increase the ratio σ_1/σ_2 in eqn. (44) threefold, an easily detected increase.

The spin of the neutral pion cannot be determined directly. If we assume that the spin of the π^0 particle is 0 or 1 unit, it can be shown that the observation that the π^0 decays into two photons and never into three photons, implies that the intrinsic spin must be zero. The argument leading to this conclusion is lucidly presented by Matthews.†

To conserve angular momentum the spinless π^0 particle must decay by emitting two photons with equal but opposite linear momentum (in the rest system of the π^0), and both photons must be right (or left) circularly polarized from the point of view of an observer at the position of the decay. Parity conservation imposes an extra restriction: in a large number of π^0 decays neither right nor left circularly polarized photons must predominate. This prediction has been verified by Garwin††. Notice that the decay of π^0 through the virtual state $\pi^0 \rightarrow N + \overline{N}$, and the annihilation process $N + \overline{N} \rightarrow 2\gamma$, both must conserve parity.

Intrinsic Parity of the Negative Pion

The intrinsic parity of the negative pion has been established in the following way. Negative pions are slowed down and captured into Bohr orbits in deuterium gas under pressure. Nearly all the negative pions cascade down to the $1s$ orbit before they are captured by the deuterium nucleus. As the pion is a spinless particle, and a $1s$ state has zero angular momentum, no angular momentum is absorbed by the deuteron when it absorbs the negative pion. Three reactions have a positive Q, and these are

$$\pi^- + d \rightarrow n + n \tag{45a}$$

$$\pi^- + d \rightarrow n + n + \gamma \tag{45b}$$

$$\pi^- + d \rightarrow n + n + \pi^0 \tag{45c}$$

Reaction (45c) is, however, not observed. Panofsky proved that reaction (45a) does occur and measured the cross section ratio†††

$$S = \frac{\sigma(\pi^- + d \rightarrow n + n)}{\sigma(\pi^- + d \rightarrow n + n + \gamma)} = 2{\cdot}36 \pm 0{\cdot}74$$

† P. T. Matthews, *Rep. Progress in Physics* **18**, 453, 1955, The Physical Society London.

†† R. L. Garwin *et al.*, *Phys. Rev.* **108**, 1589, 1957.

††† W. K. H. Panofsky *et al.*, *Phys. Rev.* **81**, 565, 1951; J. A. Kuehner *et al.*, *Proc. Phys. Soc.* **73**, 551, 1959.

The initial angular momentum of the $\pi^- + d$ system is one; thus the $n + n$ system formed by reaction (45a) must be in a $J = 1$ state. The wave function of the n, n system must be antisymmetric with respect to the exchange of the two identical fermions (neutrons). Some of the possible states are

$$^1S_0;\ ^3P_0,\ ^3P_1,\ ^3P_2;\ ^1D_2$$

For L-even, the nucleon spins must be antiparallel ($S = 0$), and for L-odd, the nucleon spins must be parallel. The only state with $J = 1$, however, is the $^3P_1$ state, which has *odd* parity (L-odd). The parity of the deuteron is *even* (it is in an S plus D state, see Chapter 19), and the parity of the system $\pi^- + d$ is the product of the intrinsic parities of the negative pion and the deuteron. Conservation of parity requires the parity of the final n, n system to be the same as the $\pi^- + d$ system. Thus the intrinsic parity of the negative pion is *negative*. The negative parity of the pion implies that the pion wave function φ is a *pseudoscalar*: that is, on inversion through the origin of coordinates

$$\boldsymbol{r} \rightarrow -\boldsymbol{r}, \quad \varphi(-\boldsymbol{r}) = -\varphi(\boldsymbol{r})$$

The Scattering of Charged Pions by Protons

One of the most fruitful ways of obtaining information about the pion–nucleon interaction, is to measure the total and differential cross sections for the following elastic processes over a wide range of energy:

$$\pi^+ + p \rightarrow \pi^+ + p \tag{46}$$

$$\pi^- + p \rightarrow \pi^- + p \tag{47}$$

$$\pi^- + p \rightarrow \pi^0 + n \tag{48}$$

The third reaction is known as charge exchange scattering. At incident pion energies greater than 200 or 300 MeV competing reactions involving multi-pion production become important. These will not be considered here.

The scattering cross sections for reactions (46), (47) and (48) have been measured using a variety of experimental techniques. These include: hydrogen-filled diffusion cloud chambers, photographic emulsions, and liquid hydrogen bubble chambers. The total cross sections for the scattering of positive and negative pions by protons as a function of the incident kinetic energy of the pions in the laboratory system, up to 1600 MeV, are shown in Fig. 11. Above 500 MeV, some of the most accurate data has been obtained using elaborate scintillation counter telescopes. The detector system used by Wood† and co-workers at Berkeley is depicted in Fig. 12. An elastic scattering event is registered by a coincidence in the pion beam monitor scintillators M_1 and M_2, and a corresponding proton–pion pair

† C. D. Wood *et al., Bull. Am. Phys. Soc.* **5**, 509, 1960.

of counters (1 and 1, 2 and 2, . . ., etc). The pairs of proton–pion counters are placed at the correct angular positions to satisfy the kinematics of an elastic collision occurring in the hydrogen target.

What can be learnt about the pion–nucleon interaction from the study of the $\pi^+ - p$ and $\pi^- - p$ total scattering cross section curves shown in Fig. 11?

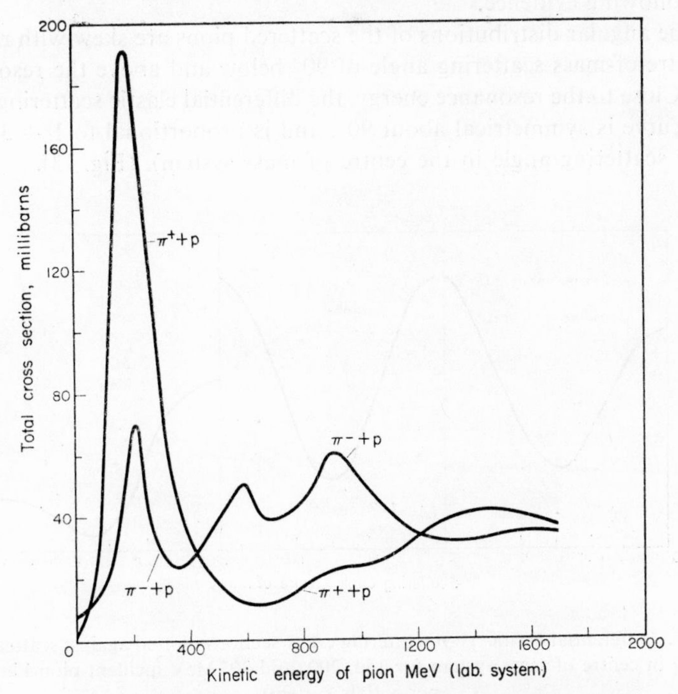

FIG. 11. Total scattering cross sections of positive and negative pions by protons as a function of the pion kinetic energy (L-system).

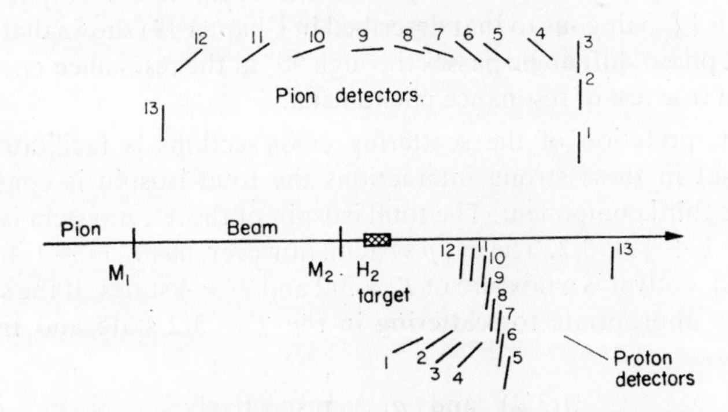

FIG. 12. Experimental arrangement for observing π–p elastic scattering (C. D. WOOD *et. al.*, *Bull. Am. Phys. Soc.* **5**, 509, 1960).

Let us, for the moment, concentrate on the pion energy range 0 to 300 MeV. The dominant features in this energy interval are the pronounced resonance type peaks in the cross sections near 200 MeV, and the considerably greater cross section for $\pi^+ + p$ scattering. That the cross section peak near 200 MeV is a true resonance phenomenon, is supported by the following evidence.

(1) The angular distributions of the scattered pions are skew with respect to a centre-of-mass scattering angle of 90° below and above the resonance energy. Close to the resonance energy, the differential elastic scattering cross section curve is symmetrical about 90°, and is proportional to $1 + 3\cos^2\theta$ (θ is the scattering angle in the centre of mass system). (Fig. 13).

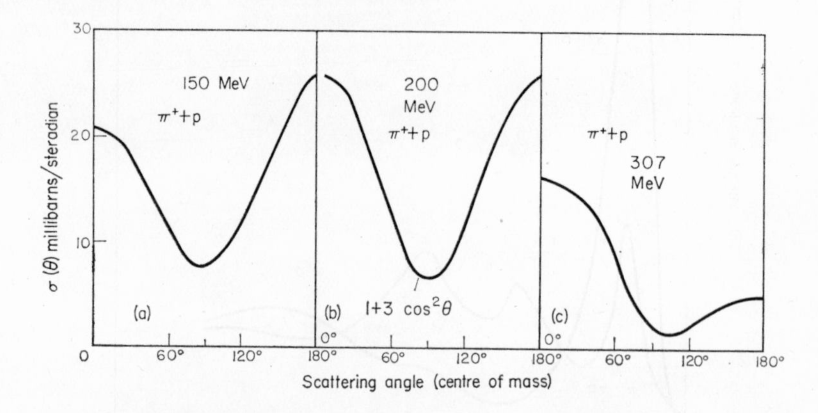

FIG. 13. Differential elastic π^+–p scattering cross sections plotted against scattering angle θ in centre of mass system for 150, 200, and 307 MeV incident pion kinetic energy (lab. system).

(2) An analysis of the cross section curves in terms of partial wave phase shifts† (analogous to that described in Chapter 19) shows that the most important phase shift angle passes through 90° at the resonance energy. This is always a true test of resonance phenomena.

The interpretation of the scattering cross sections is facilitated by assuming that in these strong interactions the total isospin is conserved as well as the third component. The total isospin of the π^+, p system is $T = 3/2$, with $T_3 = 1 + \frac{1}{2} = 3/2$. The π^-, p system, however, has $T_3 = -1 + \frac{1}{2} = -\frac{1}{2}$, and consequently it is a mixture of $T = 3/2$ and $T = \frac{1}{2}$ states. If the scattering amplitudes appropriate to scattering in the $T = 3/2$ state and the $T = \frac{1}{2}$ states are

$$a(3/2) \quad \text{and} \quad a(\tfrac{1}{2}) \quad \text{respectively,}$$

† R. H. DALITZ, *Prog. Nuclear Physics* **4**, 95, 1955.

then it can be shown†, using isospin wave functions, that the total cross sections for processes (46), (47) and (48) are

$$\sigma(+) \propto \left| a\left(\frac{3}{2}\right)\right|^2 \tag{46a}$$

$$\sigma(-) \propto \frac{1}{9}\left|2a\left(\frac{1}{2}\right) + a\left(\frac{3}{2}\right)\right|^2 \tag{47a}$$

$$\sigma(0) \propto \frac{2}{9}\left|a\left(\frac{3}{2}\right) - a\left(\frac{1}{2}\right)\right|^2 \tag{48a}$$

If the $\pi^- - p$ scattering predominantly occurs in the $T = 3/2$ state near 200 MeV, $a(3/2) \gg a(\frac{1}{2})$, and the cross sections satisfy the ratios

$$\sigma(+):\sigma(-):\sigma(0) = 9:1:2$$

This is borne out by a comparison of the cross section curves. Also $\sigma(+):\sigma(-) + \sigma(0) = 3:1$, which is in excellent agreement with the ratio of the peaks of the total $\pi^+ - p$ and $\pi^- - p$ cross section curves near 200 MeV.

Have we any information about the angular momentum state of the $\pi^+ - p$ resonance scattering? For pion energies up to 300 MeV, only s and p wave scattering is likely to be important. The d wave "impact parameter" is beyond the range of the pion–nucleon force. For resonance scattering the maximum cross section is

$$\sigma_{max} = 4\pi \lambda\!\!\!^{-2} \frac{(2J+1)}{(2s_1+1)(2s_2+1)} \tag{49}$$

s_1 is the intrinsic spin of the pion (zero), and s_2 is the intrinsic spin of the target proton ($\frac{1}{2}$). J is the total angular momentum of the $\pi - p$ system. At the peak of the resonance $\pi \lambda\!\!\!^{-2}$ is about 24 millibarns; $\lambda\!\!\!^{-}$ is the reduced wavelength of the pion in the centre of mass system. Thus for $\pi^+ - p$ scattering, where $\sigma_{max} \sim 192$ millibarns,

$$(2J+1) = \frac{2 \times 192}{4 \times 24} = 4$$

$$\therefore\ J = 3/2$$

The peak cross section of $8\pi \lambda\!\!\!^{-2}$ implies that the interaction is dominated by P wave scattering ($J = L + \frac{1}{2} = 3/2$). The resonance scattering of positive pions by protons near 200 MeV is known as the (3/2, 3/2)†† resonance, where the labels refer to the total isospin T and total angular momentum of the system, both of which are "good" quantum numbers. At the peak of the resonance, the phase shift δ_{33} goes through 90°.

† pp. 37–41 and pp. 57–58, W. O. Lock, *High Energy Nuclear Physics*.

†† Sometimes the labels are written $(2T, 2J)$ that is (3,3) in this case. The phase shifts of the partial waves in the various isospin states are labelled $\delta_{2T,\,2J}$ . . . etc.

The $\pi - p$ resonance near 200 MeV represents the fleeting existence of a nucleon in an excited state with a mean lifetime of about 10^{-23} sec, corresponding to the 100 MeV width of the resonance curve. An excited nucleon state of this type is called a nucleon isobar. The excitation energy of this nucleon isobar is about 300 MeV, of which 140 MeV is contributed by the rest mass of the pion, and the remaining 160 MeV is the centre-of-mass energy equivalent of the kinetic energy of the resonance peak in the laboratory system.

The pseudoscalar strong coupling theory of the pion–nucleon interaction† accounts in a natural way for the strong pion–nucleon attraction in the (3/2, 3/2) resonance scattering near 200 MeV. It also gives a satisfactory explanation of the marked difference in the photopion production cross section curves just above the threshold photon energy $E_\gamma \sim 150$ MeV (Fig. 14).

Above charged pion energies of 400 MeV, the $\pi^- - p$ cross section is greater than the $\pi^+ - p$ cross section (Fig. 11). Two resonance peaks occur in the total $\pi^- - p$ cross section curve at 600 and 900 MeV respectively. Peierls†† assigns the 600 MeV resonance to a $D_{3/2}$, $T = \frac{1}{2}$ scattering state. This resonance state appears at a photon energy of 750 MeV (lab.) in the photopion reaction.

The isospin assignment $T = \frac{1}{2}$ is in agreement with the absence of a resonance in the $\pi^+ - p$ cross section near 600 MeV, which has no $T = \frac{1}{2}$ component. The assignment of L and J to the 900 MeV $\pi^- - p$ resonance is less certain, but it may be a mixture of $D_{5/2}$ and $F_{5/2}$ states.†††

Photopion Production from Protons

The following pion creation process is possible with high energy bremsstrahlung;

$$\text{photon} + \text{nucleon} \rightarrow \text{nucleon} + \text{pion}$$

The photon threshold energy for this type of process is (see eqn. (64), Chapter 3)

$$m_\pi c^2 \left(1 + \frac{m_\pi}{2M}\right) \sim 150 \text{ MeV}$$

where $m_\pi c^2$ is the rest mass energy of the pion and M is the rest mass of the nucleon.

The total cross sections, as a function of photon energy E (lab.), for the pion production reactions

$$\gamma + p \rightarrow p + \pi^0$$

$$\gamma + p \rightarrow n + \pi^+$$

† K. A. Brueckner and K. M. Case, *Phys. Rev.* **83**, 1141, 1951; K. A. Brueckner, *Phys. Rev.* **86**, 106, 1952.

†† R. F. Peierls, *Phys. Rev.* **118**, 325, 1960.

††† B. J. Moyer, *Revs. Mod. Phys.* **33**, 367, 1961.

are shown in Fig. 14. The study of reactions such as $\gamma + n \rightarrow p + \pi^-$ requires the use of a deuteron target. Notice that the absolute values of the photopion cross sections are about a thousand times smaller than the $\pi^\pm - p$ scattering cross sections. Apart from this difference in scale, which is partly a consequence of the weaker electromagnetic interaction between the photon and the nucleon, the curves shown in Fig. 11 and Fig. 14 both exhibit large resonance peaks at roughly the same energy. The $\gamma + p \rightarrow p + \pi^0$ resonance at about 320 MeV corresponds to a pion kinetic energy of about 180 MeV. It is therefore reasonable to assume that the photopion resonance also arises from a (3/2, 3/2) pion–nucleon

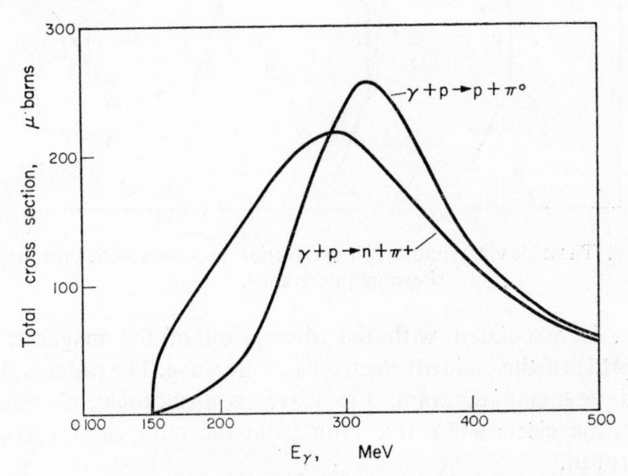

FIG. 14. Total photopion production cross sections for proton target as a function of photon energy E_γ (lab. system).

state. The neutral pion production curve is the simplest to interpret, as there is no electric interaction between the pion and the electromagnetic field; the striking difference between the shapes of the cross section curves just above the threshold photon energy of 150 MeV implies different angular momentum states for the created pion;

$$\sigma(\gamma + p \rightarrow p + \pi^0) \propto \frac{1}{\lambda\!\!\!^{-3}} \quad \text{for } E_\gamma \text{ just } > 150 \text{ MeV}$$

corresponding to an emitted P wave pion, and

$$\sigma(\gamma + p \rightarrow n + \pi^+) \propto \frac{1}{\lambda\!\!\!^{-}} \quad \text{for } E_\gamma \text{ just } > 150 \text{ MeV}$$

corresponding to an emitted S wave pion, where $\lambda\!\!\!^{-}$ is the reduced wavelength of the pion in the centre of mass system.

The theory of photopion production processes is too difficult to discuss here. An elementary account of the theory is given in Chapt. 5 of the book by Lock (see bibliography). Three Feynman diagrams corresponding to different production processes are given in Fig. 15. The first diagram represents the absorption of a photon by a proton and the subsequent emission of a pion. In Fig. 15(b), however, the pion is emitted before the photon is absorbed. This is allowed by the latitude in defining the energy of a system in a short time interval. This "shake-off" transition, to use a term coined

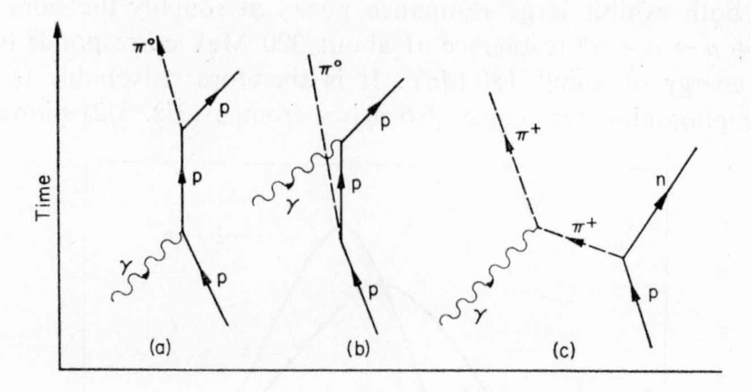

FIG. 15. Three possible photopion production processes with protons (Feynman diagrams).

by Marshak, is associated with the absorption of the magnetic dipole component ($M1$) of the incident electromagnetic wave. The process depicted by the third Feynman diagram, Fig. 15(c), is a photoelectric effect; the incoming photon ejects a positive pion from the pion cloud surrounding the target proton.

21.7. NUCLEONS AND ANTINUCLEONS

As far as we know the major contribution to the mass of the Universe is contributed by protons (if distant galaxies are composed of antimatter, presumably their main mass contribution is due to antiprotons).

The proton is a fermion of intrinsic spin $\frac{1}{2}$, with an electric charge equal but opposite to that of the antiproton. We have seen that it is useful to regard the proton as a particular charge state ($T_3 = +\frac{1}{2}$) of a single particle, the nucleon, of total isospin $T = \frac{1}{2}$.

The proton is a much more complex elementary particle than the electron. This complexity is revealed in several ways: through the strong nuclear interaction with pions, kaons, nucleons and hyperons; and in its large anomalous magnetic moment.

The proton (and the neutron) experiences a large variety of self-energy (virtual) processes. A few of these are schematically shown in the Feynman diagrams of Fig. 16. In Fig. 16(a) the virtual emission and re-absorption of a neutral pion is depicted. This is an example of a *second order* process (two vertices in the Feynman graph). The time interval Δt between the vertices 1 and 2 must, of course, be less than $\hbar/\Delta E$, where ΔE is the energy of the pion. In Fig. 16(b) another second order process is illustrated

$$p \to n + \pi^+ \text{ (virtual)} \to p$$

The nucleon–pion dimensionless coupling constant $g^2/\hbar c$ is ~ 15. This large coupling constant implies that higher order self-energy processes are *not* going to be small effects as they are in electromagnetic processes (here $e^2/\hbar c = 1/137$). A sixth order self-energy process for a neutron is depicted in Fig. 16(c). Here a neutron emits a virtual negative pion at vertex 1, changing into a proton; the negative pion at vertex 2 dissociates into a virtual neutron–antiproton pair (the baryon conservation law is not violated

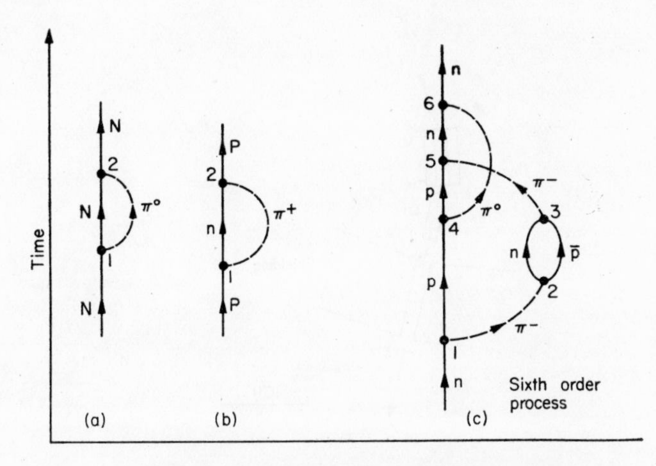

FIG. 16. Feynman diagrams of nucleon self-energy processes: (a) Second order process for proton (or neutron); (b) Second order process for proton (Two vertices); (c) Sixth order process for neutron (Six vertices).

as an antiproton counts as minus one baryon) and the pair recombines at vertex 3; meanwhile the proton emits a neutral pion at vertex 4 and then absorbs the negative pion (vertex 5) before absorbing the neutral pion at vertex 6. The time interval between vertices 1 and 6 is very short as a large amount of energy is associated with some of these virtual processes, especially the production of the neutron–antiproton pair.

The neutron is the isospin state $T_3 = -\frac{1}{2}$ of the nucleon ($T = \frac{1}{2}$). It has zero electric charge but a large anomalous magnetic moment of approximately $-1{\cdot}9$ nuclear magnetons.

The Discovery of the Antiproton

Electron–positron pairs can be created by photons of energy greater than 1·02 MeV (twice the rest mass energy of the electron) in matter. In order to create a proton–antiproton pair much more energy is required.

High energy particles in cosmic radiation should have sufficient energy to create such pairs. A number of cosmic ray events in photographic emulsions and cloud chambers has been suspected of being antiproton interactions. However, the evidence was not very convincing.

The first convincing evidence of the existence of the antiproton (the negative proton) came from the experiment of Chamberlain, Segrè, Wiegand and Ypsilantis† using a beam of 6·3 GeV protons from the Berkeley synchrotron. The apparatus is shown in Fig. 17.

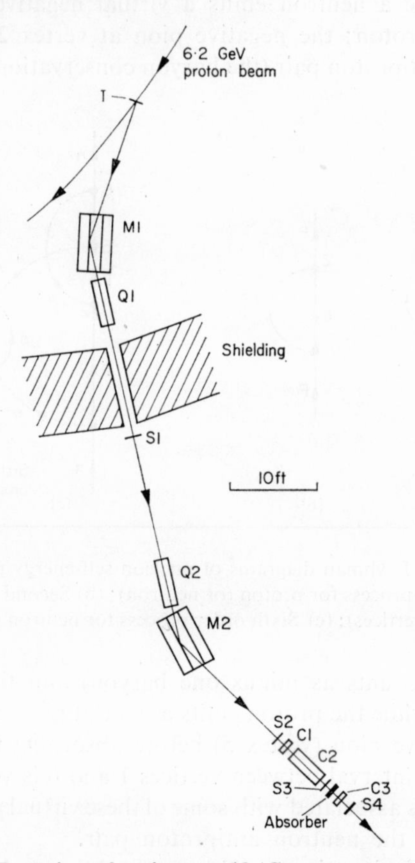

FIG. 17. Detection of antiproton (O. CHAMBERLAIN *et. al.*†).

An internal copper target T of the Berkeley proton synchrotron was bombarded with protons of kinetic energy 6·3 GeV. Antiprotons are produced by collisions between the incoming protons and protons in the target nuclei

$$p + p \rightarrow p + p + (p + \bar{p}) \tag{50}$$

† O. CHAMBERLAIN *et al., Phys. Rev.* **100**, 947, 1955

Negatively charged particles of momentum 1·19 GeV/c were selected by a mass spectrograph consisting of a series of bending magnets M1 and M2 and quadrupole focusing magnets Q1 and Q2.† This selected beam of particles was expected to contain about 50,000 negative pions to every antiproton, thus presenting a formidable detection problem. The identification of the antiprotons was based on the following requirements:

(1) A time-of-flight of 51 nsec between the plastic scintillation counters S1 and S2, which are spaced 40 ft apart (a 1·19 GeV/c antiproton has a speed of 0·78 c); a pion of the same momentum has a speed of 0·99 c and a shorter time of flight of 40 nsec.

(2) No pulse from the Cherenkov counter Cl. This counter of chemical composition $C_8F_{16}O$ and refractive index 1·28 has a threshold velocity of 0·79 c, above the threshold for antiprotons but below the pion threshold. If there is a pulse from Cl then it cannot be due to an antiproton so such pulses are discarded.

(3) The second Cherenkov counter C2 (fused quartz, refractive index 1·46) is of special design so that it only responds to charged particles in the velocity range $0{\cdot}75\,c < v < 0{\cdot}78\,c$. C2 is connected in anti-coincidence with Cl: an antiproton should give a pulse in C2 but not in Cl, whereas a negative pion produces a pulse in Cl but not in C2.

(4) The third scintillation counter S3 certifies that an antiproton has not been scattered through a large angle in C2.

An antiproton is certified by the sequence of events: pulse from S1, pulse from S2 (51 nsec later); coincidence pulses from S2, C2 and S3 in anti-coincidence with C1 (N.B. the distance between S2 and S3 is only a few inches).

An approximate determination of the rest mass of the antiproton was possible in this experiment. An experimental value of 1824 ± 51 electron mass units was obtained.

Soon after the identification of the antiproton by counters, an antiproton track and annihilation star were recognized†† in a stack of photographic emulsions exposed to a selected beam of negatively charged particles from a proton bombarded target. Measurements of ionization by grain counting, coupled with residual range measurements of the antiproton, led to an antiproton mass within 2 per cent of the expected value.

Antineutrons have been observed in the following way. A high energy antiproton enters a bubble chamber containing a high proportion of protons. The antiproton is recognized by the density of ionization of its track and its curvature in a magnetic field. At A (Fig. 18), the antiproton track vanishes, because it exchanges its charge with a target proton producing a neutron–antineutron pair $\bar{p} + p \rightarrow \bar{n} + n$

† For an account of the optics of focusing high energy particles see O. CHAMBERLAIN, *Ann. Rev. Nucl. Sci.* **10**, 161, 1960.

†† W. H. BARKAS *et al.*, *Phys. Rev.* **105**, 1037, 1957.

After travelling a few centimeters through the liquid of the bubble chamber, the antineutron annihilates at the point B in a collision with a nucleon, producing an annihilation star.

Many stars due to the annihilation of antiprotons in flight and at rest in photographic emulsions and bubble chambers have now been observed and carefully analysed. When an antiproton annihilates with a nucleon the energy available is

$$2m\,c^2 + T - B$$

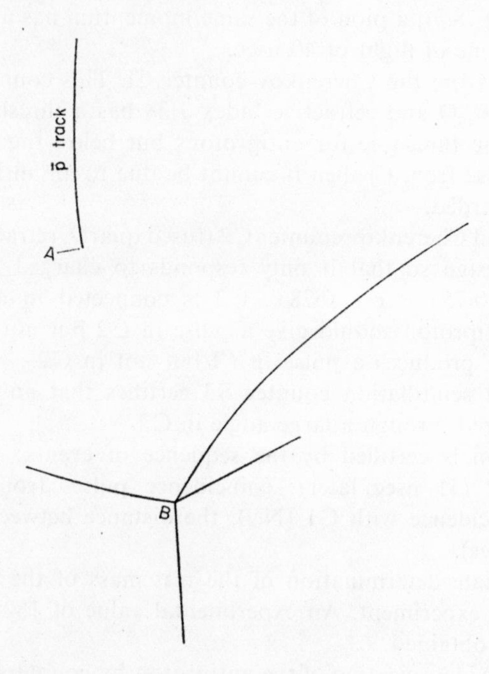

FIG. 18. Antiproton undergoes charge exchange at A with a proton. The antineutron travels from A to B (no ionization track) and annihilates with a nucleon at B giving rise to several charged particles (mainly pions).

where $m\,c^2$ is the nucleon (or antinucleon) rest mass energy ($\sim$ 930 MeV) T is the kinetic energy in the centre-of-mass system, and B is the binding energy of the annihilating nucleon in the target nucleus ($\sim$ 8 MeV). The particles observed as the products of the annihilation include: pions, protons, occasionally (if sufficient kinetic energy T is supplied) deuterons and other very light nuclei, and K mesons.

Measurements of the cross sections of antiprotons for annihilation, scattering, and charge exchange have all shown unexpectedly large values. Thus the $p - \bar{p}$ scattering cross section for antiprotons of 140 MeV (lab.) is 74 millibarns in contrast to the $p - p$ scattering cross section of 29 millibarns at the same energy†. The theory of antinucleon interactions cannot be considered to be in a satisfactory state. This is reflected in the large variety of theoretical approaches to the subject.†† Of the various models, that of Ball and Chew seems to be the most promising.††† The theoretical cross section of nucleon–nucleon scattering can be discussed in terms of a nucleon–nucleon potential energy function which includes a repulsive core of radius r_c of the order of one third of the Compton reduced pion wavelength ($r_c \sim 0{\cdot}4$ fermi). In an antinucleon–nucleon collision, Ball and Chew assume that the repulsive core is replaced by an attractive core. An approaching antinucleon which overlaps this core is immediately annihilated. This accounts in a qualitative way for the high annihilation cross section. The pion clouds surrounding an isolated nucleon and antinucleon are presumably opposite in sign.

Electric and Magnetic Structure of the Proton and Neutron

High energy electron–proton and electron–deuteron scattering cross section measurements have been used to investigate the electric charge and magnetic moment spatial distributions of the proton and neutron. The experimental technique has been described in Chapter 9, Section 2.

The scattering cross section for a point proton charge and point magnetic moment has been calculated by Rosenbluth‡. The observed scattering cross section is well below the point proton theoretical prediction. In extending the theory to include the effect of finite spatial distribution of charge and magnetic moment, it is convenient to introduce two "form factors"‡‡ F_{1p} and F_{2p} for the proton and two for the neutron, F_{1n} and F_{2n}. The form factor F_{1p} is determined by the spatial distribution of the electric charge and the normal (Dirac) component of the magnetic moment of the proton. F_{2p} is determined by the spatial distribution of the anomalous (Pauli) component of the magnetic moment of the proton. The anomalous component is $2{\cdot}79 - 1{\cdot}00 = 1{\cdot}79$ nuclear magnetons, as the Dirac value is exactly one nuclear magneton.

The following properties of the proton and neutron form factors have been established.‡‡‡

(1) At large momentum transfers $\hbar \boldsymbol{q}$ in electron–proton scattering (see eqn. (10), Chapter 9 for a definition of $\boldsymbol{q}$), the form factors F_{1p} and F_{2p} diverge, F_{2p} being considerably smaller than F_{1p}.

† J. Button *et al.*, *Phys. Rev.* **108**, 1557, 1957.

†† J. McConnell, pp. 207–256, *Progress in Elementary Particle and Cosmic Ray Physics*, Vol. 5, North-Holland., Amsterdam 1960.

††† J. S. Ball and G. F. Chew, *Phys. Rev.* **109**, 1385, 1958.

‡ M. N. Rosenbluth, *Phys. Rev.* **79**, 615, 1950.

‡‡ The concept of form factor is discussed in Chapter 9, Section 2.

‡‡‡ R. Hofstadter *et al.*, *Phys. Rev. Letters* **6**, 290, 1961, also *Phys. Rev. Letters*, **6** 293, 1961.

(2) The root-mean-square radius of the charge and Dirac magnetic moment distribution of the proton, obtained from the Fourier transform of F_{1p} expressed as a function of q^2, is

$$a_{1p} = 0{\cdot}85 \text{ fermi}$$

(3) The corresponding root-mean-square radius for the neutron is zero

$$a_{1n} = 0{\cdot}00 \text{ fermi}$$

(4) The root-mean-square radius of the anomalous magnetic moment distribution of the proton is

$$a_{2p} = 0{\cdot}94 \text{ fermi}$$

(5) The root-mean-square radius of the anomalous magnetic moment distribution of the neutron (the whole moment of the $-1{\cdot}9$ nuclear magnetons is anomalous) is

$$a_{2n} = 0{\cdot}76 \text{ fermi}$$

The zero root-mean-square radius of the charge distribution of the neutron is in agreement with measurements of the electron–neutron interaction in neutron scattering by atomic electrons.† The near equality of the anomalous magnetic root-mean-square radii of the neutron and proton is a reflection of the fact that the anomalous magnetic moments are equal, but opposite, to within 5 per cent. The form factors and root-mean-square radii of the neutron must be viewed with some caution for the only suitable neutron target is the deuteron and it is not easy to correct for the influence of the proton in the deuteron on the electron scattering cross section.

21.8. THE STRANGE PARTICLES: *K* MESONS AND HYPERONS

So far we have discussed the properties of fourteen elementary particles: γ, e^+, e^-, ν, $\bar{\nu}$, μ^+, μ^-, π^+, π^-, π^0, p, $\bar{p}$, n, $\bar{n}$. Several of these particles had been predicted before their discovery, notably the antiproton and the antineutron. Between 1947 and 1955 a whole group of *unpredicted* unstable particles (strange particles) was discovered in the cosmic radiation and in the emerging beams from the multi-GeV proton synchrotrons at Brookhaven and Berkeley.

The new particles have rest masses greater than that of the pion. The first observation of one of these strange particles was made by Rochester and Butler†† in a cloud chamber photograph. The event they recorded was probably the decay of the neutral particle the lambda hyperon, of rest mass 2182 electron mass units,

$$\Lambda^0 \rightarrow p + \pi^- + 37 \text{ MeV} \tag{51}$$

† L. L. Foldy, *Revs. modern Phys.* **30**, 471, 1958.

†† G. D. Rochester and C. C. Butler, *Nature* **160**, 855, 1947; R. Armenteros *et al.*, *Phil. Mag.* **42**, 1113, 1951.

The tracks of the proton and the negative pion diverge from the point where the Λ^0 particle decayed (the Λ^0 particle, of course, leaves no track).

The term hyperon is reserved for particles with rest mass between that of the neutron and the deuteron.

The first convincing evidence of a K meson, that is, of a particle of rest mass between that of the charged pion and the proton, came from Powell and his school† at Bristol who recorded, in a photographic emulsion, the track of a secondary cosmic ray particle

$$\tau^+ \rightarrow \pi^+ + \pi^+ + \pi^- + 75 \text{ MeV} \tag{52}$$

The problem of studying the properties and decays of the strange particles was considerably eased by the introduction of multi-GeV proton accelerators; K mesons and hyperons are produced in considerable numbers when high energy protons bombard a suitable target. With increasing proton energy the fraction of K mesons relative to pions increases significantly. Thus as many as 25 per cent of the negatively charged particles, produced by bombarding a target with 25 GeV protons in the Geneva synchrotron, are K^- particles. The invention of the bubble chamber has proved to be very timely, for it is especially suitable for studying the production and decay of strange particles.

An enormous amount of painstaking observation and analysis in the last ten years has led to accurate estimates of the masses, decay modes, and mean lifetimes of the hyperons and K mesons. This data is listed in Tables 2 and 3.

TABLE 2. HYPERONS

Symbol	Spin	Mass (MeV)	Decay modes	Q (MeV)	Mean lifetime (sec)
Λ^0	$\frac{1}{2}$	$1115{\cdot}36 \pm 0{\cdot}14$	$\Lambda^0 \rightarrow p + \pi^-$ (67%)	36·9	$2{\cdot}8 \times 10^{-10}$
			$\Lambda^0 \rightarrow n + \pi^0$ (33%)	40	$2{\cdot}8 \times 10^{-10}$
Σ^+	$\frac{1}{2}$	$1189{\cdot}40 \pm 0{\cdot}20$	$\Sigma^+ \rightarrow p + \pi^0$ (55%)	115·8	$(0{\cdot}81 \pm 0{\cdot}06) \times 10^{-10}$
			$\Sigma^+ \rightarrow n + \pi^+$ (45%)	109·9	$(0{\cdot}81 \pm 0{\cdot}06) \times 10^{-10}$
Σ^0	$\frac{1}{2}$	$1191{\cdot}5 \pm 0{\cdot}5$	$\Sigma^0 \rightarrow \Lambda^0 + \gamma$ (100%)	74	$< 10^{-11}$
Σ^-	$\frac{1}{2}$	$1195{\cdot}96 \pm 0{\cdot}30$	$\Sigma^- \rightarrow n + \pi^-$ (100%)	117	$(1{\cdot}61 \pm 0{\cdot}10) \times 10^{-10}$
Ξ^0	?	1311 ± 8	$\Xi^0 \rightarrow \Lambda^0 + \pi^0$(100%)	61	$\sim 10^{-10}$
Ξ^-	?	$1318{\cdot}4 \pm 1{\cdot}2$	$\Xi^- \rightarrow \Lambda^0 + \pi^-$(100%)	64	$(1{\cdot}28 \pm 0{\cdot}34) \times 10^{-10}$

The hyperons in Table 2 are all classified as baryons, and are all assumed to have antiparticles. Notice that the sigma hyperon Σ^+ is not the antiparticle of the Σ^-.

All the K mesons are assumed to be spinless particles. In Table 3 the decay modes of the K^+ and the K^0 mesons are given. There is not much

† R. H. BROWN *et al.*, *Nature* **163**, 82, 1949.

collected evidence on the decay of K^- particles as they tend to be captured into Bohr orbits and then by the nuclei of the stopping medium, before they decay. K-mesonic X-rays should be emitted by the negative kaons as they cascade down through the last few bound orbits. To date (1961), however, K-mesonic X-rays have not been observed. There is no reason to doubt that the decay modes of the K^+ mesons differ from those of the K^- variety, apart from the appropriate changes in sign of the decay particles.

TABLE 3. *K* MESONS

K^+ rest mass is 493·9 ± 0·2 MeV, K^0 rest mass is 497·8 ± 0·6 MeV

Symbol	Mode of decay		Q-value MeV	Mean lifetime (sec)
K^+	$\theta^+ : K^+ \rightarrow \pi^+ + \pi^0$	(~25%)	219	
	$\tau : K^+ \rightarrow \pi^+ + \pi^- + \pi^+$	(~ 6%)	75	
	$\tau' : K^+ \rightarrow \pi^+ + \pi^0 + \pi^0$	(~ 2%)	84	$(1{\cdot}224 \pm 0{\cdot}013) \times 10^{-8}$
	$K_{\mu 2} : K^+ \rightarrow \mu^+ + \nu$	(~58%)	388	
	$K_{\mu 3} : K^+ \rightarrow \mu^+ + \pi^0 + \nu$	(~ 5%)	253	
	$K_{e 3} : K^+ \rightarrow e^+ + \pi^0 + \nu$	(~ 4%)	358	
K^0	$K_1^0 : K_1^0 \rightarrow \pi^+ + \pi^-$	(~88%)*	215	$(1{\cdot}00 \pm 0{\cdot}038) \times 10^{-10}$
	$K_1^0 \rightarrow \pi^0 + \pi^0$	(~12%)*	224	
	$K_2^0 : K_2^0 \rightarrow \mu^+ + \pi^- + \nu$			
	$K_2^0 \rightarrow \mu^- + \pi^+ + \bar{\nu}$			
	$K_2^0 \rightarrow e^+ + \pi^- + \nu$			$(6{\cdot}1 \pm 1{\cdot}3) \times 10^{-8}$
	$K_2^0 \rightarrow e^- + \pi^+ + \bar{\nu}$			
	$K_2^0 \rightarrow \pi^0 + \pi^0 + \pi^0$			
	$K_2^0 \rightarrow \pi^+ + \pi^- + \pi^0$			

* These percentages refer to K_1^0 decay mode alone.

The various decay modes of the K^+ are denoted by symbols, θ^+, τ, τ', $K_{\mu 2}$, . . ., etc. This confusing terminology dates from the time when it seemed likely that the θ^+, τ, . . . decays sprang from different parent particles. The notation $K_{\mu 2}$ represents a decay into two particles, one of which is a muon.

The reader who is interested in the experimental evidence for the data listed in Tables 2 and 3 is referred to the book by Cohen, Crowe and DuMond, and the review articles by Dalitz and Walker. The short review article by Snow and Shapiro has an extensive list of references.

An accurate determination of the mass of the K^+ meson has been made from measurements of the kinetic energies of the three charged pions emitted in the τ^+ mode of decay. The kinetic energies are obtained from known range–energy relations for charged pions in nuclear emulsion.

The masses of the K^- meson and the Σ^+ hyperon have been determined in the following way†. The range R of the protons emitted in the decay

† M. S. SWAMI, *Phys. Rev.* **114**, 333, 1959.

of stopped Σ^+hyperons in nuclear emulsions has been accurately measured

$$R = 1686{\cdot}5 \pm 6{\cdot}0 \text{ microns}$$

This range corresponds to a proton of about 18 MeV kinetic energy in the decay

$$\Sigma^+ \rightarrow p + \pi^0 \tag{53}$$

From the accurately known rest masses of the proton and the neutral pion, the Q of the decay can be calculated

$$Q = 116{\cdot}37 \pm 0{\cdot}4 \text{ MeV}$$

From the Q value and the known masses of the proton and neutral pion the mass of the Σ^+ is calculated as

$$m(\Sigma^+) = (2328{\cdot}1 \pm 0{\cdot}8)\, m_e$$

Consider the hyperon production reactions

$$K^- + p \rightarrow \Sigma^+ + \pi^- + Q \tag{54}$$

$$K^- + p \rightarrow \Sigma^- + \pi^+ + Q' \tag{55}$$

If the Q value of reaction (54) is determined from the measured kinetic energies of the particles, the mass of the K^- meson can be found using the known mass of the Σ^+ hyperon

$$m(K^-) = (965{\cdot}8 \pm 1{\cdot}5)\, m_e$$

Moreover, if the Q value of reaction (55) is determined, the mass difference of the negative and positive sigma hyperons is equal to $Q - Q'$. The mass difference is

$$m(\Sigma^-) - m(\Sigma^+) = (13 \pm 1)\, m_e$$

The determination of the mass difference of the charged and neutral K mesons can be made by measuring the kinetic energies of the particles involved in the reactions

$$\pi^- + p \rightarrow \Lambda^0 + K^0 \tag{56}$$

$$\pi^- + p \rightarrow \Sigma^- + K^+ \tag{57}$$

Using the known masses of the lambda and negative sigma hyperons, the mass difference of the neutral and positive K mesons is

$$m(K^0) - m(K^+) = (7{\cdot}6 \pm 1{\cdot}2)\, m_e$$

As the mean lifetime of the charged K meson is as long as 10^{-8} sec, it is possible to measure it accurately using fast delayed coincidence circuits. In one such determination, the $K^+_{\mu 2}$ mode of decay was examined using a scintillation and Cherenkov counter telescope†. The time distribution

† V. Fitch and R. Motley, *Phys. Rev.* **105**, 265, 1957; L. Alvarez *et al.*, p. VIII-29. *Proc. Seventh Rochester Conference*, Interscience, New York 1957.

of the decay of stopped K^+ mesons in the mode $K^+ \rightarrow \mu^+ + \nu$ fits an exponential curve of time constant (mean lifetime)

$$T = 1{\cdot}22 \times 10^{-8} \text{ sec}$$

In contrast to the charged K decays, the neutral K particle exhibits two quite distinct lifetimes. The faster decay is the two pion decay

$$K_1^0 \rightarrow \pi^+ + \pi^- \quad \text{or} \quad K_1^0 \rightarrow \pi^0 + \pi^0$$

This fast mode of decay is indicated by the symbol K_1^0. Observations of the decay in flight of neutral K particles into $\pi^+ \pi^-$ pairs, lead to an estimation of the K_1^0 mean lifetime†

$$T(K_1^0) = (1{\cdot}00 \pm 0{\cdot}04) \times 10^{-10} \text{ sec}$$

The slower decay modes of the neutral K particle (denoted by the symbol K_2^0) are more difficult to observe. There are at least six different decay modes of the K_2^0 particle. One decay mode definitely does not occur: the decay of the K_2^0 into a $\pi^+ \pi^-$ pair. The approximate branching ratios of the various three-body modes of decay and the mean lifetime of the K_2^0 particle have been estimated from cloud chamber observations.††

The masses of the hyperons have been determined by several methods. The Λ^0 mass is best determined from a Q measurement of the decay (in a nuclear emulsion)

$$\Lambda^0 \rightarrow p + \pi^-$$

The determination of the masses of the positive and negative sigma particles has been discussed above. The neutral sigma particle mass has been found from measurements of the energy of the lambda particle in the decay

$$\Sigma^0 \rightarrow \Lambda^0 + \gamma$$

The masses of the xi particles (often referred to as "cascade" hyperons because they do not decay directly into nucleons, but cascade to the nucleon state via an intermediate hyperon state) have been determined from the Q value of the decay

$$\Xi^- \rightarrow \Lambda^0 \quad \text{and} \quad \pi^-, \text{ for the } \Xi^- \text{ particle},$$

and from the measured kinetic energies of the particles involved in the reaction†††

$$K^- + p \rightarrow \Xi^\circ + K^\circ, \quad \text{for the } \Xi^0 \text{ particle}.$$

The majority of hyperon lifetimes have been estimated from studies of the spatial and therefore the time distributions of hyperon decays in nuclear emulsions, cloud chambers, and bubble chambers. For example, the mean life of the lambda hyperon has been determined from many observations

† F. S. Crawford *et al.*, *Phys. Rev. Letters* **2**, 266, 1959.
†† M. Bardon *et al.*, *Ann. Phys.* **5**. 156, 1958.
††† L. Alvarez *et al.*, *Phys. Rev. Letters* **2**, 215, 1959.

of the decay

$$\Lambda^0 \rightarrow p + \pi^-$$

There is good evidence for the belief that charged K mesons have zero intrinsic angular momentum (spin). Some of this evidence is:

(1) The absence of asymmetry in the θ^+ decay mode

$$K^+ \rightarrow \pi^+ + \pi^0$$

As the pions are spinless this strongly suggests that the K^+ spin is zero.

(2) The decay $K^+ \rightarrow \pi^+ + \gamma$ is not observed. This is understandable if the K^+ is spinless, as the decay would be a $0 \rightarrow 0$ transition. Dalitz† has shown that this decay mode would have a high branching ratio if the K^+ spin is finite.

(3) The observed polarization†† of the positrons emitted in the decay of the positive muons resulting from $K^+_{\mu 2}$ decays

$$K^+_{\mu 2} \rightarrow \mu^+ + \nu : \mu^+ \rightarrow e^+ + \nu + \bar{\nu}$$

The K^- particle, being the antiparticle of the K^+, presumably has zero spin.

The angular distribution of the decay products of K^0 particles is isotropic, subsequent to the production reaction $\pi^- + p \rightarrow \Lambda^0 + K^0$. This result suggests that the neutral K meson is spinless.

The discovery that parity conservation is violated in K meson decays implies that it is meaningless to assign an intrinsic parity to K mesons.

The Λ^0 intrinsic spin has been determined as follows. Λ^0 particles are produced by the reaction

$$\pi^- + p \rightarrow \Lambda^0 + K^0 \tag{58}$$

The decays of the lambda hyperons are not symmetrical with respect to the production plane defined by the linear momenta of the π^-, the Λ^0,

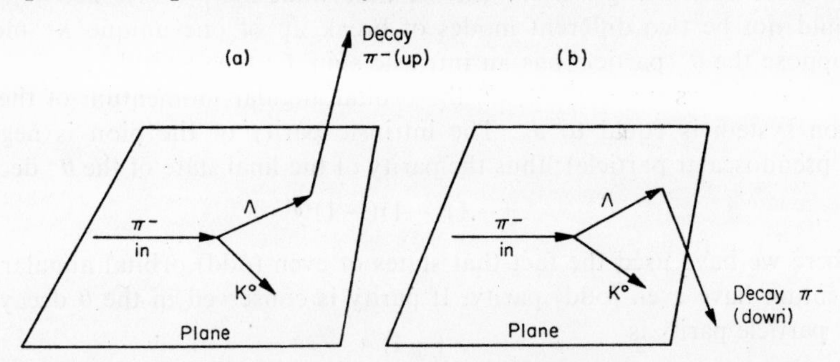

FIG. 19. The production of a Λ-hyperon by the reaction $\pi^- + p \rightarrow \Lambda^0 + K^0$, and the subsequent decay $\Lambda^0 \rightarrow p + \pi^-$. In (a) the decay pion travels "up" relative to the Λ-production plane. In (b) the decay pion travels "down". Parity violation is proved because more pions are emitted "up" than "down".

† R. H. DALITZ, *Phys. Rev.* **99**, 915, 1955.
†† C. A. COOMBES *et al.*, *Phys. Rev.* **108**, 1348, 1957.

and the K^0 particles. Experimentally it is found that more pions from the lambda decay $\Lambda^0 \to p + \pi^-$ are emitted "upwards", that is, in the direction of

$$\boldsymbol{p}_{\pi\,\mathrm{in}} \times \boldsymbol{p}_\Lambda$$

where $\boldsymbol{p}_{\pi\,\mathrm{in}}$ is the linear momentum of the negative pion of reaction (58), and $\boldsymbol{p}_\Lambda$ is the linear momentum of the created lambda particle. The up–down asymmetry in the decay of the lambda particle relative to its plane of production is depicted in Fig. 19. This asymmetry demonstrates the failure of the reflection symmetry (parity) principle in lambda decay (a weak interaction). Lee and Yang† have shown that it is possible to place an upper limit on the intrinsic spin of the lambda hyperon in terms of the magnitude of the up–down asymmetry in the lambda decay. From the observation of more than 600 charged pion decays of the lambda hyperon at Berkeley††, the up–down asymmetry strongly favours a spin assignment of $\frac{1}{2}$ for the lambda particle.

Parity Non-conservation in *K* Meson Decays

The numerous decay modes of the charged *K* mesons had originally been interpreted as evidence for the existence of a whole group of different particles with approximately the same mass of about 1000 electron mass units. Gradually, however, it was established that the six decay modes of the positive *K* mesons (Table 3) had not only the same rest masses and mean lifetimes but also exhibited the same cross sections in nuclear interactions. As the evidence accumulated that the only difference in the various types of K^+ particle lay in their different decay modes, it seemed reasonable to suppose that there is only *one* type of K^+ meson. However, Dalitz††† advanced convincing reasons (at the time) that the θ and τ decay modes could not be two different modes of break up of one unique K^+ meson. Suppose the θ^+ particle has an intrinsic spin J_θ; then as it decays into two spinless bosons ($\theta^+ \to \pi^+ + \pi^0$) the orbital angular momentum of the two pion system is equal to J_θ. The intrinsic parity of the pion is negative (a pseudoscalar particle); thus the parity of the final state of the θ^+ decay is

$$(-1)(-1)(-1)^{J_\theta}$$

where we have used the fact that states of even (odd) orbital angular momentum have even (odd) parity. If parity is conserved in the θ decay, the θ^+ particle parity is

$$(-1)^{J_\theta}$$

For a spinless theta particle, the parity is $+1$.

† T. D. Lee and C. N. Yang, *Phys. Rev.* **109**, 1755, 1958.

†† F. S. Crawford *et al.*, *Phys. Rev. Letters* **2**, 114, 1959.

††† R. H. Dalitz, *Phil. Mag.* **44**, 1068, 1953; *Phys. Rev.* **94**, 1046, 1954: see also pp. 195–206, R. H. Dalitz, *Reports on Progr. in Phys.* **20**, 1957, The Physical Society, London.

The three-pion decay of the τ^+ particle ($\tau^+ \rightarrow \pi^+ + \pi^+ + \pi^-$) is kinematically described by two momenta; $\boldsymbol{p}$ the linear momentum of the negative decay pion in the initial rest system of the τ^+ particle, and $\boldsymbol{q}$, the momentum of one of the positive pions in the centre of mass system of the two positive decay particles. The other positive pion must, of course, have a linear momentum vector $-\boldsymbol{q}$ (Fig. 20). Let L denote the orbital angular momentum quantum number of the two positive decay pions and l the orbital angular

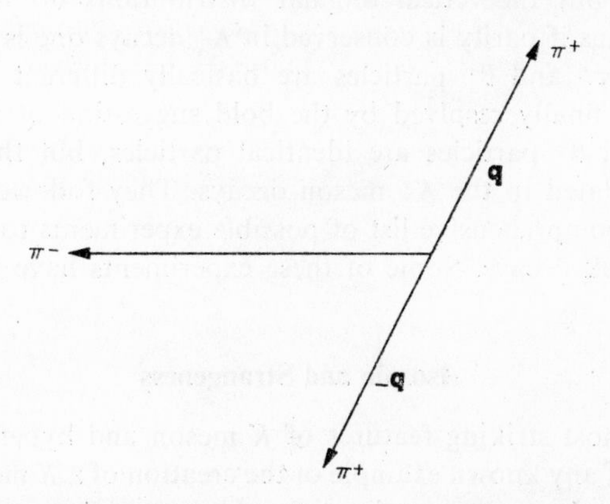

FIG. 20. Momentum diagram for the decay of τ^+. Reference frame in which the total momentum of the positive pions is zero.

momentum quantum number of the negative pion relative to the centre of mass of the two positive particles. As all the decay pions are spinless, the following angular momentum restrictions are imposed on L and l

$$|L - l| \leqq J_\tau \leqq L + l$$

where J_τ is the intrinsic angular momentum of the τ^+ particle. Thus the final state parity is the product of five terms: the intrinsic parities of the three pions and the parities associated with the quantum numbers L and l

$$(-1)^3(-1)^L(-1)^l = (-1)^{l+1}$$

L is always even, as it refers to a system of two identical spinless bosons. If the intrinsic spin of the τ^+ particle is zero ($J_\tau = 0$), $l = L$, and the final state parity is -1. If parity is conserved in the τ^+ decay, the parity of the τ^+particle, assuming it to be spinless, is

$$-1 \quad \text{(parity of spinless } \tau^+)$$

Thus a spinless θ and spinless τ particle must have opposite intrinsic parities. This is the crux of the denial that the τ and θ particles are the same. A way out of the difficulty is to assign spins $J_\theta = 1$ and $J_\tau = 1$ for the θ^+ and τ^+ particles. Then if $l = L = 2$ the parity of the τ^+ particle is

$$(-1)^3 = -1$$

and the parity of the θ^+ particle is

$$(-1)^1 = -1$$

However, these spin assignments for the τ^+ and θ^+ mesons are contradicted by the absence of an anisotropic spatial distribution of the negative pions in the centre of mass system of the two positive particles in τ^+ decays. Higher spin assignments to the τ^+ and θ^+ mesons can give the same intrinsic parities but theoretical angular distributions do not agree with observation. Thus if parity is conserved in K^+ decays one is forced to conclude that the τ^+ and θ^+ particles are basically different particles. This τ–θ puzzle was finally resolved by the bold suggestion of Lee and Yang that the τ^+ and θ^+ particles are identical particles, but that parity conservation is violated in the K^+ meson decays. They followed up this suggestion with a comprehensive list of possible experiments to test the parity principle in weak decays. Some of these experiments have been described in Chapter 14.

Isospin and Strangeness

One of the most striking features of K meson and hyperon production is the absence of any known example of the creation of a K meson (hyperon) without the simultaneous creation of a hyperon (K meson). Pais† first drew attention to this feature and coined the phrase "associated production". A few examples of associated production are

$$p + p \rightarrow p + \Lambda^0 + K^+ \tag{59}$$

$$\pi^- + p \rightarrow \Lambda^0 + K^0 \tag{60}$$

$$\pi^- + p \rightarrow \Sigma^- + K^+ \tag{61}$$

$$\pi^- + p \rightarrow \Sigma^0 + K^0 \tag{62}$$

$$p + p \rightarrow p + \Sigma^0 + K^+ \tag{63}$$

$$p + p \rightarrow p + \Sigma^+ + K^0 \tag{64}$$

The principle of associated production does not forbid the production of more than two strange particles. A Russian group at Dubna†† found five cases of multi-K production when a propane bubble chamber was exposed to a beam of 8 GeV negative pions. One observed reaction was

$$\pi^- + p \rightarrow \Lambda^0 + K^0 + \overline{K^0} + K^+ + \pi^- \tag{65}$$

Pais suggested that the phenomenon of associated production might be connected with an internal degree of freedom specified by a new quantum number, the "strangeness" number S, which is zero for the non-strange particles (pions, nucleons) but is finite for K mesons and hyperons.

† A. Pais, *Phys. Rev.* **86**, 663, 1952.

†† M. I. Soloviev, p. 388, *Proc. Intern. Conf. High Energy Physics*, Rochester 1960.

The concept of strangeness has been developed by Gell-Mann† and independently by Nakano and Nishijima†, and they showed that it is closely related to the isospin property. These authors assumed the validity of the principle of charge independence in nucleon interactions of strange particles. Charge independence is formally represented by the rotational symmetry of the total isospin vector in isospin space. In electromagnetic interactions, conservation of the total isospin T is relaxed, but the third component T_3 is conserved. The weak interactions are characterized by non-conservation of T and T_3. How are the isospin assignments of the K mesons and hyperons carried out? First, let us consider the lambda hyperon. To date there is no evidence of the existence of any charged variety of lambda particle. The lambda hyperon is a singlet particle and it is therefore reasonable to put

$$T = 0, \quad T_3 = 0, \quad \text{for the } \Lambda^0 \text{ particle.} \tag{66}$$

The observed decay processes

$$\Lambda^0 \rightarrow p + \pi^- \tag{67}$$

$$\Lambda^0 \rightarrow n + \pi^0 \tag{68}$$

do not conserve T or T_3. Remembering that for the $p + \pi^-$ system, $T_3 = \frac{1}{2} - 1 = -\frac{1}{2}$, and for the $n + \pi^0$ system, $T_3 = -\frac{1}{2} + 0 = -\frac{1}{2}$, we see that in these slow decays

$$|\Delta T_3| = \tfrac{1}{2} \tag{69}$$

The triplet of sigma states suggests the isospin assignments

$$T = 1; \quad T_3 = +1 \text{ for } \Sigma^+, \; T_3 = 0 \text{ for } \Sigma^0, \; T_3 = -1 \text{ for } \Sigma^- \tag{70}$$

The existence of the neutral xi particle was predicted by isospin considerations before it was discovered in 1959. There are two charge states for the xi hyperon corresponding to

$$T = \tfrac{1}{2}, \quad T_3 = +\tfrac{1}{2} \text{ for } \Xi^0, \; T_3 = -\tfrac{1}{2} \text{ for } \Xi^- \tag{71}$$

As regards the K mesons, we have two particles K^+ and K° (K^- and $\overline{K^\circ}$ are regarded as their antiparticles). For the K^+, K° doublet

$$T = \tfrac{1}{2}; \quad T_3 = +\tfrac{1}{2} \text{ for } K^+, \; T_3 = -\tfrac{1}{2} \text{ for } K^0 \tag{72}$$

For convenience, we recall that for the nucleon

$$T = \tfrac{1}{2}; \quad T_3 = +\tfrac{1}{2} \text{ for the proton}, \; T_3 = -\tfrac{1}{2} \text{ for the neutron} \tag{73}$$

and for the pion

$$T = 1; \quad T_3 = +1 \text{ for } \pi^+, T_3 = 0 \text{ for } \pi^0, \; T_3 = -1 \text{ for } \pi^- \tag{74}$$

† M. Gell-Mann, *Phys. Rev.* **92**, 833, 1953; T. Nakano and K. Nishijima, *Progr. Theor. Phys. Japan* **10**, 581, 1953.

The strangeness quantum number of an elementary particle is defined by the relation†

$$Q = T_3 + \frac{B}{2} + \frac{S}{2} \tag{75}$$

where Q is the electric charge of the particle (in proton units).
T_3 is the third component of the isospin vector,
B is the baryon number (B is $+1$ for nucleons and hyperons, and is minus one for antinucleons and antihyperons; for all other particles $B = 0$).

Replacing particle by antiparticle reverses the signs of Q, T_3 and B in eqn. (75). Thus particle and antiparticle have opposite S-values. The T_3 assignments given above with eqn. (75) yield the following strangeness assignments (Table 4).

TABLE 4

Particle	π	K^+, K^0	n, p	Λ^0	Σ	Ξ
Strangeness S	0	$+1$	0	-1	-1	-2

We are now in a position to appreciate why certain production reactions, which conserve charge, linear momentum, angular momentum, energy, and baryon number, are not observed. One example is

$$n + n \rightarrow \Lambda^0 + \Lambda^0$$

T and T_3 are not conserved and the reaction would involve a violation of strangeness; $|\Delta S| = 2$. In production reactions, which must involve strong interactions as the collision time is about 10^{-23} sec, with typical cross sections as high as 10^{-4} barn all the experimental evidence is in favour of strict conservation of T_3 and S: "*S is conserved in production reactions*"

Consider the reaction

$$p + p \rightarrow p + \Lambda^0 + K^+ \tag{76}$$

which has a threshold energy of 1·57 GeV. The initial strangeness is zero and in the final state the total strangeness is zero as Λ^0 and K^+ have S-values of -1 and $+1$ respectively. It is impossible in a pion–nucleon or nucleon–nucleon collision to create a single strange particle; two particles of opposite strangeness are usually produced. This explains the phenomenon of associated production.

Soon after the production of K^+ and K^- beams, by high energy proton bombardment of a suitable internal target in the Berkeley synchrotron, it was shown that the production ratio of K^- to K^+ particles at a given proton

† For $S = 0$, eqn. (75) reduces to eqn. (5).

energy is as low as a few per cent. This is a consequence of the small cross section and high threshold (2·50 GeV) of the only K^- production reaction at Bevatron proton energies

$$p + p \rightarrow p + p + K^+ + K^- \tag{77}$$

In this K-pair creation process, strangeness is conserved as the K^+ and K^- have opposite S-values. For the reactions (59) to (65) strangeness is conserved.

Consider a possible "fast" decay of the lambda hyperon. Starting with the production reaction $\pi^- + p \rightarrow \Lambda^0 + K^0$, reverse the process,

$$\Lambda^0 + K^0 \rightarrow p + \pi^-, \tag{78}$$

and transpose the neutral K^0 to the other side of the equation, changing it into its antiparticle

$$\Lambda^0 \rightarrow p + \pi^- + \overline{K^0} \tag{79}$$

Assume the proton absorbs the negative pion to form a neutron and we have

$$\Lambda^0 \rightarrow n + \overline{K^0} \tag{80}$$

Although this decay conserves charge, spin, baryon number and strangeness, the rest mass of the lambda is less than the sum of the rest masses of the neutron and the anti-K particle. Processes (79) and (80) can only be virtual and the decay represented by eqn. (80) is absolutely forbidden.

The xi hyperons have been produced by the reactions†

$$K^- + n \rightarrow \Xi^- + K^0 \tag{81}$$

$$K^- + p \rightarrow \Xi^0 + K^0 \tag{82}$$

In both reactions the total strangeness in the initial and final states is -1.

The xi particles are known as "cascade" hyperons because they do not directly decay into a nucleon and pion, but decay via the intermediate lambda hyperon state

$$\Xi^- \rightarrow \Lambda^0 + \pi^- \; |\Delta S| = 1 \tag{83}$$

$$\Xi^0 \rightarrow \Lambda^0 + \pi^0 \; |\Delta S| = 1 \tag{84}$$

Presumably the decays $\Xi^- \rightarrow n + \pi^-$ and $\Xi^0 \rightarrow p + \pi^-$, which involve a change in strangeness $|\Delta S| = 2$, are *very* slow compared to the slow decays of eqns. (83) and (84). We can now formulate a general rule: "the decays of K mesons and hyperons are very slow on a nuclear time scale because they are associated with a violation of the conservation of strangeness." In general the decay process is associated with a change in strangeness

† L. ALVAREZ *et al.*, *Phys. Rev. Letters* **2**, 215, 1959.

of one unit. As charge and baryon number are always conserved, the $|\Delta S| = 1$ rule is equivalent to the rule (differentiate eqn. (75))

$$|\Delta S| = 1 = 2|\Delta T_3|$$
$$|\Delta T_3| = \tfrac{1}{2} \text{ in slow decays} \qquad (85)$$

The $|\Delta T_3| = \frac{1}{2}$ rule for weak decays has been interpreted by several physicists as part of a more general rule, namely, $|\Delta \boldsymbol{T}| = \frac{1}{2}$ in weak decays, where $\boldsymbol{T}$ is the total isospin vector of the system.† The evidence for this more general rule comes mainly from the agreement between the predicted and observed branching ratios in strange particle decays. For instance, if $|\Delta \boldsymbol{T}| = \frac{1}{2}$ in the lambda decays

$$\Lambda^0 \rightarrow p + \pi^-$$
$$\Lambda^0 \rightarrow n + \pi^0$$

the final states must be pure $T = \frac{1}{2}$ isospin states (the $T = 3/2$ state for the $p + \pi^-$ and $n + \pi^\circ$ systems is forbidden as $|\Delta \boldsymbol{T}| = 3/2$). It can be shown that the $|\Delta \boldsymbol{T}| = \frac{1}{2}$ rule requires the branching ratio for the $p + \pi^-$ mode of decay of the lambda hyperon to be twice that of the $n + \pi^\circ$ decay. The experimental value of the branching ratio is in excellent agreement with the $|\Delta \boldsymbol{T}| = \frac{1}{2}$ prediction.††

It is instructive to apply the $|\Delta \boldsymbol{T}| = \frac{1}{2}$ rule to the θ decay mode of K^+ and K_1^0 particles. The observed two-pion decay rate of the K_1^0 is 250 times as fast as that of the two pion decay rate of the K^+ particle. Why? If the $|\Delta \boldsymbol{T}| = \frac{1}{2}$ rule is absolutely rigorous, the K^+ two-pion decay is forbidden as the following argument shows. In the decay of a K^+ particle (spinless) into two spinless bosons

$$K^+ \rightarrow \pi^+ + \pi^0$$

the final state must be an S state ($L = 0$) and as the wave function of the final state is symmetric in its space coordinates, it must be symmetric in its isospin coordinates. This symmetry imposes the restriction that T is even for the two-pion system. Now as $T = \frac{1}{2}$ for the K^+ particle, the $|\Delta \boldsymbol{T}| = \frac{1}{2}$ rule requires the final state to be a $T = 0$ state. However, this is impossible because $T = 0$ requires $T_3 = 0$, and T_3 for a $\pi^+\pi^0$ system is necessarily $+1$.

A similar argument applied to the decays

$$K_1^0 \rightarrow \pi^+ + \pi^-$$
$$K_1^0 \rightarrow \pi^0 + \pi^0$$

does not forbid these decays as T_3 for a $\pi^+\pi^-$ and $\pi^0\pi^0$ system is zero.

The question now arises why does the $K^+ \rightarrow \pi^+ + \pi^0$ decay occur at all? The answer may be that the $|\Delta \boldsymbol{T}| = \frac{1}{2}$ weak decay rule is an approx-

† M. Gell-Mann and A. H. Rosenfeld, *Ann. Rev. Nuclear Sci.* **7**, 407, 1957. This rule is only applied to decays in which leptons are not produced.

†† F. S. Crawford *et al.*, *Phys. Rev. Letters* **2**, 266, 1959.

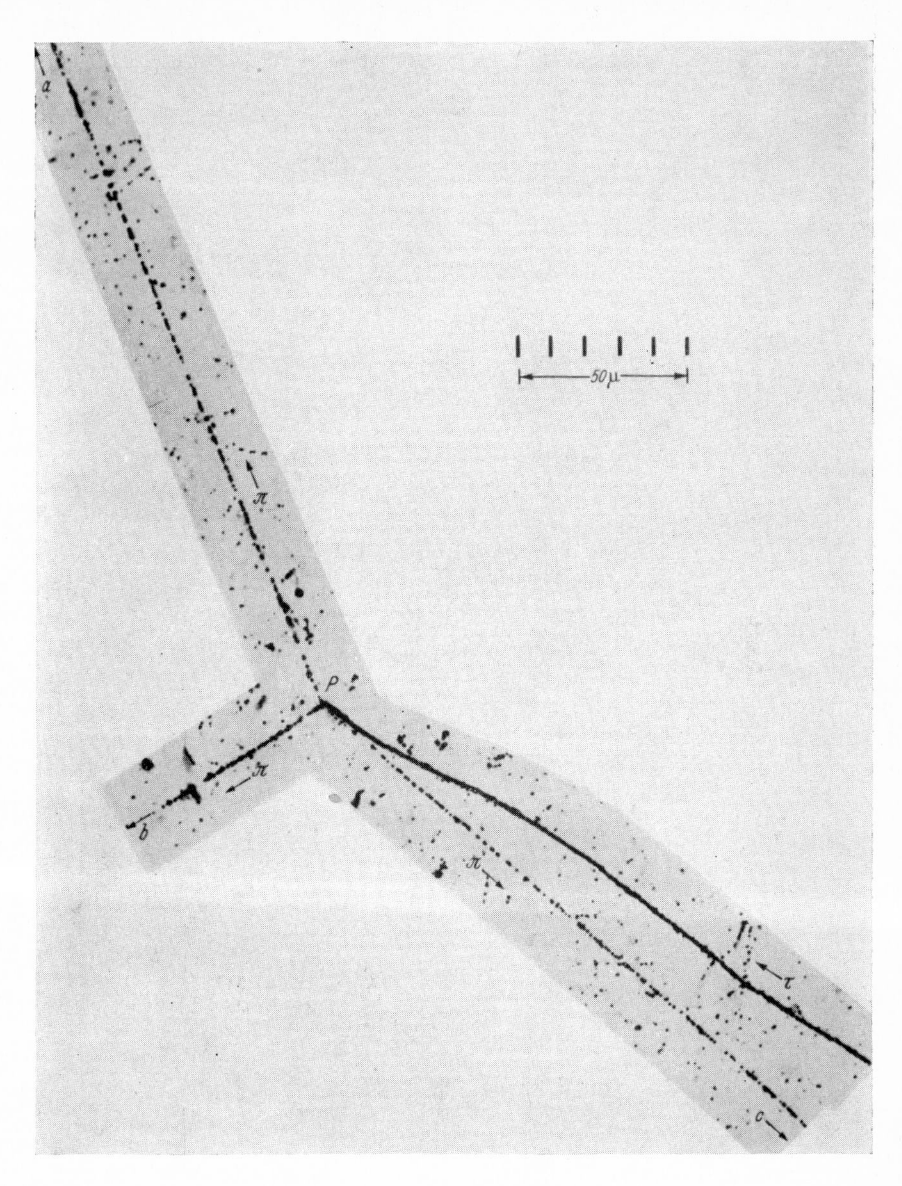

PLATE III.

Tau-mode decay of a charged *K* meson in a nuclear emulsion. (FOWLER, MENON, POWELL, ROCHAT, *Phil. Mag.*, **42** 1040 1951.)

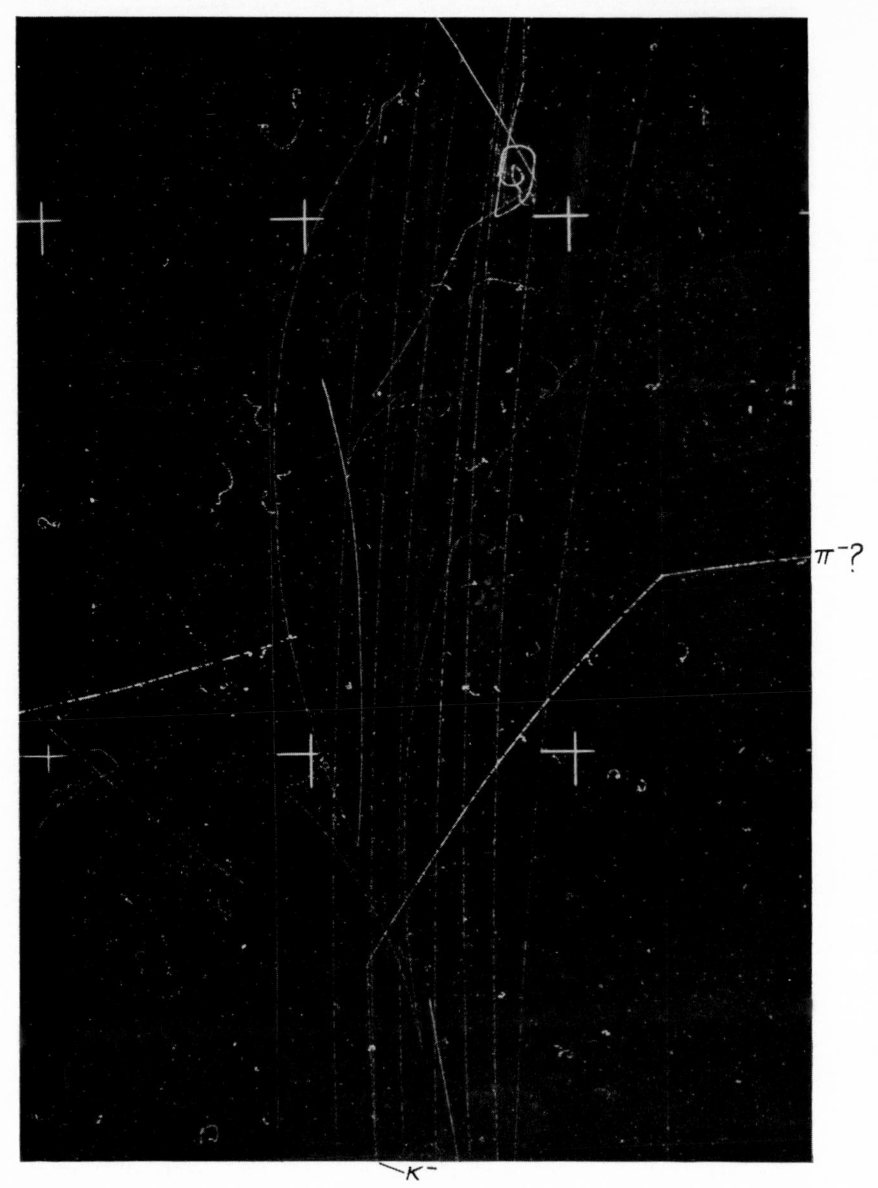

PLATE IV.

Bubble chamber photograph showing interaction of 1·5 GeV/c K^- particle with a nucleus:

$$K^- + \text{nucleus} \rightarrow \Lambda^\circ + \pi^-$$

Decay of lambda is shown

$$\Lambda^\circ \rightarrow p + \pi^-$$

(K^- enters at the bottom centre of the photograph)
(Photograph taken by Ecole Polytechnique Group of Paris at CERN, Geneva).

imation and in certain decays there is a small probability of $|\Delta T| = 3/2$ occurring. If $|\Delta T| = 3/2$ in the θ^+ mode then the two-pion system is formed in the $T = 2$ state. Confirmation of the relaxation of the $|\Delta T| = \frac{1}{2}$ rule appears in the failure of this rule to predict the observed branching ratio of the ($K^0 \rightarrow \pi^+ + \pi^- / K \rightarrow$ all 2π) decays.

21.9. NEUTRAL K MESON AS A PARTICLE MIXTURE†

In Table 3, two distinct lifetimes for the neutral K particles are given. What is the explanation of this peculiar behaviour of the neutral K particles? This behaviour is related to the fact that the antiparticle of the K^0 particle, $\overline{K^0}$, is a different particle. This is supported by the following type of argument. The virtual dissociation of a neutron

$$n \rightleftharpoons \Lambda^0 + K^0$$

is a strong interaction. Transpose the K° and change it to its antiparticle. Then the process

$$\Lambda^0 \rightleftharpoons n + \overline{K^0}$$

is also strong. If $K^0 \equiv \overline{K^0}$,

$$\Lambda^0 \rightleftharpoons n + K^0$$

is a strong interaction. Then it follows that

$$n + n \rightarrow n + \Lambda^0 + K^0 \rightarrow \Lambda^0 + \Lambda^0$$

is a strong interaction, via the intermediate $n + \Lambda^0 + K^0$ virtual state. The reaction $n + n \rightarrow \Lambda^0 + \Lambda^0$ has not been observed, implying that K^0 is not identical to $\overline{K^0}$.

The difference in identity of the K^0 and $\overline{K^0}$ particles does not rule out the possibility of a weak coupling between the $\overline{K^0}$ and K^0 states. Coupling occurs via the virtual two-pion state

$$K^0 \rightarrow \pi^+ + \pi^- \leftarrow \overline{K^0} \tag{86}$$

Notice that changing particles into antiparticles does not affect the intermediate state because $\pi^+ \rightarrow \pi^-$ and $\pi^- \rightarrow \pi^+$. In contrast to the existence of a weak coupling between the neutral K mesons, no such coupling exists for the neutron and antineutron. A neutron cannot change into an antineutron for this would violate the absolute law of baryon conservation; $|\Delta B| = 2$ is forbidden. The transformation $K^0 \leftrightarrow \overline{K^0}$ is not forbidden in a weak process as strangeness is not conserved.

Through the weak coupling between the K^0 and its antiparticle the $\overline{K^0}$, it is possible to construct two neutral K particles that are their own

† M. GELL-MANN and A. PAIS, *Phys. Rev.* **97**, 1387, 1955.

antiparticles. These states have wave functions

$$\psi(K_1^0) = \frac{1}{\sqrt{2}}[\psi(K^0) + \psi(\overline{K^0})] \tag{87}$$

$$\psi(K_2^0) = \frac{1}{\sqrt{2}}[\psi(K^0) - \psi(\overline{K^0})] \tag{88}$$

Interchanging K^0 and $\overline{K^0}$ leaves the wave function of the K_1^0 state unchanged, just like the $\pi^+ + \pi^-$ state; the wave function of the K_2^0 state, however, changes sign and the two-pion decay mode is forbidden for the K_2^0 state. Gell-Mann and Pais predicted the existence of the K_1^0 and K_2^0 states. A beam of K^0 mesons produced by the reaction $\pi^- + p \to \Lambda^0 + K^0$ is originally composed of equal numbers of K_1^0 and K_2^0 particles. From eqns. (87) and (88) we can write

$$\psi(K^0) = \frac{1}{\sqrt{2}}[\psi(K_1^0) + \psi(K_2^0)] \tag{89}$$

$$\psi(\overline{K^0}) = \frac{1}{\sqrt{2}}[\psi(K_1^0) - \psi(K_2^0)] \tag{90}$$

The K_1^0 particles decay with a mean lifetime of 10^{-10} sec into π^+ and π^- or π^0 and π^0. The K_2^0 particles decay in various three-body ways with a mean

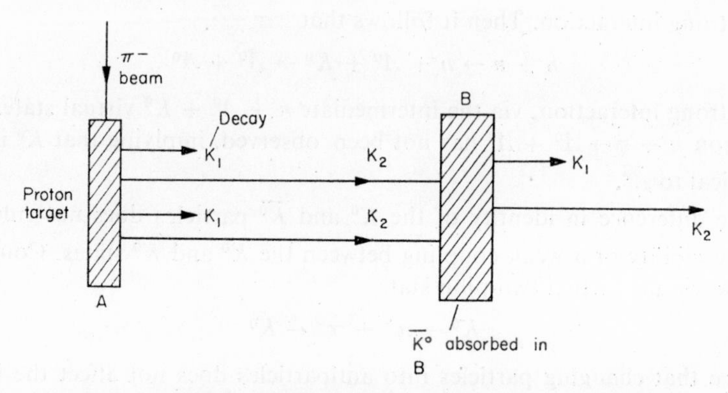

FIG. 21. The proposed experiment of A. Pais and O. Piccioni†.

lifetime of 6×10^{-8} sec. After travelling a few feet from the production target, a neutral K^0 beam consists almost exclusively of K_2^0 particles. This implies, by eqn. (88), that the neutral K beam now is a mixture of equal numbers of K^0 and $\overline{K^0}$ mesons. Pais and Piccioni proposed the following experiment† (Fig. 21). Consider a thin proton target A exposed to a high energy beam of negative pions. The pure K^0 beam emerging from A quickly

† A. PAIS and O. PICCIONI, *Phys. Rev.* **100**, 1487, 1955.

degenerates into a pure K_2^0 beam (50% K^0 and 50% $\overline{K^0}$). The K_2^0 beam enters a second target B. The $\overline{K^0}$ particles are strongly absorbed in B (not the K^0) by reactions of the type

$$\overline{K^0} + n \rightarrow \Lambda^0 + \pi^0 \tag{91}$$

$$\overline{K^0} + n \rightarrow \Sigma^{\pm} + \pi^{\mp} \tag{92}$$

For the $\overline{K^0}$ particles, $S = 1$, and strangeness is conserved, and reactions (91) and (92) are allowed reactions. Only scattering processes are possible for the K^0 component of the K_2^0

$$K^0 + n \rightarrow n + K^0$$

$$K^0 + p \rightarrow n + K^+$$

The neutral K beam emerging from the far side of B is once again nearly a pure K^0 beam; this soon degenerates into a K^0 $\overline{K^0}$ mixture through the rapid decay of the K_1^0 component. The full experiment of Pais and Piccioni has not been carried out, but the hyperons produced by $\overline{K^0}$ events (91) and (92) have been observed in emulsion stacks and bubble chambers.†

The difference in the decay modes of the K_1^0 and K_2^0 states implies the existence of a small mass difference between the particles. This mass difference, expressed in MeV/c^2, is††

$$m(K_1^0) - m(K_2^0) = \frac{(1{\cdot}5 \pm 0{\cdot}5)\,\hbar}{c^2\,\tau(K_1^0)} \sim (0{\cdot}9 \pm 0{\cdot}3) \times 10^{-5}\,\frac{\text{MeV}}{c^2}$$

where $\tau(K_1^0)$ is the mean lifetime of the K_1^0 decay.

The sequence of decay and regeneration in the Pais–Piccioni type of experiment has an analogy in classical optics. The original K^0 beam generated in the proton target A (Fig. 21) is replaced by a left circularly polarized light beam. If this beam is passed through a sheet of polaroid, one of the linearly polarized components of the left circularly polarized light is strongly absorbed (circularly polarized light is a mixture of two linear polarized components at right angles, $\pi/2$ radians out of phase). The emerging beam is linearly polarized, and this can be regarded as an equal mixture of left and right circularly polarized components. The newly generated right circularly polarized photons are analogous to the $\overline{K^0}$ mesons. Notice, however, that in this analogy the polarization property of photons is associated with their spin orientation, whereas the K mesons are spinless.

21.10. HYPERNUCLEI

A hypernucleus or hyperfragment is a metastable nucleus in which a bound hyperon replaces one of the nucleons. The symbol

$${}_{\Lambda}\text{He}^4$$

† W. B. Fowler *et al.*, *Phys. Rev.* **113**, 928, 1959; E. Boldt *et al.*, *Phys. Rev. Letters* **1**, 150, 1958.

†† F. Muller *et al.*, *Phys. Rev. Letters* **4**, 418 (539E), 1960.

denotes a hypernucleus in which one of the neutrons of the α-particle is replaced by a lambda hyperon. We shall restrict the discussion to lambda-hypernuclei. In general, sigma- or xi-hypernuclei would have very short lifetimes because of the fast (strangeness–conserving) transformations

$$\Sigma^+ + n \rightarrow \Lambda^0 + p$$
$$\Sigma^- + p \rightarrow \Lambda^0 + n$$
$$\Xi^- + p \rightarrow \Lambda^0 + \Lambda^0$$
$$\Xi^0 + n \rightarrow \Lambda^0 + \Lambda^0$$

in nuclear matter.

The Polish physicists Danysz and Pniewski† in 1952 deduced that a track in a nuclear emulsion block which had been exposed at a high altitude to cosmic radiation was due to a hypernucleus (probably Be^8). Within a short space of time many other hypernuclei events were observed. The heaviest hypernucleus observed to date (1961) is ${}_\Lambda C^{13}$ produced by exposing an emulsion block to a beam of K^- mesons

$$K^- + O^{16} \rightarrow {}_\Lambda C^{13} + p + p + n + \pi^- \tag{93}$$

From one of the observed modes of decay, viz.

$${}_\Lambda C^{13} \rightarrow N^{13} + \pi^- \tag{94}$$

the binding of the Λ^0 particle in the ${}_\Lambda C^{13}$ hypernucleus can be calculated from the observed kinetic energies of the decay particles. The calculated binding energy

$$B_\Lambda(\text{for } {}_\Lambda C^{13}) \quad \text{is} \quad (10{\cdot}8 \pm 0{\cdot}5)\ \text{MeV}$$

When lambda binding energies are plotted against mass number A of the hypernucleus, B_Λ increases monotonically with A. The hypernucleus ${}_\Lambda H^2$ has not been observed; it seems reasonable to assume that there is no bound state for the $\Lambda^0 - p$ system. The ${}_\Lambda H^3$ system has been observed, but the binding energy of the lambda particle is very small (a small fraction of one MeV). It is interesting to find that hypernuclei like ${}_\Lambda He^5$ are found (unlike He^5). ${}_\Lambda He^5$ can be regarded as a composite particle consisting of a lambda hyperon bound to an α-particle.

It is difficult to obtain accurate determinations of the mean lifetimes of hypernuclei, but it has been shown that the lifetimes are approximately equal to that of the free lambda hyperon ($\sim 10^{-10}$ sec). There are usually several competing modes of decay of a given species of hypernuclei. For example, the hypernucleus ${}_\Lambda He^4$ and ${}_\Lambda He^3$ can be studied by exposing a liquid helium bubble chamber to a K^- beam

$$K^- + He^4 \rightarrow {}_\Lambda He^4 + \pi^- \tag{95}$$

$$K^- + He^4 \rightarrow {}_\Lambda H^3 + p + \pi^- \tag{96}$$

† M. Danysz and J. Pniewski, *Phil. Mag.* **44**, 1, 348, 1953.

The $_{\Lambda}He^4$ hypernucleus has the following decay modes: (the relative frequencies are indicated by the numbers)

$$_{\Lambda}He^4 \rightarrow \text{nucleons} + \pi^0 \quad (10)$$

$$_{\Lambda}He^4 \rightarrow He^3 + p + \pi^- \quad (3)$$

$$_{\Lambda}He^4 \rightarrow H^2 + p + n \quad (1)$$

$$_{\Lambda}He^4 \rightarrow {}_1H^2 + {}_1H^2 \quad (1)$$

The first two decay modes are called pionic decays.

The decay of a $_{\Lambda}He^4$ hypernucleus into two deuterons is represented schematically in Fig. 22.

For hypernuclei with $Z > 3$ or 4, the non-pionic decay modes are dominant.

One of the interesting aspects of hypernuclear physics is that it can throw light on the parity of the lambda hyperon. Strictly speaking, as parity is

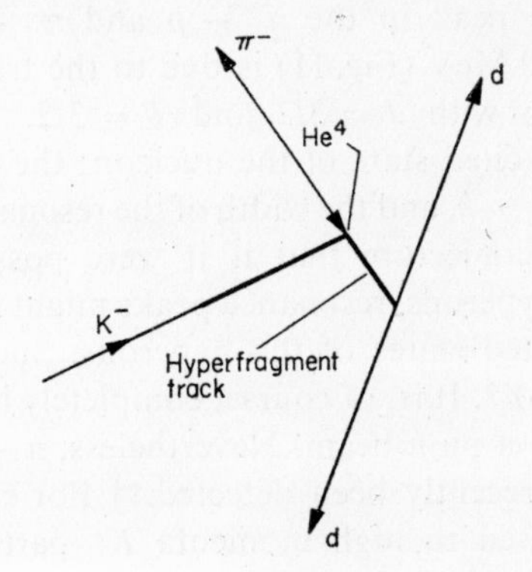

FIG. 22. Sketch of production of hyperfragment in helium bubble chamber and subsequent non-pionic decay:

$$K^- + He^4 \rightarrow {}_{\Lambda}He^4 + \pi^-$$

$$_{\Lambda}He^4 \rightarrow d + d.$$

violated in lambda decay one cannot talk about the parity of the lambda particle. However, it is meaningful to speak of the relative parity $P_{\Lambda KN}$ of the Λ–K system with respect to the nucleon parity. It is permissible to define the parity of the Λ^0 particle as even (just like the nucleon) and then identify the parity of the K particle with $P_{\Lambda KN}$. The following reactions have been observed in helium bubble chambers

$$K^- + He^4 \rightarrow {}_{\Lambda}He^4 + \pi^- \quad (97)$$

$$K^- + He^4 \rightarrow {}_{\Lambda}H^4 + \pi^0 \quad (98)$$

If the $_\Lambda He^4$ hypernucleus in reaction (97) is produced in its ground state (it seems probable that there are no bound excited states) and if we can be sure that this hypernucleus state has zero spin, then we can deduce the relative parity $P_{\Lambda KN}$. All the particles involved in reaction (97) have zero spin and as the intrinsic parity of the π^- is odd, then the relative parity of the K^- meson is odd with respect to the Λ–N system (N is a nucleon). The evidence for the zero spin of the $_\Lambda He^4$ system is not absolutely conclusive† and we can say that if the spin of the $_\Lambda He^4$ state is unity, then $P_{\Lambda KN}$ is even, provided the K^- mesons are all absorbed from zero angular momentum states. Other methods of determining the relative parities $P_{\Lambda KN}$ and $P_{\Sigma KN}$ are described in the review article by Morpurgo (see bibliography).

21.11. THE RESONANCE STATES OF ELEMENTARY PARTICLES: Y^* AND K^*

The large resonance peak in the $\pi^+ - p$ and $\pi^- - p$ scattering cross section curves near 200 MeV (Fig. 11) is due to the transient formation of a pion–nucleon system with $J = 3/2$ and $T = 3/2$. This system can be described as the first excited state of the nucleon; the mean lifetime of the state τ is $\sim 10^{-23}$ sec ($\Gamma\tau \sim \hbar$, and the width of the resonance Γ is ~ 100 MeV).

It is reasonable to conjecture that if it were possible to observe the scattering of pions by hyperons, resonance peaks might show up corresponding to short lived excited states of the hyperons. Such excited states are denoted by the symbol Y^*. It is, of course, completely impractical to expose a target of hyperons to a pion beam. Nevertheless, $\pi - Y$ and also $\pi - K$ resonance states have recently been detected.†† For example, in hydrogen bubble chambers exposed to high momenta K^- particles ($p \sim 1$ GeV/c), the following reaction is observed

$$K^- + p \to \Lambda^0 + \pi^+ + \pi^- \qquad (99)$$

The production of three particles in reaction (99) is characterized by a continuous distribution of the pion kinetic energies. However, in many cases the kinetic energy of the π^+ (or the π^-) is peaked near 280 MeV. This is characteristic of the production of two particles in reaction (99). It seems probable that in a considerable fraction of the reactions there is a two stage process

$$K^- + p \to \Lambda^* + \pi^+ \text{ (or } \pi^-) \qquad (100)$$

$$\Lambda^* \to \Lambda^0 + \pi^- \text{ (or } \pi^+) \qquad (101)$$

† Evidence for zero spin has been found; E. F. Beall *et al.*, *Phys. Rev., Letters* **8**, 75, 1962.

†† M. Alston *et al.*, *Phys. Rev. Letters* **5**, 520, 1960.

The hyperon excited state Λ^* has the following properties

Mass	$= 1380$ MeV/c^2
Resonance width	$\sim$ 55 MeV
Angular momentum	$= \frac{3}{2}\hbar$
Isospin	$= 1$
Strangeness	$= -1$
Baryon number	$= 1$

Evidence for an excited state of the K particle has been obtained from hydrogen bubble chamber events†

$$K^- + p \rightarrow \overline{K^0} + p + \pi^- \tag{102}$$

In many events, an analysis of the energies of the particles favoured a two stage process

$$K^- + p \rightarrow K^* + p \tag{103}$$

$$K^* \rightarrow \overline{K^0} + \pi^- \tag{104}$$

The K^* excited state has the following properties

Mass	$= 885$ MeV/c^2
Resonance width	$\sim$ 35 MeV
Isospin	$= \frac{1}{2}$
Strangeness	$= -1$

There is some angular distribution evidence that the K^* resonance has a spin $J = 1$, but this is not to be regarded as conclusive.

In addition to the K^* and Λ^* resonances described above, a number of others has been observed. The subject is in a rapid stage of development at the present time and it is therefore unwise to discuss the subject in any more detail.

21.12. THE TWO-PION AND THREE-PION RESONANCES

In an attempt to explain the electromagnetic form factors of the proton and the neutron, Nambu†† suggested the existence of a heavy neutral meson. Such a meson should have isospin $T = 0$ and unit angular momentum. Chew††† had also shown that such a *vector meson* should exist on dynamical grounds as a 3π resonance or bound state. Moreover, as long ago as 1936

† M. Alston *et al.*, *Phys. Rev. Letters* **6**, 300, 1961.
†† Y. Nambu, *Phys. Rev.* **106**, 1366, 1957.
††† G. F. Chew, *Phys. Rev. Letters* **4**, 142, 1960.

Breit† pointed out that a three-pion system with $T = 0$, $J = 1$ (odd parity system) would give rise to a spin–orbit force between two nucleons. Sakurai†† has argued that such a quasi-particle would produce a short range attraction between a nucleon and an antinucleon and this is compatible with the large antinucleon–nucleon annihilation cross section at high energies.

The first experimental evidence for a three-pion resonance, with $T = 0$, $J = 1$, was found by a study of four-pronged annihilation events when the 72 in. Berkeley hydrogen bubble chamber was exposed to a high energy antiproton beam.††† Previous searches for a three-pion quasi-particle or resonance had assumed that the effective mass of the three-pion "particle" was less than three times the rest mass of the pion. Maglić and his group assumed that the omega meson ω^0, as the $T = 0$, $J = 1$ three-pion resonance is called, has an effective mass greater than three pion mass units. About 10 per cent of the annihilations

$$\bar{p} + p \rightarrow \pi^+ + \pi^- + \pi^0 + \pi^+ + \pi^- \tag{105}$$

proceed via two stages

$$\bar{p} + p \rightarrow \omega^0 + \pi^+ + \pi^- \tag{106}$$

$$\omega^0 \rightarrow \pi^+ + \pi^- + \pi^0 \tag{107}$$

The ω^0 particle has an effective mass of 787 MeV/c^2 and the width of the resonance is less than 25 MeV. The ω^0 has a lifetime greater than 4×10^{-23}sec and travels a distance greater than 13 fermis before it decays into three pions. A useful relation between the resonance width Γ of a relativistic quasi-particle and the distance r it travels before decay, is $\Gamma r \sim 200$ MeV-fermi. It is, of course, impossible to measure the distance the ω^0 meson travels before decay in the bubble chamber. The effective mass of the particle was determined by plotting the number of pion triplets against effective mass: a sharp peak appears at an effective mass of 787 MeV/c^2.

The ω meson has also been detected in multipion production reactions occurring when a liquid deuterium bubble chamber is exposed to a high energy beam of positive pions

$$\pi^+ + d \rightarrow p + p + \pi^+ + \pi^- + \pi^0 \tag{108}$$

This experiment is accompanied by less background events than in $\bar{p} + p$ annihilation experiments. In addition to strong evidence that in many cases the pion triplet in reaction (108) occurs as the result of the decay of the $T = 0$, $J = 1$ omega particle, Pevsner and his group‡ also obtained good evidence for another three-pion resonance or quasi-particle, the eta meson (η)

† G. Breit, *Phys. Rev.* **51**, 248, 1936; *Phys. Rev.* **120**, 287, 1960; *Proc. Natl. Acad. Sci. U.S.* **46**, 746. 1960.

†† J. J. Sakurai, *Phys. Rev.* **119**, 1784, 1960; *Phys. Rev. Letters* **7**, 355, 1961.

††† B. C. Maglić *et al.*, *Phys. Rev. Letters* **7**, 178, 1961.

‡ A. Pevsner *et al.*, *Phys. Rev. Letters* **7**, 421, 1961.

with an effective mass of 550 MeV/c^2, and a width < 30 MeV which decays

$$\eta \rightarrow \pi^+ + \pi^- + \pi^0$$

This $T = 0$, $J = 0$ neutral vector meson, with a mass less than four pion mass units, is more in accord than the ω meson with Nambu's predicted particle to explain nucleon form factors.

The η meson has also been detected in the process

$$K^- + p \rightarrow \Lambda^0 + \eta^0$$
$$\eta^0 \rightarrow \pi^+ + \pi^- + \pi^0$$

There is good evidence for yet another quasi-particle,† the rho (ϱ) meson, which can exist in three charge states ϱ^+, ϱ^0, and ϱ^- (N.B. the omega meson is always neutral). This two-pion $T = 1, J = 1$ (odd parity) resonance has an effective mass of 750 MeV/c^2 and a width $\Gamma \sim 80$ MeV. There is some evidence that this wide resonance is, at least in the case of the neutral rho, split into two levels whose experimental widths are of the same order of magnitude as that of the omega.

The rho resonance shows up in a fairly large fraction of high energy antiproton–proton annihilations

$$\bar{p} + p \rightarrow \varrho + \pi + \pi$$

For the ϱ^0, the most probable decay is

$$\varrho^0 \rightarrow \pi^+ + \pi^-$$

There are small branching ratios for the decays

$$\varrho^0 \rightarrow \pi^+ + \pi^- + \pi^0$$
$$\varrho^0 \rightarrow \pi^+ + \pi^- + \pi^0 + \pi^0$$

The most frequent decay mode of the charged rho meson is

$$\varrho^{\pm} \rightarrow \pi^{\pm} + \pi^0$$

Although the neutral rho meson has nearly the same effective mass as the omega meson they differ in isospin ($T = 1$ for ϱ^0 and $T = 0$ for ω^0). The rho-resonance is important in relation to the charge and magnetic moment structure of the proton and the neutron. The near equality of the effective masses of the rho and omega mesons may be a consequence of the fact that the two particles are two different decay particles of the same parent particle which does not possess a definite isospin.††

The pion and the pion-resonances all have odd parity. The angular momenta J and isospins T are set out in the following table. There is a little experimental evidence for a multi-pion resonance with $J = 0$, $T = 0$.

† A. R. Erwin *et al.*, *Phys. Rev. Letters* **6**, 628, 1961; D. Stonehill *et al.*, *Phys. Rev. Letters* **6**, 624, 1961; E. Pickup *et al.*, *Phys. Rev. Letters* **7**, 192, 1961.

†† S. Fubini, *Phys. Rev. Letters* **7**, 466, 1961.

NON-STRANGE MESONS
(Odd Parity)

	$J=0$	$J=1$
$T=0$	?	ω ?
$T=1$	π	ϱ

21.13. THE UNIVERSAL WEAK INTERACTION

One of the most remarkable discoveries in recent years is the near (or possibly exact) equality of the coupling constants that characterize the various weak interaction processes. A pictorial way of representing this universal weak (Fermi) interaction is to draw the Tiomno–Wheeler† (or

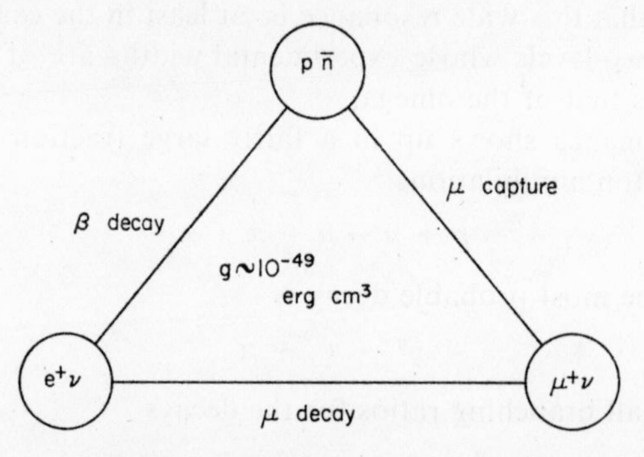

FIG. 23. The Tiomno–Wheeler (or Puppi) weak interaction triangle. (A tetrahedron can be formed by adding a (p, $\bar{\Lambda}$) vertex.

Puppi) "triangle" (Fig. 23). At each vertex of the triangle there is one neutral and one charged particle. The three sides of the triangle depict three types of weak interaction all of the same intrinsic strength. Thus the beta decay side

$$p + \bar{n} \rightarrow e^+ + \nu$$

can be transformed by "particle algebra" to read

$$n \rightarrow p + e^- + \bar{\nu}: \quad \text{negatron decay}$$

or

$$p \rightarrow n + e^+ + \nu: \quad \text{positron decay}$$

or

$$e^- + p \rightarrow n + \nu: \quad (K\,\text{capture})$$

The muon decay side

$$\mu^+ + \nu \rightarrow e^+ + \nu$$

is equivalent to

$$\mu^+ \rightarrow e^+ + \nu + \bar{\nu}$$

† J. TIOMNO and J. A. WHEELER, *Revs. Mod. Phys.* **21**, 144, 1949.

The muon capture side (analogous to K electron capture)

$$\mu^+ + \nu \rightarrow p + \bar{n}$$

is equivalent to

$$\mu^- + p \rightarrow n + \nu$$

If the fermion pair $(p, \bar{\Lambda})$ is added to the weak interaction triangle to form a tetrahedron† then the following decay processes can be incorporated in the universal scheme

$$\Lambda^0 \xrightarrow{\text{virtual}} p + (\bar{p} + n) \rightarrow p + \pi^-$$

$$K^+ \xrightarrow{\text{virtual}} \overline{\Lambda^0} + p \rightarrow \mu^+ + \nu$$

The existence of a link between the $(p, \bar{\Lambda})$ vertex and the $(e^+ \nu)$ vertex of the tetrahedron implies the existence of the decay

$$p + \overline{\Lambda^0} \rightarrow e^+ + \nu$$

i.e.,

$$\Lambda^0 \rightarrow p + e^- + \bar{\nu}$$

This beta decay mode is very infrequent but it has been detected.

21.14. CONCLUSION

It is beyond the scope of this book to include an account of the method of "dispersion relations"††, which is at the present time the most vigorous and promising branch of elementary particle physics. Dispersion relations are not new in theoretical physics; Kramers and Kronig in the nineteen-twenties showed the power of the technique in dealing with optical phenomena. The application of dispersion relations to elementary particle physics is due to many authors, notably Goldberger, Gell-Mann, Thirring and Mandelstam.

Very briefly, two of the main ideas of the method of dispersion relations are:

(1) To express the cross section for some elementary particle interaction (e.g. pion–nucleon scattering) in terms of an amplitude which is a function of a *complex variable*; the real part of the variable represents the total energy of the system. If this complex amplitude is *analytic* (i.e. "well-behaved" in a mathematical sense) in the upper half-plane of the complex variable, then it is possible to derive dispersion relations linking the real and the imaginary part of the scattering amplitude.

(2) In some applications of dispersion relations the principle of causality is built into the theory, representing the fact, for example, that the amplitude

† See the review article by M. Gell-Mann and A. H. Rosenfeld (bibliography).

†† An excellent introduction to the subject is given by J. Hamilton, *Prog. Nucl. Phys.* **8**, pp. 143–194, 1960.

of a scattered wave must be zero until an incoming wave reaches the scatterer. This "cause and effect" law has a number of non-trivial consequences.

The hope has been expressed that eventually the method of dispersion relations may yield accurate theoretical values of all elementary particle cross sections, lifetimes, branching ratios, etc. in terms of the masses and coupling constants of the fundamental particles. This stage of the theory is not yet in sight.

To offset any impression of complacency with regard to our present state of knowledge of elementary particle physics we conclude this chapter by listing *some* of the features of the subject which we do not understand.

(1) Why are there so many elementary particles and why do they have their mass values?

(2) Which of the present list of "elementary" particles is composite? Goldhaber and Györgyi have suggested that the nucleon and the K meson are the "real" elementary particles, the hyperons being compounds of a nucleon and a K particle (for example, the lambda hyperon is a tightly bound p–K^- or n–$\overline{K^0}$ system). Sakata and Okun, on the other hand, have treated the nucleon and the lambda hyperon as the "real" particles and they consider a $\overline{K^0}$ particle as a very strongly bound Λ^0–n system. Feynman †, however, expresses the view that it is impossible to tell which particles are fundamental and which are composite.

(3) Why do strong interactions satisfy more conservation laws than the weak interactions?

(4) Why do the two otherwise elementary "weak" particles the muon and the electron have such different masses? In the past, theoreticians have tended to assume that different masses are associated with different interactions.

(5) What is the connection (if any) between strangeness and parity? In decays in which S is conserved (not conserved), is parity conserved (not conserved)?

(6) Why are there no elementary charged particles with electric charges greater than one unit?

(7) Is there an intermediate boson involved in the four-fermion weak interaction?

(8) How many "new" elementary particles or "new" resonances remain to be discovered?

(9) What is the place of gravitation in the scheme of things. If the quantum of the gravitational field, the graviton, has a finite rest mass, what is the Compton wavelength of the graviton †† (i.e. the range of the gravitational potential)?

† R. P. Feynman, *Proc. Intn. Conf. High Energy Physics*, p. 501, Rochester 1960.

†† J. J. Sakurai, *Annals of Physics* **11**, 1, 1960, has tentatively estimated the graviton Compton wavelength at 3×10^8 light years, implying the absence of gravitational attraction for bodies of greater separation.

BIBLIOGRAPHY

W. O. LOCK, *High Energy Nuclear Physics*, Methuen, London 1960.

J. D. JACKSON, *The Physics of Elementary Particles*, Princeton 1958.

J. HAMILTON, *The Theory of Elementary Particles*, Oxford 1959.

P. ROMAN, *Theory of Elementary Particles*, North-Holland, Amsterdam 1960.

W. S. C. WILLIAMS, *An Introduction to Elementary Particles*, Academic Press, New York and London 1961.

R. E. MARSHAK and E. C. G. SUDARSHAN, *Introduction to Elementary Particle Physics*, Interscience, New York 1961.

In the above list, the books by Lock and Williams are the most suitable as an introduction to High Energy Physics.

Excellent accounts of the concepts of field theory are:

R. E. PEIERLS, A. SALAM, P. T. MATTHEWS and G. FELDMAN, A Survey of Field Theory in *Reports on Progress in Physics* **18**, pp. 423–477, The Physical Society, London 1955.

R. J. BLIN-STOYLE, *Contemporary Physics* **2**, pp. 325–344, Taylor and Francis, London 1960–61.

An introduction to the quantum theory of fields is, F. MANDL, *Introduction to Quantum Field Theory*, Interscience, New York 1959.

The accurate determination of the masses, spins, lifetimes, . . . of elementary particles is described in the book

E. R. COHEN, K. M. CROWE and J. W. M. DUMOND, *The Fundamental Constants of Physics*, Interscience, New York 1957.

Important review articles on elementary particles include:

G. A. SNOW and M. M. SHAPIRO, Mesons and Hyperons, *Rev. Mod. Phys.* **33**, 231, 1961.

The July issue of *Rev. Mod. Phys.* Vol. **33**, 1961.

R. H. DALITZ, *K* Mesons and Hyperons, *Rep. Progr. Phys.* **20**, pp. 163–303, Physical Society, London 1957.

W. D. WALKER, The Properties and Production of *K* Mesons, *Progr. Elementary Particle and Cosmic Ray Physics* **4**, pp. 73–103, North-Holland, Amsterdam 1958.

M. GELL-MANN and A. H. ROSENFELD, *Ann. Rev. Nucl. Sci.* **7**, 407, 1957.

J. J. SAKURAI, *Progr. Nucl. Phys.* **7**, pp. 243–312, Pergamon Press, London 1959.

E. SEGRÈ, Antinucleons, *Ann. Rev. Nucl. Sci.* **8**, 127, 1958.

W. F. FRY, Hyperfragments, *Ann. Rev. Nucl. Sci.* **8**, 105, 1958.

G. MORPURGO, Strong Interactions and Reactions of Hyperons and Heavy Mesons, *Ann. Rev. Nucl. Sci.* **11**, 41, 1961.

Recent conference volumes with articles on High Energy Physics are:

Proceedings of the International Conference on High Energy Physics, Vol. 10, Rochester 1960.

Proceedings of the Rutherford Jubilee International Conference, Manchester 1961 (Editor J. B. BIRKS), Heywood, London.

One of the best introductions to the concepts of Dispersion Theory is

J. HAMILTON, Dispersion Relations for Elementary Particles, *Progr. Nucl. Phys.* **8** pp. 143–194, London 1960.

EXAMPLES

(When necessary use data from Tables 1, 2 and 3.)

1. Verify that the weak interaction constant $\mathscr{G}^2$ is dimensionless and has the value 3×10^{-14} (assume $G = 1{\cdot}4 \times 10^{-49}$ erg cm^3).
2. Calculate the binding energy of positronium.
3. Determine the Q-value of the reaction $\bar{\nu} + p \rightarrow n + e^+$, for protons at rest. What % error in the Q-value arises if the momentum of the antineutrino is neglected.

4. Assume the neutrino and the antineutrino are identical. A cubical tank, 1 m long, is filled with carbon tetrachloride (density of liquid is 1·59 g cm^{-3}, abundance Cl^{37} is 24·6%, mean atomic weight of Cl is 35·5). The tank is exposed to an antineutrino flux of $1·5 \times 10^{13}$ particles per cm^2 per sec for 70 d. If all the argon is then extracted from the tank and put into a proportional counter what is the maximum counting rate we can expect? Assume the relevant antineutrino cross section is 1×10^{-43} cm^2. (Half-life of Ar is 35·0 d).
5. Calculate the energy (in keV) of the $4f \rightarrow 3d$ negative pion X-ray transition in phosphorus ($Z = 15$). The K absorption edge for Ce and Pr occurs at 0·3063 Å and 0·2951 Å respectively. Which of the two elements Ce or Pr absorbs the pionic X-ray most strongly?
6. Calculate the end point energy of the positron spectrum of positive muons at rest.
7. A negative pion is slowed down in hydrogen and finally captured from a $1s$ orbit

$$\pi^- + p \rightarrow n + \gamma$$

Calculate the energy of the capture γ-ray. What % error arises from (a) neglecting the recoil of the neutron, (b) the pion K-shell binding energy? The capture γ-ray is converted in a thin lead foil into an electron–positron pair. How far apart must the electron and positron detectors be placed if the electron and positron describe semicircles in a uniform field of 8000 gauss?
8. Verify eqn. (34) and calculate $(m_{\pi^-} - m_{\pi^0})\, c^2$ given $\Delta E_\gamma = 30$ MeV.
9. Calculate the velocities of a 1·19 GeV/c pion and antiproton. What is the difference in their time-of-flight over a path length of 15 m?
10. What are the kinetic energies of the proton and the pion emitted in the decay of a lambda hyperon at rest in the lab. system? Repeat the calculation for the decay into a neutron and a neutral pion.
11. What are the kinetic energies of the proton and neutral pion emitted in the decay of a positive sigma hyperon at rest in the lab. system?
12. A negative xi hyperon at rest decays into a lambda hyperon and a pion. What is the kinetic energy of the pion? If the pion is travelling *in vacuo*, what is its most probable flight distance before it decays?
13. Calculate the kinetic energy of a positive muon emitted in the $K^+_{\mu 2}$ mode of decay. If the muon is travelling *in vacuo*, what is its most probable flight distance before it decays?
14. The "eta meson" has a rest mass energy of 550 MeV. Which of the following decays are energetically possible:

$$\eta \rightarrow \pi^0 + \pi^0 + \pi^0 + \pi^0; \quad \eta \rightarrow \pi^+ + \pi^+ + \pi^- + \pi^-?$$

CHAPTER 22

THERMONUCLEAR REACTIONS IN STARS

22.1. INTRODUCTION

The problem of the source of the energy of stars is one which has stirred the imagination of scientists for generations. Not only do the stars emit an enormous amount of energy but they continue to do so for thousands of millions of years. In the last century, Helmholtz and Kelvin suggested that the slow gravitational contraction of a star might release sufficient energy to account for its observed luminosity. However, it turns out that the most optimistic estimates of this source of energy would limit the life of the sun to 20 million years. Now the age of the sun is greater than the age of the earth, and geological evidence establishes the age of the oldest rocks as well over a thousand million years. This rules out the possibility of gravitational contraction providing the main source of the sun's energy. This does not mean that gravitational contraction is not important as an energy source at certain stages in the evolution of a star. It has been shown that if gravitational contraction is the sole source of energy for the so-called cepheid variable stars (stars which vary periodically in luminosity), the period of pulsation should decrease with time. In the case of the star δ Cephei, the period of pulsation should decrease by about 40 sec every year. This star has been continuously observed since the end of the eighteenth century and its period is not changing at anything like the required amount.

Speculations have been made from time to time that a star might be heated by incoming streams of meteorites. However, it is difficult to account for the essential stability and magnitude of the radiation emitted from stars by such a variable process.

With the development of atomic physics and the establishment of the Einstein "Energy–mass" law ($E = m\,c^2$), it is not surprising that sooner or later the possibility of "sub-atomic" energy sources was seriously considered. Soon after the discovery of the radioactivity of the heavy elements uranium and thorium, it was suggested that this might be a possible source of stellar energy. For one thing, the half-lives of these elements (about 10^9 to 10^{10} y) seemed to account for the long life of a star. However, we now believe that the abundance of these elements in stellar interiors is much too low to supply enough energy. Moreover, natural radioactive decay rates are unaffected by temperature and pressure variations so there would be no self regulating energy release process maintaining the star in equilibrium. At one time, it was suggested by Jeans that protons and electrons of high energy might collide and annihilate one another converting their mass into energy. (We now know that electrons and positrons can do this, radiating γ-rays, but not electrons and protons.) By 1920, many physicists and astronomers were seriously inclined to the view that nuclear fusion reactions between the lightest nuclei were responsible for stellar energy production. Eddington in his lecture to the British Association in 1920 advanced these ideas and suggested that "... what is possible in the Cavendish Laboratory may not be too difficult in the Sun". (In 1919 Rutherford had observed the nuclear reaction $_7N^{14}(\alpha, p)\,_8O^{17}$ using a natural alpha source.) It is hardly ever true to associate a discovery with one person or event; however, one can say that the theory of thermonuclear reactions in stellar interiors began with the paper of Atkinson and Houtermans in 1927. In spite of the lack of data available at the time, they laid down the essential ideas of stellar thermonuclear reactions. Atkinson and Houtermans realized that deep in stellar interiors where the temperature exceeds 10^6 degrees, matter is completely ionized and that the energy of the nuclei should follow the Maxwell–Boltzmann distribution law. The relatively few nuclei with energies ten or twenty times the most probable value (kT) would eventually penetrate the Coulomb barrier (wave mechanical "tunnel" effect) and fuse together, releasing energy in an exoergic reaction. This theory clearly expressed the fact that the rate of energy release by these thermonuclear reactions would be very sensitive to temperature. The next major advance was made in 1938 and 1939, when the first detailed specific nuclear reactions responsible for the sun's energy were but forward independently by Bethe and von Weizsäcker. Bethe in a classic paper, systematically reviewed possible exoergic nuclear reactions and concluded that two possible processes were responsible for the sun's energy. In each process, the overall effect is to convert hydrogen into helium. The first process involves the interaction of two protons to produce deuterium, the capture of a proton by deuterium to form helium 3, and finally the interaction of two helium 3 nuclei to form helium 4 and two protons. This is known as the proton–proton chain (p–p). The other possible process is the Carbon–Nitrogen cycle, in which carbon and nitrogen act as nuclear catalysts in synthesizing helium from hydrogen.

In the post war years there has been a great advance in our detailed knowledge of nuclear reactions and stellar structure. This has led to greatly improved calculations of internal conditions in stars and in turn more accurate estimates of thermonuclear reaction rates. In the last few years it has been possible to consider in some detail possible thermonuclear reactions responsible for synthesizing the elements. In this way a remarkable theory explaining the observed abundance of the elements in our Galaxy has been developed. This will be considered later in this chapter. Before discussing thermonuclear reactions in stars, it is necessary to give a brief outline of how our knowledge of temperature and density conditions inside stars is derived. This is only a brief outline of the astrophysical background of the subject. The interested reader should consult one of the standard works listed at the end of this chapter.

22.2. ASTROPHYSICAL BACKGROUND

We must be able to deduce the conditions existing in the interior of stars before we can make much progress in discussing stellar evolution and stellar energy sources. The basic data essential to this subject are the mass M, radius R and luminosity L of the star. The luminosity L is the total amount of energy radiated per second from the surface of a star. Fortunately most stars radiate as black bodies (this is not quite true for the sun). This means that we can first deduce the surface temperature of the star from the spectral distribution of its radiation, and then deduce the luminosity L from the radius R using Stefan's law:

$$L = \sigma 4\pi R^2 T_s^4 \tag{1}$$

where σ is Stefan's constant ($5{\cdot}67 \times 10^{-5}$ ergs cm^{-2} deg K^{-4} and T_s is the effective surface temperature ($\sim 6000°$K for the sun).

For the sun we have the following values ($\odot$ is the standard symbol in astrophysics for a solar value)

$$R_\odot = 6{\cdot}96 \times 10^{10} \text{ cm}$$

$$L_\odot = 3{\cdot}86 \times 10^{33} \text{ ergs per sec}$$

$$M_\odot = 1{\cdot}99 \times 10^{33} \text{ g}$$

In spite of the enormous energy output of the sun, the power radiated is less than 2 ergs per gram per sec which is less efficient than many examples of animal metabolism!

The only method available for deducing the interior physical conditions of a star is to write down the equations representing the internal stability of the star using as few assumptions as possible. We know that stars are spherical and that they radiate steadily for millions of years. This means that a star can be considered to pass slowly through a series of equilibrium states. At any internal point, distant r from the centre, the weight of the outer shell must be just supported by the outwardly directed pressure of the stellar material interior to this point (Fig. 1). The star is said to be in hydrostatic equilibrium under its own gravitational forces. Consider a portion of the star of unit cross-sectional area, lying between radii r and $r + dr$. The pressure difference acting on this thin slice is $-\,dp$ (outwards).

This must balance the weight of the slice $g\,dm$, where dm is the mass of the slice and g is the value of the gravitational acceleration at distance r from the centre of the star.

$$\therefore\ dp = -\,g\,dm = -\,g\,\varrho\,dr$$

where ϱ is the density and dr is the volume of unit cross section.

According to Newton's universal law of gravitation $g = \dfrac{G\,M(r)}{r^2}$, where G is the constant of gravitation ($6{\cdot}67 \times 10^{-8}$, expressed in c.g.s. units), and $M(r)$ is the mass inside a radius r,

$$\therefore\ \frac{dp}{dr} = -\frac{G\,M(r)}{r^2}\,\varrho \tag{2}$$

The mass $dM(r)$ of the spherical shell of material, enclosed between radii r and $r + dr$, is given by the expression

$$\frac{dM(r)}{dr} = 4\pi\, r^2\, \varrho \tag{3}$$

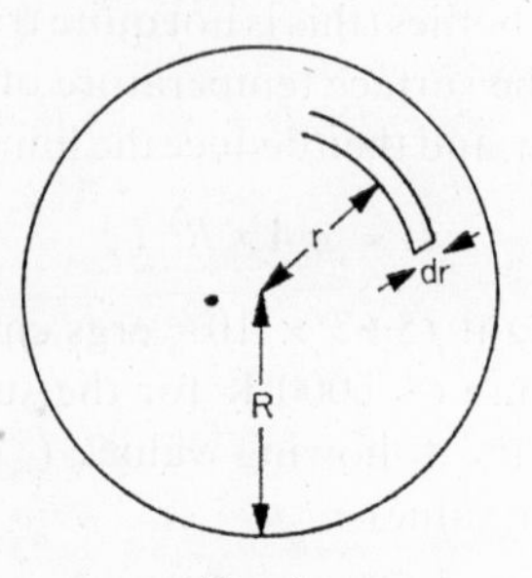

FIG. 1.

The internal pressure p is made up of two components p_r and $p_g \cdot p_r$ is the radiation pressure exerted by the outflowing radiation. As the star is very close to thermodynamic equilibrium, we can write p_r in the form $p_r = \frac{1}{3}\,a\,T^4$, where T is the absolute temperature and a is the radiation constant ($7{\cdot}55 \times 10^{-15}$ c.g.s. units). In many stars this component is much less than the second component $p_g \cdot p_g$ is the "gas" pressure due to the thermal motion of the stellar matter. In spite of the high density prevailing deep inside a star, the stellar material behaves as an ideal gas! This is a consequence of the completely ionized state of stellar matter (the plasma state) at high temperatures. Such material can be compressed to high densities (> 100 g per cm^3) and still retain the elasticity of a gas.

$p_g = \varrho\, r_g\, T,$ where r_g is the gas constant per gram

$\therefore\ p_g = \dfrac{k\,\varrho\,T}{\mu M_{\mathrm{H}}}$, where k = Boltzmann's constant ($1{\cdot}38 \times 10^{-16}$ ergs per °K)

μ = mean molecular weight,

M_{H} = mass of hydrogen atom ($1{\cdot}67 \times 10^{-24}$ g)

$\therefore$ The total internal pressure $p = p_g + p_r$ is given by

$$p = \frac{k\,\varrho\,T}{\mu\,M_H} + \frac{1}{3}\,a\,T^4 \tag{4}$$

In order to calculate the gas pressure p_g we have to estimate the mean molecular weight μ of stellar matter. At first sight this seems to demand a detailed knowledge of the chemical composition of a star. This is not necessary, as the high degree of internal ionization simplifies the problem. An atom of atomic number Z, mass number A, will have an effective mean "atomic" weight $A/(Z + 1)$, as the ionized atom will contribute Z electrons and one nucleus to the stellar material. For ionized hydrogen $\mu = 0{\cdot}5$, for ionized helium $\mu = 1{\cdot}33$ and for all other elements μ ranges from 1·75 to about 2·5.

For a star in an equilibrium state there must be a radial temperature gradient from the centre to the surface of the star. Conduction plays a negligible part in the transfer of heat inside a star. Convection can be important if the temperature gradient is steep. If the temperature gradient is less than a critical value the star is stable against convection currents and all the heat transfer is by radiation. The average temperature gradient in a typical star like the sun is of the order of 3×10^{-4} degrees per cm. The rate at which radiation flows outwards depends on the mass absorption coefficient of the ionized matter for the radiant energy. This radiation deep inside a star consists of soft and medium wavelength X-rays. The principal mechanisms of absorption are photoelectric absorption, the transfer of energy to free electrons in the field of charged ions and nuclei, and the Compton scattering of photons by free electrons. Photoelectric absorption is only possible if some of the atoms are not completely ionized. Even at the centre of a star some of the heavy atoms will not be completely ionized. Near the surface of a star the ionization will be incomplete for many elements. The problem of calculating the absorption coefficient of stellar material is not simple but it is possible to apply statistical mechanics and atomic theories of X-ray absorption to derive a value. It turns out that the stellar material is an extremely efficient absorber of X-rays. The radiation is absorbed and re-emitted many times as it slowly leaks through a star. The wavelength of the radiation adjusts itself continuously to be in thermodynamic equilibrium with the stellar matter. At the surface of the star the escaping radiation corresponds to that of a black body at the surface temperature T_s.

The technique of deducing the temperature and density conditions prevailing inside a star is to set up various stellar models, corresponding to different assumed chemical compositions. The differential equations representing the internal conditions of gravitation and radiation equilibrium are then solved so that the solutions fit the observed boundary conditions at the surface of a star (for example, the surface luminosity $L(r)$ as $r \to R$ must match the observed luminosity and radius of the star). This tedious procedure is now often carried out with the aid of high speed computers.

The results of recent stellar model calculations for the sun are given in Table 1. Each model corresponds to a different chemical composition.

In the outer zone of the star heat transfer by convection is important whereas in the inner core transfer is by radiation alone. Model 2, corresponding to a 70 per cent mass abundance of hydrogen and a 26 per cent mass abundance of helium yields values of 15 million degrees and 125 g/cm³ for the central temperature and density respectively. Calculations of stellar evolution based on these models suggest that the sun has slowly been increasing in luminosity and is now 20 per cent more luminous than at the time of its birth about 5×10^9 years ago.

TABLE 1.* (From SCHWARZSCHILD, HOWARD and HÄRM. *Astrophys. J.* **125**, 233, 1957.)
Models of the Sun.

$R_\odot = 6{\cdot}96 \times 10^{10}$ cm $M_\odot = 1{\cdot}99 \times 10^{33}$ g
$L_\odot = 3{\cdot}86 \times 10^{33}$ ergs per sec

	Model 1	Model 2	Model 3
X (Fractional mass abundance of H)	0·60	0·70	0·80
Y (Fractional mass abundance of He)	0·30	0·26	0·185
Z (Fractional mass abundance of rest)	0·10	0·04	0·013
Fraction of radius in radiative equilibrium	0·810	0·818	0·824
Fraction of mass in radiative equilibrium	0·995	0·996	0·997
Temperature at bottom of convective zone (°K)	$1{\cdot}46 \times 10^6$	$1{\cdot}27 \times 10^6$	$1{\cdot}12 \times 10^6$
Density at bottom of convective zone (g per cm³)	0·049	0·041	0·035
Central Temperature (degrees Kelvin). T_c	$17{\cdot}1 \times 10^6$	$15{\cdot}8 \times 10^6$	$14{\cdot}8 \times 10^6$
Central Density (g per cm³). ϱ_c	122	127	132

* Table reproduced from article by BURBIDGE and BURBIDGE, *Handbuch der Physik*, Vol. 51 (1958).

Gravitational contraction cannot provide sufficient energy to account for the whole output of stellar energy. Nevertheless, gravitational contraction with the consequent release of energy is an important source of energy at certain epochs in a star's evolution. The birth process of a star is one of the least well understood parts of astrophysics. It seems likely that stars are born by the slow gravitational condensation of interstellar gas and dust. Eventually the protostar† achieves sufficient density to become opaque. The temperature of the protostar increases as it contracts. Eventually the central temperature is high enough for hydrogen thermonuclear reactions to begin at a slow rate ($T_c > 10^6$ degrees). There are certain regions of the sky which seem to be the seat of protostar formation. A number of round dense globules are observed and the American astronomer Bok has suggested that these are protostars. Small interlocking patches of nebulosity occur

† Protostar is the word used for a star in the early stage of condensation from interstellar matter.

in these regions, e.g. in the Orion nebula, known as Herbig–Haro objects, which may be the early stage of star formation. It is just possible that we have direct evidence of the birth of a star. Photographs of this region of the Orion nebula taken in 1954 reveal two star-like nuclei, which were not found on photographs taken in 1946 and 1947.

When a star contracts, part of the gravitational energy is converted into internal energy of the star, the rest is radiated away. If the ratio of the specific heats C_p over C_v for stellar material is that of a monatomic gas, (5/3), one half of the energy change is converted into internal energy, thereby increasing the temperature of the star.

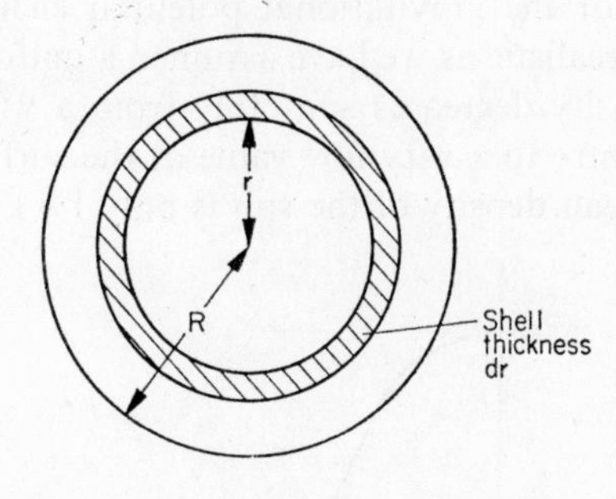

FIG. 2.

Consider the condensation of a mass M of infinite dilution to form a star of radius R. The gravitational potential at an internal point P distance r from the centre of the star

$$= \int_{\infty}^{r} \frac{G\,M(r)}{r^2}\,dr = -\frac{G\,M(r)}{r}$$

where $M(r)$ is the mass inside radial distance r. $M(r) = \frac{4}{3}\pi r^3 \varrho$, assuming a constant density ϱ for the star.

The work done in adding a thin spherical shell of mass $4\pi r^2 \varrho\, dr$ to the core of radius r (Fig. 2),

$$= -\frac{G\,M(r)}{r} \cdot 4\pi r^2 \varrho\, dr$$

Therefore total work done in condensing the star from a mass of infinite dilution is given by V,

$$V = -\int_{0}^{R} \frac{G\,M(r)}{r} \varrho \cdot 4\pi r^2 \cdot dr$$

substituting for $\qquad M(r) = \varrho \frac{4}{3}\pi r^3$

we have
$$V = -\frac{G16\pi^2 \varrho^2}{3} \int_0^R r^4\, dr$$

$$\therefore V = -\frac{G16\pi^2 \varrho^2 R^5}{15}$$

Now
$$\varrho = M / \tfrac{4}{3}\pi R^3$$

$$\therefore V = -\tfrac{3}{5}\frac{GM^2}{R} \tag{5}$$

This expression for the gravitational potential energy decrease of a condensing star is unrealistic as we have assumed a uniform density throughout the star. The density decreases smoothly from a value greater than 100 g per cm³ at the centre to a very low value at the surface, possibly as shown in Fig. 3. (The mean density of the sun is only 1·4 g per cm³.) However we

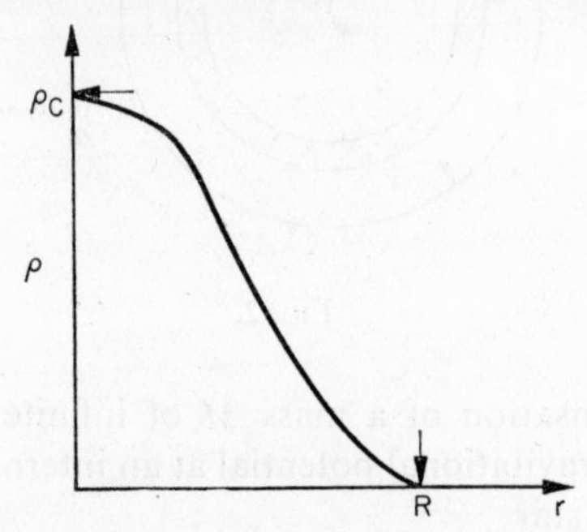

FIG. 3. Variation of density of stellar interior from the centre to the surface of a star (ϱ_c is the central density).

can say the gravitational potential energy is of the order of $-G\,M/R$. For the sun this turns out to be about -4×10^{48} ergs. If the sun has emitted radiation at its present rate L over a period of t years, and one half the potential energy release is radiated, then the maximum estimate of the age of the sun is

$$t_{\max} = \frac{1}{2}\frac{G\,M_\odot^2}{R_\odot L} \tag{6}$$

$$L \sim 4 \times 10^{33} \text{ ergs per second}$$

$$\therefore t_{\max} \text{ is } \sim 20 \text{ million years.}$$

This is much less than the age of the sun ($> 10^9$ y). For stars more massive than the sun, the time scale for gravitational contraction is less, being only 3 million years for a star of 2·3 solar masses. Gravitational contraction is responsible for the initial heating of a protostar to temperatures high enough for thermonuclear energy production to begin. At a much later stage in the evolution of a star, when the nuclear fuel source (hydrogen) at the centre of a star has all been converted into helium, the core will contract, increasing the central temperature until new thermonuclear reactions begin.

22.3. THERMONUCLEAR REACTIONS

In order that nuclear reactions can act as sources of stellar energy the following conditions must be satisfied:

(1) The reactions must be exoergic; i.e., the sum of the masses of the products of the nuclear reaction must be less than the sum of the masses of the reacting nuclei. The mass decrement Δm of the reaction is converted into kinetic energy of the products $E = c^2 \Delta m$.

(2) The temperature must be high enough for some of the nuclei to overcome the Coulomb repulsion and fuse together under the action of the short range nuclear forces.

(3) The reacting nuclei must have sufficient abundance in the region of the star where the temperature is suitable for the reaction to occur.

The first condition implies that the reactions of interest are either fusion reactions of light nuclei or fission or radioactive decay of heavy nuclei. The low abundance of heavy nuclei rules out the second possibility. Apart from irregular variations for very light nuclei, the mean binding energy per nucleon $\overline{B}$ of nuclei increases slowly with mass number A reaching a maximum around A equal to 60. Nuclei in this region of the periodic table, e.g. Fe^{56} are the most stable. The rates of fusion reactions are very sensitive to temperature changes and they decrease rapidly with increasing charge of the colliding nuclei.

The rate of a thermonuclear reaction between two types of nuclei, of density n_1 and n_2 nuclei per cm³ respectively can be written in the form

$$r = n_1 n_2 [\sigma v]_{av} \quad \text{reactions per cm}^3 \text{ per sec} \tag{7}$$

where σ is the reaction cross section (in cm²) for a relative velocity of approach v between the reacting nuclei. The product σv is then averaged over the distribution of velocities of the nuclei corresponding to the temperature T in the region of the reaction. The difficulty in computing the rate r lies in our ignorance of the cross section σ as a function of v in the region of interest. In the last few years, techniques have been developed for measuring the cross sections of some of the nuclear reactions of astrophysical interest at bombarding energies of ~ 100 keV. Even at this energy the cross sections are very difficult to measure as they are less than 10^{-10} barns! Now the energies of most of the nuclei responsible for thermonuclear reactions are in the range 10 to 20 keV. This means that the measured cross sections at energies around 100 keV must be extrapolated by theory to the thermonuclear range. This is often very uncertain as the presence of nuclear resonant levels will have a profound effect on the magnitude of the cross section.

The effect of the Coulomb barrier between the reacting nuclei can be estimated by the wave mechanical theory of the "tunnel" effect. The probability of two nuclei, of charge $Z_1 e$ and $Z_2 e$, penetrating the Coulomb barrier is given by the Gamow factor:

$$\exp\left\{-\frac{2\pi Z_1 Z_2 e^2}{\hbar v}\right\} \tag{8}$$

where v is the relative velocity of approach of the nuclei, and $\hbar$ is Planck's constant divided by 2π.

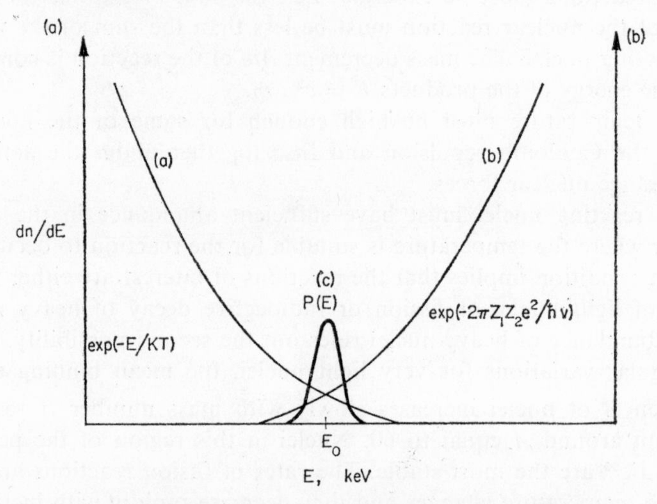

FIG. 4. Curve (a): Energy distribution of nuclei (high energy tail); Curve (b): Gamow Coulomb barrier penetration factor.

Next, we must consider the Maxwellian distribution in energy of the nuclei. The number of nuclei with a relative kinetic energy of approach E, varies with E according to the expression:

$\exp(-E/kT)$, where kT is the most probable particle energy (the peak of the Maxwell curve). The reaction probability $P(E)$ for the colliding nuclei will be peaked in the energy region where the product of these two factors is a maximum. This effect is illustrated by the graphs in Fig. 4. Most of the reactions are confined to a fairly narrow region of energy in the vicinity of $20\,kT$, that is, in the high energy tail of the Maxwell distribution. At temperatures of the order of 20 million degrees, the reactions are confined to a band of energies in the range 15 to 20 keV.

The reaction cross section σ in the formula for the rate of the reaction $r = n_1 n_2 [\sigma v]_{av}$ varies with the relative kinetic energy of the colliding particles E in the following way:

$$\sigma = \frac{S_0}{E} \exp\{-31{\cdot}3\, Z_1 Z_2 A^{1/2} E^{-1/2}\} \quad \text{barns} \tag{9}$$

where E is measured in keV and A is the reduced mass of the particles

$$A = \frac{A_1 A_2}{A_1 + A_2}$$

where A_1 and A_2 are the masses of the nuclei in atomic mass units.

S_0 must be deduced from experiment; it is measured in keV-barns. The peak of the curve (c) in Fig. (4) corresponds to an energy E_0 given by

$$E_0 = 1{\cdot}22(Z_1^2 Z_2^2 A T_6)^{1/3} \text{ keV} \tag{10}$$

where T_6 is the temperature of the stellar matter measured in units of one million degrees (Kelvin).

When the reaction cross section σ is averaged over the Maxwellian distribution of particle energies we finally obtain a complicated expression for the energy ε liberated per g per sec:

$$\varepsilon = (7{\cdot}57 \times 10^{26})\, Q \cdot S_0\, \varrho\, x_1 x_2 \frac{d\, Z_1^{1/3} Z_2^{1/3}}{A_1 A_2 A^{1/3}} \frac{e^{-\tau}}{T_6^{2/3}} \text{ ergs per gram per sec} \tag{11}$$

where Q is the energy liberated per reaction in MeV.

S_0 corresponds to the peak of the reaction probability curve

ϱ is the density of stellar material in g per cm³, x_1 and x_2 are the fractional mass abundances of the reacting nuclei

A_1, A_2, A have already been defined

Z_1, Z_2 are the atomic numbers of the reacting nuclei

τ is given by the expression

$$\tau = 42{\cdot}483 \left(\frac{Z_1^2 Z_2^2 A}{T_6}\right)^{1/3} \tag{12}$$

For the carbon–nitrogen cycle reaction $d = 1$

For the proton–proton chain reaction $d = \frac{1}{2}$.

The complexity of eqn. (11) tends to obscure the essential data which is required for calculating the rate of energy production in a stellar thermonuclear reaction. The data required is

(1) The density ϱ and temperature T_6 of the region in question.

(2) The chemical abundance of the reacting nuclei in this region of the star.

These are the essential astrophysical data.

From the nuclear physics viewpoint we need to know

(1) The Q of the nuclear reaction. This can be computed from precise atomic mass values.

(2) The extrapolated value of S_0 in eqn. (9) to the energy E_0 (see Fig. 4). This is the most difficult factor of all to determine. It has already been emphasized that extrapolation of experimental values in the region of 100 keV is uncertain, particularly if the nuclear reaction at the energy E_0 is affected by a resonance state of the compound nucleus found in the reaction.

22.4. THERMONUCLEAR REACTIONS IN THE SUN

The most abundant element in the Universe is hydrogen. We believe that hydrogen is by far the most abundant element in the so-called "Main Sequence" stars, of which our sun is a typical middle-aged member. The only thermonuclear reactions of interest in stars with central temperatures less than 50 million degrees are those involving protons. For other reacting nuclei, the Coulomb barrier is too high or the abundance of the reacting nuclei is too low. The two possible thermonuclear reactions involving hydrogen were considered in detail by Bethe. These are the "proton–proton" chain reaction and the "carbon–nitrogen" cycle. In each reaction chain, helium 4 nuclei are synthesized from four protons. The high binding energy of the helium 4 nucleus means that the hydrogen–helium fusion process liberates a considerable amount of energy. A few years ago, it was held that the major portion of the sun's energy was derived from the carbon–nitrogen cycle. Recent modification of the estimates of the central temperature of the sun now favour the proton–proton chain.

The proton–proton chain reactions in the sun are:

	Reaction Lifetimes
(a) ${}_1H^1 + {}_1H^1 \rightarrow {}_1H^2 + e^+ + \nu + 0{\cdot}42$ MeV	(7×10 y)
(b) ${}_1H^2 + {}_1H^1 \rightarrow {}_2He^3 + \gamma$	(4 sec)
(c) ${}_2He^3 + {}_2He^3 \rightarrow 2\,{}_1H^1 + {}_2He^4$	(4×10^5 y)

Total Q for the p–p chain $= 26{\cdot}2$ MeV.
(Reaction times based on a central temperature T_c of about 15 million degrees.)

The first reaction of the chain was originally considered by Bethe and Critchfield in 1938. It is unlikely that the cross section of this reaction will be measured in the laboratory in the foreseeable future. Theoretical considerations indicate that the cross section of reaction (a) at a lab. energy of 1 MeV will be as low as 10^{-23} barns! The very small probability of this reaction occurring during the short collision time of two colliding protons is a consequence of the fact that the compound nucleus He^2 must be formed and undergo beta decay to form a deuteron (${}_1H^2$ nucleus) in this time. This is very unlikely as the He^2 system must have the two proton spins antiparallel to satisfy the Pauli exclusion principle, and one of the protons must reverse its spin axis when the positron e^+ and neutrino ν are emitted (the bound state of the deuteron has the proton and neutron spins parallel).

The value of S_0 appearing in eqn. (9) is given by beta decay theory for reaction (a) as

$$S_0 = (4{\cdot}4 \pm 0{\cdot}8) \times 10^{-22} \text{ keV-barns}$$

Some energy is irretrievably lost from the star by the neutrino emission. The mean lifetime of a proton at the centre of the sun before it experiences this reaction is estimated to be $\sim 7 \times 10^9$ y! This is not surprising in view of the very low cross section. Once a deuteron is formed it reacts after about 4 sec with a proton to form He^3 (a (p, γ) reaction). The final reaction of the p–p chain is a slow one as the probability of two He^3 nuclei colliding is very small. Another factor inhibiting the reaction is the greater Coulomb repulsion ($Z_1 = 2$, $Z_2 = 2$). On average the lifetime of a He^3 nucleus at the centre of the sun is of the order of 4×10^5 y.

In 1958, Holmgren and Johnston, detected in the laboratory the reaction: $He^3(\alpha, \gamma)\, Be^7$. The cross section was found to be more than one thousand times the previous estimates. This means that the following reactions may compete with the third step in the p–p chain (reaction (c)). These are:

(d) ${}_2He^3 + {}_2He^4 \rightarrow {}_4Be^7 + \gamma$: ${}_4Be^7 + e^- \rightarrow {}_3Li^7 + \nu$ (K capture)
and ${}_3Li^7 + {}_1H^1 \rightarrow {}_2He^4 + {}_2He^4$

and/or

(e) ${}_2He^3 + {}_2He^4 \rightarrow {}_4Be^7 + \gamma$: ${}_4Be^7 + {}_1H^1 \rightarrow {}_5B^8 + \gamma$
${}_5B^8 \rightarrow {}_4Be^8 + e^+ + \nu$ and ${}_4Be^8 \rightarrow {}_2He^4 + {}_2He^4$

These reactions are likely to occur in stars with a high abundance of He^4. It is just possible that the neutrino flux from the beta decay of B^8 estimated as 2×10^9 neutrinos per cm^2 per sec at the Earth could be detected by the reaction

$${}_{17}Cl^{37} + \nu \rightarrow {}_{18}Ar^{37} + e^-$$

using a 10,000 gallon tank of carbon tetrachloride placed in a deep mine.

Carbon–Nitrogen Cycle

Bethe has suggested that the following series of reactions is responsible for the energy production in main sequence stars:

	Reaction Lifetimes
${}_6C^{12} + {}_1H^1 \rightarrow {}_7N^{13} + \gamma$	10^6 y
${}_7N^{13} \rightarrow {}_6C^{13} + e^+ + \nu$	10 min
${}_6C^{13} + {}_1H^1 \rightarrow {}_7N^{14} + \gamma$	2×10^5 y
${}_7N^{14} + {}_1H^1 \rightarrow {}_8O^{15} + \gamma$	2×10^7 y
${}_8O^{15} \rightarrow {}_7N^{15} + e^+ + \nu$	2 min
${}_1N^{15} + {}_1H^1 \rightarrow {}_6C^{12} + {}_2He^4$	10^4 y

In the C–N cycle, carbon and nitrogen nuclei are not permanently destroyed, but act as catalysts in the nuclear reactions. The average lifetimes of C^{12}, N^{13}, C^{13}, N^{14}, O^{15} and N^{15} nuclei at the centre of the sun before they are destroyed show an enormous range from 2×10^7 y to 2 min. The complete cycle involves the creation of one α-particle, two positrons and two neutrinos for the loss of four protons. The mean free path of neutrinos is very much greater than the radius of the sun and therefore the neutrino energy escapes. When the cycle has been in operation for several million years, a steady state distribution of the nuclei involved will be established. In the steady state the number of nuclei of each type is proportional to its mean lifetime. The concentration of N^{13} and O^{15} will be very small as they quickly decay by positron emission. The crucial reaction in the cycle is the last one ... $N^{15}(p, \alpha) C^{12}$. Why does this reaction occur instead of the $N^{15}(p, \gamma) O^{16}$? There is in fact a small probability of the (p, γ) reaction occurring. The great stability of the C^{12} nucleus, an $N = Z = 2n$ type, ensures the exoergic character of the (p, α) reaction. The $N^{15}(p,\gamma)O^{16}$ reaction is also exoergic, but particle emission is more probable than γ-emission, provided the Coulomb barrier is not too high. In the last year or so the estimates of the $N^{15}(p, \gamma)O^{16}$ cross section have increased. If the new estimates are correct more C^{12} will be eventually converted into O^{16} than was previously thought.

The Q of the complete cycle is 25·0 MeV, 1·2 MeV less than the value of the proton–proton chain. The difference is due to the different neutrino energy losses. The calculations on the rates of the reaction in the C–N cycle in stellar interiors are based on recent laboratory measurements of the various (p, γ) reaction cross sections. A great advance has been made at the Livermore Radiation Laboratory (California) as a result of the successful operation of a proton linear accelerator with a high beam current of several hundred milliamperes! Lamb and Hester determined the $N^{14}(p, \gamma) O^{15}$ reaction cross section at an energy of 100 keV as $0{\cdot}9 \times 10^{-11}$ barn (the nitrogen was in the form of a titanium nitride target). The extrapolation of the experimental values of S_0 to the thermonuclear reaction energy region for the (p, γ) reactions of interest in the C–N cycle is very uncertain as these are strongly affected by the existence of resonant energies. To take one example, it is uncertain whether an energy level exists for O^{15} in the vicinity of 7·37 MeV. If such a level exists, it would act as a resonance level in the $N^{14}(p, \gamma) O^{15}$ reaction at stellar energies with the result that the rate of the $N^{14}(p, \gamma)$ reaction would be much faster than present estimates.

There is no doubt that future experimental and theoretical advances in determining reaction cross sections and the excited states of the various nuclei concerned will enable much more reliable estimates to be made of the rates of stellar nuclear reactions.

In addition to the C–N cycle, other cycles involving "alpha" particle nuclei may occur at higher temperatures than that of the central regions of the sun. The Coulomb barrier effect requires higher temperatures as the nuclear charge increases. Cycles of interest are:

C–N cycle: C^{12}, C^{13}, N^{14}, $N^{15}(p, \alpha) C^{12} + 5{\cdot}0$ MeV
$N^{15}(p, \gamma) O^{16} + 12{\cdot}2$ MeV

Ne–Na cycle: Ne^{20}, Ne^{21}, Ne^{22}, $Na^{23}(p, \alpha) Ne^{20} + 2{\cdot}4$ MeV
$Na^{23}(p, \gamma) Mg^{24} + 11{\cdot}5$ MeV

Mg–Al cycle: Mg^{24}, Mg^{25}, Mg^{26}, $Al^{27}(p, \alpha) Mg^{24} + 1{\cdot}6$ MeV
$Al^{27}(p, \gamma) Si^{28} + 11{\cdot}6$ MeV

(The positron emitters in each cycle have been omitted.)

In each cycle, the (p, γ) reaction competing with the more probable (p, α) reaction which completes the cycle, is given. In each case the (p, γ) reaction yields more energy than the (p, α) reaction, although the latter reaction has the higher cross-section.

Why is the C–N cycle the first to occur? For $n = 1$, 2, and 4, where n is the number of α-particles in the nucleus, no cycles occur. For $n = 1$, there is no cycle as the $He^4(p, \gamma)\,Li^5$ reaction does not occur since the isotope Li^5 does not exist. The next possibility, a Be–B cycle ($n = 2$), almost occurs, but the B^8 nucleus is unstable against fission into two α-particles. For $n = 4$,

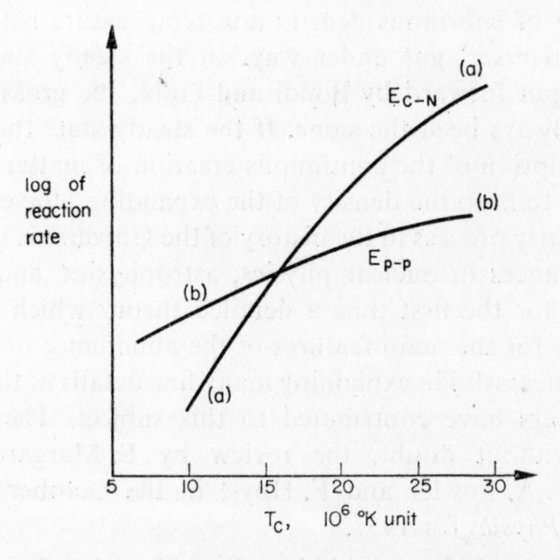

FIG. 5. Variation in rate of energy produced as a function of central temperature T_c (a) in the C–N cycle, (b) in the proton–proton chain.

there is no O–F cycle, because (p, α) reactions on O^{17} and O^{18} occur. The great advance in the subject of stellar energy sources by Bethe and von Weizsäcker was partly a realisation of what chain reactions or cycles could *not* occur.

Which of the two "hydrogen–helium" fusion processes plays the major role in energy production in a star? The answer is based on our knowledge of the stellar temperature. Assuming the existence of C^{12} at the centre of a star, the C–N cycle is the major energy process at temperatures above ~ 18 million degrees. At lower temperatures the "proton–proton" chain is more important. The carbon cycle rate is very sensitive to temperature, the rate varying approximately as the eighteenth power of the temperature in the vicinity of 18 million degrees! The p–p chain reaction rate, on the other hand, varies more slowly with temperature, roughly as T^4. Present estimates for the sun are $T_c \sim 15 \times 10^{6}$°K with the p–p chain contributing ~ 96 per cent of the nuclear energy. The reaction rates as a function of temperature for the two "hydrogen–helium" processes are shown in Fig. 5.

22.5. THE ORIGIN OF THE ELEMENTS

It is possible to explain the observed abundance of the chemical elements in the Universe? Why is hydrogen the most abundant element? Why, if a plot of abundance against mass number is made, does it exhibit peaks in the vicinity of certain elements, such as iron? Have the different elements always been present in the Universe or are they currently being produced inside stars? Ten years ago the answers to these questions were very uncertain. Some people thought that the elements heavier than helium were produced at some very early stage in the history of the Universe, possibly during some epoch of enormous density and temperature before the "expansion of the Universe" got under way. In the steady state theory of the Universe, first put forward by Bondi and Gold, the gross structure of the Universe has always been the same. If the steady state theory is valid, involving the assumption of the continuous creation of matter (presumably hydrogen) in order to keep the density of the expanding Universe constant, then some violent early process in the history of the Universe is very unlikely. As a result of advances in nuclear physics, astrophysics, and cosmology, there has emerged for the first time a detailed theory which not only accounts qualitatively for the main features of the abundance of the elements but is remarkably successful in explaining many fine details of the abundance curve. Many workers have contributed to this subject. The outstanding contribution is, without doubt, the review by E. Margaret Burbidge, G. R. Burbidge, W. A. Fowler and F. Hoyle in the October issue of the *Review of Modern Physics* for 1957.

The essential ideas of the "Burbidge, Burbidge, Fowler and Hoyle" theory are the following. They assume that hydrogen is the primeval element in the universe. All other elements are synthesized from hydrogen deep in the interior of stars at various stages in the history of evolution of the star. Now a large part of the matter in the Universe is not condensed into stars but exists as extremely rarefied gas and fine dust between the stars and nebulae. The discovery by radio astronomers of 21 cm wavelength radiation emitted by neutral atomic hydrogen gas in agreement with the theoretical prediction of van de Hulst has become an invaluable tool in mapping the hydrogen gas clouds in our Galaxy, which are often obscured by dark clouds from the optical telescopes. There is strong evidence that during the evolution of stars, some of them lose mass from their surfaces. Giant stars, like Betelgeuse, have a very low surface gravitational intensity and are therefore continuously losing matter. Some giant stars rotate rapidly and may spray matter into space. Some stars eventually become unstable and explode. The less violent explosions are those of the novae stars. The most violent explosions involving enormous increases in luminosity and ejection of matter are the supernovae stars. By these and other means, it seems very probable that there is a continuous slow circulation of matter between stars and the interstellar medium. Eventually in certain regions of space the right conditions arise for the birth of new stars by gravitational contraction of gas and dust. The newly born star will have an *initial* chemical composition corresponding to the chemical nature of the interstellar medium. As the star evolves on to the Main Sequence, the hydrogen thermonuclear reactions begin when the central temperature rises above a few million degrees. As a star evolves eventually nearly all the hydrogen in the central core is converted into helium. The proton–proton and carbon–nitrogen cycles die away and the helium core contracts thereby increasing the central density. The star now begins to evolve away from the main sequence group of stars towards the red giant group. At higher temperatures and densities new thermonuclear reactions set in, synthesizing new heavier nuclei. This is the key point in the whole theory. The nuclei of the chemical elements are continuously being produced inside stars, different elements being produced in different stars or at different stages in the evolution of a star. Eight different types of nuclear reaction are required. In addition, it is essential that at a certain stage in stellar evolution nuclear reactions releasing a copious supply of neutrons should occur.

Before describing the nuclear reactions responsible for element synthesis, we shall briefly discuss the evolution of stars and the empirical evidence we have of the abundance of elements and isotopes in the Universe.

Astrophysicists find it convenient to represent stars by plotting them in the "Hertzsprung–Russell" diagram, which is a graph of luminosity L of the star (total energy radiated per second), against its "spectral type", or what usually amounts to the same thing, its effective surface temperature T_s. (T_s is calculated assuming the star radiates as a perfect black body, which is not quite true for the sun.) See Fig. 6. The majority of stars is represented by points lying within a narrow diagonal band crossing the "H–R" diagram from the region of low surface temperature and luminosity to the region of high surface temperature and luminosity. These are the main sequence stars of which the sun is a middle region member. Notice that high luminosity for a main sequence star goes with a large mass. The finite width of the main sequence band is a consequence of the different chemical composition of the stars and therefore of their age. According to the theory the stars evolve chemically. If a selection of main sequence stars is plotted, which have very similar chemical composition, a much narrower band is obtained. In addition to the main sequence group, two other important groups are shown: the Red Giants and White Dwarfs. (There are other groups but we have omitted these for simplicity.) The red giants are large, very luminous, tenuous stars of *low* surface temperature (red in colour). The white dwarfs, on the other hand, have low luminosity and radius, and represent a freakish state of matter of enormous density (about a ton per cubic inch!). Matter exhibits very peculiar properties in this superdense state. The theory of stellar evolution is still in an early stage of development, and there are many uncertain stages in the theory. Nevertheless, in the case of the sun, we believe that the sun has evolved "up the main-sequence" and has increased its luminosity about 20 per cent during the last 5×10^9 y. The sun is likely to stay on the main sequence for a further 6×10^9 y and then evolve rapidly off the main sequence towards the red giant branch. This will

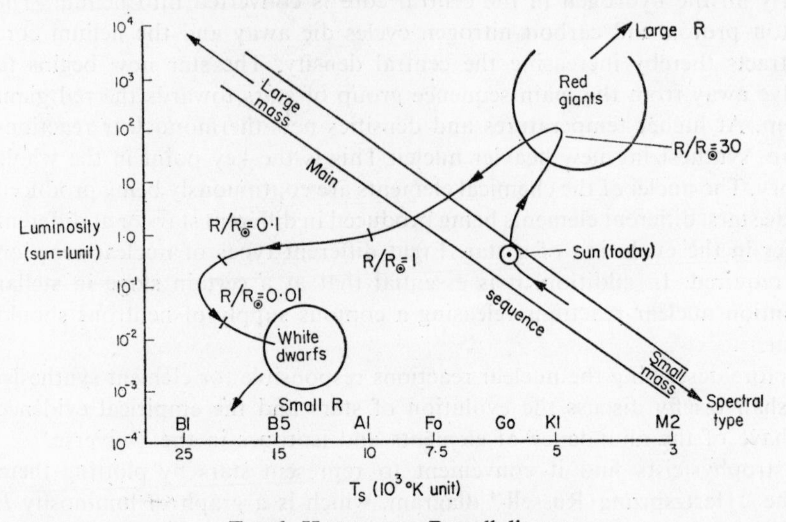

FIG. 6. Hertzsprung–Russell diagram.

correspond to the gravitational contraction of the helium core of the sun and the expansion of the outer zones. It may eventually expand to thirty times its present radius (life will have long since perished on the Earth). It will then contract, decrease in luminosity, its surface temperature increasing as shown in the diagram. At some time in its later evolution, it may go through a pulsating stage, or undergo a supernova catastrophic explosion. Finally it will enter the white dwarf stage and very slowly cool. The essential idea is that the red giants, white dwarfs, etc. represent different stages in the history of stars. The time scales for the different parts of the evolution path of a star in the H–R diagram are vastly different, the longest stage being the main sequence stage.

Let us turn now to the empirical data concerning the atomic abundances in the Universe. Sampling the composition of the Earth's crust and atmosphere is of little use in arriving at any estimate of universal elemental abundances. For example, many gases and vapours (hydrogen), have been lost from the atmosphere, and the composition of surface rocks is quite different from the much deeper lying rocks. There are three main ways of estimating atomic abundances: chemical analysis of meteorites which reach the earth;

spectroscopic analysis of solar and stellar radiation; and possibly measurements of the relative abundances of the particles comprising the primary cosmic radiation. Each of these methods is full of pitfalls in interpretation. The most comprehensive recent survey of the subject is that of Suess and Urey. Figure 7 is a plot of the relative atomic abundance of the elements as a function of mass number A from the data of Suess and Urey.

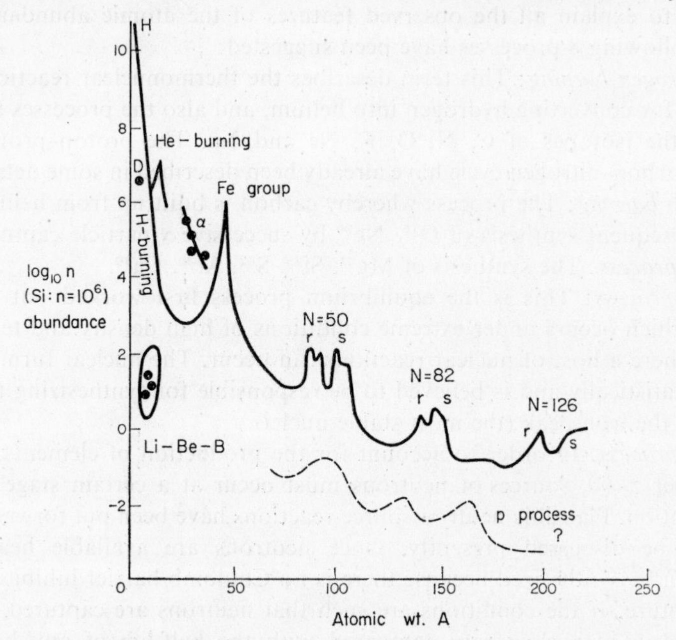

FIG. 7. Logarithmic plot of atomic abundance (value for Si set arbitrarily at $n = 10^6$ atoms) against atomic weight A (Based on Suess and Urey). N.B. Peaks near closed shell neutron numbers 50, 82, 126.

Abundances are expressed in terms of silicon (Si) arbitrarily chosen to have an abundance of 10^6 for convenience. Certain general features stand out in the abundance data.

(1) Hydrogen is by far the most abundant element, and helium the next most abundant.

(2) The so-called "L" group nuclei ($Z = 3$ to 5: Li, Be, B) have abnormally low abundances.
(The abundance of this group of nuclei in the primary cosmic radiation is $\sim 10^4$ to 10^5 times as great).

(3) There is a general exponential decrease in abundance from $A = 1$ to $A =$ about 100. For A greater than 100 there is no systematic decline in abundance.

(4) Nuclei consisting of an integral number of α-particles are over-abundant relative to their immediate neighbours: C^{12}, O^{16}, Ne^{20}, Mg^{24}, etc.

(5) There is a prominent increase in abundance near the element Fe^{56}.

(6) Twin peaks occur at $A = 80$ and 90, at 130 and 138, and at 194 and 208.

22.6. THE EIGHT SYNTHESIZING PROCESSES

In order to explain all the observed features of the atomic abundance curve the following 8 processes have been suggested:

1. *Hydrogen burning*: This term describes the thermonuclear reactions responsible for converting hydrogen into helium, and also the processes for producing the isotopes of C, N, O, F, Ne and Na. The proton–proton chain and carbon–nitrogen cycle have already been described in some detail.

2. *Helium burning*: The process whereby carbon is built up from helium and the subsequent synthesis of O^{16}, Ne^{20} by successive α-particle capture.

3. *The α-process*: The synthesis of Mg^{24}, Si^{28}, S^{32}, Ar^{36}, Ca^{40}.

4. *The e-process*: This is the equilibrium process first worked out by F. Hoyle, which occurs under extreme conditions of high density and temperature, where a host of nuclear reactions can occur. The nuclear turmoil is treated statistically and is believed to be responsible for synthesizing the elements of the iron peak (the most stable nuclei).

5. *The s-process*: In order to account for the production of elements of mass number > 60, sources of neutrons must occur at a certain stage in stellar evolution. Plausible neutron source reactions have been put forward. These will be discussed presently. Once neutrons are available heavy elements can be synthesized because there is no Coulomb barrier inhibiting neutron capture. If the conditions are such that neutrons are captured by a given nucleus at a slow rate compared with the half-life of any beta unstable isotope produced, then the nucleus will decay to its daughter, one place higher up in the periodic table, before capturing the next neutron. This neutron capture process is known as the *s*-process.

The majority of the iostopes in the range $A = 23$ to 46 are produced in this way. The abundance peaks at $A = 90$, 138 and 208 also are produced by the *s*-process. Most of the lead, barium and strontium in the universe has been produced by the *s*-process.

6. *The r-process*: If at some stage in the history of a star an enormous neutron flux is unleashed (it seems probable that this will accompany Nature's most spectacular explosion . . . a supernova explosion), neutrons will be captured so rapidly by certain nuclei that they do not have time to undergo beta decay. Many elements in the range $70 < A < 209$ are produced in this way. The platinum group of metals and uranium and thorium are produced in this way. It is an ironic thought that Nature's thermonuclear bomb, the supernova explosion, has synthesized the fissionable elements uranium and thorium used by man thousands of millions of years later! An interesting by-product of the *r*-process is that it enables us to

make reasonably accurate estimates of the production ratio of uranium 235 and uranium 238. From the present-day abundance ratios and the known half-lives of the two isotopes we can calculate the age of our galaxy.

7. *The p-process*: This process is required to produce proton-rich nuclei by proton capture (p, γ) or by the equivalent (γ, n) process.

8. *The x-process*: The nuclei of D, Li, Be and B are very low in abundance. In fact it is easier to explain their *total* absence in stellar interiors as they are all easily destroyed by nuclear reactions. Tentative ideas have been put forward that these isotopes may be produced in the outer atmosphere of stars by the impact of very high energy protons and other light nuclei on medium weight nuclei. Such high energy disintegrations are observed in our upper atmosphere due to the primary cosmic radiation. It is assumed that the nuclei, D, Li, Be and B are fragments of these *spallation* reactions. Spallation reactions may occur in the outer regions of magnetic stars if the latter are sources of high energy cosmic rays. However, it is true to say that our understanding of the x-process is very imperfect.

We now consider some of these processes in more detail. The hydrogen burning process has already been described in relation to the energy production of the sun. The essential point is that gradually over a time of thousands of millions of years the central core of hydrogen in a main sequence star is converted into helium. Eventually the hydrogen burning reactions die out for lack of fuel and the helium core contracts under the weight of the rest of star. This gravitational contraction liberates energy and *increases* the core temperature and density. The outer part expands and the star evolves towards the red giant region of the H–R diagram. At central temperatures around 10^8 degrees and densities about 10^5 g per cm^3, helium burning commences.

Helium Burning

In his classic paper, in which he set out the details of the carbon cycle, Bethe rejected the possibility of element synthesis in stars on the grounds that carbon cannot be synthesized from helium. The difficulty is that Be^8 formed by the fusion of two α-particles would break up into two α-particles within 10^{-15} sec. The probability of a mutual collision of three α-particles leading directly to the formation of C^{12} ($3He^4 \rightarrow C^{12}$), Bethe considered to be vanishingly small. However, it has been shown by E. Salpeter that under stellar conditions of ϱ about 10^5 g per cm^3 and T about 10^{8}°K, the helium core of a red giant will be converted into carbon. A statistical equilibrium is set up so that the rate of formation of Be^8 is equal to its rate of fission. A ratio of Be^8 to He^4 of about 10^{-9} is established. Once some Be^8 is produced, C^{12} can be formed by α-particle capture. The basic reactions in helium-burning are

$$He^4 + He^4 \rightleftharpoons Be^8$$

$$Be^8 + He^4 \rightleftharpoons C^{12*} \rightarrow C^{12} + \gamma$$

The reaction rate for the second stage of the process is aided by the second excited state of C^{12} at 7·65 MeV. In other words, the $Be^8 (\alpha, \gamma) C^{12}$ reaction is a resonant thermonuclear reaction.

With $\varrho = 10^5$ g per cm³, $T = 10^8$ degrees and a pure helium core, the rate of release of energy in the He burning reactions is about 600 ergs per g per sec.

It is important to realise that in addition to the helium burning in the core of a red giant, hydrogen burning begins in a thin shell between the helium core and the outer zone of the star.

Once an appreciable amount of C^{12} has been produced further α-particle capture will result in the production of O^{16}, Ne^{20} and Mg^{24}:

$$C^{12} + He^4 \rightarrow O^{16} + \gamma$$
$$O^{16} + He^4 \rightarrow Ne^{20} + \gamma$$
$$Ne^{20} + He^4 \rightarrow Mg^{24} + \gamma$$

The different rates of these reactions depend sharply on temperature, so different stars will synthesize different relative abundances. However, for temperatures in the range 1·0 to 1·3 × 10⁸ degrees, the relative abundances are according to Suess and Urey

$$C^{12} : O^{16} : Ne^{20} : Mg^{24} = 1 : 6 : 2 : 0{\cdot}2$$

The α-Process

Eventually the helium core is converted into a mixture of C^{12}, O^{16}, Ne^{20} and a little Mg^{24}. Again we have the same story. Nuclear reactions die out and core contraction begins. Gravitational contraction heating continues until a temperature of $\sim 10^9$°K is obtained. So far we have said little about the electrons in the hot plasma of a star. These undergo many nuclear collisions per second in the dense core radiating bremsstrahlung. At the centre of the sun (15 million degrees) the radiation is X-rays. At the centre of a red giant at the end of its helium burning epoch, when $T \rightarrow 10^9$ the radiation will be high energy γ-rays. Some of the γ-rays can induce the *endothermic* reaction

$$Ne^{20} + \gamma \rightarrow O^{16} + He^4 - 4{\cdot}75 \text{ MeV}$$

Then we get: $$Ne^{20} + He^4 \rightarrow Mg^{24} + \gamma + 9{\cdot}31 \text{ MeV}$$

The two reactions release a net energy of 4·56 MeV. This process, however, cannot occur at an appreciable rate until the core temperature raises the gamma energy spectrum so that a significant number of γ rays have energies > 4·75 MeV.

Once an appreciable amount of Mg^{24} has been created, further (α, γ) processes will occur:

$$Mg^{24} + He^4 \rightarrow Si^{28} + \gamma$$

and also possibly to some extent,

$$Si^{28} + He^4 \rightarrow S^{32} + \gamma$$
$$S^{32} + He^4 \rightarrow Ar^{36} + \gamma$$
$$Ar^{36} + He^4 \rightarrow Ca^{40} + \gamma$$

These "α-particle" nuclei are produced in decreasing amounts for two reasons. First, the reaction cannot begin until a considerable amount of the preceding nuclear species has been produced and second, the Coulomb barrier between the nuclei and the α-particles is increasing. The α-process probably occurs during the temperature range 1 to 3×10^9 degrees. Above 3×10^9 the *e*-process begins.

The *e*-Process

If the central temperature exceeds $\sim 3 \times 10^9$ degrees and the density is in the range 10^5 to 10^9 g per cm^3, a large number of nuclear reactions, such as (γ, α), (γ, p), (γ, n), (α, n), (p, γ), (n, γ), (p, n) compete and a state of statistical equilibrium is reached. The central core nuclei will tend to form the most stable nuclei, that is, nuclei in the neighbourhood of Fe^{56}. At this stage the star will have a rough zonal chemical composition, assuming little mixing between the zones (Fig. 8).

The star has a layer structure, with different nuclear processes occurring in the different regions. The *e*-process occurs at a very fast rate, and the iron group of nuclei may be produced in a few seconds. It is possible that the *e*-process immediately precedes a supernova outburst. We shall return to this point later.

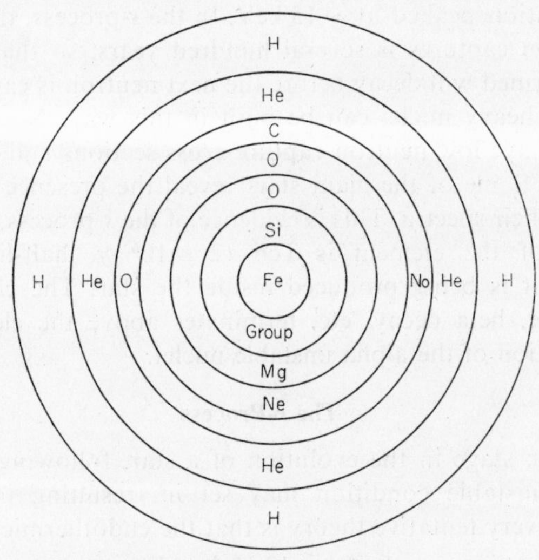

FIG. 8. Hypothetical zonal composition for advanced evolutionary stage of a Red Giant with $T_c = 3 \times 10^{9}$°K; $\varrho_c = 10^6$ g · cm^{-3}.

22.7. STELLAR NEUTRON SOURCES

To build nuclei of mass number A greater than 60 a source of *free* neutrons is required. In stars, with He-burning cores, there is a supply of He^4 and C^{12}. If there is some mixing between the hydrogen and helium burning zones, C^{13} will be produced by the (p, γ) process on C^{12}. The abundance of C^{13} in the C–N cycle of a hydrogen burning zone is not likely to be high enough to release sufficient neutrons by the reaction:

$$C^{13} + He^4 \rightarrow O^{16} + n + 2{\cdot}2 \text{ MeV}$$

If N^{14} is abundant in this region the released neutrons will be lost by the process

$$N^{14}\,(n, p)\,C^{14}$$

Cameron has suggested that the main source of neutrons occurs in the boundary between the central He-burning core of a red giant and the outer hydrogen zone.

Other possible neutron sources are

$$O^{17} + He^4 \rightarrow Ne^{20} + n + 0{\cdot}60 \text{ MeV}$$
$$Ne^{21} + He^4 \rightarrow Mg^{24} + n + 2{\cdot}58 \text{ MeV}$$
$$Mg^{25} + He^4 \rightarrow Si^{28} + n + 2{\cdot}57 \text{ MeV}$$

The $Ne^{21}\,(\alpha, n)\,Mg^{24}$ reaction might occur where Ne^{20} mixes with the hydrogen zone of a red giant and produces Ne^{21} by the (n, γ) reaction.

The *s*-Process

The neutrons released by one or more of the reactions discussed above will quickly lose energy by collisions with nuclei until they have a Maxwellian distribution peaked at $\sim$ 15 keV. In the *s*-process, the average time between neutron captures is several hundred years, so that any beta unstable nuclei formed will decay before the next neutron is captured. A large number of the heavy nuclei can be built in this way. Nuclei with closed neutron shells have low neutron capture cross sections and will tend to be over abundant. Some of the giant stars reveal the presence of the element technetium by their spectra. This is evidence of the *s*-process, for the longest lived isotope of the element is Tc^{99} (2×10^5 y, half-life), indicating that the element is being produced inside the star. The chain of events, neutron capture, beta decay, etc. terminates above the element bismuth with the formation of the alpha unstable nuclei.

The *r*-Process

At a very late stage in the evolution of a star, following the *e*-process, an extremely unstable condition may set in, resulting in a supernova explosion. One very tentative theory is that the endothermic process

$$_{26}Fe^{56} \rightarrow 13\,_2He^4 + 4n$$

may occur at temperatures $> 5 \times 10^9$ degrees.

The only possible energy supply for the disintegration of the very stable iron nuclei into α-particles and neutrons is the gravitational potential energy of a rapid contraction. This contraction is so fast, taking only a few seconds, that the centre of the star implodes and collapses. The surrounding shell is unsupported and it too collapses producing a rapid rise in temperature. The unburnt hydrogen and helium in this collapsing zone will burn at an enormous rate at a temperature $> 10^8$ degrees, leading to an explosion blasting the outer shell of the star into space as an expanding shell of gas. Today the expanding shell of the supernova explosion, observed by Chinese astronomers in 1054, has expanded to a glowing shell of gas corresponding to a 900 year expansion at a velocity of 1300 km per sec. This is the object known as the Crab nebula.† It is an usual object in two ways. It is one of the strongest radio sources that has been detected and its visible light is a continuous spectrum which is strongly polarized. Shklovski, the Russian astronomer, has suggested that these effects can be explained in terms of relativistic electrons accelerating in a magnetic field and emitting synchrotron radiation. The Crab nebula may also be a region for accelerating cosmic rays to high energies. Our ideas about such explosions are very uncertain, but it is not too much to expect that enormous fluxes of neutrons and other particles are unleashed. It has been estimated that a neutron flux as high as 10^{32} neutrons per cm^2 per sec might occur in the outer envelope of the exploding star.

These neutrons are captured on average one every second or so, that is, at a rapid rate compared to beta decay rates. Starting with Fe^{56}, neutrons are captured in rapid succession until the neutron binding energy is so small that (γ, n) reactions will compete with the (n, γ) capture process. The r-process quickly builds proton-poor nuclei, which are more stable to alpha emission and fission than their stable isobars. At mass numbers ~ 260 the process terminates by neutron induced fission. The fission nuclei of mass numbers about 108 and 146 are returned to the r capture process. There is one very interesting piece of evidence in favour of the r-process in supernova explosions. It is this: a certain class of supernovae increase their light output very rapidly after which it dies away with an exponential decay of half-life about 56 d. The supernova of 1054 was visible in daytime at its maximum and was probably somewhat brighter than Venus. In one of the hydrogen bomb tests carried out in the Pacific in 1952, the transuranic isotope Cf^{254} was detected in the fall out. This isotope was synthesized by the r-process by the successive rapid capture of sixteen neutrons by U^{238}. The U^{254} then decays by successive beta emissions to Cf^{254}. Cf^{254} decays by spontaneous fission with a half-life of 56 d! It is the only beta stable isotope with a spontaneous fission half-life between a few days and 10^4 y. This suggests that the 56 d decay light curve of supernovae may indirectly be

† The distance of the Crab Nebula is $\sim$1250 parsecs (1 parsec = 3·26 light years).

associated with the radioactive decay of Cf^{254} synthesized by the *r*-process during the supernova explosion.

The neutron capture paths of the *s*- and *r*-processes are depicted in Fig. 9. The capture path of the *s*-process wanders along the stability line in the *Z*, *A* plane and terminates by alpha decay above bismuth. The *r*-process is a result of an intense neutron flux which drives the nuclear matter to the neutron-rich side of the stability line.

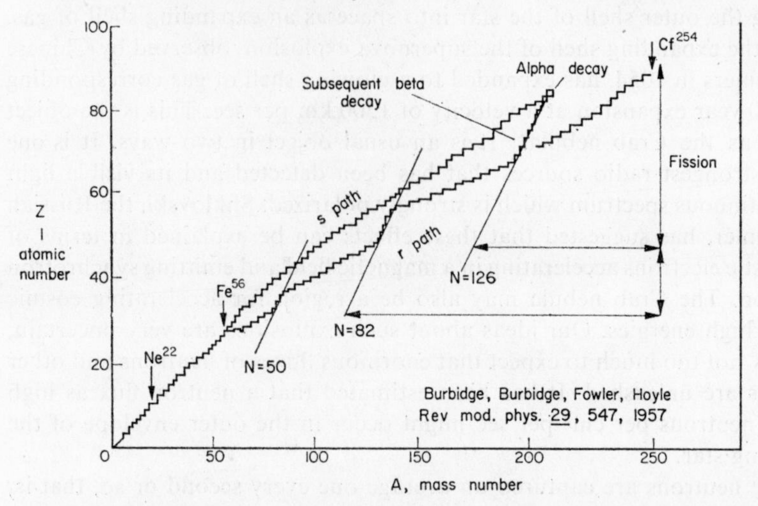

FIG. 9. Neutron capture paths of *s* and *r* (n, γ) capture process. Ne^{22} and Fe^{56} are indicated as "seed" nuclei. *s* process terminates above Bi by α-decay. *r* process caused by intense neutron flux terminates at $A \sim 254$ in fission. N.B. Sharp rise in *Z* in *r* path at neutron shell closures.

Time Scale of Nuclear Synthesis

The different synthesizing processes occur at different stages in the evolution of a star. Hydrogen burning occurs over a period of 10^{10} y when the star is on the main sequence. This is followed by core contraction and the onset of helium burning, etc. The approximate time scales and temperatures appropriate to the various processes are given in Table 2.

TABLE 2

Process	Temperature °K	Time
H-Burning	10^7 to 5×10^7	10^{10} y
He-Burning	10^8	10^7 y
s-Process	$>10^8$	10^5 to 10^6 y
α-Process	$>10^8$	10^3 y
e-Process	$>10^9$	<1 y
r-Process	$>3 \times 10^9$	sec
p-Process	$>3 \times 10^9$	sec

The most striking feature illustrated in Table 2 is the enormous range of time scale involved in the different synthesizing processes. In general as the central temperature of the star increases the reaction rates increase very rapidly.

22.8. THE AGE OF OUR GALAXY

An interesting application of element synthesis theory is the estimation of the age of our galaxy. This estimate is based on the assumption that the transuranic elements are built by the r-process. Nuclei with mass number $235 + 4n$, where n is an integer, will decay by α-particle emission to form U^{235}, unless spontaneous fission is more likely to occur. There are five nuclei which will eventually form U^{235} by alpha decay; those of mass number 239, 243, 247, 251, and 255. The formation of U^{238} is more restricted. The beta stable nuclei of mass number 238, 242, 246 decay by α-emission. On the other hand nuclei of mass number 250 decay predominantly by spontaneous fission. In order to estimate the production rate ratio of U^{235} to U^{238} in the r-process, the above considerations are taken into account along with the well established nuclear stability rule that even-A nuclei tend to be more abundant than odd-A nuclei. Hoyle has estimated the production ratio of U^{235} to U^{238} to be:

$$\frac{\text{No of atoms of } U^{235} \text{ built in } r\text{-process}}{\text{No of atoms of } U^{238} \text{ built in } r\text{-process}} = 1{\cdot}64$$

Present-day analysis of uranium ores show that the atomic abundance ratio of U^{235} to U^{238} is 0·0072. Now the half-lives of U^{235} and U^{238} are $7{\cdot}13 \times 10^8$ y and $4{\cdot}51 \times 10^9$ y respectively. If all the uranium in our galaxy was the result of a single supernova explosion t_0 years ago, we can calculate t_0 as follows:

$$n = n_0 \exp\left\{-\frac{0{\cdot}693 \times t_0}{7{\cdot}13 \times 10^8}\right\}$$

and

$$n' = n_0' \exp\left\{-\frac{0{\cdot}693 \times t_0}{4{\cdot}51 \times 10^9}\right\}$$

where n_0 and n_0' are the original number of atoms of U^{235} and U^{238} respectively (t_0 years ago).

n, n' are the present-day values of U^{235} and U^{238} respectively. Dividing the equations and substituting

$$\frac{n}{n'} = 0{\cdot}0072 \quad \text{and} \quad \frac{n_0}{n_0'} = 1{\cdot}64 \quad \text{we have}$$

$$0{\cdot}0072 = 1{\cdot}64 \exp\left\{\frac{0{\cdot}693\ t_0}{10^9}\left(\frac{1}{4{\cdot}51} - \frac{1}{0{\cdot}713}\right)\right\}$$

$$\therefore \frac{0{\cdot}693\ t_0}{10^9}\left(\frac{1}{0{\cdot}713} - \frac{1}{4{\cdot}15}\right) = \ln\left(\frac{1{\cdot}64}{0{\cdot}0072}\right)$$

This gives a value of t_0 of $6{\cdot}6 \times 10^9$ y. Uncertainties in the initial isotope ratio have little effect on t_0. For a ratio of 1·0 instead of 1·64 we find that t_0 is equal to $6{\cdot}0 \times 10^9$ y.

Another possibility must be considered. The uranium in our galaxy may have been produced in a series of supernova explosions extending over an epoch from t_0 to t_1 years ago. If the uranium production rate ratio was constant over this epoch, we can estimate t_0 for different assumed values of t_1 as follows.

We have already found that if $t_0 = t_1$ (that is all the uranium was produced at the same time, t_0 years ago) and if the U^{235} to U^{238} production ratio was 1·64 then $t_0 = 6{\cdot}6 \times 10^9$ y.

Now $\qquad t_1 \leqq t_0; \quad t_1 \leqq 6{\cdot}6 \times 10^9$ y

Suppose $\qquad t_1 = 5{\cdot}0 \times 10^9$ y

then we can calculate the abundance ratio of U^{235} to U^{238} t_1 years ago, as the present day value is 0·0072 and *no more* uranium has been produced since this time t_1 years ago. This gives a ratio of 0·43, t_1 years ago (5×10^9 y).

t_0 years ago the production of U^{235} and U^{238} started and continued at a constant rate until t_1 years ago.

We can write down the following equations for this epoch:

$$\frac{dn}{dt} = k - \lambda n$$

and

$$\frac{dn'}{dt} = k' - \lambda' n'$$

where n and n' are the numbers of atoms of U^{235} and U^{238} at time t. k and k' are the production rates of the two isotopes and λ and λ' are the radioactive decay constants.

Solving each equation, remembering $n = n' = 0$ at $t = 0$, where we are taking $t = 0$ as t_0 years ago, we find

$$n = \frac{k}{\lambda}\{1 - \exp(-\lambda T\}$$

$$n' = \frac{k'}{\lambda'}\{1 - \exp(-\lambda' T)\}$$

where T is the production time (from t_0 to t_1 years ago).

Dividing and substituting 1·64 for k/k' and the half-lives for the two isotopes we have

$$\frac{n}{n'} = 1{\cdot}64 \times \frac{7{\cdot}13 \times 10^8}{4{\cdot}51 \times 10^9} \frac{\left\{1 - \exp\left(-\dfrac{0{\cdot}693T}{7{\cdot}13 \times 10^8}\right)\right\}}{\left\{1 - \exp\left(-\dfrac{0{\cdot}693T}{4{\cdot}51 \times 10^9}\right)\right\}}$$

this ration of n/n' is the abundance ratio of U^{235} to U^{238} at the end of the production period i.e. t_1 years ago. We have already found this ratio for an assumed value of $5{\cdot}0 \times 10^9$ y for t_1, namely $n/n' = 0{\cdot}43$. This now enables us to solve the cumbersome equation and we find $T = 6{\cdot}5 \times 10^9$ y. This means $t_0 = 11{\cdot}5 \times 10^9$ y if $t_1 = 5{\cdot}0 \times 10^9$ y. In Table 3 the values of t_0 for different *assumed* values of t_1 are tabulated. The abundance ratios of U^{235} to U^{238} at the end of the production period (t_1 years ago) corresponding to the known present day value of 0·0072 are also given.

TABLE 3

t_1 (in 10^9 y)	4·5	5·0	5·5	6·0	6·6
t_0 (in 10^9 y)	18	11·5	8·5	7·4	6·6
U^{235}/U^{238} ratio (t_1 years ago)	0·29	0·43	0·65	0·98	1·64

The value obtained for t_0 is very sensitive to t_1, if t_1 is in the range 4·5 to $5{\cdot}5 \times 10^9$ y. There is some evidence based on the analysis of meteorites which favours a value of $t_1 \geqq 5 \times 10^9$ y. This limits the age of our galaxy to the range 6·6 to $11{\cdot}5 \times 10^9$ y.

22.9. CONCLUSION

The impact of nuclear physics on astrophysics has been emphasized by M. Schwarzschild in his Introduction to his book *Structure and Evolution of the Stars* as follows:

"A little more than a decade ago research on the stellar interior underwent a profound change. The central cause of this change was the introduction of nuclear physics into astronomy. Nuclear physics has provided the theory of the stellar interior with the last but not the least of the fundamental physical processes which determines stellar structure and evolution."

On the other hand developments in the theory of evolution of stars has led to a satisfactory theory of the synthesis of elements. Eight different nuclear processes are invoked in order to account for the abundance of the elements, including the isotopic ratios of a given element. The theory is based on the idea, for which there is quite a lot of evidence, that matter is continuously being ejected from certain stars and that this interstellar matter will eventually condense to form new stars. If this theory is correct, the heavy element content of our Galaxy is continuously increasing. Estimates show that if star formation has been going on at a steady rate for the past 6×10^9 y, 45 per cent of the mass of our Galaxy has been condensed into stars which have by now gone through a complete path of evolution. A young star should have a much higher concentration of metal atoms than a middle-aged main sequence star like the sun. The sun in its turn, should have a metal element concentration ten times greater than very old stars. There is some spectroscopic evidence to support this view. Some of the oldest stars in our Galaxy are found in globular clusters. Although these are very faint stars, work is under way at Mount Wilson and Mount Palomar to analyse their spectra.

The realization that the conversion of helium into carbon could occur in red giant stars with central temperatures in excess of 100 million degrees was a vital link in the theory of element synthesis. Elements beyond the iron peak ($A > 60$), will only be built in stellar interiors if at some stage copious neutron fluxes are released. The Coulomb barrier becomes too high for charged particle reactions in spite of extreme temperatures in red giants. Neutrons may be released by (α, n) reactions in the region between the core of a red giant and the hydrogen burning shell around it. The released neutrons are absorbed either slowly in the *s*-process or very quickly in the *r*-process. In giant stars where heavy elements are synthesized by the *s*-process, the most abundant nuclei are those with a closed neutron shell (once a shell is filled the capture cross section abruptly decreases). Nuclei synthesized by the *s*-process include strontium, zirconium, barium, lead and bismuth. Nuclei built by the *r*-process in the expanding shell of a supernova explosion include selenium, bromine, krypton, iodine, platinum, gold and uranium. It is an interesting thought that solar systems may exist in the Universe which condensed from interstellar matter which had not been through the *r*-process. Such a solar system if it possessed any civilizations would have to manage without gold and uranium!

At the moment we know little about the stage of evolution beyond the red giant stage. We should like to know a lot more about isotopic ratios from stellar spectra. There is also the problem of mixing in stars; observation is limited to the surface layers, we have to infer the chemical composition at greater depths. The recent improvements in proton beam intensities in linear accelerators has made possible the measurement of charged particle nuclear reaction cross sections (e.g. (p, γ)) of astrophysical importance. More detailed information is needed about the positions of the energy levels of certain nuclei. Specific nuclear reactions such as the $C^{12}(\alpha, \gamma)O^{16}$ and $O^{16}(\alpha, \gamma)Ne^{20}$ should be studied in the laboratory.

In spite of the lack of data available, it does seem as if the new theory of element synthesis has succeeded in explaining the main features, and in some cases detailed features, of the abundance of the elements.

BIBLIOGRAPHY

A. S. EDDINGTON, *Stars and Atoms*, Oxford University Press, 1927. An excellent popular account of the problem of internal conditions inside stars.

J. A. HYNEK (Editor), *Astrophysics*, McGraw-Hill, New York 1951. A general background of astrophysics can be obtained from this book. Chapter 14, *The Structure, the Composition, and the Source of the Energy of the Stars* by S. Chandrasekhar is particularly relevant to the subject matter of this chapter.

E. Margaret BURBIDGE and G. R. BURBIDGE, Stellar Evolution. Vol. LI. *Handbuch der Physik*, Springer-Verlag, Berlin 1958. Section D of this article deals with the theory of chemical evolution in stars.

M. SCHWARZSCHILD, *Structure and Evolution of the Stars*, Princeton University Press, 1958.

E. Margaret BURBIDGE, G. R. BURBIDGE, W. A. FOWLER, and F. HOYLE, The Synthesis of the Elements, *Rev. Mod. Phys.* **29**, 547, 1957. This is a full and detailed account of the theory of stellar synthesis in terms of eight nuclear reaction processes.

L. H. ALLER, *The Abundance of the Elements*, Interscience, New York 1961.

H. E. SUESS and H. C. UREY, Abundance of the Elements, *Rev. Mod. Phys.* **28**, 53, 1956.

Two excellent relatively short review articles are:

E. E. SALPETER, Stellar Energy Sources, *Rev. Mod. Phys.* **29**, 244, 1957.

A. G. W. CAMERON, Nuclear Astrophysics, *Ann. Rev. of Nucl. Sci.* **8**, 229, 1958, Annual Reviews, 1958.

EXAMPLES

1. Calculate the mass of the Sun, assuming the Earth describes a circular orbit of radius $1{\cdot}50 \times 10^8$ km. G is $6{\cdot}67 \times 10^{-8}$ c.g.s. units.
2. Derive an expression for the gravitational potential energy of a star of mass M and radius R, assuming the density decreases linearly with distance from the centre of the star to a vanishingly small value at the surface. Calculate the change in potential energy when a star of mass 2×10^{33} g contracts from a radius of 14×10^5 km to 7×10^5 km.
3. (a) Evaluate the normal flux of solar energy at the top of the Earth's atmosphere, assuming the sun is a black body with a surface temperature of 6000°K. The solar radius is $6{\cdot}96 \times 10^5$ km, its mean distance from the Earth is $1{\cdot}50 \times 10^8$ km. Stefan's constant is $5{\cdot}67 \times 10^{-5}$ ergs cm^{-2} sec^{-1} °K^{-4}.
   (b) Find the rate of decrease in the mass of hydrogen in the Sun given that the atomic masses of H^1 and He^4 are 1·008145 and 4·003874 a.m.u. respectively.
4. Calculate the gas and radiation pressure at the centre of a star, whose central temperature and density are 20 million degrees and 100 g cm^{-3}. The chemical composition of the star is 80 per cent by mass hydrogen and 20 per cent by mass helium. Repeat the calculations for a central temperature and density of 100 million degrees and 10,000 g cm^{-3}, the chemical composition now being 20 per cent hydrogen, 80 per cent helium.
5. What is the relative kinetic energy of approach of a proton and carbon 12 nucleus in the centre of a star at 18 million degrees corresponding to the peak of the reaction probability $P(E)$ curve? (Fig. 4.)
6. Verify the values of t_0 given in Table 3 for different assumed values of t_1. The production rate ratio of U^{235} to U^{238} is 1·64. The half-lives of U^{235} and U^{238} are $7{\cdot}13 \times 10^8$ and $4{\cdot}51 \times 10^9$ y respectively.

APPENDIX A

TABLE OF PHYSICAL CONSTANTS†

Speed of light in free space	$c = 299793{\cdot}0 \pm 0{\cdot}3$ km sec^{-1}
The Faraday (physical scale)	$F = 96521{\cdot}9 \pm 1{\cdot}1$ coulomb mole^{-1}
Avogadro's number (physical scale)	$N = (6{\cdot}02486 \pm 0{\cdot}00016) \times 10^{23}$ (g. mole)$^{-1}$
Electronic charge	$e = (4{\cdot}80286 \pm 0{\cdot}00009) \times 10^{-10}$ e.s.u.
	$e = (1{\cdot}60206 \pm 0{\cdot}00003) \times 10^{-19}$ coulomb
Planck's constant	$h = (6{\cdot}6252 \pm 0{\cdot}0002) \times 10^{-27}$ erg sec
	$\hbar = (1{\cdot}05443 \pm 0{\cdot}00003) \times 10^{-27}$ erg sec
1 a.m.u.	$= 931{\cdot}14$ MeV
Electron rest mass	$m_e = (9{\cdot}1083 \pm 0{\cdot}0003) \times 10^{-28}$ g
	$m_e = (0{\cdot}51098 \pm 0{\cdot}0002)$ MeV/c^2
Specific charge of the electron	$\dfrac{e}{m_e} = (1{\cdot}75890 \pm 0{\cdot}00002) \times 10^7$ e.m.u./g
Proton rest mass	$m_p = (1{\cdot}67239 \pm 0{\cdot}00004) \times 10^{-24}$ g
	$m_p = (938{\cdot}211 \pm 0{\cdot}004)$ MeV/c^2
	$m_p = (1{\cdot}007593 \pm 0{\cdot}000002)$ a.m.u.
Ratio of proton mass to electron mass	$\dfrac{m_p}{m_e} = 1836{\cdot}12 \pm 0{\cdot}02$
Neutron rest mass	$m_n = (1{\cdot}67470 \pm 0{\cdot}00004) \times 10^{-24}$ g
Hydrogen atom rest mass	$m_H = (1{\cdot}008142 \pm 0{\cdot}000003)$ a.m.u.
Deuterium atom rest mass	$m_D = (2{\cdot}014735 \pm 0{\cdot}000006)$ a.m.u.
Neutron rest mass	$m_n = (1{\cdot}008982 \pm 0{\cdot}000003)$ a.m.u.
Bohr magneton	$\mu_B = (0{\cdot}92731 \pm 0{\cdot}00002) \times 10^{-20}$ erg gauss^{-1}
Nuclear magneton	$\mu_N = (0{\cdot}505038 \pm 0{\cdot}000018) \times 10^{-23}$ erg gauss^{-1}
Electron magnetic moment	$\mu_e = 1{\cdot}00114536\ \mu_B$
Proton magnetic moment	$\mu_p = (2{\cdot}79275 \pm 0{\cdot}00003)\ \mu_N$
Fine structure constant α,	$\dfrac{1}{\alpha} = 137{\cdot}0373 \pm 0{\cdot}0006$
Classical electron radius	$\dfrac{e^2}{m_e c^2} = (2{\cdot}81785 \pm 0{\cdot}00004) \times 10^{-13}$ cm
Compton wavelength of electron	$\dfrac{h}{m_e c} = (24{\cdot}2626 \pm 0{\cdot}0002) \times 10^{-11}$ cm

Rydberg constant for $Z = 1$, infinite mass atom	$R_{\infty} = 109737{\cdot}309 \pm 0{\cdot}012)\ \mathrm{cm}^{-1}$
Rydberg constant for H^1 atom	$R_{H} = (109677{\cdot}576 \pm 0{\cdot}02)\ \mathrm{cm}^{-1}$
Molar gas constant (physical scale)	$R = (8{\cdot}31662 \pm 0{\cdot}00038) \times 10^{7}\ \mathrm{erg\,mole}^{-1}\,{}^{\circ}\mathrm{C}^{-1}$
Boltzmann's constant	$k = (1{\cdot}38044 \pm 0{\cdot}00007) \times 10^{-16}\ \mathrm{ergs}\ {}^{\circ}\mathrm{C}^{-1}$
	$kT = (8{\cdot}6164 \pm 0{\cdot}0004)\,T \times 10^{-5}\ \mathrm{eV}$

† Based mainly on COHEN, CROWE, and DUMOND, *The Fundamental Constants of Physics*, Interscience, New York 1957.

APPENDIX B

PAULI SPIN OPERATORS AND ISOSPIN (ISOTOPIC SPIN) OPERATORS

ELEMENTARY fermions all have an intrinsic angular momentum (spin) $\boldsymbol{s}\,\hbar$, where $\boldsymbol{s}^2$ is equal to

$$\frac{1}{2}\left(1+\frac{1}{2}\right)=\frac{3}{4}$$

The maximum observable component of the spin angular momentum s_z is, however, $\frac{1}{2}$. If a magnetic field is applied in the z-direction it removes the energy degeneracy of the magnetic states $s_z = +\frac{1}{2}$ and $s_z = -\frac{1}{2}$.

It is simpler to work with the Pauli spin operator as this avoids using fractions, where

$$\boldsymbol{s} = \tfrac{1}{2}\boldsymbol{\sigma}$$

The three components of $\boldsymbol{\sigma}$ in space are $\sigma_x, \sigma_y, \sigma_z$. $\pm\frac{1}{2}\sigma_z$ are the observed components of $\boldsymbol{\sigma}$.

Pauli showed that the following commutation laws hold for the spin operators $\sigma_x, \sigma_y, \sigma_z$

$$\sigma_x\sigma_y - \sigma_y\sigma_x = 2i\,\sigma_z \qquad \sigma_y\sigma_z - \sigma_z\sigma_y = 2i\,\sigma_x \qquad (1)$$
$$\sigma_z\sigma_x - \sigma_x\sigma_z = 2i\,\sigma_y$$

The spin operators are conveniently represented by the 2×2 matrices

$$\sigma_x = \begin{pmatrix}0 & 1\\ 1 & 0\end{pmatrix}; \quad \sigma_y = \begin{pmatrix}0 & -i\\ i & 0\end{pmatrix}; \quad \sigma_z = \begin{pmatrix}1 & 0\\ 0 & -1\end{pmatrix} \qquad (2)$$

The third component σ_z has finite diagonal elements corresponding to the two possible values of s_z; namely, $+\frac{1}{2}$ and $-\frac{1}{2}$. It is a simple example in matrix algebra to verify that the matrices of eqns. (2) satisfy the commutation rules defined by eqns. (1).

Isospin of the Nucleon

The concept of isospin (or isotopic spin) was first applied to the proton and neutron. These particles have nearly the same mass and it is helpful to regard the proton and neutron as different "charge" sub-states of the same fundamental particle, the nucleon. To develop this idea mathematically, introduce an abstract space, isospin or charge space, and associate an isospin vector $\boldsymbol{t}$ with the nucleon. The vector $\boldsymbol{t}$ is formally analogous to the spin vector $\boldsymbol{s}$ of the nucleon but it must be emphasized that $\boldsymbol{t}$ has no existence in ordinary space. Just as the vector $\boldsymbol{s}$ can assume one of two possible orientations with respect to the z-axis of ordinary space, there are two possible components of $\boldsymbol{t}$ in the direction of the third axis in isospin space. Thus a nucleon has the following isospin properties

$$t = \frac{1}{2}, \quad \boldsymbol{t}^2 = \frac{1}{2}\left(1 + \frac{1}{2}\right) = \frac{3}{4} \tag{3}$$

The third component t_3 can assume the values

$$t_3 = +\tfrac{1}{2} \text{ for the proton state:} \tag{4a}$$

$$t_3 = -\tfrac{1}{2} \text{ for the neutron state.} \tag{4b}$$

The charge Q in units of e is related to t_3 by

$$Q = t_3 + \tfrac{1}{2}. \tag{5}$$

The z-component of the total angular momentum vector always behaves as an *additive* quantum number. Similarly the third component T_3 of a number of nucleons is given by the addition of the t_3 values of all the nucleons in the system. For a nucleus with Z protons, N neutrons and $A = Z + N$, the third component for the *nucleus* is

$$T_3 = \frac{Z}{2} - \frac{N}{2} = \frac{A}{2} - N. \tag{6}$$

The law of conservation of electric charge implies the conservation of T_3 in all reactions and decays.

If we introduce a new nucleon isospin operator defined by the identity $\boldsymbol{t} = \frac{1}{2}\boldsymbol{\tau}$ (analogous to the definition $\boldsymbol{s} = \frac{1}{2}\boldsymbol{\sigma}$ for "ordinary" spin) we again have a set of commutation rules and matrix operators

$$\tau_1 = \begin{pmatrix} 0 & 1 \\ 1 & 0 \end{pmatrix}; \quad \tau_2 = \begin{pmatrix} 0 & -i \\ i & 0 \end{pmatrix}; \quad \tau_3 = \begin{pmatrix} 1 & 0 \\ 0 & -1 \end{pmatrix} \tag{7}$$

$$\tau_1 \tau_2 - \tau_2 \tau_1 = 2i\tau_3; \quad \tau_2 \tau_3 - \tau_3 \tau_2 = 2i\tau_1; \quad \tau_3 \tau_1 - \tau_1 \tau_3 = 2i\tau_2$$

where τ_1, τ_2, τ_3 are the three components of the vector $\boldsymbol{\tau}$ in isospin space.

For a system of two nucleons, the total isospin vector is

$$\boldsymbol{T} = \boldsymbol{t}_1 + \boldsymbol{t}_2 = \tfrac{1}{2}(\boldsymbol{\tau}_1 + \boldsymbol{\tau}_2) \tag{9}$$

where the subscripts 1 and 2 refer to the first and second nucleon respectively.

$$\boldsymbol{T}^2 = \frac{1}{4}(\boldsymbol{\tau}_1 + \boldsymbol{\tau}_2)^2$$

$$T(T+1) = \frac{1}{4}(\boldsymbol{\tau}_1^2 + \boldsymbol{\tau}_2^2 + 2\boldsymbol{\tau}_1\boldsymbol{\tau}_2)$$

Now as $\quad \boldsymbol{\tau} = 2\boldsymbol{t}, \quad \boldsymbol{\tau}_1^2 = 1(2+1) = 3, \quad \boldsymbol{\tau}_2^2 = 1(2+1) = 3$

Hence

$$T(T+1) = \tfrac{1}{2}(3 + \boldsymbol{\tau}_1 \cdot \boldsymbol{\tau}_2)$$

For two nucleons $T = 1$ or $T = 0$, so that

$$4 = 3 + \boldsymbol{\tau}_1 \boldsymbol{\tau}_2$$

or

$$0 = 3 + \boldsymbol{\tau}_1 \boldsymbol{\tau}_2$$

and

$$\boldsymbol{\tau}_1 \cdot \boldsymbol{\tau}_2 = +1 \text{ or } -3 \tag{10}$$

It is sometimes convenient to write the complete wave function of a system of particles as the product of spatial, spin, and isospin wave functions. For a single nucleon the isospin part of the wave function can be represented by the two column matrices

$$\chi_p = \begin{pmatrix}1\\0\end{pmatrix}; \quad \chi_n = \begin{pmatrix}0\\1\end{pmatrix} \tag{11}$$

where the square of χ_p expresses the probability of the nucleon being in the proton charge state and the square of χ_n that of it being in the neutron state.

Consider two nucleons, labelled (1) and (2). Four isospin states may be obtained, three belonging to $T = 1$ (a charge triplet) and one belonging to the antisymmetrical neutron–proton state. These four states are (the symbols p and n refer to proton and neutron; the subscripts 1, 0, etc. refer to the values of T and T_3):

$$\left.\begin{aligned} \chi_{(1,1)}(p, p) &= \chi_p(1)\,\chi_p(2) && \text{(a)} \\ \chi_{(1,0)}(p, n) &= \frac{1}{\sqrt{2}}[\chi_p(1)\,\chi_n(2) + \chi_n(1)\,\chi_p(2)] && \text{(b)} \\ \chi_{(1,-1)}(n, n) &= \chi_n(1)\,\chi_n(2) && \text{(c)} \end{aligned}\right\} \begin{matrix} S \\ \text{Symmetric} \\ \text{states} \\ T = 1 \end{matrix} \tag{12}$$

$$\chi_{(0,0)}(p, n) = \frac{1}{\sqrt{2}}[\chi_p(1)\,\chi_n(2) - \chi_n(1)\,\chi_p(2)] \quad \begin{matrix} A \\ \text{Antisymmetric} \\ \text{state} \\ T = 0 \end{matrix} \tag{13}$$

For a system of two nucleons, $T = 1$ for two protons or two neutrons; for the p, n system, however as $T_3 = \frac{1}{2} - \frac{1}{2} = 0$, there are two possible values for T, one and zero. The (1, 0) charge state is symmetric with respect to the interchange of the two particles and it corresponds to the case with $\boldsymbol{T}$ oriented perpendicular to the z-axis of charge space.

The complete wave function of a system of two nucleons can be written

$$\psi = \varphi\,\alpha\,\chi$$

where φ is a function of spatial coordinates

α is a function of spin coordinates

and χ is the isospin wave function discussed above.

The Pauli exclusion principle can now be expressed by stating that the product of $\varphi\,\alpha\,\chi$ for a system of two nucleons (that is, two identical particles) must be antisymmetric (A). Thus if χ is represented by one of the three $T = 1$ states given by eqn. (12), the product $\varphi\,\alpha$ must be A. The (p, n) system in the A state ($T = 0$) however, must have $\varphi\,\alpha$ symmetric.

Isospin of the Pion

The pion has an isospin $T = 1$, with $T^2 = 1(1 + 2) = 3$. The three possible orientations of T in isospin space have third components

$$T_3 = +1, \quad \text{for the } \pi^+ \text{ charge state}$$
$$T_3 = 0, \quad \text{for the } \pi^0 \text{ charge state} \tag{14}$$
$$T_3 = -1, \quad \text{for the } \pi^- \text{ charge state}$$

For the pion, the electric charge Q is equal to T_3

$$Q = T_3 \tag{15}$$

In the pion theory of nuclear forces it is possible to describe the pion field by a vector $\boldsymbol{\varphi}$ in isospin space with three components φ_1, φ_2 and φ_3 parallel to the three axes. However only φ_3 represents one of the observed charged states†; viz.

$$\varphi_3 = \varphi_0 \quad \text{corresponding to a } \pi^0 \text{ state} \tag{16a}$$

The pion field operators representing π^+ and π^- states are

$$\varphi_+ = \frac{1}{\sqrt{2}}(\varphi_1 + i\varphi) \tag{16b}$$

$$\varphi_- = \frac{1}{\sqrt{2}}(\varphi_1 - i\varphi_2) \tag{16c}$$

To show the close formal resemblance of isospin T_3-components and magnetic quantum states we compare the field equations, eqns. (16), with the angular momentum wave functions for the case with $l = 1$, $m = 1, 0, -1$. The angular momentum eigenfunctions are the spherical harmonics Y_l^m which are proportional to

$$P_l^m(\cos\theta)\, e^{im\varphi}$$

where the $P_l^m(\cos\theta)$ are Legendre polynomials.

For $\quad l = 1, \quad m = +1, \quad Y_1^1 = \frac{1}{\sqrt{2}} \sin\theta\, e^{i\varphi} = \frac{1}{\sqrt{(2)}\, r}(x + iy) \qquad (17b)$

$$l = 1, \quad m = 0, \quad Y_1^0 = \cos\theta = \frac{1}{r} z \tag{17a}$$

$$l = 1, \quad m = -1, \quad Y_1^{-1} = \frac{1}{\sqrt{2}} \sin\theta\, e^{-i\varphi} = \frac{1}{\sqrt{(2)}\, r}(x - iy) \tag{17c}$$

r, θ and φ are polar coordinates and x, y, z Cartesian coordinates in "ordinary space". Note the formal resemblance between eqns. (16) and the corresponding eqns. (17)

† For a neutral particle, the field operator φ_3 can be a hermitian operator. This is not possible for a charged particle such as π^+ or π^-. φ^+ and φ^- can, however, be expressed as linear combinations of two hermitian operators φ_1 and φ_2 in a definite phase relation.

Sometimes it is permissible to treat φ_+, φ_- and φ_0 as creation and annihilation operators. Thus φ_+ will create a positive pion or destroy a negative pion, . . . , etc.

The real or virtual processes

$$n \to p + \pi^- \tag{18a}$$

and

$$p \to n + \pi^+ \tag{18b}$$

can be represented by the operator equations

$$\tfrac{1}{2}(\tau_1 + i\,\tau_2)\,\chi(n) = \chi(p) \tag{19a}$$

and

$$\tfrac{1}{2}(\tau_1 - i\,\tau_2)\,\chi(p) = \chi(n) \tag{19b}$$

τ_1 and τ_2 are two of the components of the nucleon matrix operator $\boldsymbol{\tau}$ (eqns. 7) and $\chi(n)$ and $\chi(p)$ are the neutron and proton isospin column matrices (eqns. 11). Equations (19) can easily be verified by matrix algebra. The operator

$$\tau_+ = \frac{1}{2}(\tau_1 + i\,\tau_2) = \begin{pmatrix} 0 & 1 \\ 0 & 0 \end{pmatrix} \tag{20a}$$

$$\tau_- = \frac{1}{2}(\tau_1 - i\,\tau_2) = \begin{pmatrix} 0 & 0 \\ 1 & 0 \end{pmatrix} \tag{20b}$$

Notice the close resemblance between the operators φ_+ and τ_+ and φ_- and τ_-. Thus τ_+ is an operator which annihilates a neutron and creates a proton, and τ_- is an operator which annihilates a proton and creates a neutron.

APPENDIX C

RECENT ADDITIONS

C 1. The Antisigma Hyperon

The antiparticle of the negatively charged sigma hyperon, which is predicted by the Gell-Mann–Nishijima strangeness scheme, has recently been observed at CERN† and Brookhaven.†† The antisigma particle was detected through the following high energy antiproton reaction in a hydrogen bubble chamber

$$p + \bar{p} \rightarrow \Xi^{-} + \overline{\Xi^{+}} \qquad (1)$$

The decay of the antisigma hyperon and the subsequent decay of the anti-lambda particle were observed

$$\overline{\Xi^{+}} \rightarrow \pi^{+} + \overline{\Lambda^{0}} \qquad (2)$$

$$\overline{\Lambda^{0}} \rightarrow \pi^{+} + \bar{p} \qquad (3)$$

A careful analysis of the kinematics of processes (1), (2) and (3) constituted the identification of the $\overline{\Xi^{+}}$ particle and the estimated mass is in fair agreement with that of the sigma particle.

C 2. Two Kinds of Neutrino and Antineutrino

In Chapter 21, Section 4, the feasibility of detecting high energy neutrino and antineutrino reactions is discussed. During the first six months of 1962 a remarkable high energy antineutrino experiment has been performed with the Brookhaven A-G proton synchroton.††† High energy neutrinos and antineutrinos (1 GeV) were produced by the decay in flight of pions and kaons generated by the impact of 15 GeV protons with a 3-in. thick Be target in the synchroton. The flux of particles emitted at 7·5° with respect to the proton beam entered a 13·5-metre thick iron shield 21 metres from the Be target. All types of particle except neutrinos and antineutrinos were attenuated by the enormous factor of 10^{25} in the iron shield. Behind this shield was mounted a well screened 10 ton Al spark chamber. The following anti-

† *Phys. Rev. Letters,* **8**, 257, 1962.

†† H. N. BROWN *et al., Phys. Rev. Letters,* **8**, 255, 1962.

††† G. DANBY, J. M. GAILLARD, K. GOULIANOS, L. M. LEDERMAN, N. MISTRY, M. SCHWARTZ and J. STEINBERGER, *Phys. Rev. Letters,* **9**, 36, 1962.

neutrino reactions were looked for in the spark chamber

$$\bar{\nu} + p \rightarrow n + e^{+} \tag{1}$$

$$\bar{\nu} + p \rightarrow n + \mu^{+} \tag{2}$$

The antineutrinos were produced by the decay in flight of the very high energy negative pion beam from the synchrotron

$$\pi^{-} \rightarrow \mu^{-} + \bar{\nu} \tag{3}$$

In several hundreds of hours of operation, in which more than 3×10^{17} protons struck the Be target, fifty spark chamber tracks identified as positive muons of reaction (2) were observed. A few electron tracks were observed but none of them were attributed to reaction (1). The antineutrino cross section is so low ($< 10^{-38}$ cm^2) that a very elaborate coincidence system switched off the spark chamber except for 2 μsec intervals during each second when bursts of pions were generated by the synchrotron. This greatly minimised the number of cosmic ray muon tracks photographed in the spark chamber. The ten ton spark chamber consisted of ten units, each containing nine aluminium plates 44 in. × 44 in. × 1 in. thick separated by 3/8 in. lucite spacers. The proton targets for reactions (1) and (2) are protons in the Al nuclei of the spark chamber.

For high energy antineutrinos the cross sections of reactions (1) and (2) should be equal. In Chapter 21, Section 4, it is assumed that there is only one type of neutrino in addition to its antiparticle the antineutrino. If, however, the sort of antineutrino produced by pion decay is different in kind from that created in beta decay, then the cross section of reaction (1) should be zero. The Brookhaven experiment favours this hypothesis. Thus we must in future distinguish between the muon coupled antineutrino $\bar{\nu}_{\mu}$

$$\pi^{-} \rightarrow \mu^{-} + \bar{\nu}_{\mu}$$

and the electron coupled antineutrino

$$n \rightarrow p + e^{-} + \bar{\nu}_{e}$$

Presumably the muon coupled and the electron coupled neutrino are different in kind

$$\nu_{\mu} \neq \nu_{e}$$

Recent measurements† of the branching ratio

$$\mu^{-} \rightarrow e^{-} + \gamma / \mu^{-} \rightarrow e^{-} + \nu + \bar{\nu}$$

are compatible with the assumption that the radiative decay of the muon is forbidden. This result is credible if ν_e and ν_{μ} are different particles. Feinberg†† has shown on theoretical grounds that the above branching ratio should be $\geqq 10^{-4}$ if ν_e is identical with ν_{μ}.

† D. Bartlett, S. Devons, A. M. Sachs, *Phys. Rev. Letters*, **8**, 120, 1962; S. Frankel *et al.*, *Phys. Rev. Letters*, **8**, 123, 1962.

†† G. Feinberg, *Phys. Rev.*, **110**, 1482, 1958.

The fundamental difference between the two sorts of neutrino is presumably associated with some new quantum number not yet discovered. One difference between ν_e and ν_μ may lie in their rest masses. The evidence for zero rest mass of the muon coupled neutrino is much less precise than that for the electron coupled neutrino. If it turns out that the rest mass of ν_μ is finite then the longitudinal polarization of the muon emitted in pion decay will be less than 100 per cent.

To return to the Brookhaven antineutrino experiment. The observed number of reactions $\bar{\nu}_\mu + p \rightarrow n + \mu^+$, is in reasonable agreement with the theoretical cross section. However, no decisive information concerning the existence of the intermediate boson W was obtained.

C 3. Magnetic Moment of the Λ^0 Hyperon

A group† at Brookhaven have measured the magnetic moment of the lambda hyperon and obtained the result $\mu_\Lambda = -(1{\cdot}5 \pm 0{\cdot}5)$ nuclear magnetons. In spite of the large error this is a fine achievement when we recall that the mean lifetime of the lambda particle is $2{\cdot}25 \times 10^{-10}$ sec. Our knowledge of the properties of hyperons is so meagre that the establishment of the fact that the Λ^0 has a finite negative magnetic moment is well worth knowing. Unfortunately, a considerable improvement in accuracy must be obtained before it is possible to test various theories of the structure of the lambda particle (the Sakata model of baryons predicts identical magnetic moments for the neutron and lambda particles whereas the Gell-Mann–Ne'eman model predicts $\mu_\Lambda = 0{\cdot}5\,\mu_n$).††

The measurement of the magnetic moment of the lambda particle (strictly speaking the gyromagnetic ratio) is only possible because parity is not conserved in the decay $\Lambda^0 \rightarrow p + \pi^-$.

The decay negative pion tends to be emitted in the direction of the normal $\mathbf{p}_1 \times \mathbf{p}_\Lambda$, where $\mathbf{p}_1$ is the momentum vector of the positive pion creating the Λ^0 particle in the reaction

$$\pi^+ + n \rightarrow K^+ + \Lambda^0 \tag{1}$$

and $\mathbf{p}_\Lambda$ is the momentum of the Λ^0.

The Λ^0 is polarized with its spin normal to the production plane and the subsequent decay pion is emitted preferentially along the lambda spin direction.

In the Brookhaven experiment a beam of positive pions of momentum ~ 1 GeV/c from the Cosmotron was incident on a Be target. Lambda hyperons of momentum ~ 680 MeV/c ($\beta \sim 0{\cdot}52$) produced by reaction (1) travelled a few inches parallel to a strong magnetic field before decaying

† R. L. Cool, E. W. Jenkins, T. F. Kycia, D. A. Hill, and R. A. Schluter, *Phys. Rev.*, **127**, 2223, 1962.

†† A. Salam, *Proc. Phys. Soc.*, **80**, 13, 1962.

in a spark chamber. The only lambda decay events recorded were those in coincidence with the detection of the K^+ particle produced in reaction (1). As the lambda particle is created with its spin axis perpendicular to $\boldsymbol{p}_\Lambda$, it will precess around the magnetic field H at the Larmor angular frequency

$$\omega_L = \mu_\Lambda H/I\hbar$$

If the distance of travel parallel to H is d, then in the flight time $t = d/\beta c$, the spin axis will rotate through an angle

$$\varepsilon = 5{\cdot}48 \times 10^5 \mu H(1 - \beta^2)^{1/2} \frac{d}{\beta c} \quad \text{degrees}$$

where μ is the magnetic moment of the lambda particle in nuclear magnetons. (For $\mu = 1$, $\beta = 0{\cdot}52$, and the field integral $\int_0^d H\,dl = 540$ kilogauss-cm, $\varepsilon = 16{\cdot}5^0$.) From a statistical analysis of the direction of emission of the negative pions in more than two hundred lambda decays a value of $\varepsilon = 25^0 \pm 8^0$ was obtained. This corresponds to

$$\mu_\Lambda = -(1{\cdot}5 \pm 0{\cdot}5) \quad \text{nuclear magnetons}.$$

The negative sign was determined by observing the sense of precession of the lambda spin in the magnetic field.

C 4. The Neutral Antixi Hyperon

The last of the predicted antiparticles, the $\overline{\Xi}{}^0$, has been observed at Brookhaven.† This antiparticle was produced by exposing a liquid hydrogen bubble chamber to a 3·69 GeV/c beam of antiprotons

$$\bar{p} + p \rightarrow \Xi^- + \overline{\Xi^0} + \pi^+$$

The following decays were observed

$$\Xi^- \rightarrow \Lambda^0 + \pi^-$$
$$\Lambda^0 \rightarrow p + \pi^-$$
$$\overline{\Xi^0} \rightarrow \overline{\Lambda^0} + \pi^0$$
$$\overline{\Lambda^0} \rightarrow \bar{p} + \pi^+$$

† C. Baltay *et al.*, *Phys. Rev. Letters*, **11**, 165, 1963.

APPENDIX D

MORE RECENT ADDITIONS

D 1. Semiconductor Counters (p. 345)

The recent improvements in the performance of semiconductor junction detectors means that they seriously rival scintillation counters in low energy physics. Under favourable circumstances alpha particles have been detected by semiconductor counters with an energy resolution as good as 0·5 per cent. One of the most important developments is the successful production of depletion layer thicknesses of 5 mm or more (lithium ion drift technique).

The situation as regards the spectrometry of gamma photons has improved but there is still a great need for efficient gamma conduction counters. Gallium arsenide, with an energy gap of 1·4 eV, is one of the most promising semiconductor materials. A conduction counter in the form of a cube 1 or 2 cm in length would be a most valuable addition to the armoury of gamma detectors.

D 2. Elementary Particle Resonances and the Ω^- Particle (p. 742)

A large number of mesonic and baryonic resonant states has been discovered since 1961, (see bibliography). Meanwhile a considerable degree of order in classifying these resonant states has been achieved following the independent suggestions of Gell-Mann and Ne'eman in 1961, that the strong interactions are invariant with respect to a special group of unitary transformations known as SU(3). More than two hundred papers on group theoretical aspects of elementary particle physics have been published in the last four years. It is not possible in a short appendix to do justice to these symmetry ideas and the reader is advised to consult the excellent short articles by Chew et al. and Devons and the book by Lipkin (see Bibliography).

The most spectacular result of the unitary symmetry scheme was the prediction in 1962, by Gell-Mann, of the existence of a new "particle" or resonant state, the Ω^- of rest mass energy 1676 MeV. This prediction followed the announcement of two new resonances at 1530 MeV rest mass energy. Nine baryonic resonant states, all with spin 3/2 and even parity were known. If the group theoretical arguments of Gell-Mann and Ne'eman were correct, there should be a *tenth* resonance of spin 3/2 and even parity, completing a *decuplet* family of states. The ten members of this family (supermultiplet) differ in mass, electric charge, strangeness and isospin. The splitting of the supermultiplet into four multiplets is due to some symmetry breaking interaction. The members of this decuplet are split into four isospin multiplets as follows:

(a) 4 states of hypercharge $Y = 1$ (Y is defined as baryon number B plus strangeness number S). These states correspond to the four possible values of the third component of isospin of the (3/2, 3/2) π-nucleon resonance at 1238 MeV. (p. 714)

(b) 3 states of hypercharge $Y = 0$, these correspond to a triplet of $T = 1$ resonances at 1385 MeV.

(c) 2 states of hypercharge $Y = -1$, corresponding to two states of a $T = 1/2$ resonance at 1530 MeV.

N.B. The energy spacing of states (b) and (a), 147 MeV, is nearly equal to that of (c) and (b), 145 MeV.

(d) The tenth state, a $Y = -2$ ($S = -3$) singlet of electric charge minus one unit, to complete the super multiplet should occurat a rest mass energy of 1530 + 146 = 1676 MeV. This is the predicted Ω^- "particle". The lifetime of this "particle" should be as long as 10^{-10} sec, for it should be stable against strong and electromagnetic decays, its lifetime being determined by the $|\Delta S| = 1$ weak interaction decay rule.

The first Ω^- event was reported early in 1964 by a group† (33 authors!) using a 5 BeV beam of K^- mesons from the Brookhaven A-G proton synchrotron. In this experiment the Ω^- particle was created by a $K^- - p$ collision in the 80 inch hydrogen bubble chamber

$$K^- + p \rightarrow \Omega^- + K^+ + K^\circ$$

Strangeness is conserved in this production reaction.

The Ω^- particle travelled about one inch in the bubble chamber before decaying

$$\Omega^- \rightarrow \Xi^0 + \pi^-$$

After travelling a few centimetres the Ξ^0 particle decayed:

$$\Xi^0 \rightarrow \Lambda^0 + \pi^0$$

$$\pi^0 \rightarrow \gamma + \gamma$$

Both gamma photons were converted into electron–positron pairs in the bubble chamber and the Λ^0 decayed into a proton and a π^- meson.

† V. E. Barnes *et al.*, *Phys. Rev. Letters*, **12**, 204, 1964.

A few weeks after the first Ω^- event a second event† was reported, in this case, however, the decay mode was different

$$\Omega^- \rightarrow \Lambda^0 + K^-$$

followed by $$K^- \rightarrow \pi^- + \pi^+ + \pi^-$$

and $$\Lambda^0 \rightarrow p + \pi^-$$

The estimated production cross section in 5 BeV $K^- - p$ collisions is $\sim 10^{-6}$ barn. The estimated rest mass energy of the Ω^- from these two events is (1675 ± 3) MeV, in excellent agreement with the theoretical prediction.

Unitary symmetry arguments also lead to some interesting mass formulae, notably those of Gell-Mann and Okubo,†† connecting the masses of the isospin components of supermultiplets. Coleman and Glashow††† have derived an interesting relation for the mass differences within isospin multiplets, e.g.

$$\begin{aligned} M(\Xi^-) - M(\Xi^0) &= [M(\Sigma^-) - M(\Sigma^+)] + [M(p) - M(n)] \\ &= 8{\cdot}25 - 1{\cdot}29 = 7{\cdot}0 \text{ MeV} \end{aligned}$$

in good agreement with the latest experimental values.‡

D 3. Violation of Time Reversal Invariance in Neutral *K* Meson Decay

Neutral K mesons have remarkable properties (p. 737). As far as decay properties are concerned, the states $\Psi(K_1^0)$ and $\Psi(K_2^0)$ behave like particles, with mean lifetimes of 10^{-10} sec and $6{\cdot}10^{-8}$ sec respectively (Table 3, p. 726). The K_1^0 and K_2^0 wave functions can be defined in terms of those of the K^0 and $\overline{K^0}$ states (eqns. (87) and (88) p. 738). Examination of these equations shows that

$\Psi(K_1^0)$ is an eigenstate of CP with eigenvalue $+1$

$\Psi(K_2^0)$ is an eigenstate of CP with eigenvalue -1

CP is the combined operation of C (charge conjugation) and P (parity).

Consider a system of two neutral pions. As these are spinless bosons they must be in a state of even orbital angular momentum and even parity (p. 175). The charge conjugation transformation changes π^0 into π^0, therefore two neutral pions have a CP value of $+1$. Similarly a system $\pi^+ + \pi^-$ has

† W. B. Fowler and N. P. Samios, *Scientific American*, **211**, 36, Oct. 1964.

†† M. Gell-Mann, *Phys. Rev.*, **125**, 1067, 1962.
S. Okubo, *Progr. Theoret. Phys.* (Kyoto), **27**, 949, 1962.

††† S. Coleman and S. L. Glashow, *Phys. Rev. Letters*, **6**, 1423, 1961.

‡ D. Duane Carmody *et al.*, *Phys. Rev. Letters*, **12**, 482, 1964.

a CP value of $+1$, charge conjugation transforms π^+ into π^-, π^- into π^+, and the parity of the system is even.

Assuming CP invariance in weak decay processes

$$K_1^0 \to \pi^+ + \pi^-$$

$$K_1^0 \to \pi^0 + \pi^0$$

is allowed, whereas

$$K_2^0 \to \pi^+ + \pi^-$$

$$K_2^0 \to \pi^0 + \pi^0$$

is forbidden.

The shorter lifetime of the K_1^0 meson is a consequence of the allowed two pion decays.

If any K_2^0 mesons are observed to decay into two pions then CP invariance is broken and, if we accept the validity of the CPT theorem (p. 451), this implies violation of time-reversal invariance.†

Several experiments have shown that about two or three K_2^0 mesons out of every thousand do decay into two charged pions instead of three pions.

The first experiment†† revealing the two-pion decay mode of the K_2^0 meson was carried out by a Princeton group using a 1 BeV/c beam of neutral K mesons generated by the 30 BeV proton beam of the Brookhaven synchrotron. The decay of neutral K mesons from a region about 300 K_1^0 decay lengths from their production point ensures that the number of observed K_1^0 decays is negligible. The K_2^0 decays (in helium gas) into $\pi^+ \pi^-$ pairs were registered as coincidences in two elaborate magnetic spectrometers, involving the use of spark chambers, scintillation and Cherenkov counters.

Confirmation of the Brookhaven results quickly followed from the Geneva ††† and the Rutherford laboratories.‡ The most interesting conclusions from these two experiments is that the relative number of two-pion decay modes of K_2^0 mesons does not rise rapidly with increasing K meson energy. (In the Geneva experiment, the K_2^0 momentum was ~ 10 BeV/c, about ten times the magnitude of the Brookhaven experiment.) If the observed two-pion decays are not due to CP violation but to the effect of a weak cosmic force, then the number of K_2^0 two-pion decays should increase as the square of the K meson energy. These experiments do not agree with this prediction.

† The possibility that there may exist a long-range weak force responsible for occasionally changing a K_2^0 meson into a K_1^0 meson seems to be ruled out by the later experiments. J. Bernstein, N. Cabibbo, T. D. Lee, *Phys. Letters*, **12**, 146, 1964.
J. S. Bell and J. K. Perring, *Phys. Rev. Letters*, **13**, 348, 1964.

†† J. H. Christenson, J. W. Cronin, V. L. Fitch, R. Turlay *Phys. Rev. Letters*, **13**, 138, 1964.

††† X. de Bouard *et al.*, *Phys. Letters*, **15**, 58, 1965.

‡ W. Galbraith *et al.*, *Phys. Rev. Letters*, **14**, 383, 1965.

At the moment, the evidence is in favour of a violation of CP and therefore of T-invariance. One curious aspect of this violation is the *weakness* of it in contrast to the *strong* violation of parity in beta and other weak interactions.

D 4. Magnetic Moment of the $\Lambda°$ Hyperon (p. 791)

Two recent determinations of the magnetic moment of the lambda hyperon give the following results

$$\mu_\Lambda = -(1{\cdot}39 \pm 0{\cdot}72) \text{ nuclear magnetons}\dagger$$
$$\mu_\Lambda = -(0{\cdot}5 \pm 0{\cdot}28) \text{ nuclear magnetons}\dagger\dagger$$

The second experiment is interesting as the decay products of the hyperon were observed in a stack of nuclear emulsion plates (this technique is now nearly obsolete in high energy experiments†††).

The accuracy of these experiments and the previous one of Cool *et al.* (p. 791) is not sufficient to establish the correctness of the unitary symmetry prediction,

$$\mu(\Lambda^0) = \tfrac{1}{2}\mu(n) = -0{\cdot}95 \text{ nuclear magnetons}$$

where $\mu(n)$ is the neutron magnetic moment.
Other unitary symmetry magnetic moment predictions, which are beyond the range of present experimental techniques, are

$$\mu(p) = \mu(\Sigma^+); \quad \mu(\Xi^-) = \mu(\Sigma^-)$$
$$\mu(n) = \mu(\Xi^0) = -[\mu(\Sigma^+) + \mu(\Sigma^-)]$$

D 5. No Sign of the Intermediate W Boson (p. 699)

An intensive search has been made to establish whether or not high energy neutrino reactions take place through the creation of the W boson (p. 699 and p. 791). The evidence at the time of writing (July 1965) is against the existence of the intermediate boson, provided that its rest mass is less than 1·8 BeV.

The Cern‡ and Brookhaven‡‡ methods of search depend on the high energy muon neutrino reactions

$$\nu_\mu + Z \rightarrow W^+ + \mu^- + Z$$
$$\bar{\nu}_\mu + Z \rightarrow W^- + \mu^+ + Z$$

here Z denotes a proton or nucleus.

† J. A. ANDERSON and F. S. CRAWFORD, *Phys. Rev. Letters*, **13**, 167, 1964.
†† G. CHARRIÈRE *et al.*, *Phys. Letters*, **15**, 66, 1965.
††† E. H. S. BURHOP, *Proc. Roy. Soc. A.*, **278**, 350, 1964.
‡ G. BERNARDINI *et al.*, *Phys. Letters*, **13**, 86, 1964.
‡‡ R. BURNS *et al.*, *Phys. Rev. Letters*, **15**, 42, 1965.

Within about 10^{-18} sec, the hypothetical boson decays in one of three ways:

$$W^+ \rightarrow \mu^+ + \nu_\mu$$

$$W^+ \rightarrow e^+ + \nu_e$$

or

$$W^+ \rightarrow \text{pions and/or kaons}$$

No lepton pair events, $\mu^- \mu^+$, $\mu^- e^+$, with the expected energy were observed in the large detection spark chambers.

BIBLIOGRAPHY

D 1. J. M. TAYLOR, *Semiconductor Particle Detectors*, Butterworths, London, 1963.
G. DEARNALEY, *Semiconductor Counters* in *Prog. Nucl. Phys.* **9**, 29, 1964.

D 2. G. F. CHEW, M. GELL-MANN, A. H. ROSENFELD, *Scientific American*, **210**, 74, Feb., 1964.
S. DEVONS, *Science Progress*, **52**, 543, 1964.
H. J. LIPKIN, *Lie Groups for Pedestrians*, North-Holland Publishing Co., Amsterdam, 1965.
G. PUPPI, *Pionic Resonances*, in *Annual Review of Nuclear Science*, **13**, 287, 1963.
R. H. DALITZ, *Strange-Particle Resonant States* in *Annual Review of Nuclear Science*, **13**, 339, 1963.
A recent compilation of resonant states is given by:
A. H. ROSENFELD *et al.*, *Revs. Mod. Phys.*, **36**, 977, 1964.

ANSWERS TO PROBLEMS

CHAPTER 1

1. $1{\cdot}16 \times 10^7$ °K.
2. r.m.s., 410 m sec^{-1}; 490 m sec^{-1}; mean, 378 m sec^{-1}, 451 m sec^{-1}; 0·55.
3. $1{\cdot}8 \times 10^{-8}$ cm. **4.** 5·14 km, 4·36.
5. 171 erg sec^{-1}; $6{\cdot}05 \times 10^{-2}$ erg cm^{-2} sec^{-1}.
7. $3{\cdot}91 \times 10^{-12}$ cm; 57° 50′. **8.** $2{\cdot}34 \times 10^{-6}$.

CHAPTER 2

1. 2·38 eV; $3{\cdot}61 \times 10^7$ cm sec^{-1}. **2.** $0{\cdot}902 \times 10^{-3}$.
3. $-13{\cdot}62$ eV, $2{\cdot}19 \times 10^8$ cm sec^{-1}, $5{\cdot}29 \times 10^{-9}$ cm; $-54{\cdot}48$ eV, $4{\cdot}38 \times 10^8$ cm sec^{-1}, $2{\cdot}64 \times 10^{-9}$ cm; $4{\cdot}27 \times 10^{-12}$ cm, $1{\cdot}31 \times 10^9$ cm sec^{-1}.
4. $3{\cdot}7 \times 10^{-3}$ eV, $4{\cdot}95 \times 10^{-3}$ eV.
5. $5{\cdot}443 \times 10^{-3}$; $1{\cdot}77 \times 10^7$ e.m.u.g^{-1}.
6. $5{\cdot}7 \times 10^2$ m sec^{-1}, $5{\cdot}75 \times 10^2$ m sec^{-1}; $9{\cdot}4 \times 10^2$ m sec^{-1}, $9{\cdot}6 \times 10^2$ m sec^{-1}.

CHAPTER 3

1. 0·866 *c*, 0·943 *c*, 0·996 *c*. **2.** 14·8 days, 0·135 light years.
3. 1 year. **4.** 0·731 m, 43°53′. **5.** 32°12′.
6. $1{\cdot}64 \times 10^8$ parsec. **7.** 26·7 gauss, 3·83 cm.
9. $2{\cdot}65 \times 10^7$ m sec^{-1}, $7{\cdot}04 \times 10^{16}$ m sec^{-2}; $2{\cdot}49 \times 10^8$ m sec^{-1}, $1{\cdot}24 \times 10^{16}$ m sec^{-2}. **11.** 27 cm.

CHAPTER 4

1. $6{\cdot}197 \times 10^{-9}$ cm, $2{\cdot}6 \times 10^{14}$ sec^{-1}, 2×10^8 sec^{-1}, No, 2·68 keV.
2. 111, 200, 220, 311, 222, 400, f.c.c.; $3{\cdot}60 \times 10^{-8}$ cm.
3. $2{\cdot}6 \times 10^{-5}$ °C^{-1}. **4.** 103, 204. **5.** 63.
6. $6{\cdot}62 \times 10^{-27}$ erg sec. **7.** $I(200) : I(222) = 6{\cdot}5$.
9. 0·51 MeV, 30°; 0·68 MeV, 18°26′; 0·765 MeV, 10°53′; 0·816 MeV, 0°.

CHAPTER 5

1. 5·1 cm; 5·9 cm; 8·4 cm, 9·8 cm.
2. 12·4 fermi, 2·48 fermi, $6{\cdot}2 \times 10^{-2}$ fermi; $1{\cdot}78 \times 10^{-8}$ cm (most probable); $1{\cdot}98 \times 10^{-9}$ cm.

CHAPTER 6

1. 5·95 eV (even parity), 5·97 eV (odd), 23·3 eV (even), 23·5 eV (odd).
2. 7×10^{-15}.

CHAPTER 7

1. 36·42 cm, 1·008143 a.m.u.
2. 3723 eV, 3286 eV, 437 eV, 0·833%.

CHAPTER 9

1. 1·4 fermi. **2.** 8·45 fermi. **3.** 245·2 MeV, 4·81 MeV, 66°10′; $qa = 1{\cdot}613$, $F(qa) = 0{\cdot}648$; $1{\cdot}295 \times 10^{-29}$ cm² steradian⁻¹, $5{\cdot}43 \times 10^{-30}$ cm² steradian⁻¹.

CHAPTER 10

1. 640 : 1·71 : 1. **2.** After 3·97 days, 0·111. **3.** 24,100 years.
4. 1020 disintegrations sec⁻¹, 11·0 disintegrations sec⁻¹.
5. $1{\cdot}50 \times 10^9$ years. **6.** $1{\cdot}26 \times 10^{-12}$.
7. 0·863 milliwatts, $3{\cdot}29 \times 10^5$ joule. **8.** $1{\cdot}29 \times 10^9$ years.
9. 2·46 ± 0·43 c.p.m., 40 days.

CHAPTER 11

1. 0·105 MeV cm⁻¹, 0·131 MeV cm⁻¹, 0·178 MeV cm⁻¹, 0·292 MeV cm⁻¹.
2. 2950 ion pairs cm⁻¹, 3680, 5000, 8200.
4. $0{\cdot}409 \times 10^{-6}$ sec, 50×10^{-6} V.
5. −25·96 V sec⁻¹, 173×10^{-6} V, 230×10^{-6} V.
6. 0·06%. **7.** $5{\cdot}1 \times 10^{-8}$ A. **8.** 8 ± 1.

CHAPTER 12

2. +0·314, −1·006 V. **3.** After 2×10^{-6} sec, $78{\cdot}6 \times 10^{-6}$ V.
4. Anode load currents, 2·5 mA, 0·366 mA; anode potentials, 60 V, 158 V; grid potentials, 37 V, 19 V.

CHAPTER 14

1. 37 keV, Yes. **2.** 1·97 MeV. **3.** 0·572 MeV, 0·657 MeV, 1·671 MeV.

CHAPTER 15

1. 12·5 barns, 5 eV, 0·4 eV. **2.** 150 μsec, 12 msec.
3. +7·8 fermi. **4.** $2{\cdot}72 \times 10^9$ sec⁻¹. **5.** 12·8 ± 2 min.

CHAPTER 16

1. 42·58 Mc/s, 2140 c/s. **2.** 2·216.
3. $2{\cdot}36 \times 10^{16}$, 1·61 msec, $4{\cdot}35 \times 10^{-4}$ °C hr^{-1}, $2{\cdot}35 \times 10^{-4}$ °C hr^{-1}.

CHAPTER 18

1. 36·3 MeV, 10·67 Mc/s, − 88·6 gauss.
2. 11·44 Mc/s, 172 MeV, 500 km. **3.** 300 gauss, $2{\cdot}6 \times 10^{7}$ m/sec, 360 kc/s, 14 kgauss, 4·2 Mc/s.
4. 100 MeV, 4 msec. **5.** 2·1 cm, 1·2 cm.

CHAPTER 20

1. 0·3875, 0·3867, 0·3612, 0·3600, 0·3500 W m^{-2} m. Yes.
2. 1·98 MeV. **3.** 1·65 MeV, −1·45 MeV.
4. 9·670 MeV, 0·25 MeV, 135 MeV/c, 89 MeV/c; 73·5 MeV/c, 0·053.
5. $10^{-18{\cdot}3}$, $4{\cdot}3 \times 10^{-4}$.
6. 8 : 1, 20 : 1, 60 : 1, 80 : 1, 45 : 1, 20 : 1.

CHAPTER 21

2. 6·7 eV. **3.** 1·81 MeV, 0·1%. **4.** 25 counts/hr.
5. 40·67 keV, Ce. **6.** 53 MeV.
7. 129·3 MeV, 7%, 3×10^{-3}%, 1·075 m. **8.** 4·6 MeV.
9. 0·992 c, 0·785 c, $13{\cdot}3 \times 10^{-9}$ sec.
10. 5·3 MeV, 31·7 MeV, 5·6 MeV, 34·4 MeV.
11. 19 MeV, 98 MeV. **12.** 55·6 MeV, 7·5 m.
13. 152·5 MeV, 1490 m. **14.** Yes, no.

CHAPTER 22

1. $1{\cdot}98 \times 10^{33}$ grams. **2.** $-0{\cdot}743$ GM^{2}R^{-1}.
3. 0·15 W cm^{-2}, $6{\cdot}6 \times 10^{14}$ sec^{-1}.
4. 30×10^{14}, 4×10^{14}; 9×10^{19}, $2{\cdot}5 \times 10^{17}$ dyne cm^{-2}.
5. 24 keV.

NAME INDEX

SUBJECT INDEX

ERRATA

Page 200, line 20, read:
R. W. GURNEY, Elementary Quantum Mechanics, ...

Page 304, line 23, read:
where K is a constant, n is the number ...

Page 336, penultimate line, read:
of about one per cent, ...
(see Appendix D 1)

Page 416, line 10, read:
mass change $\delta M = E/c^2$

Page 437, six lines from the bottom, read:

$g = 1{\cdot}42 \times 10^{-49}$ erg-cm^3

Page 559, line 20, read:
of the order of 0.003 Ω

Page 616, line 11, read:
$V(r)$ L. S

Page 620, line 24, read:
famous for its interpretation ...

Page 665, last line, read:
$j = l \pm \frac{1}{2}$, except for $l - 0$ when $j = +\frac{1}{2}$.

Page 728, The "firm" statement on lines 13 and 14 is incorrect:
(see Appendix D 3)

Page 762, line 18, read:
(7×10^9 y)